# ELECTRICITY

### AND

# MAGNETISM

# ELECTRICITY
# AND
# MAGNETISM

BY

## B. I. BLEANEY

*Formerly Fellow of St. Hugh's College, Oxford*

AND

## B. BLEANEY

*Dr. Lee's Professor of*
*Experimental Philosophy*
*University of Oxford*

SECOND EDITION

OXFORD
AT THE CLARENDON PRESS

*Oxford University Press, Ely House, London W.1*

GLASGOW NEW YORK TORONTO MELBOURNE WELLINGTON
CAPE TOWN SALISBURY IBADAN NAIROBI LUSAKA ADDIS ABABA
BOMBAY CALCUTTA MADRAS KARACHI LAHORE DACCA
KUALA LUMPUR HONG KONG TOKYO

FIRST EDITION 1957
REPRINTED LITHOGRAPHICALLY IN GREAT BRITAIN
AT THE UNIVERSITY PRESS, OXFORD
BY VIVIAN RIDLER, PRINTER TO THE UNIVERSITY
FROM CORRECTED SHEETS OF THE FIRST EDITION 1959
SECOND EDITION 1965
REPRINTED (WITH CORRECTIONS) 1968

# PREFACE TO THE FIRST EDITION

In teaching for the Final Honour School of Physics in Oxford the authors have long felt the need for an up-to-date text on *Electricity and Magnetism* which would cover the whole field, both the theory and the practice. This book is an attempt to supply this need, and to make it as comprehensive as possible chapters have been included which may form part of a graduate course rather than an undergraduate course. The plan of the book is as follows : the first eight chapters cover the fundamentals of the theory and include accounts of electrical conductors and magnetism at an elementary level ; chapters 9 to 11 deal with the theory of alternating currents and waves ; the next five chapters cover the experimental aspects of generators, radio, and alternating current measurements ; the final section is devoted to fuller accounts of noise, dielectrics, conductors, and magnetism, and a chapter on magnetic resonance, with particular reference to measurements of some fundamental constants.

The writing of any book on electricity and magnetism is bedevilled by the question of units. The authors were brought up on the two centimetre-gramme-second systems, and the practical system. To these is now added the metre-kilogramme-second system, making four systems at present in use. General adoption of the m.k.s. system would reduce this to one system, which is such an obvious advantage that the rationalized m.k.s. system has been adopted in this book. Unfortunately no general agreement on the definition of magnetization obtained while this book was in preparation ; the authors have therefore adopted the definition which is closest to the c.g.s. systems, which has the advantage that magnetostatics is closely parallel to electrostatics. This choice has been made to simplify as far as possible the transition from c.g.s. systems to the m.k.s. system, since many students who may wish to use this book will have been brought up on the former. For these students, a chapter on units has been included where methods are detailed for translating all the numbered equations into their equivalents in one of the c.g.s. systems. The choice of the rationalized m.k.s. system makes this translation more cumbersome, and the rather minor advantages of 'rationalization' are outweighed by the disadvantages of changes in the defining equations of a number of the fundamental quantities. These will disappear when the c.g.s. systems fall out of use, and the authors have therefore adopted the rationalized m.k.s. system to conform with present practice.

The authors are much indebted to their colleagues—in particular Drs. D. M. S. Bagguley, A. H. Cooke, J. H. E. Griffiths, H. G. Kuhn, and G. W. Series—who have criticized parts of the manuscript and made many helpful suggestions; to M. H. W. Gall, Esq., of Messrs. H. Tinsley & Co. Ltd., Professor L. F. Bates, F.R.S., and A. Hart, Esq., of Nottingham University, and to Messrs. L. J. Arundel and R. A. Kamper of the Clarendon Laboratory, for the considerable trouble they took in obtaining the photographs for Figs. 7.3, 21.6, 16.3, and 23.7 respectively; and to a number of pupils who have read various chapters and eliminated numerous errors. The authors are not so sanguine as to believe that no errors remain in other parts of the book, and they will be grateful to readers who inform them of any errors.

B. I. B.<br>B. B.

*Clarendon Laboratory*
*Oxford*
*April 1955*

# PREFACE TO THE SECOND EDITION

SINCE the first edition of this book appeared in 1957 there has been considerable progress, both experimental and theoretical, in understanding the electrical and magnetic properties of materials. Much of this is too advanced in approach for a book intended primarily for undergraduates or graduates starting research, but the authors have attempted to distil a suitable fraction of appropriate density for presentation at this level in the second edition. This is not always easy, and the authors apologize both to those who find sections lacking in the simple clarity which the ideal textbook should possess, and to those who find that over-simplification has resulted in a lack of accuracy.

The plan of the book is substantially the same as in the first edition. The first eight chapters cover the fundamentals of the theory and include accounts of electrical conductors and magnetism at an elementary level; Chapters 9–11 deal with the theory of alternating currents and waves; the next four chapters cover the experimental aspects of radio and alternating current measurements; the final part is devoted to fuller accounts of noise, dielectrics, conductors, and magnetism, ending with a chapter on magnetic resonance. This part, which overlaps with solid state physics, has been considerably rewritten; the section on semiconductors has been expanded into a separate chapter, with some account of the principles of junctions but stopping short of transistor circuitry; that on anti-ferromagnetism has been incorporated in a new chapter which also includes ferrimagnetism and the rare-earth metals. The discussion of conduction in metals, paramagnetism and ferromagnetism, and magnetic resonance, has been considerably revised and somewhat enlarged. Material elsewhere has been pruned wherever possible to minimize the increase in overall size; in particular the chapter on electrical machines has been omitted, except for low frequency transformers, whose equivalent circuit is discussed at the end of Chapter 9 on alternating current theory.

In the first edition the electromagnetic dipole moment of an elementary current circuit was defined in such a way as to retain $\mathbf{H}$ as the force (couple) vector on a magnetic dipole, while $\mathbf{B}$ is the force vector on a current. This was a compromise, intended to reduce the gap between the older c.g.s. system and the new m.k.s. system. However, the definition $\mathbf{m} = \mu\mu_0 \, I \, \mathbf{dS}$ had obvious difficulties in ferromagnetic media, and led to inconsistencies between dia- and paramagnetism, where the atomic formulae contained $\mu_0$ in the numerator in one case and in the denominator in the other. In common with other books using the m.k.s. system, the authors have therefore adopted the definition $\mathbf{m} = I\,\mathbf{dS}$ in the second edition, which gives a more logical treatment in which $\mathbf{B}$ is the force vector both for currents and magnetic dipoles. This has necessitated considerable changes in Chapter 5, and the opportunity has been taken to revise the treatment to give a more rigorous approach. Amongst other minor changes a fuller treatment of spherical harmonics is included in Chapter 2, together with the multipole expansion.

The authors are much indebted to Drs. B. V. Rollin, R. J. Elliott, and R. A. Stradling, who read part of the manuscript and made suggestions for improvements; also to many colleagues in Oxford and readers elsewhere who took the trouble to send comments on the first edition. With their help the authors have endeavoured to eliminate the errors that remained, but no doubt a fresh crop has been sown in the second edition, and the authors will be grateful to readers who inform them of such errors.

B. I. B.
B. B.

*Clarendon Laboratory*
*Oxford*
*April 1964*

I N the second impression we have made a number of minor changes, and we are grateful to many of our colleagues in Oxford and to readers elsewhere who have taken the trouble to point out errors and make suggestions for improvements. In particular we are indebted to Dr. G. D. Peskett, who suggested the new version of § 19.8 describing the more generally used common-emitter junction transistor circuit; we have also inserted in § 23.3 a more modern circuit for the detection of nuclear magnetic resonance.

*Clarendon Laboratory*
*Oxford*
*December 1967*

# ACKNOWLEDGEMENTS

THE authors are indebted to the following for permission to use published diagrams as a basis for figures in the text: the late Sir K. S. Krishnan; G. Benedek; R. Berman; D. F. Cochran; S. Dresselhaus; G. Duyckaerts; R. D. Frauenfelder; S. A. Friedberg; M. P. Garfunkel; W. E. Henry; A. F. Kip; C. Kittel; J. F. Koch; B. T. Matthias; K. A. G. Mendelssohn; D. E. Nagle; H. M. Rosenberg; C. G. Shull; J. S. Smart; J. W. Stout; R. A. Stradling; W. Sucksmith; R. W. Taylor; P. Vigoureux; W. E. Willshaw; W. P. Wolf; American Institute of Physics; American Physical Society; Institution of Electrical Engineers; Institute of Physics and the Physical Society (London); Royal Society (London); Bell Telephone Laboratories; A.E.I. Research Laboratories; G.E.C. Research Laboratories; North Holland Publishing Co.

# CONTENTS

1. ELECTROSTATICS I
 1.1 The electrical nature of matter  1
 1.2 Coulomb's law and fundamental definitions  3
 1.3 Gauss's theorem  8
 1.4 Electric dipoles  13
 1.5 The theory of isotropic dielectrics  16
 1.6 Properties of capacitors and systems of conductors  21
 1.7 Stress in the electrostatic field  26

2. ELECTROSTATICS II
 2.1 The equations of Poisson and Laplace  33
 2.2 Solutions of Laplace's equation in spherical coordinates  35
 2.3 The multipole expansion  38
 2.4 Some electrostatic problems  44
 2.5 Electrical images  48
 2.6 Line charges  52
 2.7 Images in dielectrics  55

3. STEADY CURRENTS
 3.1 Introduction  61
 3.2 Flow of current in conductors  63
 3.3 The voltaic circuit  66
 3.4 Resistance networks  68
 3.5 Wheatstone's bridge, and the measurement of resistance  71
 3.6 The potentiometer  73
 3.7 Electron optics  75
 3.8 The electrolytic tank  81

4. PROPERTIES OF ELECTRICAL CONDUCTORS
 4.1 Free electrons in metals—classical theory  85
 4.2 Free electrons in metals—quantum theory  88
 4.3 Work function and contact potential  95
 4.4 Emission of electrons from metals  97
 4.5 Thermoelectricity  103
 4.6 Conduction of electricity through liquids  109
 4.7 Voltaic cells  113
 4.8 Conduction of electricity through gases  116
 4.9 Plasma oscillations  123

5. THE MAGNETIC EFFECTS OF CURRENTS AND MOVING CHARGES, AND MAGNETOSTATICS

5.1 Forces between currents     126
5.2 Magnetic shells     130
5.3 Magnetostatics and magnetic media     135
5.4 Solution of magnetostatic problems     139
5.5 Steady currents in magnetic media     142
5.6 Calculation of the magnetic fields of simple circuits     148
5.7 Moving charges in electric and magnetic fields     151

6. ELECTROMAGNETIC INDUCTION AND VARYING CURRENTS

6.1 Faraday's laws of electromagnetic induction     158
6.2 Self-inductance and mutual inductance     161
6.3 Transient currents in circuits containing inductance, resistance, and capacitance     165
6.4 Magnetic energy and mechanical forces in inductive circuits     172
6.5 Magnetic energy in magnetic media     175

7. DIRECT CURRENT MEASUREMENTS

7.1 Galvanometers, ammeters, and voltmeters; the wattmeter     179
7.2 Galvanometer damping     184
7.3 The ballistic galvanometer and fluxmeter     186
7.4 Absolute measurements     190

8. MAGNETIC MATERIALS AND MAGNETIC MEASUREMENTS

8.1 Origins of magnetism     195
8.2 Diamagnetism     198
8.3 Paramagnetism     201
8.4 Ferromagnetism     204
8.5 Production of magnetic fields     207
8.6 Measurement of magnetic fields     214
8.7 Measurement of susceptibility     216
8.8 Experimental investigation of the hysteresis curve     221
8.9 Terrestrial magnetism     223

9. ALTERNATING CURRENT THEORY

9.1 Forced oscillations     227
9.2 Use of vectors and complex numbers     231
9.3 Tuned circuits     236
9.4 Coupled resonant circuits     243
9.5 Low-frequency transformers     247

## 10. ELECTROMAGNETIC WAVES

10.1 Maxwell's equations of the electromagnetic field            256

10.2. Plane waves in isotropic dielectrics                       260

10.3 The Poynting vector of energy flow                          263

10.4 Plane waves in conducting media                             265

10.5 The skin effect                                             267

10.6 Reflection and refraction of plane waves at the boundary of two
dielectrics                                                      269

10.7 Reflection from the surface of a metal                      277

10.8 The pressure due to radiation                               278

10.9 Radiation from an oscillating dipole                        281

## 11. FILTERS, TRANSMISSION LINES, AND WAVEGUIDES

11.1 Elements of filter theory                                   291

11.2 Some simple types of filter                                 297

11.3 Travelling waves on transmission lines                      302

11.4 Terminated loss-free lines                                  306

11.5 Attenuation on lossy lines, and resonant lines              311

11.6 Guided waves—propagation between two parallel conducting
planes                                                           315

11.7 Waveguides                                                  321

## 12. THERMIONIC VACUUM TUBES

12.1 Construction of the thermionic vacuum tube                  329

12.2 The diode                                                   331

12.3 The three-halves power law                                  332

12.4 Uses of the diode                                           335

12.5 The triode                                                  339

12.6 Characteristics of the triode                              340

12.7 Equivalent circuit of the triode                           343

12.8 Input impedance of the triode                              344

12.9 The screen-grid tetrode                                    347

12.10 The pentode                                               349

## 13. APPLICATIONS OF THERMIONIC VACUUM TUBES

13.1 Audio-frequency voltage amplifiers                         351

13.2 Negative feed-back amplifiers                              354

13.3 Audio-frequency power amplifiers                           355

13.4 Radio-frequency amplifiers                                 359

13.5 Tuned anode and tuned grid oscillators                     364

13.6 Power oscillators                                          368

13.7 The Kipp relay and the multivibrator                       370

13.8 Amplitude modulation and detection                         375

13.9 Frequency changing                                         380

13.10 Frequency modulation                                      383

13.11 Radio receivers                                           386

14. THERMIONIC VACUUM TUBES AT VERY HIGH FRE-
QUENCIES
    14.1 Effects of electrode impedance    390
    14.2 Effect of transit time on input conductance    393
    14.3 Modified circuits and tubes for metre and decimetre wavelengths    395
    14.4 The klystron    400
    14.5 The magnetron    405
    14.6 Crystal diodes    411
    14.7 Travelling wave tubes    412

15. ALTERNATING CURRENT MEASUREMENTS
    15.1 Measurement of voltage, current, and power    414
    15.2 Measurement of impedance at low frequencies    423
    15.3 Measurement of impedance at radio frequencies    429
    15.4 Measurement of frequency and wavelength    434
    15.5 Measurement of dielectric constant    442
    15.6 Measurement of the velocity of radio waves    445

16. FLUCTUATIONS AND NOISE
    16.1 Brownian motion and fluctuations    452
    16.2 Fluctuations in galvanometers    454
    16.3 The relation between resistance noise and thermal radiation    458
    16.4 Shot noise    462
    16.5 Design of receivers for optimum performance (minimum noise
        figure)    466
    16.6 Measurement of receiver noise    470

17. THEORY OF THE DIELECTRIC CONSTANT
    17.1 Molecular structure and the dielectric constant    475
    17.2 Dielectric constant of non-polar gases    477
    17.3 Static dielectric constant of polar gases    480
    17.4 Dispersion in gases    483
    17.5 Static dielectric constants of liquids and solids    488
    17.6 Static dielectric constants of polar liquids    491
    17.7 Radio-frequency dispersion in polar liquids    493
    17.8 Scattering    498

18. ELECTRONS IN METALS
    18.1 Kinetics of free electrons in metals    504
    18.2 The energy band approximation    506
    18.3 Conductors and insulators on the band theory    515
    18.4 Specific heat of the conduction electrons    517
    18.5 Electrical and thermal conductivity of metals    521
    18.6 The Hall effect    528
    18.7 Dia- and paramagnetism of conduction electrons    529

## 19. SEMICONDUCTORS

19.1 Intrinsic and extrinsic conductivity 536
19.2 Elementary and compound semiconductors 538
19.3 Electron distribution and the Fermi level 543
19.4 Optical properties 548
19.5 Transport properties 553
19.6 Metal-semiconductor junctions 560
19.7 The $p$–$n$ junction 565
19.8 The junction transistor 569

## 20. THE ATOMIC THEORY OF PARAMAGNETISM

20.1 A general precession theorem 574
20.2 The vector model of the atom 576
20.3 Magnetic moments of free atoms 585
20.4 The measurement of atomic magnetic moments—the Stern–Gerlach experiment 590
20.5 Curie's law and the approach to saturation 591
20.6 Susceptibility of paramagnetic solids—the $4f$ group 593
20.7 Susceptibility of paramagnetic solids—the $3d$ group 598
20.8 Susceptibility of paramagnetic solids—strongly bonded compounds 606
20.9 Electronic paramagnetism—a summary 609
20.10 Nuclear moments and hyperfine structure 610

## 21. FERROMAGNETISM

21.1 Exchange interaction between paramagnetic ions 618
21.2 The Weiss theory of spontaneous magnetization 622
21.3 Ferromagnetic domains 266
21.4 The gyromagnetic effect 634
21.5 Thermal effects in ferromagnetism 637
21.6 Measurement of the spontaneous magnetization $M_0$ as a function of temperature 640
21.7 Foundations of the theory of ferromagnetism 644
21.8 Spin waves 648
21.9 Mechanisms of exchange interaction 650

## 22 ANTI-FERROMAGNETISM AND FERRIMAGNETISM

22.1 Anti-ferromagnetism 657
22.2 The molecular field—two sub-lattice model 659
22.3 Ferrimagnetism 664
22.4 The lanthanide ('rare earth') metals 670
22.5 Neutron diffraction 673

23. MAGNETIC RESONANCE

    23.1  The magnetic resonance phenomenon                                677
    23.2  Molecular beams and nuclear magnetic resonance                   681
    23.3  Nuclear magnetic resonance in bulk material                     685
    23.4  Relaxation effects in nuclear magnetic resonance               689
    23.5  Applications of nuclear resonance                               692
    23.6  Electron magnetic resonance in atomic beams                     697
    23.7  Electron magnetic resonance in solids                           703
    23.8  Cyclotron resonance with free charged particles                 710
    23.9  Cyclotron resonance of charge carriers in semiconductors        717
    23.10 Azbel–Kaner resonance in metals                                 722

24. UNITS

    24.1  Unrationalized c.g.s. systems                                   729
    24.2  Practical units                                                 733
    24.3  The rationalized m.k.s. system                                  733
    24.4  Conversion factors from rationalized m.k.s. system             736
    24.5  Equivalent equations in unrationalized c.g.s. systems          737

APPENDIX A. VECTORS

    A.1  Definition of scalar and vector quantities                       744
    A.2  Vector addition and subtraction                                  744
    A.3  Multiplication of vectors                                        745
    A.4  Differentiation and integration of vectors                       747
    A.5  The divergence of a vector                                       748
    A.6  The curl of a vector                                             750
    A.7  Laplace's operator                                               751
    A.8  Stokes's theorem                                                 751
    A.9  The divergence theorem                                           752
    A.10 Transformation from a rotating coordinate system                 753
    A.11 Larmor's theorem                                                 753

APPENDIX B. THE UNIQUENESS THEOREM                                       755

APPENDIX C. NUMERICAL VALUES OF THE FUNDA-
MENTAL CONSTANTS                                                         756

APPENDIX D. SOME ATOMIC FORMULAE IN M.K.S. UNITS                         757

INDEX                                                                    759

# 1

## ELECTROSTATICS I

### 1.1. The electrical nature of matter

THE fundamental laws of electricity and magnetism were discovered by experimenters who had little or no knowledge of the modern theory of the atomic nature of matter. It should therefore be possible to present these laws in a textbook by dealing at first purely in macroscopic phenomena and then introducing gradually the details of atomic theory as required. In this way the subject might be developed almost in the historical order of discovery, and these opening sentences would talk of amber and cat's fur. It is more interesting, however, to discuss here and there throughout this book the interpretation of the macroscopic laws in terms of present atomic theory. In the later chapters a considerable knowledge of such theory will be assumed, since to give an adequate account of it would greatly increase the size of the book. This will not be attempted, but in the following paragraphs a summary is presented of what may be regarded almost as common knowledge of the nature of the atom.

On modern theory the atom consists of a central core, or nucleus, of diameter about $10^{-12}$ cm, surrounded by a number of electrons. These electrons move round the nucleus in orbits whose diameter is about $10^{-8}$ cm, and these determine the size of the atom. The nucleus contains two kinds of particles: protons, which are particles roughly 1836 times as heavy as electrons, but with a positive electric charge $+e$, and neutrons, of very nearly the same mass as protons, but with no electric charge. The number of electrons surrounding the nucleus is equal to the number of protons, and each electron has a negative charge $-e$, so that the atom as a whole is electrically neutral. The physical and chemical properties of the atoms are determined by the number of electrons they contain, and hence the number of protons in the nucleus is characteristic of a particular element. The number of neutrons is roughly equal to the number of protons in light elements but is over 1·5 times as great in the heaviest elements. The mass of the nucleus is determined by the total number of protons and neutrons, and a given element may have several stable forms of different nuclear mass, corresponding to nuclei with different numbers of neutrons, but the same number of protons. These are called isotopes. Thus the oxygen nucleus

B

has 8 protons, and there are three stable isotopes, oxygen 16, 17, and 18, with 8, 9, and 10 neutrons respectively, although the percentage of isotopes 17 and 18 occurring in nature is very small.

It is now established that the electronic charge is the fundamental unit of charge, and all charges are integral multiples of $+e$ or $-e$. It is therefore assumed that the electron is indivisible, and is a fundamental particle of matter; so also is the proton. We may summarize the properties of electron, proton, and neutron as follows:

| Particle | Charge | Mass |
|----------|--------|------|
| Electron | $-e$ | $m$ |
| Proton | $+e$ | $1836m$ |
| Neutron | $0$ | $1838m$ |

$e = 1 \cdot 602 \times 10^{-19}$ coulomb; $m = 0 \cdot 911 \times 10^{-27}$ g.

Since charges of opposite sign attract one another, the electrons are bound to the atom by the electrical attraction of the protons in the nucleus. The forces which hold the nucleus together are of different character, and operate only at very short ranges, of the order of the nuclear diameter.

## Conductors and insulators

For the purpose of electrostatic theory all substances can be divided into two fairly distinct classes: conductors, in which electrical charge can flow easily from one place to another; and insulators, in which it cannot. In the case of solids, all metals and a few other substances such as carbon are conductors, and their electrical properties can be explained by assuming that a number of electrons (roughly one per atom) are free to wander about the whole volume of the solid instead of being rigidly attached to one atom. Atoms which have lost one or more electrons in this way have a positive charge, and are called ions. They remain fixed in position in the solid lattice. In solid substances of the second class, insulators, each electron is firmly bound to the lattice of positive ions, and cannot move from point to point. Typical solid insulators are sulphur, paraffin wax, and mica.

When a substance has no net electrical charge, the total numbers of positive and negative charges within it must just be equal. Charge may be given to or removed from a substance, and a positively-charged substance has an excess of positive ions, while a negatively-charged substance has an excess of electrons. Since the electrons can move so much more easily in a conductor than the positive ions, a net positive charge is usually produced by the removal of electrons. In a charged conductor the electrons will move to positions of equilibrium under the influence of the forces of mutual repulsion between them, while in an insulator they are fixed in position and any initial distribution of charge will remain almost indefinitely. In a good conductor the movement of charge is almost instantaneous, while in a good insulator it is extremely slow. While there is no such thing as a perfect conductor or perfect insulator, such concepts are useful in developing electrostatic theory; metals form a good approximation to the former, and substances such as sulphur to the latter.

## 1.2. Coulomb's law and fundamental definitions

The force of attraction between charges of opposite sign, and of repulsion between charges of like sign, is found to be inversely proportional to the square of the distance between the charges (assuming them to be located at points), and proportional to the product of the magnitudes of the two charges. This law was discovered experimentally by Coulomb in 1785. In his apparatus the charges were carried on pith balls, and the force between them was measured with a torsion balance. The experiment was not very accurate, and a modern method of verifying the inverse square law with high precision will be given later (§ 1.3). From here on we shall assume it to be exact.

If the charges are $q_1$ and $q_2$, and $r$ is the distance between them, then the force $F$ on $q_2$ is along $r$. If the charges are of the same sign, the force is one of repulsion, whose magnitude is

$$F = C\frac{q_1 q_2}{r^2}.$$

The vector equation for the force is

$$\mathbf{F} = C\frac{q_1 q_2}{r^3}\mathbf{r}. \tag{1.1}$$

Here $\mathbf{F}$, $\mathbf{r}$ are counted as positive when directed from $q_1$ to $q_2$. Equation (1.1) is the mathematical expression of Coulomb's law.

The units of $\mathbf{F}$ and $\mathbf{r}$ are those already familiar from mechanics; it remains to determine the units of $C$ and $q$. Here there are two alternatives: either $C$ is arbitrarily given some fixed numerical value, when equation (1.1) may be used to determine the unit of charge, or the unit of charge may be taken as some arbitrary value, when the constant $C$ is to be determined by experiment. The electrostatic system of units (e.s.u.) makes the use of the first method. The force $F$ is in dynes, and the distance $r$ in centimetres (i.e. both are measured in the centimetre-gramme-second system), and the constant $C$ is set equal to unity. Then $q_1$, $q_2$ are measured in e.s.u. of charge, the unit being defined as that charge which repels an equal charge at a distance of 1 cm *in vacuo* with a force of 1 dyne. In the metre-kilogramme-second-coulomb system (m.k.s.), which will be used throughout this book, the unit of charge is the coulomb, the standard practical unit of charge (equal to one-tenth of the unit of charge in the electromagnetic system of units). For the present purpose it may be regarded as defined by the charge required to deposit a certain mass of silver in a silver voltameter, being thus defined in an arbitrary manner in the same way as the standard metre and standard kilogramme. Equation (1.1) for Coulomb's law is then analogous to that for gravitational attraction, except that it deals with electrical charges instead of masses, and the unknown constant of proportionality $C$ must be determined by experiment. In the 'rationalized' metre-kilogramme-second-coulomb system, the constant $C$ is written as $1/4\pi\epsilon_0$, the factor $4\pi$ being introduced to simplify certain equations which appear later in the theory. Equation (1.1) therefore becomes

$$\mathbf{F} = \frac{1}{4\pi\epsilon_0} \frac{q_1 q_2}{r^3} \mathbf{r}, \tag{1.2}$$

where $\mathbf{F}$ is in newtons, $\mathbf{r}$ in metres, and $q$ in coulombs. The quantity $\epsilon_0$ is known as the 'permittivity of free space' (see § 1.5); its experimental value is found to be (see § 7.4) $8 \cdot 85 \times 10^{-12}$ coulomb$^2$ newton$^{-1}$ metre$^{-2}$ (this unit can be more conveniently called farad metre$^{-1}$ (see § 1.6)). Since 1 newton $= 10^5$ dyne, and 1 metre $= 10^2$ cm, it may readily be shown that 1 coulomb $= 2 \cdot 998 \times 10^9$ e.s.u.

*Electric field and electric potential*

The force which a charge $q_2$ experiences when in the neighbourhood of another charge $q_1$ may be ascribed to the presence of an 'electric field' $\mathbf{E}$ produced by the charge $q_1$. Since the force on a charge $q_2$ is proportional to the magnitude of $q_2$, we define the field $\mathbf{E}$ by the equation

$$\mathbf{F} = \mathbf{E} q_2. \tag{1.3}$$

From this definition and Coulomb's law it follows that $\mathbf{E}$ does not depend on $q_2$, and is a vector quantity, like $\mathbf{F}$. From equation (1.2) we find that

$$\mathbf{E} = \frac{q_1}{4\pi\epsilon_0 r^3} \mathbf{r} \tag{1.4}$$

is the electric field due to the charge $q_1$.

If a unit positive charge is moved an infinitesimal distance **ds** in a field **E**, then the work done by the field is **E.ds**, and the work done against the field is −**E.ds**. This follows from the fact that the force on unit charge is equal to the electric field **E**. The work done against the field in moving a unit positive charge from a point $A$ to a point $B$ will therefore be

$$V = -\int_A^B \mathbf{E.ds}.$$

This is a scalar quantity known as the electric potential. If the field **E** is due to a single charge $q$ at $O$, as in Fig. 1.1, then the force on unit

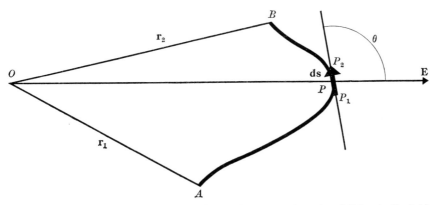

Fig. 1.1. Calculation of the potential difference between points $A$ and $B$ due to the field of a point charge $q$ at $O$.

charge at an arbitrary point $P$ is along $OP$, and **ds** is the vector element $P_1 P_2$. Now $\mathbf{E.ds} = E\cos\theta\, ds = E\,dr$, and hence

$$V_B - V_A = -\int_A^B E\,dr = -\frac{q}{4\pi\epsilon_0}\int_{r_1}^{r_2}\frac{dr}{r^2} = \frac{q}{4\pi\epsilon_0}\left(\frac{1}{r_2} - \frac{1}{r_1}\right).$$

Thus the difference of potential between $A$ and $B$ depends only on the positions of $A$ and $B$, and is independent of the path taken between them.

The potential at a point distance $r$ from a charge $q$ is the work done in bringing up unit charge to the point in question from a point at zero potential. By convention, the potential is taken as zero at an infinite distance from all charges, that is, $V = 0$ for $r = \infty$. Therefore the potential at a point distance $r$ from a charge $q$ is

$$V = q/(4\pi\epsilon_0 r). \tag{1.5}$$

The difference in potential $dV$ between $P_1$ and $P_2$ (Fig. 1.1) distance **ds** apart is

$$dV = -\mathbf{E.ds} = -(E_x\,dx + E_y\,dy + E_z\,dz).$$

Hence $$E = -\text{grad}\, V = -\nabla V, \tag{1.6}$$

where in Cartesian coordinates grad $V = \mathbf{i}\,\partial V/\partial x + \mathbf{j}\,\partial V/\partial y + \mathbf{k}\,\partial V/\partial z$ and $\mathbf{i}, \mathbf{j}, \mathbf{k}$ are unit vectors parallel to the $x$, $y$, and $z$-axes. The components of $\mathbf{E}$ along the three axes are

$$E_x = -\frac{\partial V}{\partial x}, \qquad E_y = -\frac{\partial V}{\partial y}, \qquad E_z = -\frac{\partial V}{\partial z}.$$

The negative sign shows that of itself a positive charge will move from a higher to a lower potential, and work must be done to move it in the opposite direction. (For vector relations, see Appendix A.)

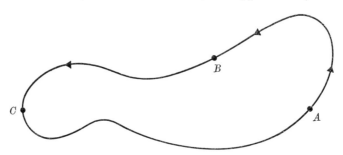

FIG. 1.2. The work done in taking an electric charge round a closed path in an electrostatic field is zero.

The work done in taking a charge $q$ round a closed path in an electrostatic field is zero. This can be seen from Fig. 1.2. The work done in taking the charge $q$ round the path $ABCA$ is

$$W = -q \oint \mathbf{E}.\mathbf{ds} = q(V_B - V_A) + q(V_C - V_B) + q(V_A - V_C) = 0,$$

and is independent of the path taken provided it begins and ends at the same point. Therefore the electric potential is a single-valued function of the space coordinates in any stationary distribution of electric charges; it has only one value at any point in the field.

Since potential is a scalar quantity the potential at any point is simply the algebraic sum of the potentials due to each separate charge. On the other hand, $\mathbf{E}$ is a vector quantity, and the resultant field is the vector sum of the individual fields. Hence it is nearly always simpler to work in terms of potential rather than field; once the potential distribution is found, the field at any point is found by using equation (1.6).

*Units*

From equation (1.3) we obtain the definition of electric field. An electric field of 1 unit exerts a force of 1 newton on a charge of 1 coulomb. Electric fields can therefore be expressed in newton/coulomb.

The unit of potential is defined as follows: When 1 joule of work is done in transferring a charge of 1 coulomb from $A$ to $B$, the potential difference between $A$ and $B$ is 1 volt. From equation (1.6) $E$ can be expressed in volts/metre, and this is the unit which is customarily used. It is easily verified that the two alternative units for $E$ are equivalent.

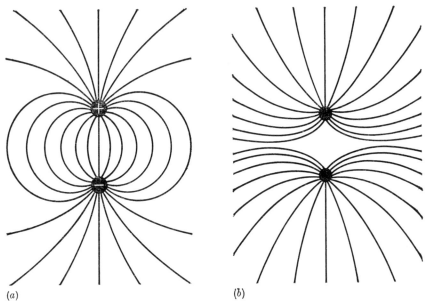

(a)                                      (b)

FIG. 1.3. (a) Lines of force between equal charges of opposite sign. (b) Lines of force between equal charges of the same sign.

## Lines of force

A line drawn in such a way that it is parallel to the direction of the field at any point is called a line of force. Figure 1.3 shows the lines of force for two equal charges. Lines of force do not intersect one another since the direction of the field cannot have two values at one point; they are continuous in a region containing no free charges, and they begin and end on free charges. The number of lines of force drawn through unit area normal to the direction of $\mathbf{E}$ is equal to the value of $E$ at that point.

If a series of curves is drawn, each curve passing through points at a given potential, these equipotential curves cut the lines of force orthogonally. Equipotential curves are generally drawn for equal increments of potential; then $\mathbf{E}$ is greatest where the equipotentials are closest together.

### 1.3. Gauss's theorem

Let $S$ be a closed surface surrounding a charge $q$, and let $q$ be distant $r$ from a small area $\mathbf{dS}$ on the surface $S$ at $A$ (Fig. 1.4 (a)). The electric intensity $\mathbf{E}$ at $A$ has the value

$$E = \frac{q}{4\pi\epsilon_0 r^2}.$$

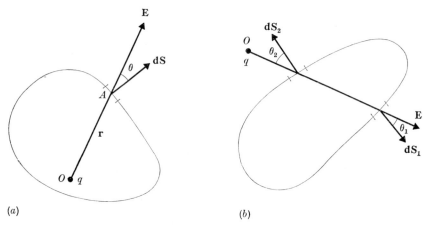

Fig. 1.4. Illustrating Gauss's theorem.

The number of lines of force passing through an element of area $dS$ is

$$\mathbf{E}.\mathbf{dS} = E\cos\theta \, dS = \frac{q\cos\theta \, dS}{4\pi\epsilon_0 r^2},$$

where the outward normal to the surface element makes an angle $\theta$ with $\mathbf{E}$. Now the solid angle subtended by $dS$ at $O$ is $d\omega = \cos\theta \, dS/r^2$, and the value of $E\cos\theta \, dS$ is therefore $q\, d\omega/(4\pi\epsilon_0)$. Hence the total number of lines of force passing through the whole surface is

$$\int E\cos\theta \, dS = \frac{q}{4\pi\epsilon_0}\int d\omega = \frac{q}{\epsilon_0}, \qquad (1.7\,\text{a})$$

since a closed surface subtends a total solid angle of $4\pi$ at any point within the volume enclosed by the surface. If there are a number of charges $q_1, q_2, ..., q_n$ inside $S$, the resultant intensity of $\mathbf{E}$ at any point is the vector sum of the intensities due to each separate charge, and the integration of equation (1.7 a) may be carried out separately for each charge. In this way it is found that $\int E\cos\theta \, dS = \sum q/\epsilon_0$. On the other hand, the contribution of any charge outside $S$ is zero, as may be seen from Fig. 1.4 (b), since in this case

$$\int E \cos \theta \, dS = \frac{q}{4\pi\epsilon_0}\left[\int \frac{dS_1 \cos \theta_1}{r_1^2} - \int \frac{dS_2 \cos \theta_2}{r_2^2}\right] = 0.$$

We may summarize these results in the form

$$\int E \cos \theta \, dS = \int \mathbf{E}.\mathbf{dS} = \sum q/\epsilon_0, \qquad (1.7\,b)$$

where the summation is to be taken only over the charges lying within the closed surface $S$. This is known as Gauss's theorem. We see that the integral of the normal component of $\mathbf{E}$ over the surface is equal to the total charge enclosed, divided by $\epsilon_0$, irrespective of the way in which the charge is distributed.

If there exists throughout a volume enclosed by a surface $S$ a charge distribution of varying density $\rho$, we have

$$\frac{1}{\epsilon_0}\int \rho \, d\tau = \int \mathbf{E}.\mathbf{dS} = \int \mathrm{div}\, \mathbf{E} \, d\tau, \qquad (1.7\,c)$$

where $d\tau$ is an element of volume. The two volume integrals must be equal whatever the volume over which the integration takes place, and it therefore follows that the integrands themselves must be equal. Hence

$$\mathrm{div}\, \mathbf{E} = \frac{\partial E_x}{\partial x} + \frac{\partial E_y}{\partial y} + \frac{\partial E_z}{\partial z} = \rho/\epsilon_0, \qquad (1.8)$$

and this is the expression in differential form of Gauss's theorem. The transformation from a surface to a volume integral used above is due to Gauss (see Appendix A).

One of the consequences of Gauss's theorem is that there can be no field within a conductor, nor can there be any volume distribution of charge within it. For, if there were such a charge distribution, a field would exist within the conductor, which would act on the charges. Since they are free to move in a conductor, they cannot then be in a state of equilibrium. Thus no electrostatic field can exist within the body of a conductor, and all parts of it must be at the same potential. If the conductor has a total charge different from zero, then this charge must reside entirely in a thin layer on the outer surface.

The fact that there can be no electric field within the body of a conductor has an important consequence in the case of a hollow closed conductor. If we apply Gauss's theorem to a surface $S$ lying entirely within the conducting substance, as in Fig. 1.5 (b), then $\int E \cos \theta \, dS = 0$, since $\mathbf{E} = 0$ everywhere over the surface. Hence the net charge inside the surface must be zero. This can be realized in two ways: (a) if there is a total charge $q$ in the hollow space within the conductor, the lines of force from the charges comprising $q$ must end on a distribution of charge on the inner surface of the conductor, and the total charge in this layer must be equal to $-q$; (b) if there is no charge in the hollow space, then there can be no field in this space. This last result is important, for many proofs of the inverse square law (see below) depend

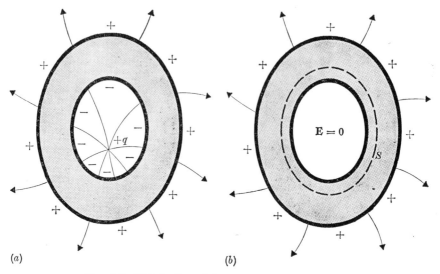

FIG. 1.5. Distribution of charge on a hollow conductor.

(a) A hollow conductor with a point charge $+q$ inside, and induced charges $-q$ and $+q$ on the inside and outside surfaces.

(b) The same conductor with no charge inside, and total charge $+q$ on the surface.

on it. It means that if we put a closed conductor into a field, a charge distribution on the outer surface will be set up such that the field inside remains exactly zero.

*Experimental proof of the inverse square law*

Coulomb's attempts to check the inverse square law using a torsion balance were not capable of great accuracy, and most subsequent attempts have relied on the fact that the field inside a closed conductor is only zero if the inverse square law holds. We shall prove this for the special case of a spherical conductor.

In Fig. 1.6 let an elementary cone of solid angle $d\omega$ be drawn with vertex at the point $O$ within the sphere. This cone intersects the surface of the sphere in the elementary areas $dS_1$, $dS_2$ at distances $r_1$, $r_2$ from $O$.

If the charge on the sphere has a uniform density $\sigma$ per unit area, then the field at $O$ due to the elements $dS_1$ and $dS_2$ will be

$$dE = \frac{\sigma}{4\pi\epsilon_0}\left[\frac{dS_1}{r_1^n} - \frac{dS_2}{r_2^n}\right]$$

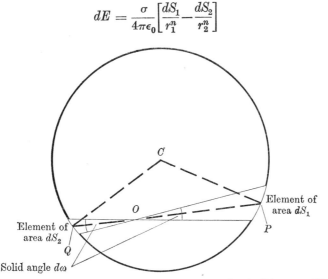

FIG. 1.6. The field inside a spherical conductor at a point $O$. Distances $OP = r_1$, $OQ = r_2$. From the geometry of the circle, $\angle OPC = \angle OQC = \theta$. Hence

$$d\omega = \frac{dS_1\cos\theta}{r_1^2} = \frac{dS_2\cos\theta}{r_2^2}.$$

assuming that the field of a point charge falls off as $r^{-n}$. But the solid angle $d\omega = dS_1\cos\theta/r_1^2 = dS_2\cos\theta/r_2^2$, and we can therefore write

$$dE = \frac{\sigma\,d\omega}{4\pi\epsilon_0\cos\theta}\left[\frac{1}{r_1^{n-2}} - \frac{1}{r_2^{n-2}}\right].$$

This gives a resultant field towards the nearer element if $n < 2$, and towards the further element if $n > 2$. Clearly, the whole surface of the sphere can be divided into elementary areas in this way, and the vector resultant of the fields at $O$ will not be zero unless all the individual $dE$ are zero, since there will be a resultant towards the nearer portion of the spherical surface if $n < 2$, and vice versa. Thus, if it is shown experimentally that there is no field inside a charged sphere, it follows that the power of $n$ in the inverse power law must be exactly 2.

This result was used to test the validity of the inverse square law by Cavendish and, later, by Maxwell. Maxwell had a spherical air condenser consisting of two concentric insulated spherical shells. The outer sphere had a small hole in it so that the inner one could be tested for charge by inserting through the hole an electrode connected to an electrometer. The two spheres were initially connected by a wire and charged to a high potential, and then insulated from one another. After earthing the outer sphere, the inner one was tested and found to have no charge. In this way Maxwell found that the value of $n$ did not differ from 2 by more than one part in 21 600.

The experiment has been repeated by Plimpton and Lawton (1936) with a more sensitive detector, the electrometer being replaced by an

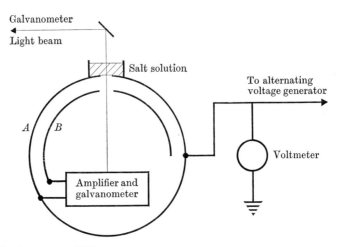

FIG. 1.7. Apparatus of Plimpton and Lawton for verifying the inverse square law.

amplifier and galvanometer. The detecting apparatus was placed inside the sphere $A$ (see Fig. 1.7), and its conducting case, together with the hemisphere $B$, formed the inner conductor (it was shown that this does not necessarily have to be spherical in shape). The galvanometer deflexion was observed through a small hole in the sphere $A$, covered by a wire grid immersed in salt solution so that $A$ was effectively a closed conductor. It was found that this was essential for the field inside to be rigorously zero when $n = 2$. The galvanometer was un-damped so that it could swing at its natural period ($\frac{1}{2}$ sec), and an alternating voltage of 3000 V, whose frequency was adjusted to syn-chronism with the galvanometer, was applied to the outer sphere. No potential difference between the inner and outer spheres was found, though a voltage of $10^{-6}$ V could have been detected. It was found that this was only true if the hole in $A$ was covered with the salt solution. The galvanometer deflexion observed if this was removed was used to check that the frequency of the alternating voltage was equal to the natural period of the galvanometer. From this experiment, Plimpton and Lawton concluded that $n$ did not differ from 2 by more than one part in $10^9$.

## 1.4. Electric dipoles

An electric dipole consists of two charges equal in magnitude but of opposite sign, separated by a small distance. Figure 1.8 shows such a dipole with charges $+q$ and $-q$ separated by a distance $a$. Then the potential at a point $P$ is

$$V = \frac{q}{4\pi\epsilon_0}\left(\frac{1}{r_2} - \frac{1}{r_1}\right), \qquad (1.9)$$

and if $a \ll r$, so that quantities of the order $(a/r)^2$ may be neglected,

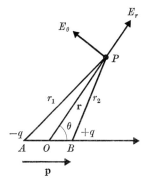

FIG. 1.8. The electric potential and the field due to an electric dipole.

$$\begin{aligned}
V &= \frac{q}{4\pi\epsilon_0}\left(\frac{1}{r-\tfrac{1}{2}a\cos\theta} - \frac{1}{r+\tfrac{1}{2}a\cos\theta}\right)\\
&= \frac{qa\cos\theta}{4\pi\epsilon_0}\left(\frac{1}{r^2-\tfrac{1}{4}a^2\cos^2\theta}\right) \approx \frac{qa\cos\theta}{4\pi\epsilon_0 r^2} = \frac{p\cos\theta}{4\pi\epsilon_0 r^2}.
\end{aligned}$$

$$(1.10\,\mathrm{a})$$

Here the product $qa$ has been written as $p$, and is known as the dipole moment. If $\mathbf{r}$ is a vector drawn from $O$ as origin to $P$, then

$$p\cos\theta = (\mathbf{p}.\mathbf{r})/r,$$

where $\mathbf{p}$ is a vector whose magnitude is equal to the dipole moment and whose direction is from the negative charge to the positive charge. Then

$$V = \frac{\mathbf{p}.\mathbf{r}}{4\pi\epsilon_0 r^3}. \qquad (1.10\,\mathrm{b})$$

If $O$ is a fixed point and $P$ is regarded as a variable point, then

$$\mathbf{r}/r^3 = -\mathrm{grad}(1/r),$$

so that the formula for the potential may also be written as

$$V = -\frac{1}{4\pi\epsilon_0}\{\mathbf{p}.\mathrm{grad}_P(1/r)\}. \qquad (1.11\,\mathrm{a})$$

Here the subscript $P$ is added to the operator grad to denote that differentiation is with respect to $P$ as the variable point. If we regard $P$ as fixed, and move from $A$ to $B$, then equation (1.9) could have been written in the form

$$V = \frac{1}{4\pi\epsilon_0}\{\mathbf{p}.\mathrm{grad}_O(1/r)\}, \qquad (1.11\,\mathrm{b})$$

since the vector **r** in (1.10 b) is now drawn in the opposite sense, where the subscript $O$ denotes that $O$ is now the variable point, and there is a change of sign from equation (1.11 a) because **r** is now measured in the opposite direction.

The components of the electric field at $P$ can be calculated by

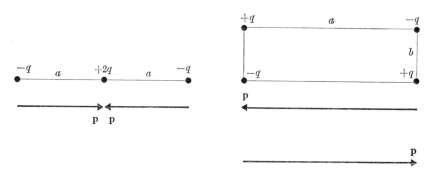

FIG. 1.9. Two quadrupole moments represented as an assembly of charges or a pair of dipoles; note that the net charge and net dipole moment are zero in each case.

differentiating the potential given by equation (1.10 a). The radial and azimuthal components are

$$
\left.
\begin{aligned}
E_r &= -\left(\frac{\partial V}{\partial r}\right)_\theta = \frac{1}{4\pi\epsilon_0}\left(\frac{2p\cos\theta}{r^3}\right) \\
E_\theta &= -\frac{1}{r}\left(\frac{\partial V}{\partial\theta}\right)_r = \frac{1}{4\pi\epsilon_0}\left(\frac{p\sin\theta}{r^3}\right)
\end{aligned}
\right\}. \tag{1.12}
$$

These equations show that the electric field of a dipole falls off as $1/r^3$, and its potential as $1/r^2$, whereas the corresponding laws for a single pole are $1/r^2$ and $1/r$. The significance of this difference is that at large distances the fields of the two equal and opposite charges which comprise a dipole cancel one another in the first approximation (that is, terms varying as $1/r^2$ vanish), but terms in the next order ($1/r^3$ in the field) remain. Similarly, if two dipoles are placed end to end, giving a set of charges as in Fig. 1.9 (known as a quadrupole), their fields annul one another at large distances, and the potential of a quadrupole falls off as $1/r^3$ (see Problem 1.1), and its field as $1/r^4$.

If a dipole consisting of two charges $-q$ and $+q$ a distance **a** apart is placed in a uniform field, its potential energy $U_P$ is (see Fig. 1.10)

$$
U_P = q(V_B - V_A) = -qa\cos\theta\,E = -q\mathbf{a}.\mathbf{E} = -\mathbf{p}.\mathbf{E}, \tag{1.13}
$$

where **p** is the dipole moment. This shows that the energy depends only on the angle which **p** makes with **E**, and not on the position of the dipole. Hence there is no translational force acting on the dipole, but there is a couple

$$\Gamma = -(dU_P/d\theta) = pE\sin\theta = \mathbf{p}\wedge\mathbf{E},\qquad(1.14)$$

which tends to turn the dipole into a position parallel to the field.

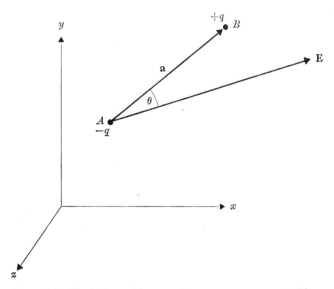

FIG. 1.10. Dipole formed by two charges $-q$, $+q$ separated by a distance $\mathbf{a}$, in a field $\mathbf{E}$.

If the dipole is placed in a non-uniform field, a translational force is exerted on it, and we shall derive an expression for the $x$-component of this force. If $E_x$ is the value of the $x$-component of the field at $A$, its value at $B$ may be written as

$$E'_x = E_x + \left(\frac{\partial E_x}{\partial x}\right)a_x + \left(\frac{\partial E_x}{\partial y}\right)a_y + \left(\frac{\partial E_x}{\partial z}\right)a_z,$$

where $a_x$, $a_y$, $a_z$ are the components of $\mathbf{a}$ along the three axes. The $x$-component of the force on the dipole is therefore

$$F_x = -qE_x + qE'_x = qa_x\left(\frac{\partial E_x}{\partial x}\right) + qa_y\left(\frac{\partial E_x}{\partial y}\right) + qa_z\left(\frac{\partial E_x}{\partial z}\right)$$

$$= p_x\left(\frac{\partial E_x}{\partial x}\right) + p_y\left(\frac{\partial E_x}{\partial y}\right) + p_z\left(\frac{\partial E_x}{\partial z}\right).$$

Now

$$\frac{\partial E_x}{\partial y} = \frac{\partial}{\partial y}\left(-\frac{\partial V}{\partial x}\right) = \frac{\partial}{\partial x}\left(-\frac{\partial V}{\partial y}\right) = \frac{\partial E_y}{\partial x},$$

since the order of differentiation is immaterial, and similarly

$$\frac{\partial E_x}{\partial z} = \frac{\partial E_z}{\partial x}.$$

Hence the force component may be written as

$$F_x = p_x\frac{\partial E_x}{\partial x} + p_y\frac{\partial E_y}{\partial x} + p_z\frac{\partial E_z}{\partial x} \qquad (1.15)$$

with similar expressions for the other components.

## 1.5. The theory of isotropic dielectrics

Faraday found that if a slab of insulating material was inserted between two metal plates across which a constant voltage was applied by means of a battery, the charge on the plates increased. If the insulator entirely filled the intervening space, the charge increased by a factor $\epsilon$, where $\epsilon$ is called the dielectric constant, relative permittivity, or specific inductive capacity of the insulator. It varies between 1 and 10 for most solid substances, being 1 for vacuum and 1·00057 for air at room temperature and pressure. To find how $\epsilon$ is related to the intrinsic properties of the material, or dielectric, it is necessary to consider what happens inside a dielectric when an electric field is applied to it.

Dielectric substances are insulators, and therefore do not contain free electrons. Each electron is bound to the ionic lattice by the electrostatic attraction between the negative electronic charge and the positive charges on the nuclei. In the absence of any external field, the electrons are distributed symmetrically with respect to the nuclei, but when a field is applied, the electrons are displaced in the direction opposite to that of the field, while the more massive nuclei are slightly displaced in the direction of the field. (The centre of gravity remains fixed, since there is no translational force on the system as a whole.) Each ion thus acquires an electric dipole moment which is parallel to and in the same direction as the applied field. If a slab of dielectric is placed between parallel metal plates as in Faraday's experiment and the voltage across the plates is constant, there will be an induced negative charge on the dielectric surface near the positive plate, Fig. 1.11, and a similar positive charge on the surface near the negative plate. There will be no resultant charge density at any point within the dielectric as all the individual dipoles are aligned parallel to the field and hence each negative charge of one dipole is next to the positive charge of the next dipole. The surface charges on the dielectric will induce charges of opposite sign on the plates, and the charge on the plates is increased when the dielectric is inserted, if the voltage is kept constant, as Faraday found in his experiments.

The action of the electric field in giving each atom of the dielectric an induced dipole moment is termed polarization. The polarization of the substance **P** is defined as the electric dipole moment per unit volume, and it is proportional in magnitude to the applied field **E** at all ordinary

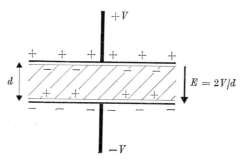

Fig. 1.11. Effect of a dielectric in increasing the capacitance between two parallel plates.

field strengths. **P** is a vector and in an isotropic substance it is parallel to **E** so that we may write

$$\mathbf{P} = \chi\epsilon_0\,\mathbf{E}. \tag{1.16}$$

Here $\chi$ is a constant for any given substance, known as the polarizability or the electric susceptibility.

The resultant moment for an element of volume $d\tau$ is $\mathbf{P}\,d\tau$, and the potential of such an element a distance $r$ away is, by equation (1.11 b),

$$dV = \frac{1}{4\pi\epsilon_0}(\mathbf{P}\,d\tau).\text{grad}(1/r),$$

where the differentiation is with respect to the coordinates of the volume element containing the dipoles. The potential due to a finite volume of dielectric is then

$$V = \int \frac{1}{4\pi\epsilon_0}\{\mathbf{P}.\text{grad}(1/r)\}\,d\tau.$$

But

$$\text{div}(\mathbf{P}/r) = \frac{1}{r}\text{div}\,\mathbf{P} + \mathbf{P}.\text{grad}(1/r).$$

Hence

$$V = \int \frac{1}{4\pi\epsilon_0}\text{div}(\mathbf{P}/r)\,d\tau - \int \frac{1}{4\pi\epsilon_0}\frac{1}{r}\text{div}\,\mathbf{P}\,d\tau$$

$$= \int \frac{1}{4\pi\epsilon_0}\frac{1}{r}\mathbf{P}.d\mathbf{S} - \int \frac{1}{4\pi\epsilon_0}\frac{1}{r}\text{div}\,\mathbf{P}\,d\tau, \tag{1.17}$$

where Gauss's theorem of divergence has been used in the transformation from a volume to a surface integral. These two terms in equation (1.17) show that the resultant potential can be attributed to an apparent surface charge of density $P\cos\theta$, where $\theta$ is the angle which $\mathbf{P}$ makes with the normal to the surface of the dielectric, and an apparent volume distribution of charge whose density is

$$-\text{div}\,\mathbf{P} = -(\partial P_x/\partial x + \partial P_y/\partial y + \partial P_z/\partial z).$$

If $\chi$ is uniform, isotropic, and independent of field, and there is no volume distribution of real charge, $\text{div}\,\mathbf{P} = \chi\epsilon_0\,\text{div}\,\mathbf{E} = 0$, and there is no volume distribution of apparent charge. The surface distribution vanishes only when there is no applied field. These apparent charges are often called 'polarization charges'. Note that in the derivation of equation (1.17) it has not been assumed that the dielectric is isotropic.

*Gauss's theorem in dielectrics*

In § 1.3 it was shown by Gauss's theorem that the integral $\int \mathbf{E}.\mathbf{dS}$ of the normal component of $\mathbf{E}$ over any closed surface is equal to the total charge within the surface, divided by $\epsilon_0$. If the surface is within a dielectric medium, the total charge must include both the free charges and the polarization charges. The volume charge density is thus $\rho-(\text{div}\,\mathbf{P})$, so that

$$\int \mathbf{E}.\mathbf{dS} = \int \text{div}\,\mathbf{E}\,d\tau = \frac{1}{\epsilon_0}\int (\rho-\text{div}\,\mathbf{P})\,d\tau$$

so that
$$\int \text{div}(\epsilon_0\,\mathbf{E}+\mathbf{P})\,d\tau = \int \rho\,d\tau.$$

Comparison of this with equation (1.7 c) shows that, in effect, $\epsilon_0\,\mathbf{E}$ has been replaced by $(\epsilon_0\,\mathbf{E}+\mathbf{P})$. We may define a new vector $\mathbf{D}$, such that

$$\mathbf{D} = \epsilon_0\,\mathbf{E}+\mathbf{P}. \tag{1.18}$$

$\mathbf{D}$ is known as the 'electric displacement', and equation (1.18) is valid even in an anisotropic medium where $\mathbf{P}$ is not necessarily parallel to $\mathbf{E}$. We may now write Gauss's theorem, in a dielectric medium, in the form

$$\int \mathbf{D}.\mathbf{dS} = \int \text{div}\,\mathbf{D}\,d\tau = \int \rho\,d\tau. \tag{1.19}$$

Since the volume integrals must be equal over any arbitrary volume, it follows that their integrands must be equal, i.e.

$$\text{div}\,\mathbf{D} = \rho, \tag{1.20}$$

which is the differential form of Gauss's theorem. It is easy to see that these equations reduce to those of § 1.3 *in vacuo*, where $\mathbf{P} = 0$. An alternative way of deriving equation (1.20) directly for the special case of Cartesian coordinates is given in Appendix A.

In an isotropic dielectric, $\mathbf{P}$ is parallel to $\mathbf{E}$, and hence so also is $\mathbf{D}$. Since $\mathbf{P} = \chi\epsilon_0\,\mathbf{E}$, $\mathbf{D} = \epsilon_0(1+\chi)\mathbf{E}$, and if we write

$$\epsilon = 1+\chi \tag{1.21}$$

we have
$$\mathbf{D} = \epsilon\epsilon_0\,\mathbf{E}, \tag{1.22}$$

where $\epsilon$ is the 'dielectric constant' and $\chi$ is the susceptibility; for vacuum (or air, for most purposes), $\chi = 0$, and $\epsilon = 1$. The ratio of $\mathbf{D}$ to $\mathbf{E}$ is known as the 'permittivity'; in free space $\mathbf{D}/\mathbf{E} = \epsilon_0$, and thus $\epsilon_0$ is the 'permittivity of free space'. When a medium is present $\mathbf{D}/\mathbf{E}$ is increased by the factor $\epsilon$, known also as the 'relative permittivity'.

If we have a single point charge $q$ in a uniform dielectric of constant $\epsilon$, we may apply Gauss's theorem over a sphere of radius $r$ with centre at $q$. Then the surface integral reduces to $4\pi r^2 D = 4\pi r^2\epsilon\epsilon_0\,E = q$, whence

$$\epsilon\epsilon_0\,\mathbf{E} = \mathbf{D} = \frac{q\mathbf{r}}{4\pi r^3}. \tag{1.23}$$

It follows that the force between two charges $q_1$, $q_2$ a distance $r$ apart is

$$\mathbf{F} = \frac{q_1 q_2}{4\pi\epsilon\epsilon_0\,r^3}\mathbf{r} \tag{1.24}$$

and the potential at a distance $r$ from a point charge is

$$V = \frac{q}{4\pi\epsilon\epsilon_0\,r}. \tag{1.25}$$

*Some properties of* $\mathbf{D}$ *and* $\mathbf{E}$

It is important to distinguish clearly between the two vector quantities electric field $\mathbf{E}$ and electric displacement $\mathbf{D}$. $\mathbf{E}$ is defined as the force acting on unit charge, irrespective of whether a dielectric medium is present or not. This definition is expressed in equation (1.3). The displacement $\mathbf{D}$ is defined by equation (1.18). The quantity $\mathbf{D}.\mathbf{dS}$ is sometimes known as the electric flux through the element of area $\mathbf{dS}$. From (1.19) the total flux is $q$ through an area surrounding a charge $q$, and this flux is unaltered by the presence of a dielectric medium. The unit of flux is the coulomb, and the unit of $D$ is coulomb/metre$^2$.

Since $\mathbf{D}$ is a vector we may draw lines of displacement analogous to lines of force, such that the number passing through unit area is equal to the displacement. Also by Gauss's theorem lines of displacement are continuous in a space containing no free charges; they begin and end only on free charges. At the boundary of two dielectrics $\epsilon_1$ and $\epsilon_2$, if no free charge resides there, lines of $\mathbf{D}$ are continuous but lines of $\mathbf{E}$ are not, because lines of force end on both free and polarization charges, whereas lines of $\mathbf{D}$ end only on free charges. There is a polarization charge on the surface separating two dielectrics, since the induced moment per unit volume is different in the two media. Lines of E begin

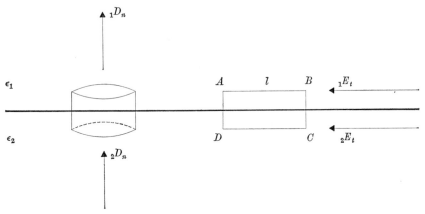

F<small>IG</small>. 1.12. Boundary conditions at the surface between two dielectrics.

and end on this surface charge, but not lines of $\mathbf{D}$. The rules governing the behaviour of $\mathbf{E}$ and $\mathbf{D}$ at the surface of a dielectric, or the boundary between two dielectrics, are embodied in two 'boundary conditions', which will now be derived.

To find the boundary condition for $\mathbf{D}$, we apply Gauss's theorem to a small cylinder which intersects the boundary, as in Fig. 1.12, and whose axis is normal to the boundary. If the height of the cylinder is very small compared with its cross-sectional area, the only contribution to $\int \mathbf{D}.\mathbf{dS}$ over its surface will come from the components of $\mathbf{D}$ normal to the boundary. Since there is no free charge on the boundary, $\int \mathbf{D}.\mathbf{dS} = 0$, and hence

$$_1D_n = {}_2D_n, \tag{1.26}$$

where the symbols refer to the normal components of $\mathbf{D}$ on the two sides of the boundary.

The boundary condition for $\mathbf{E}$ is found by considering the work done in taking unit charge round a small rectangular circuit such as $ABCDA$ in Fig. 1.12. If the sides $BC$, $AD$ are very small compared with $AB$, $CD$, then the work done will be $l({}_1E_t - {}_2E_t) = 0$. Hence

$$_1E_t = {}_2E_t, \tag{1.27}$$

where the symbols refer to the tangential components of $\mathbf{E}$ on either side of the boundary. Thus equations (1.26) and (1.27) are our two

fundamental boundary conditions. It follows from them that lines of
**D** will in general be refracted at the boundary between two dielectrics.
A typical example is shown in Fig. 1.13.

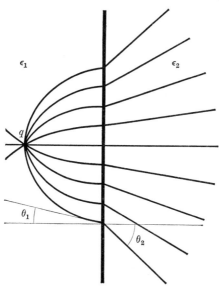

FIG. 1.13. Refraction of lines of displacement at the boundary between two dielectrics
($\epsilon_2 > \epsilon_1$). From equations (1.26) and (1.27) we have

$$D_1 \cos \theta_1 = D_2 \cos \theta_2,$$

$$E_1 \sin \theta_1 = (D_1/\epsilon_1 \, \epsilon_0)\sin \theta_1 = E_2 \sin \theta_2 = (D_2/\epsilon_2 \, \epsilon_0)\sin \theta_2.$$

Hence
$$\epsilon_1 \cot \theta_1 = \epsilon_2 \cot \theta_2.$$

Similar boundary conditions may be applied at the surface of a conductor. Since there can be no field inside the conductor, the tangential
component of **E** just outside the conductor must also be zero, and any
field at the surface must be normal to the surface. If we apply Gauss's
theorem to an elementary cylinder intersecting the surface, as in Fig. 1.12
we have $_1D_n \, dS = \sigma \, dS$ (since $_2D_n = 0$ within the conductor), where $\sigma$ is
the charge density on the conducting surface. Since $_1$**D** must be normal
to the surface, we have $_1\mathbf{D} = {}_1D_n$, and hence (dropping the subscripts)

$$D = \epsilon\epsilon_0 E = \sigma \qquad (1.28)$$

at the surface of the conductor immersed in a medium of dielectric
constant $\epsilon$.

## 1.6. Properties of capacitors and systems of conductors

If a charge $Q$ is given to an isolated conductor its voltage is increased
by an amount $V$. For a given conductor the ratio $Q/V$ is independent

of $Q$ and depends only on the size and shape of the conductor. The ratio $Q/V$ is called the capacitance of the conductor, and is denoted by $C$. If a second conductor which is earthed is brought close to the first one, a charge of opposite sign is induced on it, and the potential falls. Since $Q$ is constant if the conductor is isolated, the capacitance has increased. The two conductors together form a capacitor, and the capacitance of the capacitor is defined as the ratio of the charge on either conductor to the potential difference between them. A capacitor is an instrument for storing charge, and a capacitor of large capacitance can store a correspondingly large quantity of charge for a given potential difference between the plates. The capacitance depends on the geometry of the conductors and the dielectric constant of the medium separating them.

In general, calculation of the capacitance of a conductor or a capacitor is difficult unless simple geometrical shapes are involved. The principle of the calculation may be illustrated by the case of an isolated sphere, of radius $a$, in an infinite dielectric. Suppose this carries a charge $Q$. Then by applying Gauss's theorem over a spherical surface of radius $r$, concentric with the sphere, we have

$$4\pi r^2 D = 4\pi r^2 \epsilon\epsilon_0 E = Q,$$

since, by symmetry, $\mathbf{D}$ and $\mathbf{E}$ are constant over the spherical surface and everywhere normal to it. Hence

$$E = \frac{Q}{4\pi\epsilon\epsilon_0 r^2},$$

which is the same as equation (1.23) for a point charge $Q$. The potential of the sphere is

$$V = -\int_{\infty}^{a} E \, dr = \frac{Q}{4\pi\epsilon\epsilon_0 a}.$$

Hence $$C = Q/V = 4\pi\epsilon\epsilon_0 a. \qquad (1.29)$$

If instead of an isolated sphere we have a capacitor formed by two concentric spheres as in Fig. 1.14 of radii $a$, $b$ ($b > a$), we may place a charge $Q$ on the inner sphere and a charge $-Q$ on the outer sphere. Then the formula given above for $E$ holds in the dielectric-filled space between the spheres, while everywhere else $E$ is zero. Hence the potential difference between the two spheres is

$$V = \frac{Q}{4\pi\epsilon\epsilon_0}\left(\frac{1}{a} - \frac{1}{b}\right)$$

and the capacitance is $$C = 4\pi\epsilon\epsilon_0 \, ab/(b-a). \qquad (1.30)$$

Another simple type of capacitor is formed by two plane parallel plates of area $S$ and separation $t$. If the lateral dimensions of the plates are large compared with their separation (or if the plates are surrounded by 'guard rings' at the same potential), then the field between them is

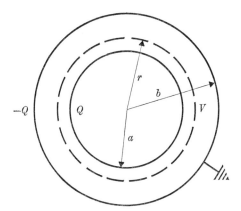

Fig. 1.14. A spherical capacitor.

uniform and normal to the planes, being given by equation (1.28) with $\sigma = Q/S$. Since the field is uniform, the potential difference between the plates is simply $V = Et$, and the capacitance is thus

$$C = Q/V = \epsilon\epsilon_0 S/t. \tag{1.31}$$

This equation (and also equations (1.29) and (1.30)) shows that the capacitance increases by a factor $\epsilon$ if the space between the plates is filled with a medium of dielectric constant $\epsilon$. This agrees with the original definition of dielectric constant by Faraday, mentioned at the beginning of § 1.5.

The unit of capacitance is called the farad (F); the plates of a capacitor of 1 F carry a charge of 1 coulomb if their potential difference is 1 V. Reference to equations (1.29) to (1.31) above, or more fundamentally, to equation (1.25), shows that a capacitance has the dimensions of $\epsilon_0$ multiplied by a length; hence the unit of $\epsilon_0$ is the farad/metre. The farad is a very large unit (a sphere the size of the earth would have a capacitance of about $10^{-3}$ F), and the subdivisions microfarad ($\mu$F) $= 10^{-6}$ F, and micromicrofarad ($\mu\mu$F or pF) $= 10^{-12}$ F are commonly used instead.

A result often required is the net capacitance of a number of capacitors joined either in series, or in parallel, as in Fig. 1.15. If $n$ capacitors $C_1$, $C_2$,..., $C_n$ are joined in series, and a voltage $V$ applied across them, a charge $+Q$ appears on the plate $A$ and $-Q$ on the plate $B$. The plate 2 of the first capacitor will have charge $-Q$, and plate 1 of the second capacitor must therefore have charge $+Q$ since the two, though connected together, are otherwise isolated and their total charge must remain zero on connecting the battery. Thus each capacitor carries

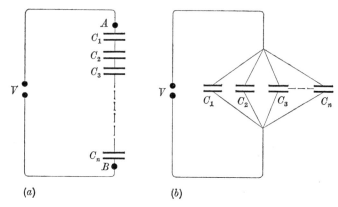

(a)                              (b)

FIG. 1.15. (a) Capacitors in series. (b) Capacitors in parallel.

the same charge, irrespective of its size, and the potential across the $k$th capacitor is $Q/C_k$. Hence the total potential is $\sum\limits_{1}^{n} (Q/C_k)$, and this equals $Q/C$, where $C$ is the net capacitance. Equating these two results gives

$$\frac{1}{C} = \frac{1}{C_1} + \frac{1}{C_2} + ... + \frac{1}{C_k} + ... + \frac{1}{C_n}. \tag{1.32}$$

If the capacitors are joined in parallel, the voltage across each capacitor is equal to $V$. The total charge carried by all the capacitors is $Q = Q_1 + Q_2 + ... + Q_k + ... + Q_n = V(C_1 + C_2 + ... + C_k + ... + C_n) = VC$, where $C$ is the net capacitance. Hence

$$C = C_1 + C_2 + ... + C_k + ... + C_n. \tag{1.33}$$

*The potential energy of a system of charges and charged conductors*

A system of electric charges possesses potential energy, since work must be done in bringing up any particular charge through the electrostatic field of the remaining charges. The energy depends only on the final state of the system and not on how the charges are established. We may therefore suppose that each charge is increased from zero to its final value in infinitesimal steps so that at any given instant each charge is $\alpha q_k$, where $q_k$ is its final value and $\alpha$ is a number less than unity which is the same for all charges. Then if $V_k$ is the final value of the potential at the point occupied by $q_k$, the instantaneous value of the potential will be $\alpha V_k$, and the work done in increasing the charge by $q_k\, d\alpha$ will be $(\alpha V_k)(q_k\, d\alpha)$. Thus the work done in increasing all the charges by a corresponding amount will be $\alpha\, d\alpha \sum\limits_k q_k V_k$. The total work done is equal to the stored energy, which will therefore be

$$U = \sum_k q_k V_k \int_0^1 \alpha\, d\alpha = \tfrac{1}{2} \sum_k q_k V_k. \tag{1.34}$$

We may apply this result to a capacitor with two plates at potentials $V_1$, $V_2$ carrying charges $+Q$ and $-Q$ respectively. The energy of the capacitor will be

$$U = \tfrac{1}{2}QV_1 - \tfrac{1}{2}QV_2 = \tfrac{1}{2}QV = \tfrac{1}{2}CV^2 = \tfrac{1}{2}Q^2/C, \tag{1.35}$$

where $V = V_1 - V_2$ is the potential difference between the plates.

The energy of the system may be expressed in a different way which implies that it is distributed over the space between the charges occupied by their electrostatic field. Consider two nearby equipotential surfaces in this space which differ in potential by a small amount $V$, and are a distance $ds$ apart. If two parallel conducting plates of area $dS$ were inserted so as to coincide with these equipotentials, they would not alter the field distribution in any way. They would form a parallel plate capacitor of capacity $C$ and energy $\tfrac{1}{2}CV^2$. But $C = \epsilon\epsilon_0\, dS/ds$ and $V = -E\, ds$, where $E$ is the electric field at this point. The capacitor occupies a volume $d\tau = dS ds$ and its energy is $\tfrac{1}{2}\epsilon\epsilon_0\, E^2(dS ds) = \tfrac{1}{2}DE\, d\tau$. We may therefore regard the energy as distributed throughout the field, the energy density at any point being $\tfrac{1}{2}DE$. This equation may be derived more rigorously by vector analysis, as follows.

In Fig. 1.16 suppose there exists a volume distribution of charge of density $\rho$ per unit volume and a surface distribution of density $\sigma$ per unit area. Then from equation (1.34), if the summation is replaced by integrations, we have for the total energy

$$U = \tfrac{1}{2} \int \rho V\, d\tau + \tfrac{1}{2} \int \sigma V\, dS,$$

where the surface integral is taken over the surfaces of all the conductors present. By Gauss's theorem, $\rho = \operatorname{div} \mathbf{D}$, and hence, using a vector transformation (see Appendix A), $\rho V = V \operatorname{div} \mathbf{D} = \operatorname{div}(V\mathbf{D}) - \mathbf{D} . \operatorname{grad} V$. Therefore

$$\tfrac{1}{2} \int \rho V\, d\tau = \tfrac{1}{2} \int \operatorname{div}(V\mathbf{D})\, d\tau - \tfrac{1}{2} \int \mathbf{D} . \operatorname{grad} V\, d\tau$$

$$= \tfrac{1}{2} \int V\mathbf{D} . \mathbf{dS} + \tfrac{1}{2} \int \mathbf{D} . \mathbf{E}\, d\tau.$$

The first integral must be taken over a closed surface bounding the whole volume, and also over the surface of each conductor. The first surface may be taken at an infinitely large distance from all the charges, and its contribution to the surface integral then vanishes. For, at large distances, $V$ varies as $r^{-1}$ and $D$ as $r^{-2}$, while $dS$ increases with $r^2$; thus

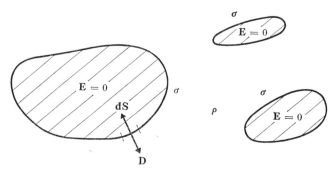

FIG. 1.16. Diagram to illustrate the calculation of the energy density of a system of surface and volume charges.

the integral is proportional to $r^{-1}$ and tends to zero as $r$ tends to infinity. The total energy may now be written

$$U = \tfrac{1}{2} \int \mathbf{D}.\mathbf{E}\, d\tau + \tfrac{1}{2} \int V\mathbf{D}.\mathbf{dS} + \tfrac{1}{2} \int \sigma V\, dS,$$

where the surface integrals are taken over the surfaces of all the conductors. Since the integration is over the surface of the medium, $\mathbf{dS}$ is a vector drawn outwards from the medium and hence into the conducting surface as in Fig. 1.16. But the normal component of $\mathbf{D}$ in this direction is $-\sigma$, from equation (1.28), and hence $\mathbf{D}.\mathbf{dS} = -\sigma\, dS$, so that the two surface integrals in our expression for $U$ cancel. Our final expression for $U$ becomes

$$U = \tfrac{1}{2} \int \mathbf{D}.\mathbf{E}\, d\tau. \tag{1.36}$$

Since $\mathbf{E}$ is zero within any conductor, we may regard the energy as distributed throughout the surrounding dielectric medium, with density $\tfrac{1}{2}\mathbf{D}.\mathbf{E}$. This expression is valid in anisotropic dielectrics, where $\mathbf{D}$ is not necessarily parallel to $\mathbf{E}$, but it assumes that $\mathbf{D}$ is always proportional to $\mathbf{E}$.

## 1.7. Stress in the electrostatic field

It has already been shown that the charge on a conductor resides in a thin surface layer. This is due to the mutual repulsion between charges of like sign, so that each portion of the charge on the conductor is trying to get as far away as possible from the remainder. This results in a tension acting on the surface of the conductor, whose magnitude will now be calculated. We shall assume that the charge of surface density $\sigma$ is in a thin layer just outside the conducting surface, in a medium of dielectric constant $\epsilon$, as in Fig. 1.17. By applying Gauss's theorem to a small cylinder with its axis normal to the surface, and with one end inside the conductor and the other within the surface layer, the field $\mathbf{E}'$

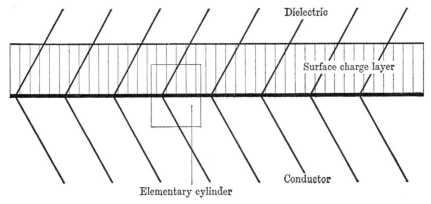

FIG. 1.17. Deduction of the tension on a charged conductor.

at this latter point is found to be $\mathbf{E}' = (\sigma\alpha)/\epsilon\epsilon_0$, where $\sigma\alpha$ is the portion of the surface charge density lying between the conductor and the end of the cylinder. The force on the element of charge density $\sigma\,d\alpha$ at the end of the cylinder is therefore $\mathbf{E}'(\sigma\,d\alpha) = \sigma^2\alpha\,d\alpha/\epsilon\epsilon_0$, and the total force per unit area is

$$T = \frac{\sigma^2}{\epsilon\epsilon_0} \int_0^1 \alpha\,d\alpha = \frac{\sigma^2}{2\epsilon\epsilon_0}. \tag{1.37}$$

At first sight the assumption that the charge layer resides in the dielectric may appear rather artificial, but the same result may be obtained by application of the principle of virtual work to special cases. For example, consider a parallel plate capacitor with a medium of dielectric constant $\epsilon$ between the plates. If the separation between the plates is $x$, and their area $S$, the capacitance $C = \epsilon\epsilon_0 S/x$, and the stored energy is $\frac{1}{2}Q^2/C = \frac{1}{2}\sigma^2 S^2/C$, where $\sigma$ is the charge density on the plates. If $\sigma$ is kept constant, and the separation of the plates is increased, the rate of change of the stored energy is

$$\frac{dU}{dx} = \frac{d}{dx}(\sigma^2 S x/2\epsilon\epsilon_0) = \frac{\sigma^2 S}{2\epsilon\epsilon_0}.$$

But $(dU/dx) = -ST$, where $T$ is the tension per unit area on the plate, and hence $T = -\sigma^2/2\epsilon_0$, where the minus sign denotes that the tension acts in the opposite direction to the movement of the one plate, i.e. in the direction of diminishing $x$.

It is interesting to derive the tension on the plates of this capacitor if the voltage, rather than the charge, is kept constant. In this case we must include the work done by the battery maintaining the constant potential difference. If the capacitance increases by $dC$, the charge increases by $V\,dC$, and the work done by the battery is $V(V\,dC) = V^2\,dC$. The increase in the stored energy is $dU = d(\tfrac{1}{2}CV^2) = \tfrac{1}{2}V^2\,dC$, and the external work $dW$ required is therefore

$$\tfrac{1}{2}V^2\,dC - V^2\,dC = -\tfrac{1}{2}V^2\,dC = -dU.$$

Hence the tension on the plates is

$$T = -\frac{1}{S}\left(\frac{\partial W}{\partial x}\right) = -\frac{1}{S}\left(\frac{\partial W}{\partial C}\right)\left(\frac{\partial C}{\partial x}\right)$$

$$= -\frac{1}{S}\left(-\frac{V^2}{2}\right)\left(-\frac{\epsilon\epsilon_0 S}{x^2}\right) = -\frac{\epsilon\epsilon_0 E^2}{2} = -\frac{\sigma^2}{2\epsilon\epsilon_0},$$

which is the same as before, as we should expect. The fact that the work done by the battery in maintaining the system at constant potential is just twice the increase in the stored energy is generally true, and our example is just a particular case. It is, however, probably more instructive for the student to remember to put in the work done by the battery in working a particular problem at constant potential rather than avoiding the issue by making use of a general theorem.

*Stresses in dielectric media*

Both Faraday and Maxwell used the concept of tubes of force. A tube of force contains an arbitrary but very large number of lines of force, and the number of tubes crossing unit area is equal to the electric intensity; similarly, the number of tubes of displacement per unit area is equal to $\mathbf{D}$. They imagined these tubes to be in a state of tension, so that the force of attraction between two charges of opposite sign, for example, was transmitted along the tubes of force. It was also necessary to stipulate that there was a force of repulsion between tubes of force in a direction normal to their length, otherwise the tubes would all contract until they passed straight from one charge to another. These forces can be expressed in terms of the 'Maxwell Stress Tensor', and we shall quote the results (a complete treatment is given in Panofsky and Phillips, 1955). The $x$-component $dF_x$ of the force $dF$ transmitted across a surface element $dS$ is

$$dF_x = T_{xx}\,dS_x + T_{xy}\,dS_y + T_{xz}\,dS_z \tag{1.38}$$

with similar equations for $dF_y$, $dF_z$. The quantities $T_{xx}$, $T_{xy}$, etc., form the nine components of a tensor $T$, which can be written as

$$T = \begin{pmatrix} \tfrac{1}{2}(E_xD_x - E_yD_y - E_zD_z) & E_xD_y & E_xD_z \\ E_yD_x & \tfrac{1}{2}(E_yD_y - E_zD_z - E_xD_x) & E_yD_z \\ E_zD_x & E_zD_y & \tfrac{1}{2}(E_zD_z - E_xD_x - E_yD_y) \end{pmatrix}. \tag{1.39}$$

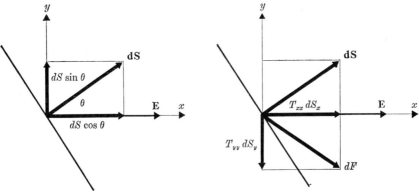

FIG. 1.18. A surface element $dS$, and its stress components. From equation (1.40) these are $dF_x = T_{xx}\,dS_x = \tfrac{1}{2}ED\,dS\,\cos\theta$, $dF_y = T_{yy}\,dS_y = -\tfrac{1}{2}ED\,dS\,\sin\theta$, so that $dF = (dF_x^2 + dF_y^2)^{\frac{1}{2}} = \tfrac{1}{2}ED\,dS$.

This tensor is symmetric (that is, $T_{xy} = T_{yx}$, etc.), and by choosing a special set of axes, the off-diagonal terms can be made zero. If we choose the $x$-axis to be parallel to $\mathbf{E}$, $T$ takes the form

$$T = \begin{pmatrix} \tfrac{1}{2}ED & 0 & 0 \\ 0 & -\tfrac{1}{2}ED & 0 \\ 0 & 0 & -\tfrac{1}{2}ED \end{pmatrix} \tag{1.40}$$

whose significance is that we have a force component $= +\tfrac{1}{2}ED(dS_x)$ parallel to $\mathbf{E}$, and components $-\tfrac{1}{2}ED(dS_y)$, $-\tfrac{1}{2}ED(dS_z)$ normal to $\mathbf{E}$. These are shown in Fig. 1.18 for a surface element for which $dS$ is normal to the $z$-axis, and in Fig. 1.19 for the special cases where $\mathbf{E}$ is normal and parallel to the surface.

It must be realized that these stresses must be regarded as present in the field irrespective of whether $dS$ is an element of a real boundary or not. If $dS$ is not a real boundary, there will be equal and opposite stresses on the other side, so that equilibrium is maintained. If, however, $dS$ is part of a real boundary, and the vectors $\mathbf{E}$, $\mathbf{D}$ are different on the two sides, there will be a net force acting at the bounding surface. The charged conductor considered above is a special case where **E**, **D** are zero on one side, and normal to the boundary on the other, and it is easily seen that the tension given by equation (1.37) agrees with that given by the Maxwell Stress Tensor. The tensor representation is of course more general, and makes it possible to compute the stress on

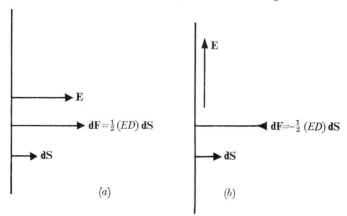

FIG. 1.19. The stress at a surface which is (a) normal and (b) parallel to an electric field **E**.

a dielectric boundary. This is equal to the difference $\Delta T$ of the Maxwell Stress Tensors on the two sides of the boundary, and it is easy to show that the resultant force is always normal to the boundary. For, if the latter is taken to be normal to the $z$-axis, so that the only component of **dS** is $dS_z$, then we have

$$dF_x = (\Delta T_{xz})\, dS_z = ({}_1E_x\, {}_1D_z - {}_2E_x\, {}_2D_z)\, dS_z = 0,$$
$$dF_y = (\Delta T_{yz})\, dS_z = ({}_1E_y\, {}_1D_z - {}_2E_y\, {}_2D_z)\, dS_z = 0,$$

which both vanish because the boundary conditions make $E_x$, $E_y$, $D_z$ continuous across the boundary.

## REFERENCES

PANOFSKY, W. K. H., and PHILLIPS, M., 1955, *Classical Electricity and Magnetism* (Addison-Wesley Publishing Co., U.S.A.).

PLIMPTON, S. J., and LAWTON, W. E., 1936, *Phys. Rev.* **50**, 1066.

## PROBLEMS

**1.1.** An electric quadrupole is formed by a charge $-2e$ at the origin and charges $+e$ at the points $(\pm a, 0, 0)$. Show that the potential $V$ at a distance $r$ large compared with $a$ is approximately given by $V = +ea^2(3\cos^2\theta - 1)/4\pi\epsilon_0 r^3$, where $\theta$ is the angle between $r$ and the line through the charges.

**1.2.** Show that there is no translational force or couple on such an electric quadrupole in a uniform field. Prove that the couple on the quadrupole at a distance $r$ from a point charge $q$ is $C = \dfrac{3ea^2 \sin 2\theta \cdot q}{4\pi\epsilon_0 r^3}$, where $\theta$ is the angle between $r$ and the line through the charges. (Assume $r \gg a$.)

**1.3.** Show that the force on an elementary dipole of moment $\mathbf{p}$, distance $r$ from a point charge $q$, has components

$$F_r = -\frac{qp\cos\theta}{2\pi\epsilon_0 r^3}, \qquad F_\theta = \frac{qp\sin\theta}{4\pi\epsilon_0 r^3}$$

along and perpendicular to $\mathbf{r}$ in the plane of $\mathbf{p}$ and $\mathbf{r}$, where $\theta$ is the angle which $\mathbf{p}$ makes with $\mathbf{r}$.

**1.4.** Show that the potential energy of two coplanar dipoles $p_1$ and $p_2$ a distance $r$ apart is

$$\frac{p_1 p_2}{4\pi\epsilon_0 r^3}(\sin\theta_1 \sin\theta_2 - 2\cos\theta_1 \cos\theta_2),$$

where $\theta_1$, $\theta_2$ are the angles made by $p_1$ and $p_2$ respectively with the line joining their centres.

**1.5.** A charge $q$ is placed at each of the four corners $(\pm a, 0, 0)$, $(0, \pm a, 0)$ of a square. Show that the potential at a point $(x, y, z)$ near the origin is

$$V = \frac{q}{4\pi\epsilon_0 a}[4 + (x^2 + y^2 - 2z^2)/a^2 + \ldots].$$

Verify that a charge of the same sign placed at the centre of the square is in stable equilibrium against a small displacement in the plane of the square, but is unstable for a displacement normal to this plane. This is an example of Earnshaw's theorem, which shows that a charge cannot rest in stable equilibrium in an electrostatic field.

**1.6.** The values of the vertical potential gradient of the earth at heights of 100 and 1000 metres above its surface are 110 and 25 V/metre respectively. What is the mean electrostatic charge per cubic metre of the atmosphere between these heights ?      (*Answer:* $0.835 \times 10^{-12}$ coulombs/metre³.)

**1.7.** A parallel plate capacitor with plates of area $S$ and separation $d$ has a block of dielectric, of constant $\epsilon$, of cross-sectional area $S$, and thickness $t$ $(t \ll d)$, inserted in between the plates. Find the values of $E$ and $D$ in the space between the plates, in both air and dielectric. Show that the capacitance of the capacitor is $C = \dfrac{S\epsilon\epsilon_0}{\epsilon d - (\epsilon - 1)t}$, and calculate the change in stored energy of the system when the dielectric is inserted (a) if the plates have a constant charge $Q$, and (b) if they are connected to a battery at a constant potential $V$.

$$\left(Answer:\ (a)\ \Delta U = -\frac{Q^2(\epsilon-1)t}{2\epsilon\epsilon_0 S}; \qquad (b)\ \Delta U = +\frac{\epsilon_0 S V^2(\epsilon-1)t}{2d\{\epsilon d - (\epsilon-1)t\}}.\right)$$

**1.8.** Find an expression for the capacitance per unit length of a cylindrical capacitor consisting of two concentric cylinders, radii $a$ and $b$, separated by a medium of dielectric constant $\epsilon$. (Neglect edge effects.)

(*Answer:* $C = 2\pi\epsilon\epsilon_0/\log(b/a)$.)

**1.9.** A capacitor is formed by two coaxial cylinders of radii $a$ and $b$. The axes of the cylinders are vertical and the inner cylinder is suspended from a balance so that it hangs only partly within the outer cylinder. Find an expression for the mass which must be added to the other pan of the balance to maintain equilibrium when a voltage $V$ is connected between the two cylinders.

$$(\textit{Answer: } mg = \pi \epsilon \epsilon_0 V^2 / \log(b/a).)$$

**1.10.** The electrometer is an instrument for measuring voltages by means of the force on a charged conductor. An attracted disk electrometer has a moving plate of area $100 \text{ cm}^2$, separated by a distance of 1 mm from the fixed plate. Calculate the force between the plates when the potential difference across them is 100 V. Calculate the sensitivity at this voltage in newtons per volt.

$$(\textit{Answer: } F = 4 \cdot 42 \times 10^{-4} \text{ newtons, } dF/dV = 8 \cdot 85 \times 10^{-6} \text{ newton/V.})$$

**1.11.** The upper disk of such an electrometer is suspended by a spring. In equilibrium, the separation between the two disks is $x$ when a voltage $V$ is applied and $a$ when $V = 0$. Show that the equilibrium in the former case is stable provided that $x > 2a/3$.

**1.12.** A sphere carrying a charge density $\sigma$ per unit area is immersed in an infinite dielectric medium. Verify equation (1.37) by using the principle of virtual work and allowing the radius to change infinitesimally.

**1.13.** Assuming that the total charge $Ze$ of an atomic nucleus is uniformly distributed within a sphere of radius $a$, show that the potential at a distance $r$ from the centre $(r \leqslant a)$ is

$$V = \left\{ \frac{3}{2} - \frac{1}{2} \left( \frac{r}{a} \right)^2 \right\} Ze / 4\pi \epsilon_0 a.$$

Show that the electrostatic energy of such a nucleus is

$$U = \frac{3(Ze)^2}{20 \pi \epsilon_0 a}.$$

This electrostatic energy must be provided at the expense of a small decrease $\delta m$ in the mass of the nucleus, such that $U = \delta m c^2$, where $c = $ velocity of light, by the Einstein relation. $\delta m$ is part of the 'mass defect'.

**1.14.** An atom with an electron in an $s$-state has a finite density $-\rho$ of electronic charge inside the nucleus. Using the formula for the potential inside the nucleus given in the previous problem, show that the potential energy associated with the electron density $-\rho$ inside the sphere of radius $a$ is $-2Ze\rho a^2 / 5\epsilon_0$, and that this is greater by $Ze\rho a^2 / 10\epsilon_0$ than it would have been if the nucleus were a point charge.

Since isotopes of the same element have different nuclear radii, this energy forms part of the 'isotope shift'; that is, the difference in frequency of spectrum lines from different isotopes.

# ELECTROSTATICS II

## 2.1. The equations of Poisson and Laplace

IN a region where there exists a charge distribution of density $\rho$ per unit volume, the differential form of Gauss's theorem is (equation (1.20))

$$\operatorname{div} \mathbf{D} = \rho.$$

Now $\mathbf{E} = -\operatorname{grad} V$, and in an isotropic dielectric $\mathbf{D} = \epsilon\epsilon_0 \mathbf{E}$. Hence

$$\nabla^2 V = \operatorname{div}(\operatorname{grad} V) = -\operatorname{div} \mathbf{E} = -\rho/\epsilon\epsilon_0. \tag{2.1}$$

This is known as Poisson's equation. If there is no free charge present, $\rho = 0$, and we have Laplace's equation

$$\nabla^2 V = 0. \tag{2.2}$$

The operator denoted by $\nabla^2$ is a scalar operator, which has its simplest form in Cartesian coordinates, where Poisson's equation becomes

$$\frac{\partial^2 V}{\partial x^2} + \frac{\partial^2 V}{\partial y^2} + \frac{\partial^2 V}{\partial z^2} = -\frac{\rho}{\epsilon\epsilon_0}. \tag{2.3}$$

Two other coordinate systems will be considered. These are spherical polar coordinates, where Poisson's equation becomes

$$\frac{1}{r^2}\frac{\partial}{\partial r}\left(r^2\frac{\partial V}{\partial r}\right) + \frac{1}{r^2\sin\theta}\frac{\partial}{\partial\theta}\left(\sin\theta\frac{\partial V}{\partial\theta}\right) + \frac{1}{r^2\sin^2\theta}\frac{\partial^2 V}{\partial\phi^2} = -\frac{\rho}{\epsilon\epsilon_0}, \tag{2.4}$$

and cylindrical polar coordinates, where we have

$$\frac{1}{r}\frac{\partial}{\partial r}\left(r\frac{\partial V}{\partial r}\right) + \frac{1}{r^2}\frac{\partial^2 V}{\partial\theta^2} + \frac{\partial^2 V}{\partial z^2} = -\frac{\rho}{\epsilon\epsilon_0}. \tag{2.5}$$

In principle, equation (2.1) enables us to calculate the potential distribution due to any given set of charges and conductors. A formal solution of Poisson's equation can be found,

$$V = \int \frac{\rho\, d\tau}{4\pi\epsilon\epsilon_0 r}, \tag{2.6}$$

but this holds only in a vacuum or an infinite dielectric medium. If there are conductors present we should have to allow for the effect of the charge distribution on their surfaces, but we do not in general know what this distribution is. We have therefore to resort to a number of special methods, but we must be sure that any solution we obtain which

D

satisfies the boundary conditions is the correct and only answer. That this is the case is shown by an important theorem, known as the Uniqueness Theorem. This theorem (see Appendix B) shows that if two different potential distributions are assumed to satisfy Laplace's equation and the boundary conditions, their difference is zero. We now discuss a number of methods for the case of no free charges, where the solutions needed are of Laplace's rather than Poisson's equation.

The required solution may be a sum of a number of functions, each of which satisfies Laplace's equation; for, if the functions $V_1$, $V_2$,..., $V_n$ are each individual solutions of Laplace's equation, then

$$V = a_1 V_1 + a_2 V_2 + ... + a_n V_n,$$

where $a_1$, $a_2$,..., $a_n$ are a set of numerical coefficients, is also a solution. A series of functions, each of which is a solution of Laplace's equation, may sometimes be found by making use of the fact that if $V_1$ is a solution, so also are any differentials of $V_1$ with respect to the space coordinates. Thus in Cartesian coordinates the functions $\partial V_1/\partial x$, $\partial V_1/\partial y$, $\partial V_1/\partial z$, $\partial^2 V_1/\partial x^2$ $\partial^2 V_1/\partial x \partial y$, etc., all satisfy equation (2.2) if $V_1$ does. The proof of this can be seen from a single example. On partial differentiation of equation (2.3) with respect to $x$, we have (setting $\rho = 0$)

$$0 = \frac{\partial}{\partial x}\left(\frac{\partial^2 V_1}{\partial x^2} + \frac{\partial^2 V_1}{\partial y^2} + \frac{\partial^2 V_1}{\partial z^2}\right)$$
$$= \frac{\partial^2}{\partial x^2}\left(\frac{\partial V_1}{\partial x}\right) + \frac{\partial^2}{\partial y^2}\left(\frac{\partial V_1}{\partial x}\right) + \frac{\partial^2}{\partial z^2}\left(\frac{\partial V_1}{\partial x}\right) = \nabla^2\left(\frac{\partial V_1}{\partial x}\right),$$

since the order of differentiation is immaterial when $x$, $y$, $z$ are independent coordinates. The value of this method lies in the fact that once a series of functions which satisfy equation (2.2) is established, any linear combination of these functions may be taken, and if they can be chosen in such a way as to satisfy the boundary conditions by adjustment of the coefficients, they give the unique solution to the problem.

In theory, any problem involving electrostatic fields may be solved by finding a solution which satisfies equation (2.2) and gives the right boundary conditions. In practice the problem is almost insoluble by ordinary mathematical methods except in cases where there is a high degree of symmetry. These may be handled by the use of a series of known functions, and some examples of this method are given below. We shall consider also another special method which can be applied to the case of one or two point charges near to a conducting surface of simple shape. Though a number of other problems may be handled by mathematical methods which are beyond the scope of this volume (see the general references at the end of Chapter 1), most of the problems met with in practice, such as the design of electron guns to give a focused beam in a cathode ray tube, are dealt with either by use of approximate solutions, or by plotting the lines of equal potential using a scale model as described in Chapter 3.

## 2.2. Solutions of Laplace's equation in spherical coordinates

We shall consider first the case of spherical coordinates, and assume initially that we have symmetry about the polar axis so that $V$ is independent of $\phi$. Then Laplace's equation reduces to

$$\frac{\partial}{\partial r}\left(r^2\frac{\partial V}{\partial r}\right)+\frac{\partial}{\partial \mu}\left\{(1-\mu^2)\frac{\partial V}{\partial \mu}\right\} = 0, \tag{2.7}$$

where $\mu$ has been written for $\cos\theta$. This has solutions of the form $V = r^l P_l$, where $P_l$ is a function of $\mu = \cos\theta$ only, and $l$ is an integer. If we substitute such a function in equation (2.7), and divide through by $r^l$, we obtain Legendre's differential equation for $P_l$

$$\frac{d}{d\mu}\left\{(1-\mu^2)\frac{\partial P_l}{\partial \mu}\right\}+l(l+1)P_l = 0.$$

It is readily seen that replacing $l$ by $-(l+1)$ leaves this equation unaltered, so that $P_l = P_{-(l+1)}$; that is, $V = r^l P_l$ and $V = r^{-(l+1)}P_l$ are both solutions of equation (2.7).

Solutions of Legendre's equation may be obtained by standard methods, but a quick alternative method is as follows. We know that $V = 1/r$ is a solution, and hence so is any partial derivative of this such as $(\partial V/\partial z)$ under the conditions $x$, $y$ constant. Since $r^2 = x^2+y^2+z^2$, we have $2r(\partial r/\partial z) = 2z$ when $x$, $y$ are kept constant, so that

$$\left(\frac{\partial r}{\partial z}\right)_{x,y} = \frac{z}{r}.$$

Hence
$$-\left(\frac{\partial}{\partial z}\right)_{x,y}\left(\frac{1}{r}\right) = \frac{1}{r^2}\left(\frac{\partial r}{\partial z}\right)_{x,y} = \frac{z}{r^3} = r^{-2}\cos\theta$$

if we take $z$ to lie along the polar axis, so that $z = r\cos\theta$. The two functions $V = r^{-1}$ and $r^{-2}\cos\theta$ are the first two types of solution in the inverse powers $r^{-(l+1)}$, and correspond to values of $l = 0$ and $1$ respectively. Thus $P_0 = 1$, and $P_1 = \cos\theta$. Further functions may be generated by successive differentiation; thus

$$(\partial/\partial z)(z/r^3) = (1-3z^2/r^2)r^{-3} = (1-3\cos^2\theta)r^{-3}$$

gives the next function, which is proportional to $P_2$. A general formula for $P_l$ is

$$P_l = \frac{1}{2^l l!} \left( \frac{\partial}{\partial \mu} \right)^l (\mu^2 - 1)^l, \tag{2.8}$$

where the numerical coefficients are such that $P_l = 1$ at $\mu = 1$, i.e. at $\theta = 0$. The first few functions are given in Table 2.1, together with the radial functions $r^{-(l+1)}$ and $r^l$ with which they combine to give solutions of Laplace's equation.

## TABLE 2.1

### Some spherical harmonic functions

| Legendre function | Function of $r$ | |
|---|---|---|
| $P_0 = 1$ | $r^{-1}$ | $1$ |
| $P_1 = \cos\theta$ | $r^{-2}$ | $r$ |
| $P_2 = \frac{1}{2}(3\cos^2\theta - 1)$ | $r^{-3}$ | $r^2$ |
| $P_3 = \frac{1}{2}(5\cos^3\theta - 3\cos\theta)$ | $r^{-4}$ | $r^3$ |
| $P_4 = \frac{1}{8}(35\cos^4\theta - 30\cos^2\theta + 3)$ | $r^{-5}$ | $r^4$ |
| $P_5 = \frac{1}{8}(63\cos^5\theta - 70\cos^3\theta + 15\cos\theta)$ | $r^{-6}$ | $r^5$ |
| $P_6 = \frac{1}{16}(231\cos^6\theta - 315\cos^4\theta + 105\cos^2\theta - 5)$ | $r^{-7}$ | $r^6$ |

## Associated Legendre functions

Table 2.1 clearly does not contain all possible solutions of Laplace's equation, since we can find others by differentiation with respect to $x, y$. For example,

$$-\left( \frac{\partial}{\partial x} \right)_{y,z} \left( \frac{z}{r^3} \right) = \frac{3z}{r^4} \left( \frac{\partial r}{\partial x} \right)_{y,z} = \frac{3zx}{r^5} = 3r^{-3}\cos\theta\sin\theta\cos\phi$$

must also be a solution. The fact that it contains $\phi$ shows that it is not a solution of equation (2.7), but of the more general equation which includes the dependence on $\phi$. This is

$$\frac{\partial}{\partial r}\left( r^2 \frac{\partial V}{\partial r} \right) + \frac{\partial}{\partial \mu}\left\{ (1 - \mu^2) \frac{\partial V}{\partial \mu} \right\} + \frac{1}{(1-\mu^2)} \frac{\partial^2 V}{\partial \phi^2} = 0, \tag{2.9}$$

where we have again written $\mu$ for $\cos\theta$. As before, we assume that there exists a solution of the form $V = r^l \Theta \Phi$, where $\Theta$, $\Phi$ are functions only of $\theta$, $\phi$ respectively. Then the differential equation for $\Theta\Phi$ is

$$\frac{\partial}{\partial \mu}\left\{ (1-\mu^2)\frac{\partial(\Theta\Phi)}{\partial \mu} \right\} + l(l+1)(\Theta\Phi) + \frac{1}{1-\mu^2}\frac{\partial^2(\Theta\Phi)}{\partial \phi^2} = 0, \tag{2.10}$$

which can be written in the form

$$\frac{(1-\mu^2)}{\Theta}\left[ \frac{\partial}{\partial \mu}\left\{ (1-\mu^2)\frac{\partial\Theta}{\partial \mu} \right\} + l(l+1)\Theta \right] = m^2 = -\frac{1}{\Phi}\frac{\partial^2\Phi}{\partial\phi^2}, \tag{2.11}$$

where the variables are separated. The right-hand side has the solution

$$\Phi_m = (2\pi)^{-\frac{1}{2}}e^{im\phi} \qquad (2.12)$$

and the equation for $\Theta$ becomes

$$\frac{\partial}{\partial\mu}\left\{(1-\mu^2)\frac{\partial\Theta}{\partial\mu}\right\} + \left\{l(l+1) - \frac{m^2}{1-\mu^2}\right\}\Theta = 0. \qquad (2.13)$$

It is apparent that the functions listed in Table 2.1 are solutions of this equation for the special case $m = 0$, where there is no dependence on $\phi$. The solutions of equation (2.13) are

$$P_{l,m} = \sin^m\theta\left(\frac{\partial}{\partial\mu}\right)^m P_l = (1-\mu^2)^{\frac{1}{2}m}\left(\frac{\partial}{\partial\mu}\right)^m P_l$$

$$= \frac{(1-\mu^2)^{\frac{1}{2}m}}{2^l l!}\left(\frac{\partial}{\partial\mu}\right)^{m+l}(\mu^2-1)^l. \qquad (2.14)$$

The functions $\Phi$ defined by equation (2.12) are 'normalized'; that is

$$\int_0^{2\pi}\Phi_m^*\Phi_m\,d\phi = \int_0^{2\pi}(2\pi)^{-1}e^{-im\phi}e^{im\phi}\,d\phi = 1 \qquad (2.15)$$

and they are also 'orthogonal'; that is $(m' \neq m)$

$$\int_0^{2\pi}\Phi_{m'}^*\Phi_m\,d\phi = \int_0^{2\pi}(2\pi)^{-1}e^{-im'\phi}e^{im\phi}\,d\phi = 0. \qquad (2.16)$$

By using the Kronecker $\delta$, whose properties are that $\delta(m',m) = 1$ if $m' = m$, but $\delta(m',m) = 0$ if $m' \neq m$, we can write these two equations in the short form

$$\int_0^{2\pi}\Phi_{m'}^*\Phi_m\,d\phi = \delta(m',m). \qquad (2.17)$$

The functions $P_{l,m}$ are orthogonal but not normalized, and hence it is often convenient to work in terms of 'spherical harmonics' defined by

$$Y_{l,m} = \Theta_{l,m}\Phi_m, \qquad (2.18)$$

where $\qquad \Theta_{l,m} = (-1)^m\left\{\frac{(2l+1)(l-|m|)!}{2(l+|m|)!}\right\}^{\frac{1}{2}}P_{l,m} \quad$ for $m \geqslant 0$,

$$\Theta_{l,m} = (-1)^m\Theta_{l,|m|} \qquad\qquad \text{for } m < 0. \qquad (2.19)$$

The functions $Y_{l,m}$ are both orthogonal and normalized; that is

$$\int_0^{2\pi}\int_0^\pi Y_{l',m'}^*Y_{l,m}\sin\theta\,d\theta d\phi = \delta(l',l)\delta(m',m), \qquad (2.20)$$

where the integration is over the solid angle $4\pi$. Here the significance of the $\delta$ functions is that the integral is zero unless both $l' = l$ and $m' = m$, in which case it is unity.

Expressions for the first members of the series of spherical harmonics are listed in Table 2.2 (note that the signs of the functions used by different authors sometimes differ; we have followed the definition adopted by Ramsey (1956) and Brink and Satchler (1962)). A general proof of the orthogonality and normalization relations is tedious, but the reader may verify that they are correct by evaluating the integrals for some of the functions given in Table 2.2.

### TABLE 2.2

*Some spherical harmonic functions*

| | | | |
|---|---|---|---|
| $Y_{10}$ | $+(3/4\pi)^{\frac{1}{2}} \cos \theta$ | $C_{10}$ | $+\cos \theta$ |
| $Y_{1+1}$ | $-(3/8\pi)^{\frac{1}{2}} \sin \theta\, e^{+i\phi}$ | $C_{1+1}$ | $-2^{-\frac{1}{2}} \sin \theta\, e^{+i\phi}$ |
| $Y_{1-1}$ | $+(3/8\pi)^{\frac{1}{2}} \sin \theta\, e^{-i\phi}$ | $C_{1-1}$ | $+2^{-\frac{1}{2}} \sin \theta\, e^{-i\phi}$ |
| $Y_{20}$ | $+(5/16\pi)^{\frac{1}{2}} (3 \cos^2\theta - 1)$ | $C_{20}$ | $+\frac{1}{2}(3 \cos^2\theta - 1)$ |
| $Y_{2+1}$ | $-(15/8\pi)^{\frac{1}{2}} \cos \theta \sin \theta\, e^{+i\phi}$ | $C_{2+1}$ | $-(3/2)^{\frac{1}{2}} \cos \theta \sin \theta\, e^{+i\phi}$ |
| $Y_{2-1}$ | $+(15/8\pi)^{\frac{1}{2}} \cos \theta \sin \theta\, e^{-i\phi}$ | $C_{2-1}$ | $+(3/2)^{\frac{1}{2}} \cos \theta \sin \theta\, e^{-i\phi}$ |
| $Y_{2+2}$ | $+(15/32\pi)^{\frac{1}{2}} \sin^2\theta\, e^{+i2\phi}$ | $C_{2+2}$ | $+(3/8)^{\frac{1}{2}} \sin^2\theta\, e^{+i2\phi}$ |
| $Y_{2-2}$ | $+(15/32\pi)^{\frac{1}{2}} \sin^2\theta\, e^{-i2\phi}$ | $C_{2-2}$ | $+(3/8)^{\frac{1}{2}} \sin^2\theta\, e^{-i2\phi}$ |
| $Y_{30}$ | $+(7/16\pi)^{\frac{1}{2}}(5 \cos^3\theta - 3 \cos \theta)$ | $C_{30}$ | $+\frac{1}{2}(5 \cos^3\theta - 3 \cos \theta)$ |
| $Y_{3+1}$ | $-(21/64\pi)^{\frac{1}{2}}(5 \cos^2\theta - 1)\sin \theta\, e^{+i\phi}$ | $C_{3+1}$ | $-(3/16)^{\frac{1}{2}}(5 \cos^2\theta - 1)\sin \theta\, e^{+i\phi}$ |
| $Y_{3-1}$ | $+(21/64\pi)^{\frac{1}{2}}(5 \cos^2\theta - 1)\sin \theta\, e^{-i\phi}$ | $C_{3-1}$ | $+(3/16)^{\frac{1}{2}}(5 \cos^2\theta - 1)\sin \theta\, e^{-i\phi}$ |
| $Y_{3+2}$ | $+(105/32\pi)^{\frac{1}{2}} \cos \theta \sin^2\theta\, e^{+i2\phi}$ | $C_{3+2}$ | $+(15/8)^{\frac{1}{2}} \cos \theta \sin^2\theta\, e^{+i2\phi}$ |
| $Y_{3-2}$ | $+(105/32\pi)^{\frac{1}{2}} \cos \theta \sin^2\theta\, e^{-i2\phi}$ | $C_{3-2}$ | $+(15/8)^{\frac{1}{2}} \cos \theta \sin^2\theta\, e^{-i2\phi}$ |
| $Y_{3+3}$ | $-(35/64\pi)^{\frac{1}{2}} \sin^3\theta\, e^{+i3\phi}$ | $C_{3+3}$ | $-(5/16)^{\frac{1}{2}} \sin^3\theta\, e^{+i3\phi}$ |
| $Y_{3-3}$ | $+(35/64\pi)^{\frac{1}{2}} \sin^3\theta\, e^{-i3\phi}$ | $C_{3-3}$ | $+(5/16)^{\frac{1}{2}} \sin^3\theta\, e^{-i3\phi}$ |

The functions $C_{lm}$ are related to $Y_{lm}$ by $C_{lm} = \left(\dfrac{4\pi}{2l+1}\right)^{\frac{1}{2}} Y_{lm}$. Note that $C_{l0} = P_l$.

The spherical harmonics have many applications, some of which are discussed in the next section. From the atomic viewpoint, their particular interest is that $Y_{l,m}$ represents the angular variation of the wavefunction for an electron in an atom which has orbital angular momentum $\sqrt{\{l(l+1)\}}(h/2\pi)$, and a component $m(h/2\pi)$ of angular momentum along the $z$-axis (the polar axis), where $h$ is Planck's constant.

### 2.3. The multipole expansion

If we have a charge distribution with density $\rho$ in a region where the potential $V$ is varying, the potential energy is

$$U_P = \int \rho V \, d\tau. \tag{2.21}$$

If the charge extends only over a small volume, we can expand $V$ in a series

$$V = V_0 + x(\partial V/\partial x) + y(\partial V/\partial y) + z(\partial V/\partial z) +$$
$$+ \tfrac{1}{2}x^2(\partial^2 V/\partial x^2) + \tfrac{1}{2}y^2(\partial^2 V/\partial y^2) + \tfrac{1}{2}z^2(\partial^2 V/\partial z^2) +$$
$$+ \tfrac{1}{2}xy(\partial^2 V/\partial x \partial y) + \tfrac{1}{2}yx(\partial^2 V/\partial y \partial x) + \text{etc.} \quad (2.22)$$

The potential energy then becomes

$$U_P = \int \rho V_0 \, d\tau + \int \rho x(\partial V/\partial x) \, d\tau + \int \rho y(\partial V/\partial y) \, d\tau + \int \rho z(\partial V/\partial z) \, d\tau + \text{etc.} \quad (2.23)$$

Here the first term is simply $qV_0$, where $q = \int \rho \, d\tau$ is the total charge. Since $\partial V/\partial x = -E_x$, etc., we can write the next three terms as

$$p_x(\partial V/\partial x) + p_y(\partial V/\partial y) + p_z(\partial V/\partial z)$$
$$= -(p_x E_x + p_y E_y + p_z E_z) = -\mathbf{p}.\mathbf{E}, \quad (2.24)$$

and by comparison with equation (1.13) we identify the quantities $p_x$, $p_y$, $p_z$ as the components of the electric dipole moment of the charge distribution. This gives a general definition of the dipole moment of a charge distribution, the components being

$$p_x = \int \rho x \, d\tau, \quad p_y = \int \rho y \, d\tau, \quad p_z = \int \rho z \, d\tau, \quad \text{or} \quad \mathbf{p} = \int \rho \mathbf{r} \, d\tau. \quad (2.25)$$

If we have a number of point charges rather than a continuous distribution, the integrals can be replaced by a summation (a dipole consisting of two equal and opposite charges separated by a small distance, as defined in Chapter 1, is thus a special case). Note that in equation (2.24) we have implicitly assumed that the first differentials of $V$ are constant over the region occupied by charge, since only then can we take them outside the integration.

If the charge distribution has reflection symmetry in the plane $z = 0$, that is, if the charge density $\rho$ at the point $(x, y, z)$ is the same as that at the point $(x, y, -z)$, the component $p_z$ of the dipole moment will be zero, since in the integral $\int \rho z \, d\tau$ the contributions from the points $(x, y, z)$ and $(x, y, -z)$ will be equal and opposite. Thus in a diatomic molecule, an electric dipole moment can exist parallel to the line joining the two nuclei if they are different (i.e. if the molecule is heteronuclear, such as HCl), but not if they are identical, as in a homonuclear molecule ($H_2, Cl_2$).

Similar considerations apply to $p_x$, $p_y$ of course, and show that a diatomic molecule can have no electric dipole moment perpendicular to the internuclear axis. The method can be extended to more complicated molecules, such as $CH_3Cl$, $C_2H_6$, $C_6H_6$.

In an atom or nucleus the charge distribution is expected to have reflection symmetry in three mutually perpendicular planes, so that there will be no permanent electric dipole moment in any direction. Note that three such reflections change the point $(x, y, z)$ into $(-x, -y, -z)$ and are equivalent to inversion through the origin. The assumption we have made about the charge distribution is equivalent to assuming that the system is 'invariant under the parity operation', i.e. that its properties are unaltered by inversion.

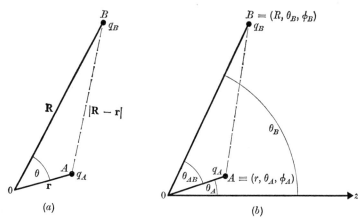

FIG. 2.1. Expansion of the potential at $A$ due to a point charge $q_B$ at $B$ (or of the potential at $B$ due to charge $q_A$ at $A$) using spherical harmonics. In $(b)$, the points $A, B$ are not necessarily in the plane $\phi = 0$.

### Expansion in spherical harmonics

Similar considerations can be applied to the higher terms in equation (2.23), but it is obvious that the large number of terms makes the expansion in Cartesian coordinates clumsy to handle. We therefore turn to another method of expanding the potential of a point charge which makes use of spherical harmonics.

Assume that we have a charge at the point $B$ and wish to know how its potential varies in the neighbourhood of the point $O$, e.g. at the point $A$ (Fig. 2.1 $(a)$). This requires evaluation of the quantity $(R^2 - 2Rr\cos\theta + r^2)^{-\frac{1}{2}}$, which is the inverse of the distance $AB$. If $r < R$, this function can be expanded in powers of $(r/R)$:

$$\frac{1}{|\mathbf{R}-\mathbf{r}|} = (R^2 - 2Rr\cos\theta + r^2)^{-\frac{1}{2}}$$

$$= \frac{1}{R} + \frac{r}{R^2}P_1 + \frac{r^2}{R^3}P_2 + \ldots + \frac{r^l}{R^{l+1}}P_l + \ldots. \tag{2.26}$$

Here the functions $P_l$ are the Legendre functions defined by equation (2.8), as can readily be verified by direct expansion for the first terms.

A more general formula can be found where the points $A, B$ in spherical coordinates are at $(r, \theta_A, \phi_A)$ and $(R, \theta_B, \phi_B)$ respectively. In Fig. 2.1 $(b)$, $Oz$ is the polar axis, and the lines $OA$, $OB$ (which are not necessarily coplanar) make angles $\theta_A$, $\theta_B$ with it; the angle $AOB$ is denoted by $\theta_{AB}$. It can be shown that the Legendre function $P_l(\cos\theta_{AB})$ can be expressed in terms of $\theta_A$, $\phi_A$ and $\theta_B$, $\phi_B$ by the formula

$$P_l(\cos\theta_{AB}) = \frac{4\pi}{2l+1} \sum_{m=-l}^{+l} (-1)^{|m|} Y_{l,m}(\theta_A, \phi_A) Y_{l,-m}(\theta_B, \phi_B)$$

$$= \sum_{m=-l}^{+l} (-1)^{|m|} C_{l,m}(\theta_A, \phi_A) C_{l,-m}(\theta_B, \phi_B), \qquad (2.27)$$

where the function $\qquad C_{l,m} = \left(\frac{4\pi}{2l+1}\right)^{\frac{1}{2}} Y_{l,m} \qquad (2.28)$

is also listed in Table 2.2. By the use of equation (2.27) the potential at the point $A$ due to a charge $q_B$ at $B$ may be written as

$$V = \frac{q_B}{4\pi\epsilon_0} \frac{1}{|\mathbf{R}-\mathbf{r}|}$$

$$= \frac{q_B}{4\pi\epsilon_0} \sum_{l=0}^{\infty} \sum_{m=-l}^{+l} (-1)^{|m|} \frac{r^l}{R^{l+1}} C_{l,m}(\theta_A, \phi_A) C_{l,-m}(\theta_B, \phi_B). \qquad (2.29)$$

This shows that if we take $A$ as a variable point, the potential at $A$ due to the charge $q_B$ at $B$ has a series of components, and the magnitude of the component which varies as $r^l C_{l,m}(\theta_A, \phi_A)$ is determined by the value of $R^{-(l+1)} C_{l,-m}(\theta_B, \phi_B)$ at the point $B$. We may equally well take $B$ to be a variable point at which we wish to find the potential due to a charge $q_A$ at $A$; this is given by equation (2.29) on replacing $q_B$ by $q_A$. The potential at $B$ then has a series of components, where the magnitude of the component varying as $R^{-(l+1)} C_{l,-m}(\theta_B, \phi_B)$ is determined by the value of $r^l C_{l,m}(\theta_A, \phi_A)$ at the point $A$.

If we have a number of point charges $q_B$ at large distances, the magnitude of a given component in the potential at $A$ near $O$ can be found by the summation $\sum_B q_B R^{-(l+1)} C_{l,-m}(\theta_B, \phi_B)$, an example of which is given in Problem 2.18. Conversely, if we have a number of point charges $q_A$ close to $O$, the magnitude of a given component in the potential at a distant point such as $B$ can be found by the summation $\sum_A q_A r^l C_{l,m}(\theta_A, \phi_A)$. In either case the summation is replaced by an integration if we have a continuous distribution of charge. Note that the series expansion for the potential does not assume that $r \ll R$, but the terms will only converge rapidly if this is so.

The electrostatic energy of two charges $q_A$, $q_B$ at the points $A$, $B$ may be written by means of equation (2.29) as

$$U_P = \frac{1}{4\pi\epsilon_0} \sum_{l=0}^{\infty} \sum_{m=-l}^{+l} (-1)^{|m|} \{q_A \, r^l C_{l,m}(\theta_A, \phi_A)\}\{q_B \, R^{-(l+1)} C_{l,-m}(\theta_B, \phi_B)\},$$

$$(2.30)$$

which has the advantage that the terms involving the coordinates of the two charges have been separated. Thus if we have distributed charges with densities $\rho_A$, $\rho_B$ at the points $A$, $B$ the electrostatic energy is

$$U_P = \frac{1}{4\pi\epsilon_0} \int\int \frac{\rho_A \rho_B \, d\tau_A \, d\tau_B}{|\mathbf{R}-\mathbf{r}|}$$

$$= \frac{1}{4\pi\epsilon_0} \sum_{l=0}^{\infty} \sum_{m=-l}^{l} (-1)^{|m|} \int \rho_A \, r^l C_{l,m}(\theta_A, \phi_A) \, d\tau_A \times$$

$$\times \int \rho_B \, R^{-(l+1)} C_{l,-m}(\theta_B, \phi_B) \, d\tau_B$$

$$= \frac{1}{4\pi\epsilon_0} \sum_l \sum_m A_{l,m} B_{l,-m}, \qquad (2.31)$$

where

$$A_{l,m} = \int \rho_A \, r^l C_{l,m}(\theta_A, \phi_A) \, d\tau_A, \qquad (2.32)$$

$$B_{l,-m} = \int (-1)^{|m|} \rho_B \, R^{-(l+1)} C_{l,-m}(\theta_B, \phi_B) \, d\tau_B. \qquad (2.33)$$

The quantities $A_{l,m}$ may be regarded as defining the components of the multipole moments of degree $l$, of the charge distribution near $O$, and it will be seen that they interact only with the conjugate components $B_{l,-m}$ which have the same value of $l$, $m$. The monopole component ($l = 0$) contains only one term, while the dipole ($l = 1$) components contain three terms which may easily be shown (Problem 2.15) to give the same interaction as equation (2.24). In general the interaction energy involving $r^l$ and $R^{-(l+1)}$ contains $(2l+1)$ terms, but the advantage of the quantities $A_{l,m}$, $B_{l,m}$ is that they can be expressed in terms of functions $C_{l,m}$ which are tabulated. We shall go no further than the quadrupole terms ($l = 2$), which can be written out using Table 2.2. It can then readily be verified that, for the particular case where either charge distribution is symmetrical about the axis $\theta = 0$, all the terms in equation (2.31) vanish except that with $m = 0$. If $\rho_A$ has such symmetry (i.e. it is independent of $\phi$), its quadrupole interaction can be expressed in terms of a single component

$$A_{2,0} = \int \rho_A \tfrac{1}{2} r^2 (3 \cos^2 \theta_A - 1) \, d\tau_A = \tfrac{1}{2} q Q, \qquad (2.34)$$

where the quantity (writing $r \cos \theta_A = z$)

$$Q = \frac{1}{|q|} \int \rho_A (3z^2 - r^2) \, d\tau_A \qquad (2.35)$$

is called the 'quadrupole moment' of the charge distribution, and has the dimensions of an area. It might be expected that one would take $q = \int \rho_A \, d\tau_A$, the total charge in the distribution, but for a nucleus, by convention, $q$ is taken as the charge on a single proton (not the total nuclear charge), and $Q$ is expressed in terms of the unit of a 'barn' $= 10^{-24}$ cm$^2$. This unit is chosen because it is of the same order as the square of the nuclear radius (for an atom the quadrupole moment would be of order $10^{-16}$ cm$^2$).

It has already been shown that invariance under the parity operation excludes the possibility of permanent electric dipole moments in atoms and nuclei. This may be expressed more generally using spherical harmonics. Inversion through the origin is equivalent to changing the point $(r, \theta, \phi)$ into $(r, \pi - \theta, \pi + \phi)$. Since

$$P_{l,m}(\pi - \theta) = (-1)^{l-m} P_{l,m}(\theta), \qquad e^{im(\pi + \phi)} = (-1)^m e^{im\phi},$$

we have

$$C_{l,m}(\pi - \theta, \pi + \phi) = (-1)^l C_{l,m}(\theta, \phi), \qquad (2.36)$$

and it follows that

$$\int \rho r^l C_{l,m} \, d\tau = 0 \quad \text{if } l \text{ is odd}. \qquad (2.37)$$

Thus invariance under the parity operation excludes the possibility of electric multipole moments of any odd degree.

The form in which the interaction energy is expressed in equation (2.31) is very suitable to a case where one charge distribution (such as that of a nucleus) is confined to a small volume, but interacts with another charge distribution which is comparatively far away (such as the atomic electrons). The series then converges very rapidly, since $(r/R) \ll 1$; experimentally, nuclear electric multipole interactions higher than quadrupole are very difficult to detect. The convergence is much less rapid in atomic cases, such as the interaction between electrons within an atom, or between atomic electrons and the surrounding ions in a solid (which strongly affects their magnetic properties, see Chapter 20). However, integrals involving all but the first few values of $l$ can be shown to vanish by means of orthogonality theorems, since the wave functions are themselves spherical harmonics.

## 2.4. Some electrostatic problems

*Conducting sphere in a uniform field*

Suppose an earthed conducting sphere of radius $R$ is placed in a uniform field $\mathbf{E}_0$. Then the field immediately around the sphere will become distorted owing to the induced charges on the surface of the sphere (Fig. 2.2), but the field at large distances will approach the value $\mathbf{E}_0$.

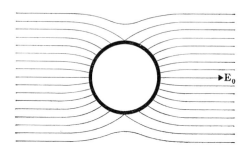

FIG. 2.2. The lines of force near a conducting sphere in a uniform electric field.

In general the potential distribution can be expressed as a sum of terms of the type given in Table 2.1, with the condition that $V = 0$ over the surface of the sphere. If we take a whole series of terms, it would turn out that the coefficients of most of them are zero. It is simpler to try a possible solution with a few terms whose nature is suggested by the symmetry of the problem; if it is then possible to satisfy the boundary condition $V = 0$ at $r = R$ (taking the centre of the sphere as origin of coordinates), then this is the only correct solution.

If the polar axis is taken parallel to the uniform field $\mathbf{E}_0$, then the potential at large distances is that of this field alone, so that

$$V = -E_0 r \cos \theta \quad \text{for } r \to \infty.$$

In order to make $V = 0$ at $r = R$ for all values of $\theta$, it seems likely that we can only add terms which vary with the same power of $\cos \theta$. Hence we try as a solution

$$V = -E_0 r \cos \theta + A r^{-2} \cos \theta. \tag{2.38}$$

It is clear that this satisfies our boundary condition if $E_0 R = A R^{-2}$; that is, $A = E_0 R^3$. Hence we have

$$V = -E_0 r \cos \theta (1 - R^3/r^3).$$

This shows that the potential outside the sphere is that due to the uniform field together with that of a dipole of moment $\mathbf{p} = 4\pi\epsilon_0 \mathbf{E}_0 R^3$ situated at the centre of the sphere. Inside the sphere a solution of the type (2.38) is not acceptable, since it would give an infinite potential at the origin. Instead we must add a term $E_0 r \cos\theta$, which will just cancel the potential of the external field so that $V = 0$ everywhere inside the sphere.

The magnitude of the induced charge at any point on the sphere can be found from the normal component of the field at the surface. This is

$$E_r = -\partial V/\partial r = E_0 \cos\theta + 2E_0(R^3/r^3)\cos\theta$$
$$= 3E_0 \cos\theta \quad \text{at } r = R.$$

Hence the charge $\sigma$ per unit area will be (from equation (1.28))

$$\sigma = \epsilon\epsilon_0 E_r = 3\epsilon\epsilon_0 E_0 \cos\theta,$$

where $\epsilon$ is the dielectric constant of the medium surrounding the sphere.

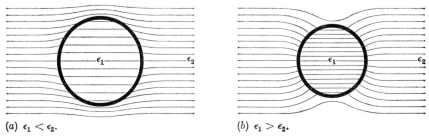

(a) $\epsilon_1 < \epsilon_2$.    (b) $\epsilon_1 > \epsilon_2$.

Fig. 2.3. The lines of electric displacement $\mathbf{D}$ due to a dielectric sphere, $\epsilon_1$, in a uniform electric field, in a medium of dielectric constant $\epsilon_2$.

*Dielectric sphere in a uniform field*

A slightly harder problem is that of a dielectric sphere of radius $R$ and dielectric constant $\epsilon_1$, surrounded by a medium of dielectric constant $\epsilon_2$, and placed in a uniform field $\mathbf{E}_0$, as in Fig. 2.3. Two separate potential functions must now be taken, one for inside and the other for outside the sphere (in effect, this was also required for the conducting sphere, but then inside we had just $V = 0$). We must also satisfy the boundary conditions at the surface of the sphere, which are, from equations (1.26) and (1.27),

$$\epsilon_1 E_{1r} = \epsilon_2 E_{2r} \quad \text{and} \quad E_{1t} = E_{2t},$$

where subscripts 1 and 2 refer to inside and outside the surface, and subscripts $r$ and $t$ refer to normal and tangential components respectively. Guided by the potential function for the case of the conducting sphere, we shall assume

$$V_2 = -E_0 r \cos\theta + A_2 r^{-2} \cos\theta,$$
$$V_1 = B_1 r \cos\theta + B_2 r^{-2} \cos\theta$$

for outside and inside the sphere respectively. Clearly we cannot have $V_1 \to \infty$ for $r \to 0$, so that the coefficient $B_2$ must be zero. It is also obvious that $V$ must be continuous at the boundary, since a discontinuity would give an infinite electric field there. Thus $V_1 = V_2$ at $r = R$; this automatically satisfies our second boundary condition since

$$E_t = E_\theta = -\frac{1}{r}\left(\frac{\partial V}{\partial \theta}\right),$$

and gives $\qquad B_1 R \cos \theta = -E_0 R \cos \theta + A_2 R^{-2} \cos \theta,$

or $\qquad\qquad B_1 = A_2 R^{-3} - E_0.$ $\qquad\qquad$ (2.39)

The normal components of $E$ at the surface are

$$E_{1r} = -(\partial V_1/\partial r)_{r=R} = -B_1 \cos \theta$$

and $\qquad E_{2r} = -(\partial V_2/\partial r)_{r=R} = E_0 \cos \theta + 2A_2 R^{-3} \cos \theta.$

Hence the first boundary condition gives

$$-B_1 = (\epsilon_2/\epsilon_1)(E_0 + 2A_2 R^{-3}).$$ $\qquad\qquad$ (2.40)

The solution of equations (2.39) and (2.40) is

$$B_1 = -\left(\frac{3\epsilon_2}{\epsilon_1+2\epsilon_2}\right)E_0 \quad \text{and} \quad A_2 = \left(\frac{\epsilon_1-\epsilon_2}{\epsilon_1+2\epsilon_2}\right)R^3 E_0,$$

so that the potential functions inside and outside the sphere are

$$V_1 = -\left(\frac{3\epsilon_2}{\epsilon_1+2\epsilon_2}\right)E_0 r \cos \theta,$$ $\qquad\qquad$ (2.41)

$$V_2 = -\left(1 - \frac{R^3}{r^3}\frac{\epsilon_1-\epsilon_2}{\epsilon_1+2\epsilon_2}\right)E_0 r \cos \theta.$$ $\qquad\qquad$ (2.42)

These equations show that the field $\mathbf{E}_1$ inside the sphere is parallel to $\mathbf{E}_0$, and of magnitude

$$\mathbf{E}_1 = \frac{3\epsilon_2}{\epsilon_1+2\epsilon_2}\,\mathbf{E}_0.$$ $\qquad\qquad$ (2.43)

If $\epsilon_1 > \epsilon_2$, $\mathbf{D}_1 > \mathbf{D}_0$ (see Fig. 2.3), but $\mathbf{E}_1 < \mathbf{E}_0$, the reduction being due to the reverse field of the polarization charges on the surface of the sphere; this reverse field is known as the 'depolarizing field'. The potential distribution outside the sphere is that of a dipole of magnitude $4\pi\epsilon_2\epsilon_0 R^3 E_0(\epsilon_1-\epsilon_2)/(\epsilon_1+2\epsilon_2)$, situated at the centre of the sphere, superimposed on that due to the uniform field. If $\epsilon_2 = 1$, the size of this dipole moment is just equal to the volume of the sphere times the polarization $\mathbf{P}_1$ induced by the field within the sphere since then $\mathbf{P}_1 = \epsilon_0(\epsilon_1-1)\mathbf{E}_1 = 3\epsilon_0(\epsilon_1-1)E_0/(\epsilon_1+2)$. Note that as $\epsilon_1 \to \infty$, the solutions tend to those obtained for the conducting sphere; this follows from the fact that the boundary condition then requires that the field in the sphere be zero.

*Problems with cylindrical symmetry—conducting cylinder in a uniform field*

In some three-dimensional problems the potential may be independent of one coordinate, and the problem then reduces to a two-dimensional one. It is often convenient to use cylindrical coordinates in such a case, taking the $z$ direction as that in which the potential is invariant. Then

TABLE 2.3

*Some cylindrical harmonic functions*

| Cylindrical harmonic | Corresponding solutions of Laplace's equation | |
|:---:|:---:|:---:|
| $D_0$ | $\log r$ | $1$ |
| $D_1$ | $r^{-1}(A\cos\theta + B\sin\theta)$ | $r(A\cos\theta + B\sin\theta)$ |
| $D_2$ | $r^{-2}(A\cos 2\theta + B\sin 2\theta)$ | $r^2(A\cos 2\theta + B\sin 2\theta)$ |
| $D_3$ | $r^{-3}(A\cos 3\theta + B\sin 3\theta)$ | $r^3(A\cos 3\theta + B\sin 3\theta)$ |

putting $\rho = 0$ and $\partial^2 V/\partial z^2 = 0$ in equation (2.5), we have for Laplace's equation

$$r\frac{\partial}{\partial r}\left(r\frac{\partial V}{\partial r}\right) + \frac{\partial^2 V}{\partial\theta^2} = 0. \tag{2.44}$$

This is satisfied by a function of the form $V = r^n D_n$, where $D_n$ is a function of $\theta$ alone (known as a cylindrical harmonic) which must satisfy the differential equation

$$\frac{\partial^2 D_n}{\partial\theta^2} + n^2 D_n = 0. \tag{2.45}$$

This equation is unchanged by the substitution of $-n$ for $n$, so that if $V = r^n D_n$ is a solution of Laplace's equation, so also is $V = r^{-n} D_n$. One solution is $V = \log_e r$, and other solutions may be obtained either by partial differentiation with respect to $x = r\cos\theta$, or by direct solution of equation (2.45).

A number of the simplest functions are given in Table 2.3; note that the general form of $D_n$ will be $A_n\cos n\theta + B_n\sin n\theta$, where $A_n$ and $B_n$ are constants.

The type of problem to which the solutions may be applied is illustrated by the case of a conducting circular cylinder, initially uncharged, lying with its axis at right angles to a uniform field $\mathbf{E}_0$. If the axis of the cylinder is taken as the $z$-axis, it is clear that the potential distribution will be independent of $z$. At large distances the potential will tend to $V = -E_0 r\cos\theta$, and we will assume that other terms required must also vary as $\cos\theta$. Then the potential outside the cylinder will be of the form

$$V = -E_0 r \cos\theta + A r^{-1} \cos\theta.$$

To satisfy the boundary condition $V = 0$ at $r = R$ for all values of $\theta$, we must have $E_0 R = A R^{-1}$, so that the potential is

$$V = -E_0 r \cos\theta (1 - R^2/r^2). \tag{2.46}$$

The first term is the potential of the external field, the second that of an extended dipole consisting of two parallel lines of positive and negative charge close to the $z$-axis.

In these problems, we have assumed a potential containing just the required number of terms. This is a matter of intelligent anticipation rather than guesswork or knowing the answer beforehand. If we had taken any less terms, we could not have satisfied the boundary conditions. If we had taken more terms, the coefficients of the additional terms would have been found to be zero. In the case just considered, terms such as $\cos n\theta$ or $\sin n\theta$ could not satisfy the condition $V = 0$ at $r = R$ for *all values of* $\theta$, because the potential of the external field varies only as $\cos\theta$. We are justified in assuming that the solution we have found is the correct and only solution because of the uniqueness theorem. This theorem also justifies the use of another special method, which we shall now consider.

## 2.5. Electrical images

If we have two equal point charges of opposite sign separated by a certain distance $2a$, the plane passing through the midpoint of the line joining them and normal to this line is an equipotential surface at zero potential. Therefore if the negative charge (say) is replaced by a plane conducting sheet $AB$ in Fig. 2.4, the field to the right of $AB$ will remain unaltered. Conversely, if a point charge is placed in front of an infinite conducting plane, the resultant electric field to the right of $AB$ will be the same as that produced by the original charge plus a negative charge an equal distance from the plane on the opposite side. The negative charge is the 'electrical image' of the original charge in the plane $AB$.

The method of images thus consists in replacing a conductor by a point charge such that the conducting surface is still an equipotential surface. Then Laplace's equation is still satisfied at all points outside the conductor, and by the principle of uniqueness, the problem of a point charge and its image is identical with that of a point charge and an infinite conducting surface as regards the region outside the conducting

surface. Electrical images are entirely virtual; a field on one side of a
closed equipotential surface cannot be represented by an image on the
same side of the surface, since this would give a singularity at the point
occupied by the image charge. The field on the one side of the surface
is identical with that which would be produced if the surface were
replaced by an image charge on the other side of it.

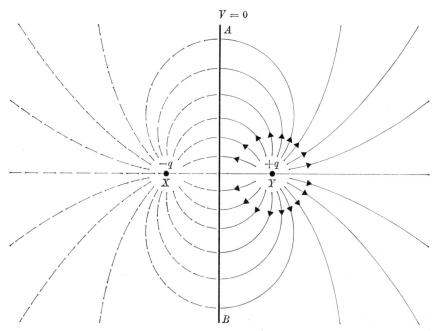

FIG. 2.4. A point charge $q$ and its image charge $-q$ in an infinite conducting plane $AB$,
showing the lines of force from $q$ on the right of the plane which end on the surface charge
on $AB$. $XY = 2a$.

### Point charge and infinite conducting plane

The method of images will now be applied to a number of special cases,
the simplest of which is that of a point charge $q$ placed a distance $a$ from
an infinite conducting plane at zero potential. In this case it is obvious
that the image must be a charge $-q$ at a distance $a$ behind the plane,
as in Fig. 2.5. The potential at an arbitrary point $P$ is then

$$V = \frac{q}{4\pi\epsilon\epsilon_0}\left\{\frac{1}{r} - \frac{1}{\{r^2 + 4a^2 + 4ar\cos\theta\}^{\frac{1}{2}}}\right\},$$

where $\epsilon$ is the dielectric constant of the medium outside the conductor.
In order to calculate the charge density at any point on the plane, we

must find the component of the electric field normal to the plane. This is (see Fig. 2.5)

$$E_x = E_r \cos\theta - E_\theta \sin\theta = -\frac{\partial V}{\partial r}\cos\theta + \frac{1}{r}\frac{\partial V}{\partial\theta}\sin\theta$$

$$= \frac{q}{4\pi\epsilon_0}\left[\frac{\cos\theta}{r^2} - \frac{r\cos\theta + 2a}{\{r^2 + 4a^2 + 4ar\cos\theta\}^{\frac{3}{2}}}\right]$$

at the point $P$. At a point $Q$ on the plane, $r\cos\theta = -a$, so that at $Q$

$$E_x = -qa/2\pi\epsilon_0 r^3$$

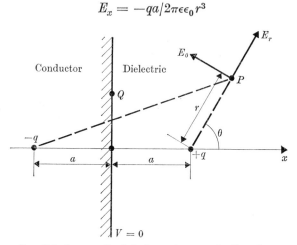

FIG. 2.5. Image of point charge in a conducting plane.

(cf. Problem 2.6), where $r$ is the distance of $Q$ from the charge $+q$. The induced charge per unit area at $Q$ is then

$$\sigma = \epsilon\epsilon_0 E_x = -qa/2\pi r^3. \tag{2.47}$$

The force exerted on the point charge by the induced charge on the plane is just equal to the force exerted on the charge by its image. That is, $F = -q^2/16\pi\epsilon_0 a^2$, where the negative sign indicates that the charge is attracted towards the plane (see Problem 2.6).

*Point charge and conducting sphere*

A more difficult problem is that of a point charge $q$ placed (*in vacuo*) a distance $a$ from the centre of a conducting sphere of radius $R$ (Fig. 2.6). We shall consider first the case where the sphere is earthed and at zero potential. By symmetry, the image charge must be on the line through $q$ to the centre of the sphere $O$, and we will assume that it consists of a single charge $q'$ at a distance $b$ from $O$. The potential at a point $Q$ on the surface of the sphere is then

$$V = \frac{1}{4\pi\epsilon_0}\left(\frac{q}{r}+\frac{q'}{r_1}\right)$$

$$= \frac{1}{4\pi\epsilon_0}\left[\frac{q}{(R^2+a^2+2aR\cos\theta)^{\frac{1}{2}}}+\frac{q'}{(R^2+b^2+2bR\cos\theta)^{\frac{1}{2}}}\right].$$

It is only possible to make $V = 0$ over the whole surface of the sphere (i.e. for all values of $\theta$) if the functions in the denominators are similar

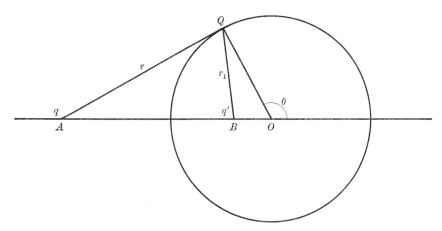

FIG. 2.6. A point charge $q$ and its image $q'$ in a conducting sphere.
$OA = a, \quad OB = b.$

functions of $\theta$. This requires that we choose $b$ so that $b/R = R/a$; that is, $B$ is the inverse point to $A$ in the sphere. Then the potential at $Q$ is

$$V = \frac{q+(a/R)q'}{4\pi\epsilon_0(R^2+a^2+2Ra\cos\theta)^{\frac{1}{2}}},$$

and this will be zero if we make $q' = -q(R/a)$. Hence the image charge is of magnitude $-q(R/a)$ at the inverse point in the sphere, and the reader may verify, by integrating the charge density on the sphere, that the total charge on the sphere is equal to the image charge.

If the sphere is insulated and initially uncharged, the total charge on it must remain zero. It is therefore necessary to add a second image charge $-q'$ at such a point that the surface of the sphere remains an equipotential surface. This is accomplished by placing a charge $+q(R/a)$ at the centre of the sphere in addition to the charge $-q(R/a)$ at the inverse point. If the sphere is insulated but carries an initial charge $Q$ the total charge at the centre would of course be $Q+q(R/a)$.

## 2.6. Line charges

Just as we have considered the mathematical abstraction of a point charge, so we may postulate a 'line charge' in which charge is uniformly distributed along an infinite straight line. Its strength is denoted by $\lambda$, the charge per unit length. To find the field of such a line charge, immersed in a medium of dielectric constant $\epsilon$, we apply Gauss's theorem to a section of length $t$ of a cylinder of radius $r$ whose axis coincides with the line charge. This gives

$$\epsilon\epsilon_0 \, E(2\pi rt) = \lambda t,$$

since by symmetry the field $E$ is everywhere normal to the axis. Hence $E = \lambda/(2\pi\epsilon\epsilon_0 r)$, and the potential at a distance $r$ from the axis is

$$V = -\frac{\lambda}{2\pi\epsilon\epsilon_0} \int \frac{dr}{r} = -\frac{\lambda}{2\pi\epsilon\epsilon_0} \log_e r + V_0. \qquad (2.48)$$

Here the constant $V_0$ cannot be defined by assuming $V = 0$ at $r = \infty$ since the line charge itself extends to infinity.

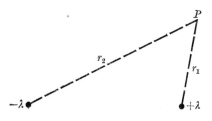

If we have two parallel line charges of equal strength but opposite sign, as in Fig. 2.7, the potential at a point whose perpendicular distances from the line charges are $r_1$, $r_2$ respectively is

FIG. 2.7. Two parallel line charges normal to the plane of the paper, with charge $+\lambda$ and $-\lambda$ per unit length.

$$V = \frac{\lambda}{2\pi\epsilon\epsilon_0} \log(r_2/r_1) + V_0. \qquad (2.49)$$

The equipotential surfaces given by this equation are shown in Fig. 2.8. They have the form of cylinders whose cross-sections form a set of coaxial circles with limiting points at the line charges. The surface whose potential is $V_0$ is the median plane (for which $r_1 = r_2$) between the two line charges. From this it follows that the problem of a line charge parallel to a conducting plane can be solved by the method of images, using a line charge of opposite sign as image. We shall apply our results to a more realistic problem.

*Capacitance between two parallel infinite circular cylinders*

Consider first an infinite line charge of strength $\lambda$ which is parallel to an infinite cylinder of radius $a$. In the cross-section shown in Fig. 2.9, the line charge is at $P$ and the axis of the cylinder at $O$. We imagine

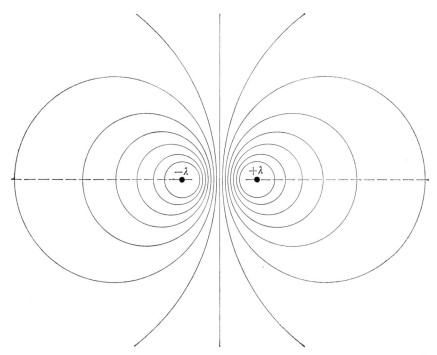

Fig. 2.8. The lines of constant potential for two parallel infinite line charges $\lambda$ and $-\lambda$, normal to the plane of the paper. They form systems of coaxial circles with limiting points at the charges.

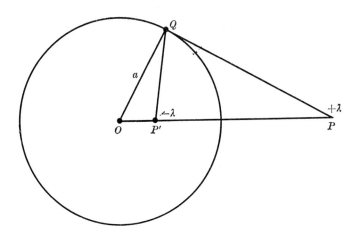

Fig. 2.9. The image of an infinite line charge in an infinite conducting cylinder.

an image line charge of strength $-\lambda$ to be placed at $P'$, the position of $P'$ being chosen so that the circle formed by the cross-section of the conducting cylinder coincides with one of the family of coaxial circles which are the equipotentials of the line charge and its image. Then the potential at any point $Q$ on the surface of the cylinder is

$$V = -\frac{\lambda}{2\pi\epsilon_0} \log \frac{QP}{QP'} + V_0.$$

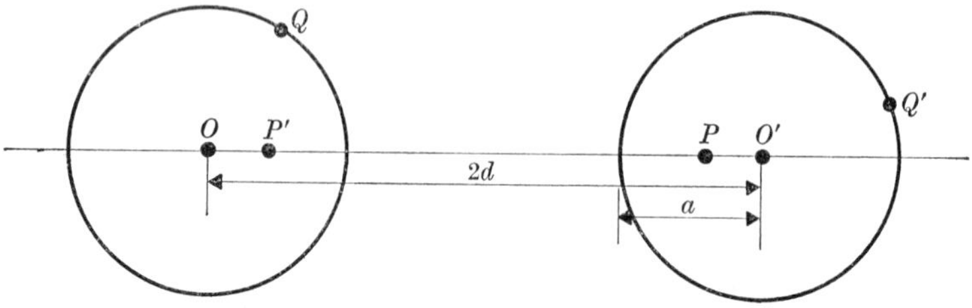

Fig. 2.10. Two infinitely long parallel conducting cylinders.

Since $P$ and $P'$ are the limiting points of the family of coaxial circles, it follows that they are inverse points with regard to any one of these circles. Hence

$$QP/QP' = OP/OQ = OP/a,$$

and the potential at $Q$ is

$$V = -\frac{\lambda}{2\pi\epsilon_0} \log \frac{OP}{a} + V_0,$$

which is independent of the position of $Q$ on the surface of the cylinder, showing that this is an equipotential.

We turn now to the case of two infinite parallel cylinders, each of radius $a$, whose axes are a distance $2d$ apart. Then in Fig. 2.10 the distance $OO'$ is $2d$, and $P$, $P'$ are the limiting points of a family of coaxial circles. $P$ and $P'$ are chosen so that two of the circles coincide with the surfaces of the cylinders, making each of these an equipotential if line charges of strength $\lambda$ and $-\lambda$ were placed at $P$ and $P'$ respectively. Then the potential at an arbitrary point whose distance is $r_1$ from $P$ and $r_2$ from $P'$ is

$$V = -\frac{\lambda}{2\pi\epsilon_0} \log(r_1/r_2),$$

where the constant $V_0$ is zero if we take the median plane $(r_1 = r_2)$ between the cylinders to be at zero potential. Then the potentials of the two cylinders are

$$V_Q = -\frac{\lambda}{2\pi\epsilon_0} \log(OP/a) \quad \text{and} \quad V_{Q'} = +\frac{\lambda}{2\pi\epsilon_0} \log(OP/a)$$

respectively. But $OP+OP' = 2d$, and $OP.OP' = a^2$, since $P$, $P'$ are inverse points in the circle of radius $a$, centre $O$. Hence

$$OP = d+\sqrt{(d^2-a^2)},$$

and the capacitance per unit length between the two cylinders is

$$C = \lambda/(V_{Q'}-V_Q)$$

$$= \frac{\pi\epsilon\epsilon_0}{\log[\{d+\sqrt{(d^2-a^2)}\}/a]}. \qquad (2.50)$$

When $d \gg a$, this approaches the limiting value

$$C = \pi\epsilon\epsilon_0/\log(2d/a). \qquad (2.51)$$

A similar problem is the capacitance of a horizontal telegraph wire with respect to the earth. This may be treated as an infinite cylinder of radius $a$ a distance $d$ above an infinite conducting plane. It is clear that the potential distribution will be the same as in the case of the two parallel cylinders if we assume that the conducting plane coincides with the median plane between the cylinders, which is the equipotential surface $V = 0$. Then the charge on the wire per unit length is $\lambda$, and the potential difference between it and the plane is just half that between the two cylinders in the previous problem. Hence the capacitance per unit length will be (assuming $d \gg a$)

$$C = \frac{2\pi\epsilon\epsilon_0}{\log(2d/a)}. \qquad (2.52)$$

Note that the approximation $d \gg a$ is tantamount to assuming that the wire behaves as if it had a line charge $\lambda$ per unit length along its axis, since as $(a/d)$ approaches zero the point $P'$ moves towards $O$ in Fig. 2.10 and $OP \to 2d$.

## 2.7. Images in dielectrics

The potential distribution due to a point charge near a dielectric surface may sometimes be found by the method of images. We shall illustrate this type of problem by considering the case of a point charge $q$ a distance $a$ from a semi-infinite dielectric bounded by a plane surface. This problem is more complex than that of a point charge and conducting plane since a second image system is required to represent the field within the dielectric. It is not obvious that the field can be represented by that of a single point charge, but we shall assume that this is possible (if our assumption is wrong we shall not be able to satisfy the boundary conditions). We take therefore a single charge $q_2$ at a point $B$, as in

Fig. 2.11, and the potential at a point $Q$ in the dielectric will then be

$$V_Q = \frac{q_2}{4\pi\epsilon_0\, r_2}. \tag{2.53}$$

The field of the point charge $q$ will polarize the dielectric and there will therefore be a surface charge on the dielectric which affects the field outside. We assume that this can be represented by an image charge $q_1$

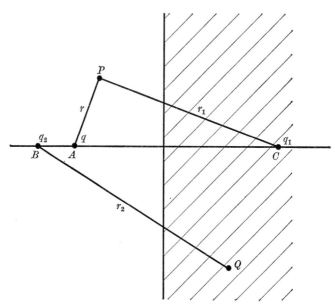

FIG. 2.11. Image systems for a point charge $q$ and a semi-infinite dielectric. The field outside the dielectric is that of $q$ and $q_1$; the field inside the dielectric is that of $q_2$.

at $C$ in the dielectric, and the potential at a point $P$ outside the dielectric is then

$$V_P = \frac{1}{4\pi\epsilon_0}\left\{\frac{q}{r}+\frac{q_1}{r_1}\right\}. \tag{2.54}$$

By symmetry, $q$, $q_1$, and $q_2$ will all lie on a normal to the dielectric surface. Note that the dielectric constant $\epsilon$ does not appear in these equations since the effect of the dielectric is replaced by two image systems *in vacuo*.

To avoid an infinite electric field at the boundary we must assume that $V_P = V_Q$ at the boundary, and this automatically satisfies our first boundary condition, that the tangential components of $E$ must be the same on either side of the boundary. It is clear that the condition

$V_P = V_Q$ everywhere on the boundary can only be satisfied if $r$, $r_1$, and $r_2$ vary at the same rate as we move along the boundary, and we must therefore have $r = r_1 = r_2$, so that $B$ coincides with $A$, and $C$ is as far behind the surface as $A$ is in front. In addition, $q+q_1 = q_2$. Our second boundary condition is that the normal components of $D$ must be continuous at the boundary; i.e. $(\partial V_P/\partial z) = \epsilon(\partial V_Q/\partial z)$ at the surface, which we take to be the plane $z = 0$. Now at an arbitrary point $(x, y, z)$, $r_2 = \{x^2+y^2+(a+z)^2\}^{\frac{1}{2}}$, and $r_1 = \{x^2+y^2+(a-z)^2\}^{\frac{1}{2}}$, so that

$$\frac{\partial}{\partial z}\left(\frac{1}{r}\right) = \frac{\partial}{\partial z}\left(\frac{1}{r_2}\right) = -\frac{a+z}{r^3}, \qquad \frac{\partial}{\partial z}\left(\frac{1}{r_1}\right) = \frac{a-z}{r_1^3}.$$

Using these relations for the case $z = 0$, our second boundary condition becomes

$$\frac{a(q-q_1)}{4\pi\epsilon_0 r^3} = \frac{\epsilon a q_2}{4\pi\epsilon_0 r^3}.$$

Hence we have the relations

$$q+q_1 = q_2 \quad \text{and} \quad q-q_1 = \epsilon q_2,$$

which give $q_2 = 2q/(\epsilon+1)$ and $q_1 = -q(\epsilon-1)/(\epsilon+1)$ for the image charges. The force of attraction on the charge $q$ towards the dielectric is therefore

$$F = -\frac{qq_1}{4\pi\epsilon_0(2a)^2} = \frac{q^2(\epsilon-1)}{16\pi\epsilon_0 a^2(\epsilon+1)}. \tag{2.55}$$

The lines of displacement for the case of a point charge and an infinite dielectric are shown in Fig. 1.13.

## REFERENCES

BRINK, D. M., and SATCHLER, G. R., 1962, *Angular Momentum* (O.U.P.).
RAMSEY, N. F., 1956, *Molecular Beams* (O.U.P.).

## PROBLEMS

2.1. The polarization charge on the surface of a spherical cavity is $-\sigma_0 \cos\theta$, at a point whose radius vector from the centre makes an angle $\theta$ with a given axis $Oz$. Prove that the field at the centre is $\sigma_0/3\epsilon_0$, parallel to $Oz$.

If the cavity is in a uniform dielectric subject to a field $\mathbf{E}_0$ parallel to the direction $\theta = 0$, show that $\sigma_0 = 3E_0\epsilon_0(\epsilon-1)/(1+2\epsilon)$, where $\epsilon$ is the relative permittivity of the dielectric. Verify that this gives the correct value for the field at the centre of the cavity (equation (2.43)) and note that $\sigma_0$ is not simply $(\epsilon-1)\epsilon_0 E_0$ because of the distortion of the field in the dielectric caused by the presence of the cavity.

2.2. A dipole $\mathbf{p}$ is situated at the centre of a spherical cavity of radius $a$ in an infinite medium of dielectric constant $\epsilon$. Show that the potential in the dielectric medium is the same as would be produced by a dipole $\mathbf{p}'$ immersed in a continuous dielectric, where

$$\mathbf{p}' = \mathbf{p}\,\frac{3\epsilon}{2\epsilon+1},$$

and that the field inside the cavity is equal to $\mathbf{E}_d + \mathbf{E}_r$, where $\mathbf{E}_d$ is the field which the dipole would produce in the absence of the dielectric, and

$$\mathbf{E}_r = \frac{2(\epsilon - 1)}{2\epsilon + 1} \frac{\mathbf{p}}{4\pi\epsilon_0 a^3}.$$

$\mathbf{E}_r$ is known as the 'reaction field'. These formulae are used in the theory of dielectrics (see Chapter 17).

2.3. Show that the field inside a cylindrical cavity in a dielectric of constant $\epsilon$ is $\dfrac{2\epsilon}{\epsilon + 1} \mathbf{E}_0$, when the axis of the cylinder is at right angles to a uniform field $\mathbf{E}_0$.

2.4. Find an expression for the surface density of charge on an infinitely long conducting cylinder of radius $a$, placed with its axis at right angles to a uniform electric field $\mathbf{E}_0$, as a function of the polar angle $\theta$.

(*Answer*: $\sigma = 2\epsilon_0 E_0 \cos\theta$.)

2.5. A uniform electric field $\mathbf{E}$ is set up in an infinite dielectric. Show that (a) if a long needle-shaped cavity, whose lateral dimensions are very small compared with its length, is cut in the dielectric with its axis parallel to $\mathbf{E}$, then the field in this cavity is $\mathbf{E}$; (b) if a flat disk-shaped cavity, whose lateral dimensions are very large compared with its thickness, is cut with its plane normal to the direction of $\mathbf{E}$, then the field in the cavity is $\mathbf{D}/\epsilon_0$, where $\mathbf{D}$ is the displacement in the dielectric.

Verify that the field in an intermediate shape of cavity (such as in Problems 2.1 and 2.3) lies between these extreme values.

2.6. A point charge $q$ is placed near an infinite conducting plane. Verify that the total charge on the plane is $-q$ by integrating equation (2.47), and calculate the total force on the plane by integration of the tension per unit area (equation (1.37)) over the area of the plane. Verify the expression given in the text for the field at $Q$ (Fig. 2.5) by vector addition of the fields of the point charge and its image.

2.7. Show that the work done in bringing up a charge $q$ from infinity to a distance $a$ from a conducting plane at zero potential is $-q^2/16\pi\epsilon\epsilon_0 a$. Verify that the same result is obtained using equation (1.34) (remember that the induced charge on the plane is at zero potential).

2.8. Show that the force on a charge $q$ distance $a$ *in vacuo* from the centre of an insulated and uncharged conducting sphere of radius $R$ is $(a > R)$

$$F = \frac{q^2}{4\pi\epsilon_0} \left( \frac{R}{a^3} - \frac{Ra}{(a^2 - R^2)^2} \right).$$

2.9. A point charge is placed in a hollow metal sphere of radius $R$. If the charge is $q$ and is a distance $b$ from the centre of the sphere show that the force on it is

$$\frac{q^2}{4\pi\epsilon_0} \frac{Rb}{(R^2 - b^2)^2}.$$

(*Hint*: Find the image of $q$ outside the sphere such that the sphere is an equipotential surface.)

2.10. A point charge $q$ is placed at a distance $3R$ from the centre of an isolated conducting sphere of radius $R$ which already has a charge equal to $q$. Prove that the surface densities at points on the sphere nearest to and farthest from the point charge are in the ratio $8:29$.

**2.11.** An elementary dipole of strength $p$ is placed at a point $P$, outside and at a distance $a$ from the centre $C$ of an earthed conducting sphere of radius $R$. The axis of the dipole is in the direction $CP$. Prove that its image system consists of a point charge $pR/a^2$ and a dipole of strength $pR^3/a^3$, both situated at the point $P'$ which is inverse to $P$ in the sphere.

**2.12.** Show that if an infinite line charge $\lambda$ per unit length is at a distance $d$ from an infinite conducting plane in a medium of dielectric constant $\epsilon$, the surface density of charge in the plane is $\sigma = -d\lambda/\pi r^2$, where $r$ is the shortest distance from the line of charge to the point in question.

**2.13.** Calculate the force per unit length on the infinite line charge of the last question.

$$(Answer: \quad F = -\lambda^2/4\pi\epsilon_0 d.)$$

**2.14.** Electric charge is distributed over a thin spherical shell with a density which varies in proportion to the value of a single function $P_l(\cos\theta)$ at any point on the shell. Show, by using the expansions (2.26) and (2.27) and the orthogonality relations for the Legendre functions, that the potential varies as $r^l P_l(\cos\theta)$ at a point $(r, \theta)$ inside the sphere and $r^{-(l+1)}P_l(\cos\theta)$ at a point $(R, \theta)$ outside.

**2.15.** Show that, for $l = 1$, the quantities defined by equation (2.32) are

$$A_{1,0} = p_z, \qquad A_{1,1} = -2^{-\frac{1}{2}}(p_x + ip_y), \qquad A_{1,-1} = 2^{-\frac{1}{2}}(p_x - ip_y),$$

while for a point charge at $B$ in Fig. 2.1 $(b)$,

$$\frac{1}{4\pi\epsilon\epsilon_0}B_{1,0} = -E_z, \qquad \frac{1}{4\pi\epsilon\epsilon_0}B_{1,1} = -2^{-\frac{1}{2}}(E_x + iE_y), \qquad \frac{1}{4\pi\epsilon\epsilon_0}B_{1,-1} = 2^{-\frac{1}{2}}(E_x - iE_y),$$

and verify that this gives the same interaction energy as equation (2.24).

**2.16.** For an atom in a $p$-state, the wave function is $\psi = f(R)Y_{1,0}$, and the charge density is $-e\psi^2$. Show that the atomic quadrupole moment (as defined by equation (2.35)) is $\frac{4}{5}\langle R^2\rangle$, where $\langle R^2\rangle$ is the mean square distance of the electron from the nucleus.

**2.17.** The isotope of mass 35 of chlorine has a nuclear electric quadrupole moment $Q$. Show that if it were in a chlorine atom whose wave function $\psi = f(R)Y_{1,0}$, the energy of interaction between the nuclear electric quadrupole moment and the electron is

$$U_P = -\left(\frac{1}{4\pi\epsilon_0}\right)(\tfrac{1}{5}e^2 Q\langle R^{-3}\rangle),$$

where $\langle R^{-3}\rangle$ is the mean inverse cube of the distance of the electron from the nucleus, and $e$ the electronic charge.

If $Q = -0.079$ barns $= -7.9 \times 10^{-30}$ m$^2$, and $\langle R^{-3}\rangle = 5 \times 10^{31}$ m$^{-3}$, show that the energy of interaction $(U_P/h)$ expressed in frequency units ($h$ is Planck's constant) is about 27 Mc/s.

**2.18.** Six equal charges $q$ are placed at the points $(\pm R, 0, 0)$, $(0, \pm R, 0)$, $(0, 0, \pm R)$. Show that the terms of lowest degree in the potential at a point $(x, y, z) = (r, \theta, \phi)$ near the origin are

$$V = \frac{6q}{4\pi\epsilon_0 R} + \left(\frac{q}{4\pi\epsilon_0}\right)\left(\frac{r^4}{R^5}\right)\left(\frac{7}{2}\right)\{C_{4,0} + (5/14)^{\frac{1}{2}}(C_{4,4} + C_{4,-4})\},$$

where $C_{4,0} = P_4$ (which is given in Table 2.1), and

$$C_{4,\pm 4} = (35/128)^{\frac{1}{2}} \sin^4\theta \, e^{\pm i4\phi}.$$

[*Hints*: Since the system has inversion symmetry through the origin, terms in odd powers of $r$ must vanish. Also $V$ must have fourfold symmetry about the polar ($z$-)axis, so that rotations changing $\phi$ by $\frac{1}{2}\pi$ must leave $V$ unchanged: only functions with $m = 0$ or $4$ satisfy this condition.]

Note that in Cartesian coordinates

$$V = \frac{6q}{4\pi\epsilon_0}\frac{1}{R} + \left(\frac{q}{4\pi\epsilon_0}\right)\left(\frac{1}{R^5}\right)\left(\frac{35}{4}\right)(x^4 + y^4 + z^4 - \tfrac{3}{5}r^4),$$

showing that the $x$, $y$, $z$ axes are all equivalent (cubic symmetry).

# 3

## STEADY CURRENTS

### 3.1. Introduction

In the previous chapters on electrostatics we have been concerned with stationary electric charges. If a free charge is placed in an electric field it will be acted on by a force, and will move in the direction of the lines of force. Thus, if an initial difference of potential exists in a conductor, the charges will move until they reach positions of equilibrium, and the whole of the conductor becomes an equipotential surface. But by connecting a battery between two points of a conductor, a permanent difference of potential may be maintained between these two points, and there will then be a continuing flow of charge. This constitutes an electric current, and the strength of the current $I$ is defined by the rate at which charge passes any given point in the circuit. If we are dealing with a current extended in space, then we may define the current density **J** as the quantity of charge passing per second through unit area of a plane normal to the line of flow. The total current flowing through any surface is found by integrating the normal component of the current density: that is

$$I = \int \mathbf{J}.\mathbf{dS}. \tag{3.1}$$

If the current is carried by particles of charge $e$ with density $n$ per unit volume and velocity **v**, then the current density is

$$\mathbf{J} = ne\mathbf{v}. \tag{3.2}$$

Thus **J** is a vector whose direction is that of the velocity **v** of the carriers.

In early experiments on electricity there was no evidence for the sign of the charges forming the current, since there was no means of distinguishing between a flow of positive charges in one direction and a flow of negative charges in the opposite direction. The positive direction of current flow was therefore taken as that in which a positive charge would move in an electric field. Thus in a circuit, the conventional direction for the flow of current is from the higher potential to the lower potential; i.e. from the positive pole of a battery round the external circuit to the negative pole. It is customary to retain this convention, although the modern theory of metallic conduction shows that the positively charged ions are fixed, while a certain number of electrons are free to move about the body of the metal. Since the electrons are negatively charged, their direction of movement is opposite to that of the conventional current flow.

*Measurement of e/m for carriers of electric current in a metal*

The first direct experimental evidence that the carriers of electricity in a metal are electrons was supplied by the measurements of Tolman and Stewart (1917). The principle of this experiment depends on a comparison of the electric current with the momentum carried by the particles. If the current density is $nev$, and the particles have mass $m$, then the momentum associated with the current crossing unit area of a plane normal to the direction of flow is $nmv$. Thus the ratio of the electric current density to the momentum 'current density' is simply equal to the ratio of charge to mass $(e/m)$ of the carriers. The sign of $e/m$ is obtained from comparison of the directions of flow of the electric current and momentum current. The method we shall now describe is that of a later experiment by Kettering and Scott (1944).

A circular coil is suspended by a thin fibre so that its plane is horizontal and it forms a torsional pendulum with very small damping. The coil, consisting of $N$ turns of radius $r$, carries a current $I$. If the number of electrons per unit length of the wire is $n$, and they move with a mean velocity $v$, their angular momentum about the axis of the coil is

$$\Gamma = mrvn(2\pi rN),$$

since the total number of electrons in the coil is $n(2\pi rN)$. The current $I = nev$, and hence we have

$$\Gamma = 2\pi r^2 N(m/e)I = 2AN(m/e)I,$$

where $A$ is the area of the coil. In the experiment, a current $I$ is maintained in the coil, and then suddenly reversed. This imparts an impulse $2\Gamma$ to the coil, whose angular momentum is thus altered by $4AN(m/e)I$. In practice the amplitude of swing of the coil is observed with the current flowing in one direction, and the current is reversed at the moment when the coil passes through its equilibrium position. This changes the amplitude of swing $\theta_0$ by an amount

$$\Delta\theta_0 = 2\Gamma(T/2\pi\mathfrak{I}),$$

where $2\Gamma$ is the change of angular momentum due to the current reversal, $T$ is the time of swing, and $\mathfrak{I}$ the moment of inertia of the coil. The value of $e/m$ can thus be determined by measurement of the change in amplitude of oscillation for a given current $I$.

Although the theory of the experiment is simple there were many practical difficulties. Leads to the coil had to be brought in so that the free suspension by the torsion fibre was not affected. To eliminate vibration and disturbance due to changing magnetic fields, the apparatus was installed in an underground vault. The experiment was performed both with coils made of copper and aluminium. The values of $m/e$ obtained were 5·64, 5·67, and 5·79 × 10⁻⁹ g/coulomb for three different copper coils, and 5·66 × 10⁻⁹ g/coulomb for an aluminium coil. The mean of these results, 5·69 × 10⁻⁹, is in very close agreement with the reciprocal (5·68 × 10⁻⁹ g/coulomb) of the most accurate determinations of $e/m$ for free electrons. The sign of $m/e$, obtained from the direction of the change of amplitude, corresponded to the carriers being negatively charged.

## 3.2. Flow of current in conductors

Since electric charge can neither be created nor destroyed, it follows that the rate of increase of the total charge inside any arbitrary volume must be equal to the net flow of charge into this volume. We have therefore

$$\frac{\partial}{\partial t}\left(\int \rho \, d\tau\right) = \int \frac{\partial \rho}{\partial t} d\tau = -\int \mathbf{J}.\mathbf{dS},$$

where the integrals are taken respectively over the volume and the surface bounding it. On transforming the surface integral into a volume integral, we have

$$\int \frac{\partial \rho}{\partial t} d\tau = -\int \operatorname{div} \mathbf{J} \, d\tau$$

or

$$\int \left(\operatorname{div} \mathbf{J} + \frac{\partial \rho}{\partial t}\right) d\tau = 0.$$

This integral must be zero whatever the volume over which we integrate, and this can only be true if the integrand is itself zero. We may therefore write

$$\operatorname{div} \mathbf{J} = -\frac{\partial \rho}{\partial t}, \tag{3.3}$$

which is known as the equation of continuity. In the steady state $\partial \rho/\partial t = 0$, and therefore

$$\operatorname{div} \mathbf{J} = 0 \tag{3.4}$$

in any region of current flow which does not contain a source or sink of current. Such a source or sink by which current may be injected into or withdrawn from a conducting region is known as an electrode. The total current flow to or from an electrode may be found by integrating the current density over any surface which totally encloses the electrode.

*Ohm's law*

It is found experimentally that in a metallic conductor at constant temperature the current density is linearly proportional to the electric field. This is expressed by the equation

$$\mathbf{J} = \sigma \mathbf{E}. \tag{3.5}$$

The constant $\sigma$ is known as the specific conductivity, and its reciprocal as the specific resistance or resistivity. The latter is usually denoted by $\rho$, and it is generally clear from the context whether this symbol is being used to denote charge density or specific resistance.

If a conducting wire of cross-section $A$ carries a current $I$, then $I = JA$; if the current enters at a point where the potential is $V_1$ and leaves at a point a distance $l$ away where the potential is $V_2$, then $E = -(V_2-V_1)/l$. Hence

$$I = \sigma EA = \sigma A(V_1-V_2)/l = (V_1-V_2)/R, \tag{3.6}$$

where $R = l/(A\sigma) = \rho l/A$ is known as the resistance of the wire. Equation (3.6), which expresses the fact that the voltage between the ends of a conductor is proportional to the current flowing in the conductor is known as Ohm's law. In the m.k.s. system (see Chapter 24) $V$ is measured in volts, $I$ in amperes, and the unit of resistance is the ohm. Its reciprocal, the unit of conductance, is called the mho, or reciprocal ohm. Since $\rho = AR/l$, the dimensions of specific resistance are those of resistance $\times$ length, and the unit is therefore the ohm-metre.

Values of the resistivity $\rho$ at room temperature are given in Table 3.1 for a number of metals, alloys, and insulators. All metals are good conductors; silver is the best, but is expensive, so that copper is generally used instead. The specific resistance of all metals is independent of the current density over an extremely large range, but increases with the temperature. If $R_0$ is the resistance at the ice-point $T_0$, the resistance $R$ at a temperature $T$ can be written as

$$R = R_0[1+a(T-T_0)+b(T-T_0)^2+c(T-T_0)^3+...], \tag{3.7}$$

where $a$, $b$, and $c$ are constants which decrease rapidly in order of magnitude as the powers of the brackets increase. In the range between the ice-point and the steam-point only $a$ is appreciable except in very accurate work. It is known as the temperature coefficient of resistance, and some values are given in Table 3.1. It will be seen that manganin and constantan can be considered to have a resistance independent of temperature over the range for which $b$ is negligible.

There is another class of substances called semiconductors, examples of which are carbon, germanium, silicon, and some compounds such as zinc oxide. The conductivity depends on the purity of the specimen, but can be represented in many cases by an equation of the form

$$\sigma = \sigma_0 e^{-b/T} \quad \text{or} \quad \rho = \rho_0 e^{b/T}, \tag{3.8}$$

where $\sigma_0$, $\rho_0$, and $b$ are constants.

TABLE 3.1

*Specific resistance of some typical materials*

| Substance | | Specific resistance at 20° C (ohm-metres) | Temperature coefficient (°C)$^{-1}$ |
|---|---|---|---|
| Pure metals | Silver | $1\cdot6 \times 10^{-8}$ | $3\cdot8 \times 10^{-3}$ |
| | Copper | $1\cdot72 \times 10^{-8}$ | $3\cdot9 \times 10^{-3}$ |
| | Aluminium | $2\cdot83 \times 10^{-8}$ | $3\cdot9 \times 10^{-3}$ |
| | Platinum | $10 \times 10^{-8}$ | $3\cdot9 \times 10^{-3}$ |
| Alloys | Constantan | $44\cdot2 \times 10^{-8}$ | $\sim 10^{-6}$ |
| | Manganin | $44 \times 10^{-8}$ | $\sim 10^{-6}$ |
| Semiconductors | Pure silicon | $\sim 2 \times 10^{3}$ | negative |
| | Pure germanium | $\sim 0\cdot5$ | negative |
| Insulators | Glass plate | $2 \times 10^{11}$ | — |
| | Sealing wax | $\sim 10^{14}$ | — |
| | Sulphur | $\sim 10^{15}$ | — |
| | Fused quartz | $> 5 \times 10^{16}$ | — |

By combining equations (3.2), (3.5) we find that

$$\sigma = ne(\mathbf{v}/\mathbf{E}) = neu. \tag{3.9}$$

Here $u$ is a quantity known as the mobility, and is equal to the mean drift velocity which the electrons acquire in unit electric field. It is generally expressed in units of (cm/sec) per (volt/cm), or cm$^2$/volt-sec; in m.k.s. units it must be converted to m$^2$/volt-sec, and the number then obtained for the mobility will be smaller by a factor $10^{-4}$ than that expressed in the more customary units. From equation (3.9) we see that the conductivity depends on $n$, the number of carriers per unit volume, and $u$, their mobility. In a metal $n$ is virtually independent of temperature, but $u$ varies roughly inversely as the absolute temperature except at very low temperatures; in a semiconductor the very rapid change in the conductivity with temperature is mainly due to the fact that $n$ varies exponentially with $(1/T)$. The properties of metallic conductors and of semiconductors are discussed further in Chapters 18 and 19.

*Current flow in an extended medium*

From equations (3.4) and (3.5) it follows that in a medium where $\sigma$ is constant, $\sigma \operatorname{div} \mathbf{E} = 0$. But since $\mathbf{E} = -\operatorname{grad} V$, we have

$$\nabla^2 V = 0,$$

so that Laplace's equation holds, as in electrostatics. If two perfectly conducting electrodes are immersed in an infinite medium of finite conductivity, the potential distribution in the medium is the same as in a condenser, whose plates are formed by the two conductors; for the potential must satisfy Laplace's equation in each case with the boundary conditions $V = \text{constant}$ on the surface of the conductors. In the medium, the lines of current flow are orthogonal to the lines of constant $V$, and coincide with the lines of $\mathbf{E}$. Since the resistance $R$ of the solution between the conductors, and the capacity $C$ of the condenser formed when the solution is replaced by a dielectric, depend essentially on the distribution of the lines of $\mathbf{E}$, there is a simple relation between them.

The analogous equations for the two cases are:

$$\left.\begin{array}{cc} \mathbf{D} = \epsilon\epsilon_0\,\mathbf{E} & \mathbf{J} = \sigma\mathbf{E} \\ \epsilon\epsilon_0\operatorname{div}(\operatorname{grad} V) = 0 & \sigma\operatorname{div}(\operatorname{grad} V) = 0 \\ \int \mathbf{D}.\mathbf{dS} = Q & \int \mathbf{J}.\mathbf{dS} = I \end{array}\right\}. \tag{3.10}$$

Since $C = Q/V$, and $1/R = I/V$, $C/\epsilon\epsilon_0$ is equivalent to $(1/R)/\sigma$; that is,

$$R \equiv \frac{\epsilon\epsilon_0}{\sigma C}. \tag{3.11}$$

The fact that the potential distribution in a conducting medium is the same as in the electrostatic case may be made the basis of a method of finding experimentally the distribution in a case where it is not amenable to calculation (see § 3.8).

### 3.3. The voltaic circuit

The mechanism by which a battery acts as the source of a constant potential will be discussed in Chapter 4. For the present purpose the battery will merely be regarded as maintaining a potential difference between its two terminals. Fig. 3.1 illustrates the usual notation for the case of a battery $B$ which causes a current $I$ to flow through the resistance $R$ connected across the terminals $P$, $Q$. Since the battery drives the current round any circuit attached to it, the potential difference it produces is often called the 'electromotive force' or e.m.f. The total e.m.f. is equal to the line integral $\oint \mathbf{E}.\mathbf{ds}$ taken round the circuit;

since no work is done by any external agency we must have

$$0 = V - \oint \mathbf{E}.\mathbf{ds}.$$

Hence, using equation (3.6),

$$V = \oint \mathbf{E}.\mathbf{ds} = El = I(l/\sigma A) = IR \tag{3.12}$$

if the battery of e.m.f. $V$ is connected to a single conductor of conductivity $\sigma$, cross-section $A$, and length $l$. Equation (3.12) is the basis of all calculations on resistance networks.

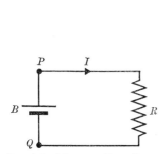

FIG. 3.1. A battery $B$ sending a current $I$ through a resistance $R$.

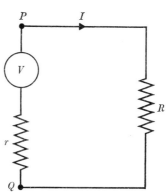

FIG. 3.2. Representation of a battery by an open-circuit e.m.f. $V$ and an internal resistance $r$.

When a current flows through a conductor of finite resistance, charge is being transferred from a point at one potential to a point at a different potential. The direction of positive current flow is to a place at a lower potential so that there is a loss of electrical energy which appears as heat in the conductor. If a charge $dQ$ flows between two points differing in potential by $V$ in a time $dt$, the energy lost per second (power) is

$$W = V(dQ/dt) = VI = V^2/R = I^2 R, \tag{3.13}$$

where $R$ is the resistance between the two points. The unit of power is the volt-ampere, known as the watt. In an extended medium of conductivity $\sigma$, the power dissipated in an element of cross-section $dS$ and length $ds$ is $VI = (E\,ds)(\sigma E\,dS) = \sigma E^2\,d\tau$, where $d\tau$ is the volume of the element. The total power dissipated is then found by integration over the whole volume of the conductor.

In practice it is found that the e.m.f. produced by a battery is not quite constant, but drops slightly when a current is drawn from it. The variation is the same as would be produced by an ideal source of e.m.f. $V$ equal to that produced by the battery on open circuit, less the potential drop in a resistance $r$. The equivalent circuit is shown in Fig. 3.2, and $r$ is known as the 'internal resistance' of the battery. If the battery is used to supply power to a load of resistance $R$, as in Fig. 3.2, the current $I$ which flows is given by the equation $V = I(r+R)$. The power dissipated in the load is therefore

$$W = I^2R = V^2R/(r+R)^2.$$

If the load can be varied, so that $R$ is adjustable, then by differentiating this expression for $W$ it is found that it has a maximum value when $R = r$. This is an example of the 'Maximum Power Theorem', which states that, if a variable load is to be matched to a source of power so that the maximum power is to be dissipated in the load, its resistance must be adjusted to be equal to the internal resistance of the source. The greatest value of $W$ which can be obtained is thus $V^2/4r$, and this is known as the 'available power' of the source. It should be noted that with a given load, and a range of batteries of the same voltage but of different internal resistance, maximum power is obtained with the battery of lowest internal resistance, so that the maximum power theorem does not apply to the converse problem.

## 3.4. Resistance networks

In a complicated network of resistances containing many branches, the calculation of the currents in the various branches is based on two laws due to Kirchhoff. They are:

(1) the algebraic sum of all the currents meeting at a point is zero;
(2) the algebraic sum of the potential differences across the resistances in any closed circuit is equal to the total e.m.f. in that circuit.

The first law follows from the equation of continuity, since there can be no accumulation of charge at any point. It can be written

$$\sum I_k = 0.$$

The second law is an extension of equation (3.12), and can be written

$$\sum_k I_k R_k = \sum_j V_j,$$

where $I_k$ is the current in the resistance $R_k$.

These laws can immediately be applied to find the equivalent resistance of a number of resistances $R_1, R_2, ..., R_n$ in series or in parallel, as in Fig. 3.3. In the former case the voltage across all the resistances is

$$V = IR_1 + IR_2 + ... + IR_n = I(R_1 + R_2 + ... + R_n) = IR,$$

where $R$ is the equivalent resistance. Hence

$$R = R_1 + R_2 + \ldots + R_n = \sum_k R_k.$$

When the resistances are in parallel, the voltage across each is the same. The total current $I$ is

$$I = \frac{V}{R_1} + \frac{V}{R_2} + \ldots + \frac{V}{R_n} = V\left(\frac{1}{R_1} + \frac{1}{R_2} + \ldots + \frac{1}{R_n}\right) = V/R,$$

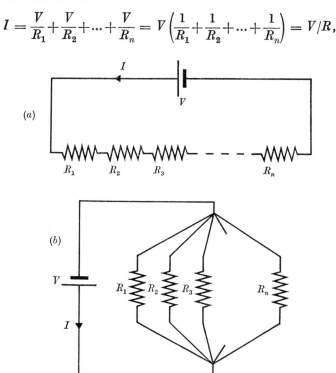

FIG. 3.3. Resistance arranged $(a)$ in series, $(b)$ in parallel.

where $R$ is the equivalent resistance. Hence in this case

$$\frac{1}{R} = \frac{1}{R_1} + \frac{1}{R_2} + \ldots + \frac{1}{R_n} = \sum_k \frac{1}{R_k}.$$

If a network has many branches, the problem of finding the current in each branch is best solved by the method of cyclic currents. Fig. 3.4 is part of a network in which there are $n$ cyclic currents all flowing in an anticlockwise sense. Such a system of currents satisfies the first of Kirchhoff's laws automatically. Then the current through $R_1$ is $I_1$, but the current through $R_{12}$ is $(I_1 - I_2)$. For circuit (1), for example, we have

$$V_1 = I_1 R_1 + (I_1 - I_3) R_{13} + (I_1 - I_2) R_{12} = I_1 R_{11} - I_2 R_{12} - I_3 R_{13},$$

where $R_{11} = R_1 + R_{12} + R_{13}$. In general, if $R_{qq} = R_q + \sum_p R_{qp}$,

$$V_1 = +R_{11} I_1 \pm R_{12} I_2 \pm R_{13} I_3 \pm \ldots \pm R_{1q} I_q \pm \ldots \pm R_{1n} I_n,$$
$$V_2 = \pm R_{21} I_1 + R_{22} I_2 \pm R_{23} I_3 \pm \ldots \pm R_{2q} I_q \pm \ldots \pm R_{2n} I_n,$$
$$\cdot \quad \cdot \quad \cdot \quad \cdot \quad \cdot \quad \cdot \quad \cdot \quad \cdot \quad \cdot$$
$$V_q = \pm R_{q1} I_1 \pm R_{q2} I_2 \pm R_{q3} I_3 \pm \ldots + R_{qq} I_q \pm \ldots \pm R_{qn} I_n,$$
$$\cdot \quad \cdot \quad \cdot \quad \cdot \quad \cdot \quad \cdot \quad \cdot \quad \cdot \quad \cdot$$
$$V_n = \pm R_{n1} I_1 \pm R_{n2} I_2 \pm R_{n3} I_3 \pm \ldots \pm R_{nq} I_q \pm \ldots + R_{nn} I_n.$$

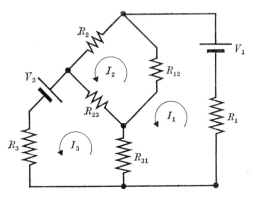

FIG. 3.4. A general network with cyclic currents.

$V_q$ is the total e.m.f. in the $q$th circuit, and is positive if it acts in the direction of $I_q$. The subscripts to the resistances denote the currents which flow through them. Then if $\Delta_{pq}$ is the cofactor of $R_{pq}$ in the determinant

$$\Delta = \begin{vmatrix} +R_{11} & \cdot & \cdot & \pm R_{1q} & \cdot & \cdot & \pm R_{1n} \\ \cdot & \cdot & \cdot & \cdot & \cdot & \cdot & \cdot \\ \pm R_{p1} & \cdot & \cdot & \pm R_{pq} & \cdot & \cdot & \pm R_{pn} \\ \cdot & \cdot & \cdot & \cdot & \cdot & \cdot & \cdot \\ \pm R_{n1} & \cdot & \cdot & \pm R_{nq} & \cdot & \cdot & +R_{nn} \end{vmatrix}$$

$\Delta_{pq} = \Delta_{qp}$, since $R_{pq}$ is identical with $R_{qp}$.

If we solve these equations for the current $I_q$ when there is only one source of e.m.f. $V_p$ in the circuit, then we find

$$I_q = V_p \Delta_{pq}/\Delta.$$

Similarly, the current $I_p$, when there is only the e.m.f. $V_q$ in circuit, is

$$I_p = V_q \Delta_{qp}/\Delta.$$

Since $\Delta_{pq} = \Delta_{qp}$, we have the Reciprocity Theorem, which states that a given e.m.f. in the $p$th branch will produce the same current in the $q$th

branch of a circuit as the same e.m.f. in the $q$th branch would produce
in the $p$th branch.

## 3.5. Wheatstone's bridge and the measurement of resistance

As an example of network analysis we shall take the arrangement
shown in Fig. 3.5, consisting of a battery and five resistances. It is
required to find the current through the resistance $G$. By making the
substitutions shown in the figure for $I_3$ and $I_2$, the first of Kirchhoff's

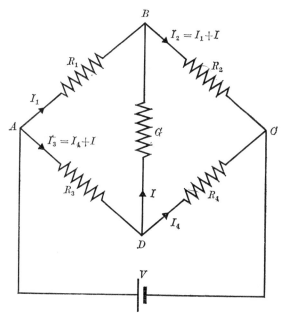

FIG. 3.5. Wheatstone's bridge. The current $I = 0$ if $R_1 R_4 = R_2 R_3$.
(In Callendar's notation, $R_4 = R$, $R_2 = mR'$, $R_3 = nR'$, $R_1 = nmR'$.)

laws is satisfied and two unknowns are eliminated from the equations
at once. Then from the second of Kirchhoff's laws we have

$$
\left.
\begin{aligned}
V &= I_3 R_3 + I_4 R_4 = (I_4 + I)R_3 + I_4 R_4 \\
0 &= I_1 R_1 - IG - I_3 R_3 = I_1 R_1 - IG - (I_4 + I)R_3 \\
0 &= I_2 R_2 - I_4 R_4 + IG = (I_1 + I)R_2 - I_4 R_4 + IG
\end{aligned}
\right\}.
\tag{3.14}
$$

Elimination of $I_1$ and $I_4$ from these equations gives

$$
I = \frac{V(R_1 R_4 - R_2 R_3)}{D + G(R_1 + R_2)(R_3 + R_4)},
\tag{3.15}
$$

where $D = R_1 R_2 R_3 + R_2 R_3 R_4 + R_3 R_4 R_1 + R_4 R_1 R_2$. Similar expressions can be found for the currents through the other resistances.

Inspection of equation (3.15) shows that $I = 0$ provided that

$$R_1 R_4 = R_2 R_3,$$

and this is the basis of the Wheatstone's bridge method of comparing resistances or measuring an unknown resistance $R_4$ in terms of three known resistances $R_1$, $R_2$, $R_3$. A galvanometer (see Chapter 7) is inserted in the arm $BD$ to detect when $I$ is zero, and $G$ then represents the galvanometer resistance. The resistance in one of the arms $R_1$, $R_2$, $R_3$ is varied until the balance point is found.

Wheatstone's bridge can be used to measure an unknown resistance whose value can have a very wide range. The currents used must not be large enough to heat the resistances and so alter their values appreciably; the standard resistances are generally made of constantan or manganin so that their values do not change with the external temperature. Like all bridge methods, it is a null method, and the galvanometer is required only to detect the balance point so that its calibration is not necessary. The bridge is accurate, and quick to use; a simple version is the slide wire form described below. When measuring small resistances, care must be taken to ensure that the resistances of leads and contacts are not appreciable. For resistances of from $10^{-1}$ to $10^{-3}$ ohms the Kelvin double bridge (see Problem 3.5) is more suitable.

*Sensitivity of a bridge*

The accuracy with which the null point can be determined in a bridge depends on how rapidly the galvanometer current changes near the balance point for a given fractional change of the resistance in one arm of the bridge. Thus if $R_2$ is variable, the sensitivity is defined as $R_2(\partial I/\partial R_2)$ at the point $I = 0$; this may be evaluated from the equations for Wheatstone's bridge, but the resulting expression is very cumbersome. We shall follow a treatment due to Callendar (1910). The resistances in the four arms of the unbalanced bridge of Fig. 3.5 are written in the form $R_4 = R$ (the unknown), $R_2 = mR'$, $R_3 = nR'$, $R_1 = nmR'$, where $m$ and $n$ are simple numbers and the currents are as before. When $R = R'$ the bridge is balanced, $I = 0$ and $I_4 = I_3$. From equations (3.14) it can be shown that the ratio of the current through the galvanometer (resistance $G$) to that through the unknown resistance is

$$\frac{I}{I_4} = \frac{R-R'}{G(1+1/n)+R'(1+m)}. \tag{3.16}$$

The ratio $I/I_4$ is a measure of the sensitivity which is especially useful when the current which can be put through the unknown resistance is limited; it is independent of the e.m.f. and resistance in the battery circuit. For a given value of $(R-R')$, $I/I_4$ is a maximum when $n$ is made large and $m$ small, the limiting value being

$$I/I_4 = (R-R')/(G+R') \quad (n = \infty, m = 0).$$

This is, however, only twice as great as when $n = m = 1$, so that little is gained by using a large value of $n$ and a small value of $m$. On the other hand, if $n$ is made small and $m$ large, the sensitivity will be greatly reduced (see also Problem 3.6).

To obtain the greatest accuracy in detection of the null point, the galvanometer used must be as sensitive as possible. The sensitivity is proportional to the number of turns on the galvanometer coil (see Chapter 7), but if this number is greatly increased the resistance may become too high. With a given size of coil, the cross-sectional area of the wire used must be decreased in inverse proportion to the number of turns, so that the resistance will increase with the square of the number of turns. Hence the galvanometer deflexion will be proportional to $\sqrt{G}$ for a given current, and the sensitivity of the bridge will vary as $I\sqrt{G}$. From differentiation of equation (3.16) (multiplied by $\sqrt{G}$) it is found that $I\sqrt{G}$ is a maximum at the balance point $R = R'$ when

$$G = Rn(1+m)/(1+n) \tag{3.17}$$

if $G$ is treated as the variable. It is readily shown that this is just equal to the net resistance of the branches $BAD$ and $BCD$ in parallel (see Problem 3.3).

## 3.6. The potentiometer

If a pair of resistances $R_1$, $R_2$ are connected in series to a battery of potential $V_1$, the potential across the first resistance is $V_1 R_1/(R_1+R_2)$, and this potential may be varied by adjusting $R_1$ or $R_2$. Such a device is called a potential divider and is the basis of a method of comparing two potentials by means of a 'potentiometer'. The basic circuit of this instrument is shown in Fig. 3.6, where a battery of potential $V_1$ is connected across a slide wire $AB$. An unknown e.m.f. $V_2$ is connected in series with a galvanometer between the point $A$ and a point $C$ which can be slid along the wire. The tapping point is adjusted until there is no current through the galvanometer, and then, if the wire is uniform, we have

$$V_2 = V_1 l_1/(l_1+l_2).$$

The purpose of the large resistance $R_3$ is to protect the galvanometer from excessive currents during the initial stages of finding a balance.

As the balance point is neared, $R_3$ is reduced to give greater sensitivity in finding the null. At the balance point no current is taken from the battery $V_2$, so that its open-circuit e.m.f. is measured. Current is taken from the battery $V_1$, and its e.m.f. will depend on the amount of current and also on other factors such as temperature and the time since charging if $V_1$ is an accumulator. The uncertainty due to this is eliminated by comparison with a standard cell, whose e.m.f. is measured on open circuit and is very constant with time, etc. The circuit for this is

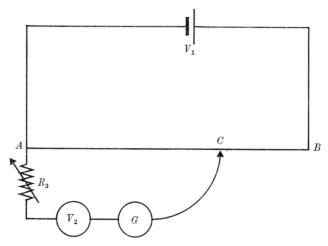

Fig. 3.6. The slide-wire potentiometer.

$$AC = l_1, \quad CB = l_2.$$

illustrated in Fig. 3.7, which shows a general type of potentiometer. The slide wire is replaced by a resistance chain $R_1$, $R_2$, whose total resistance is constant and has tapping points every 10 ohms, say. This is in series with a slide wire $DB$ whose total resistance $r$ is exactly 10 ohms. The total potential drop across the resistances $R_1$, $R_2$ and the slide wire is first adjusted to a standard value in the following way. $R_1$ is made zero, so that the tapping point $C_1$ is at $A$. The standard cell $V_s$ is then brought in circuit by closing the key $K_1$, and the resistance $R_4$ is adjusted until the potential across $R$ is exactly equal to that of the standard cell. The current supplied by $V_1$ and flowing through $R$ is then exactly $I = V_s/R$. $K_1$ is now opened and $K_2$ closed to bring the unknown voltage $V_2$ in circuit instead. The balance point is found first by adjusting the position of $C_1$, giving a course adjustment in steps, and then varying $C_2$, the tapping point on the slide wire to give the ultimate balance. The potential $V_2$ is then given by (writing $DC_2 = l_1$, $C_2 B = l_2$)

$$V_2 = I\{R_2 + rl_1/(l_1 + l_2)\}.$$

By suitable choice of the values of $R$ and the other resistances, a direct reading potentiometer may be made. The accuracy of commercial instruments of this type is of the order of 1 part in $10^5$, so that a potential of 0·1 V can be measured to a microvolt.

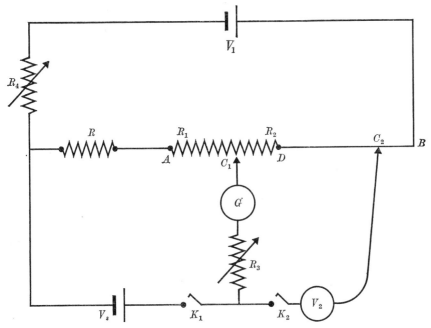

FIG. 3.7. General potentiometer circuit.
$$DC_2 = l_1, \quad C_2 B = l_2.$$

The potentiometer has many uses of which we shall mention here only the calibration of a voltmeter and an ammeter. The circuits for these measurements are shown in Fig. 3.8. To calibrate a voltmeter a variable voltage is applied to it from a battery and potential divider, and the voltage $V_2$ on the voltmeter is measured by the potentiometer. To calibrate an ammeter a known resistance $R_5$ is connected in series with it, and from the potential across this resistance, measured by the potentiometer, the actual current through the ammeter is found.

## 3.7. Electron optics

In a conducting solid or liquid electrons make very frequent collisions with the atoms, and the mean velocity which they acquire in the direction of an electric field is proportional to the field; the motion is similar to that of a particle in a viscous medium (see Problem 3.9). In a rarefied gas collisions with atoms are infrequent, and conduction phenomena are quite different (see § 4.8); at sufficiently low pressures collisions cease to play any role in determining the motion of the electrons. This is the

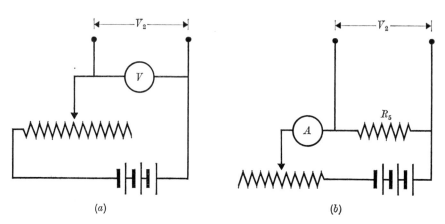

FIG. 3.8. Calibration of $(a)$ a voltmeter, and $(b)$ an ammeter. The voltage $V_2$ is applied to the potentiometer as in Fig. 3.7.

position in thermionic vacuum tubes, where the electrons move directly from one electrode to another. It is often necessary to direct the electrons to a particular electrode, or to cause a beam of electrons to pass through as small an area as possible, as in a cathode-ray tube, where the beam must strike the fluorescent screen in a small spot. The principles employed in the design of such tubes are outlined below, without reference to particular applications.

In an evacuated field-free space electrons travel in straight lines, and a beam of electrons leaving an electrode will eventually diverge. Under the action of a suitable electric (or magnetic) field the path of the electrons is bent, and the beam may be made to converge. This is called 'focusing' the electrons: the use of the word 'focus' is borrowed from optics and it may be shown that there is a very close analogy between the behaviour of electrons in an electrostatic field and that of light in a refracting medium. The basis of geometrical optics is Snell's law: when a light ray passes from a medium of refractive index $n_1$ through a plane boundary to another medium $n_2$, the angles of incidence and refraction obey the relation

$$n_1 \sin \alpha_1 = n_2 \sin \alpha_2.$$

In electron optics the corresponding case is that of an electron in a field-free space (i.e. a region of constant potential $V_1$) crossing into a region at another potential $V_2$, as in Fig. 3.9. At the boundary there exists an electric field which accelerates the electron in the direction normal to the boundary, while the component of velocity parallel to the boundary remains unchanged. If the initial and final velocities are $v_1$ and $v_2$, the

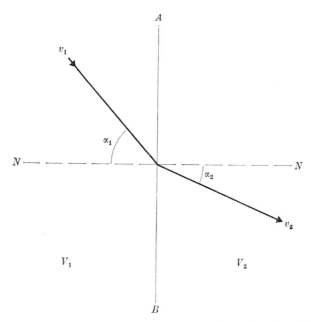

FIG. 3.9. 'Refraction' of an electron on crossing a boundary $AB$ between two regions of potential $V_1$ and $V_2$. $NN$ is the normal to this boundary.

components parallel to the boundary are $v_1 \sin \alpha_1$ and $v_2 \sin \alpha_2$, so that we have
$$v_1 \sin \alpha_1 = v_2 \sin \alpha_2.$$

If the electron started from rest at a point where the potential is zero, this may be written
$$\sqrt{V_1} \sin \alpha_1 = \sqrt{V_2} \sin \alpha_2, \qquad (3.18)$$

since $v$ is proportional to $\sqrt{V}$. Note that the electron velocity plays the same role as the refractive index and does not correspond to the velocity of light in the medium.

The example just given is a special case of a more general correspondence based on Fermat's principle of least time in optics and Hamilton's principle of least action in mechanics. The former states that the path of a light ray is such that the time taken between any two points of the path is an extremum (generally a minimum). Thus we have

$$t = \int dt = \int \frac{ds}{v} = \frac{1}{c} \int n \, ds = \text{minimum}. \qquad (3.19)$$

Hamilton's principle states that the path of a particle is such that the line integral of its momentum is a minimum; i.e.

$$\int mv \, ds = \text{minimum}. \qquad (3.20)$$

So long as the mass of the particle is constant (i.e. so long as relativity corrections are negligible) the analogy between electron velocity and refractive index is complete.

Although the formula for the focal length of a thin lens can be calculated quite simply in optics, the equivalent calculation for electron optics is generally very difficult. We shall content ourselves by showing how a focusing action can be obtained in a simple case. Fig. 3.10 shows a pair of parallel conducting planes each with a small circular aperture. The planes are at potentials $V_1$, $V_2$, and the potentials outside the planes away from the aperture are constant and equal to $V_1$ and $V_2$. Near the aperture the equipotentials are curved and bulge out as shown. If an electron travelling parallel to the $z$-axis (i.e. normal to the planes) enters the aperture, it finds itself in a region where the lines of electric field, which are normal to the equipotentials, have a radial component. This gives the electron an acceleration normal to the axis, and it emerges into the field-free region with a component of velocity to or away from the axis. If the electron is in the $xz$ plane as shown in the diagram, the $x$ component of velocity given to it is

$$v_x = -\int_0^t \frac{e}{m} E_x \, dt = +\frac{e}{m} \int_0^t \left(\frac{\partial V}{\partial x}\right) dt. \qquad (3.21)$$

If the electron enters the aperture at a small distance $h$ from the axis, then we may make the approximation

$$\left(\frac{\partial V}{\partial x}\right)_{x=h} = \left(\frac{\partial V}{\partial x}\right)_{x=0} + h\left(\frac{\partial^2 V}{\partial x^2}\right).$$

Since the potential satisfies Laplace's equation

$$\frac{\partial^2 V}{\partial x^2} + \frac{\partial^2 V}{\partial y^2} + \frac{\partial^2 V}{\partial z^2} = 0,$$

where, by symmetry, $\partial^2 V/\partial x^2 = \partial^2 V/\partial y^2$, and $(\partial V/\partial x) = (\partial V/\partial y) = 0$

on the axis, we have

$$\left(\frac{\partial V}{\partial x}\right)_{x=h} = -\frac{h}{2}\left(\frac{\partial^2 V}{\partial z^2}\right),$$

from which

$$v_x = -\int \frac{1}{2}\frac{e}{m}h\left(\frac{\partial^2 V}{\partial z^2}\right)dt = -\frac{1}{2}\frac{e}{m}h\int\left(\frac{\partial^2 V}{\partial z^2}\right)\frac{dz}{v_z},$$

where $v_z = dz/dt$ is the $z$ component of the instantaneous velocity at any point. On emerging from the aperture the electron has a velocity $v_2 = (2eV_2/m)^{\frac{1}{2}}$ which is independent of $h$, and it moves at an angle $\theta$

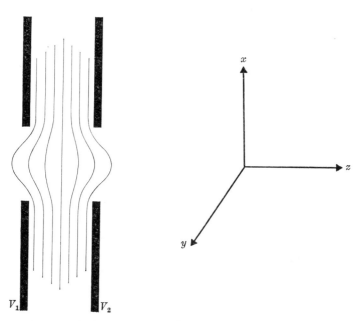

FIG. 3.10. A simple electron lens, consisting of two parallel conducting planes at potentials $V_1$, $V_2$ with apertures. The bulging of the equipotential surfaces near the apertures is shown.

with the axis where $\sin\theta = v_x/v_2$. Since $v_x$ is proportional to $h$, for small values of $\theta$ (where the difference between $\sin\theta$ and $\tan\theta$ is negligible) all electrons will move towards (or appear to diverge from) a particular point on the axis, whose distance from the aperture is

$$-h/\tan\theta = -hv_2/v_x.$$

As the electrons were assumed to enter parallel to the axis, this is one focal point of the lens. If $v_x$ is negative when $h$ is positive we have a converging lens whose focal length is given by

$$\frac{1}{f_2} = -\frac{v_x}{hv_2} = \frac{e/2m}{(2eV_2/m)^{\frac{1}{2}}} \int \left(\frac{\partial^2 V}{\partial z^2}\right) \frac{dz}{v}$$

$$= \frac{e/2m}{(2eV_2/m)^{\frac{1}{2}}} \int \left(\frac{\partial^2 V}{\partial z^2}\right) \frac{dz}{(2eV/m)^{\frac{1}{2}}} = \frac{1}{4\sqrt{V_2}} \int \frac{1}{\sqrt{V}} \left(\frac{\partial^2 V}{\partial z^2}\right) dz, \quad (3.22)$$

where we have assumed that $v_z = v$, the actual velocity at any point, and substituted $(2eV/m)^{\frac{1}{2}}$ for it inside the integral.

If the electrons had entered the lens from the right, they would have been brought to a focus at a point $f_1$, where

$$\frac{1}{f_1} = -\frac{1}{4\sqrt{V_1}} \int \frac{1}{\sqrt{V}} \left(\frac{\partial^2 V}{\partial z^2}\right) dz. \quad (3.23)$$

Hence $f_1/f_2 = -\sqrt{V_1}/\sqrt{V_2}$, a formula which is exactly analogous to the optical case of a thin lens with initial and final media of different refractive indices $n_1$ and $n_2$.

Inspection of equations (3.22) and (3.23) for the focal lengths shows that they require a knowledge of the variation of the potential on the axis of the lens. It is only possible in very simple cases to derive an analytical expression for $V$ in the aperture, and in general the variation of $V$ must either be calculated by numerical methods, by which an approximate solution of Laplace's equation with the required boundary conditions may be found, or experimentally by the use of an electrolytic tank (see below). The variation of $V$ always occupies a finite distance, and if it occupies a distance comparable with either of the focal lengths the electron lens is a 'thick lens' rather than a 'thin lens'. The behaviour of the system is again similar to that of an optical system, and is defined if the cardinal points are determined. These can be found by tracing the paths of a number of electrons through the system. One method of doing this is to divide the potential field into thin slices along the equipotential surfaces, and treat each slice as a thin lens.

The approximations made above in expanding $(\partial V/\partial x)$ near the axis and retaining only the first term are equivalent to the approximations made in 'Gaussian optics' in treating only rays near the axis. It is to be expected, therefore, that electron lens systems will suffer from defects similar to those of optical systems, such as spherical aberration, etc. The equivalent of 'chromatic aberration' arises when not all electrons enter the system with the same velocity, since this corresponds to a variable refractive index. If the spread in velocity is due only to the Maxwellian distribution of velocity on emission from the cathode, chromatic aberration is small. An additional effect in electron lenses, not present in optical systems, arises from the mutual repulsion of the charged particles, which will cause a beam of electrons initially moving parallel to each other to diverge.

## 3.8. The electrolytic tank

It was shown in § 3.2 that the equipotential lines in a conducting medium between two conductors of fixed shape and position remain unaltered if the conducting medium is replaced by a dielectric. The electrolytic tank is a device for plotting the lines of constant $V$ experimentally using electrodes immersed in a conducting solution (tap water is usually sufficiently conducting for this purpose). Such a device is often used in cases where theoretical calculation of the potential distribution is difficult; it is not usually feasible to construct a scale model for a three-dimensional problem, but often the problem can be reduced to a two-dimensional one. The simplest case is one where the conductors extend indefinitely in one dimension (e.g. the $z$-axis) without change of cross-section. A slab of conducting solution with parallel plane faces may then be used to simulate a section normal to the $z$-axis. Since no current can flow out of the sides of the slab, the equipotential surfaces in the solution will always be normal to the sides, and it is essential that these sides be normal to the equipotential surfaces in the three-dimensional electrostatic problem of which the solution gives a model. In the case under consideration the water can be contained in an insulating tank whose bottom is plane and horizontal. The tank must be sufficiently large in comparison with the region over which the potential distribution is important so that the distortion of the equipotentials at the sides of the tank does not affect the problem.

The apparatus is shown in Fig. 3.11. The tank contains two electrodes $A$, $C$ which are scale models of those in the electrostatic problem where the potential distribution is desired. They are connected to a low-frequency alternating-current generator to avoid polarization effects and electrolysis of the solution (see Chapter 4), and also to two variable resistances $R_1$, $R_2$ in series. A detector of alternating current such as a pair of headphones is connected between the mid-point $B$ of the resistances and a small vertical probe $D$ immersed in the solution. The resistances of the solution between the probe $D$ and the electrodes $A$, $C$ then form a Wheatstone's bridge with $R_1$ and $R_2$, so that no current flows through the detector when the potential at $B$ is the same as that at $D$. If $C$ is at zero potential, and $A$ at potential $V$, then the potential at $B$ is $V R_2/(R_1+R_2)$. The equipotential line in the solution with this potential can then be traced out by moving the probe so that the detector current is always zero. The probe is fixed to a framework which slides along two perpendicular guides with scales, and its position can be read in terms of these two coordinates and plotted on graph paper.

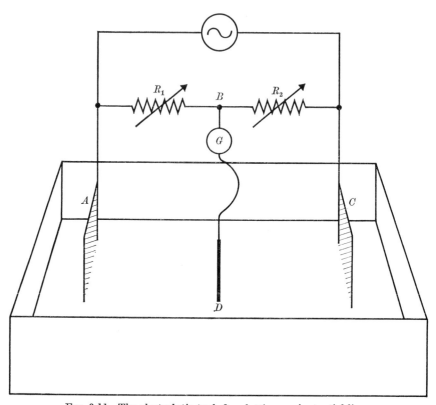

FIG. 3.11. The electrolytic tank for plotting equipotential lines.

## REFERENCES

CALLENDAR, H. L., 1910, *Proc. Phys. Soc.* **22**, 220.
KETTERING, C. F., and SCOTT, G. G., 1944, *Phys. Rev.* **66**, 257.
TOLMAN, R. C., and STEWART, T. D., 1917, ibid. **9**, 64.

## PROBLEMS

**3.1.** Deduce equation (3.17) directly from equations (3.14) and (3.15).

**3.2.** In Fig. 3.5 show that if the galvanometer is removed ($G = \infty$) the open circuit voltage across the terminals $BD$ is

$$v = V(R_1 R_4 - R_2 R_3)/(R_1+R_2)(R_3+R_4)$$

while if also the battery is short-circuited, the resistance measured at the terminals $BD$ would be

$$r = \frac{R_1 R_2}{R_1 + R_2} + \frac{R_3 R_4}{R_3 + R_4}.$$

Show that with the galvanometer and battery in place, the bridge behaves as a generator of e.m.f. equal to $v$, and internal resistance $r$, the galvanometer being the load. This is an example of Thévenin's theorem, which may be stated as follows:

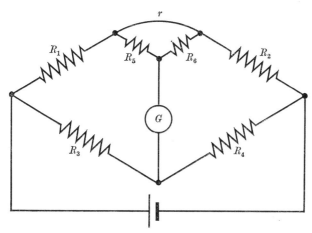

Fɪɢ. 3.12. Kelvin's double bridge.

If the open circuit voltage across terminals $B$, $D$ of a network is $v$, and if when $B$ and $D$ are short-circuited a current $I$ flows between them, then the resistance of the network measured between $B$ and $D$ after all sources of e.m.f. have been short-circuited is $r = v/I$. Thus the effect on any circuit connected across $BD$ will be the same as that of a generator of e.m.f. equal to $v$ and internal resistance $r$.

(For a proof of this theorem, see W. R. Smythe, *Static and Dynamic Electricity*, McGraw-Hill.)

**3.3.** Derive equation (3.17) from the results of the last problem and the maximum power theorem.

**3.4.** Resistances $P$, $Q$, $R$ each of 10 ohms are placed in three arms of a Wheatstone's bridge, and a resistance $S$ is adjusted in the fourth arm so that the bridge is balanced. The resistance $R$ is now replaced by a resistance $X$, and the balance is restored by shunting $S$ with a resistance of 10 123 ohms. What is the value of $X$ ?

Discuss the advantages and disadvantages of this method of measuring resistances when high accuracy is required.

**3.5.** In Fig. 3.12, show that a balance condition for the bridge (i.e. no current through the galvanometer) which is independent of the value of $r$ is

$$R_1/R_2 = R_3/R_4 = R_5/R_6.$$

This is Kelvin's double bridge for measuring small resistances of the order of 0·01 ohm. The resistance $r$ represents the contact resistance between the two small resistances $R_1$, $R_2$, and its value does not affect the balance. If readings are taken with the currents flowing in both directions, so that errors due to thermoelectric e.m.f.s at the junctions are avoided, an accuracy of about $0.02$ per cent can be achieved.

**3.6.** The total amount of power $W$, which can be dissipated in the four arms of a Wheatstone's bridge is fixed. Show from equation (3.16) that close to balance

$$I = \frac{(R-R')}{G(1+1/n)+R'(1+m)} \left\{ \frac{mW}{R'(1+m)(1+n)} \right\}^{\frac{1}{2}}.$$

Hence, by differentiation with respect to $m$ and to $n$, and using equation (3.17), show that the most sensitive arrangement of the bridge is when

$$n = m = 1, \qquad G = R.$$

**3.7.** Six 1-ohm resistances are joined to form a regular tetrahedron, and a potential of 1 V is maintained across one of the resistances. Find the current flowing in each conductor.

(*Answer:* $1, \frac{1}{2}, \frac{1}{2}, \frac{1}{2}, \frac{1}{2}$, and 0 A.)

**3.8.** Two long parallel copper rods of radius of cross-section $0.25$ cm are placed with their axes 20 cm apart within a large tank of copper sulphate solution. If the conductivity of the solution is $4.1$ ohm$^{-1}$ metre$^{-1}$, find the conductance per unit length between the rods.

(*Answer:* $3.0$ ohm$^{-1}$/metre.)

**3.9.** A particle of mass $m$ and charge $e$ moves in a viscous medium where there is uniform electric field $\mathbf{E}$ parallel to the $x$-axis. Show that the equation of motion may be written as

$$\frac{d\dot{x}}{dt} + \dot{x}/\tau = eE/m,$$

and that its solution, for a particle starting from rest at $t = 0$ is

$$\dot{x} = (eE\tau/m)\{1 - \exp(-t/\tau)\}.$$

For an electron in a metal, the effect of collisions is similar to that of a viscous force, and the value of $\tau$ is $\approx 10^{-14}$ sec (see § 4.1). Thus the exponential term in the equation for $x$ above quickly falls to zero and the velocity is proportional to the electric field strength; $\tau$ is known as the 'relaxation time', since it gives a measure of the time required to reach the new equilibrium velocity when the field strength is altered.

The mobility of the electron is $u = \dot{x}/E = (e/m)\tau$, and hence the conductivity of a metal containing $n$ electrons per unit volume is $\sigma = n(e^2/m)\tau$ (see equation 4.3).

# PROPERTIES OF ELECTRICAL CONDUCTORS

## 4.1. Free electrons in metals—classical theory

A SIMPLE explanation of metallic conductivity was put forward by Drude in 1900, based on classical theory. It was assumed that in a metal some electrons are free to move about the whole volume of the metal like the molecules of a perfect gas in a container. In the absence of an electric field the electrons move in random directions, making collisions from time to time with the positive ions (which are fixed in the lattice) or other free electrons. When an electric field $\mathbf{E}$ is applied to the metal, the electrons are accelerated in the direction of the field and acquire an average drift momentum $\mathbf{p}$, parallel to $\mathbf{E}$. The value of $\mathbf{p}$ can be calculated as follows. In a time $dt$ an electron of charge $-e$ acquires an additional momentum $-e\mathbf{E}\,dt$ through the acceleration by the field $\mathbf{E}$. In the time $dt$ a fraction $dn$ of the total number of electrons $n$ per unit volume make collisions, where

$$dn/n = dt/\tau. \tag{4.1}$$

The parameter $\tau$ is the mean time between collisions, as can be verified by reference to textbooks on kinetic theory, or to Shockley (1950). We now make the assumption that immediately after collisions the electron velocities are completely random, so that the momentum gained under the influence of the electric field is lost. The momentum gained in time $dt$ is $-ne\mathbf{E}\,dt$, while the momentum destroyed in collisions is

$$\mathbf{p}\,dn = n\mathbf{p}\,dt/\tau.$$

For equilibrium these must balance, so that

$$n\mathbf{p}\,dt/\tau = -ne\mathbf{E}\,dt$$

or
$$\mathbf{p} = -e\mathbf{E}\tau. \tag{4.2}$$

The current density is

$$\mathbf{J} = n(-e/m)\mathbf{p} = n(e^2/m)\mathbf{E}\tau$$

and hence the conductivity is

$$\sigma = \mathbf{J}/\mathbf{E} = n(e^2/m)\tau. \tag{4.3}$$

An estimate of the value of $\tau$ can be found for copper if we assume that there is just one free electron per atom; then from the specific resistance given in Table 3.1, a value of $\tau \approx 2 \times 10^{-14}$ seconds is obtained at $20°$ C.

As is obvious from equation (4.3), the conductivity is independent of the sign of the charge on the carriers, since reversing this sign changes the direction of their drift motion but not the direction of the current flow. Equation (4.2) shows that the mean drift velocity $\mathbf{v} = \mathbf{p}/m$ is proportional to the applied field, and the ratio $|\mathbf{v}/\mathbf{E}|$ (irrespective of the sign) is defined (see equation 3.9) as the mobility $u$. This quantity is a useful parameter, since it is directly proportional to $\tau$:

$$u = |\mathbf{v}/\mathbf{E}| = |e/m|\tau. \tag{4.4}$$

The unit of $u$ is metres per second divided by volts per metre $= \mathrm{m}^2/\mathrm{V}$ sec; however it is nearly always quoted in $\mathrm{cm}^2/\mathrm{V}$ sec. For copper at 20° C we find $u \approx 40\ \mathrm{cm}^2/\mathrm{V}$ sec, where again we have assumed one free electron per atom.

Since metals are much better conductors of heat than electrical insulators, we may assume that the thermal conduction in a metal is also mainly due to the free electrons. If we apply the ordinary kinetic theory formula for the thermal conductivity $K$ of a gas to the 'electron gas' in a conductor, we have

$$K = \tfrac{1}{3}ncl(dW/dT), \tag{4.5}$$

where $c$ is the random electron velocity and $W$ its kinetic energy $= \tfrac{1}{2}mc^2$. Taking the mean free path $l$ as equal to $c\tau$, we find a simple expression for the ratio of thermal to electrical conductivity:

$$\frac{K}{\sigma} = \frac{mc^2}{3e^2}\frac{dW}{dT} = \frac{2W}{3e^2}\frac{dW}{dT}.$$

If the electrons obey classical statistics, then $W = \tfrac{1}{2}mc^2 = \tfrac{3}{2}kT$, and

$$K/\sigma = \frac{3}{2}\left(\frac{k}{e}\right)^2 T. \tag{4.6}$$

This equation shows that the ratio of the thermal and electrical conductivities should be proportional to the absolute temperature for a given metal, and should be the same for all metals at a given temperature. This is in accordance with an empirical law discovered by Wiedemann and Franz in 1853, and the numerical value of $(K/\sigma T)$ given by equation (4.6) is in good agreement with the experimental values for copper, silver, and gold over the limited temperature range of the experiments. The experimental values of $K$ and $\sigma$ themselves and their variation with temperature do not, however, fit with Drude's theory. From equation (4.3), if $l = c\tau$ is fixed, $\sigma$ should vary as $T^{-\frac{1}{2}}$ because of the variation in the average velocity $c$ of the electrons. Similarly, $K$ should vary as $T^{\frac{1}{2}}$. In practice, at ordinary temperatures $K$ is found to be practically constant and $\sigma$ varies roughly as $T^{-1}$. At low temperatures $\sigma$ varies more rapidly still; Fig. 4.1 shows the resistivity of sodium at various temperatures as a fraction of its value at 273° K. The thermal conductivity also varies at low temperatures but in a different way so that

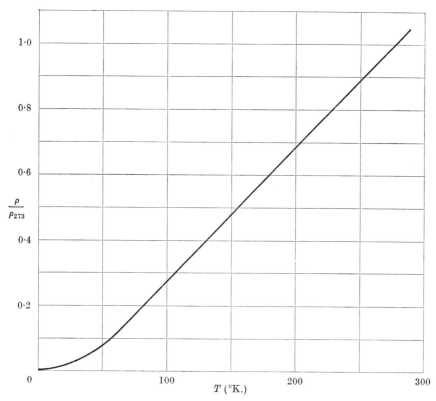

FIG. 4.1. The resistivity of sodium as a function of temperature.

$(K/\sigma T)$ is not constant. The chief objection to Drude's theory arises, however, from the fact that the atomic heat of metals should be greater than that of insulators by $3R/2$, corresponding to the expression for the average energy $W$ assumed above. In practice the atomic heats of metals at ordinary temperatures are not significantly greater than those of insulators, showing that the contribution from the electrons is much smaller than $3R/2$. This difficulty was not overcome until it was realized that electrons should obey quantum statistics rather than the Maxwell–Boltzmann statistics assumed in the classical model of a 'free-electron gas'. In fact, since the electrons have an intrinsic spin angular momentum of $\frac{1}{2}\hbar = \frac{1}{2}(h/2\pi)$, where $h$ is Planck's constant, they must be treated by the type of quantum statistics associated with the names of Fermi and Dirac.

## 4.2. Free electrons in metals—quantum theory

On the free electron model the conduction electrons are confined to the volume of the metal, but are quite free to move about inside this volume, like gas molecules in a box. On classical theory the kinetic energy of such a particle can have any value, and there is a continuous distribution of values of the energy, though some are more probable than others. When the temperature falls the average energy of the particles decreases linearly with the temperature, becoming zero at $0°$ K; at absolute temperature $T$ the total translational energy of $N$ particles is $\frac{3}{2}NkT$, and the differential of this gives the contribution $3R/2$ to the molar heat. On quantum mechanics not every value of the energy is allowed, and the continuous distribution of energies is replaced by a discrete set of allowed energy levels. The spacing is extremely small, however, and the difference between this and the assumed classical continuous distribution produces no observable effect for real gases. It would become appreciable only at temperatures so low that ordinary substances have negligible vapour pressure, and at higher temperatures it is always masked by deviations from the perfect gas laws owing to the van der Waals forces. In the case of electrons in a metal, the spacing of the energy levels is rather larger because of the smaller mass of the electron, and the number per unit volume is much larger than in any real gas. The result of this is to emphasize the role played by the Pauli exclusion principle, which states that no two electrons in a given system can have the same set of quantum numbers. When allowance is made for the intrinsic spin angular momentum of the electron, this means that only two electrons can occupy any given translational energy level. Hence the kinetic energy of the electrons cannot be zero at $0°$ K, since this would mean that all the electrons were in one particular energy level. In fact the electrons occupy the lowest possible set of energy levels consistent with the Pauli exclusion principle, and their mean energy is very far from zero at $0°$ K. At a finite temperature the energy distribution can only be found using the Fermi–Dirac statistics; i.e. the quantum statistics which take account of the Pauli exclusion principle. At ordinary temperatures it turns out that the energy distribution differs very little from that at $0°$ K; the latter can be found when the values of the allowed energy levels are known, and a simple method of computing the levels will now be given.

The fact that electrons and other particles have a wave-like aspect is well established from experiments on electron and neutron diffraction; the wavelength associated with a particle of linear momentum **p** is given by the de Broglie relation

$$2\pi/k = \lambda = h/p \quad \text{or} \quad \mathbf{k} = \mathbf{p}(2\pi/h) = \mathbf{p}/\hbar, \tag{4.7}$$

where **k** is the 'wave vector' which is parallel to the direction in which the wave is travelling, and $h$ is Planck's constant and $\hbar = h/2\pi$. For example, the wavelength is $12\cdot3\times10^{-8}$ cm for an electron of kinetic energy equal to 1 eV. (One eV is the energy acquired by an electron in falling through a potential difference of 1 volt.) Free electrons confined within a metal rebound from the surface of the metal without losing any energy; on the wave aspect this means that the waves are totally reflected at the boundaries, and standing waves are set up. These standing waves are the allowed solutions of the wave equation for a particle in a box, in the same way that standing waves of certain wavelengths are allowed in a waveguide resonator (see § 11.7). By analogy with the theory of heat radiation, the number $di$ of allowed wavelengths in the range $\lambda$ to $\lambda+d\lambda$ is

$$di = V\,4\pi\,d\lambda/\lambda^4, \tag{4.8}$$

where $V$ is the volume of the box. For particles the wavelength is determined by the momentum, and from equation (4.7) the number $di$ of possible values of the momentum in the range $p$ to $p+dp$ is found to be

$$di = (V/h^3)4\pi p^2\,dp. \tag{4.9}$$

This relation may be derived in another way by the use of the uncertainty relation. The momentum of a particle is completely specified in magnitude and direction by the components $p_x$, $p_y$, $p_z$ along three Cartesian axes, and the square of the momentum is $p^2 = p_x^2+p_y^2+p_z^2$. A 'momentum space' may be constructed as in Fig. 4.2 where the coordinates are the components of the momentum $(p_x, p_y, p_z)$ instead of the components of position $(x, y, z)$, and the momentum of a particle is then specified by a point in this space; the magnitude and direction of the momentum are given by the length and direction of a radius vector drawn from the origin to the point. All values of the momentum which lie between $p$ and $p+dp$ are represented by points which lie within the spherical shell bounded by the radii $p$ and $p+dp$, and the volume of this shell is $4\pi p^2\,dp$. By the uncertainty relation, the momentum component $p_x$ cannot be determined more precisely than to an amount $\Delta p_x$, where

$$\Delta p_x\,\Delta x = h,$$

where $\Delta x$ is the uncertainty in its position coordinate; and similar relations hold for the other two axes. Hence

$$\Delta p_x \Delta p_y \Delta p_z = h^3/(\Delta x \Delta y \Delta z) = h^3/V$$

if the particle is only constrained to be within the volume $V$. Now $\Delta p_x \Delta p_y \Delta p_z$ is an element of volume in 'momentum space', and the Pauli exclusion principle may be stated in the form that only one point

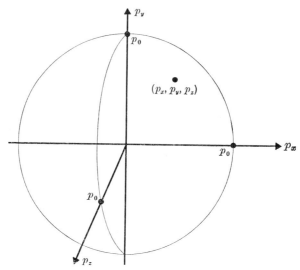

FIG. 4.2. The momentum $\mathbf{p}$ of a particle is specified by its components $(p_x, p_y, p_z)$, corresponding to a point in 'momentum space'. At $0°$ K all electrons are specified by points within the sphere of radius $p_0$, since this makes the energy a minimum.

in momentum space is allowed in each element of volume of size $h^3/V$. Hence in the volume $4\pi p^2\,dp$ of momentum space the allowed number of points is $4\pi p^2\,dp/(h^3/V)$, which is the same as equation (4.9). In addition we have to consider the angular momentum of the electron $\frac{1}{2}\hbar$ due to its intrinsic spin, which can have one of two components $\pm\frac{1}{2}\hbar$ along any axis (see § 20.2). The Pauli principle then allows two electrons, with opposite values of these angular momentum components, to have the same translational energy, i.e. we can assign a maximum of two electrons to each point in the (linear) momentum space.

The translational energy $W$ of an electron of momentum $p$ and mass $m$ is $p^2/2m$, and the total kinetic energy will be smallest when $\sum (p^2/2m)$ has its minimum value. It is readily seen that this occurs when the points in momentum space just fill a sphere of the least volume which will accommodate all the electrons, since if we replace any point within the sphere by one outside, the value of $p$ and hence of the energy will be larger. If the radius of this sphere is $p_0$, then its volume is $\frac{4}{3}\pi p_0^3$ and the number of possible points (i.e. allowed values of the momentum) is $(V/h^3)(\frac{4}{3}\pi p_0^3)$. Since we can have a maximum of two electrons per point, if the total number of electrons in the volume $V$ of metal is $N$, we must have

$$\tfrac{1}{2}N = (V/h^3)(\tfrac{4}{3}\pi p_0^3), \tag{4.10}$$

and hence

$$W_F = p_0^2/2m = \frac{\hbar^2}{2m}(3\pi^2 n)^{\frac{2}{3}}. \tag{4.11}$$

Here $n = N/V$ is the number of electrons per unit volume of the metal and $W_F$ is the energy of the highest level occupied at $0°$ K; $W_F$ is known as the 'Fermi energy'.

It is convenient to express the distribution in terms of energy rather than momentum. By using the relation $W = p^2/2m$, and equations (4.9–11), the number $(2/V)\,di$ of states per unit volume which have kinetic energy in the range $W$ to $W+dW$ is found to be

$$g(W)\,dW = (2/V)\,di = 8\pi p^2\,dp/h^3$$

$$= \frac{1}{2\pi^2}\left(\frac{2m}{\hbar^2}\right)^{\frac{3}{2}} W^{\frac{1}{2}}\,dW \tag{4.12}$$

$$= \frac{3n W^{\frac{1}{2}}\,dW}{2W_F^{\frac{3}{2}}}. \tag{4.13}$$

If the quantity $g(W)$ is plotted against $W$, as in Fig. 4.3, a parabola is obtained; at $T = 0$ each state is occupied by an electron up to the sharp cut-off at the Fermi energy $W_F$. The mean energy $\overline{W}$ of the electrons may be found in the usual way:

$$\overline{W} = \frac{1}{n}\int_0^{W_F} W g(W)\,dW = \tfrac{3}{2}W_F^{-\frac{3}{2}}\int_0^{W_F} W^{\frac{3}{2}}\,dW = \tfrac{3}{5}W_F, \tag{4.14}$$

and the total internal energy $U_0$ of $n$ electrons at $0°$ K is then

$$U_0 = \tfrac{3}{5}n W_F. \tag{4.15}$$

The great difference between this type of energy distribution and the Maxwell–Boltzmann distribution can only be appreciated if numerical values are considered. Equation (4.11) shows that $W_F$ depends on the metal only in so far as $n$, the number of electrons per unit volume, varies. If we take sodium as a typical example and assume that just the one valence electron per atom is released in the metal as a free electron, then

$$n = 2 \cdot 5 \times 10^{22}/\text{cm}^3 = 2 \cdot 5 \times 10^{28}/\text{m}^3,$$

and $W_F$ is found to be 3·1 eV. The mean energy $\overline{W}$ is $\frac{3}{5}$ of this, or 1·9 eV. This is very large indeed. On the classical Maxwell–Boltzmann statistics, where the mean energy is $\frac{3}{2}kT$ at an absolute temperature $T$, it is equivalent to a temperature of 20 000° K. The values for other metals calculated in a similar way are given in Table 4.1.

TABLE 4.1

*Values of $W_F$ (the 'Fermi' energy), the work function $\phi$ (as deduced from measurements of the photoelectric effect and thermionic emission), and the thermionic emission constant $A$*

| Substance | $W_F$ (eV) | Work function $\phi$ | | $A$ (amp cm$^{-2}$ deg$^{-2}$) |
| | | Photoelectric effect (eV) | Thermionic emission (eV) | |
| --- | --- | --- | --- | --- |
| Li | 4·7 | 2·2 | | |
| Na | 3·1 | 1·9 | | |
| K | 2·1 | 1·8 | | |
| Cu | 7·0 | 4·1 | 4·5 | 110 |
| Ag | 5·5 | 4·7 | 4·3 | 107 |
| Au | 5·5 | 4·8 | 4·25 | 100 |
| Mo | 5·9 | | 4·2 | 50–115 |
| W | 5·8 | 4·49 | 4·5 | 20–60 |
| Pt | 6·0 | $> 6·2$ | 5·3 | 30 |
| Ni | 7·4 | 4·9 | 4·5 | 120 |
| Thoriated tungsten | | | 2·6 | 60 |
| (BaO,SrO) mixture | | | 1·8 | 3 |

By way of comparison, we will calculate the value of $W_F$ for a monatomic gas of the rare isotope of mass 3 of helium, atoms of which should also obey the Fermi–Dirac statistics. The boiling-point of this gas is 3·2° K, and the number of atoms per cm³ at atmospheric pressure in the gas at this temperature is $2·3 \times 10^{21}$. This gives $W_F = 1·15 \times 10^{-4}$ eV, which is equivalent only to a temperature of 1·3° K. This is small compared with the actual temperature, indicating that deviations from the perfect gas laws due to quantum effects will not be large. It is obvious that the low value of $W_F$ for this, or any other real gas, as compared with the electron gas in a metal, is due primarily to the difference in the mass of the particles (which comes in the denominator of equation (4.11)), and also partly to the smaller number per unit volume. When $W_F \ll kT$, the particles have all energies up to those of order $kT$, and the density of occupied points in momentum space is low; that is, the chance of finding an occupied point in the fundamental volume ($h^3/V$) is small. Under these circumstances the classical statistics are a valid approximation. For an electron gas, on the other hand, $W_F \gg kT$ at all ordinary temperatures, and every fundamental volume $(h^3/V)$ of momentum space contains an occupied point, only one such point (or two electrons, allowing for the spin) in each such volume being allowed by the exclusion principle. If we tried to use the classical picture, with the average energy of the order $kT$, this would correspond to putting a large number of electrons in each volume $(h^3/V)$ of momentum space, and the exclusion principle would be violated.

The energy distribution at a finite temperature is given by Fermi–Dirac statistical mechanics, and we quote the results. Each 'point' in momentum space corresponds to a quantized state of translational motion, and inclusion of the electron spin gives two quantum states to each point. The number of such states $g(W)\,dW$ per unit volume in the energy range $W$ to $W+dW$ is known as the 'density of states', and from equation (4.12)

$$g(W) = \frac{1}{2\pi^2}\left(\frac{2m}{\hbar^2}\right)^{\frac{3}{2}} W^{\frac{1}{2}} = Cm^{\frac{3}{2}} W^{\frac{1}{2}}, \qquad (4.16)$$

where $C$ is a constant. If $f$ is the probability that an electron occupies a given state, then the number $dn$ of electrons with energy between $W$ and $W+dW$ is $dn = fg(W)\,dW$. The quantity $f$ is a function both of energy and of temperature, being given by

$$f = \frac{1}{\exp\{(W-W_F)/kT\}+1}. \qquad (4.17)$$

Hence
$$dn = \frac{Cm^{\frac{3}{2}} W^{\frac{1}{2}}}{\exp\{(W-W_F)/kT\}+1}\,dW \qquad (4.18)$$

and the total number of electrons per unit volume $n$ is

$$n = Cm^{\frac{3}{2}} \int_0^\infty \frac{W^{\frac{1}{2}}}{\exp\{(W-W_F)/kT\}+1}\,dW. \qquad (4.19)$$

This integral can be evaluated numerically, but at temperatures where $kT \ll W_F$ approximate methods can be used. At $T = 0$ the denominator is infinite for $W > W_F$, and unity for $W < W_F$, so that $f = 0$ in the former case and 1 in the latter. This corresponds to the sharp cut-off in the occupation of states already discussed. At a finite temperature $f$ is still very close to unity when $W < W_F$ and to zero when $W > W_F$ except for the range of energies which lie within a few $kT$ of $W_F$. The distribution appropriate to a temperature of about 2000° K is shown in Fig. 4.3.

From equation (4.17) $W_F$ may be defined as the energy at which the probability of a state being occupied by an electron is $f = \frac{1}{2}$, since the denominator is then $e^0 + 1 = 2$. The actual value of $W_F$ can only be

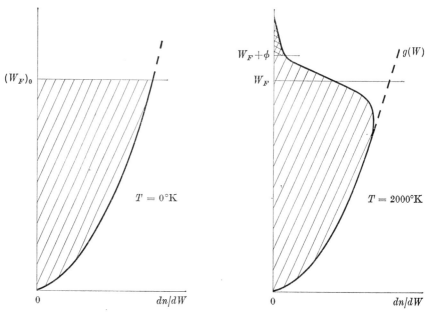

FIG. 4.3. The number of free electrons $dn$ with kinetic energy between $W$ and $W + dW$ in a metal, as given by the Fermi–Dirac distribution. At $0°$ K the electrons have energies only up to the Fermi level $(W_F)_0$; the distribution at $2000°$ K is shown on the right. At room temperature the distribution is much closer to that on the left, since $dn/dW$ is only altered for electrons whose energy lies within $\approx kT$ of $W_F$.

found from equation (4.19); if we denote the value for $T = 0$ defined by equation (4.11) by $(W_F)_0$, it can be shown that

$$W_F \doteqdot (W_F)_0 - \frac{\pi^2}{12} \frac{(kT)^2}{W_F}. \tag{4.20}$$

The difference is of order $(kT)^2/W_F$, and at ordinary temperatures can be neglected for many purposes, but not in calculating differentials such as the specific heat. The basic reason is that because of the Exclusion Principle an electron can only move into an unoccupied state, and as the temperature increases the extra energy available is of order $kT$. Thus only the electrons with energies differing from $W_F$ by amounts of this order can move to higher levels, and this is a fraction of order $kT/W_F$ of the total number. Thus the increase in internal energy is of order $nkT(kT/W_F)$, and the specific heat is smaller than the classical value $3R/2$ per mole by a factor of order $kT/W_F$. The electronic specific heat will be discussed further in § 18.4, but in the following paragraphs we can usually neglect the difference between the actual Fermi–Dirac distribution and that at 0° K, since at room temperature $kT$ is equivalent to 0·025 electron volts while $W_F$ is several volts.

### 4.3. Work function and contact potential

The energy required to remove an electron from the top of the energy distribution out of the metal to infinity is called the work function, $\phi$, and values of $\phi$ for different metals are also given in Table 4.1. The fact that $\phi$ varies from metal to metal gives rise to the phenomenon of 'contact potential'. It has long been known that when two metals are placed in contact, there is a potential difference between them, but it was not at first generally accepted that this was a fundamental property of the metals. From Fig. 4.4 it will be seen that if metal $A$ has a smaller work function than metal $B$, electrons from the top of the energy band in $A$ can flow into metal $B$ when contact is made, since they will then have a lower energy. This flow creates a potential difference between $B$ and $A$ which increases until the tops of the two energy distributions reach the same level, when no more electrons will be transferred, and equilibrium is attained. The actual number of electrons transferred is only an insignificant fraction of the total, so that the areas in Figs. 4.4 (a) and (b) are equal. Hence the contact potential is equal to the difference of the work functions.

In Fig. 4.4 the distributions are shown appropriate to $T = 0$, but in fact the equilibrium condition at any temperature is $W_{FA} = W_{FB}$; this makes the distribution functions $f_A$, $f_B$ match for every value of $W$, since

$$f_A = \frac{1}{\exp\{(W-W_{FA})/kT\}+1}, \qquad f_B = \frac{1}{\exp\{(W-W_{FB})/kT\}+1}.$$

A detailed statistical treatment shows that $W_F$ is equivalent to the 'thermodynamic potential', which must have the same value for all systems when they are in thermal equilibrium (see, for example, Dekker, A. J., 1958, *Solid State Physics* (Macmillan)).

The work function of a metal, and hence also the contact potential between two metals, is very sensitive to the state of the surface. For this reason measurements of $\phi$ show rather a wide scatter, and the best determinations are made with metallic films newly deposited by evaporation *in vacuo* (for metals with low boiling-points), or (for a high melting-point metal such as tungsten) with a surface cleaned by 'flashing'

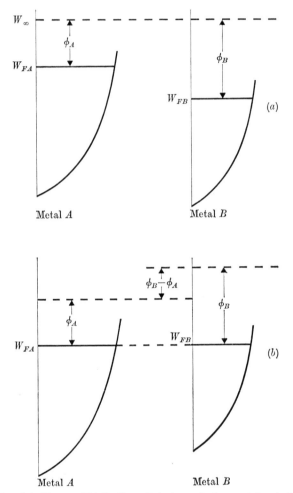

Fig. 4.4.  Energy distribution of electrons in two metals, $A$, $B$.

(a) Before contact: $\phi_A$, $\phi_B$ are the energies required to remove an electron to rest at infinity.

(b) After contact: electrons flow to metal $B$, changing its potential relative to $A$ until the tops of the two energy distributions are level (the transfer of electrons required is an insignificant fraction of the whole). The contact potential difference thus set up is practically equal to $\phi_B - \phi_A$, and an electron released from $B$ (e.g. by the photo-electric effect) would gain this amount of energy in moving from a point just outside $B$ to a point just outside $A$.

the metal at a temperature close to the melting-point *in vacuo*. Each of these processes removes traces of absorbed gas from the metal which affect the work function. The contact potential between two surfaces is measured indirectly as follows (see, for example, Mitchell and Mitchell, 1951). A narrow beam of electrons from an electron gun is directed on

to the metallic surface, and the current reaching the surface is plotted
as a function of the retarding potential applied to the surface. When
a second metallic surface is substituted, and the current to it plotted, a
curve of similar shape is obtained but displaced by an amount equal to
the contact potential difference between the two surfaces. The work of
Mitchell and Mitchell gave the following mean values for the contact
potential relative to a clean tungsten surface: copper $-0\cdot05\pm0\cdot02$ V;
silver $+0\cdot23\pm0\cdot03$ V; aluminium $+0\cdot31\pm0\cdot03$ V.

## 4.4. Emission of electrons from metals

If an electron can acquire an excess energy at least equal to the work
function, it can escape from the metal, and it will then travel to a nearby
electrode held at a positive potential with respect to the emitting surface. A continuous flow of such electrons constitutes a current, and the
possibility of producing a continuous emission of electrons is the basis
of thermionic vacuum tubes. Electrons can acquire sufficient energy to
escape in two important ways; (a) if the metal is heated, the energy
distribution amongst the electrons changes, developing a pronounced
'tail' as in curve $B$ in Fig. 4.3, in which an appreciable number of electrons have energy greater than $(\phi+W_F)$; the escape of electrons from the
metal is then known as 'thermionic emission': (b) if light of a sufficiently
short wavelength shines on the metal, electrons acquire energy from
collisions with the photons and can escape if the photon energy is greater
than the work function $\phi$; this is known as 'photoelectric emission'.
Electrons can also be emitted if an intense electric field is applied at
the metal surface ('field emission'), or if the surface is bombarded by
electrons ('secondary emission'). We shall discuss these effects separately.

*Thermionic emission*

If a metal is heated *in vacuo* and an electrode at a positive potential
with respect to it collects the emitted electrons, as in Fig. 4.5, a continuous current of microamperes up to milliamperes may be obtained.
Such a device is known as a 'thermionic vacuum tube'. The magnitude
of the current depends on the work function of the emitter, and varies
very rapidly with temperature; copious emission can be obtained from
pure metals only at temperatures of the order of 2000° C (see Chapter
12). In order to escape, an electron must have an energy greater than
$(\phi+W_F)$, and at a given temperature the number represented by the
hatched area in Fig. 4.3 will be able to leave the surface. The close
parallel between thermionic emission and evaporation was recognized by

Richardson, who showed that the current emitted per unit area should be given by the equation

$$J = AT^2 e^{-\phi/kT},\qquad(4.21)$$

where $\phi$ is the work function, $k$ is Boltzmann's constant, and $A$ should be a universal constant for all metals, equal to 120 amp cm$^{-2}$ deg$^{-2}$. (For the derivation of equation (4.21), see, for example, Slater, 1939,

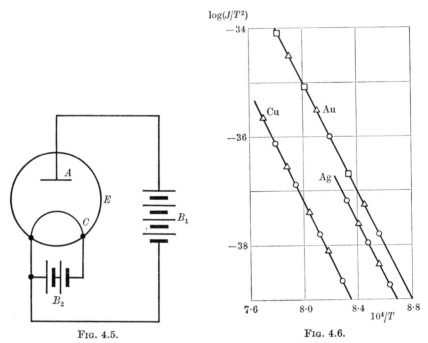

FIG. 4.5.        FIG. 4.6.

FIG. 4.5. A thermionic vacuum tube. $B_2$ is a battery of about 4 V for heating electrode $C$ (the cathode): electrons flow from the cathode to the anode $A$ maintained at a positive potential by the battery $B_1$ ($\approx$ 100 V). The whole is enclosed in an evacuated glass or metal envelope.

FIG. 4.6. Plot of $\log_e(J/T^2)$ against $10^4/T$ for the thermionic emission from copper, silver, and gold (after Jain and Krishnan, 1953).

or Zemansky, 1957). This equation has been verified experimentally, though the variation of the exponential term with temperature is so much more rapid than that of the $T^2$ term that in early experiments it was difficult to be certain that the latter was correct. However, if $\log(J/T^2)$ is plotted against $1/T$, a linear graph is obtained, as shown in Fig. 4.6. Representative values of the constants $A$ and $\phi$ are given in Table 4.1; the values of $A$ vary considerably, an effect generally attributed to a partial reflection of electrons attempting to leave the surface of the emitter, though there will also be a slight variation in $\phi$ with temperature, similar to that in $W_F$ (see Problem 4.6), which will affect the value of $A$ obtained from the use of equation 4.21). There is also evidence that the emission is different from different faces of a single crystal, and that the values of $A$ obtained from a polycrystalline surface are too low. Thermionic emission will be considered in more detail in Chapter 12.

*Field emission*

The emission of electrons from a metal under the influence of an applied field is closely related to thermionic emission, so that we shall discuss it next. As we should expect, it occurs only when the direction of the applied field is such that electrons are attracted out of the metal, and we must consider the effect of an applied field on the potential barrier at the surface of a metal.

The potential energy jump at the surface is $W_F + \phi$, since it represents the energy which we should have to give an electron of zero kinetic energy to extract it from the metal. The potential jump is not infinitely sharp because of the 'image force' which acts on an electron just outside the metal (§ 2.5). If the electron is at a distance $x$ from the surface it will have potential energy $W = -e^2/(16\pi\epsilon_0 x)$ when $x$ is large compared with atomic dimensions, but will deviate from this for small values of $x$. The shape of the potential energy curve is shown in Fig. 4.7; when a field $E$ is applied, the potential energy outside the metal becomes

$$W = -e^2/(16\pi\epsilon_0 x) - Eex, \tag{4.22}$$

and this has a maximum as shown. Thus the apparent work function is reduced by a large electric field, and at temperatures where the thermionic emission is appreciable it will be correspondingly increased. At any temperature field emission will occur also through the quantum mechanical 'tunnel effect', by which an electron with insufficient energy to surmount the potential barrier can 'leak' through it; this requires fields $\sim 10^8$ V/metre to produce appreciable emission.

*Photoelectric emission*

The energy associated with a quantum of radiation of frequency $\nu$ (a 'photon') is $h\nu$, where $h$ is Planck's constant, and in many respects the photons behave like corpuscles with this energy. In an inelastic collision the whole of this energy may be transferred to an electron. If $h\nu > \phi$, the electron may be ejected from a metallic surface with maximum kinetic energy $w$ such that

$$h\nu = \phi + w.$$

Measurement of the lowest frequency (longest wavelength) of light which can just cause photoelectric emission therefore provides another method of determining the work function $\phi$, assuming Planck's constant to be known; the values of $\phi$ given in Table 4.1 were obtained by this method. The cut-off wavelength lies in the visible region only for the

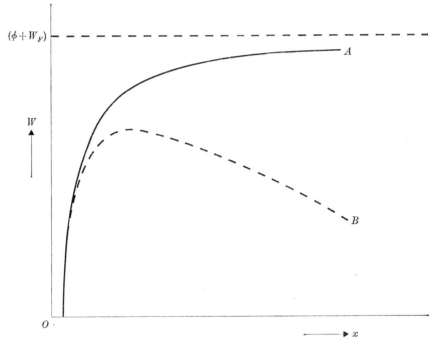

FIG. 4.7. Variation of potential energy $W$ of an electron with distance $x$ from a conductor. Curve $A$. No external field.     Curve $B$. With external field (equation 4.22).

alkali metals and barium and strontium, which have low work functions; for other metals it lies in the ultraviolet.

A device for detecting visible radiation (sometimes called a 'photo-tube') makes use of the photoelectric current. A typical construction is shown in Fig. 4.8. An electrode at a positive potential (the anode) in the form of a long thin rod is placed along the axis of a cylindrical cathode from which one section is removed so that light can enter and fall on the inside of the cylinder, which is the photoelectric surface. The whole is placed within an evacuated glass envelope. The current to the anode reaches a value independent of the anode potential when the latter is more than about 15 V, since all the emitted photoelectrons then reach the anode. For a given wavelength of light, this saturation current is strictly proportional to the light intensity over a very wide range of intensities, and the tube can therefore be used as an intensity meter. The currents are of the order $10^{-5}$ A, and can be read either on a micro-ammeter, as shown in Fig. 4.8, or, to obtain greater sensitivity, the current can be passed through a large resistance and the voltage developed across this resistance amplified by a vacuum tube amplifier (see Chapter 13). This method is particularly useful for rapidly fluctuating light intensities, since the response of the photo-tube is virtually instantaneous (the time delay in emission of electrons after switching on a source of light is less than $10^{-9}$ sec). Gas-filled photo-tubes are also used. They give a greater current, since the initial photoelectrons give rise to additional electrons and ions on collision with gas molecules, but suffer from the disadvantages that the current is strongly dependent on the anode voltage and the response is not as rapid as in the vacuum type.

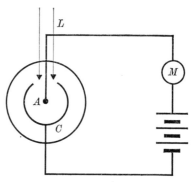

Fig. 4.8. An instrument using the phenomenon of photoelectric emission for the measurement of light intensities.

A    Anode.
C    Negative electrode, whose inner surface is the source of electrons.
M    Microammeter.
L    Incident light.

*Secondary emission*

When a solid surface is struck by electrons or ions of appreciable energy, secondary electrons are emitted from the surface; if the bombarding particles (primaries) are electrons, they must have an energy of at least a few electron volts to eject an appreciable number of secondary electrons, and, at higher energies, the number of secondaries may be greater than the number of incident primaries. The phenomenon of 'secondary emission' is commonly encountered in thermionic vacuum tubes with several electrodes, and also from the fluorescent screen of a cathode ray tube. It is very sensitive to impurities and to contamination of the surface; for pure metals the secondary emission ratio

$\delta$ = (number of secondary electrons/number of incident primaries)

has a maximum value varying from 0·5 to 1·6. At low energies there is an initial rise in $\delta$ because the number of secondaries released within the metal increases with the energy of the incident primary. However, the production of secondaries is most copious near the end of the primary path, and their chance of escape declines rapidly as the primaries penetrate deeper into the metal at higher energies, causing δ to fall again after passing through a maximum at about 200–400 eV in the primary energy.  For composite surfaces (such as a layer of $Cs_2O$ on a base of silver, with a surface film of absorbed caesium on the $Cs_2O$) δ may rise

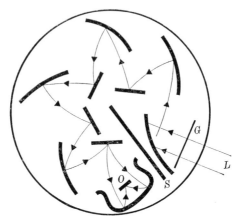

FIG. 4.9.  A photo-multiplier tube, showing one arrangement of the electrodes (a linear arrangement is also used).

| | | | |
|---|---|---|---|
| G | Grill. | O | Final electrode. |
| S | Shield. | L | Incident light. |

to values as high as 10.  There is still much uncertainty as to the mechanism of secondary emission, but there are reasons for believing that the secondary electrons come from those tightly bound to the metallic ions rather than from the free electrons.  The shape of the curve of secondary emission ratio against energy of the incident electrons is similar for all substances, and resembles that for the probability of ionization of a gaseous atom; high ratios can also be obtained from insulators.

The chief use of secondary emission is for current amplification.  For example, the photoelectrons from a photo-sensitive surface may be accelerated to strike a secondary emitting electrode, so arranged that the secondary electrons are accelerated to another secondary emitting electrode, and so on.  The electrode arrangement in such a 'photo-multiplier' tube is shown very schematically in Fig. 4.9.  The current amplification that can be obtained is very large indeed; with a secondary emission ratio of 3 at each of 10 surfaces, the overall amplification is $3^{10}$ or about

$6 \times 10^4$. The main difficulty is the production of stable surfaces with a high ratio; in practice there is generally some change in the amplification with time. The potential of each successive electrode is about 75 V higher than the previous one, and the necessary voltages are obtained from a potentiometer system.

## 4.5. Thermoelectricity

When two metals are joined together, a contact potential difference is set up between them. If a second junction is made between them, so that a closed circuit is established, the contact potential difference at the second junction is just equal and opposite to that at the first junction, so that there is no net e.m.f. in the circuit provided that the two junctions are at the same temperature. The work function of a metal varies slightly with temperature, however (for tungsten it changes at the rate of 6 to $7 \times 10^{-5}$ eV/°K; compare Problem 4.6) and so also will the contact potential. Hence, if the junctions are at different temperatures, the contact potentials will be slightly different, and a net e.m.f. will exist which can drive a current round the circuit. This is known as the thermoelectric e.m.f., and was discovered by Seebeck in 1821; it is generally of the order of microvolts per degree temperature difference between the junctions. The converse effect was discovered by Peltier in 1834. If the Seebeck e.m.f. is from metal $A$ to metal $B$ at the hot junction, an external e.m.f. applied in this direction will produce a cooling at this junction and a heating at the other junction. Both effects are entirely reversible.

Since the energy of the free electrons in a metal depends on the temperature, the presence of a temperature gradient in a metal produces a region at one end where the electrons have more energy than those at the other end. Owing to their higher velocities, electrons from the end with higher energy will diffuse down the metal faster than those from the other end, and the flow will continue until a potential difference is set up which is just sufficient to counterbalance this flow. This is known as the Thomson effect. In general the e.m.f. is from the lower temperature to the higher temperature, but it can have either sign. Like the Seebeck and Peltier effects, the Thomson effect is reversible.

The Peltier coefficient $\Pi$ is defined as follows: the heat absorbed when a charge $Q$ passes from metal $A$ to metal $B$ is $\Pi Q$ joules when $Q$ is in coulombs. The Thomson coefficient $\sigma$ is defined as such that the potential difference is $\sigma_A dT$ (in volts) between two points in the metal $A$ where the temperature difference is $dT$ (°K). In tables $\sigma$ is given as positive when the direction of the e.m.f. is from the cold to the hot end.

*Thermoelectric theory*

When a charge is passed round a circuit such as that in Fig. 4.10, there will be an irreversible heating throughout the circuit due to its resistance, as well as thermal changes due to the Peltier and Thomson

Metal $A$

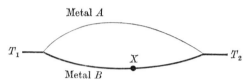

$T_1$ ——————— $X$ ——————— $T_2$

Metal $B$

FIG. 4.10. Figure to illustrate the thermoelectric effect.

effects. However, the irreversible heating is proportional to the square of the current, and can be neglected for very small currents. If a charge $Q$ is passed, the external work done is $QV$, where $V$ is the total e.m.f. in the circuit; the net heat absorbed at the junctions is $(\Pi_{T_1} - \Pi_{T_2})Q$; and the increase in internal energy is $-Q \int_{T_2}^{T_1} (\sigma_A - \sigma_B) \, dT$, since this represents the energy required to heat the electrons from temperature $T_2$ to $T_1$ in metal $A$ less that emitted in the reverse process in metal $B$. Hence from the first law of thermodynamics (dividing by $Q$),

$$V = \Pi_{T_1} - \Pi_{T_2} + \int_{T_2}^{T_1} (\sigma_A - \sigma_B) \, dT. \qquad (4.23)$$

In order to detect this e.m.f., the circuit must be broken and a voltmeter introduced at, say $X$, in Fig. 4.10. Although the voltmeter may contain metals different from $A$ and $B$, the total e.m.f. in the circuit will be unaffected provided that both junctions to the instrument are at the same temperature. For, if the meter $M$ has junctions at a temperature $T$,

$$V = (\Pi_{T_1} - \Pi_{T_2})_{A \to B} + (\Pi_T)_{B \to M} + (\Pi_T)_{M \to B} + \int_{T_2}^{T_1} (\sigma_A - \sigma_B) \, dT$$

$$= (\Pi_{T_1} - \Pi_{T_2}) + \int_{T_2}^{T_1} (\sigma_A - \sigma_B) \, dT,$$

which is the same as before. The same result holds if any number of metals at different temperatures are connected in the circuit, provided that each pair of junctions to a given metal are at the same temperature.

Since no temperature changes occur in the circuit, the external work $QV$ is also the free energy of the system, so that we have from the second law of thermodynamics

$$QV = U + T\frac{d(QV)}{dT}, \quad \text{where } U = Q\int_0^T (\sigma_A - \sigma_B)\,dT.$$

Hence

$$V = \int_0^T (\sigma_A - \sigma_B)\,dT + T\frac{dV}{dT}$$

and differentiation with respect to $T$ gives

$$\sigma_A - \sigma_B = -T\frac{d^2V}{dT^2}. \tag{4.24}$$

Then elimination of $\sigma_A - \sigma_B$ with the help of equation (4.23) yields

$$\Pi_{T_1} - \Pi_{T_2} = [T(dV/dT)]_{T_2}^{T_1},$$

or

$$\frac{dV}{dT} = \frac{\Pi}{T}. \tag{4.25}$$

Although the Peltier and Thomson effects are reversible, the application of reversible thermodynamics to a thermoelectric circuit is open to a number of objections, since irreversible effects such as resistive heating and thermal conduction are always present. A better method is to use irreversible thermodynamics (see Zemansky, 1957) or to consider the change of entropy at a junction (see Cusack, 1958), and to relate this to the net heat absorbed at that temperature. A more rigorous treatment on these lines confirms that equations (4.24) and (4.25) are valid, and they have been tested experimentally over a large temperature range for many substances.

The quantity $dV/dT$ is called the 'thermoelectric power', and from equation (4.24) we have

$$dV/dT = -\int \frac{\sigma_A - \sigma_B}{T}\,dT + \text{constant}.$$

By the third law of thermodynamics (see, for example, Wilks, 1961) $dV/dT \to 0$ as $T \to 0$, and we can therefore eliminate the constant by taking the integral from 0 to $T$ (to avoid infinities in the integrand this requires $\sigma$ to vary at least as the first power of $T$). Then

$$dV/dT = \int_0^T \frac{\sigma_B}{T}\,dT - \int_0^T \frac{\sigma_A}{T}\,dT = S_B - S_A, \tag{4.26}$$

where the quantity

$$S = \int_0^T \frac{\sigma}{T}\,dT \tag{4.27}$$

is known as the 'absolute thermoelectric power' and is a property of each substance separately. Our identification of the quantity $Q \int_{T_1}^{T_2} \sigma \, dT$ as the change in the internal energy suggests that

$$\sigma = (1/Q)(dU/dT) = (1/Q)C_e,$$

TABLE 4.2

*Values of the thermoelectric coefficients $\alpha$ and $\beta$ (equation (4.29)) with t in °C*

| Substance | $\alpha$ $(\mu V/deg)$ | $\beta$ $(\mu V/deg^2)$ |
|---|---|---|
| Aluminium . . . . | − 0·76 | +0·0039 |
| Bismuth (commercial) . . | −43·7 | −0·465 |
| Copper . . . . | + 1·34 | +0·0094 |
| Constantan (60% Cu–40% Ni) | −38·1 | −0·089 |
| Gold . . . . . | + 2·80 | +0·010 |
| Iron . . . . . | +17·2 | −0·048 |
| Palladium . . . . | − 7·4 | −0·039 |
| Platinum . . . . | − 3·04 | −0·033 |
| 90% platinum–10% rhodium . | + 7·0 | +0·0064 |

where $C_e$ is the specific heat of the electrons. Hence using equation (18.16 a) we have, since $Q = -ne$,

$$S = \int_0^T \frac{\sigma}{T} dT = \int_0^T (C_e/QT)\, dT = -\int_0^T \frac{\pi^2 k^2 n T}{2W_F \, ne T}\, dT$$

$$= -(\pi^2 k^2 / 2eW_F)T = \beta T \qquad (4.28)$$

and the e.m.f. between a pair of metals $A$, $B$ whose junctions are at $T_1$, $T_2$ should take the form $(t = T_1 - T_2; \beta = \beta_B - \beta_A)$

$$V = \int_{T_2}^{T_1} S_B \, dT - \int_{T_2}^{T_1} S_A \, dT = \tfrac{1}{2}\beta(T_1^2 - T_2^2) = \alpha t + \tfrac{1}{2}\beta t^2. \qquad (4.29)$$

Though this relation is obeyed by many pairs of metals over a large temperature range, our derivation not only predicts $\alpha = \beta T_2$, but also that $\beta$ is negative (equation (4.28)), neither of which holds generally (see Table 4.2).

The quantity $S$ (see equation 4.26) is analogous to entropy per unit charge since the free energy $F$ per unit charge is $V$, and the entropy is $-dF/dT$. Our simple theory predicts that $S$ should be proportional to $T$ for a metal, and at temperatures above 100° K this is true to a large extent. At lower temperatures $S$ ceases to vary linearly with $T$, and this cannot be accounted for by considering the energy distribution of the conduction electrons alone. The vibrations of the crystal lattice must also be included, since these alter the potential fields through which the electrons move and provide a mechanism by which energy can be exchanged between electrons and lattice. This effect is particularly important at low temperatures and in semiconductors, where thermoelectric effects are much larger. For germanium at room temperature $S$ is about 1 millivolt per degree (metals have values of order $10^{-6}$ V/deg: see Problem 4.7), and these high values, combined with values of thermal conductivity which are much lower than in metals, make refrigeration using the Peltier effect in a semiconductor a practicable possibility.

*Thermocouples*

If one junction is maintained at a fixed temperature, the thermoelectric e.m.f. can be used to measure the temperature of the other junction. The values of $\alpha$, $\beta$ can be found from the differences (taking due account of sign) between the values given in tables (such as Table 4.2, where the one junction is assumed to be at 0° C). The values are tabulated for each substance against lead, which is used as a reference metal because its Thomson coefficient is very small. It is obviously desirable to work on the steep part of the $(V, t)$ curve, in order that $V$ shall vary almost linearly with $t$ and that $dV/dt$ shall be large. As $dV/dt = 0$ at the temperature $t = -\alpha/\beta$, different pairs of metals are used for different temperature ranges. A copper-constantan couple is useful in the range $-200°$ to 400° C, and a platinum-rhodium against platinum couple is used up to 1700° C. For accurate work each thermocouple must be calibrated at two known temperatures to determine $\alpha$ and $\beta$, and then a calibration curve is drawn from which any unknown temperature can be read off in terms of the e.m.f. $V$. It is possible to obtain millivoltmeters which read off the temperature directly, but for accurate work a potentiometer and standard cell should be used. Thermocouples have the advantage that the junction has a very small heat capacity, so that it rapidly reaches the required temperature without altering the experimental conditions; they are therefore suitable for measuring varying temperatures. It is also easy to ensure that the junction is in good thermal contact with the substance whose temperature is required.

*Measurement of the Thomson coefficient*

The Thomson coefficient of one metal relative to another may readily be found by making a thermocouple from the two metals, measuring the e.m.f. as a function of temperature, and applying equation (4.24). The Thomson effect is a characteristic of each metal, however, and it is desirable to know its absolute value. If this can be determined for one metal, then all the others follow from thermocouple measurements. We shall describe a method of Borelius, Keesom, and Johansson (1928) which can also be used at low temperatures.

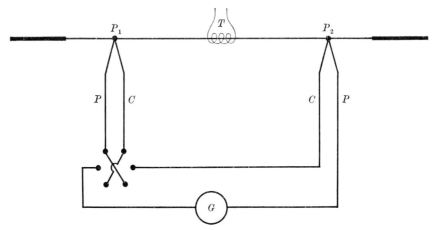

Fig. 4.11. Diagram of the apparatus used by Borelius, Keesom, and Johansson (1928) to measure the absolute value of the Thomson coefficient of a metal.

$T$   Platinum resistance thermometer for measurement at low temperatures.
$G$   High resistance galvanometer.
$P_1, P_2$   Thermocouple junctions of platinum ($P$) and constantan ($C$).

A thin wire of the metal is stretched *in vacuo* between two heavy leads maintained at a constant temperature. When a current is passed through the wire, the Joule heating raises the temperature at the centre so that in one half of the wire the Thomson effect gives a voltage in the same direction as the applied e.m.f., while in the other half it is opposed to it. The temperature of the wire is measured at two symmetrical points $P_1$, $P_2$ as in Fig. 4.11 by a pair of thermocouples which are electrically insulated from the wire by means of thin paper. Two measurements are made. First, the thermocouples are connected in series, so that the mean increase of temperature at the two points is found; this gives the temperature increase due to the Joule heating alone. Second, the couples are connected in opposition to give the difference in temperature between the two points due to the Thomson effect. Temperature differences due to asymmetry in the position of the points $P_1$, $P_2$ can be eliminated by repeating the measurement with the direction of current flow reversed.

In the theory it is assumed that heat is lost only by conduction along the wire. The net heat flow into a section $dx$ of the wire a distance $x$ from the centre by conduction is then

$$-KA(\partial T/\partial x)+KA\{(\partial T/\partial x)+(\partial^2 T/\partial x^2)\,dx\} = KA(\partial^2 T/\partial x^2)\,dx,$$

where $K$ is the thermal conductivity of the wire and $A$ its cross-section. The heat generated in the section is $I(IR\,dx-\sigma\,dT)$, where $I$ is the current flowing and $R$ the resistance per unit length. Hence the differential equation is

$$KA\frac{\partial^2 T}{\partial x^2} - I\sigma\frac{\partial T}{\partial x} + I^2 R = 0. \qquad (4.30)$$

The exact solution of this equation is

$$T = c\{e^{fx} - \cosh fa - (x/a)\sinh fa\},$$

where $f = I\sigma/KA$ and $c^{-1} = (\sigma/IaR)\sinh fa$; the temperature at the ends of the wire $x = \pm a$ is taken to be zero. If the thermocouple readings are $t$ when connected in series, and $\tau$ when in opposition, then these are proportional to the sum and difference of the temperatures at $+b$ and $-b$ respectively. Hence

$$\frac{\tau}{tfb} = \frac{(1/fb)\sinh fb - (1/fa)\sinh fa}{\cosh fb - \cosh fa} = \frac{1}{3} \quad \text{when } f \text{ is small.}$$

This gives

$$\sigma = \frac{3\tau KA}{tIb}. \qquad (4.31)$$

In this treatment the resistivity of the wire has been assumed independent of temperature, and in practice a small correction must be made for the slight change in temperature distribution due to the varying resistance.

## 4.6. Conduction of electricity through liquids

Certain liquids, such as hydrocarbons, are extremely good insulators, while others, such as water, have an appreciable conductivity. Solutions of some salts in water have a conductivity of the order of $10^{-5}$ times that of metals, and such salts are known as ionic compounds. An example is sodium chloride, which in a simple picture is formed by the transfer of one electron from the sodium atom to the chlorine atom, so that the molecule consists of a positively charged sodium ion and a negatively charged chlorine ion. Such a molecule has a permanent electric dipole moment, and is called a 'polar molecule'; in a non-polar molecule, such as hydrogen, the electrons are shared equally between the two atoms, and there is no permanent dipole moment. The water molecule is itself strongly polar, and when a substance such as sodium chloride is dissolved in it, the electric fields of the water molecules are strong enough to dissociate the solute molecules into separate sodium ions and chlorine ions. There are also composite ions formed by groups of molecules which have gained or lost an electron. The solution is called an 'electrolytic solution', the solute being known as the 'electrolyte'. The degree of dissociation of the electrolyte in solution is determined by the dynamic equilibrium between recombination and dissociation. With 'strong electrolytes', such as NaCl, the dissociation is practically complete at all ordinary concentrations; for 'weak electrolytes', such as acetic acid, the degree of dissociation is greatest at high dilution and falls steadily with increasing concentration according to the law

$$\alpha^2/(1-\alpha) = K/c,$$

where $\alpha$ is the fraction of solute molecules dissociated, $c$ the concentration, and $K$ is a constant which depends on the temperature.

If a potential difference is applied between two electrodes in an electrolytic solution, a current will flow through the solution. The current is carried by both positive and negative ions, which are produced by the decomposition of the electrolyte; the hydrogen or metallic radical always travels to the cathode, or negative electrode, and the acid radicals travel to the anode, or positive electrode. This transfer of charged ions by an electric current is called electrolysis. For example, if two copper electrodes are immersed in copper sulphate solution, copper is dissolved off the anode, and is deposited on the cathode. With carbon electrodes in a brine solution, hydrogen appears at the cathode, and chlorine at the anode. There are two fundamental laws, discovered by Faraday, which are obeyed by all electrolytes.

*Faraday's laws of electrolysis*

(1) The mass of a given substance liberated at one electrode is proportional to the total charge which has passed.

(2) The mass of a given substance liberated at an electrode by unit charge is proportional to the chemical equivalent of that substance.

These two laws can be condensed into the following form: If the mass liberated at an electrode is $m$ when a current $I$ passes for $t$ seconds, then $m = ZIt$, where $Z$ is a constant for a given element, called the *electrochemical equivalent*. The chemical equivalent of an ion is the atomic weight divided by the valency, the valency being equal to the number of electronic charges carried by the ion. Then if $A$ is the atomic weight, and $v$ the valency,

$$m = (A/v)It/F, \qquad (4.32)$$

where $F$ is a universal constant known as the Faraday. The Faraday is the charge of electricity which liberates one gramme equivalent $(A/v)$ of an ion in electrolysis. If $N$ (Avogadro's number) is the number of atoms in a gramme atom, the total charge carried by a gramme equivalent is $(N/v)(ve)$, since each atom (more correctly, each ion) has a charge $ve$, and this total charge $Ne$ must just be equal to $F$. Hence we have the important relation

$$F = Ne. \tag{4.33}$$

Basically, the value of the Faraday is found by determining the mass of electrolyte liberated when a known current is passed through a solution for a measured length of time. Some very accurate determinations are those of Craig and Hoffman (1950). Using silver electrodes in a solution containing silver perchlorate and perchloric acid, they obtained

$$F = 96523 \cdot 3 \pm 6 \cdot 2 \text{ coulomb/g,}$$

while in another experiment in which oxalate ions are oxidized to carbon dioxide $(C_2O_4^{--} - 2e^- \rightarrow 2CO_2)$ at the anode in a solution of sodium oxalate in sulphuric acid they obtained

$$F = 96519 \cdot 3 \pm 2 \cdot 6 \text{ coulomb/g.}$$

Although the primary reaction in electrolysis is simply the flow of ions of positive and negative sign to the cathode and anode respectively, secondary processes may occur at the electrodes so that different products appear there which do not correspond to the primary ions. The first product may be unstable, as in the case

$$NH_4 + H_2O \rightarrow NH_4OH + H,$$

or it may react with the solvent, the solute, or the electrode in a chemical reaction such as

$$Na + H_2O \rightarrow NaOH + H.$$

In these examples the hydrogen atoms or ions will combine to form hydrogen molecules which appear as a mass of small bubbles of gas covering the electrode. In a cell where gas appears at the electrodes, the phenomenon of 'polarization' of the electrodes is generally observed. For example, in the electrolysis of acidulated water using polished platinum electrodes, no electrolysis occurs until the applied e.m.f. $V$ exceeds a certain critical value $V'$, known as the decomposition potential of the electrolyte. If $V > V'$, the current $I$ flowing obeys a modified Ohm's law relation

$$V - V' = IR,$$

but if $V < V'$, no current flows. The cell therefore becomes irreversible owing to 'polarization' of the electrodes. This is probably due to the presence of positively-charged hydrogen ions in the gas bubbles, which repel other positive ions and so give the effect of a back e.m.f. Practical cells incorporate a 'depolarizer' consisting of a substance which reacts chemically with the hydrogen ions appearing at the electrode and so prevents the formation of gas bubbles.

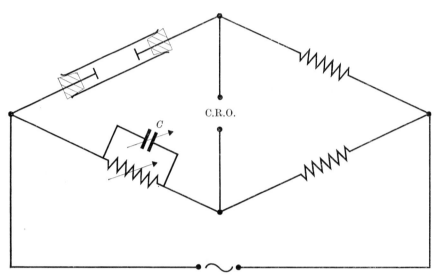

Fig. 4.12. Alternating current bridge for measuring the conductivity of an electrolyte. $C$ is a small variable capacitor to balance out the capacitance between the electrodes.

### Conductivity

Polarization effects do not appear instantaneously, but after current has been passed in one direction for a finite time. They can be avoided if alternating current is used, since the direction of the current is then reversed before such effects can be established. The conductivity of electrolytic solutions is therefore measured with alternating current and a Wheatstone bridge, the detector being an amplifier with earphones or cathode ray oscilloscope (see Chapter 15). The solution is contained in a cell with two platinum electrodes; the geometrical arrangement is not important if only relative measurements of conductivity are required, but should be such as to minimize the capacitance between the electrodes. In general this capacitance will require balancing with a variable capacitance in another arm of the bridge in order to obtain a balance with alternating current, as in Fig. 4.12.

The current density at any point in the solution will be

$$J = (n_1 v_1 u_1 + n_2 v_2 u_2)|e|E = \sigma E,$$

where $n_1$, $n_2$ are the numbers of positive and negative ions per unit volume, $v_1$, $v_2$ their valencies, and $u_1$, $u_2$ their mobilities; that is, the mean velocity of an ion in a field of unit intensity. Hence the specific conductivity $\sigma$ is

$$\sigma = |e|(n_1 v_1 u_1 + n_2 v_2 u_2). \tag{4.34}$$

$\sigma$ is found to be proportional to the concentration for very dilute solutions, but increases less rapidly at higher concentrations. For weak electrolytes, the conductivity is determined by the degree of dissociation, i.e. the number of ions present, indicating that the mobility is independent of concentration. For strong electrolytes, where dissociation is practically complete at all concentrations, the mobility falls at high concentrations because each ion attracts round itself an 'atmosphere' of ions of opposite sign which retard its progress through the solution when an electric field is applied.

## 4.7. Voltaic cells

If two metal electrodes are put into an electrolytic solution, it is found that under certain circumstances a potential difference exists between them. In the 'concentration cell', the two electrodes are of the same metal but are immersed in two solutions of the same electrolyte with different concentrations, usually separated by a permeable membrane which allows ions to pass from one solution to the other. The e.m.f. developed is normally of the order of hundredths of a volt, and such cells are not of practical importance. In the 'chemical cell' the electrodes are of different metals, and an e.m.f. is set up of the same order as the contact potential difference between the two metals. If a metallic contact is established between the two electrodes a current will flow, the energy required for this current being derived from the chemical reactions which take place at the electrodes.

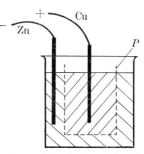

FIG. 4.13. The Daniell cell.

$P$ is a porous pot containing copper sulphate solution in which the copper rod is immersed. The zinc rod is in a solution of dilute sulphuric acid.

The essential processes involved may be illustrated by reference to the simple Daniell cell, consisting of a zinc electrode immersed in dilute sulphuric acid (or acidulated zinc sulphate solution) and a copper electrode in copper sulphate solution, with a membrane through which ions can pass from one solution to the other (Fig. 4.13). At the former electrode Zn ions pass into solution, and at the latter copper ions are deposited; thus the effective chemical change is essentially

$$Zn^{++} + CuSO_4 \rightarrow ZnSO_4 + Cu^{++}.$$

The physical change at one electrode is the detachment of an ion from the surface of the metal and its passage into solution where it is surrounded by water molecules and becomes hydrated, and vice versa at the other electrode. This may be treated in the following schematic way. The potential energy curve of a positive ion near the surface

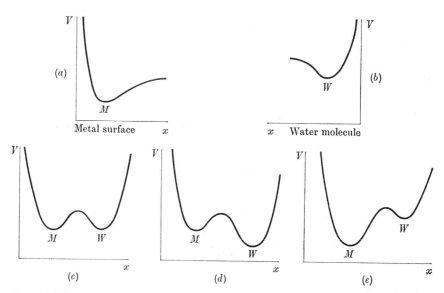

Fig. 4.14. Potential energy curves for a positive ion in the region of a metallic surface or a water molecule. The minima marked $M$ denote the equilibrium positions for the ion at the surface of the metal; those marked $W$, the equilibrium positions for the ion in the solution.

of the metal is roughly as shown in Fig. 4.14 (a); the steep rise to the left occurs when the ion overlaps with other ions in the metal lattice, when strong repulsive forces are set up, while the slow rise to the right is due to the image force attracting an ion just outside the metal back to the metal. The normal equilibrium position of the ion will be in the potential minimum. If we now take an isolated ion its potential energy curve as it approaches a water molecule will be of the type shown in Fig. 4.14 (b); at large distances there will be an attractive force due to induced polarization of the water molecule, while at short distances repulsive forces will be more important. For an ion at the surface of a metal immersed in a solution the combined potential energy curve will have one of the three forms shown in Fig. 4.14 (c), (d), and (e); in (c) ions can pass readily from metal to solution and vice versa, since the two potential minima are equal; in (d) an ion can only pass from the electrode into solution, while in (e) an ion can pass only from the solution to the electrode. With a single electrode in the solution the passage of charged ions in one direction or the other will quickly set up a reverse potential difference between electrode and solution, which displaces the two un-equal potential minima of situations (d) or (e) until we reach situation (c), the equilibrium situation.

If now two electrodes are placed in the solution and an external junc-tion is made between the metals, the usual contact potential difference is set up at the metal–metal contact because electrons can pass very much more readily across this contact than metal ions can move into and out of the solution. Electrons move across the metal–metal contact from the zinc to the copper (in our example), thereby lowering the electron energy levels in the zinc, but raising the positive ion levels in the zinc because of their opposite charge. The situation at the zinc–solution junction will therefore be as in (d), and zinc ions will pass into solution. The positive ion levels in the copper will be lowered and situation (e) will prevail at the copper-solution junction, copper ions being deposited on the electrode. At both these two junctions the move-ment of the metal ion is towards lower energy, and this makes available energy to drive the current round the circuit. Thus the contact potential difference plays an essential role in determining the direction of current flow, but the energy is derived from the chemical processes at each elec-trode. Since heats of reaction are additive it is not necessary to consider each chemical reaction in detail, and the available energy can be calcu-lated from the heat of reaction of the effective chemical change, the displacement of copper by zinc in the sulphate.

It is impossible to measure separately the potential difference set up at each electrode, but it is convenient to have one standard electrode against which the e.m.f. of other electrodes can be measured. This standard is the 'hydrogen electrode', consisting of a piece of platinum covered with platinum black saturated with hydrogen gas at atmospheric pressure. Each e.m.f. listed in Table 4.3 is measured for the hydrogen electrode against the metal electrode immersed in a standard solution. The e.m.f. developed in a cell with any two metal electrodes immersed in the standard solution is the algebraic difference of the potentials listed. Thus the e.m.f. of the Daniell cell, copper against zinc, is approximately $(0\cdot345+0\cdot762) = 1\cdot1$ V.

*Application of thermodynamics to voltaic cells*

Since in a reversible cell the chemical reactions taking place when a current is passed through it in one direction may be reversed by sending the current through it in the opposite direction, the standard equations of thermodynamics may be applied to the cell. In an ideal case we may suppose the current to be infinitely small so that Joule heat losses, which

TABLE 4.3

*Standard electrode potentials in volts, with respect to the hydrogen electrode, at 25° C*

| | | | |
|---|---|---|---|
| $Li^+$ | $-2 \cdot 959$ | $Sn^{+++}$ | $-0 \cdot 336$ |
| $Rb^+$ | $-2 \cdot 926$ | $Pb^{++}$ | $-0 \cdot 12$ |
| $K^+$ | $-2 \cdot 924$ | $Pt,H_2,H^+$ | $0 \cdot 0000$ |
| $Na^+$ | $-2 \cdot 715$ | $Cu^{++}$ | $+0 \cdot 345$ |
| $Zn^{++}$ | $-0 \cdot 762$ | $Hg^{++}$ | $+0 \cdot 799$ |
| $Fe^{++}$ | $-0 \cdot 44$ | $Ag^+$ | $+0 \cdot 798$ |
| $Cd^{++}$ | $-0 \cdot 402$ | | |

depend on the square of the current, can be made negligibly small in comparison with the chemical energy changes which vary with the first power of the current. Then the equation for the change in the free energy $F$ of a cell when a charge $Q$ is passed at constant temperature is

$$F = U + T(\partial F/\partial T)_V,$$

where $U$ is the change in internal energy and $F$ is the energy available for external work provided the cell volume is constant (i.e. no gases are liberated at the electrodes). If $V$ is the e.m.f. of the cell, then $F = VQ$, and we have

$$V = (U/Q) + T(\partial V/\partial T)$$
$$= h + T(\partial V/\partial T), \qquad (4.35)$$

where $h = U/Q$ is the heat of reaction when unit charge is passed. The reason why $VQ$ is not just equal to $U$ is because it may be necessary for the cell to exchange heat with its surroundings in order to remain at constant temperature, and this flow of heat may be related, by the second law of thermodynamics, to the temperature coefficient of the e.m.f.

## 4.8. Conduction of electricity through gases

Under perfect conditions a gas consists of uncharged molecules, and therefore behaves as an insulator since there are no charged particles present to carry a current. In practice, due to cosmic rays and radioactive background (especially in the walls of the containing vessel), there are always a few ions present, which are sufficient to initiate a spark discharge at sufficiently high electric fields (of the order of 30 000 V/cm in air at atmospheric pressure), but at low fields the current passing is negligibly small unless ions are deliberately produced in the gas, or electrons are liberated at one of the electrodes (the cathode). The essential distinction between the two cases is that at low fields the current is

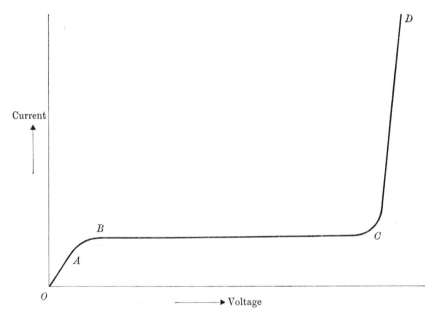

FIG. 4.15.  Current-voltage characteristic of a gas.

OA    Ohm's law is obeyed; most ions formed are lost by recombination.
BC    all ions formed are swept to electrodes before recombination can take place.
CD    fresh ions are formed by collision when electrons can reach the ionization potential of the gas molecules between collisions (Townsend discharge).

limited by the supply of ions through external action (X-rays or ultraviolet light releasing electrons from the electrodes or from the gas molecules) while at high fields new ions are created by collisions between charged particles (accelerated by the applied electric field) and neutral molecules. A typical current-voltage characteristic is shown in Fig. 4.15. At very low voltages the current is proportional to the voltage, but at higher voltages it rises less rapidly and reaches a constant value, independent of the voltage over a wide range.

At points on the initial part OA of this characteristic (corresponding to currents of $10^{-13}$–$10^{-14}$ A) the situation is analogous to that in an electrolytic solution, and equation (4.34) may be applied. The density of ions is determined by the equilibrium between the rate of formation by the X-rays and the rate of loss by recombination within the gas and diffusion to the walls. As the voltage increases the ions move proportionately faster and appreciable numbers are lost to the electrodes so that the ion density decreases. When the electric field reaches about 20 V/cm at atmospheric pressure, the ions reach the electrodes so quickly that practically none is lost by recombination. The current then becomes independent of the applied voltage, being limited solely by the rate of formation of ions by the X-rays. The saturation current is proportional to the number of X-rays incident on the gas, and so forms a convenient measure of the X-ray intensity.

The mobility of the ion is much greater than in a liquid, and may be estimated in the following way. After collision with a gas molecule the ion is initially moving in a random direction, and is then accelerated by the external field $E$. The average velocity acquired in the direction of the field can be determined in the same way as for the electrons in a metal (see equation (4.2)). It is $eE\tau/M$, where $\tau$ is the mean time between collisions, $e$ the charge on the ion and $M$ its mass, so that the mobility is

$$u = e\tau/M = el/Mv, \qquad (4.36)$$

where $l$ is the mean free path, and $v$ the random molecular velocity. For ions of molecular dimensions, $l$ and $v$ have the usual values given by kinetic theory: $l = 1/\sqrt{2}n\pi\sigma^2$, where $n$ is the number of molecules per unit volume of diameter $\sigma$; and $v = (8kT/\pi M)^{\frac{1}{2}}$, where $k$ is Boltzmann's constant and $T$ is the absolute temperature.

At atmospheric pressure, both positive and negative ions have mobilities of the order of a cm/sec per V/cm, in fair agreement with values calculated using equation (4.36). As the pressure is lowered, the mobility increases inversely with the density for positive ions, corresponding to the expected increase in mean free path, but for negative ions it increases much more rapidly. This is due to the fact that at low pressures most of the negative ions are electrons rather than heavy charged molecules. At a given pressure, the ratio of electrons to heavy negative ions varies markedly from gas to gas; some molecules, such as $Cl_2$, readily attach electrons to form negative ions, while others such as $H_2$ do not. The mobility of electrons is much greater than that of heavy ions, mainly owing to their small mass, but also partly due to their longer mean free paths. Since the diameter of an electron is negligible, its collision diameter with a gas molecule is only $\frac{1}{2}\sigma$, and since its velocity is much greater than that of the gas molecules the factor $\sqrt{2}$ introduced by Maxwell to allow for the relative velocities is absent, so that the electron mean free path is $4/n\pi\sigma^2$, or $4\sqrt{2}$ times that of a heavy ion. In addition, the average loss of energy by an electron in an elastic collision with a molecule is very small (see Problem 4.4), and the average energy of the electrons when a field is applied is much higher than that of the gas molecules or heavy ions. We may express this by saying that the 'mean temperature' of the electrons is higher than that of the gas. As the pressure is reduced, and the mean free path increases, the energy gained by an electron from the applied field increases and the effective electron temperature rises. The energy gained is proportional to the product of the mean free path and the applied field $E$, and since the mean free path is inversely proportional to the pressure $p$ it follows that the conditions are a function of $E/p$. At low values of $E/p$ the energy gained by an electron between collisions is small, and it makes only elastic collisions with the gas molecules, but at high values of $E/p$ the mean electron temperature rises and the number of electrons in the high energy tail of the energy distribution increases rapidly. Those which have a few electron volts of energy can make inelastic collisions in which most of the energy is transferred to the colliding molecule. The effect on the molecule will now be discussed.

On quantum theory the total energy, kinetic plus potential, of an electron bound in an atom can only have certain allowed values, and in the normal state the electrons in an atom are in the lowest allowed levels; this is the 'ground state' of the atom. The different energy levels can be plotted on an 'energy level diagram' (such as Fig. 20.2). The atom cannot exist with intermediate values of the energy, and if it is in an excited state (one of the higher energy levels) it may return to the ground state by emitting its excess energy as a quantum of light whose frequency $\nu$ is defined by the equation

$$W_1 - W_2 = h\nu. \tag{4.37}$$

For a molecule the energy level diagram is similar to but rather more complicated than that of an atom.

If an electron with sufficient energy collides with an atom or molecule in its ground state, it may transfer some of its kinetic energy to the molecule and raise it to an excited state. For this to be possible the electron must have at least as much energy as the difference between the ground state and the first excited state of the molecule, and the potential through which the electron must be accelerated to obtain this energy is called the 'resonance potential' of the molecule. In general the molecule will get rid of this extra energy by emitting a photon (light quantum) within about $10^{-8}$ sec, and the gas thus becomes luminous when the electrons gain sufficient energy from the applied electric field to raise the molecules into these excited states. As the energy of the electrons increases, the molecules are raised into higher excited states, corresponding to a bound electron being in an orbit of larger radius, and finally the molecule may be ionized; that is, an electron is completely removed, leaving the molecule as a positively-charged ion. The energy required to do this (expressed in electron volts) is called the ionization potential of the molecule. This process of ionization through electron impact increases the number of charged ions and electrons, and when the value of $E/p$ is large enough for it to occur, the current through the gas is greatly increased. The steep rise in current $CD$ with applied voltage shown after the saturation plateau $BC$ in Fig. 4.15 is due to the formation of ions by collision; it was extensively investigated by Townsend, and is known as the Townsend discharge. With specially designed electrodes the voltage in this region becomes almost independent of current, and small gas-filled tubes are used as voltage stabilizers.

Ionization by electron collision is the primary process in producing fresh ions in the body of the gas. Experiments have shown that collisions with positive ions are much less effective in causing ionization (owing to their shorter mean free paths, heavy ions pick up less energy from the applied field than electrons), and this process can be neglected in comparison. The most important secondary processes for producing further charged particles occur at the cathode, from which electrons are emitted under the action of (a) bombardment by positive ions, (b) the photo-electric effect caused by photons emitted by excited molecules, (c) bombardment by excited molecules. The relative importance of these three processes varies with the conditions; in general (a) is more important with cathode surfaces of high work function, and (b) with surfaces of low work function. The main type of excited molecules reaching the cathode are those in 'metastable states', i.e. molecules in certain excited states which cannot return to the ground state by emitting a photon, and so have much longer lives than the $10^{-8}$ sec mentioned above.

Secondary ionization processes occurring within the body of the gas, which (except at high pressure) appear to be less important than those at the cathode, are (d) photoionization, in which high energy photons emitted by one molecule are absorbed by another, and may have sufficient energy to ionize it. This occurs mostly with the high frequency ultraviolet radiation which is found in high voltage discharge tubes; (e) as the temperature of the gas rises owing to the conversion of electrical energy to heat energy through collisions between molecules and ions, neutral molecules may have sufficient kinetic energy of random motion to ionize other molecules by collision. This process is sometimes called thermal ionization.

*The Townsend discharge*

Suppose we have two plane parallel electrodes a distance $d$ apart and an electric field is applied between them. Let the negative electrode (the cathode) be illuminated with ultraviolet light which causes $n_0$ electrons to be emitted per second. These electrons are accelerated, and if the value of $E/p$ is sufficiently high, they will produce further ions by collision. If $n$ electrons cross a plane at a distance $x$ from the cathode per second, then the number formed by ionization in the next element of distance $dx$ will be proportional both to $n$ and $dx$, so that we can write

$$dn = C_1 n \, dx,$$

which on integration gives $n = n_0 e^{C_1 x}$, and the current at the anode is therefore

$$I = ne = n_0 e \cdot e^{C_1 d} = I_0 e^{C_1 d}, \tag{4.38}$$

where $I_0$ is the current due to the original $n_0$ electrons alone. For low currents this equation is in good agreement with experiment, but at high currents the current shoots up rapidly towards infinity. This is due to the secondary processes, which increase the supply of ions, principally by causing the emission of more electrons from the cathode. If now the total emission of electrons from the cathode is $n_0'$, the number of extra electrons produced in the gas by primary ionization must be $n_0'(e^{C_1 d} - 1)$, and this will also be the number of positive ions. The number of excited molecules emitting photons, and the number of molecules in excited states, will also be proportional to this number, and hence so also will be the number of secondary electrons emitted from the cathode, whatever the mechanism. Hence

$$n_0' = n_0 + C_2 n_0'(e^{C_1 d} - 1), \tag{4.39}$$

from which     $n_0'/n_0 = \{1 - C_2(e^{C_1 d} - 1)\}^{-1},$

and the total current will be

$$I = n_0' e \cdot e^{C_1 d} = I_0 \frac{e^{C_1 d}}{1 - C_2(e^{C_1 d} - 1)}. \tag{4.40}$$

The total current will become infinite when the denominator is zero, that is when

$$e^{C_1 d} = (C_2 + 1)/C_2. \tag{4.41}$$

This implies that a finite current will pass when this condition is satisfied, even if $I_0$ is zero. The voltage at which this occurs is known as the sparking or breakdown potential $V_s$. Experimentally it was discovered by Paschen that for a given gas $V_s$ depends only on the product $pd$ of the gas pressure $p$ and the electrode separation $d$. This is known as Paschen's law, and it holds up to very high pressures; it follows from the Townsend theory (above), for the constant $C_1$ is the number of ions produced by an electron in going unit distance. This number must be proportional

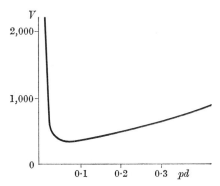

FIG. 4.16. Breakdown voltage $V$ for air plotted against $pd$. $V$ in volts, $p$ in cm of mercury, and $d$ in cm.

to the number of molecules per unit volume, and hence to the pressure, and it also depends on the average energy gained by an electron between collisions. This energy varies as $El$, where $l$ is the mean free path, and since $E = V/d$ and $l$ is inversely proportional to $p$, we have

$$C_1 d = (pd)F(V/pd), \tag{4.42}$$

where $F(V/pd)$ is some single-valued function of $(V/pd)$. Since $C_2$ is a constant it follows from equation (4.41) that the sparking potential $V_s$ is a function only of $pd$ for a given gas.

Inspection of equation (4.39) shows that when the condition of equation (4.41) is fulfilled, $C_2(e^{C_1 d}-1) = 1$; that is, the secondary processes produce all the electrons leaving the cathode. These electrons increase at an exponential rate, and the discharge current rises very rapidly (in a time of the order $10^{-7}$ sec at atmospheric pressure) and a spark passes. A typical curve for the variation of $V_s$ with the product (pressure × electrode separation) is shown in Fig. 4.16. The sharp rise at the low pressure end is due to the low density, when the chance of an electron encountering a molecule is small and few ions are formed by collision. In the high pressure region collisions are frequent, but the mean free path is small so that few electrons gain sufficient energy from the field between collisions to cause ionization. Thus for any given electrode separation $d$, there is always a certain pressure at which the sparking potential is a minimum.

Later work on the Townsend discharge (see Llewellyn Jones, 1953) shows that the theory given above holds over a very wide range of values of $pd$. At the higher pressures ($pd$ greater than about 20 cm Hg × cm and sparking potentials of 10–100 kV) positive ions cannot reach the cathode in the duration $\approx 10^{-7}$ sec found experimentally for a spark, and most of the secondary emission from the cathode is due to photons; however, cathode emission is then probably less important than ionization in the body of the gas. At pressures of the order of 100 atm, and with gaps of the order of centimetres, Paschen's law breaks down. This is due to the high fields at the cathode ($\sim 10^6$ V/cm), which cause appreciable field emission, a process which does not depend on the number of ions formed in the body of the gas, as assumed in equation (4.39). Since both field emission and photoelectric emission depend on the work function, the nature of the cathode surface becomes increasingly important at high pressures.

## 4.9. Plasma oscillations

Interest in gas discharge physics, under the modern title of plasma physics, has been renewed in the quest for thermonuclear power. A plasma may be defined as an assembly of charged and neutral particles in static or dynamic equilibrium, but this equilibrium may be disturbed locally. Suppose that at some instant a momentary excess of charge occurs in one region; the mutual repulsion of the charged particles pushes them apart, so that the excess quickly disappears. However, the velocity gained by the particles through their mutual repulsion may carry them too far, and the excess is replaced by a defect in the charge density, and the particles are attracted back. Repetition of this process sets up a periodic disturbance known as 'plasma oscillations'; these are a common feature of gas discharges (where they may be visible as striations), and electron or ion beams. We shall not discuss these phenomena (which are very complex), but content ourselves with a simple derivation of the frequency of such oscillations.

In a gas at low pressure the relative permittivity may be taken as unity, so that from Gauss's theorem (equation 1.20) we have

$$\epsilon_0 \operatorname{div} \mathbf{E} = \rho. \tag{4.43}$$

Through the movement of charges a drift current $\mathbf{J} = \rho\mathbf{v}$ occurs, and the conservation of charge as expressed in the continuity equation (3.3) gives

$$-d\rho/dt = \operatorname{div} \mathbf{J} = \operatorname{div}(\rho\mathbf{v}). \tag{4.44}$$

Differentiation of equation (4.43) gives, together with equation (4.44),

$$\epsilon_0 \, \text{div}(d\mathbf{E}/dt) = -\text{div}(\rho \mathbf{v})$$

or
$$\epsilon_0 \dot{\mathbf{E}} = -\rho \mathbf{v} = -\mathbf{J}, \qquad (4.45)$$

where the constant of integration is zero since in the absence of particle movement ($v = 0$) the time derivative of the electric field is also zero.

In a plasma where both positive and negative ions are present, the negative ions are mostly electrons which move very much more rapidly than the more massive ionized atoms, and we can assume that all the current is carried by electrons; i.e. by one type of particle, of mass $m$ and charge $q$. The equation of motion of these particles is $m\dot{\mathbf{v}} = q\mathbf{E}$, so that (using equation (4.45))

$$d\mathbf{J}/dt = \rho\dot{\mathbf{v}} = (\rho q/m)\mathbf{E},$$
$$d^2\mathbf{J}/dt^2 = (\rho q/m)\dot{\mathbf{E}} = -(\rho q/m\epsilon_0)\mathbf{J}.$$

If we assume that oscillations are of vanishingly small amplitude, the departure of $\rho$ from its mean value $\bar{n}q$, where $\bar{n}$ is the average number per unit volume, is negligible, and we can write

$$d^2\mathbf{J}/dt^2 = -(\bar{n}q^2/m\epsilon_0)\mathbf{J}. \qquad (4.46)$$

This is the equation of simple harmonic motion, showing that the current will oscillate at a frequency

$$2\pi f_p = (\bar{n}q^2/m\epsilon_0)^{\frac{1}{2}}. \qquad (4.47)$$

This is known as the plasma frequency. We can estimate its magnitude by taking as an example a plasma of fully ionized hydrogen at a pressure of $10^{-5}$ atm ($0{\cdot}0076$ mm Hg), for which $\bar{n} = 2{\cdot}7 \times 10^{20}$ per cubic metre. Then

$$f_p = (\bar{n}e^2/4\pi^2\epsilon_0 m)^{\frac{1}{2}}$$
$$= 9{\cdot}0\bar{n}^{\frac{1}{2}}$$
$$= 1{\cdot}5 \times 10^{11}. \qquad (4.48)$$

This frequency corresponds to a wavelength of 2 mm for electromagnetic waves, and its measurement is an important tool in plasma physics since it gives the density of electrons. In ordinary gas discharges the degree of ionization is relatively low, and the plasma frequency may lie in the region $10^3$ to $10^8$ c/s. In metals, on the other hand, the electron density is very much higher, and the plasma frequency is about $10^{15}$ c/s.

## REFERENCES

BORELIUS, G., KEESOM, W. H., and JOHANSSON, C. H., 1928, *Proc. Acad. Sci. Amsterdam*, **31**, 1046.

CRAIG, D. N., and HOFFMAN, J. I., 1950, *Phys. Rev.* **80**, 487.

CUSACK, N., 1958, *The Electrical and Magnetic Properties of Solids* (Longmans, Green).

JAIN, S. C., and KRISHNAN, K. S., 1953, *Proc. Roy. Soc.* A, **217**, 451.
LLEWELLYN JONES, F., 1953, *Ann. Rep. Progr. Phys.* (Physical Society, London), **16**, 216.
MITCHELL, E. W. J., and MITCHELL, J. W., 1951, *Proc. Roy. Soc.* A, **210**, 70.
SHOCKLEY, W., 1950, *Electrons and Holes in Semiconductors* (Van Nostrand).
SLATER, J. C., 1939, *Introduction to Chemical Physics* (McGraw-Hill).
WILKS, J., 1961, *The Third Law of Thermodynamics* (O.U.P.).
ZEMANSKY, M. W., 1957, *Heat and Thermodynamics* (McGraw-Hill).

## PROBLEMS

**4.1.** It is found that the thermoelectric power $dV/dt$ of a copper–nickel thermocouple in the range $0°$ C to $100°$ C can be expressed as $20·4 + 0·0450t \, \mu V/°C$, where $t$ is the centigrade temperature measured on a particular hydrogen gas thermometer. The Peltier coefficient can be expressed as $1330 + 7·78t + 0·0107t^2 \, \mu cal/$ coulomb. Verify that in this thermometer the hydrogen behaves as a perfect gas, and deduce the absolute temperature of the ice-point.

**4.2.** Find the equation of motion of a free electron in an electric field $E = E_0 \sin \omega t$.

If the field strength $E_0$ is $10^4$ V/metre, and the frequency is 100 Mc/s, show that the amplitude of oscillation of the electron is $0·0045$ m and that its maximum energy is $22·5$ eV.

**4.3.** A spark passes between two electrodes 1 cm apart in air at atmospheric pressure when a uniform field of 10 kV/cm is applied across the gap. If the mean free path of an oxygen molecule in air is $6 \times 10^{-6}$ cm show that the time required for a singly ionized oxygen molecule to cross the gap is $4·5 \times 10^{-5}$ sec.

**4.4.** An electron of mass $m$ collides with a molecule of mass $M$. Show that if the molecule is stationary the fraction of the electron energy which is transferred to the molecule in a head-on collision is $4Mm/(m+M)^2$ and evaluate this for the case $M = 200 \times$ mass of the proton.

(*Answer:* $\approx 1·1 \times 10^{-5}$.)

**4.5.** Calculate the neutral temperature $(t = -\alpha/\beta)$ for the thermocouples copper/iron and platinum/platinum-rhodium.

(*Answer:* $+276$ and $-255°$ C.)

**4.6.** Use equation (4.20) to show that the temperature coefficient $(dW_F/dT)$ for tungsten $(W_F = 5·8 \text{ eV})$ at $3000°$ K is about $-0·6 \times 10^{-5}$ eV per degree. $W_F$ will also vary because of thermal expansion, since the number of electrons per unit volume changes. If $\alpha$ is the linear coefficient of expansion, show that

$$dW_F/dT = -2\alpha W_F.$$

For tungsten at $3000°$ K, $\alpha$ is about $6 \times 10^{-6}$, from which $dW_F/dT = -7 \times 10^{-5}$ eV per degree, showing that the effect of expansion is considerably more important than the second term in equation (4.20).

**4.7.** Calculate the value of the absolute thermoelectric power $S$ for gold from equation (4.28), taking $W_F = 5·5$ eV, and compare it with the value obtained from Table 4.2, at $273°$ K.

(*Answer:* $-1·9$ and $+2·7 \, \mu V/$deg.)

# 5

## THE MAGNETIC EFFECTS OF CURRENTS AND MOVING CHARGES, AND MAGNETOSTATICS

### 5.1. Forces between currents

THE first experimental investigation of the interaction between coils carrying electric currents was performed by Ampère during the years 1820–5, and the work was continued by Oersted, Biot, and Savart. They found that two long parallel wires carrying currents in opposite directions repel one another, whereas when carrying currents in the same direction they attract one another, so that the direction of the force is reversed when the current is reversed. Ampère used circular coils, the leads to the coils being twisted together, and as these leads each carried equal currents in opposite directions they exerted no force on other circuits, and any forces observed were due only to the coils. He found that, if the dimensions of the coils were small compared with their distance apart, one coil exerts a force and a couple on another coil exactly similar to the force and couple which one electric dipole exerts on another. The magnitude of this force and couple is proportional to the current through the coil, the number of turns, and the area. If the plane of each coil is normal to the line joining the centre of each coil, the force is along this line. It is found also that if a coil carrying a current is placed near a magnet it experiences both a force and a couple. At distances large compared with the dimensions of either coil or magnet, this force and couple are similar in nature to those due to a second coil carrying a current. Thus both a magnet and a current-carrying coil are said to produce a magnetic induction **B**, which exerts forces on other coils or magnets. **B** is a vector quantity and lines of **B** can be drawn whose direction at any point is that of **B**, in the same way as lines of electric force are drawn in an electric field. The strength of **B** is shown by making the number of lines per unit area normal to **B** numerically equal to the value of **B**.

The force exerted on an element of wire $\mathbf{ds}_1$ carrying a current $I_1$ at a place where the magnetic induction is **B** can be expressed in the simple form (see Fig. 5.1)

$$\mathbf{dF} = I_1(\mathbf{ds}_1 \wedge \mathbf{B}). \tag{5.1}$$

This equation then defines the unit of magnetic induction as that amount of induction which exerts unit force on unit length of a wire carrying one unit of current. In the m.k.s.a. system, the unit of force is the newton, that of length the metre, and the unit of current the ampere. The unit of **B** is then newtons (ampere metre)$^{-1}$; we shall see later that this can be expressed as weber/metre$^2$ (see § 5.5) and this is the more usual term for the unit.

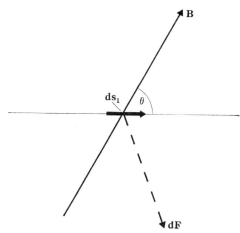

FIG. 5.1. Diagram to illustrate equation (5.1). $ds_1$ and **B** are in the plane of the paper, the angle between them being $\theta$. **dF** is normal to the paper, towards the reader, and has magnitude $ds_1 B \sin \theta$.

The experiments of Ampère and others showed that the force on an element **ds**$_1$ carrying a current $I_1$ due to another element **ds**$_2$ carrying a current $I_2$ is

$$\mathbf{dF}_1 = \frac{\mu_0 I_1 I_2}{4\pi r^3} \{\mathbf{ds}_1 \wedge (\mathbf{ds}_2 \wedge \mathbf{r})\}, \qquad (5.2)$$

where $\mu_0$ is a constant. **r** is the vector joining the two elements, being positive when drawn from **ds**$_2$ to **ds**$_1$, as in Fig. 5.2. The force **dF**$_2$ on the element **ds**$_2$ due to **ds**$_1$ is given by a similar expression with **ds**$_1$ and **ds**$_2$ interchanged, and **r** must then be taken as positive when drawn from **ds**$_1$ to **ds**$_2$. The directions of the forces for the special case of two coplanar elements are shown in Fig. 5.2, and it will be seen that they are not equal and opposite unless the current elements are parallel. This apparent violation of Newton's third law of motion has caused much discussion, but Page and Adams (1945) have shown that there is no real violation, since the electromagnetic field of the current elements possesses momentum which is changing at a rate just equal to the difference of the two forces. Ampère's original formulation of the law of force between two current elements was different from equation (5.2), but gave the correct result when integrated over a closed circuit carrying a constant current.

Comparison of equations (5.1) and (5.2) shows that we may say that

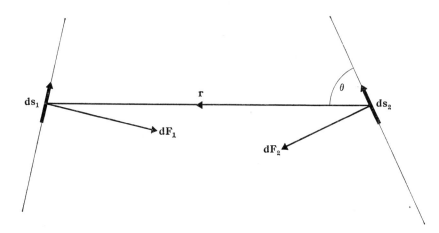

Fig. 5.2. Diagram showing the direction of the forces between two current elements. $\mathbf{ds_1}$ and $\mathbf{ds_2}$ are in the plane of the paper. The vector $(\mathbf{ds_2}\wedge\mathbf{r})$ is normal to the plane of the paper, and the vector $\{\mathbf{ds_1}\wedge(\mathbf{ds_2}\wedge\mathbf{r})\}$ is in the plane of the paper, normal to $\mathbf{ds_1}$. The magnetic field $\mathbf{dB}$ due to $\mathbf{ds_2}$ is parallel to $(\mathbf{ds_2}\wedge\mathbf{r})$, and the force $\mathbf{dF_1}$ on $\mathbf{ds_1}$ due to it is parallel to $\{\mathbf{ds_1}\wedge(\mathbf{ds_2}\wedge\mathbf{r})\}$.

the current $I_2$ in the element $\mathbf{ds_2}$ produces a magnetic induction $\mathbf{dB}$ at a distance $\mathbf{r}$ given by the formula

$$\mathbf{dB} = \left(\frac{\mu_0}{4\pi r^3}\right) I_2(\mathbf{ds_2} \wedge \mathbf{r}). \tag{5.3}$$

These equations may be used to calculate the field $\mathbf{B}$ produced by a current in an infinite straight wire, and hence the force between currents in two parallel infinite straight wires. In Fig. 5.3 we have two such wires a distance $a$ apart, carrying currents $I_1$, $I_2$; we choose a coordinate system where the first wire lies along the $z$-axis, and the second is parallel to it but passes through the point $x = a$, $y = 0$. We first calculate the field $\mathbf{B}$ at the point $(0, 0, 0)$ due to the current $I_2$ in the second wire, using equation (5.3). Then the element $\mathbf{ds_2}$ has components $(dx, dy, dz) = (0, 0, dz)$ and $\mathbf{r}$ has components $(-a, 0, -z)$ since it is defined by the coordinates of the point $(0, 0, 0)$ relative to the point $A(a, 0, z)$ at which $\mathbf{ds_2}$ is placed. Then the components of $(\mathbf{ds_2} \wedge \mathbf{r})$ are $(0, -a\,dz, 0)$, showing that $\mathbf{dB}$ at $O$ is antiparallel to the $y$-axis, wherever the point $A$ lies along the second wire. Hence $\mathbf{B} = \int \mathbf{dB}$ will also be antiparallel to the $y$-axis, so that $B_x = B_z = 0$, and integration yields for $B_y$ the result

$$B_y = \frac{\mu_0 I_2}{4\pi} \int_{-\infty}^{+\infty} \frac{-a\,dz}{(a^2+z^2)^{\frac{3}{2}}} = -\frac{\mu_0 I_2}{4\pi a} \int_{-\frac{1}{2}\pi}^{+\frac{1}{2}\pi} \cos\theta\,d\theta = -\frac{\mu_0 I_2}{2\pi a}, \quad (5.4)$$

where we have used the substitution $z = a\tan\theta$. Equation (5.4) shows that the field of a current $I_2$ in an infinite wire is proportional to $I_2$ and

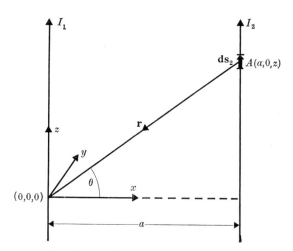

FIG. 5.3. Parallel wires carrying currents.

inversely proportional to the distance $a$ from the wire. **B** is normal to the plane containing the wire and the radius vector **r**, so that lines of constant $B$ form closed circles centred on the wire.

We can now use equation (5.1) to find the force **dF** on an element **ds**$_1$ of the first wire. Since **B** is in the $y$-direction, and **ds**$_1$ in the $z$-direction, the force is in the $x$-direction, its only component being

$$dF_x = \frac{\mu_0 I_1 I_2 ds_1}{2\pi a}. \quad (5.5)$$

If the currents are in the same direction the force is one of attraction, if the currents are opposed the force is one of repulsion, as stated above.

The value of the constant $\mu_0$ depends on the system of units employed. In the electromagnetic system $\mu_0/4\pi$ is taken to be unity, the force in dynes, and the distance in centimetres. This gives a c.g.s. system, where the unit of current may be defined by the use of equation (5.5), being that current which, flowing in a straight infinite wire at a distance of 1 cm from a parallel wire carrying an equal current, produces a force of

2 dynes per centimetre length. Similarly, 1 electromagnetic unit (1 gauss) of magnetic field **B** exerts a force of 1 dyne on 1 cm of a conductor carrying 1 electromagnetic unit of current (1 gauss $= 10^{-4}$ weber/metre$^2$). In the m.k.s.a. system, the forces are in newtons and lengths in metres, and the currents in absolute amperes. Hitherto we have regarded the ampere (or coulomb, since 1 A is a current of 1 coulomb/sec) as a standard of current (or charge) defined in some arbitrary way, similar to the kilogramme and metre. The value of $\mu_0$ is then a constant to be determined. In practice $\mu_0$ is defined to be exactly $4\pi \times 10^{-7}$ (newton/ampere$^2$) since this makes the unit of current exactly equal to one-tenth of the old electromagnetic unit, and hence equal to the practical unit (the ampere) as generally used in the past. Equation (5.5) then shows that for two parallel wires 1 metre apart, each carrying 1 ampere of current, the force per metre length of wire is $2 \times 10^{-7}$ newtons. This may be regarded as a convenient way of defining the ampere. The quantity $\mu_0$ is known as the 'permeability of free space' (see § 5.4), and its unit is generally called the henry/metre (see § 6.2) rather than newton/ampere$^2$; the two units are equivalent.

### 5.2. Magnetic shells

The investigations of Ampère of the forces between two small coils showed that they were similar to those between two dipoles. Comparison with equation (1.14) shows that we should expect such a dipole, if placed in a uniform field, to experience a couple, and we shall now derive this couple by use of equation (5.1). A small plane coil is placed in a region of uniform magnetic induction **B**. We divide the area of the coil into thin strips, as in Fig. 5.4, by drawing lines parallel to the $x$-axis, which is taken to be the projection of **B** on the plane of the coil. The current $I$ flowing round the coil may be regarded as made up of a current $I$ flowing round each of the rectangular strips in the same sense; for there is then flowing along each line such as $CD$ two currents, from neighbouring strips, of opposite sign so that they annul, leaving only the current along the periphery. In order to compute the forces on the strip $CDEF$ we resolve **B** into a component $B\cos\theta$ normal to the plane of the strip (where $\theta$ is the angle between **B** and this normal) and a component $B\sin\theta$ in the plane, parallel to the $x$-axis. The force on each side of the strip due to the normal component $B\cos\theta$ is in the plane of the coil, normal to the side and proportional to the length of the side. It is readily seen that they form a set of forces in equilibrium, for they can be drawn as a set of vectors forming a closed figure similar to the strip, turned through a right angle. The forces due to the component $B \sin \theta$ are zero on $CD$ and $EF$, while those on $DE$ and $FC$ are proportional to the projections of these elements on the $y$-axis (being thus equal and opposite), and normal to the plane of the coil. They therefore form a couple of magnitude $I \times CD \times \delta y \times B \sin \theta$ tending to turn the coil about

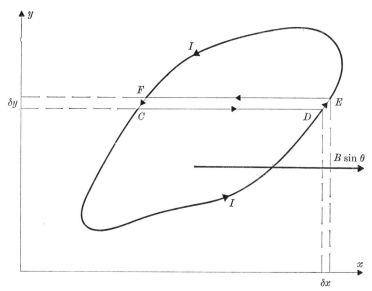

Fig. 5.4. Diagram showing the couple on a current circuit due to a field of magnetic induction **B** which makes an angle $\theta$ with the normal to the plane of the circuit, and whose projection on the plane is parallel to the $x$-axis.

the $y$-axis; but $(CD \times \delta y)$ is the area of the strip, which can be represented by a vector **dS** normal to the plane, whose sense is that of a right-handed screw turned in the direction of the current. The couple can then be written in the form

$$d\mathbf{\Gamma} = I\,\mathbf{dS} \wedge \mathbf{B} = \mathbf{dm} \wedge \mathbf{B}, \tag{5.6}$$

where

$$\mathbf{dm} = I\,\mathbf{dS} \tag{5.7}$$

is defined as the magnetic dipole moment of the strip $CDEF$. The couple acting on the whole plane coil is proportional to the area, and so also is the moment of the equivalent dipole. That is,

$$\mathbf{\Gamma} = \mathbf{m} \wedge \mathbf{B}, \tag{5.8}$$

$$\mathbf{m} = I\mathbf{S}. \tag{5.9}$$

Comparison of equation (5.8) with equation (1.14) shows that it is of the same form, the magnetic field **B** playing the same role as the electric field **E**. We may therefore expect that it can be written as the gradient of a scalar potential $\phi$, so that

$$\mathbf{B} = -\mu_0 \operatorname{grad} \phi. \tag{5.10}$$

Although the derivation above was given for a plane coil, it is clear that a coil of any shape can be divided up in the same way (as in Fig. 5.5) by using any surface which is bounded by the circuit formed by the coil.

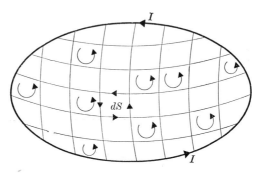

FIG. 5.5. A large coil divided into a number of small magnetic shells.

Each element of area $dS$ may be regarded as having a current $I$ flowing round its edge, and summation of the currents in all the elements comprising the entire surface leaves only the current in the circuit as the resultant. If $dS$ is taken as infinitesimal in both directions, rather than the narrow strip assumed above, it can be regarded as a plane element and will have an associated magnetic dipole moment given by equation (5.7), and the couple on the whole circuit is obtained by integration of equation (5.6). The surface forms a magnetic 'double layer', or 'magnetic shell', with a certain dipole moment per unit area. The potential due to such a shell will now be calculated using equation (5.3).

The field at a point $P$ due to the current circuit is found by integration of equation (5.3) round the circuit. In Fig. 5.6 if the point $P$ is displaced a distance $\delta\mathbf{s}$ the change in potential will be

$$\delta\phi = -\frac{1}{\mu_0}\mathbf{B}.\,\delta\mathbf{s} = -I\,\delta\mathbf{s}.\int \frac{(\mathbf{da} \wedge \mathbf{r})}{4\pi r^3} = -I\int \frac{\delta\mathbf{s}.(\mathbf{da} \wedge \mathbf{r})}{4\pi r^3}, \tag{5.11}$$

where $\delta\mathbf{s}$ can be taken inside the integral sign because it is a constant during the integration. It is clear that we should obtain the same change in potential if the point $P$ were kept fixed and the circuit were displaced by an amount $-\delta\mathbf{s}$. In such a displacement the circuit element **da** sweeps out an area $-(\delta \mathbf{s} \wedge \mathbf{da})$, and this area subtends a solid angle at the point $P$ of

$$-\frac{\mathbf{r}.(\delta \mathbf{s} \wedge \mathbf{da})}{r^3} = -\frac{\delta \mathbf{s}.(\mathbf{da} \wedge \mathbf{r})}{r^3}.$$

Hence the line integral in equation (5.11) is the total solid angle subtended at $P$ by the area swept out by the circuit when it is displaced

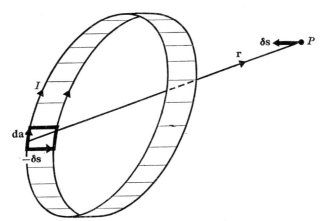

Fig. 5.6. Displacement of a current element, in order to calculate the potential at $P$ due to a magnetic shell.

by $-\delta \mathbf{s}$, and this is equal to the change $\delta \omega$ in the solid angle due to the displacement of $P$ by $\delta \mathbf{s}$. Hence we may write the change in potential as

$$\delta \phi = I \frac{\delta \omega}{4\pi},$$

and the potential at $P$ is

$$\phi = \frac{I\omega}{4\pi}, \tag{5.12}$$

where $\omega$ is the solid angle which the circuit subtends at $P$. But

$$\omega = \int \frac{\mathbf{dS}.\mathbf{r}}{r^3},$$

where $\mathbf{dS}$ is an element of area of any surface bounded by the circuit, and hence

$$\phi = \int \frac{I \mathbf{dS}.\mathbf{r}}{4\pi r^3} = \int \frac{\mathbf{dm}.\mathbf{r}}{4\pi r^3}. \tag{5.13}$$

Here the integration is over the surface of the magnetic shell, and the potential of an individual dipole $\mathbf{m}$ must therefore be

$$\phi = \frac{\mathbf{m}.\mathbf{r}}{4\pi r^3}. \tag{5.14}$$

This is of the same form as equation (1.10 b), except that $\mu_0$, which we might expect to replace the constant $\epsilon_0$, does not occur here but in equation (5.10). The reason for this choice will appear later (see equation (5.28)).

The quantity $\phi$ is related to the line integral of **B** between two points, since

$$\int \mathbf{B}.\mathbf{ds} = -\mu_0 \int \operatorname{grad}\phi.\mathbf{ds} = -\mu_0\phi. \tag{5.15}$$

By analogy with electromotive force, which is the line integral of **E** (see equation (3.12)), the quantity $-\phi$ is sometimes known as the 'magneto-motive force', or m.m.f.

In the electrostatic case, the work done in traversing a closed circuit is zero, and this would also be the case for a true magnetic double layer. If we take the integral $\int \mathbf{B}.\mathbf{ds}$ from a point $P$ very close to a magnetic shell round to a point $P'$ just on the other side of the magnetic shell, the difference in the solid angle which the shell subtends at these two points is $-4\pi$, and the m.m.f. between these two points is

$$-\Delta\phi = -I\,\Delta\omega/4\pi = I,$$

from equation (5.12). With a real magnetic shell, if we now move from $P'$ to $P$ through the shell, there would be a contribution to the m.m.f. which would just make the total zero, but with a current circuit there is no such contribution. We have therefore an important difference, that the m.m.f. increases by $I$ every time we go round a closed path which threads the coil positively (i.e. in the same direction as the lines of **B**). Thus the magnetostatic potential is not single-valued and cannot be used in a region where there are currents flowing. On the other hand, if the path does not thread a current circuit, the change in solid angle is zero, and the potential is single-valued. If the path does encircle a current $i$, we have

$$\oint \mathbf{B}.\mathbf{ds} = \mu_0 I. \tag{5.16}$$

In a region of distributed current flow, the total current threaded by the path is $\int \mathbf{J}.\mathbf{dS}$, where **J** is the current density in an element **dS** of a surface bounded by the path. Hence

$$\oint \mathbf{B}.\mathbf{ds} = \int \operatorname{curl}\mathbf{B}.\mathbf{dS} = \mu_0 \int \mathbf{J}.\mathbf{dS},$$

where the transformation from a line integral of **B** to a surface integral of curl **B** is an example of Stokes's theorem (see Appendix A). Since the integrals must be equal over any surface, the integrands must be equal, and we have

$$\operatorname{curl}\mathbf{B} = \mu_0\mathbf{J}. \tag{5.17}$$

Equation (5.16) is known as Ampère's law, and equation (5.17) is its representation in differential form. Since any function such as curl(grad $\phi$) is identically zero (see Appendix A), we note again that **B** can only be derived from a scalar potential $\phi$ in a region where $\mathbf{J} = 0$.

## 5.3. Magnetostatics and magnetic media

The theory so far has been concerned with the magnetic effects of currents *in vacuo*, i.e. in the absence of any magnetizable media. It is found experimentally that a material substance acquires a magnetic polarization when placed in a magnetic field, just as a dielectric medium acquires an electric polarization in an electric field. The magnetic dipole per unit volume of the material is called the intensity of magnetization (or often, simply the magnetization), and is represented by a vector **M**. All such magnetic effects are produced by current loops of atomic dimensions, which arise from the circulation of electric charge within the atom. The relation between the magnetic moment of such a loop and the circulating current is given by equation (5.9). If a magnetic medium has a magnetization **M**, which is not necessarily uniform throughout the substance, the equivalent current flow can be found by considering elementary current loops, as in Fig. 5.5. There the currents were all equal, and cancelled one another except at the perimeter, but in general this will not be the case. In Fig. 5.7 both **M** and $I$ are functions of the space coordinates. We consider an element of volume $d\tau = dxdydz$ at the point $(x, y, z)$, for which the magnetic moment has a component $M_z dxdydz$ in the $z$-direction. This is equivalent to a current flowing round the loop, the strength of the current being

$$I = (M_z dxdydz)/(dxdy) = M_z dz,$$

since the area of the loop is $dxdy$. The adjacent loop at the point $(x+dx, y, z)$ has a current

$$I' = I + (\partial I/\partial x) dx = M_z dz + (\partial M_z/\partial x) dxdz.$$

Hence the net current flow on the interface between the two elements has a component in the $y$-direction of magnitude

$$I - I' = -(\partial M_z/\partial x) dxdz$$

and if **J** is the current density, this component must equal $J_y dxdz$. By considering similar current loops in the $yz$-plane, we find there is another current component in the $y$-direction of magnitude $(\partial M_x/\partial z) dxdz$ associated with th ecomponent of magnetization $M_x$. Hence the total $y$-component of the current density is $J_y = (\partial M_x/\partial z) - (\partial M_z/\partial x)$, with similar expressions for the other components of **J**. These are the components of the vector curl $\mathbf{M}$, so that we can write for the current density $\mathbf{J}_m$ associated with a magnetization $\mathbf{M}$

$$\mathbf{J}_m = \operatorname{curl}\mathbf{M}. \tag{5.18}$$

It follows that if $\mathbf{M}$ is uniform in space, $\mathbf{J}_m = 0$, so that an equivalent current flow exists only in regions where $\mathbf{M}$ is varying.

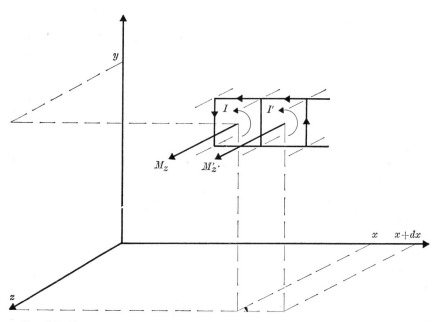

Fig. 5.7. Representation of a non-uniform magnetization by circulating currents.

$$M_z' = M_z + \frac{\partial M_z}{\partial x}\,dx.$$

In a medium which is both electrically conducting and magnetizable, the total current density will be the sum of the real current density $\mathbf{J}$ and the equivalent magnetization current density $\mathbf{J}_m$, both of which must be counted in Ampère's law. Hence equation (5.17), which was derived for a vacuum, must be replaced by

$$\operatorname{curl}\mathbf{B} = \mu_0(\mathbf{J} + \mathbf{J}_m) = \mu_0(\mathbf{J} + \operatorname{curl}\mathbf{M}),$$

or

$$\operatorname{curl}(\mathbf{B} - \mu_0\mathbf{M}) = \mu_0\mathbf{J}. \tag{5.19}$$

This is the form which Ampère's law takes in the presence of a magnetizable medium, and the quantity $(\mathbf{B} - \mu_0\mathbf{M})$, whose curl is related to the flow of real current, is used to define a new vector such that $\mathbf{B} - \mu_0\mathbf{M} = \mu_0\mathbf{H}$, or

$$\mathbf{B} = \mu_0(\mathbf{H} + \mathbf{M}). \tag{5.20}$$

Then Ampère's law takes the simple form

$$\operatorname{curl} \mathbf{H} = \mathbf{J}, \tag{5.21}$$

which is more general than equation (5.17), since it holds both *in vacuo* and in a medium. Obviously, *in vacuo* $\mathbf{B} = \mu_0 \mathbf{H}$, so that equation (5.17) is a special case of (5.21), which is the general differential form of Ampère's law. Similarly, equation (5.16) must be replaced by the more general equation

$$\int \mathbf{H}.\mathbf{ds} = \int \operatorname{curl} \mathbf{H}.\mathbf{dS} = \int \mathbf{J}.\mathbf{dS} = I. \tag{5.22}$$

It is clear from this equation that the dimensions of $\mathbf{H}$ must be amperes per metre, since the line integral of $\mathbf{H}$ round a circuit is equal to the total current threading the circuit. From equation (5.20), $\mathbf{M}$ must have the same dimensions as $\mathbf{H}$, and this can be readily verified, since $\mathbf{M} =$ magnetic moment per unit volume, and magnetic moment $=$ current $\times$ area, from equation (5.9).

The process by which we have introduced a new vector $\mathbf{H}$ in modifying our equations to allow for the presence of a polarizable medium is analogous to that in electrostatics, where a new vector $\mathbf{D}$ was introduced. There, this vector followed from the modification of Gauss's theorem needed in the presence of a polarizable medium; the force vector $\mathbf{E}$ is related by Gauss's theorem to the sum of the real charge density and the polarization charge density, and the advantage of $\mathbf{D}$ is that div $\mathbf{D}$ is related only to the real charge density. In the magnetic case, the force vector $\mathbf{B}$ is related by Ampère's law to the sum of the real current density and the magnetization current density, and the advantage of $\mathbf{H}$ is that curl $\mathbf{H}$ is determined only by the real current density.

We return now to equation (5.3) to derive an important relation for div $\mathbf{B}$. For a volume distribution of current, this equation may be written

$$\mathbf{dB} = \frac{\mu_0}{4\pi} \left( \frac{\mathbf{J} \wedge \mathbf{r}}{r^3} \right) d\tau = -\frac{\mu_0}{4\pi} \left( \mathbf{J} \wedge \operatorname{grad} \frac{1}{r} \right) d\tau. \tag{5.23}$$

To find $\mathbf{dB}$ we must remember that we are dealing with a fixed current density in the volume element $d\tau$ and deriving a relation concerning the way in which $\mathbf{dB}$ at a distance $r$ from the element $d\tau$ varies with $r$. Any differentiation with respect to the space coordinates is a partial differentiation operating on $r$ and not on $\mathbf{J}$. Thus in such a differentiation, curl $\mathbf{J} = 0$ and using the last equation of § A.7 we have

$$\operatorname{div} \mathbf{dB} = -\frac{\mu_0 \, d\tau}{4\pi} \operatorname{div} \left( \mathbf{J} \wedge \operatorname{grad} \frac{1}{r} \right) = -\mathbf{J}.\operatorname{curl}\left( \operatorname{grad} \frac{1}{r} \right).$$

Since curl grad$(1/r) = 0$ (§ A.7), we have div $\mathbf{dB} = 0$, and if this is true for the contribution $\mathbf{dB}$ from any volume element $d\tau$, it must be true also for the sum of all such contributions. Hence we can write

$$\text{div } \mathbf{B} = 0. \tag{5.24}$$

This relation has been derived only for a current *in vacuo*. However, we have shown that any magnetization $\mathbf{M}$ present can be replaced by

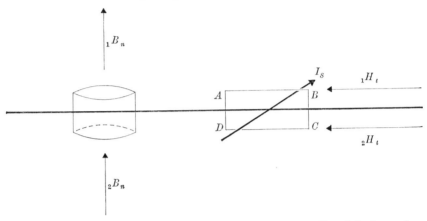

Fig. 5.8. Boundary conditions at the surface between two media. $I_s$ is the surface current per unit width normal to the plane of the circuit $ABCDA$.

an equivalent current density $\mathbf{J}_m$ for which it will also be true that div $\mathbf{B} = 0$. Hence equation (5.24) holds also in a magnetizable medium.

This equation is similar to that derived for div $\mathbf{D}$ in electrostatics, except that div $\mathbf{D} = \rho_e$, where $\rho_e$ is the density of true electric charge, while div $\mathbf{B} = 0$ because we have no true magnetic charges. Again, as in electrostatics, we can use Gauss's theorem applied to an elementary flat box surrounding the boundary between two magnetic media as in Fig. 5.8 to show that $\int \mathbf{B}.\mathbf{dS} = 0$ over the surface of the box. If the height of the box is very small compared with its cross-section, the only contributions to $\int \mathbf{B}.\mathbf{dS}$ come from the components of $\mathbf{B}$ normal to the boundary. Hence we have

$$_1B_n = {_2}B_n. \tag{5.25}$$

The boundary conditions for $\mathbf{H}$ are found by using Ampère's law applied to a small rectangular circuit $ABCDA$ whose sides $BC$, $AD$ are very small compared with $AB$, $CD$. If there is a surface current $I_s$ per unit length of the surface normal to the circuit, then equation (5.22) leads immediately to the result

$$_1H_t - {_2}H_t = I_s. \tag{5.26}$$

If there is no surface current,

$$_1H_t - _2H_t = 0, \tag{5.27}$$

showing that the tangential components of **H** are continuous, while from equation (5.25) the normal components of **B** are continuous. These boundary conditions are similar to those in electrostatics, but note that the formal equivalence here is between **B** and **D**, and between **H** and **E**. This equivalence can be carried a stage further, since if no currents are present, we have curl **H** = 0, and we can therefore write

$$\mathbf{H} = -\operatorname{grad}\phi, \tag{5.28}$$

which is analogous to **E** = $-\operatorname{grad} V$. Equation (5.28) is true both *in vacuo* and in a magnetizable medium, our earlier equation (5.10) being a special case.

## 5.4. Solution of magnetostatic problems

In many materials it is found that the magnetization **M** is linearly proportional to the field **H**, so that we can write

$$\mathbf{M} = \chi\mathbf{H}. \tag{5.29}$$

Here $\chi$ is known as the magnetic susceptibility; if we wish to distinguish it from the electric susceptibility (§ 1.5) we may write them as $\chi_m$ and $\chi_e$ respectively, but where there is no danger of confusion the subscripts may be omitted. Representative values of $\chi$ for different substances vary widely, and will be discussed in Chapter 8. At ordinary temperatures $\chi$ is small and independent of **H** for most substances, the exceptions being ferromagnetics, where $\chi$ is large and very dependent on field strength; **M** may even be non-zero when **H** = 0.

From equation (5.20) we have

$$\mathbf{B} = \mu_0(\mathbf{H}+\mathbf{M}) = \mu_0\mathbf{H}(1+\chi)$$
$$= \mu\mu_0\mathbf{H}, \tag{5.30}$$

where the quantity

$$\mu = 1+\chi \tag{5.31}$$

is known as the magnetic permeability of the medium, or sometimes, since $\mu_0$ is called the 'permeability of free space', as the 'relative permeability'. It is clear that $\mu$ plays a similar role in magnetostatics to that played by the dielectric constant $\epsilon$ in electrostatics.

Since div **B** = 0, we have, when $\mu$ is independent of **H**,

$$\operatorname{div}\mathbf{B} = \operatorname{div}(\mu\mu_0\mathbf{H}) = -\mu\mu_0\operatorname{div}\operatorname{grad}\phi$$
$$= -\mu\mu_0\nabla^2\phi = 0,$$

or

$$\nabla^2\phi = 0, \tag{5.32}$$

showing that the magnetostatic potential obeys Laplace's equation. The theory of Chapter 2 may therefore be adapted to magnetostatic problems, and we shall illustrate this by treating a special case.

The problem of a polarizable sphere in a uniform electric field was solved by means of spherical harmonics in § 2.4. The corresponding magnetic problem may be approached in the same way, but we shall

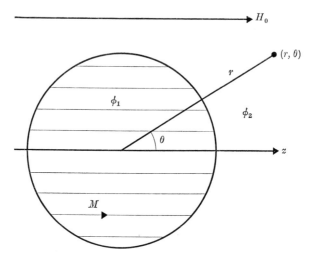

FIG. 5.9. A magnetizable sphere in a uniform field $\mathbf{H_0} = -\partial\phi_2/\partial z$.

extend it slightly by assuming that $\mathbf{M}$ is not necessarily proportional to $\mathbf{H}$, though still parallel to it. Then, from equation (5.20)

$$\operatorname{div}\mathbf{B} = -\mu_0 \operatorname{div}\operatorname{grad}\phi + \mu_0 \operatorname{div}\mathbf{M} = 0,$$

whence
$$\nabla^2\phi = \operatorname{div}\mathbf{M}. \tag{5.33}$$

In the corresponding electrostatic case we found that the sphere was uniformly polarized, and we shall assume that this is true also in the magnetic case. Then $\operatorname{div}\mathbf{M} = 0$, and the potentials required are solutions of Laplace's equation.

In Fig. 5.9, the potentials inside and outside the sphere are assumed to be

$$\phi_1 = -H_1 r\cos\theta \qquad (r < a),$$
$$\phi_2 = -H_0 r\cos\theta + Ar^{-2}\cos\theta \quad (r > a).$$

As in the electrostatic case, there can be no term in $r^{-2}\cos\theta$ inside the sphere, since it would become infinite at $r = 0$; thus the field inside is uniform and equal to $H_1$. Outside the sphere the field at large distances is uniform and equal to $H_0$; we take $H_0$ to be given, so that $H_1$ and $A$ are the unknowns to be determined from the boundary conditions.

The first boundary condition, that the tangential components of **H** be continuous at the boundary, is equivalent to making $\phi_1 = \phi_2$ at $r = a$, giving

$$H_1 = H_0 - Aa^{-3}.$$

The radial components of **B** are

$$\mu_0 M \cos\theta - \mu_0(\partial\phi_1/\partial r) = \mu_0(M + H_1)\cos\theta \quad \text{(inside)}$$

and

$$-\mu_0(\partial\phi_2/\partial r) = \mu_0(H_0 + 2Ar^{-3})\cos\theta \quad \text{(outside)}.$$

Hence, equating the two at $r = a$, we have

$$M + H_1 = H_0 + 2Aa^{-3},$$

and elimination of $A$ between this equation and the first boundary condition gives

$$H_1 = H_0 - \tfrac{1}{3}M, \tag{5.34}$$

so that $H_1$ is smaller than $H_0$ by an amount $\tfrac{1}{3}M$. Thus the magnetization produces a reverse field inside the sphere known as the 'demagnetizing field' which is proportional to $M$; the factor $\tfrac{1}{3}$ is known as the 'demagnetizing factor'. Its value depends on the shape of the specimen, and it is only a meaningful concept for a number of simple shapes where the internal field is uniform and parallel to $H_0$.

A full solution of the problem is possible only if we know how **M** depends on $H_1$. If $\mathbf{M} = \chi\mathbf{H_1} = (\mu - 1)\mathbf{H_1}$, we find $\mathbf{H_1} = 3\mathbf{H_0}/(\mu + 2)$, $\mathbf{M} = 3\mathbf{H_0}(\mu - 1)/(\mu + 2)$. As in the electrostatic case, the field outside the sphere is equal to $\mathbf{H_0}$ plus the field of a dipole at the centre of the sphere of magnitude equal to the total moment of the sphere. In the ferromagnetic case we can have a finite **M** even when $\mathbf{H_0} = 0$. This is a spherical permanent magnet, whose external field is that of a point dipole, and whose internal field is just the demagnetizing field

$$\mathbf{H_1} = -\tfrac{1}{3}\mathbf{M}.$$

We conclude the discussion of magnetostatics by finding a general expression for the magnetic potential due to a magnetized substance. In an element $d\tau$ the dipole moment is $\mathbf{M}\,d\tau$, and the potential equation (5.13) may be written in the form

$$\phi = \frac{1}{4\pi} \int \mathbf{M}\,.\,\text{grad}(1/r)\,d\tau, \tag{5.35}$$

where the differentiation is with respect to the coordinates of the volume element $d\tau$ (cf. equation (1.11 b)). Then, by a vector transformation similar to that used in deriving equation (1.17), we find

$$\phi = \frac{1}{4\pi} \int \frac{1}{r}\left(\mathbf{M}\,.\,\mathbf{dS}\right) - \frac{1}{4\pi} \int \frac{1}{r}(\text{div}\,\mathbf{M}\,d\tau), \tag{5.36}$$

showing that the potential can be attributed to an apparent surface distribution of magnetic charge of surface density $M \cos \theta$, where $\theta$ is the angle which $\mathbf{M}$ makes with the normal $\mathbf{dS}$ to the surface, and an apparent volume distribution of volume density $-\mathrm{div}\,\mathbf{M}$, which, since $\mathrm{div}\,\mathbf{B} = 0$, is equal to $+\mathrm{div}\,\mathbf{H}$. Thus the field lines of $\mathbf{H}$ terminate on the polarization charges, while the field lines of $\mathbf{B}$ are all closed loops since there are no real magnetic charges. If the substance is uniformly magnetized, $\mathrm{div}\,\mathbf{M} = 0$ and there are no volume charges, but there is a surface distribution corresponding to the 'magnetic poles' of classical magnetic theory.

## 5.5. Steady currents in magnetic media

In § 5.3 the effects of the presence of a magnetizable medium were considered, and it was shown that Ampère's law takes the simple form

$$\mathrm{curl}\,\mathbf{H} = \mathbf{J} \tag{5.21}$$

or in integral form
$$\int \mathbf{H}.\mathbf{ds} = I. \tag{5.22}$$

It follows from these equations that in an infinite uniform magnetizable medium of permeability $\mu$ the value of the field $\mathbf{H}$ is unaltered by the presence of the medium, provided the current flow is unaltered, and is independent of $\mu$. Returning to equation (5.3), which holds *in vacuo* where $\mathbf{B} = \mu_0\mathbf{H}$, we see that it may be rewritten in terms of $\mathbf{H}$ as

$$\mathbf{dH} = \frac{1}{4\pi r^3}I(\mathbf{ds}\wedge\mathbf{r}) \tag{5.37}$$

$$= \frac{1}{4\pi r^3}(\mathbf{J}\wedge\mathbf{r})\,d\tau, \tag{5.38}$$

where the first form refers to a current $I$ in an element $\mathbf{ds}$ and the second to a current density $\mathbf{J}$ in an element $d\tau$. From the preceding remarks it is obvious that these equations are unaltered in a magnetizable medium, and are known as the law of Biot and Savart.

We consider now the force vector $\mathbf{B}$. We know from § 5.4 that

$$\mathbf{B} = \mu\mu_0\mathbf{H} \tag{5.30}$$

and it follows that in a magnetizable medium the value of the force vector due to a given current distribution is proportional to $\mu$. Thus the forces between two current elements are also proportional to $\mu$, and the more general form of equation (5.2) becomes

$$\mathbf{dF}_1 = \frac{\mu\mu_0 I_1 I_2}{4\pi r^3}\{\mathbf{ds}_1\wedge(\mathbf{ds}_2\wedge\mathbf{r})\}. \tag{5.39}$$

We see from this that in a magnetizable medium the force between two current elements is proportional to the permeability $\mu$, in contrast with the electrostatic case where the force between two electric poles is inversely proportional to the dielectric constant $\epsilon$.

So far we have not considered the potential energy of a current circuit in a field $\mathbf{B}$, but this may be found in a simple manner. It was shown in § 5.2 that the couple on a circuit in a field $\mathbf{B}$ may be written as

$$\mathbf{\Gamma} = \mathbf{m} \wedge \mathbf{B}, \tag{5.8}$$

where

$$\mathbf{m} = I\mathbf{S} \tag{5.9}$$

is the equivalent magnetic dipole moment of the circuit. The equation for the couple is similar to that for an electric dipole equation (1.14), which was found from differentiation of the potential energy, equation (1.13). The formal mathematical equivalence shows that the potential energy of a magnetic dipole must be

$$U_P = -\mathbf{m} \cdot \mathbf{B}. \tag{5.40}$$

Hence the potential energy of a circuit carrying an invariant current $I$ is

$$U_P = -\int \mathbf{dm} \cdot \mathbf{B} = -I \int \mathbf{dS} \cdot \mathbf{B} = -IN, \tag{5.41}$$

where

$$N = \int \mathbf{B} \cdot \mathbf{dS} \tag{5.42}$$

is known as the total flux of $B$ through the circuit. From equation (5.41) its unit is equal to one joule per ampere, and is known as the weber. Thus from equation (5.42), as already mentioned in § 5.1, the unit of $\mathbf{B}$ is weber/metre².

The energy is expressed in equation (5.41) in terms of a surface integral, but it is useful to be able to express it as a line integral taken round the current circuit. This transformation may be effected by means of Stokes's theorem if we introduce a new vector $\mathbf{A}$, such that $\mathbf{B} = \operatorname{curl} \mathbf{A}$. Since $\mathbf{A}$ is essentially derived from $\mathbf{B}$ by an integration, this definition is not complete, for we could add another term (equivalent to a constant of integration) such as $\operatorname{grad} \psi$, and still have

$$\operatorname{curl}(\mathbf{A} + \operatorname{grad} \psi) = \operatorname{curl} \mathbf{A} = \mathbf{B}.$$

We therefore add a supplementary condition, and define $\mathbf{A}$ by the relations

$$\operatorname{curl} \mathbf{A} = \mathbf{B}, \qquad \operatorname{div} \mathbf{A} = 0. \tag{5.43}$$

The vector $\mathbf{A}$ is known as the 'magnetic vector potential', and we note that the definition in equation (5.43) is consistent with $\operatorname{div} \mathbf{B} = 0$, since $\operatorname{div} \operatorname{curl} \mathbf{A} \equiv 0$ (see Appendix A).

The potential energy of a current circuit may now be expressed as

$$U_P = -I \int (\operatorname{curl} \mathbf{A}) . \, d\mathbf{S} = -I \int \mathbf{A} . \, d\mathbf{s}, \tag{5.44}$$

where the line integral is taken round the current circuit, or, for a volume current of density $\mathbf{J}$, since $I \, d\mathbf{s} = \mathbf{J} \, d\tau$,

$$U_P = - \int (\mathbf{A} . \mathbf{J}) \, d\tau. \tag{5.45}$$

In an isotropic magnetic medium, $\mathbf{B} = \mu\mu_0 \mathbf{H}$, and we can combine equations (5.21) and (5.43) to give

$$\mu\mu_0 \mathbf{J} = \mu\mu_0 \operatorname{curl} \mathbf{H} = \operatorname{curl} \mathbf{B} = \operatorname{curl}(\operatorname{curl} \mathbf{A}) = \operatorname{grad} \operatorname{div} \mathbf{A} - \nabla^2 \mathbf{A},$$

whence, since div $\mathbf{A} = 0$,

$$\nabla^2 \mathbf{A} = -\mu\mu_0 \mathbf{J}. \tag{5.46}$$

This equation is similar to Poisson's equation, equation (2.1), except that the operand is a vector instead of a scalar quantity. This should not cause any difficulty if we remember that equation (5.46) implies that each of the components of the vector separately must satisfy the equation. Then a formal solution similar to equation (2.6) can be found for each of the components

$$A_x = \frac{\mu\mu_0}{4\pi} \int \frac{J_x \, d\tau}{r}, \quad \text{etc.,}$$

which may be expressed in vector form as

$$\mathbf{A} = \frac{\mu\mu_0}{4\pi} \int \frac{\mathbf{J}}{r} \, d\tau. \tag{5.47}$$

This solution may be obtained directly from equation (5.38), which gives

$$\mathbf{H} = \frac{1}{4\pi} \int \frac{(\mathbf{J} \wedge \mathbf{r})}{r^3} \, d\tau = -\frac{1}{4\pi} \int \left\{ \mathbf{J} \wedge \operatorname{grad}\left(\frac{1}{r}\right) \right\} \, d\tau, \tag{5.48}$$

where the integration is over the region of current flow and the gradient is with respect to a displacement of the field point (cf. equation (1.11 a)). By a vector identity (Appendix A)

$$\operatorname{curl}\left(\frac{\mathbf{J}}{r}\right) = \frac{1}{r} \operatorname{curl} \mathbf{J} - \mathbf{J} \wedge \operatorname{grad}\left(\frac{1}{r}\right) = - \mathbf{J} \wedge \operatorname{grad}\left(\frac{1}{r}\right)$$

since the curl operator acts only on the field point and $\mathbf{J}$ is invariant in this operation. Hence in a uniform medium

$$\mathbf{B} = \mu\mu_0 \mathbf{H} = \frac{\mu\mu_0}{4\pi} \int \operatorname{curl}\left(\frac{\mathbf{J}}{r}\right) d\tau = \frac{\mu\mu_0}{4\pi} \operatorname{curl} \int \left(\frac{\mathbf{J}}{r}\right) d\tau,$$

where the order of the curl operation and the integration can be interchanged because the integration is over the current distribution while the curl operation refers to the field point. Since $\mathbf{B} = \text{curl}\,\mathbf{A}$, we have found a solution for $\mathbf{A}$ which agrees with equation (5.47) above.

For a current circuit carrying a current $I$, the solution for $\mathbf{A}$ is

$$\mathbf{A} = \frac{\mu\mu_0 I}{4\pi} \int \frac{\mathbf{ds}}{r} \tag{5.49}$$

and we can use this to find the value of the magnetic vector potential for an elementary current circuit and hence for a point dipole. We take

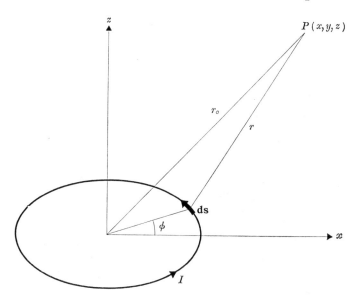

FIG. 5.10. The magnetic vector potential due to a plane circular coil carrying a current $I$.

a small circular current of radius $a$, and calculate the value of $\mathbf{A}$ at a point $P$. For convenience we take Cartesian coordinates, whose $z$-axis is normal to the plane of the coil and whose origin is at the centre of the coil. Then $P$ is at $r_0 \equiv (x, y, z)$, and $r$ is the distance of $P$ from an element $\mathbf{ds}$ of the circuit. In terms of the azimuthal angle $\phi$ (see Fig. 5.10), the components of $\mathbf{ds}$ are $(-a\,d\phi \sin\phi,\ a\,d\phi \cos\phi,\ 0)$ so that $A_z = 0$. Since

$$r^2 = (x - a\cos\phi)^2 + (y - a\sin\phi)^2 + z^2 = r_0^2 - 2ax\cos\phi - 2ay\sin\phi + a^2,$$

and $a \ll r$, we have

$$\frac{1}{r} = \frac{1}{r_0} + \frac{ax\cos\phi + ay\sin\phi}{r_0^3} + \cdots$$

and hence

$$A_x = \frac{\mu\mu_0 I}{4\pi} \int_0^{2\pi} \frac{-a\sin\phi\,d\phi}{r}$$

$$= -\frac{a\mu\mu_0 I}{4\pi} \int_0^{2\pi} \left(\frac{1}{r_0} + \frac{ax\cos\phi + ay\sin\phi}{r_0^3}\right)\sin\phi\,d\phi = -\frac{\mu\mu_0}{4\pi}\{\pi a^2 I(y/r_0^3)\}.$$

Similarly,

$$A_y = \frac{\mu\mu_0 I}{4\pi} \int_0^{2\pi} \frac{a\cos\phi\,d\phi}{r} = +\frac{\mu\mu_0}{4\pi}\{\pi a^2 I(x/r_0^3)\}.$$

The dipole moment equivalent to the current circuit can be represented by a vector $\mathbf{m}$ of size $\pi a^2 I$ directed along the $z$-axis, and the components of $\mathbf{A}$ are then proportional to those of the vector $\mathbf{m}\wedge\mathbf{r}_0$. Hence, dropping the subscript on $\mathbf{r}_0$, we can write

$$\mathbf{A} = \frac{\mu\mu_0}{4\pi r^3}(\mathbf{m}\wedge\mathbf{r}). \tag{5.50}$$

It can readily be verified that the lines of constant $A$ are circles about the $z$-axis, and it is generally true that for simple current circuits the lines of $\mathbf{A}$ are similar in their geometry to those of the current flow, as in the case just discussed.

Equation (5.50) may be compared with equation (5.14). The vector potential is proportional to the vector product $(\mathbf{m}\wedge\mathbf{r})$, the scalar potential to the scalar product $(\mathbf{m}.\mathbf{r})$; in addition the quantity $\mu\mu_0$ appears in the vector potential but not in the scalar potential because the former is connected with $\mathbf{B}$ and the latter with $\mathbf{H}$.

In § 2.3 a general expression was found for the equivalent electric dipole moment of a distributed charge, and some applications on the atomic scale were given. A similar expression may be found for the equivalent magnetic dipole moment of a current distribution, and it is convenient to do this from the formula for the energy in a uniform field $\mathbf{B}$, using the magnetic vector potential. For a uniform field,

$$\mathbf{A} = \tfrac{1}{2}(\mathbf{B}\wedge\mathbf{r}) \tag{5.51}$$

as can readily be verified by calculating the components of curl $\mathbf{A}$ in cartesian coordinates. Then from equation (5.45) the potential energy of a distributed current is

$$U_P = -\int(\mathbf{A}.\mathbf{J})\,d\tau = -\tfrac{1}{2}\int\{(\mathbf{B}\wedge\mathbf{r}).\mathbf{J}\}\,d\tau$$

$$= -\tfrac{1}{2}\int\mathbf{B}.(\mathbf{r}\wedge\mathbf{J})\,d\tau = -\mathbf{B}.\int\tfrac{1}{2}(\mathbf{r}\wedge\mathbf{J})\,d\tau,$$

where $\mathbf{B}$ can be taken out of the integral because it is constant and independent of the space coordinates. The equivalent magnetic dipole moment may be found by equating this expression for the energy to that in equation (5.40), $U_P = -\mathbf{m}.\mathbf{B}$, giving

$$\mathbf{m} = \int \tfrac{1}{2}(\mathbf{r} \wedge \mathbf{J})\, d\tau. \qquad (5.52)$$

We may check that this agrees with our earlier definition of the dipole moment equivalent to a current circuit, since for the latter equation (5.52) becomes

$$\mathbf{m} = I \int \tfrac{1}{2}(\mathbf{r} \wedge \mathbf{ds}) = I \int \mathbf{dS} = I\mathbf{S},$$

in agreement with equation (5.9).

TABLE 5.1

*Comparison of various formulae*

| Electrostatics | Magnetostatics | Currents |
|:---:|:---:|:---:|
| $\mathbf{D} = \epsilon_0\,\mathbf{E} + \mathbf{P}$ | $\mathbf{B} = \mu_0(\mathbf{H} + \mathbf{M})$ | $\mathbf{H} = (\mathbf{B}/\mu_0) - \mathbf{M}$ |
| $= \epsilon\epsilon_0\,\mathbf{E}$ | $= \mu\mu_0\,\mathbf{H}$ | $= \mathbf{B}/\mu\mu_0$ |
| div $\mathbf{D} = \rho$ | div $\mathbf{B} = 0$ | div $\mathbf{B} = 0$ |
| curl $\mathbf{E} = 0$ | curl $\mathbf{H} = 0$ | curl $\mathbf{H} = \mathbf{J}$ |
| $\mathbf{E} = -\mathrm{grad}\,V$ | $\mathbf{H} = -\mathrm{grad}\,\phi$ | $\mathbf{B} = \mathrm{curl}\,\mathbf{A}$ |
| $\nabla^2 V = -\rho/\epsilon\epsilon_0$ | $\nabla^2\phi = 0$ | $\nabla^2\mathbf{A} = -\mu\mu_0\,\mathbf{J}$ |
| $V = \dfrac{1}{4\pi\epsilon\epsilon_0}\displaystyle\int \dfrac{\rho\,d\tau}{r}$ | | $\mathbf{A} = \dfrac{\mu\mu_0}{4\pi}\displaystyle\int \dfrac{\mathbf{J}\,d\tau}{r}$ |
| $\mathbf{D} = \dfrac{q\mathbf{r}}{4\pi r^3}$ | | $\mathbf{H} = \dfrac{I\,\mathbf{ds} \wedge \mathbf{r}}{4\pi r^3}$ |
| $\mathbf{p} = \int \rho\mathbf{r}\,d\tau$ | | $\mathbf{m} = \int \tfrac{1}{2}(\mathbf{r} \wedge \mathbf{J})\,d\tau$ |
| $V = \dfrac{\mathbf{p}.\mathbf{r}}{4\pi\epsilon\epsilon_0\,r^3}$ | $\phi = \dfrac{\mathbf{m}.\mathbf{r}}{4\pi r^3}$ | $\mathbf{A} = \dfrac{\mu\mu_0}{4\pi r^3}(\mathbf{m} \wedge \mathbf{r})$ |
| $U_P = -\mathbf{p}.\mathbf{E}$ | $U_P = -\mathbf{m}.\mathbf{B}$ | $U_P = -I N$ |
| $U_P = \int \rho V\,d\tau$ | | $U_P = -\int (\mathbf{A}.\mathbf{J})\,d\tau$ |
| $U = \int \tfrac{1}{2}\mathbf{D}.\mathbf{E}\,d\tau$ | | $U = \int \tfrac{1}{2}\mathbf{B}.\mathbf{H}\,d\tau$ |

The formulae derived in this chapter are summarized in Table 5.1 in a form which gives a ready comparison with electrostatics. It is assumed that the permeability $\mu$ is independent of $\mathbf{H}$ and isotropic, and that there is no spontaneous magnetization. In a ferromagnetic medium these conditions are not satisfied, and formulae must be derived using the relation $\mathbf{B} = \mu_0(\mathbf{H} + \mathbf{M})$ rather than $\mathbf{B} = \mu\mu_0\mathbf{H}$ (see Problem 5.1).

The formula $U = \int \frac{1}{2} \mathbf{B} . \mathbf{H} \, d\tau$ for the stored energy is quoted for convenience, and is derived in § 6.5.

### 5.6. Calculation of the magnetic fields of simple circuits

The magnetic field of a circuit of simple shape may be found in a number of ways, the chief of which are:

(a) use of equation (5.22). This is possible only when the field has a high degree of symmetry as in the rather similar use of Gauss's theorem in electrostatics;

(b) use of the potential of the equivalent magnetic shell, equation (5.12);

(c) use of the Biot–Savart law, equation (5.37);

(d) use of the magnetic vector potential, equations (5.43) and (5.49).

Simple illustrations will be given of the use of the various methods.

The field due to an infinite straight wire carrying a current $I$ was calculated by (c) in § 5.1, but is very quickly found by method (a). By symmetry, $\mathbf{H}$ can only be a function of the radial distance from the wire, and by applying equation (5.22) to a circle of radius $r$ about the wire we find $\int \mathbf{H} . \mathbf{ds} = 2\pi r H = I$. Hence the azimuthal component of $\mathbf{H}$ is $I/2\pi r$; since this depends only on $r$, the lines of force are concentric circles about the wire, and no other components of $\mathbf{H}$ exist.

If the wire has radius $a$, and the current density is uniform, the field inside the wire can be found by a similar application of equation (5.22). In this case the current threading a circle of radius $r$ is $I(r^2/a^2)$, so that $\int \mathbf{H} . \mathbf{ds} = 2\pi r H = I(r^2/a^2)$ and $H = Ir/2\pi a^2$, showing that $H$ increases linearly from the centre to the surface of the wire.

The case of a straight wire serves also as a simple example where the vector potential can be found by solving equation (5.46). Taking the axis of the wire to be along the $z$-axis, it is obvious that the only component of current density is $J_z$, and hence the only component of $\mathbf{A}$ is $A_z$, so that the lines of $\mathbf{A}$ are parallel to the wire. Inside the wire (permeability $\mu_1$)

$$\nabla^2 A_z = -\mu_1 \mu_0 J_z = -\mu_1 \mu_0 I/(\pi a^2).$$

Since $J_z$ is independent of $z$ and $\theta$ (making use of cylindrical coordinates $r$, $\theta$, $z$), so also is $A_z$ and the differential equation becomes

$$\frac{1}{r} \frac{\partial}{\partial r} \left( r \frac{\partial A_z}{\partial r} \right) = -\mu_1 \mu_0 I/(\pi a^2).$$

Integration gives    $r(\partial A_z/\partial r) = -\mu_1 \mu_0 I r^2/2\pi a^2,$

where the constant of integration vanishes, because $\partial A_z/\partial r = 0$ at $r = 0$ (otherwise we should have a discontinuity in $\partial A_z/\partial r$ on crossing the axis.) A second integration gives

$$A_z = \frac{\mu_1 \mu_0 I}{4\pi}\left(1 - \frac{r^2}{a^2}\right) \quad \text{(inside),} \tag{5.53}$$

where for convenience we make $A_z = 0$ at $r = a$.

Outside the wire (assuming a medium of permeability $\mu_2$)

$$\frac{1}{r}\frac{\partial}{\partial r}\left(r\frac{\partial A_z}{\partial r}\right) = 0,$$

whence $\partial A_z/\partial r = c/r$, and

$$A_z = c\ln(r/a) \quad \text{(outside),}$$

where the second constant of integration is chosen to make $A_z$ continuous at the boundary; i.e. $A_z = 0$ at $r = a$. The constant $c$ is determined by the boundary condition for $\partial A_z/\partial r$ at $r = a$. By writing $r^2 = x^2+y^2$ and finding the components of curl $\mathbf{A}$, it can be verified that

$$B_x = (\partial A_z/\partial r)(y/r), \qquad B_y = -(\partial A_z/\partial r)(x/r),$$

so that $B_\theta = -\partial A_z/\partial r$. Since $B_\theta$ is purely tangential (the other components are zero), the boundary condition is that $H_\theta$ must be continuous at $r = a$, and it is easily shown then that

$$A_z = -\frac{\mu_2 \mu_0 I}{2\pi}\ln(r/a) \quad \text{(outside).} \tag{5.54}$$

Methods (b) and (c) may be compared in finding the magnetic field on the axis of a plane circular coil. We will assume that the coil has $n$ turns each carrying a current $I$, and the radius of the coil is $a$. Then, at a point on the axis a distance $z$ away, the solid angle subtended by the coil is $2\pi\left\{1 - \dfrac{z}{(z^2+a^2)^{\frac{1}{2}}}\right\}$ (this formula may be verified by the integration $\omega = \displaystyle\int\frac{d\mathbf{S}.\mathbf{r}}{r^3}$, taken over the plane surface bounded by the coil). Hence

$$H_z = -d\phi/dz = -(nI/4\pi)(d\omega/dz) = \tfrac{1}{2}nIa^2/(z^2+a^2)^{\frac{3}{2}}. \tag{5.55}$$

When $a \ll z$, this formula is the same as that for the field of a dipole of moment $\mathbf{m} = nI(\pi a^2)$ at a point on its axis (cf. equation 5.9).

In applying the formula of Biot and Savart we consider first the field $d\mathbf{H}$ due to an element of wire $d\mathbf{s}$, as in Fig. 5.11. Since $d\mathbf{H}$ is normal both to $d\mathbf{s}$ and to $\mathbf{r}$, it will have the direction shown in the figure. On integrating round the coil it is clear that the sum of all the components

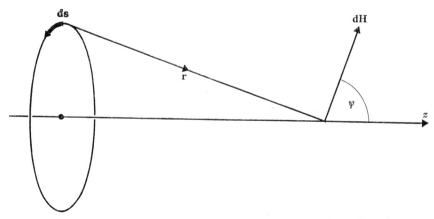

FIG. 5.11. The magnetic field due to a circular coil at a point on its axis.

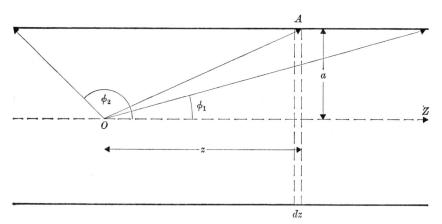

FIG. 5.12. Magnetic field on the axis of a solenoid.

normal to the axis will be zero. The components parallel to the axis will sum to

$$H_z = nI \int (\cos\psi/4\pi r^2)\, ds = 2\pi anI \cos\psi/4\pi r^2 = \tfrac{1}{2}nIa^2/(z^2+a^2)^{\tfrac{3}{2}}.$$

This formula may be extended to the case of a solenoid with $m$ turns per unit length, uniformly wound round a cylinder of radius $a$ (Fig. 5.12). If the turns are closely wound, we may regard them as being equivalent to a uniform current flowing round the cylinder, so that an element $dz$ of it forms a plane coil with a current $mI\, dz$. At the point $O$ this gives a field along the axis equal to

$$dH_z = \tfrac{1}{2}mIa^2\, dz/(z^2+a^2)^{\tfrac{3}{2}} = -\tfrac{1}{2}mI \sin\phi\, d\phi,$$

where $\phi$ is the angle $AOZ$. Hence

$$H_z = -\tfrac{1}{2}mI \int_{\phi_2}^{\phi_1} \sin\phi \, d\phi = \tfrac{1}{2}mI(\cos\phi_1 - \cos\phi_2). \qquad (5.56)$$

For an infinite solenoid, $\phi_1 = 0$ and $\phi_2 = \pi$, so that

$$H_z = mI \qquad (5.57)$$

and is uniform inside the solenoid.

We shall end this section by calculating the force between two small plane circular coils, each of one turn of radius $a$ carrying a current $I$, with a common axis, and separated by a distance $z$ ($a \ll z$). From equation (5.55) the field on the axis at the centre of the second coil is

$$H_z = \tfrac{1}{2}Ia^2/z^3.$$

Since $a \ll z$, $H_z$ will not vary appreciably for a small distance off the axis, and the flux through the second coil is therefore

$$N = \int \mathbf{B}.\mathbf{dS} = \mu\mu_0(\tfrac{1}{2}Ia^2/z^3)(\pi a^2) = \tfrac{1}{2}\mu\mu_0\pi Ia^4/z^3.$$

The potential energy of the second coil is $U_P = -NI$, and hence the force on it is

$$F = -dU_P/dz = -\tfrac{3}{2}\mu\mu_0\pi a^4 I^2/z^4. \qquad (5.58)$$

It is instructive to see just how this force arises. Since div $\mathbf{B} = 0$ in the region away from the second coil, we have

$$\frac{\partial B_x}{\partial x} + \frac{\partial B_y}{\partial y} + \frac{\partial B_z}{\partial z} = 0,$$

where $x$ and $y$ are normal to the common axis of the coils. By symmetry, $\partial B_x/\partial x = \partial B_y/\partial y$, and hence each equals $-\tfrac{1}{2}(\partial B_z/\partial z)$. At a small distance $a$ from the axis there will be a radial component of field equal to $a(\partial B_x/\partial x) = -\tfrac{1}{2}a(\partial B_z/\partial z) = 3\mu\mu_0 a^3 I/4z^4$. There will therefore be a force $I(\mathbf{ds} \wedge \mathbf{B})$ on each element of the coil, of which the components due to $B_z$ are radial and sum to zero over the whole coil, while the force components due to the radial component of $B$ all act in the negative $z$-direction (assuming the currents in each coil flow in the same sense). These sum to $-I(2\pi a)\mu\mu_0(3a^3 I/4z^4)$, which gives the same result as in equation (5.58) (see also Problem 5.4).

### 5.7. Moving charges in electric and magnetic fields

The fundamental equations (5.1) and (5.37) for the force on and the field produced by a current element both involve the quantity $I\,\mathbf{ds}$. This may be transformed to give the corresponding formulae for a moving charge, which is equivalent to a current. The magnitude of the current

$I = dq/dt$, the rate at which charge passes a given point. If the charge moves with velocity $\mathbf{v}$, we have $I\,\mathbf{ds} = (dq/dt)\mathbf{v}\,dt = dq\,\mathbf{v}$, and the Biot–Savart law (equation (5.37)) thus becomes

$$\mathbf{H} = \int \frac{I(\mathbf{ds} \wedge \mathbf{r})}{4\pi r^3} = \int \frac{dq(\mathbf{v} \wedge \mathbf{r})}{4\pi r^3}.$$

If all the charge is located at a point, $\mathbf{v}$ and $\mathbf{r}$ are constant in the integration over $dq$, and for a point charge $q$ we have

$$\mathbf{H} = \frac{q(\mathbf{v} \wedge \mathbf{r})}{4\pi r^3}, \tag{5.59}$$

while the force on a moving charge becomes

$$\mathbf{F} = q(\mathbf{v} \wedge \mathbf{B}). \tag{5.60}$$

If an electric field $\mathbf{E}$ is also present, the total force is

$$\mathbf{F} = q(\mathbf{E} + \mathbf{v} \wedge \mathbf{B}). \tag{5.61}$$

It may be remarked that though equation (5.60) has here been introduced as an additional postulate, it follows as a consequence of equation (1.3) when we apply the special theory of relativity. An observer in whose system a charge is at rest will ascribe the forces on it to a purely electrostatic field $\mathbf{E}$. On applying the laws for the transformation of mechanical force we find that a moving observer would measure a force of the type given by equation (5.61); that is, he would ascribe the effects to the action of both electric and magnetic fields. In a similar manner, equation (5.59) can be deduced from the electrostatic formula for $\mathbf{D}$, equation (1.23).

The motion of charged particles, usually electrons or positive ions, under the action of electric and magnetic fields is the basis of many fundamental experiments in physics, a few of which will be used as illustrations here. The motion in purely electrostatic fields has already been discussed (§ 3.7), and we shall begin by considering the motion of a charge in a uniform magnetic induction $\mathbf{B}$. If the charge is initially moving in a plane normal to $\mathbf{B}$, then the force on it (assuming $\mathbf{E} = 0$) is also in this plane and normal to its direction of motion. Thus no work is done on the particle, since $\mathbf{F}.\mathbf{v} = q\mathbf{v}.(\mathbf{v} \wedge \mathbf{B}) = 0$, and its velocity remains constant in magnitude. The charge will therefore move in a circle in this plane, the force towards the centre being

$$Mv^2/r = qvB,$$

where $M$ is the mass of the charged particle, and $r$ the radius of the circle. Hence we have

$$r = Mv/qB \quad \text{and} \quad \omega_c = v/r = B(q/M), \tag{5.62}$$

where $\omega_c$ is the angular velocity. This equation shows that $\omega_c$, and hence the time taken to make one revolution, is independent of the velocity of the particle (so long as the relativistic change of mass with velocity can be neglected). This fact is made use of in many applications.

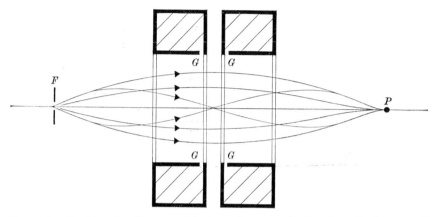

Fɪɢ. 5.13. Double solenoid encased in iron, for magnetic focusing. $G$, $G$ are small annular gaps in the iron casing.

*Magnetic focusing*

If the initial velocity of the charge is not normal to **B**, but makes an angle $\theta$ with the direction of **B**, then we can resolve the velocity into a component $v \cos \theta$ parallel to **B**, and a component $v \sin \theta$ normal to **B**. The vector product $(\mathbf{v} \wedge \mathbf{B})$ has no component parallel to **B**, and the component of velocity $v \cos \theta$ will therefore continue unaltered. The projection of the motion on a plane normal to **B** will be a circle of radius $r = Mv \sin \theta / qB$, and the actual path of the particle will be a helix. One revolution of the helix is completed in a time $2\pi/\omega = 2\pi M/qB$, and the particle has then moved a distance $z = 2\pi Mv \cos \theta / qB$ in the direction of **B**. For small values of $\theta$, this distance is independent of $\theta$ in the first approximation (since $\cos \theta \approx 1 - \frac{1}{2}\theta^2$), and this is the principle used in magnetic focusing.

In Fig. 5.13 electrons leave a point $F$, and it is desired to focus them so that they all reach a point $P$ a distance $z$ away. If the electrons emerge from a gun with electrostatic focusing, they all have closely the same velocity $v$, but are not moving quite parallel to the line $FP$. By means of a solenoid, a magnetic field is applied in the direction $FP$, and the current in the solenoid adjusted so that the time taken to reach $P$ is equal to one or more periods of revolution in the helical motion caused by the magnetic field. It is often impracticable to use a long solenoid, and one or more short solenoids, encased in iron with a small annular gap round the inner circumference, as shown in Fig. 5.13, are used instead. Such coils give a localized, non-uniform field, which acts like a thin lens; their design is largely empirical.

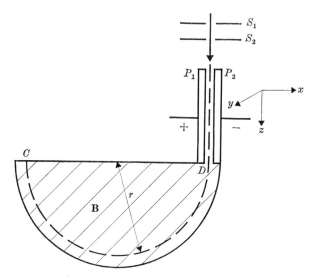

Fɪɢ. 5.14.  Diagram illustrating the principle of Bainbridge's mass spectrometer.

*Measurement of specific charge*

Determination of the ratio of charge to mass (or 'specific charge') of atomic particles is of prime importance in atomic physics. All such particles carry a charge (positive or negative) equal to the electronic charge $e$, or a small integral multiple of it, and the ratio of the charge to the mass for the electron and the proton are fundamental constants. From equation (5.62) it will be seen that an accurate measurement of $\omega_c$ and $B$ for particles moving in a circle suffices to determine $q/M$, and recent methods based on this principle are described in Chapter 23. For positive ions of heavier nuclei, the main interest lies in the measurement of the mass, and instruments for measuring the specific charge ($q/M$) for this purpose are known as 'mass spectrometers'. In general they make use of both electric and magnetic fields, and two measurements are required since both the velocity of the particle and the value of $q/M$ are unknown. The positive ions are usually formed in a gaseous discharge and more than one type of ion with varying velocity may be present; the instruments are therefore designed to sort these out, and bring all particles with the same specific charge to a common focus.

Many such instruments have been designed, but since our purpose here is just to illustrate the principles, we shall describe only one, due to Bainbridge. It makes use of a 'velocity selector', formed by the flat plates $P_1$, $P_2$ in Fig. 5.14, which have a very small separation. Ions enter these plates from a source through slits $S_1$, $S_2$, so that they are travelling with velocity $v$ parallel to the $z$-axis of the coordinate system shown in the figure. A voltage is maintained between the plates, so that there is an electric field $\mathbf{E}$ in the $x$-direction. By means of a pair of Helmholtz coils (see Problem 5.2) a uniform induction $\mathbf{B}$ is maintained in the $y$-direction, and the total force on an ion between the plates is therefore $q(E-vB)$ in the $x$-direction. If the plates are long and close together, only ions for which this force is zero will emerge, and their velocity must therefore be $v = E/B$. The device therefore selects ions of a particular velocity determined by this ratio. On emerging from the plates the ions travel in a semicircular path under the influence of the field $\mathbf{B}$ alone until they strike a detector at $C$. The distance $DC$ is twice the radius of the orbit and is thus

$$2r = 2Mv/qB = 2(M/q)E/B^2. \tag{5.63}$$

Hence the distance $DC$ is linearly proportional to the mass of the ion. In Problem 5.11 it is shown that the distance $DC$ is independent (to the first order) of the angle to the $z$-axis at which an ion emerges from the plates, provided this is small, so that we have 'first order' focusing of the ions with a given value of $q/M$.


## REFERENCE

PAGE, L., and ADAMS, N. I., 1945, *Am. J. Phys.* **13**, 141.


## PROBLEMS

5.1. Show that if the relation $\mathbf{B} = \mu_0(\mathbf{H}+\mathbf{M})$ is used rather than $\mathbf{B} = \mu\mu_0\mathbf{H}$, the differential equations for the potentials $\phi$ and $\mathbf{A}$ become

$$\nabla^2\phi = \operatorname{div}\mathbf{M} \quad \text{(in regions where } \mathbf{J} = 0\text{)},$$

$$\nabla^2\mathbf{A} = -\mu_0\mathbf{J} - \mu_0\operatorname{curl}\mathbf{M}.$$

These apply in media such as ferromagnetics, where $\mathbf{M}$ is not linearly proportional to $\mathbf{H}$, and may even be finite (spontaneous magnetization) in the absence of an applied field.

5.2. Two identical circular coils, each of $n$ turns of radius $a$, are placed with their planes parallel and normal to the line joining them, a distance $r$ apart. Calculate the magnetic field on the axis midway between the coils due to a current $I$ through each coil. Show that, if $r = a$, the field midway between the coils is uniform over a considerable region; that is, $\partial H/\partial r$ for one coil is equal to $-\partial H/\partial r$ for the other coil, and $\partial^2 H/\partial r^2 = 0$. Such an arrangement of coils was used by Helmholtz for a galvanometer, a small magnetic needle suspended by a torsion fibre at the centre being deflected by the current through the coils.

5.3. Two infinite cylindrical conductors are placed parallel to one another at a distance $2a$ apart. They carry equal and opposite currents. Show that in the equatorial plane the gradient of the magnetic field is greatest at a distance $a/\sqrt{3}$ from the plane through the axes of the cylinders.

5.4. Deduce equation (5.58) by treating each coil as a point dipole of moment $I(\pi a^2)$, and using the formula for the force on a dipole in a non-uniform field

$$F = m(\partial B/\partial z)$$

equivalent to the electrostatic formula $F = p(\partial E/\partial z)$.

5.5. Show that, if a magnet of moment $\mathfrak{m}$ is suspended by a torsionless fibre so that it is free to swing in a horizontal plane in a horizontal field $B$, the period of small oscillations about the equilibrium position is $T = 2\pi(\mathfrak{I}/\mathfrak{m}B)^{\frac{1}{2}}$, where $\mathfrak{I}$ is the moment of inertia of the magnet about the axis of rotation.

5.6. Two short magnets are attached to a cork so that they float on water with their axes horizontal. One magnet lies with its centre on the axis of the other, but with its own axis perpendicular to the line joining them. Assuming that the distance between the magnets is large compared with their lengths, so that they can be treated as point dipoles, calculate the force and the couple on each magnet, and satisfy yourself that there is no resultant force or couple on the system as a whole.

5.7. Show that the magnetic field inside a spherical air bubble in a paramagnetic substance of permeability $\mu$ is $3\mu H/(2\mu+1)$, if the field in the substance away from the bubble is $H$. Will any translational force act on the bubble?

5.8. A spherical shell has radii $a$ and $b$ respectively ($b > a$), and is made of a material of permeability $\mu$. It is placed in a uniform field $H$. Show that the field inside the shell is

$$H_i = \frac{9\mu H}{(2\mu+1)(\mu+2)-2(\mu-1)^2(a/b)^3}$$

and that for large values of $\mu$, this approximates to

$$H_i = 9H/\{2\mu(1-a^3/b^3)\}.$$

Thus if $\mu$ is large, $H_i$ is much smaller than $H$, and an instrument can be shielded from stray magnetic fields by placing it in an iron case. Magnetic shielding is much less efficient than electrostatic shielding (especially if $a/b$ is close to unity), for the effective value of $\epsilon$ in the equivalent expression for a conductor is infinite.

5.9. A hollow sphere of internal radius $a$, external radius $b$, has a uniform spontaneous magnetization $M$ per unit volume. Show that the field in the internal cavity ($r < a$) is zero, and that the external field ($r > b$) is the same as that of a dipole moment $\mathbf{m} = 4\pi\mathbf{M}(b^3-a^3)/3$, the total moment of the hollow sphere.

Show also that the square of the field outside the sphere at a point $(r, \theta)$, measured from the centre of the sphere and with respect to the direction of magnetization, is

$$H^2 = (3\cos^2\theta + 1)\left\{\frac{M(b^3 - a^3)}{3r^3}\right\}^2.$$

If the angle of dip $\delta$ is defined as the angle which the lines of force at a point on the external surface of the sphere make with the tangent at that point, show that

$$\tan\delta = 2\cot\theta.$$

5.10. A particle of mass $M$ and charge $q$ is rotating in a circular orbit of radius $r$ with angular velocity $\omega$. Show that a magnetic dipole moment $\mathbf{m}$ is associated with the motion of the charge, such that

$$\mathbf{m} = (q/2M)\mathbf{G},$$

where $\mathbf{G} = Mr^2\omega$ is the angular momentum of the particle. (The orbit may be regarded as a small circuit carrying a current $I = q \times$ the frequency at which the charge passes any point in the orbit per unit time.)

5.11. In Bainbridge's mass spectrometer the ions emerge in a wedge-shaped beam of small semi-vertical angle $\theta$ (see Fig. 5.14). If the resolution of the instrument as a mass spectrometer is defined as the reciprocal of the smallest fractional change of mass which will produce non-overlapping traces on the plane $CD$, show that the resolution is $2/\theta^2$.

5.12. A charged particle starts from rest at the origin of coordinates in a region where there is a uniform electric field $\mathbf{E}$ parallel to the $x$-axis, and a uniform magnetic induction $\mathbf{B}$ parallel to the $z$-axis. Show that the coordinates of the particle at a time $t$ later will be

$$x = (E/\omega B)(1 - \cos\omega t),$$
$$y = -(E/\omega B)(\omega t - \sin\omega t),$$
$$z = 0,$$

where $\omega = eB/m$. (The path of the particle is a cycloid.)

Electrons are liberated with zero velocity from the negative plate of a parallel plate condenser, to which is applied an induction $\mathbf{B}$ parallel to the plates. Show that they will not reach the positive plate if the plate separation $d$ is greater than $2mE/eB^2$, where $\mathbf{E}$ is the field between the plates.

# ELECTROMAGNETIC INDUCTION AND VARYING CURRENTS

## 6.1. Faraday's laws of electromagnetic induction

THE experiments of Oersted and others showed that 'electricity can produce magnetism', and established the laws governing the magnetic field set up by a current. Many experiments were devised to detect the inverse effect, the flow of electric current due to a magnetic field, without success, mainly because a steady current flow was looked for. In 1831 it was found by Faraday that a transient flow of current occurred in a closed circuit when the flux of magnetic induction through the circuit was changed. The change of flux could be brought about in a number of ways: in his first experiment two coils of wire were wound on a ring of soft iron as in Fig. 6.1. The presence of a current in the second coil was detected by connecting it to another coil near a small suspended magnet. When the first coil was connected to a battery, a momentary oscillation of the magnet occurred, after which it settled in its original position. A similar oscillation, though with an initial kick in the opposite direction, was observed on disconnecting the battery. In other experiments Faraday showed that similar effects were observed if a permanent magnet was moved near the second coil, or if the coil was moved in the neighbourhood of a magnet. His results were summed up in the two laws:

(a) when the flux of magnetic induction through a circuit is changing, an electromotive force is induced in the circuit;

(b) the magnitude of the e.m.f. is proportional to the rate of change of the flux.

The sign of the e.m.f. is given by Lenz's law, which states that it is such that any current flow is in the direction which would oppose the flux change causing the e.m.f. Thus, in Fig. 6.2, if the magnet is moved towards the closed loop of wire so that the magnetic flux through the coil is increased, the induced current will flow in such a direction that its own field opposes the increased field of the magnet threading the loop.

These laws are expressed in the equation

$$V = -\frac{dN}{dt},$$

(6.1)

where $V$ is the electromagnetic force round the circuit, and $N$ is the instantaneous value of the magnetic flux through the circuit. Now $N = \int \mathbf{B}.\mathbf{dS}$ and $V = \int \mathbf{E}.\mathbf{ds}$, where the former integral is taken over

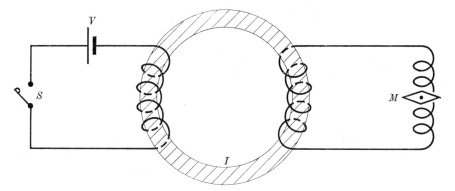

FIG. 6.1. Faraday's experiment on electromagnetic induction.

$V$  battery,                                    $S$  switch,
$M$  suspended magnetic needle,      $I$  iron ring.

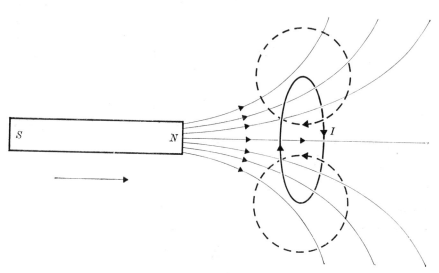

FIG. 6.2. Current induced in a loop by a moving magnet (broken lines represent lines of magnetic field produced by the induced current when the magnet moves towards the loop).

any area bounded by the circuit and the latter integral is taken round the circuit. Hence we have

$$\int \mathbf{E}.\mathbf{ds} = -\frac{d}{dt}\int \mathbf{B}.\mathbf{dS}. \qquad (6.2)$$

Using the transformation $\int \mathbf{E} \cdot \mathbf{ds} = \int \text{curl} \, \mathbf{E} \cdot \mathbf{dS}$, and the fact that the time and space coordinates are independent variables, this can be re-written in the form

$$\int \text{curl} \, \mathbf{E} \cdot \mathbf{dS} = - \int \frac{d\mathbf{B}}{dt} \cdot \mathbf{dS},$$

and since this must hold over any surface area, the integrands must be equal, giving the differential form

$$\text{curl} \, \mathbf{E} = -\frac{d\mathbf{B}}{dt}. \tag{6.3}$$

At first sight it would have been expected that equation (6.1) would have contained a multiplying constant to be determined either experimentally or from theory. This constant is in fact unity, as can be seen in the following way. Let us assume we have a very thin conductor carrying no current, which is moved with a velocity **v** in a uniform field of magnetic induction **B**. Since the wire is a conductor, it carries charges (electrons) which are free to move along the wire; let the velocity of a charge $q$ in the conductor be **u** relative to the conductor. Since the conductor is very thin **u** must be parallel to the direction of the wire at any point. The velocity of the charge $q$ relative to the observer is $\mathbf{v}+\mathbf{u}$, and the force on it will therefore be $\mathbf{F} = q(\mathbf{v}+\mathbf{u}) \wedge \mathbf{B}$. If the charge moves a distance **dr** along the wire, the work done is $\mathbf{F} \cdot \mathbf{dr}$; since $(\mathbf{u} \wedge \mathbf{B}) \cdot \mathbf{dr} = 0$ because **u**, **dr** are parallel, this is the same as if there existed in **dr** an e.m.f.

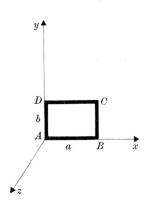

FIG. 6.3. Relation between Faraday's law of induction and the force on a moving conductor.

$$dV = (\mathbf{v} \wedge \mathbf{B}) \cdot \mathbf{dr}. \tag{6.4}$$

For a closed circuit in a uniform induction **B**, since $(\mathbf{v} \wedge \mathbf{B})$ is constant, the total e.m.f. $V = \int (\mathbf{v} \wedge \mathbf{B}) \cdot \mathbf{dr} = 0$. If the induction is not uniform, the flux through the circuit will change as the circuit moves, and we can relate $V$ to the rate of change of flux. Consider a small rectangular circuit $ABCD$ (Fig. 6.3) with sides $a$, $b$ parallel to the $x$, $y$ axes of a Cartesian system. The e.m.f. in an anti-clockwise direction (the sense in which a right-handed screw would turn to advance along the

$z$-axis) is

$$V = a(v_y B_z - v_z B_y) + b\left(v_z\left\{B_x + a\frac{\partial B_x}{\partial x}\right\} - v_x\left\{B_z + a\frac{\partial B_z}{\partial x}\right\}\right) -$$

$$- a\left(v_y\left\{B_z + b\frac{\partial B_z}{\partial y}\right\} - v_z\left\{B_y + b\frac{\partial B_y}{\partial y}\right\}\right) - b(v_z B_x - v_x B_z)$$

$$= -ab\left(v_x\frac{\partial B_z}{\partial x} + v_y\frac{\partial B_z}{\partial y} - v_z\left\{\frac{\partial B_x}{\partial x} + \frac{\partial B_y}{\partial y}\right\}\right)$$

$$= -ab\left(v_x\frac{\partial B_z}{\partial x} + v_y\frac{\partial B_z}{\partial y} + v_z\frac{\partial B_z}{\partial z}\right) \tag{6.5}$$

since div $\mathbf{B} = 0$. But $abB_z = N$, the flux through the circuit, and since $v_x = dx/dt$, etc.,

$$V = -\left(\frac{\partial N}{\partial x}v_x + \frac{\partial N}{\partial y}v_y + \frac{\partial N}{\partial z}v_z\right) = -dN/dt$$

in agreement with equation (6.1). The unit of magnetic flux $N$ is the weber, and an e.m.f. of 1 V is generated in a circuit where the flux is changing at the rate of 1 weber/sec.

Equation (6.3) may be combined with the relation $\mathbf{B} = \text{curl}\,\mathbf{A}$ (equation (5.43)) to give

$$\text{curl}\,\mathbf{E} = -\frac{\partial}{\partial t}\,\text{curl}\,\mathbf{A} = -\text{curl}(\partial \mathbf{A}/\partial t),$$

whence

$$\mathbf{E} = -\frac{\partial \mathbf{A}}{\partial t} + \text{constant} = -\frac{\partial \mathbf{A}}{\partial t} - \text{grad}\,V. \tag{6.6}$$

This is a more general equation than equation (1.6) which applies only to steady fields. For a particle of charge $q$ the rate of change of momentum $\mathbf{p}$ is (assuming grad $V = 0$)

$$\partial \mathbf{p}/\partial t = q\mathbf{E} = -q(\partial \mathbf{A}/\partial t),$$

which on integration gives

$$\mathbf{p} = \mathbf{p}_0 - q\mathbf{A}, \tag{6.7}$$

assuming that $\mathbf{A} = 0$ when $\mathbf{p} = \mathbf{p}_0$. This relation plays an important role in quantum mechanics, where the effect of a magnetic field on a charged particle can be introduced by replacing $\mathbf{p}$ by $\mathbf{p}_0 - q\mathbf{A}$.

## 6.2. Self-inductance and mutual inductance

If a current $I$ is flowing in a circuit, a magnetic field is set up and there will be a flux $N$ of magnetic induction through the circuit associated with its own magnetic field. The magnetic field at any point is proportional to the current $I$, and hence so also is the induction and the flux $N$. We may therefore write

$$N = LI, \tag{6.8}$$

where $L$ is a constant which depends on the geometry of the circuit and the permeability of the medium in which it is immersed. $L$ is called the self-inductance of the circuit, and is equal to the total flux through the circuit when unit current is flowing. A circuit has unit self-inductance (one henry) if it is threaded by one weber of flux when one ampere of current is flowing.

If a second coil is brought near to a coil carrying a current $I$, there will in general be a flux $N_2$ of magnetic induction through the second coil due to the current in the first coil. Since $N_2$ is again linearly proportional to $I_1$, we may write

$$N_2 = M_{21} I_1, \tag{6.9a}$$

where $M_{21}$ is called the mutual inductance between the two circuits. The unit of mutual inductance is again the henry. There will also be a flux $N_1$ through the first circuit due to a current $I_2$ in the second circuit, given by

$$N_1 = M_{12} I_2. \tag{6.9b}$$

The coefficients $M_{12}$ and $M_{21}$ are equal, as can be seen from energy considerations. The potential energy of the system can be found from the flux of either coil due to the field of the other; from equation (5.41)

$$U_P = -N_2 I_2 = -M_{21} I_1 I_2 = -N_1 I_1 = -M_{12} I_2 I_1,$$

showing that

$$M_{12} = M_{21}. \tag{6.10}$$

By using equations (5.44) and (5.47) we can derive a formula for the mutual inductance, since

$$U_P = -I_1 \int \mathbf{A}_{21}.\mathbf{ds}_1 = -I_1 \int \left( \frac{\mu\mu_0}{4\pi} \int \frac{I_2\,\mathbf{ds}_2}{r} \right).\mathbf{ds}_1$$

$$= -\frac{\mu\mu_0}{4\pi} I_1 I_2 \int\int \frac{\mathbf{ds}_1.\mathbf{ds}_2}{r} = -M_{12} I_1 I_2, \tag{6.11}$$

where, by symmetry,

$$M_{12} = M_{21} = \frac{\mu\mu_0}{4\pi} \int\int \frac{\mathbf{ds}_1.\mathbf{ds}_2}{r}. \tag{6.12}$$

This result is known as Neumann's formula. Since the unit of mutual inductance is the henry, this formula shows that the dimensions of $\mu_0$ are henry/metre.

If the two coils are closely wound, so that all the flux generated by the first coil passes through the second, and vice versa, then the ratio of the two fluxes $N_1$ and $N_2$ will just be equal to the ratio of the number of turns $n_1$, $n_2$ on the two coils. For a current $I_1$ in the first coil we have (writing $M$ for $M_{12} = M_{21}$)

$$N_1/N_2 = (L_1 I_1)/(M I_1) = L_1/M = n_1/n_2,$$

while for the flux generated by a current $I_2$ in the second coil

$$N_2/N_1 = (L_2 I_2)/(M I_2) = L_2/M = n_2/n_1.$$

Hence        $$L_1/M = M/L_2 = n_1/n_2 \quad \text{and} \quad M^2 = L_1 L_2. \tag{6.13}$$

If the flux through the two coils is changing, the voltages induced in the two coils will be in the ratio

$$V_1/V_2 = (dN_1/dt)/(dN_2/dt) = n_1/n_2 = 1/n.$$

Hence such a device may be used as a transformer, since if a changing voltage $V_1$ is applied to the 'primary' coil, a changing voltage of different magnitude will be induced in the 'secondary' coil. The voltage transformation ratio is $n = V_2/V_1$, the 'turns ratio' of secondary to primary. In general not all the flux of one circuit passes through the other, and $M$ is less than $(L_1 L_2)^{\frac{1}{2}}$; it may be written as

$$M = k(L_1 L_2)^{\frac{1}{2}} \quad (0 \leqslant k \leqslant 1), \tag{6.14}$$

where $k$ is called the 'coefficient of coupling'. The theory of transformers is considered further in § 9.5.

The magnitude of an inductance may be calculated from first principles by computing the field produced by a given current in the coil, and then finding the total flux through the same or another coil, according to whether the self-inductance of the first coil or the mutual inductance between the two coils is required. The calculations are illustrated below for a number of simple shapes of coil.

*Long solenoid*

For an infinitely long solenoid, wound with $m$ turns per unit length and carrying a current $I$, the magnetic field inside is uniform and given by equation (5.57):
$$H = mI.$$

If the core of the solenoid has permeability $\mu$, the flux through each turn is $N' = \mu\mu_0 A m I$, where $A$ is the cross-sectional area of the solenoid. The self-inductance per unit length is therefore $L' = mN'/I = \mu\mu_0 m^2 A$; for a solenoid of length $l$, large compared with its diameter, this formula is still very nearly correct, and we may write for the total self-inductance

$$L = \mu\mu_0 m^2 A l. \tag{6.15}$$

If a second short coil of $n$ turns, insulated from the first, is wound on the solenoid as in Fig. 6.4, the mutual inductance is

$$M = \mu\mu_0 mnA.$$                               (6.16)

*Two coaxial coils*

Another simple case is that of two plane coaxial coils $A$ and $B$ as in Fig. 6.5, of radii $a$ and $b$, and total numbers of turns $n_1$ and $n_2$ respectively, whose centres are a distance $z$ apart, where $z \gg a, b$. The field

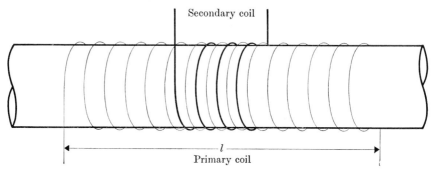

Secondary coil

$l$

Primary coil

FIG. 6.4. Solenoid with primary and secondary coils.

FIG. 6.5. Mutual inductance between two plane coaxial coils. $AB = z$.

at the centre of $B$ due to a current $I$ in $A$ is, from equation (5.55),

$$H = \tfrac{1}{2}Ia^2n_1/z^3,$$

and the total flux through $B$ is $\pi b^2 n_2(\mu\mu_0 H)$, since the field through the coil will be uniform in the first approximation when the inequality $z \gg a, b$ holds. Hence the mutual inductance is

$$M = \frac{\mu\mu_0 \pi a^2 b^2 n_1 n_2}{2z^3}.$$          (6.17)

*Pair of coaxial cylinders*

An important method of carrying radio-frequency alternating currents is by means of a pair of coaxial cylinders of radii $a, b$ ($b > a$), as

in Fig. 6.6. At any point the current in the inner cylinder is $I$, while
that in the outer cylinder is $-I$; that is, it is exactly equal in magnitude
but flowing in the opposite direction. The magnetic field at a distance $r$
from the axis when $r < b$ is the same as that due to a straight wire, so
that
$$H = I/2\pi r.$$

Application of the same equation shows that there will be no field outside
the larger cylinder, since any circuit drawn round it is threaded by two

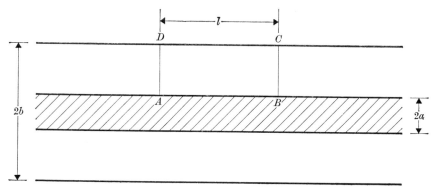

FIG. 6.6. Self-inductance of coaxial cylinders.

equal and opposite currents. To compute the self-inductance of a length
$l$, we find the flux through a circuit such as $ABCD$ in Fig. 6.6. This flux is

$$l \int_a^b (\mu\mu_0 H)\, dr = \frac{\mu\mu_0 lI}{2\pi} \int_a^b \frac{dr}{r} = \frac{\mu\mu_0}{2\pi} lI \log_e\!\left(\frac{b}{a}\right).$$

The flux and hence also the inductance are proportional to the length.
Hence the inductance per unit length is

$$\frac{\mu\mu_0}{2\pi} \log_e\!\left(\frac{b}{a}\right) \text{ henry/metre.} \tag{6.18}$$

For another method of deriving this formula, which avoids the use of
the hypothetical circuit $ABCD$, see Problem 6.1.

## 6.3. Transient currents in circuits containing inductance, resistance, and capacitance

If a circuit containing a battery $V$ and a resistance $R$ is connected
to a coil through which the flux $N$ is changing, the total voltage $V'$
applied to the resistance $R$ will be the sum of the battery voltage $V$ and
the e.m.f. developed in the coil. Hence $V' = V - dN/dt = RI$, or

$$V = RI + dN/dt. \tag{6.19}$$

We can apply this equation to a number of problems, the first being a circuit containing a self-inductance $L$ and a resistance $R$, as shown in Fig. 6.7, which is connected at time zero to a battery of constant e.m.f. $V$. Since $dN/dt = L(dI/dt)$, we have

$$V = IR + L\,(dI/dt),\qquad(6.20)$$

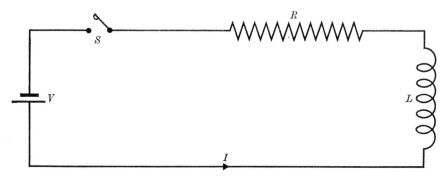

FIG. 6.7. Battery driving current through $R$ and $L$.

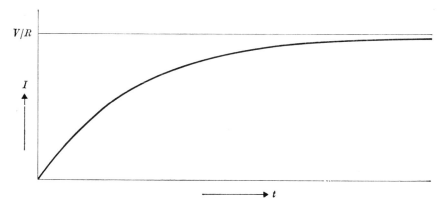

FIG. 6.8. Rise of current in circuit of Fig. 6.7.

which is the fundamental differential equation relating the current $I$ to the voltage $V$. Integration of this equation, with the condition $I = 0$ at $t = 0$, gives

$$I = \frac{V}{R}\,(1 - e^{-(R/L)t}),\qquad(6.21)$$

showing that the current approaches exponentially the value $V/R$ which it would have if there were no inductance present (see Fig. 6.8). The rate of approach to this steady value depends on the ratio of resistance to inductance. If $R = 0$, the steady state, corresponding to infinite current, is never reached, but the current rises linearly according to the equation $I = (V/L)t$, obtained by direct integration of equation (6.20) with $R = 0$. When $R$ is finite, the initial rate of rise of current, given by the tangent at the origin in Fig. 6.8, is $dI/dt = V/L$, but as the current through the resistance increases, the voltage across the inductance falls, with a corresponding decrease in $dI/dt$.

The converse problem, in which a battery has been connected to the circuit for a long time so that a steady current $I_0$ is flowing, and then at time zero the battery is replaced by a short circuit, leads to the same differential equation (6.20), but with $V = 0$. Its solution is

$$I = I_0 e^{-(R/L)t}, \tag{6.22}$$

showing that the effect of the inductance is to prevent the current from falling instantaneously to zero. If the battery is suddenly open-circuited,

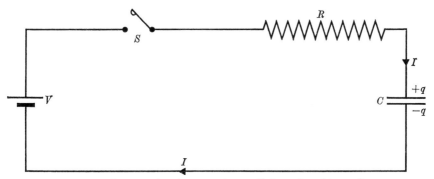

Fig. 6.9. Battery charging capacitance $C$ through resistance $R$.

the sudden cessation of the current produces a large impulse voltage $-L (dI/dt)$ in the inductance, which may be sufficient to cause a spark across the point at which the circuit is broken. With large inductances such as are found in electromagnets (see § 8.5) very high voltages may arise in this way which can damage the insulation if the circuit is broken suddenly.

In both the cases considered above the exponential is of the form $e^{-t/\tau}$, and the exponential rate of change of the current is the same; the quantity $\tau = L/R$ is called the time constant of the circuit.

*Circuit with capacitance and resistance*

An analogous problem is that of a capacitance $C$ in series with a resistance $R$, to which a battery $V$ is connected at time zero (see Fig. 6.9). At any instant the charge on the capacitor is $q$, and the voltage across it is $q/C$. Since the current $I = dq/dt$, we have

$$V = q/C + RI = q/C + R\,(dq/dt).\qquad(6.23)$$

The solution of this equation gives

$$q = CV(1 - e^{-t/RC})\qquad(6.24)$$

showing that the charge on the capacitor builds up in a manner similar to the current in the previous problem. The time constant of the circuit is now $\tau = RC$, and the current at any instant is

$$I = dq/dt = \frac{V}{R}\,e^{-t/RC} = \frac{V}{R}\,e^{-t/\tau}.\qquad(6.25)$$

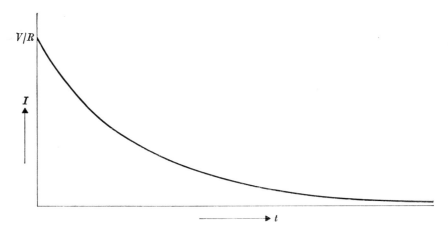

Fɪɢ. 6.10. Current in circuit of Fig. 6.9 after switch is closed.

It therefore falls exponentially from its initial value $(V/R)$ to zero, as shown in Fig. 6.10. The voltage across the capacitor increases from zero to its steady value $V$, when no more current can flow in the circuit.

If we have an isolated capacitor initially at a voltage $V_0$, and a resistance $R$ is then connected across it at time $t = 0$, the differential equation for the charge at a subsequent time is given by equation (6.23) with $V = 0$. The solution is

$$q = CV_0\,e^{-t/RC} = CV_0\,e^{-t/\tau}\qquad(6.26)$$

showing that the charge decays exponentially to zero.

*Circuit containing L, C, R*

An inductance, a capacitance, and a resistance are connected in series, as in Fig. 6.11, and the circuit is closed at an instant $t = 0$ when the charge on the capacitor is $q_0$. Since the total voltage in the circuit is always zero, we have

$$L\frac{dI}{dt}+IR+\frac{q}{C}=0.$$

Since $I = dq/dt$, $q$ may be eliminated by differentiation, giving

$$L\frac{d^2I}{dt^2}+R\frac{dI}{dt}+\frac{I}{C}=0. \tag{6.27}$$

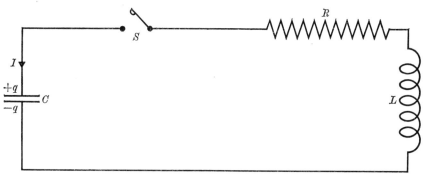

FIG. 6.11. Discharge of a capacitance $C$ through resistance $R$ and inductance $L$.

This equation has a general solution of the form

$$I = e^{-(R/2L)t}\{Ae^{nt}+Be^{-nt}\}, \tag{6.28}$$

where

$$n^2 = (R/2L)^2-(1/LC)$$

and $A$, $B$ are constants determined by the initial conditions. Since $I = 0$ at time $t = 0$, we must have $B = -A$, and the value of $A$ can be found by integration of (6.28) and setting $q = q_0$ at $t = 0$.

The nature of the solution depends on whether $n$ is real or imaginary. Three cases can be distinguished:

(a) $n$ real, that is, $(R/2L) > 1/(LC)^{\frac{1}{2}}$. The discharge of the capacitor is aperiodic, as shown in Fig. 6.12.

(b) $n = 0$; that is, $(R/2L) = 1/(LC)^{\frac{1}{2}}$. In this case the solution is of the form

$$q = q_0(1+tR/2L)e^{-(R/2L)t} \tag{6.29}$$

and the aperiodic discharge is most rapid.

(c) $n$ imaginary; that is, $(R/2L) < 1/(LC)^{\frac{1}{2}}$. The discharge is now oscillatory, as in Fig. 6.13, and the current may be written as

$$I = Ae^{-(R/2L)t}\sin \omega t, \tag{6.30}$$

where $\omega^2 = 1/LC-R^2/4L^2$. If the resistance is small, so that

$$(R/2L) \ll 1/(LC)^{\frac{1}{2}} \quad \text{(i.e. } \tfrac{1}{2}R(C/L)^{\frac{1}{2}} \ll 1),$$

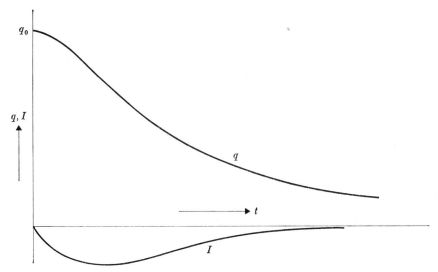

FIG. 6.12. Charge on capacitor and current in circuit of Fig. 6.11 (non-oscillatory discharge).

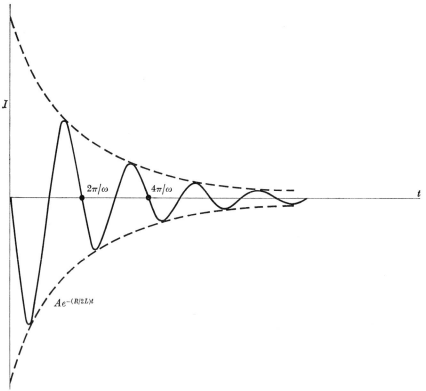

FIG. 6.13. Oscillatory discharge in a circuit containing a capacitance, a resistance, and an inductance.

$$I = Ae^{-(R/2L)t}\sin \omega t.$$

the angular frequency $\omega$ will be close to $1/(LC)^{\frac{1}{2}}$. We may call

$$f_0 = 1/\{2\pi\sqrt{(LC)}\}$$

the natural frequency of oscillation of the circuit in the absence of damping. When the damping is small the amplitude of the oscillations decays slowly, and the maxima, which lie on the exponential curve

$$\left[A\Big/\sqrt{\left\{1+\left(\frac{R}{2\omega L}\right)^2\right\}}\right]e^{-(R/2L)t}$$

occur very nearly at the points where $\tan \omega t = (2\omega L/R)$. These points occur at intervals of time $T$, where $T = 2\pi/\omega \approx 2\pi(LC)^{\frac{1}{2}}$ (where we

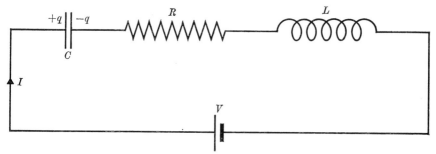

FIG. 6.14. Battery $V$ charging capacitance $C$ through resistance $R$ and inductance $L$.

have again assumed that the damping is small), and the amplitude of successive maxima (of the same sign) therefore decreases by the constant ratio $\exp(-TR/2L)$. If we denote successive maxima by $I_m$, $I_{m+1}$, the quantity

$$\log_e(I_m/I_{m+1}) = TR/2L \approx \pi R(C/L)^{\frac{1}{2}} = \pi/Q \tag{6.31}$$

is known as the 'logarithmic decrement' of the circuit. The quantity

$$Q = \frac{1}{R}\sqrt{\Big/\left(\frac{L}{C}\right)}$$

is known as the 'quality factor' of the circuit. Either of these quantities serves as an important criterion for the performance of an oscillatory circuit, but in electricity it is customary to use the quality factor $Q$ rather than the logarithmic decrement. Further relations involving $Q$ will be obtained in Chapter 9.

The converse problem, where a battery of e.m.f. $V$ is connected at time zero to a circuit containing $L$, $C$, $R$ in series (Fig. 6.14), is left as an exercise for the reader. The differential equation is the same as (6.27), and the solutions are similar to those above, with an aperiodic or oscillatory approach to the equilibrium state where no current flows and the voltage across the capacitance is equal to $V$. An important point is that the approach to the equilibrium state in the $L$, $C$, $R$ circuit is most rapid at the change-over point from an aperiodic to an oscillatory condition; that is, when $(R/2L) = (LC)^{-\frac{1}{2}}$ or $Q = (L/C)^{\frac{1}{2}}/R = \frac{1}{2}$.

## 6.4. Magnetic energy and mechanical forces in inductive circuits

In the circuit of Fig. 6.14 the relation between the applied voltage $V$ and the current is given by the equation

$$V = L\frac{dI}{dt} + RI + \frac{q}{C},$$

where $q$ is the charge on the capacitance. The rate at which work is done is found by multiplying by $I$, giving

$$VI = LI\frac{dI}{dt} + RI^2 + \left(\frac{dq}{dt}\right)\frac{q}{C}$$

since $I = dq/dt$. The work done in a time interval $t$, in which the current changes from $I_1$ to $I_2$, and the charge on the capacitance from $q_1$ to $q_2$, will be

$$W = \int_0^t VI\,dt = \tfrac{1}{2}L(I_2^2 - I_1^2) + \int_0^t RI^2\,dt + \frac{1}{2C}(q_2^2 - q_1^2).$$

Now $W$ is the total work done by the battery, and the integral of $RI^2$ is the energy dissipated as heat in the resistance, which is always positive. The last term, $\tfrac{1}{2}(q_2^2 - q_1^2)/C$, represents the change in the stored energy of the capacitance, and we interpret the first term $\tfrac{1}{2}L(I_2^2 - I_1^2)$ as the change in the energy stored in the inductance. We note that this change is reversible, since if the current is first increased to $I_2$ and then returned to its initial value $I_1$, the change in the stored energy is zero. If $I_1 = 0$, and a current $I$ is established in the inductance, an energy $\tfrac{1}{2}LI^2$ will be associated with it.

An expression for the energy stored in a series of inductances will now be derived in a more general way. If $N_k$ is the flux through the $k$th circuit, the voltage induced in it is $V_k = dN_k/dt$, and the rate of doing work is $I_k V_k = I_k(dN_k/dt)$. We assume that currents in all the circuits were initially zero and increased proportionately with time, so that at an intermediate instant $t'$ the values are $I'_k = \alpha I_k$, $N'_k = \alpha N_k$. Then the total work done is

$$\int_0^t I'_k V'_k\,dt' = I_k N_k \int_0^t \alpha(d\alpha/dt')\,dt'$$

$$= I_k N_k \int_0^1 \alpha\,d\alpha = \tfrac{1}{2}I_k N_k. \tag{6.32}$$

On summing over all the circuits, we have

$$U = \tfrac{1}{2} \sum_k I_k N_k. \tag{6.33}$$

If each coil has both self and mutual inductance,

$$N_k = L_k I_k + \sum_{j \neq k} M_{kj} I_j. \tag{6.34}$$

Hence equation (6.33) can be written in the form

$$U = \tfrac{1}{2} \sum_k L_k I_k^2 + \tfrac{1}{2} \sum_j \sum_k^{j \neq k} M_{kj} I_k I_j. \tag{6.35}$$

Since $M_{kj} = M_{jk}$, each term in the second summation occurs twice. This is clearly seen if we consider just two coils, for which (writing $M$ for $M_{12}$)

$$N_1 = L_1 I_1 + M I_2, \qquad N_2 = L_2 I_2 + M I_1,$$

so that the energy becomes

$$\begin{aligned} U &= \tfrac{1}{2} I_1 (L_1 I_1 + M I_2) + \tfrac{1}{2} I_2 (L_2 I_2 + M I_1) \\ &= \tfrac{1}{2} (L_1 I_1^2 + L_2 I_2^2) + M I_1 I_2. \end{aligned} \tag{6.36}$$

It is important to realize the distinction between this stored energy $U$ and the potential energy of one circuit carrying an invariant current $I_1$ in the field of a second circuit carrying an invariant current $I_2$, given by equation (6.11). The difference lies in the fact that the formula for $U_P$ assumes that the currents are invariant, and no account is taken of any work done by the batteries in maintaining the currents, whereas the stored energy $U$ includes the work done by the batteries in setting up the current flow, starting from zero current. Thus $U_P$ is the potential energy function from which any mechanical force can be calculated by the usual formulae such as

$$F_x = -dU_P/dx \tag{6.37}$$

for the $x$-component of the force, under the condition that the currents are kept constant.

The distinction between $U$ and $U_P$ can be seen from a simple example, that of two rigid circuits as in Fig. 6.15, one of which is moving with velocity $dx/dt$ with respect to the other. Then the rate at which work is done by the batteries is

$$dW/dt = (dU/dt) + F_x(dx/dt) + R_1 I_1^2 + R_2 I_2^2, \tag{6.38}$$

where $dU/dt$ is the rate at which the stored energy changes. Now from equation (6.37) $F_x(dx/dt) = -(dU_P/dx)(dx/dt) = -dU_P/dt$ and hence

$$dW/dt = (dU/dt) - (dU_P/dt) + R_1 I_1^2 + R_2 I_2^2.$$

Now the flux through each circuit is

$$N_1 = L_1 I_1 + M I_2, \qquad N_2 = L_2 I_2 + M I_1,$$

and the rate at which work is done by the batteries is

$$dW/dt = I_1(R_1 I_1 + dN_1/dt) + I_2(R_2 I_2 + dN_2/dt)$$
$$= 2(dM/dt)I_1 I_2 + R_1 I_1^2 + R_2 I_2^2,$$

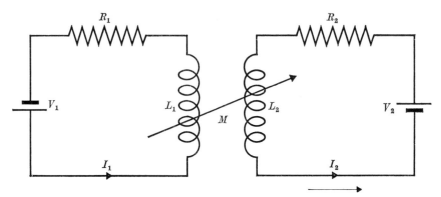

FIG. 6.15. Two circuits with a mutual inductance $M$. Circuit (2) is moving relative to circuit (1) so that $M$ is varying, but $L_1$, $L_2$ and $I_1$, $I_2$ are constant.

since $I_1$, $I_2$ are constant. Comparing these two equations, we see that

$$dU/dt = dU_P/dt + 2(dM/dt)I_1 I_2. \qquad (6.39)$$

Now from equation (6.36), since only $M$ is changing,

$$dU/dt = (dM/dt)I_1 I_2$$

and hence $\qquad dU_P/dt = -(dM/dt)I_1 I_2 = -dU/dt.$

Thus the component of the mechanical force is

$$F_x = -dU_P/dx = +dU/dx. \qquad (6.40)$$

From equation (6.39) we see that the difference in sign between the two expressions for the force in (6.40) arises from the fact that the batteries do work at the rate $2(dM/dt)I_1 I_2$ (apart from the irreversible Joule heating represented by the terms $R_1 I_1^2$, etc.) which is just twice the rate of increase $(dU/dt)$ of the stored energy. This situation with regard to the magnetic energy, and the calculation of the mechanical forces in a system where the currents are kept constant, is similar to that in electrostatics when changes take place in a system where the conductors are maintained at constant potential. It was shown in § 1.7 that in a change where the stored energy increases by $dU$, the batteries do work $2dU$, so that the amount of external work $dW$ done on the system is

$-dU$. Hence the component of the force in the $x$-direction is given by

$$F_x = -dU_P/dx = +(dU/dx)_V,$$

where the subscript $V$ denotes that this formula is to be used under the condition $V = $ constant. Similarly, we may emphasize that in equations such as (6.40) the current is kept constant by writing them in the form

$$F_x = +(dU/dx)_I, \text{ etc.}$$

As we should expect, the torque on a coil can be shown to be

$$\Gamma = -(dU_p/d\theta) = +(dU/d\theta)_I = (dM/d\theta)I_1 I_2, \qquad (6.41)$$

where $\theta$ is the angle which the coil makes with some fixed axis.

## 6.5. Magnetic energy in magnetic media

Since for any circuit

$$N = \int \mathbf{B}.\mathbf{dS} = \int \operatorname{curl} \mathbf{A}.\mathbf{dS} = \oint \mathbf{A}.\mathbf{ds} \qquad (6.42)$$

we can transform equation (6.33) as follows:

$$U = \tfrac{1}{2} \sum_k I_k N_k = \tfrac{1}{2} \sum_k I_k \oint \mathbf{A}.\mathbf{ds}.$$

For a system of distributed currents, we write $I\,\mathbf{ds} = \mathbf{J}\,d\tau$, and take the integral over all space, since contributions arise only from regions where $\mathbf{J}$ is finite, giving

$$U = \tfrac{1}{2} \int (\mathbf{A}.\mathbf{J})\,d\tau. \qquad (6.43)$$

However, $\mathbf{J} = \operatorname{curl}\mathbf{H}$, and using the vector identity

$$\operatorname{div}(\mathbf{A}\wedge\mathbf{H}) = \mathbf{H}.\operatorname{curl}\mathbf{A} - \mathbf{A}.\operatorname{curl}\mathbf{H},$$

we have
$$U = \tfrac{1}{2} \int (\mathbf{H}.\operatorname{curl}\mathbf{A})\,d\tau - \tfrac{1}{2} \int \operatorname{div}(\mathbf{A}\wedge\mathbf{H})\,d\tau$$
$$= \tfrac{1}{2} \int (\mathbf{H}.\mathbf{B})\,d\tau - \tfrac{1}{2} \int (\mathbf{A}\wedge\mathbf{H})\,\mathbf{dS}.$$

If the volume integral is extended over all space, the surface integral is taken over the sphere at infinity. For a finite system of closed circuits, the fields $\mathbf{H}$, $\mathbf{B}$ at large distances will fall off at least as rapidly as those of dipoles; hence $\mathbf{H} \sim r^{-3}$ and $\mathbf{A} \sim r^{-2}$, so that the integrand diminishes as $r^{-5}$ and the integral vanishes as $r \to \infty$. Hence we have

$$U = \tfrac{1}{2} \int (\mathbf{H}.\mathbf{B})\,d\tau. \qquad (6.44)$$

This formula shows that the energy may be regarded as distributed throughout the region occupied by the fields with density $\tfrac{1}{2}\mathbf{H}.\mathbf{B}$, which is clearly analogous to the result $\tfrac{1}{2}\mathbf{D}.\mathbf{E}$ obtained in electrostatics (1.36). In each case it has been derived under the assumption that $\mathbf{B}$ ($\mathbf{D}$) is linearly proportional to $\mathbf{H}$ ($\mathbf{E}$), i.e. that the media have values of $\mu$ ($\epsilon$),

which are independent of field strength, We may relax this assumption
by considering infinitesimal changes of flux, for which $\delta U = \sum_k I_k \delta N_k$.

Then by applying transformations exactly similar to those above, we
find

$$\delta U = \int \mathbf{J}.\delta\mathbf{A}\, d\tau = \int \mathbf{H}.\delta\mathbf{B}\, d\tau, \qquad (6.45)$$

a result which can then be integrated over any finite change in $\mathbf{B}$ if we
know how $\mathbf{H}$ and $\mathbf{B}$ are related at every point during the change. If $\mathbf{B}$
is linearly proportional to $\mathbf{H}$, this result clearly gives again equation
(6.44).

We close this discussion by finding the work done when the mag-
netization changes by $\delta\mathbf{M}$ in a field $\mathbf{B}_0$ which is due to other sources,
i.e. $\mathbf{B}_0$ does not include the field due to the magnetic material itself.
A simple example would be a piece of magnetizable material inside a
solenoid; $\mathbf{B}_0$ is then just equal to the field $\mu_0\mathbf{H}_0$ which the solenoid would
produce in the absence of the magnetizable substance, and can be cal-
culated from the standard formulae. We start by considering two
circuits, for which, from equation (6.39), in an infinitesimal change,

$$\delta U = \delta U_P + 2\delta(MI_1 I_2).$$

But $U_P = -\mathbf{m}_2.\mathbf{B}_1 = -I_2 \int \mathbf{B}_1.d\mathbf{S}_2$, and the flux through the second
circuit is $MI_1 = \int \mathbf{B}_1.d\mathbf{S}_2$. Hence

$$\delta U = +\delta I_2 \int \mathbf{B}_1.d\mathbf{S}_2 = \delta(\mathbf{B}_1.\mathbf{m}_2),$$

where $\mathbf{m}_2$ is the equivalent magnetic moment of the second coil, and
we assume that $\mathbf{B}_1$ is constant over the area of this coil. If $\mathbf{B}_1$ is fixed,
and $\mathbf{m}_2$ increases by $\delta\mathbf{m}$, then $\delta U = \mathbf{B}_1.\delta\mathbf{m}$. Clearly it does not matter
what the source of $\mathbf{B}_1$ is, so that we can write in general

$$\delta U = \mathbf{B}_0.\delta\mathbf{m} = \int (\mathbf{B}_0.\delta\mathbf{M})\, d\tau, \qquad (6.46)$$

where $\mathbf{B}_0$ excludes the field contribution from the magnetized substance
itself.

## PROBLEMS

6.1. Two infinite coaxial cylinders carry equal and opposite currents $I$. Calculate
the self-inductance $L$ per unit length (equation (6.18)) by equating the stored
energy per unit length to $\frac{1}{2}LI^2$.

6.2. Prove that the inductance per unit length of two infinite parallel wires of
radius $a$ separated by a distance $2d$ $(2d \gg a)$ is

$$L = (\mu\mu_0/\pi)\log_e(2d/a).$$

**6.3.** Prove that the inductance of a long solenoid of length $l$, radius $a$, with $m$ turns per unit length is approximately

$$L = \pi m^2 a^2 \mu \mu_0 \{(l^2 + a^2)^{\frac{1}{2}} - a\}$$

(assume that the field is uniform over any cross-section: if $l > 10a$, this formula is accurate within 2 per cent).

**6.4.** Show that the mutual inductance between two coplanar coaxial coils of radii $a$ and $b$ ($b \gg a$), with turns $n_1$ and $n_2$ respectively, is approximately (*in vacuo*)

$$M = \mu_0 \pi a^2 n_1 n_2 / 2b.$$

Use this result to show that the flux through the larger coil due to a small magnet $\mathfrak{m}$ placed at its centre and pointing along its axis is

$$N = \mu_0 \mathfrak{m} n_2 / 2b.$$

**6.5.** If the magnet in the last problem is withdrawn along the axis at a uniform velocity $v$, show that the e.m.f. induced in the coil when the magnet is at a distance $z$ from the centre of the coil is

$$V = 3\mu_0 \mathfrak{m} n_2 z v b^2 / 2(b^2 + z^2)^{\frac{5}{2}}.$$

If the resistance of the coil is $R$, show that the total charge which flows when the magnet is removed from the centre to infinity is

$$Q = \mu_0 \mathfrak{m} n_2 / 2b R.$$

**6.6.** A plane circular disk of radius $a$ rotates at a speed of $f$ revolutions per second about an axis through its centre normal to its plane. A uniform induction $B$ exists parallel to this axis. Show from first principles that there is an e.m.f. between the centre of the disk and its rim of magnitude $V = f B \pi a^2$. (Lorenz's method of determining the unit of resistance depends on this result; see § 7.4.)

**6.7.** A circular coil of $n$ turns of radius $a$, total resistance $R$, and no self-inductance is rotated with uniform angular velocity $\omega$ about a vertical diameter in a horizontal induction $B$. Prove that the mean power required to maintain the coil in motion is

$$W = \tfrac{1}{2} n^2 \pi^2 a^4 B^2 \omega^2 / R,$$

and that this is equal to the power dissipated in the resistance of the coil.

A small magnetic needle, which is free to turn slowly in a horizontal plane, is placed at the centre of the coil. Show that it will set at an angle $\phi$ to $B$ where

$$\cot \phi = 4R/(\pi n^2 \mu_0 \omega a).$$

(Rayleigh's method of determining the unit of resistance is based on an experiment of this type.)

**6.8.** A torsional pendulum consists of two spheres of 1 cm diameter at either end of a thin rod 10 cm long suspended at its mid-point. It swings in a horizontal plane so that its instantaneous angular deflexion is $\pi \cos \frac{1}{2}\pi t$. Find the magnitude and direction of the current flowing in the rod at any instant, assuming that the capacity of each sphere is the same as if each were isolated in space, and the rod and suspension have negligible resistance.

Show that there will be damping of the swing if the suspension has a finite resistance, but not otherwise.

(Vertical component of earth's magnetic field = $6 \times 10^{-5}$ weber/m².)

$$(\textit{Answer}: 3\cdot2 \times 10^{-19} \cos \tfrac{1}{2}\pi t \text{ amp.})$$

6.9. An aeroplane is in level flight at a ground speed of 300 km/hr. Its metal propeller measures 3 m from tip to tip and rotates at 3000 r.p.m. Find an expression for the p.d. between the ends of the propeller when the aeroplane is flying along the magnetic meridian.

(Vertical component of earth's magnetic field $= 6 \times 10^{-5}$ weber/m².)

(*Answer*: $0.015 \cos 100\pi t$ volts.)

6.10. Show that for a uniformly magnetized spherical permanent magnet, $\int \frac{1}{2}\mathbf{B}.\mathbf{H} \, d\tau$, integrated over the volume inside the sphere, is just equal and opposite to the value of the integral over the volume outside the sphere. Thus $\int \frac{1}{2}\mathbf{B}.\mathbf{H} \, d\tau$ over the whole of space is zero. (This follows because there are no currents—see the derivation of $U = \int \frac{1}{2}\mathbf{B}.\mathbf{H} \, d\tau$ in § 6.5.)

6.11. The magnetostatic energy of a permanent magnet is $\int \frac{1}{2}\mu_0 H^2 \, d\tau$ taken over all space. A solid spherical permanent magnet of radius $b$ is uniformly magnetized with a magnetization $M$ per unit volume. Show that the total energy stored in the field outside the sphere is $\mu_0 V M^2/9$, where $V$ is the volume of the sphere. Show also that the energy (thus defined) stored in the field inside the sphere is $\mu_0 V M^2/18$. Thus the total energy is $\mu_0 V M^2/6$, and this is the magnetostatic energy of the sphere.

(*Hint*: Use the result of Problem 5.9. The question of the magnetostatic energy of a permanent magnet is discussed by V. Heine (1956), *Proc. Camb. Phil. Soc.* **52**, 546.)

# DIRECT CURRENT MEASUREMENTS

## 7.1. Galvanometers, ammeters, and voltmeters; the wattmeter

A GALVANOMETER is an instrument for detecting and measuring electric current; if it is provided with a scale already calibrated, it is called an ammeter. The only type of galvanometer now in common use is the moving-coil type, where the current is passed through a coil, usually rectangular in shape, which is suspended in a uniform constant magnetic induction, as in Fig. 7.1. The suspension is adjusted so that the plane of the coil is parallel to the lines of magnetic field when no current is passing. Flow of current through the coil gives it a magnetic moment, and the action of the magnetic field on this moment produces a couple which tends to turn the coil; this is balanced by the restoring torque due to the suspension, and an equilibrium position is reached where the two are equal. If the coil has $n$ turns, each of area $A$, and the current is $I$, the magnetic moment $\mathbf{m}$ will be $nAI$. When the coil is deflected through an angle $\theta$, the couple on it due to the suspension is $c\theta$, and on equating this to the couple exerted by the magnetic field, we have

$$c\theta = \mathbf{m} \wedge \mathbf{B} = InAB\cos\theta. \tag{7.1}$$

In practice the lines of $B$ are shaped so that they are always parallel to the plane of the coil, and the term $\cos\theta$ will then be unity, so that the equilibrium deflexion $\theta$ will be linearly proportional to the current.

The magnetic induction, usually $\approx 0.4$ weber/metre$^2$ (4,000 gauss), is produced by a small permanent magnet, with pole faces shaped as in Fig. 7.2. The centre of the gap is filled with iron, so that the lines of force in the gap are as nearly radial as possible. The coil is wound on a former which fits in the gap between this piece of iron and the pole faces without touching either. In the less sensitive but more rugged type of instrument the coil is suspended by two spiral metal springs which also serve as leads for the current, and the deflexion of the coil is indicated by a pointer moving over a scale. In a common type of instrument full-scale deflexion (corresponding to rotation of the coil through about 60° of arc) is obtained for a current of 1 mA, though more sensitive instruments can be obtained. This higher sensitivity is achieved by winding more turns on the coil; this increases the resistance, which rises to more than a hundred ohms. Such a high resistance is undesirable in many uses, and in galvanometers for currents of the order of microamperes a light suspension of phosphor bronze wire is used

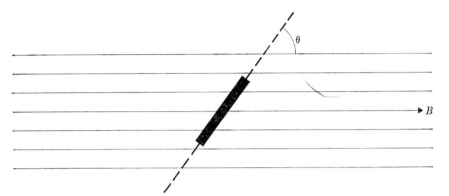

FIG. 7.1. Coil in a flux of magnetic induction $B$. Area of coil $= A$, number of turns $n$.

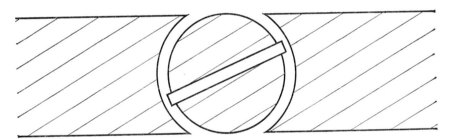

FIG. 7.2. Pole pieces of a permanent magnet in a moving-coil galvanometer.

instead of springs. This gives a small restoring torque and a greater sensitivity. This type of suspension is not strong enough to support a pointer, and the deflexion is observed by means of a lamp and scale, a small mirror being attached to the suspension just above the coil. With the scale at 1 metre distance, a common type of galvanometer gives a deflexion of about 100 mm/$\mu$A, with a coil resistance of about 10 ohms. Thus the increased sensitivity is obtained partly from use of a suspension with a smaller restoring torque, and partly from the greater reading accuracy of the lamp and scale method (the deflexion just quoted corresponds to a rotation of the galvanometer coil through about 3°). The period of swing of such an instrument is about 2 sec. Higher sensitivity can be obtained by use of a weaker suspension (giving also a longer period) and more turns on the coil (giving a higher resistance, and also

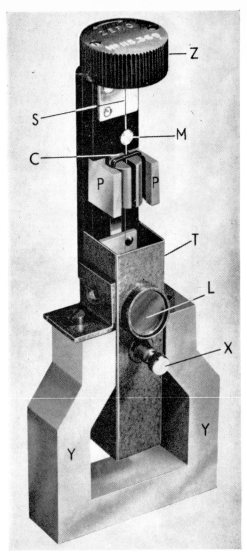

*(Courtesy of Messrs. H. Tinsley & Co.)*

Fig. 7.3. A modern galvanometer suspension and magnet.

| | |
|---|---|
| C—coil | Z—zero adjustment |
| M—mirror | L—lens |
| S—suspension strip | X—clamping mechanism |
| P—magnet pole pieces | Y—magnet yoke |
| | T—suspension tube |

When ready for use the coil assembly is lowered so that the mirror is behind the lens and the pole pieces in line with the yoke.

increasing the period through the greater moment of inertia of the coil unless correspondingly thinner wire is used). A typical galvanometer construction is shown in Fig. 7.3.

The pointer type of instrument described above is commonly known as a milliammeter. It may readily be adapted to make the full-scale reading correspond to any given greater current by use of a shunt. If the coil resistance is $R$, and the current required for full-scale reading

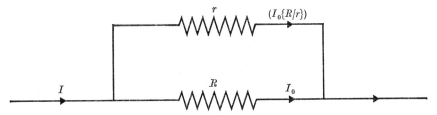

Fig. 7.4. Shunting a milliammeter.

is $I_0$, then by connecting a shunt of resistance $r$ across the coil as in Fig. 7.4, full-scale reading will be given by a current $I = I_0(1+R/r)$. Hence if $R$ is known, the sensitivity may be reduced by any given amount by the correct choice of $r$. The net resistance of the instrument becomes $rR/(r+R)$, and so becomes very low if the coil is shunted to read high currents. This is a desirable feature, since the ideal ammeter should have the lowest possible resistance in order to minimize its effect on the circuit in which it is introduced to measure the current.

The e.m.f. required to produce full-scale deflexion in the instrument just considered is $RI_0$, and hence the meter can be used to measure voltage if $R$ is known. Since $R$ is about 50 ohms for an instrument with a full-scale reading of 1 mA, the voltage required is about 50 mV. To reduce the sensitivity, a resistance $r$ is added in series with the coil, since this makes the voltage required for full-scale reading $I_0(r+R)$. By adjustment of $r$, any given full-scale reading can be obtained, and the instrument is then called a voltmeter. Use of a series resistance increases the net resistance of the instrument; since a voltmeter is connected across the circuit between the points where the voltage drop is to be measured, it is desirable that its resistance shall be as high as possible in order to change the current flow by the minimum amount. It is obvious that, whatever the reduction in sensitivity by adding series resistance, the current drawn by the meter at full-scale deflexion is $I_0$; thus a meter with the smallest possible value of $I_0$ should be used to construct a voltmeter. Similarly, if the meter is shunted to make an ammeter, the voltage across it for full-scale deflexion is constant and equal to $RI_0$; thus a meter with the lowest value of $RI_0$ should be used to make an ammeter.

The most accurate measurements of voltage are made with a potentiometer, as described in § 3.6; since no current is drawn from the source of voltage to be measured when the potentiometer is balanced, it behaves as a voltmeter with infinite resistance. Currents can be measured by determining the voltage drop across a known resistance, as in the calibration of an ammeter described in § 3.6.

In some applications it is more important to obtain the maximum galvanometer reading than to have an instrument with very low resistance, and we shall now discuss the factors involved in the correct choice of galvanometer for this purpose. Obviously the sensitivity of a moving-coil instrument is increased by using a higher value of $B$, and we shall assume that $B$ is already made as high as possible by the correct design of the permanent magnet. This means that the magnet gap in which the coil moves is fixed, and the dimensions of the coil itself are fixed. This determines also the suspension, since this depends mostly on the mass of the coil, and the restoring torque is therefore also fixed. Thus the only variables left are the number of turns $n$ on the coil, and the cross-section of wire used. If the available cross-section of the coil is $\alpha$, the cross-section of the wire must be $\alpha/n$; if the perimeter of the coil is $t$, the total length of wire is $nt$. Hence the coil resistance will be

$$R = nt\rho/(\alpha/n) = n^2 t\rho/\alpha,$$

where $\rho$ is the specific resistance of the wire. If the source of voltage $V$ has internal resistance $r$, as in Fig. 3.2, and drives a current $I$ through the galvanometer coil resistance $R$, then $I = V/(R+r)$, and from equation (7.1) the coil deflexion will be

$$\theta = \frac{nABI}{c} = \frac{ABV}{c}\left(\frac{n}{r+(n^2 t\rho/\alpha)}\right). \tag{7.2}$$

Differentiation with respect to $n$ shows that $\theta$ is a maximum when $n^2 t\rho/\alpha = r$, or $R = r$. Hence for optimum sensitivity the number of turns on the coil should be adjusted so that the coil resistance is just equal to the internal resistance of the source (cf. § 3.5). In practice it is only necessary to choose a galvanometer whose coil resistance is approximately equal to that of the load, since a factor 2 in the ratio of the resistances only causes the deflexion to fall by 6 per cent below the optimum. The analysis shows that a low resistance instrument should be used to measure, for example, the e.m.f. of a thermocouple, which has a low internal resistance. On the other hand, a high resistance instrument should be used to measure an ionization current (such as is caused by the passage of X-rays through a gas) since this behaves as a very high resistance source.

In the moving-coil instruments considered so far the magnetic induction $B$ is constant and provided by a permanent magnet. In another class of moving-coil instruments, known as dynamometers, the induction $B$ is provided by a second set of fixed coils carrying a current $I_1$

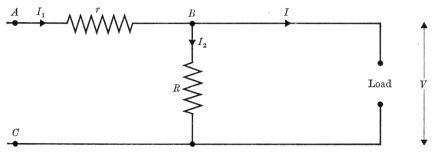

FIG. 7.5. A wattmeter.

surrounding the moving coil which carries a current $I_2$. Since $B$ is proportional to $I_1$, it is obvious that the torque on the moving coil will be proportional to $I_1 I_2$; more exactly, if $M$ is the mutual inductance between the fixed and moving coils, by equation (6.41) the torque is $I_1 I_2 (dM/d\theta)$, and hence the equilibrium deflexion will be given by the equation

$$c\theta = I_1 I_2 (dM/d\theta),$$

where $c\theta$ is the restoring torque due to the suspension (usually a spiral spring). The factor $(dM/d\theta)/c$ is found by calibration with known currents.

If a current $I$ to be measured is allowed to flow through the fixed and moving coils in series, so that $I = I_1 = I_2$, the instrument will act as a milliammeter with a square law deflexion; with a pointer type dynamometer the full-scale reading is about 10 mA. A more important application is its use as a wattmeter; the coils are then connected as follows. The fixed coil $r$ is connected in series with the load, so that $I_1$ is nearly equal to $I$, the current in the load; the moving coil is connected in series with a large resistance $R$ across the load, as in Fig. 7.5. Then the current $I_2 = V/R$, where $V$ is the voltage across the load. The deflexion is proportional to $I_1 I_2 = IV/R = W/R$, where $W$ is the power being dissipated in the load. Thus the instrument may be calibrated to measure power directly. Note that with the coils connected as in Fig. 7.5, the current through the fixed coil is really $I+I_2$, so that the power measured is the sum of that in the load and in $R$ (see Problem 7.6).

## 7.2. Galvanometer damping

So far we have considered only the equilibrium deflexion of a galvanometer when a steady current flows; the behaviour during the time interval between switching on the current and the attainment of the final deflexion must also be discussed. When the current starts to flow through the galvanometer coil, a couple is exerted on it which gives it an angular acceleration. This couple diminishes as the coil nears its equilibrium position, owing to the reverse couple exerted by the suspension, but if the damping is small, the coil may overshoot and oscillate about its final position. If the damping is large no overshoot may occur, and the coil approaches the final position very slowly. In either case some time must elapse before the equilibrium deflexion can be observed, and the effect of the damping is thus of considerable importance. Though air resistance and other sources of energy loss contribute to the damping, the most important source is electromagnetic damping, due to the motion of the coil in the magnetic field of the permanent magnet. With the notation of Fig. 7.1, the flux through the coil $N = nAB\sin\theta$, and there will therefore be an e.m.f. induced in the coil equal to

$$-dN/dt = -nAB\cos\theta(d\theta/dt).$$

If $\theta$ is small, or if the lines of magnetic induction are always radial (as in Fig. 7.2), we can put $\cos\theta = 1$. If $V$ is the external source of e.m.f. and $R$ is the total resistance in the circuit (including the galvanometer coil resistance), then the current $I$ will be given by the equation

$$V - \frac{dN}{dt} = RI$$

at any instant. The equation of motion of the coil will therefore be

$$\Im\frac{d^2\theta}{dt^2} + b\frac{d\theta}{dt} + c\theta = nABI = \frac{nAB}{R}\left(V - \frac{dN}{dt}\right) = \frac{nAB}{R}V - \frac{(nAB)^2}{R}\frac{d\theta}{dt},$$

(7.3)

where $\Im$ is the moment of inertia of the coil, $b(d\theta/dt)$ the torque due to air damping, etc., and $c\theta$ the restoring torque due to the suspension. Rearranging the equation gives

$$\Im\frac{d^2\theta}{dt^2} + \left\{b + \frac{(nAB)^2}{R}\right\}\frac{d\theta}{dt} + c\theta = \frac{nAB}{R}V,$$

(7.4)

from which it is seen that the effect of the e.m.f. induced by the motion
of the coil is to increase the damping torque by an amount

$$(nAB)^2 \, (d\theta/dt)/R.$$

The differential equation is similar to that for the oscillatory circuit of
§ 6.3, and the same analysis may be applied. There are three types of
solution, according to whether the damping is large or small:

(a) *Small damping,* $b' < 2(\Im c)^{\frac{1}{2}}$, where $b' = b+(nAB)^2/R$. The motion
is a damped harmonic motion, of period nearly equal to $2\pi(\Im/c)^{\frac{1}{2}}$.
The coil overshoots its equilibrium deflexion $\theta = (nAB)V/cR$, and
then oscillates with diminishing amplitude about this position.

(b) *Critical damping,* $b' = 2(\Im c)^{\frac{1}{2}}$. The coil approaches its equilibrium
without overshoot.

(c) *High damping,* $b' > 2(\Im c)^{\frac{1}{2}}$. The coil approaches its final position
without overshoot, but more slowly than in case (b).

In general the electromagnetic damping is much greater than other
sources of damping, unless the total resistance $R$ of the galvanometer
circuit is very large. As $R$ decreases the electromagnetic damping increases, and critical damping will be obtained with a certain value of
resistance $R_c$ given by the relation

$$R_c = \tfrac{1}{2}(nAB)^2/(\Im c)^{\frac{1}{2}}, \tag{7.5}$$

assuming that $b$ is negligible under these conditions. It is important to
operate a galvanometer at or near critical damping since it then takes
up its equilibrium deflexion (or, more precisely, comes to a deflexion
within a certain fraction of its equilibrium value) in the shortest possible
time. If the galvanometer is either highly over-damped or very much
under-damped it will take much longer to settle down, and this reduces
the rate at which readings can be taken. If the source of voltage varies
within the time required for the galvanometer to settle, the reading will
always lag behind the true value; in detecting the balance point of a
bridge, quite misleading indications can be obtained if the bridge arms
are altered too rapidly.

Since the critical damping resistance is of such importance, it is always
specified for a galvanometer, together with the coil resistance, the sensitivity, and the period. As a rough rule, the critical damping resistance
is 10 to 20 times the coil resistance in a modern reflecting galvanometer.
In a pointer instrument the coil may carry a short-circuited turn, or the
coil former may be made of metal, in order to give adequate damping.

## 7.3. The ballistic galvanometer and fluxmeter

The ballistic galvanometer is a suspended moving-coil instrument with very light damping, which can be used for the measurement of charge by observing the maximum deflexion in its oscillatory motion. For this purpose the charge must pass through the galvanometer in a time short compared with its period of swing, so that the coil does not deflect appreciably during the passage of the charge. If the current at any instant during this passage is $I$, the couple exerted on the coil is $nABI$, and the impulse of angular momentum given to the coil will be

$$\int nABI \, dt = nABQ,$$

where $Q$ is the total charge flowing through the coil. The effect of this impulse is to give the coil an initial angular velocity $(d\theta/dt)_{t=0} = nABQ/\mathfrak{I}$, where $\mathfrak{I}$ is the moment of inertia of the coil. We analyse the subsequent motion of the coil assuming it to remain connected to a circuit of total resistance $R$ (including the coil resistance) but with no external e.m.f. The differential equation of the motion will be the same as (7.4) but with $V = 0$, so that we have

$$\mathfrak{I}\frac{d^2\theta}{dt^2} + b'\frac{d\theta}{dt} + c\theta = 0, \tag{7.6}$$

where $b' = b + (nAB)^2/R$ is the total effective damping, which we shall assume to be small. Then the solution is

$$\theta = De^{-b't/2\mathfrak{I}} \sin \omega t,$$

where $\omega = (c/\mathfrak{I})^{\frac{1}{2}}$ to a good approximation. The constant $D$ is found by differentiation, and setting the initial angular velocity equal to $nABQ/\mathfrak{I}$, giving

$$nABQ/\mathfrak{I} = (d\theta/dt)_{t=0} = D\omega,$$

whence
$$\theta = (nABQ/\mathfrak{I}\omega)e^{-b't/2\mathfrak{I}} \sin \omega t. \tag{7.7}$$

If there were no damping the deflexion would oscillate between maximum and minimum values $\pm\theta_0$ occurring at the instants when $\sin \omega t = 1$, and the charge $Q$ would be given by

$$Q = \mathfrak{I}\omega\theta_0/(nAB) = c\theta_0/(\omega nAB) = \theta_0\left(\frac{\tau}{2\pi}\right)\left(\frac{c}{nAB}\right), \tag{7.8}$$

where we have used in succession the relations $(\mathfrak{I}/c)\omega^2 = 1$, and $\omega = 2\pi/\tau$, where $\tau$ is the period of swing of the galvanometer. This can be measured experimentally, and the constant $(c/nAB)$ can be found from the deflexion produced by passing a steady current through the galvanometer.

The effect of the damping is to make successive deflexions smaller as in Fig. 7.6, and also to make the first throw $\theta_1$ (at $t = \frac{1}{4}\tau$) smaller than $\theta_0$, since from equation (7.7)

$$\theta_1 = \theta_0 e^{-b'\tau/8\Im}.$$

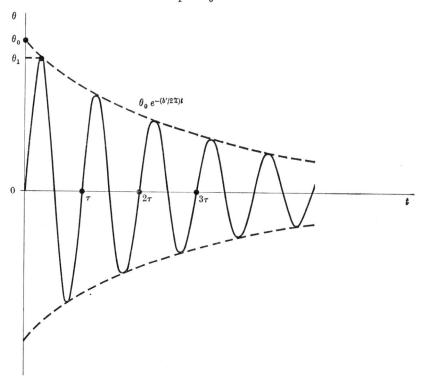

FIG. 7.6. The deflexion of a ballistic galvanometer plotted as a function of the time
$$\theta = \theta_0 e^{-(b'/2\Im)t} \sin \omega t.$$

The size of the correction can be found by measuring the logarithmic decrement $\lambda$ of successive swings on the same side, since

$$\lambda = \log(\theta_1/\theta_2) = \log(\theta_2/\theta_3), \text{ etc.}$$
$$= b'\tau/2\Im.$$

Hence,          $$\theta_0 = \theta_1 e^{\frac{1}{4}\lambda} \qquad (7.9)$$

or, since $\lambda$ is small,          $$\theta_0 = \theta_1(1 + \tfrac{1}{4}\lambda).$$

For accurate use the damping of the ballistic galvanometer should be small and the resistance of the external circuit must therefore be high. If used to measure the charge on a capacitor by connecting the capacitor to the galvanometer and allowing it to discharge through the galvanometer, this condition is fulfilled because the capacitor is effectively an open circuit for the slowly varying induced e.m.f. produced by the galvanometer swing. A convenient method of calibrating the ballistic galvanometer directly is by discharging through it a known capacitance charged to a known voltage. An alternative method is by means of a standard mutual inductance, using the circuit of Fig. 7.7. The secondary

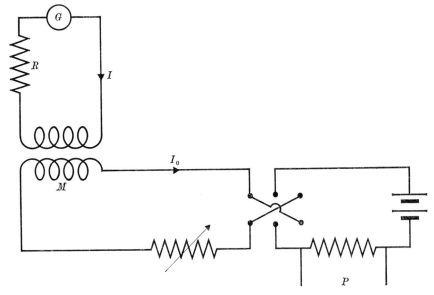

FIG. 7.7. Apparatus for calibrating a ballistic galvanometer.

G    Galvanometer.
M    Standard mutual inductance.
P    Potentiometer connected across standard 1 ohm resistance.

of the mutual inductance is connected to the galvanometer, and a known current is reversed in the primary coil. If $L$ is the inductance of the secondary windings and $R$ the total resistance in the secondary circuit, the secondary current $I$ flowing at any instant is given by the equation

$$L\frac{dI}{dt} + RI = -\frac{dN}{dt},$$

where $dN/dt$ is the rate at which the flux is changing through the secondary coil. Integrating over the duration of time occupied by the flux change (assuming that the time constant $R/L$ is very short compared with the period of the galvanometer) gives

$$\int -\frac{dN}{dt}\,dt = N_1 - N_2 = L\int \frac{dI}{dt}\,dt + R\int I\,dt = L[I]_0^0 + RQ = RQ,$$

(7.10)

showing that the charge measured by the galvanometer is just equal to the total flux change in the secondary divided by the total resistance. If $I_0$ is the current reversed in the primary, $N_1-N_2 = 2MI_0$, and so $Q = 2MI_0/R$. The current $I_0$ may either be measured by a substandard ammeter, or by means of the potential drop it produces across a known resistance. To reduce the damping of the ballistic galvanometer, either $R$ must be large, which in general will mean adding considerable resistance to the circuit and thus reducing the sensitivity of the galvanometer, or the secondary circuit must be broken immediately after the primary current is reversed and before the galvanometer has deflected appreciably.

Once the ballistic galvanometer has been calibrated, it may be used to measure a flux change or an unknown mutual inductance if the resistance $R$ is known. An alternative method is to use a fluxmeter, which gives a direct reading of the flux change. This instrument consists of a moving coil, suspended in such a way as to give almost zero restoring torque, in a strong magnetic induction of a permanent magnet. The electromagnetic damping is very strong, and if other forms of damping can be neglected, the equation of motion is

$$\Im \frac{d^2\theta}{dt^2} + \frac{(nAB)^2}{R} \frac{d\theta}{dt} = nABI = \frac{nAB}{R} \left( -\frac{dN}{dt} - L \frac{dI}{dt} \right), \qquad (7.11)$$

where $I$ is the instantaneous current produced by the e.m.f. $- dN/dt$ induced by the flux change to be measured, and $L$ is the self inductance. The effect of this current is to impart an angular momentum to the fluxmeter coil, which is then brought to rest under the action of the electromagnetic damping. Integration of equation (7.11) over the entire time occupied by the motion of the coil gives

$$\Im \left[ \frac{d\theta}{dt} \right]_0^0 + \frac{(nAB)^2}{R} [\theta]_0^{\theta_0} = \frac{nAB}{R} [N_1 - N_2] - \frac{nABL}{R} [I]_0^0$$

and, since the angular velocity and current are zero both initially and finally,

$$nAB\theta_0 = N_1 - N_2, \qquad (7.12)$$

where $\theta_0$ is the ultimate deflexion of the fluxmeter. The flux change through the fluxmeter coil is just $nAB\theta_0$, and so this equation shows that the total flux threading the system is the same at the beginning and the end. The fluxmeter is generally calibrated directly in terms of flux; since there is no restoring torque on the coil it has no stable position of equilibrium but can rest anywhere in neutral equilibrium. It is therefore necessary to level the instrument carefully to prevent the coil drifting during the measurement. As a rough rule, a fluxmeter is accurate to about 1 per cent, while a ballistic galvanometer, properly calibrated, is accurate to about 0·1 per cent.

## 7.4. Absolute measurements

Relative measurements of electrical quantities can be made using bridges or potentiometers to an accuracy of some parts in $10^5$. For absolute measurements it is necessary to have ultimate standards (for example, of resistance and current) with which an unknown quantity can be compared. The resistance of a coil was determined by Rayleigh in terms of the constant $\mu_0$ and the standard of length, by rotating the coil in a magnetic field (see Problem 6.7). Here we shall describe in some detail the method used by Lorenz, which has the two advantages of being a null method, and of not needing the resistance to be in the form of a coil. If a disk-shaped conductor is rotated in a magnetic field $B$ with a frequency of $f$ revolutions per second, and $B$ is parallel to the axis of rotation, a voltage is induced in the disk between the axis and the rim of magnitude $V = kfB$, where $k$ is a constant (with the dimensions of an area: see Problem 6.6) determined by the geometry of the apparatus. In Lorenz's experiment (Fig. 7.8) the field $B$ is produced by coils carrying a current $I$ which also flows through the resistance $R$ to be standardized. Then $B = \mu_0 I/k'$, where $k'$ is a quantity with the dimensions of a length, again fixed by the geometry of the apparatus. The voltage $V$ is balanced against the potential drop $RI$ across the resistance, so that $RI = (k/k')\mu_0 fI$, and at the balance point

$$R = (k/k')\mu_0 f. \tag{7.13}$$

The frequency $f$ can be measured accurately, $\mu_0$ is defined in the m.k.s. system as $4\pi\ 10^{-7}$ henry/metre, and $(k/k')$ has the dimensions of a length. In fact $\mu_0(k/k')$ is the mutual inductance between the field coil and the rotating conductor, which can be calculated from the dimensions and the geometry. Fundamentally the comparison is between the resistance and the product inductance × frequency, the rotating conductor being a device by which a steady voltage is developed across the inductance for balance against the voltage drop in the resistance.

The arrangement of the apparatus is shown in Fig. 7.8. The rotating conductor is formed by the disks $P$, $P'$ mounted on a shaft driven by a motor. The galvanometer $G$ reads zero when the voltage induced in the circuit $abcd$ is exactly equal to the potential across the resistance $R$, which is in series with the two coils $CC'$ and $DD'$. The current flows through these coils in the opposite sense so that the voltages induced in the two disks add round the circuit $abcd$. Contact with the disks at

$a$ and $d$ is made by brushes, and the coils are designed so that the magnetic induction at these contacts is zero; this minimizes any error in determining the actual radius of the disk; that is, the distance from the centre at which contact is made. Some trouble arises from thermal e.m.f.s. at the brush contacts, which would give a finite galvanometer

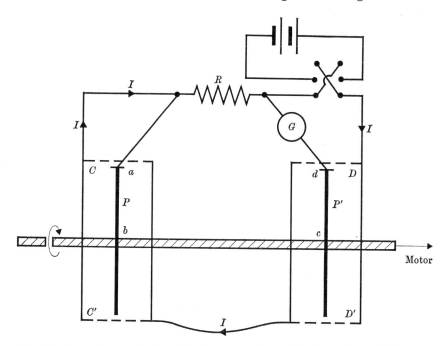

FIG. 7.8. Lorenz's apparatus for determining a resistance $R$ in terms of $\mu_0$ and the metre. $CC'$, $DD'$ are coils through which $I$ flows (in opposite senses) producing the magnetic fields in which the plates $PP'$ are rotated.

reading at the true balance point. This difficulty is overcome by reversing the current throughout the whole system, which reverses any true unbalance current but not that due to the thermal e.m.f. Hence the correct balance point is when the galvanometer reading remains unchanged on reversing the current, and this procedure also eliminates the effect of any voltages induced by stray magnetic fields. With adequate precautions it is possible to obtain an accuracy of a few parts in $10^5$; other resistances can then be determined relative to the standard by means of a Wheatstone's bridge.

From the fundamental equations of § 5.1, it can be seen that a current may be determined in absolute units by passing it through two conductors and measuring the force between them. The method of doing this, by means of a 'current balance', is illustrated in Fig. 7.9. $A$, $B$, $C$ $D$, $E$, $F$ are six single-layer coils wound on marble formers and connected in series. Coils $A$, $C$, $D$, and $F$ are fixed, while $B$ and $E$ are carried on a balance arm; the current flows through the various coils in such a direction that the force on $E$ is upwards while that on $B$ is downwards. The balance arm is brought back to its equilibrium position by moving a standard mass along a calibrated scale on the arm. From the distance of the mass from the fulcrum, the torque and hence the force

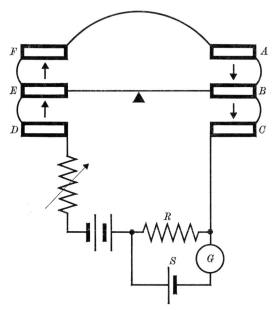

FIG. 7.9. Current balance.
$R$ standard resistance.      $G$ galvanometer.      $S$ standard cell.

between the coils can be evaluated. If $M$ is the mutual inductance between $B$ or $E$ and either of the coils $A$, $C$ or $D$, $F$, then the total torque due to the coils when carrying a current $I$ is $4I^2(dM/d\theta)$, where $\theta$ is the angle defining the rotation of the balance arm. Since $dM/d\theta$ must be calculated from the geometry, there must be no iron near the apparatus. Effects due to the more remote coils (that is, for example, the force between coil $A$ and coil $E$) are eliminated by repeating the readings with the current through all the coils on one side reversed. An accuracy of one part in $10^5$ can be achieved, but the measurements are very laborious. One such determination is carried out at a standardizing laboratory, and at the same time the voltage across a standard resistance, placed in series with the coils so that the standardized current flows through it, is compared with the e.m.f. of a standard Weston cell. By potentiometer methods, other Weston cells can be calibrated against the standard cell for use as substandards; subsequently, a current is measured by comparing the potential drop it produces in a standard resistance with the e.m.f. of the substandard cells. Ammeters can be calibrated in this way, as outlined in § 3.6.

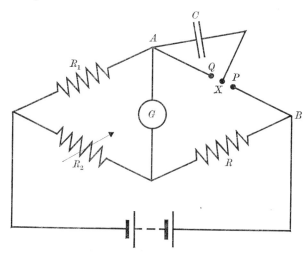

Fig. 7.10. Determination of a capacitance $C$ in terms of a standard resistance $R$.

The value of a resistance is found in absolute units by comparing it with an inductance whose value is $\mu_0$ times a factor with the dimensions of a length. The capacitance $C$ of a capacitor is $\epsilon_0 l$, where $l$ is a factor with the dimensions of a length which is determined by the geometry of the capacitor. Thus if $l$ is calculated, and the capacitance $C$ is determined by comparison with a standard resistance $R$, the value of the constant $\epsilon_0$ can be found. An accurate experiment of this type was carried out by Rosa and Dorsey in 1907; the apparatus consists essentially of the bridge circuit shown in Fig. 7.10. The contact $X$ vibrates between $P$ and $Q$ at a known frequency, and the capacitor $C$ is alternately charged and discharged $f$ times a second. The voltage $V$ across it is $q/C$, and the charging of the condenser $f$ times a second sends a current $fq$ through the arm $AB$, so that the effective resistance of this arm is $V/(fq) = 1/(fC)$. Hence at the balance point, $R_2/R_1 = fCR$. Rosa and Dorsey used both spherical and cylindrical capacitors, and took many readings to correct for a large variety of possible errors.

Their final result, expressed in our units, was

$$\epsilon_0 = (8{\cdot}8547)10^{-12} \text{ F/metre}$$

with an accuracy of about 4 parts in $10^5$.

## PROBLEMS

7.1. A bridge consists of a self-inductance $L$ and resistance of about 10 ohms in one arm and three non-inductive resistances in the remaining arms, so that an accurate steady balance is obtained. If, with the galvanometer in circuit, the battery key is depressed, a ballistic deflexion of 10 cm of the galvanometer is recorded. If in a second experiment a resistance of 0·02 ohm is connected in series with $L$, a steady deflexion of 12 cm is obtained with the key depressed. The galvanometer is a moving-coil instrument with a period of 9 sec. A switch in the galvanometer circuit is opened immediately after the flow of charge through it when it is used ballistically. Show that $L$ is approximately 24 mH.

7.2. A ballistic galvanometer is calibrated by putting it in series with a 2-V battery and a resistance of $10^6$ ohm. A steady deflexion of 17 cm is observed. The time of swing is 3·8 sec. A capacitor is charged by a 4-V battery and when discharged through the galvanometer gives a throw of 24·2 cm. Find its capacitance.

(*Answer*: $C = 0{\cdot}43\,\mu\text{F}$.)

7.3. A small search coil with 8 turns of mean area 1·5 cm² is placed between the poles of an electromagnet with its plane normal to the magnetic field. It is connected to a ballistic galvanometer and the total resistance of the circuit is 1000 ohms. When the coil is suddenly removed to a place where the field is negligible, the throw of the galvanometer is 23 divisions. When a capacitance of $1\,\mu\text{F}$ charged to 1 V is discharged through the galvanometer, the throw is 25 divisions. Calculate $B$ between the poles of the magnet.

(*Answer*: $B = 0{\cdot}77$ weber/metre².)

7.4. A ballistic galvanometer gives a throw of 10 cm when a charge of $3{\cdot}5 \times 10^{-7}$ coulombs is passed. Its period is 2·2 sec. Calculate the deflexion when a steady current of $3\,\mu\text{A}$ is passed.

(*Answer*: 30 cm.)

7.5. A capacitance is connected across a moving-coil ballistic galvanometer of negligible resistance; show that the period of the galvanometer is increased. If the capacitance is $10\,\mu\text{F}$, the current sensitivity of the galvanometer per $\mu\text{A}$ is 10 cm at a metre, the moment of inertia of the suspended system 10 g cm², and the period on open circuit 10 sec, show that the fractional change in period is about $2 \times 10^{-3}$.

7.6. In the circuit of Fig. 7.5, the moving coil (in series with $R$) may be connected either as shown or between the points $A$ and $C$. Show that the fractional error in the reading of the power in the load (resistance $Z$) is less with the latter method of connexion if $Z > (rR)^{\frac{1}{2}}$, and vice versa, where $r$ is the resistance of the fixed coil.

# 8

## MAGNETIC MATERIALS AND MAGNETIC MEASUREMENTS

### 8.1. Origins of magnetism

THE fact that a substance placed in a magnetic field acquires a magnetic moment was introduced in the theory of magnetostatics in § 5.3. The ratio of the magnetic moment per unit volume to the magnetic field $H$ is known as the susceptibility $\chi$, and substances are classed as diamagnetic, paramagnetic, or ferromagnetic according to the nature of their susceptibility. In the first two of these classes the induced magnetization is proportional to the applied field under ordinary conditions, so that the susceptibility is independent of the field strength. In diamagnetic substances the magnetization is in the opposite direction to the applied field, so that $\chi$ is negative, while in paramagnetic substances it is in the same direction, giving a positive value of $\chi$. Ferromagnetic substances are distinguished by very large (positive) values of $\chi$, which are not independent of the field strength; in addition they may possess a magnetic moment even in the absence of an applied field, as in a permanent magnet. In this chapter we shall give first a brief description of the origins of the magnetization, and describe methods of measuring magnetic properties. A fuller account of the theory of paramagnetism and ferromagnetism is given in Chapters 20 and 21.

After the discovery that a small coil carrying a current behaves like a magnet, Ampère suggested that the origin of all magnetism lay in small circulating currents associated with each atom. These 'amperean currents' would each possess a magnetic dipole moment, and the total magnetic moment of any substance would be just the vector sum of the magnetic dipole moments of its constituent atoms. This gave a natural explanation of the fact that no isolated magnetic pole had ever been observed, since even on the atomic scale only dipoles existed, and these were due to electric currents and did not consist of two actual magnetic poles of opposite sign separated by a small distance. Ampère's theory is essentially the same as that of modern atomic physics, the origin of his elementary current circuits being the motion of the negatively-charged electrons in closed orbits round the positively-charged atomic nucleus.

When a particle is moving in a closed orbit in a system where no external force is acting, its angular momentum is constant. If the particle is charged, a magnetic moment will be associated with its motion, and there is a linear relation between the angular momentum and the magnetic moment (see Problem 5.10 for the simple case of a circular orbit). A general expression for the magnetic dipole moment associated with a distributed current has already been found in § 5.5. In equation (5.52) we can replace $\mathbf{J}\,d\tau$ by $\mathbf{v}\,dq$ to find the equivalent expression for a moving charge, giving

$$\mathbf{m} = \int \tfrac{1}{2}(\mathbf{r} \wedge \mathbf{v})\,dq. \tag{8.1}$$

In the absence of an external force, the quantity $(\mathbf{r} \wedge \mathbf{v})$ is a constant, since $m(\mathbf{r} \wedge \mathbf{v})$ is equal to $\mathbf{G}$, the angular momentum for a particle of mass $m$. Hence

$$\mathbf{m} = \mathbf{G} \int (dq/2m) = (q/2m)\mathbf{G} = \gamma\mathbf{G}, \tag{8.2}$$

where $q = \int dq$ is the total charge circulating in the orbit. The quantity $\gamma = q/2m$ is called the magnetogyric ratio.

This close relation between magnetic moment and angular momentum is of great importance in atomic theories of magnetism, because on quantum theory the angular momentum of an electron in an atom, which is a constant of the motion, can only have discrete values. The electron possesses angular momentum not only in respect of its orbital motion round the nucleus, but also in respect of its intrinsic rotation (spin) about its own axis. The resultant angular momentum of an atom is the vector sum of the individual angular momenta of its electrons, and the resultant magnetic moment is a similar vector sum of the individual magnetic moments of the electrons. Because of the linear relation between the two, an atom, ion, or molecule will have no resultant permanent magnetic moment if the total angular momentum is zero. If the total angular momentum is not zero, the atom, ion, or molecule will have a permanent magnetic dipole moment. Most free atoms possess a permanent magnetic dipole moment because they have a resultant electronic angular momentum. Experiments such as the gyromagnetic effect (§ 21.4) in solids, and magnetic resonance (Chapter 23) for free particles and solids, give precise determinations of the ratio of the magnetic moment to the angular momentum for nuclei, and atoms and molecules, as well as magnetic ions in solids.

Such magnetic dipole moments are fundamentally different from electric dipole moments, where it has been shown (§ 2.3) that if parity is conserved in an atom or nucleus, no electric dipole moment can exist.

The difference is clear if we write out the components of the magnetic dipole moment given by equation (8.1); e.g.

$$m_z = \int \tfrac{1}{2}\left(x\frac{\partial y}{\partial t}-y\frac{\partial x}{\partial t}\right)dq.$$

If parity is conserved, we have inversion symmetry; that is, the value of $dq$ is the same at the point $(-x, -y, -z)$ as at the point $(x, y, z)$. So also is the quantity $\{x(\partial y/\partial t)-y(\partial x/\partial t)\}$, so that the integrand retains the same sign under the inversion operation, and the integral can have a finite value. This differs from the electric dipole moment in that the latter involves the first power of the coordinates (see equation (2.25)), while the magnetic dipole moment involves the second power. The difference shows clearly under reflection in a plane, see Fig. 8.1; also, magnetic moments change sign under time reversal, $t \to -t$.

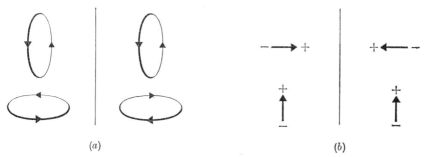

(a)                                                        (b)

FIG. 8.1. (a) Reflection of 2 circulating currents in a plane.
(b) Reflection of 2 dipoles in a plane.
Note that the circulating currents behave differently from the equivalent dipoles on reflection.

In general, however, atoms do not exist in the free state but are combined into molecules, and it so happens that the forces responsible for chemical binding strongly affect the arrangement of the individual magnetic moments of the various electrons in the molecule. As a result the stable state of the molecule is nearly always one in which the vector sum of these individual moments is just zero, so that the molecule as a whole has no resultant permanent magnetic moment. Similarly, in the majority of solids and liquids, the atomic constituents are ions with no permanent magnetic dipole moments. When such a substance is placed in a flux of magnetic induction **B**, each individual electron, being a moving charge, experiences a force. Its orbital motion round the nucleus is altered in such a way that it acquires an angular momentum and hence a magnetic dipole moment which is proportional to the applied field, but in the opposite direction. This gives a negative susceptibility, whose value will now be calculated. It should be noted that this diamagnetic effect is present in all substances, but in paramagnetic substances there is a much larger positive contribution to the susceptibility which generally far outweighs the diamagnetic contribution. The positive contribution arises from molecules (or ions) where the vector sum of the individual electron moments is not zero, so that the molecule or ion possesses a permanent magnetic moment. Thus all substances show a diamagnetic effect, giving a susceptibility of the order of $10^{-5}$ (using m.k.s. units, or $10^{-6}$ with e.m.u.), but in paramagnetic substances there is a positive susceptibility contribution which is much greater.

## 8.2. Diamagnetism

The fact that an atom placed in a magnetic field $\mathbf{B}$ acquires a magnetic moment parallel to $\mathbf{B}$ can be shown by finding the effect on the atom of establishing the field $\mathbf{B}$ from zero. In § 6.1 it was shown that this changes the momentum of a particle of charge $q$ from $m\mathbf{v}_0$ to $m\mathbf{v}$, where

$$m\mathbf{v} = m\mathbf{v}_0 - q\mathbf{A}$$

and $\mathbf{A}$ is the vector potential associated with the field $\mathbf{B}$. The corresponding current density is given by

$$\mathbf{J} = \rho\mathbf{v} = \rho\mathbf{v}_0 - \rho(q/m)\mathbf{A}. \tag{8.3}$$

If $\mathbf{A}$ is increased by $\delta\mathbf{A}$, the increase in potential energy is, by equation (5.45),

$$\delta U_P = -\int (\mathbf{J}.\delta\mathbf{A})\,d\tau = -\int \rho(\mathbf{v}_0.\delta\mathbf{A})\,d\tau + \int \rho(q/m)(\mathbf{A}.\delta\mathbf{A})\,d\tau. \tag{8.4}$$

For simplicity we take $\mathbf{B}$ to be a uniform field (which it will be over atomic dimensions), so that

$$\mathbf{A} = \tfrac{1}{2}(\mathbf{B} \wedge \mathbf{r}), \quad \text{and} \quad (\mathbf{A}.\delta\mathbf{A}) = \tfrac{1}{4}(B\,\delta B)r^2\sin^2\theta,$$

where $\theta$ is the angle between $B$ and $r$. Hence

$$\delta U_P = -\int \tfrac{1}{2}\rho\mathbf{v}_0.(\delta\mathbf{B} \wedge \mathbf{r})\,d\tau + (q/4m)\int \rho B\,\delta B\,r^2\sin^2\theta\,d\tau$$

$$= -\delta\mathbf{B}.\int \tfrac{1}{2}\rho(\mathbf{r} \wedge \mathbf{v}_0)\,d\tau + (q/4m)B\,\delta B\int \rho r^2\sin^2\theta\,d\tau$$

$$= -\delta\mathbf{B}.\mathbf{m}_0 - \delta\mathbf{B}.\mathbf{m}_i = -\delta\mathbf{B}.\mathbf{m}. \tag{8.5}$$

This result shows that the magnetic moment $\mathbf{m}$ consists of two parts, of which the first, $\mathbf{m}_0$, is clearly the permanent magnetic dipole moment (see equation 8.1), while the second $\mathbf{m}_i$ is an induced dipole moment which is proportional to the field strength B. The value of $\mathbf{m}_i$ is

$$\mathbf{m}_i = -\mathbf{B}(q/4m)\int \rho r^2\sin^2\theta\,d\tau = -\mathbf{B}(q^2/4m)\langle r^2\sin^2\theta\rangle,$$

where $q = \int \rho \, d\tau$ is the total charge. If $\rho$ is independent of $\theta$,

$$\langle r^2 \sin^2\theta \rangle = \langle r^2 \rangle \frac{1}{4\pi} \int_0^\pi \sin^2\theta \,.\, 2\pi \sin\theta \, d\theta = \tfrac{2}{3}\langle r^2 \rangle,$$

where $\langle r^2 \rangle$ is the mean square radius of the orbit. On summing over all electrons in the atom or ion, $\mathbf{m_0}$ must be replaced by the resultant (if any) of the permanent dipole moments, while the induced moment per atom becomes

$$\mathbf{m}_i = -(e^2/6m)\mathbf{B} \sum \langle r^2 \rangle, \tag{8.6}$$

where the electronic charge $-e$ has been substituted for $q$. Hence the diamagnetic susceptibility of a sample containing $n$ atoms (or ions) per unit volume will be

$$\chi = n\mathbf{m}_i/\mathbf{H} = -n\mu_0(e^2/6m) \sum \langle r^2 \rangle. \tag{8.7}$$

This result can be derived in another way using Larmor's theorem (Appendix A. 11). The result of establishing a field $\mathbf{B}$ is to set up a precessional motion of the electronic orbits with angular velocity $\boldsymbol{\omega} = -(q/2m)\mathbf{B}$, as a result of which each electron acquires an additional angular momentum

$$\mathbf{G}_i = m\langle a^2 \rangle\boldsymbol{\omega} = -m\langle a^2 \rangle(q/2m)\mathbf{B},$$

where $\langle a^2 \rangle = \langle r^2 \sin^2\theta \rangle$ is the mean square distance of the electron from an axis parallel to $B$ through the centre of gravity of the atom (the nucleus). Associated with $\mathbf{G}_i$ is an additional magnetic moment of magnitude (from equation (8.2))

$$\mathbf{m}_i = (q/2m)\mathbf{G}_i = -(q^2/4m)\langle r^2 \sin^2\theta \rangle\mathbf{B}.$$

On evaluating the average and summing over all electrons in the atom, this gives equation (8.7) above.

This equation shows that the diamagnetic susceptibility is inherently negative in sign, and does not depend, for example, on the sign of the electronic charge. Fundamentally, the negative sign follows from Lenz's law. When the external magnetic induction $\mathbf{B}$ is switched on, there is a change in flux through the electron orbits which induces a momentary e.m.f. The change in the orbits which this causes gives an induced magnetic moment to the atom which is in such a direction as to oppose the change in flux through the orbit, i.e. the magnetic moment is due to an induced current whose own lines of magnetic field through the atom are in the opposite direction to those of the external field. We have assumed that $\langle r^2 \rangle$ is unaltered by the presence of the magnetic field; this is justified because the magnetic forces at ordinary field strengths are negligible compared with the internal atomic forces (see Appendix A. 11).

As defined in Chapter 5, the susceptibility refers to unit volume of substance, and $n$ is then the number of atoms in unit volume. Since $\chi$ is linearly proportional to $n$, it is permissible to take samples of different size, and refer to the 'susceptibility per unit mass', or 'susceptibility per gramme atom'. These are simply equal to the susceptibility per unit volume (or 'volume susceptibility' for short) multiplied by the volume of the sample. Thus the 'mass susceptibility' $\chi_m = \chi/\rho$, where $\rho$ is the density, since unit mass (1 kg) occupies a volume of $(1/\rho)$ metre$^3$. Similarly, the susceptibility per gramme atom or gramme molecule will be $\chi_M = 10^{-3} M \chi_m$, where $M$ is the atomic or molecular weight in grammes. Here the factor $10^{-3}$ occurs because our $\chi_m$ refers to a kilogramme of substance. For a gramme mole equation (8.7) gives the numerical value

$$\chi_M = -3 \cdot 55 \times 10^9 \sum \langle r^2 \rangle. \tag{8.8}$$

In most reference tables the susceptibility is given in electromagnetic units, and for solids and liquids the diamagnetic volume susceptibility (per cm$^3$) is of the order $-10^{-6}$ e.m.u. (for gases it is much smaller owing to the lower number of atoms per unit volume). In our m.k.s. units the volume susceptibility (per metre$^3$) is greater by a factor $4\pi$ and so is of the order $-10^{-5}$. As a rough rule, the susceptibility (m.k.s.) per gramme atom is of order $-10^{-11}Z$, where $Z$ is the atomic number, equal to the number of electrons in the atom. This indicates that the mean value of $\langle r^2 \rangle$ is about $10^{-21}$ metres$^2$, as expected from atomic theory. The susceptibility of a diamagnetic substance is substantially independent of temperature, since $\sum \langle r^2 \rangle$ is practically unaltered by temperature.

In the first approximation $\sum \langle r^2 \rangle$ is constant for a particular type of atom or ion, and is not greatly altered by its surroundings. Thus aqueous solutions of alkali and alkaline earth halides obey quite accurately (and most substances approximately) an additivity rule known as Wiedemann's law. According to this rule the mass susceptibility $\chi_m$ of a solution containing a mass $m_1$ of a salt of mass susceptibility $\chi_1$ in a mass $m_2$ of solvent of mass susceptibility $\chi_2$ is

$$\chi_m = \frac{m_1 \chi_1 + m_2 \chi_2}{m_1 + m_2}. \tag{8.9}$$

Similar additivity rules are approximately valid for chemical compounds. Thus, for compounds which ionize in solution, the molar susceptibility of the compound is generally close to the sum of the ionic susceptibilities of its constituent ions in solution. By assuming a theoretical value for the susceptibility of one type of ion, approximate values for the susceptibilities of other ions can be obtained from measurements on compounds, and the validity of the additivity rules tested. (For a review of the diamagnetism of ions, see Myers (1952).)

## 8.3. Paramagnetism

As already pointed out, paramagnetism occurs in those substances where the individual atoms, ions, or molecules possess a permanent magnetic dipole moment. In the absence of an external magnetic field, the atomic dipoles point in random directions and there is no resultant magnetization of the substance as a whole in any direction. This random orientation is the result of thermal agitation within the substance. When an external field is applied, the atomic dipoles tend to orient themselves parallel to the field, since this is a state of lower energy than the anti-parallel position. This gives a net magnetization parallel to the field, and a positive contribution to the susceptibility. Since the thermal agitation, which tends to give a random orientation, is less at low tem-peratures, a bigger proportion of the dipoles are able to align themselves parallel to the field, and the magnetization is greater for a given field. It was discovered by Curie that, for ordinary fields and temperatures, the susceptibility of many substances follows the equation

$$\chi = \frac{M}{H} = \frac{C}{T},\qquad(8.10)$$

where $C$ is a constant, and $T$ is the absolute temperature; this is known as Curie's law. For large fields at low temperatures the magnetization produced is no longer proportional to the applied field, and tends to a constant value. This saturation effect is produced when all the atomic dipoles are aligned parallel to the field, so that the magnetization reaches a limiting maximum value.

The theoretical explanation of Curie's law was given by Langevin, using the classical statistics of Boltzmann. He assumed that each atom had a permanent magnetic moment $\mathfrak{m}$, and that the only force acting on it was that due to the external field $\mathbf{B}$. Then, if a given atomic dipole is pointing in a direction making an angle $\theta$ with $\mathbf{B}$, its magnetic poten-tial energy is $W = -\mathfrak{m}B\cos\theta$. Now, on classical statistics, the number of atoms making an angle between $\theta$ and $\theta + d\theta$ is

$$dn = ce^{-W/kT}\sin\theta\, d\theta,\qquad(8.11)$$

where $k$ is Boltzmann's constant and $T$ is the absolute temperature. $c$ is a constant defined by the fact that integration of (8.11) over the whole possible range of energies must give just $n$, the total number of atoms in the system. Hence for our case

$$dn = c \exp(\mathfrak{m}B \cos\theta / kT) . \, \mathfrak{m}B \sin\theta \, d\theta$$

and $n$ is equal to this integrated over all angles from 0 to $\pi$. The component of each dipole moment parallel to **B** is $\mathfrak{m}\cos\theta$, and hence the average component per atom is $\bar{\mathfrak{m}}$, where

$$n\bar{\mathfrak{m}} = \mathfrak{m} \int \cos\theta \, dn.$$

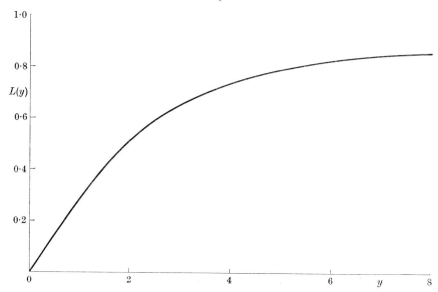

FIG. 8.2. The Langevin function $L(y) = \coth y - 1/y$.

Hence

$$\frac{\bar{\mathfrak{m}}}{\mathfrak{m}} = \frac{\displaystyle\int_0^\pi \cos\theta \, . \, c \exp(\mathfrak{m}B \cos\theta / kT) . \, \mathfrak{m}B \sin\theta \, d\theta}{\displaystyle\int_0^\pi c \exp(\mathfrak{m}B \cos\theta / kT) . \, \mathfrak{m}B \sin\theta \, d\theta} .$$

On writing $\mathfrak{m}B/kT = y$, $\cos\theta = x$, this takes the form

$$\frac{\bar{\mathfrak{m}}}{\mathfrak{m}} = \frac{\displaystyle\int_{-1}^{+1} x \exp(xy) \, dx}{\displaystyle\int_{-1}^{+1} \exp(xy) \, dx} = \coth y - \frac{1}{y} = L(y), \qquad (8.12)$$

where $L(y)$ is known as the Langevin function. It is plotted as a function of $y$ in Fig. 8.2. For large values of $y$ the function tends to unity, saturation being reached when all the atomic dipoles are parallel to **B**.

For small values of $y$ the curve is linear, and $L(y) = y/3 = \mathfrak{m}B/3kT$. Then the susceptibility is

$$\chi = \frac{n\bar{\mathfrak{m}}}{H} = \frac{\mu_0 n\mathfrak{m}^2}{3kT}, \qquad (8.13)$$

where $n$ is the number of atoms per unit volume. This is the same as Curie's law, equation (8.10), if we identify the Curie constant $C$ with $\mu_0 n\mathfrak{m}^2/3k$. The only unknown quantity in (8.13) is the atomic dipole moment $\mathfrak{m}$ so, that by measuring the susceptibility as a function of the absolute temperature in a region where $\mathfrak{m}B/kT$ is small, the magnitude of the atomic dipole moments may be found. In general these are of the order of $10^{-23}$ ampere-metre$^2$ ($10^{-20}$ e.m.u.), or slightly greater, and the volume susceptibility at room temperature of solid paramagnetic substances which obey Curie's law $\approx +10^{-3}$. Thus the paramagnetism considerably outweighs the diamagnetism which is also present.

Langevin's theory applies strictly only to gases, where the molecules are sufficiently far apart for their mutual interactions to be negligible. In liquids and solids such interactions may be large, and many substances obey the modified Curie–Weiss law

$$\chi = \frac{C}{T-\theta}. \qquad (8.14)$$

$\theta$ is called the 'Weiss constant' and is characteristic of the substance; it may be either positive or negative (see Chapters 21 and 22). Equation (8.14) holds only at temperatures where $T > |\theta|$, and for many substances no single equation represents the susceptibility variation adequately over a wide temperature range.

As already noted, the tendency in chemical combination is towards zero resultant angular momentum of the electrons and hence to zero permanent magnetic moment. Of the common gases, only oxygen $O_2$ and nitric oxide NO are paramagnetic. In the solid state paramagnetism occurs in salts of the 'transition group' ions (see Chapter 20), and the magnetic moment is associated with the metallic ion itself. Thus in compounds such as $CrK(SO_4)_2,12H_2O$ ('chrome alum') or $CuSO_4,5H_2O$ (copper sulphate) only the $Cr^{+++}$ ion and $Cu^{++}$ ion respectively have permanent magnetic moments, the other ions ($K^+, SO_4^{--}$) and water molecules giving only a diamagnetic contribution to the susceptibility. In most metals the outer electrons are detached from the individual atoms, which are thus left as diamagnetic ions. The detached electrons are free to move through the metal and form the conduction electrons; these give rise to a diamagnetic and a paramagnetic effect, both of the same order of magnitude and both independent of temperature (see § 18.7). The outstanding exceptions are the ferromagnetic metals, iron, cobalt, nickel, and a few others.

## 8.4. Ferromagnetism

Ferromagnetic substances are all solids, and each is characterized by a certain temperature known as the Curie point at which its properties change abruptly. Above the Curie point the susceptibility is independent

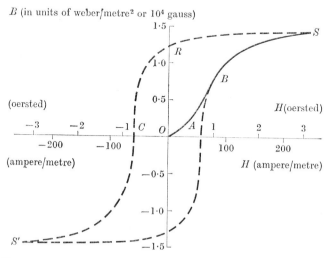

FIG. 8.3. Magnetization curve (full line $OABS$) and hysteresis loop (broken line) for iron.

of field strength, and follows approximately a Curie–Weiss law (equation (8.14)) with a Weiss constant $\theta$ whose value is close to that of the Curie point. Below the Curie temperature the behaviour is quite different; very large values of magnetization are produced by quite small fields, and the magnetization varies quite non-linearly with the field strength. This is shown by a characteristic plot of the magnetic induction $B$ as a function of the field $H$ in a sample of iron, Fig. 8.3. If the iron is initially unmagnetized, and a field of slowly increasing magnitude is applied, $B$ follows the full line in Fig. 8.3, known as the 'magnetization curve'. In a field of a few hundred ampere/metre the value of $B$ becomes practically constant at about 1·5 weber/metre². If the magnetic field $H$ is now reduced, the induction $B$ does not return along the magnetization curve but follows the broken line, and even at $H = 0$, corresponding to the point $R$ in the figure, $B$ is still near the saturation value. The value of $B$ at this point is known as the 'residual induction', and the retention

of magnetization in zero field is known as 'remanence'. On applying
a reverse field the value of $B$ falls and finally becomes zero (point $C$ in
Fig. 8.3); the value of the field at this point is called the 'coercive force'.
As the magnitude of the reverse field is further increased, a reverse induction is set up which quickly reaches the saturation value. Finally,
if the reverse field is gradually removed and a positive field applied,

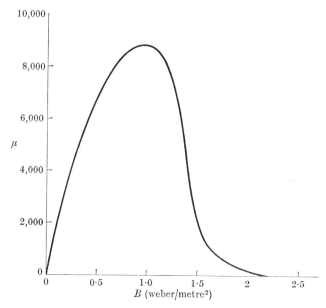

FIG. 8.4. Curve of permeability $\mu$ against induction $B$ for iron.

the induction traces out the broken curve in the direction $S'BS$. This
broken curve is called the 'hysteresis curve'. It shows that the change
in the magnetic induction always lags behind the change in the applied
magnetic field.

The magnetization curve may also be represented in the form of a
permeability curve, showing the variation of $\mu = B/(\mu_0 H)$ as a function of either $B$ or $H$. Such a curve ($\mu$ against $B$) is shown in Fig. 8.4.
When a field is applied $\mu$ goes through a maximum and then falls rapidly
as the material becomes saturated. The values of $\mu$, of the order of $10^4$,
are enormously greater than in paramagnetism ($1\cdot001$ or so at ordinary
temperatures).

To explain this behaviour, Weiss suggested that a ferromagnetic
substance contains atoms with permanent magnetic moments, as in a
paramagnetic substance, but that there are large forces acting between

neighbouring atomic dipoles which cause groups of them all to point in the same direction. The substance would then be permanently magnetized within each group; such groups are called 'domains' and their size is now known to vary from about $10^{-6}$ cm$^3$ to $10^{-2}$ cm$^3$, or greater in single crystals. In an unmagnetized polycrystalline specimen the domains are oriented at random, so that there is no resultant magnetic moment in any direction. When a field is applied, domains where the

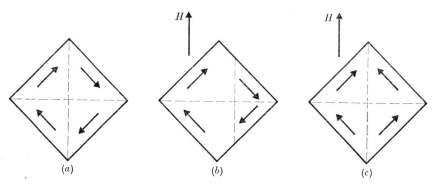

FIG. 8.5. Schematic representation of domains in a ferromagnetic substance: (a) unmagnetized; (b) magnetization through movement of domain boundary wall; domains oriented parallel to $H$ grow at the expense of anti-parallel domains; (c) magnetization by rotation of the magnetization of whole domains. The domains remain magnetized along a preferred direction in each crystallite; very large fields are required to swing the magnetization away from such a direction towards the applied field.

magnetization is parallel or at a small angle with the field grow at the expense of those where the magnetization is anti-parallel or nearly so, so that the boundary between domains is displaced. Initially ($OA$ in the full curve of Fig. 8.3) the magnetization of the substance as a whole proceeds by small (reversible) boundary displacements, but the steeper part ($AB$) of the magnetization curve is due to larger (irreversible) displacements. Above the knee of the curve, magnetization proceeds by rotation of the direction of magnetization of whole domains; such a process is rather difficult and the increase in magnetization is relatively slow. These processes are shown schematically in Fig. 8.5. When the applied field is reduced, there is little change in the domain structure so that the magnetization remains quite high until reverse fields are applied, thus giving rise to the hysteresis described above.

Ferromagnetic substances may be broadly divided into two classes: (a) magnetically soft materials, which have high permeability, and are easily magnetized and demagnetized, and (b) magnetically hard materials, which have a relatively low permeability and are difficult to magnetize or demagnetize (high coercive force). The chief uses of the former are in electromagnetic machinery and transformers, and of the latter in permanent magnets. To obtain a soft magnetic material the domain walls must be able to move easily and reversibly, so that the magnetization changes by large amounts for small changes in the magnetizing field. This requires a material as free as possible of irregularities in the crystal structure due to strains or small particles of impurities. The main treatment of such materials consists therefore of heating to a temperature where sufficient movement of the atoms is possible for them to settle into an ordered lattice, followed by a slow cooling (annealing) so as not to disturb it. On the other hand, a hard magnetic material is one in which domain wall movement is difficult owing to lattice imperfections. These are produced by heating the material and then plunging it suddenly into cold oil (quenching), which sets up internal stresses. Some alloys are then reheated to a lower temperature to cause one of the constituents partially to separate out in small particles dispersed through the alloy. In an alternative process magnets are constructed from compressed powders of very fine particles. If the particles are below a certain size, each forms a single domain and there are no domain walls within the particle. Magnetization and demagnetization can only be accomplished by rotation of the direction of magnetization of each particle, which requires a higher field than wall movements, and so gives a higher coercive force.

## 8.5. Production of magnetic fields

For many purposes it is necessary to maintain a large magnetic field which is constant over a certain volume. By 'large' is meant values of $B$ ranging from 0·1 to 10 weber/metre$^2$ ($10^3$ to $10^5$ gauss), and the volume may vary from 100 cm$^3$ up to many cubic metres in a modern accelerator for atomic particles. According to the particular application, permanent magnets or electromagnets (with or without iron) may be employed, and the principles of their construction are outlined below.

A modern permanent magnet of typical shape is shown in Fig. 8.6. The important quantities are the values of $B$ in the air gap, and the volume of the air gap; since the energy density at any point is $\frac{1}{2}\mathbf{B}.\mathbf{H}$ (equation (6.44)), the total energy stored in the air gap is $(\frac{1}{2}BH)V_a$, where $V_a$ is the volume of the gap, and the vectorial representation of $B$ and $H$ can be dropped since they are parallel to one another. The energy stored in the gap includes both the important parameters (the value of $B$ and the volume), and is simply related to the quantities involved in the magnet design, as follows. If we assume that there is no leakage, so that all the lines of magnetic induction within the magnet pass through the gap, we have

$$BA_a = B_m A_m, \qquad (8.15)$$

where $A_a$, $A_m$ are the cross-sections of the air gap and the magnet respectively, and $B_m$ is the value of the magnetic induction in the magnet.

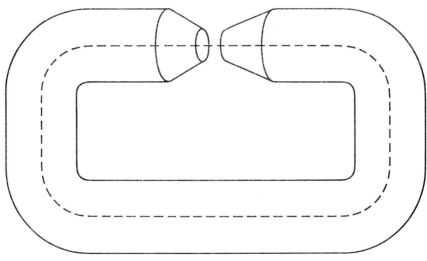

FIG. 8.6. Permanent magnet.

Now, if we consider a circuit through the gap and the magnet as indicated by the broken line in Fig. 8.6, the total magnetomotive force (see § 5.2) is zero, since no electric currents are involved. Hence

$$\int \mathbf{H}.\mathbf{ds} = Hd_a + H_m d_m = 0, \qquad (8.16)$$

where $d_a$, $d_m$ are the path lengths in the air gap and the magnet respectively, and $H_m$ is the magnetic field in the magnet. On combining equations (8.15) and (8.16) we have

$$(\tfrac{1}{2}BH)V_a = (\tfrac{1}{2}BH)A_a d_a$$
$$= -(\tfrac{1}{2}B_m H_m)A_m d_m = -(\tfrac{1}{2}B_m H_m)V_m. \qquad (8.17)$$

This important relation shows that for a magnet of given volume $V_m$, the greatest amount of energy stored in the gap is obtained if the product $(B_m H_m)$ has its maximum value.

The variation of the product $(B_m H_m)$ with $B_m$ for a typical material is shown in Fig. 8.7, together with the 'demagnetization curve'; that is, the part of the hysteresis loop corresponding to the application of a

reverse field. In a permanent magnet the field inside is the 'demagnetizing field' due to the 'free magnetic poles' near the ends of the magnet;
this field is in the opposite direction to $B_m$, and the negative sign in
equation (8.17) arises from this. The size of the demagnetizing field is

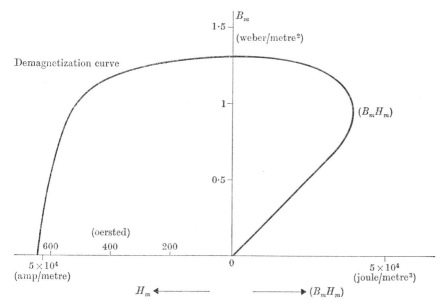

Fig. 8.7. Demagnetization curve (to the left) and plot of $(B_m H_m)$ against $B_m$
(to the right), for Alcomax III.

determined by the shape of the magnet, and this must be designed so
that the material is at the point where $(B_m H_m)$ is a maximum. A good
working rule is that at this point the ratio of $B_m$ to $H_m$ is equal to the
ratio $B_r/H_c$, where $B_r$ is the residual induction and $H_c$ the coercive force.

In practice there is always some leakage of lines of magnetic field so
that the energy stored in the gap is less than the theoretical value given
by equation (8.17). The best shape of the magnet is one in which $B_m H_m$
at every point in the material is closest to its maximum value. Since the
product $B_m H_m$ is a characteristic of the material the volume of material
required increases linearly with the energy stored in the gap. Many
special alloys, such as Alcomax (Alnico), have been developed with high
values of the energy product. Alcomax III has the composition 50%
iron, 25% cobalt, 13·5% nickel, 8% aluminium, 3% copper, and $\frac{1}{2}$%
niobium. Its coercive force $H_c \approx 5 \times 10^4$ A/metre, the residual induction
$B_r \approx 1·3$ weber/metre$^2$, and the maximum value of $(B_m H_m) \approx 4 \times 10^4$

joules/metre³. The disadvantage of most of these special alloys is that they cannot be machined, and the magnets must be cast or sintered from powder. They are very useful when constant fields up to 1 weber/metre² are required.

When fields of greater magnitude, or adjustable fields, are required, an electromagnet is used. For fields up to about 2 weber/metre² the normal type of construction is as shown in Fig. 8.8. It consists of a yoke $Y$ of soft iron or, more commonly, mild steel, which has a reasonably high magnetization for small values of the applied field. $C$, $C$ are coils of copper wire, or copper tube through which cooling water may flow, carrying current from a d.c. generator. If the coils have a total of $n$ turns each carrying a current $I$, the magnetomotive force (m.m.f.) is

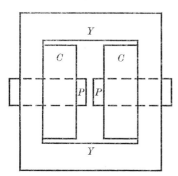

FIG. 8.8. Weiss type of electromagnet.

$C$, $C$ coils carrying electric current; $P$, $P$ pole tips; $Y$ yoke.

$$nI = \int \mathbf{H}.\mathbf{ds} = Hd_a + H_m d_m \quad (8.18)$$

round a circuit through the air gap and yoke similar to that shown in Fig. 8.6, with the same nomenclature as before. Since equation (8.15) still holds, we have

$$nI = BA_a\left[\frac{d_a}{\mu_0 A_a} + \frac{d_m}{\mu\mu_0 A_m}\right], \quad (8.19)$$

where the quantity in brackets is known as the magnetic 'reluctance' of the system. In this analogy between the m.m.f. and the e.m.f. in a circuit, the flux $(BA_a)$ is analogous to the electric current, and the flux passes through the two components—the air gap and the yoke—in series. The total reluctance of the 'magnetic circuit' is the sum of the two parts due to the gap and the iron. Since $\mu$ for iron is very large, the greater part of the reluctance is generally associated with the air gap.

In most iron-cored magnets the pole faces may be removed and replaced by others of different shape for special investigations, and the width of the air gap may be altered. To obtain higher values of $B$, coned pole pieces may be used. In the design of Fig. 8.9, if it is assumed that the magnetization is everywhere parallel to the axis and has the saturation value $M_s$, the field at the centre of the gap due to the conical portions indicated by shading may be shown to be (see Problem 8.7)

$$B = \mu_0 H = \mu_0 M_s \sin^2\phi \cos\phi \log_e(b/a). \quad (8.20)$$

This has a maximum value at $\phi = 54\cdot7°$; in practice the pole pieces are not everywhere completely saturated, and a value of about 60° gives the best results. The pole tips may be made of a special cobalt steel which has a higher saturation induction than ordinary mild steel. A plot of the field in the gap against exciting current is usually fairly linear

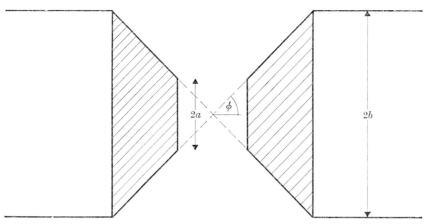

FIG. 8.9. Coned pole tips for magnet.

(apart from a small initial field due to the remanence) until the steel becomes saturated; the rate of increase then becomes much lower, any extra field being that due to the current in the coils themselves.

It was pointed out by Bitter (1936) that this arrangement, in which the iron is magnetized everywhere in the same direction, does not make the best use of the iron. In Fig. 8.10 the field at the origin $O$ due to the dipole at $A$, oriented as shown, has a component parallel to the $x$-axis equal to

$$H_x = \frac{\mathfrak{m}}{4\pi r^3}(2\cos\theta\cos\phi + \sin\theta\sin\phi).$$

If the orientation of the dipole is variable, then $H_x$ has a maximum value when $dH_x/d\theta = 0$; i.e. $\tan\theta = \frac{1}{2}\tan\phi$, and this value is then

$$(H_x)_{\max} = \frac{\mathfrak{m}}{4\pi r^3}(1+3\cos^2\phi)^{\frac{1}{2}}. \tag{8.21}$$

If, on the other hand, the dipole points parallel to the $x$-axis, so that $\theta = -\phi$, the value of $H_x$ is only

$$H_x = \frac{\mathfrak{m}}{4\pi r^3}(3\cos^2\phi - 1). \tag{8.22}$$

Both the angular functions in (8.21) and (8.22) have the value 2 at

$\phi = 0$, but the latter falls to zero at $\phi = 54\cdot7°$ and then changes sign (the reason why the coned pole pieces discussed above have this as their optimum angle is that dipoles at a larger angle oriented parallel to the axis would give a reverse field and thus reduce the field in the gap). On the other hand, at this angle $(1+3\cos^2\phi)^{\frac{1}{2}}$ has fallen only to $\sqrt{2}$, and its smallest value is 1 at $\phi = 90°$.

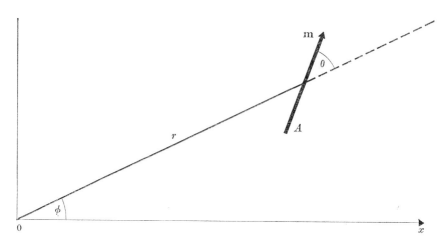

FIG. 8.10. Illustrating the calculation of the field at the origin $O$ due to a dipole $\mathbf{m}$ at $A$.

At first sight it would seem impracticable to set up a magnetization in the iron with the angular distribution of the direction of magnetization required by the equation $\tan\theta = \frac{1}{2}\tan\phi$. The orientation of the magnetization at any point is, however, just the same as the direction of the lines of force set up by a point dipole at the origin pointing along the $x$-axis, and it follows that such a dipole would magnetize the iron in just the right direction. Bitter therefore designed a magnet of the type shown in Fig. 8.11, where the magnetizing coil, whose field is approximately that of a point dipole, is surrounded by soft iron. This gave an appreciably better performance than the older type of design. Bitter considered also the question of the current distribution and shape of the magnetizing coil, and concluded that higher efficiency could be obtained if the current density were not uniform, as it is in a coil wound in the ordinary way, but fell off inversely with the radius. In the design of Fig. 8.11 this is achieved by winding a spiral out of copper strip of gradually increasing width; the current enters along a central brass tube, flows round the spiral with decreasing density as the width increases, and leaves at the outer edge. In such a magnet Bitter obtained a flux of

30 000 gauss (3 weber/metre²), using a power of 21 000 W; the m.m.f. was $5 \times 10^4$ ampere-turns, and the coil resistance about 0·03 ohm.

Since iron and other magnetic materials saturate at about 1 to 2 weber/metre², the contribution they make in magnets for still higher fields is not sufficient to justify the expense. Bitter has designed air-cored solenoid magnets on the principle outlined above. The non-uniform

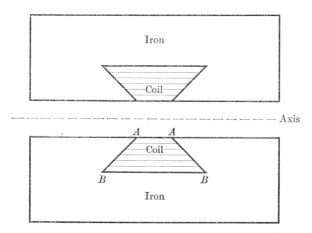

FIG. 8.11. Bitter magnet, with central coil surrounded with iron. The coil consists of a spiral strip, whose width increases with the radius; current enters at $AA$, flows round the coil producing an axial field, and leaves at $BB$.

current distribution is obtained by using flat conductors of the shape shown in Fig. 8.12; the current is led in along the edge $AA$ and out along $BB$, so that the current density varies inversely with the radius because the resistance along a path of radius $r$ increases with $r$. The solenoid is constructed of a number of such disks mounted one above the other, with holes drilled in them so that cooling water can be forced through. The low resistance of such a design ($\sim$ 0·01 ohm) reduces the chance of any breakdown in the insulation, and corrosion through electrolysis of the cooling water. In one such coil Bitter (1940) obtained a field of 10 weber/metre², uniform to 1 per cent over a volume of 25 cm³, with a supply of 10 000 A at 170 V. It can be shown that the field obtained from an air-cored coil can be expressed as $(W\lambda/\rho r)^{\frac{1}{2}}$ times a factor depending only on the shape of the coil and the current distribution; here $W$ is the power dissipation, $\lambda$ the fraction of the coil volume occupied by conductor of resistivity $\rho$ (the remainder being insulation and coolant), and $r$ a linear dimension such as the inner radius. Thus to double the field over the same volume requires four times the power.

The discovery of superconducting wires which remain in the super-conducting state up to fields of $10^5$ gauss (10 weber/metre²) or more has made it possible to construct solenoids in which a steady field can be maintained without any power consumption, since the resistance in the superconducting state is zero. The main drawback is that the super-conducting state is only attained below some critical temperature $T_c$

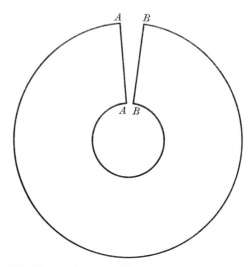

Fig. 8.12. Shape of copper disk known as a 'Bitter pancake'.

which lies below 20° K for virtually all substances, so that the solenoid must be maintained at liquid helium temperatures. A comparison of the power requirements of various types of magnets is given in Fig. 8.13; the power shown for the superconducting magnet (10 kW) is arbitrary, being that required to run the liquid helium refrigerator!

## 8.6. Measurement of magnetic fields

The commonest method of measuring the value of $B$ at any point in air is by means of a 'flip coil' and an instrument for measuring flux. The flip coil consists of a number $n$ of turns of wire wound on a small former of known area $A$; this is mounted on a handle and the leads to the coil are twisted and brought out through the handle. When the coil is placed with its axis parallel to a field $\mathbf{B}$, the flux through it is $nAB$; if the coil is then quickly removed to a point where $\mathbf{B} = 0$, the flux change is just $nAB$ and this can be measured either by a ballistic gal-vanometer or a fluxmeter (see § 7.3). For accurate results the ballistic galvanometer should be standardized as described in § 7.3 using a mutual

inductance, with the secondary winding and the flip coil in series with
the galvanometer throughout all the measurements so that the total
resistance of the circuit remains constant. Flip coils can be made with
different values of the product $nA$ (turns × area), so that by choice of
the right coil for the field to be measured a suitable deflexion can be

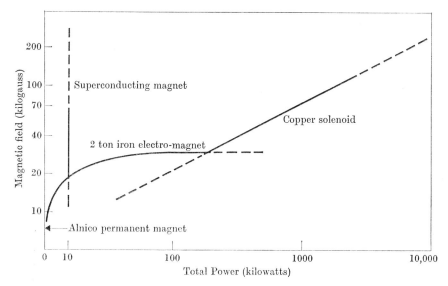

FIG. 8.13. Comparison of field produced by various types of magnet, and the power
requirements (for the superconducting magnet this is just the refrigerator power consumption). Volume of field = 500 cm³. (Courtesy Dr. J. Hulm, Westinghouse Research
Laboratories.)

obtained on the ballistic galvanometer or fluxmeter. As noted in § 7.3,
the accuracy obtainable with an average fluxmeter is about 1 per cent,
and with a ballistic galvanometer about ten times greater.

If the coil is rotated rapidly in the field, an alternating voltage is set
up which is proportional to $nAB$ times the angular velocity; measurement of this voltage requires a less sensitive instrument than the fluxmeter because the energy available is much greater than with a single
throw. In a typical instrument, a coil of 3 mm outer diameter is rotated
at 30 c/s, and gives full scale deflexion in a field of about 500 gauss;
with larger and smaller coils, fields ranging from the earth's field to $10^5$
gauss can be measured quickly with an accuracy of about 1 per cent.

An absolute method which is capable of giving higher accuracy is the
electromagnetic balance of Cotton, in which the force due to the field **B**
on a length of wire carrying a known current is measured directly. This
method can only be used for rather strong fields which are uniform over

a fair volume. A long rectangular coil is suspended from an analytical balance with the lower end of the coil in the field to be measured, this field being directed horizontally. The long sides of the coil are vertical, so that no force is exerted on them in the vertical direction; they act as leads for the current in the horizontal lower edge of the coil, and the force measured is just that on this lower edge, assuming that the value of **B** along the upper edge is negligible. If the lower edge is directed perpendicular to the lines of **B**, the net vertical force is $F = I \int B \, dx$, where the integral is measured along the lower edge. Thus the integrated value of the field along this edge is determined, and to find the value at any point the field distribution must be known. The current is measured with a standard resistance and potentiometer, and the force by the change in the balance reading when the current through the rectangular coil is reversed in direction. With a balance of this type Thomas, Driscoll, and Hipple (1950) were able to measure a field of about 0·5 weber/metre$^2$ with an accuracy of a few parts in $10^5$. The purpose of their experiment was to make an accurate absolute measurement of the magnetogyric ratio of the nuclear magnetic moment of the proton, by determining the precession frequency $(\omega/2\pi)$ of the nuclear moments in a field $B$. The principle of this method ('nuclear magnetic resonance') will be discussed in Chapter 23, but it is based on the equation

$$\omega = -\gamma B,$$

where $\gamma$ is the magnetogyric ratio (see equation (8.2)). Since the frequency $(\omega/2\pi)$ is linearly proportional to $B$, and the frequency of a radio-oscillation may readily be determined with high accuracy (see Chapter 15), this gives an accurate measure of $B$ if the value of $\gamma$ is known.

## 8.7. Measurement of susceptibility

Most methods of determining the susceptibility of weakly magnetic substances depend on measuring the force on the substance in an inhomogeneous magnetic field. By analogy with equation (1.15), the force on a magnetic dipole **m** has an $x$-component

$$F_x = \mathrm{m}_x\left(\frac{\partial B_x}{\partial x}\right) + \mathrm{m}_y\left(\frac{\partial B_y}{\partial x}\right) + \mathrm{m}_z\left(\frac{\partial B_z}{\partial x}\right). \qquad (8.23)$$

Now, if instead of a permanent dipole we have a particle of magnetizable matter of susceptibility $\chi$ and volume $v$, its moment will be

$$\mathbf{m} = \chi v \mathbf{H}$$

and the $x$-component of the force on it is

$$F_x = \chi\mu_0 v\left(H_x\frac{\partial H_x}{\partial x}+H_y\frac{\partial H_y}{\partial x}+H_z\frac{\partial H_z}{\partial x}\right) = \tfrac{1}{2}\chi\mu_0 v\left(\frac{\partial}{\partial x}H^2\right).$$

If the particle has a susceptibility $\chi_1$ and is immersed in a medium (such as the atmosphere) with susceptibility $\chi_2$, then the force on it is

$$F_x = \tfrac{1}{2}(\chi_1-\chi_2)\mu_0 v\frac{\partial H^2}{\partial x}. \qquad (8.24)$$

This can be seen from the fact that any displacement of the particle in the $x$-direction requires an opposite displacement of an equal volume of the surrounding medium.

This equation may also be derived by considering the stored energy. The effect of the presence of the particle of volume $v$ is to increase the stored energy by

$$U = v(\tfrac{1}{2}\mathbf{B_1}.\mathbf{H}-\tfrac{1}{2}\mathbf{B_2}.\mathbf{H})$$
$$= \tfrac{1}{2}v\{(1+\chi_1)-(1+\chi_2)\}\mu_0 H^2$$
$$= \tfrac{1}{2}v(\chi_1-\chi_2)\mu_0 H^2.$$

From equation (6.40) the force component is given by $F_x = +(\partial U/\partial x)$, giving the same formula as above (equation (8.24)). In both these derivations we have assumed that the magnetic field inside the specimen is the same as the value measured before the specimen was introduced. These two quantities differ only by the demagnetizing field in the specimen, whose order of magnitude is $M = \chi H$, which is negligible for the values of $\chi$ ($\approx 10^{-3}$ or less) ordinarily encountered.

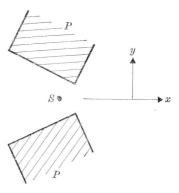

The force equation (8.24) is the basis of methods for measuring the susceptibility of small specimens, and was used by Curie. The specimen is suspended from one arm of a sensitive torsion balance, and hangs between the pole tips of an electromagnet as in Fig. 8.14. The arrangement of the pole tips gives

FIG. 8.14. Curie's method for the susceptibility of a small specimen $S$. $P, P$ are the magnet pole tips.

a large value of $\partial H_y^2/\partial x$, while along the axis the quantities $\partial H_x^2/\partial x$ and $\partial H_z^2/\partial x$ are very small. Values of the order of $10^{11}$ A²/metre³ can be obtained for $\partial H_y^2/\partial x$ with $H_y$ of the order of $10^6$ A/metre ($\sim 10^4$ oersted). The main difficulty arises from the fact that the value of $\partial H_y^2/\partial x$ is

usually constant over only a rather small volume, and different specimens must be placed rather accurately in the same position in the
magnet to obtain correct results. This difficulty is reduced by the use
of special shapes of pole tips designed to make $\partial H_y^2/\partial x$ uniform over a
larger volume.

When larger quantities of a substance are available, a better method
of measuring the susceptibility is that due to Gouy. The specimen is

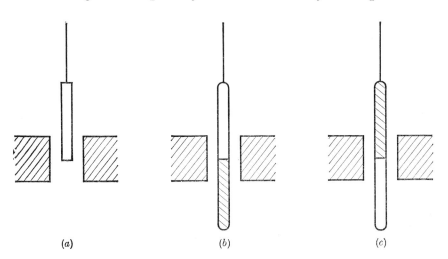

(a)                    (b)                    (c)

Fig. 8.15. Gouy's method for measuring susceptibility.

made into a long cylinder of uniform cross-section, and is suspended
from one arm of a sensitive balance so that its lower end hangs between
the poles of an electromagnet, as in Fig. 8.15 (a). If the cross-section
of the specimen is $A$, the vertical force in the $x$-direction is $dF_x$ on an
element $A\,dx$, and hence the total force is found, by integrating over
the length of the specimen, to be

$$F_x = \tfrac{1}{2}A\mu_0(\chi_1-\chi_2)\int (\partial H^2/\partial x)\,dx$$
$$= \tfrac{1}{2}A\mu_0(\chi_1-\chi_2)(H_1^2-H_2^2), \qquad (8.25)$$

where $H_1$ is the field at the lower end of the specimen and $H_2$ that at
the upper end; generally $H_2^2$ will be negligible compared with $H_1^2$. It will
be seen that, although the force arises because the specimen is in an inhomogeneous field, only the value of the homogeneous field at the centre
of the magnet gap is required. With field strengths of the order of $10^5$
to $10^6$ A/metre ($10^3$ to $10^4$ oersteds), forces of the order of milligrammes
are obtained which can be measured on an ordinary laboratory balance.

For liquids and powders, a cylindrical container of uniform cross-section may be used, half-filled with the substance or divided into two compartments (see Figs. 8.15 (b) and (c)). The mid-point of the container is in the centre of the field, and the forces on the two halves of the container are equal and opposite. They therefore cancel, leaving only the force on the specimen. For liquids, a variant of the Gouy method due to Quincke may be used, in which the force due to the magnetic field is balanced by hydrostatic pressure. In the simplest form of this method the liquid is contained in a U-tube, and the meniscus in one arm is placed in the uniform field between the magnet pole tips. When the field is switched on, the meniscus rises or falls, according to whether the liquid is more or less paramagnetic than the air in the tube above it. If the density of the liquid is known, the hydrostatic pressure caused by the magnetic forces may be found from the change in height of the meniscus in either limb of the tube. A more accurate method, which eliminates errors due to the liquid sticking on the walls of the tube, is to restore the meniscus to its original height by changing the relative levels of the two limbs (e.g. by tilting). This method was used by Auer in determining the diamagnetic susceptibility of water with an accuracy of about 0·1 per cent.

Force methods of measuring the susceptibility have the disadvantage that the force arises from an inhomogeneous magnetic field. In modern measurements, the magnetic moment of a small single crystal is often required as a function of field strength and of the direction of the field relative to the crystal axes (as well as of temperature). For this purpose it is preferable to use a uniform magnetic field, whose value can be determined accurately much more easily than a quantity such as $\partial H^2/\partial x$ which is needed in Curie's method. A number of methods have been developed where the sample is moved in and out of a coil (or from one coil to another) in the field, and the change in flux through the coil is measured. Movement of the sample is superior to movement of the coil, because the latter gives a flux change even in the absence of a sample due to residual inhomogeneity in the field. A null method is often used; one way of achieving this with a cylindrical sample is to wind a small coil round the sample and adjust the current through it until the magnetic moment of the coil just cancels that due to the sample, as shown by the zero flux change in a pick-up coil from which the (sample+coil) are suddenly removed. This is a good example of the equivalence of a current circuit and a magnetic shell, as discussed in § 5.2.

A sensitive magnetometer, due to Foner (1959), in which the sample is vibrated at 90 c/s, is shown in Fig. 8.16. The sample $S$, at the end of a long support which reaches down into a dewar vessel for work at low temperatures, is vibrated vertically by a loud-speaker transducer $T$ fed by alternating current at 90 c/s. The sample is at the mid-point between two coils $A$, $B$ whose axes are vertical; the vertical component of the flux from the horizontal magnetic moment of the sample threads

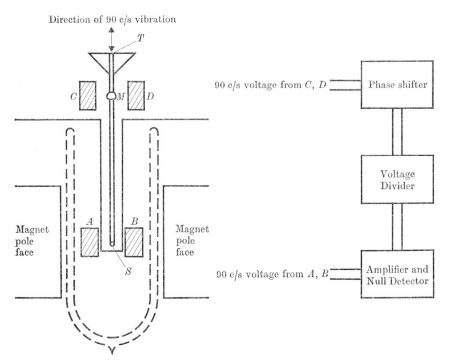

FIG. 8.16. Foner's Vibrating Magnetometer. The pair of coils $A$, $B$ (and similarly $C$, $D$) are in series but opposing, thus reducing spurious voltages due to magnetic field instability or unwanted mechanical vibration.

$S$    sample, producing 90 c/s voltage in coils $A$, $D$.
$M$    permanent magnet producing comparison voltage in coils $C$, $D$.
$T$    loudspeaker transducer driving sample $S$ and magnet $M$ in vertical vibration at 90 c/s.

the top and bottom halves of each coil in opposite sense, so that the net flux is zero if the sample is exactly opposite the mid-point. When the sample is displaced vertically during vibration, the net flux through each coil becomes finite and in first approximation is linearly proportional to the displacement of the sample. Thus an e.m.f. alternating at 90 c/s is induced in the coils, which can be balanced against a similar e.m.f. induced by a small permanent magnet $M$ in the coils $C$, $D$. This gives a null method where the magnetic moment of the sample is read off on the calibrated voltage divider (the phase shifter is required because the two alternating voltages may have a small phase difference—see Chapter 9). The accuracy is about 1 per cent, and changes in magnetic moment of about $10^{-4}$ e.m.u. ($10^{-7}$ ampere metre$^2$) can be detected, corresponding to a volume susceptibility in the sample of about $10^{-8}$ e.m.u. ($10^{-7}$ m.k.s.) in a field of $10^4$ gauss (1 weber/metre$^2$). Rotation of the whole assembly about a vertical axis enables the magnetic moment to be measured throughout a horizontal plane; permanent moments can be measured as well as induced moments.

## 8.8. Experimental investigation of the hysteresis curve

In order to determine the hysteresis curve of a substance it is necessary to know the values of $B$ and $H$ inside the substance. For this purpose the most satisfactory shape of the substance is in the form of an anchor ring, or toroid, since then there is no demagnetizing field due to the 'free poles' at the ends of the specimen. If the radius of the ring is large compared with the dimensions of its cross-section, a coil wound uniformly round the ring will produce a uniform field $H$ everywhere within the ring. If $n_1$ is the number of turns per unit length in this (the 'primary' coil), and $I$ the current flowing, then $H = n_1 I$. To measure $B$, a small secondary coil is wound over the primary at some point on the ring; if this coil has $n_2$ turns, and the cross-section of the ring is $A$, the flux through the coil is $n_2 A B$. Changes in the flux through the secondary coil are measured by connecting it to a ballistic galvanometer; the galvanometer is calibrated at the same time as described in § 7.3.

A circuit diagram of the apparatus is shown in Fig. 8.17. In order to determine the initial magnetization curve ($OABS$ in Fig. 8.3), the ring must previously have been demagnetized; this is usually accomplished by passing an alternating current through the primary coil and slowly diminishing its amplitude to zero. Then the primary coil is supplied with direct current measured on the ammeter $A$: this current can be adjusted in value by means of the variable resistance $R_1$. By adjusting $R_1$ in steps, the current in the primary coil is increased stepwise and the ballistic throw of the galvanometer measured at each step. This gives the increment in $B$ at each step, and finally the saturation value $S$ (Fig. 8.3) is reached.

Before starting to plot out the hysteresis curve, the full current in the primary should be reversed a number of times until the flux change at each reversal reaches a constant value. The material is then in a 'cyclic state' and reproducible results for the hysteresis curve can be obtained. Suppose the material is at the point $S$ in Fig. 8.3, with the full current flowing through the closed switch $S_2$ in Fig. 8.17. On opening the switch $S_2$ with a suitable value of the resistance $R_2$, the primary current is diminished and a point between $S$ and $R$ on the hysteresis curve is attained. On throwing the reversing switch in the primary

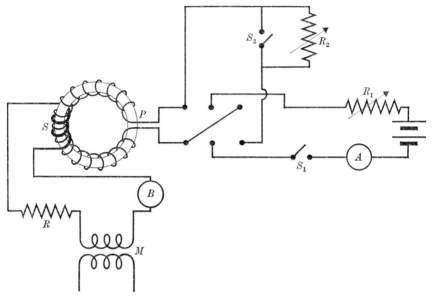

Fig. 8.17. Apparatus for **B–H** curve measurement.

$M$    is a standard mutual inductance for calibrating the ballistic galvanometer $B$.
$P$    primary winding ⎫ on toroidal specimen.
$S$    secondary winding ⎭

circuit the current is restored to its full value but flowing in the opposite sense through the primary coil, so that the material is now at $S'$, and can be returned to $S$ by returning the reversing switch to its original position after closing $S_2$. By repeating this procedure with various values of $R_2$, and then rearranging the circuit to that $R_2$ is in circuit when the current flows in the negative sense, points all round the hysteresis curve can be obtained. It is important that the cycle is always followed in the same sense, and completed by reaching the points $S$ and $S'$ every time, in order to retain the cyclic state. If the direction of movement round the hysteresis curve is reversed at some point between $S$ and $S'$, an intermediate curve will be traced out, and the cyclic state must be restored by a number of reversals of the full current.

In many cases the material to be tested is in the form of a long bar rather than a toroidal ring. Special methods (see, for example, Vigoureux and Webb, 1946) must then be used, but the general principle is similar to that given above.

The area enclosed by the hysteresis curve is of importance because it represents the work done in taking the material once round the hysteresis curve. Thus in a transformer for alternating current of frequency $f$, the hysteresis curve is traversed $f$ times per second and power is dissipated which appears as heat in the magnetic material of the core. From equation (6.45) the work done per unit volume in moving from one point on the hysteresis curve to another is the integral, taken along the curve,

$$W = \int H \, dB. \tag{8.26}$$

It is readily seen that in a complete cycle the value of the integral is just given by the area enclosed by the hysteresis curve. Since this curve is traversed once per cycle, the energy dissipated rises linearly with the frequency of the alternating current.

## 8.9. Terrestrial magnetism

It has been known since the sixteenth century that there is a small permanent magnetic field at the surface of the earth. The general nature of this field is similar to that of a uniformly magnetized sphere whose magnetization is slightly inclined to the axis of rotation. At two points the lines of force are normal to the earth's surface. These are known as the 'magnetic poles'; the north magnetic pole attracts the 'north' pole of a suspended magnet or compass needle, and the latter is more accurately termed the 'north-seeking pole', since it is a pole of opposite sign to the earth's magnetic pole. In general, the magnetic field at any point on the earth's surface makes an angle with the horizontal, known as the angle of dip. The direction of the horizontal component is called the magnetic meridian, and the angle between this and the geographical meridian is the angle of declination. In England the size of the horizontal component is about 0·18 oersted ($\approx$ 14 A/metre), and the angle of dip is 58°.

Although it is a convenient first approximation to think of the earth as a uniformly magnetized sphere, it must be remembered that this implies that the field outside it is just the same as that of a small dipole at the centre, and no immediate deductions can be drawn from the nature of this field about the actual distribution of magnetization within the earth. The magnetic potential associated with the earth's field can be analysed in a series of spherical harmonics. Apart from small localized distortions due to iron-bearing minerals in the earth's crust, there is a dipole term which has decreased in magnitude by about 5 per cent in the last hundred years, while the quadrupole and higher terms have strong and fairly rapid secular variations with lifetimes less than a hundred years. These latter terms have no constant components and it is believed that all the non-dipole field components would average to zero over a sufficiently long period of time. The variation with time of the field at any one point also contains diurnal variations which are irregular and unpredictable. These are caused by currents in the iono-sphere due to solar and lunar perturbations, and days of great magnetic disturbance can often be related to epochs of maximum sunspots, the intensity showing a similar 11-year cycle.

The origin of the main field is more difficult to account for. A plausible guess of the composition of the interior of the earth may be made by studying the composition of meteorites, the sun, stars, and other planets, and using the data on the density obtained from the velocity of seismic waves through the earth. The latter show that there is a central core, with a radius of $3473 \pm 4$ km, which is assumed to be liquid since no transverse seismic waves are transmitted through it. Although this contains much iron, the temperature and pressure are too high for it to be ferromagnetic; it is assumed to consist mostly of liquid silicates of iron, magnesium, and calcium, which have an appreciable electrical conductivity at high temperatures. The present view is that the main part of the earth's field is due to electric currents in this core, associated with convective currents caused by radioactive or chemical sources. The mathematics of the process (energy source → kinetic energy of fluid → electrical energy) has been studied by Elsasser, Bullard, and others, and it seems probable that electrical currents can be maintained in this way. For detailed accounts reference should be made to Chapman and Bartels (1940), and Elsasser (1950, 1955–6).

## REFERENCES

BITTER, F., 1936, *Rev. Sci. Instrum.* **7**, 479; **7**, 482.

—— 1937, ibid. **8**, 318.

—— 1940, ibid. **11**, 373.

CHAPMAN, S., and BARTELS, J., 1940, *Geomagnetism* (O.U.P.).

ELSASSER, W. M., 1950, *Rev. Mod. Phys.* **22**, 1.

—— 1955–6, *Am. J. Phys.* **23**, 590; **24**, 85.

FONER, S., 1959, *Rev. Mod. Phys.* **30**, 548.

MYERS, W. R., 1952, ibid. **24**, 15.

THOMAS, H. A., DRISCOLL, R. L., and HIPPLE, J. A., 1950, *Phys. Rev.* **78**, 787.

VIGOUREUX, P., and WEBB, C. E., 1946, *Electric and Magnetic Measurements* (Blackie).

# GENERAL REFERENCE

McCaig, M., 1967, *Attraction and Repulsion, Mechanical Applications of Permanent Magnets* (Oliver and Boyd).

# PROBLEMS

8.1. The susceptibility of a gramme mole of helium gas is $-2\cdot4 \times 10^{-11}$ (m.k.s. units). Show that this corresponds to a value for the mean square radius of each electronic orbit in the helium atom of $1\cdot22a_0^2$, where $a_0 = 0\cdot528 \times 10^{-10}$ metre is the radius of the first Bohr orbit in the hydrogen atom.

8.2. If the mutual repulsion of the two electrons in the helium atom is neglected, the wave function of each electron in the ground state is

$$\psi = (Z^3/\pi a_0^3)^{\frac{1}{2}} \exp(-Zr/a_0),$$

where $-e\psi^2$ is the density of electronic charge at a distance $r$ from the nucleus, and $Ze$ is the effective charge of the helium nucleus. Show that this wave function leads to a value for the mean square radius of each electronic orbit of

$$\overline{r^2} = 3a_0^2/Z^2.$$

Verify that agreement with the value of $1\cdot22a_0^2$ in the previous problem is obtained if we take $Z$ as about $1\cdot6$ (we should expect it to be less than 2 because each electron partially shields the other from the field of the nucleus).

8.3. When $23\cdot15$ g of $NiCl_2$ are dissolved in 100 g water, the density of the solution is 1255 kg/m³. Show that the maximum height of a column of the solution which can be supported by magnetic force when one surface of the column is in a uniform induction of 1 weber/metre² is $3\cdot0$ mm.

(Susceptibilities of 1 kg of $NiCl_2$ and water are $+0\cdot438 \times 10^{-6}$ and $-0\cdot0090 \times 10^{-6}$ respectively; volume susceptibility of air $= +0\cdot4 \times 10^{-6}$ (m.k.s. units).)

8.4. The susceptibility of a gramme mole of $NiK_2(SO_4)_2,6H_2O$ is found to be $1\cdot6 \ 10^{-5} \ T^{-1}$. Assuming that the diamagnetic contribution is negligible, and that the only paramagnetic contribution comes from the $Ni^{++}$ ion, calculate the size of the permanent dipole moment on each $Ni^{++}$ ion.

(*Answer*: $3\cdot0 \times 10^{-23}$ ampere-metre².)

8.5. An iron anchor ring of large mean radius $R$ and uniform cross-section has a gap of thickness $d$ cut in it. It is wound with a single layer coil. Over the range under consideration the permeability of the iron is $(1+a/H)$, where $H$ is the field in the iron. Show that, if $d \ll R$, four times as much power is required to maintain a field $3a$ in the gap as is required for a field $2a$.

8.6. It was shown by Rayleigh that at low values of the magnetic induction the hysteresis loop with tips at $B_0$, $H_0$ and $-B_0$, $-H_0$ is described by the equations

$$B = \mu\mu_0 H + \tfrac{1}{2}a(H_0^2 - H^2) \quad \text{(upper half of loop)}$$

and

$$B = \mu\mu_0 H - \tfrac{1}{2}a(H_0^2 - H^2) \quad \text{(lower half of loop)},$$

where $\mu = B_0/\mu_0 H_0$. Show that the energy loss per cycle represented by the area of the loop is

$$W = \tfrac{4}{3}aH_0^3$$

in each unit volume of the substance.

This relation is valid only for low values of $B_0$ (in iron below about 0·05 weber/metre²). At high values $W$ varies approximately as $B_0^{1\cdot6}$, an empirical law due to Steinmetz.

8.7. Deduce equation (8.20), by the use of equivalent magnetic shells and integration of equation (5.55), or from integration of the magnetic induction due to the 'free poles' (polarization charges) on the surfaces of the cones.

8.8. An air-cored solenoid of length $2l$ is constructed from $n$ equally-spaced Bitter pancakes each of thickness $t$, inner radius $a$, outer radius $b$, and resistivity $\rho$. If $n$ is large, and $W$ is the power supplied, show that the field $H$ at the centre is approximately

$$H = \left[\frac{Wtn}{8\pi l^2 \rho \log_e(b/a)}\right]^{\frac{1}{2}} \log_e \frac{b\{l + (l^2 + a^2)^{\frac{1}{2}}\}}{a\{l + (l^2 + b^2)^{\frac{1}{2}}\}}.$$

Note that this is of the form $(W\lambda/\rho r)^{\frac{1}{2}}$ times a factor depending on the shape of the solenoid (as given in § 8.5), since $\lambda = nt/2l$.

8.9. It was shown by Maxwell that stresses are present in the magnetic field which can be represented by a stress tensor similar to that in the electrostatic case (§ 1.7) if $\mathbf{E}$, $\mathbf{D}$ are replaced by $\mathbf{H}$, $\mathbf{B}$ respectively. Show that the force equation (8.25) can be obtained by considering the stresses on the end of the specimen.

# 9

## ALTERNATING CURRENT THEORY

### 9.1. Forced oscillations

In § 6.3 we considered the transient currents which flow when a capacitor, initially charged, is allowed to discharge through a circuit containing both inductance and resistance, and found that an oscillatory current of decaying amplitude flowed through the circuit provided that the resistance in the circuit was not too high. The theory of such transients is due to Lord Kelvin, and its correctness was verified by early experimenters. With the invention of the dynamo and, later, the electronic vacuum tube, it became possible to produce continuous alternating currents whose frequency of oscillation may be anything up to about $10^{11}$ c/s. In the simplest case the form of the current is that of a simple sine wave, and may be written as

$$I = I_0 \cos \omega t,$$

where $I$ is the value of the current at time $t$. The maximum value of $I$ is $I_0$, known as the 'amplitude' of the current, and the frequency of alternation is $f = (\omega/2\pi)$ c/s. The current generated by a dynamo or other device may or may not have a simple sinusoidal wave form, but whatever the actual wave form it may be resolved by Fourier analysis into a sum of sine and cosine terms whose frequencies are integral multiples of the fundamental frequency. This frequency is given by the inverse of the period between instants at which the whole wave form is repeated. Since the behaviour of a circuit is in general different at different frequencies, it is necessary to consider each component of such a Fourier series separately, and in the theory that follows we shall assume that the wave form is sinusoidal, varying at one frequency only. Except in non-linear circuits where the behaviour of a circuit element depends on the size of the current or voltage applied to it (i.e. elements in which the amplitudes of current and voltage are not linearly proportional to one another) any non-sinusoidal fluctuations may be resolved into their Fourier components, and the required solution is simply a sum of such components.

In the circuit of Fig. 9.1, a voltage $V_0 \cos \omega t$ is applied to an inductance, a resistance, and a capacitance in series. If $I$ is the current flowing at any instant, the e.m.f. set up in the inductance is $-L(dI/dt)$, and the voltage drop across the capacitance is $q/C$, where $q$ is the charge on the capacitor. We have therefore for the circuit

$$V_0 \cos \omega t - L(dI/dt) - q/C = RI$$

or

$$L\frac{dI}{dt} + RI + q/C = V_0 \cos \omega t. \tag{9.1}$$

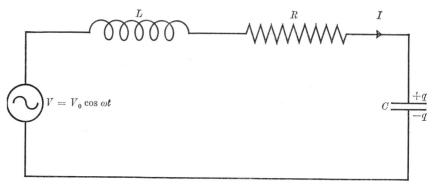

FIG. 9.1. Forced oscillations in a circuit containing $L$, $C$, $R$.

Now the rate of increase of the charge on the capacitor $dq/dt = I$, the current flowing, and hence by differentiation we have

$$L\frac{d^2I}{dt^2} + R\frac{dI}{dt} + \frac{I}{C} = dV/dt = -\omega V_0 \sin \omega t. \tag{9.2}$$

This is a differential equation whose solution consists of two parts. The first of these, known as the Complementary Function, is found by solving the equation obtained by setting the right-hand side equal to zero; that is, it is a solution of equation (6.27), and hence is of the form given by equation (6.28). This solution represents a transient flow of current produced by the act of applying the e.m.f. $V_0 \cos \omega t$, it being assumed that this starts to act at the instant $t = 0$. In all practical applications this transient current decays rapidly in amplitude, owing to the exponential term $\exp(-tR/2L)$ and becomes negligible within a few seconds or less of the circuit being closed. If conditions are such that the transient current is oscillatory, its frequency is the natural frequency determined by the values of $L$, $C$, and $R$, and not that of the applied e.m.f.

The second part of the solution is known as the Particular Integral, and for equation (9.2) it may be written as

$$I = (V_0/Z)\cos(\omega t - \phi), \tag{9.3}$$

where
$$Z = \left\{ R^2 + \left( \omega L - \frac{1}{\omega C} \right)^2 \right\}^{\frac{1}{2}} \qquad (9.4)$$

and the phase angle $\phi$ is given by
$$\tan \phi = \left( \omega L - \frac{1}{\omega C} \right) \Big/ R. \qquad (9.5)$$

This is also known as the 'steady state' solution, since it gives the current flow at any time after the transient current has become negligible. The frequency of the current is the same as that of the applied e.m.f., so that the circuit is in 'forced' oscillation. In general the phase of the current is different from that of the applied voltage, except when $\omega L - 1/\omega C = 0$. This occurs when

$$\omega = \omega_0 = 1/\sqrt{(LC)}, \qquad (9.6)$$

and hence is the same as the angular frequency of natural oscillation of the circuit in the absence of any damping resistance. The circuit is then said to be in 'resonance', and the amplitude of the current is, by equations (9.3) and (9.4), a maximum.

The quantity $Z$ in equation (9.4) is called the impedance of the circuit, and at resonance the value of $Z$ is just equal to $R$, the total resistance in the circuit. At other frequencies the value of $Z$ is related to the quantities $R$, $L$, and $C$, but is not given by the simple additive relation that holds (§ 3.4) for resistances in series. The reason for this is that the voltages across the different elements are not in phase, and the total voltage amplitude is therefore not just the sum of the individual amplitudes. In the following sections we shall see how this difficulty can be overcome by the introduction of complex numbers to represent the impedances. The use of such complex impedances enables us to apply Kirchhoff's laws (§ 3.4) to alternating current (a.c.) networks, and we can find the steady-state values of the current and voltage in any branch without having to solve a differential equation.

An important consideration in a.c. circuits is the rate of doing work. At any instant the rate $W$ at which work is done by the generator in Fig. 9.1 is

$$W = VI = (V_0 \cos \omega t) \times (V_0/Z) \cos(\omega t - \phi)$$
$$= (V_0^2/Z)\{\cos^2 \omega t \cos \phi + \cos \omega t \sin \omega t \sin \phi\}.$$

To find the mean rate $\overline{W}$ of doing work, this expression must be averaged over one or more periods of oscillation. Now the mean value of $\cos^2 \omega t$ averaged in this way is just $\frac{1}{2}$, while that of $\cos \omega t \sin \omega t$ is 0. Hence the mean power drawn from the generator is

$$\overline{W} = \tfrac{1}{2}(V_0^2/Z)\cos\phi = \tfrac{1}{2}V_0 I_0 \cos\phi = \tfrac{1}{2}I_0^2 Z \cos\phi, \qquad (9.7)$$

where $I_0 = V_0/Z$ is the amplitude of the current given by equation (9.3). From equation (9.5) it is readily shown that $\cos\phi = R/Z$, and the expression for the mean power can therefore be written

$$\overline{W} = \tfrac{1}{2}I_0^2 R. \qquad (9.8)$$

Now the mean rate at which power is dissipated in the resistance of the circuit is the average value of $RI_0^2\cos^2(\omega t - \phi)$ taken over a complete period, and this is just equal to $\tfrac{1}{2}RI_0^2$. Hence all the power delivered by the generator, averaged over a period, is dissipated in the resistance of the circuit. The term in $\cos\omega t \sin\omega t$ in the expression for $VI$ represents work done by the generator in increasing the energy stored in the inductance and capacitance; since the product $\cos\omega t \sin\omega t$ is as often negative as positive, this work is returned to the generator in other parts of the cycle and no mean power is drawn from the generator for this purpose in the steady state. Of course, power was drawn from the generator initially to provide the stored energy, and this is represented by the transient current; when this has decayed, the mean stored energy remains constant and no further work is done by the generator on the average except to supply that dissipated in the resistance.

Since the rate at which power is dissipated is proportional to the square of the current, it is convenient to specify the root mean square value $\tilde{I}$ of the current, defined by the fact that

$$(\tilde{I})^2 = \langle I^2 \rangle,$$

where the average of the square of the current is taken over a whole period. The root mean square value of the voltage $\tilde{V}$ may be defined in a similar way, $(\tilde{V})^2 = \langle V^2 \rangle$. If the wave form is sinusoidal, the root mean square value is just $(1/\sqrt{2})$ times the amplitude, and we can write equation (9.7) as

$$\overline{W} = (\tilde{V}^2/Z)\cos\phi = \tilde{V}\tilde{I}\cos\phi = \tilde{I}^2 Z \cos\phi \qquad (9.9)$$

and the ratio $\overline{W}/\tilde{V}\tilde{I} = \cos\phi$ is called the 'power factor' of the circuit. It represents the fraction of the product $\tilde{V}\tilde{I}$ which is dissipated as Joule heat. If the circuit behaves as a pure resistance, as occurs when the resonance condition (9.6) is fulfilled in the circuit of Fig. 9.1, the power factor is unity, while if the circuit contains no resistance the power factor is zero.

The general practice in a.c. circuits is to specify the root mean square values of the current and voltage, and it should be understood that any values quoted are root mean square values unless the contrary is specifically stated.

## 9.2. Use of vectors and complex numbers

The values of the voltage across the individual components of the circuit in Fig. 9.1 will now be considered in more detail. For this purpose we assume that a current $I = I_0 \cos \omega t$ flows through them all in series, as in Fig. 9.2. The voltages across the three circuit elements are:

across $R$:  $V = IR = RI_0 \cos \omega t$

across $L$:  $V = L(dI/dt) = -\omega L I_0 \sin \omega t = \omega L I_0 \cos(\omega t + \tfrac{1}{2}\pi)$

across $C$:  $V = q/C = (1/\omega C)I_0 \sin \omega t = (1/\omega C)I_0 \cos(\omega t - \tfrac{1}{2}\pi)$

where in the last case we have used the relation $q = \int I \, dt$. It will be seen that the voltage across the resistance is in phase with the current,

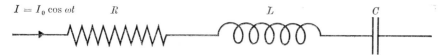

FIG. 9.2. Current $I$ flowing through $R, L, C$ in series.

the voltage across the inductance leads the current in phase by 90°, while that across the capacitance lags behind by 90°. We may represent these voltages by vectors such that, if the voltage across the resistance is represented by a vector drawn parallel to the $x$-axis, that across the inductance is represented by a vector parallel to the $y$-axis, and that across the capacitance by a vector parallel to the latter but in the opposite sense. The lengths of the vectors are proportional to $R$, $\omega L$, and $1/\omega C$, respectively.

If we require the voltage across two of the elements, say the resistance and inductance, it may be found by adding the two individual voltage vectors together, as in Fig. 9.3 (a). For the total voltage will be

$$V = IR + L(dI/dt) = RI_0 \cos \omega t - \omega L I_0 \sin \omega t$$
$$= I_0(R^2 + \omega^2 L^2)^{\frac{1}{2}} \cos(\omega t + \phi) = I_0 Z \cos(\omega t + \phi), \quad (9.10)$$

where $\tan \phi = \omega L/R$. From Fig. 9.3 (a) it will be seen that $(R^2 + \omega^2 L^2)^{\frac{1}{2}}$ is just the length of the hypotenuse of the triangle, while the phase angle $\phi$ is just the angle between the vectors $R$ and $(R^2 + \omega^2 L^2)^{\frac{1}{2}}$. Thus the magnitude of the total voltage is represented in amplitude by the hypotenuse, and its phase relative to the current is given by the angle through which this vector is rotated with respect to $R$. Similarly it can be shown that for a resistance and capacitance in series the total voltage may be found by adding the vectors $R$ and $-(1/\omega C)$ as in Fig. 9.3 (b), while the case of a resistance $R$, inductance $L$, and capacitance $C$ all in series is represented by Fig. 9.3 (c). Here the amplitude of the resultant vector is $\{R^2+(\omega L-1/\omega C)^2\}^{\frac{1}{2}}$, which is just the value of $Z$ (equation (9.4)) and the voltage leads the current by the phase angle $\phi$, where

$$\tan\phi = (\omega L-1/\omega C)/R,$$

as in equation (9.5). The term 'impedance' has already been introduced for $Z$, which represents the ratio of the amplitude of voltage to current

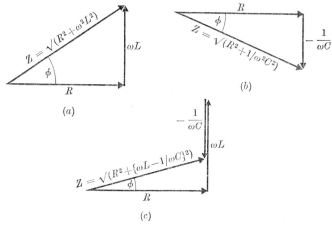

FIG. 9.3. Vector diagram for impedance. (a) $R, L$ in series; (b) $R, C$ in series; (c) $R, L, C$ in series. The voltage vectors are the same as the impedance vectors if the current is represented by a unit vector parallel to $R$.

for the whole circuit. The quantities $\omega L$ and $1/\omega C$ associated with inductance and capacitance respectively are known as reactances, and are usually denoted by the symbol $X$. Thus the total reactance of the circuit of Fig. 9.2 is $X = (\omega L-1/\omega C)$, and the impedance is given by the vector sum of $R$ and $X$, represented by mutually perpendicular vectors. Thus $Z = (R^2+X^2)^{\frac{1}{2}}$, and the phase angle is given by $\tan\phi = X/R$.

The vector representation of the impedance is similar to the representation of a complex number on the Argand diagram. Using the relation

$$e^{j\omega t} = \cos\omega t+j\sin\omega t,$$

where $j^2 = -1$, we may replace our cosine and sine functions by complex exponentials on the understanding that we are interested only in the real or imaginary parts respectively. Then we may write the current $I_0 \cos \omega t$ as $I_0 \mathscr{R}(e^{j\omega t})$, and quantities such as $dI/dt$ or $q = \int I \, dt$ become

$$dI/dt = I_0(d/dt)\cos \omega t = I_0 \mathscr{R}\left(\frac{d}{dt} e^{j\omega t}\right) = I_0 \mathscr{R}(j\omega e^{j\omega t})$$

and $\qquad q = I_0 \int \cos \omega t \, dt = I_0 \mathscr{R}\left(\int e^{j\omega t} \, dt\right) = I_0 \mathscr{R}\left(\frac{1}{j\omega} e^{j\omega t}\right)$

respectively. Hence the total voltage across the circuit of Fig. 9.2 is

$$\begin{aligned}
V &= RI + L(dI/dt) + (1/C)\int I \, dt \\
&= \left(Re^{j\omega t} + j\omega L e^{j\omega t} + \frac{1}{j\omega C} e^{j\omega t}\right)I \\
&= \left(R + j\omega L + \frac{1}{j\omega C}\right)I_0 e^{j\omega t} \\
&= \left(R + j\omega L + \frac{1}{j\omega C}\right)I. \tag{9.11}
\end{aligned}$$

If the current is $I_0 \cos \omega t$, then to find the voltage we take the real part of (9.11). Thus

$$\begin{aligned}
V &= I_0 \mathscr{R}\bigg( R \cos \omega t + jR \sin \omega t + j\omega L \cos \omega t - \omega L \sin \omega t - \\
&\qquad\qquad\qquad\qquad\qquad - \frac{j}{\omega C}\cos \omega t + \frac{1}{\omega C}\sin \omega t \bigg) \\
&= I_0\bigg( R \cos \omega t - \omega L \sin \omega t + \frac{1}{\omega C}\sin \omega t\bigg),
\end{aligned}$$

where the three component terms are just the voltages across the three circuit elements derived at the beginning of this section. Similarly, if the current had been $I_0 \sin \omega t = I_0 \mathscr{I}(e^{j\omega t})$, the voltage would be found by taking the imaginary part of (9.11), giving

$$V = I_0\bigg( R \sin \omega t + \omega L \cos \omega t - \frac{1}{\omega C}\cos \omega t\bigg).$$

The importance of equation (9.11) lies in the fact that it shows we may represent the inductance and capacitance by impedance operators $j\omega L$ and $1/(j\omega C)$ respectively, and these operators may be added to one another when the elements are in series in a similar way to resistances. The phase of the voltage, which leads the current by $\frac{1}{2}\pi$ in the inductance and lags by $\frac{1}{2}\pi$ in the capacitance, is taken care of by the presence of $j$. If, as is usual in the Argand diagram, real quantities are represented by vectors drawn parallel to the $x$-axis, and imaginary quantities by vectors parallel to the $y$-axis, then the complex impedance operator is as shown in our vector diagram Fig. 9.3 (c). The circuit impedance is given by the modulus of the complex impedance operator, and the phase angle by its argument. If we write the impedance operator as

$$\mathbf{Z} = R+j\omega L+\frac{1}{j\omega C} = R+jX = Ze^{j\phi}$$

then $Z = (R^2+X^2)^{\frac{1}{2}}$, and $\tan\phi = X/R$, as before. Then

$$V = \mathbf{Z}I = Ze^{j\phi}I_0 e^{j\omega t} = ZI_0 e^{j(\omega t+\phi)}.$$

If $I = I_0\cos\omega t$, the real part of this gives $V = ZI_0\cos(\omega t+\phi)$, as in equation (9.10). If, on the other hand, the voltage is given as $V_0\cos\omega t$, as in § 9.1, the current is found by taking the real part of

$$I = V/\mathbf{Z} = V_0 e^{j\omega t}/(Ze^{j\phi}) = (V_0/Z)e^{j(\omega t-\phi)},$$

which gives $\qquad\qquad I = (V_0/Z)\cos(\omega t-\phi),$

as in equation (9.3).

From an extension of the treatment given above it may readily be shown that the impedance operator for a circuit consisting of a number of impedances $\mathbf{Z}_1, \mathbf{Z}_2,..., \mathbf{Z}_n$ in series is

$$\mathbf{Z} = \mathbf{Z}_1+\mathbf{Z}_2+...+\mathbf{Z}_n. \tag{9.12}$$

The corresponding formula for a number of impedances in parallel is found by noting that the voltage across each is the same. The current through the impedance $\mathbf{Z}_k$ is $V/\mathbf{Z}_k$, and the total current is the sum of a number of similar terms. Hence the net impedance is given by

$$I/V = \frac{1}{\mathbf{Z}} = \frac{1}{\mathbf{Z}_1}+\frac{1}{\mathbf{Z}_2}+...+\frac{1}{\mathbf{Z}_n}. \tag{9.13}$$

When a number of elements are in parallel it is generally convenient to work in terms of the reciprocal of the impedance, known as the admittance $\mathbf{Y}$. Thus $I = V/\mathbf{Z} = \mathbf{Y}V$, and equation (9.13) may be written as

$$\mathbf{Y} = \mathbf{Y}_1+\mathbf{Y}_2+...+\mathbf{Y}_n. \tag{9.14}$$

In general $\mathbf{Y}$ is complex; thus $\mathbf{Y} = G+jS$, where $G$ is called the conductance and $S$ the susceptance. For the three simple circuit elements we have conductance $G = 1/R$; susceptance of an inductance is $S = (j\omega L)^{-1} = -j/(\omega L)$; susceptance of a capacitance is $S = j\omega C$; but note that for a circuit containing both resistance and reactance these simple reciprocal relations do not hold. For

$$\mathbf{Y} = 1/\mathbf{Z} = 1/(R+jX) = (R-jX)/(R^2+X^2),$$

so that $Y = |\mathbf{Y}| = |\mathbf{Z}^{-1}| = Z^{-1}$, but

$$G = R/(R^2+X^2) = Y\cos\phi, \qquad S = -X/(R^2+X^2) = -Y\sin\phi$$

and similarly

$$R = G/(G^2+S^2) = Z\cos\phi, \qquad X = -S/(G^2+S^2) = Z\sin\phi$$

$$(9.15)$$

In order to calculate the power consumed in a circuit we must use the relation $W = \mathscr{R}\{V\}\times\mathscr{R}\{I\}$; note that this is not the same as $\mathscr{R}\{VI\}$,

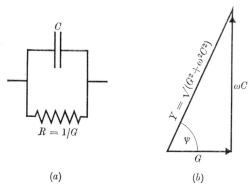

FIG. 9.4. (a) Imperfect capacitor with conductance $G$, represented by capacitance $C$ shunted by resistance $R = 1/G$; (b) corresponding admittance diagram.

for $\mathscr{R}\{V_0\exp j\omega t\}\times\mathscr{R}\{I_0\exp j(\omega t-\phi)\} = V_0\cos\omega t\times I_0\cos(\omega t-\phi)$, which does not equal $\mathscr{R}\{V_0 I_0\exp j(2\omega t-\phi)\} = V_0 I_0\cos(2\omega t-\phi)$. However, the mean energy $\overline{W}$ dissipated is given by any of the relations (where $\tilde{V}$ and $\tilde{I}$ are the root mean square values)

$$\overline{W} = \tilde{V}^2\mathscr{R}\{\mathbf{Y}\} = \tilde{V}^2 G = \tilde{V}^2 R/(R^2+X^2)$$
$$= \tilde{I}^2\mathscr{R}\{\mathbf{Z}\} = \tilde{I}^2 R = \tilde{I}^2 G/(G^2+S^2), \qquad (9.16)$$

as can be verified by comparison with equation (9.9).

The unit of reactance and impedance is the same as that of resistance, the ohm; when $\omega$ is expressed in radians/second, $L$ in henries, and $C$ in farads, the corresponding reactances are in ohms. Similarly, the unit of admittance and susceptance is the same as that of conductance, the reciprocal ohm, or mho.

We may illustrate the use of admittance by considering the case of a lossy condenser, represented by a pure capacitance $C$ shunted by a resistance $R$, as in Fig. 9.4 (a). The admittance operator is

$$\mathbf{Y} = (1/R)+j\omega C = G+j\omega C.$$

This may be represented by the admittance diagram shown in Fig. 9.4 (b). The phase angle of the admittance is given by $\tan\psi = \omega C/G = \omega CR$; by use of equation (9.15) or by plotting the corresponding impedance diagram it is readily shown that $\tan\psi = -\tan\phi$, so that $\psi = -\phi$. Hence the power factor $\cos\phi = \cos\psi = (1+\omega^2 C^2 R^2)^{-\frac{1}{2}}$. For a perfect capacitance, as for a perfect inductance, the power factor is zero; in practice this is not quite true, since at radio frequencies power is lost through eddy currents in the plates and imperfections in the dielectric. The latter are caused by hysteresis effects which cause the vector $\mathbf{D}$ to lag behind the vector $\mathbf{E}$ in the dielectric as in the corresponding case of $\mathbf{B}$ and $\mathbf{H}$ for a ferromagnetic substance. The quality of a dielectric is expressed in terms of its 'loss tangent', $\tan\delta$, where

$$\delta = \tfrac{1}{2}\pi - \psi = \tfrac{1}{2}\pi + \phi;$$

hence          $\tan\delta = \cot\psi = -\cot\phi = G/(\omega C) = (\omega CR)^{-1}.$

In an oscillating electric field the hysteresis loop is traversed once per cycle, so that the loss conductance $G$ is proportional to the frequency. The value of $\tan\delta$ should therefore be independent of frequency, and this is generally true except for strongly polar dielectrics (see Chapter 17); for a good dielectric, such as quartz, the value of $\tan\delta$ is about $10^{-4}$.

## 9.3. Tuned circuits

The circuit of Fig. 9.1 consisting of an inductance, resistance, and capacitance in series is known as a 'series resonant' circuit. The impedance operator is          $\mathbf{Z} = R + j(\omega L - 1/\omega C),$          (9.17)

and, as pointed out in § 9.1, the modulus of this has a minimum value if the frequency is adjusted to make $\omega L = 1/\omega C$. This is the resonant frequency of the circuit, given by equation (9.6)

$$\omega_0 = 1/\sqrt{(LC)}.$$

At this frequency the current through the circuit is a maximum and is in phase with the applied voltage, since $\mathbf{Z}$ is real; the magnitude of the current is $V/R$. The voltage across the resistance $R$ is thus equal to the voltage across the whole circuit, and the voltages across the inductance and capacitance are therefore equal and exactly 180° out of phase with one another, making the voltage across the two zero. The voltage across the capacitance alone at resonance is

$$V_C = I/(j\omega_0 C) = V/(j\omega_0 CR)$$

and hence, using (9.6),

$$|V_C/V| = (\omega_0 C R)^{-1} = \frac{1}{R}\sqrt{\frac{L}{C}} = \frac{\omega_0 L}{R} = Q, \qquad (9.18)$$

where $Q$ is the 'quality factor' of the circuit as defined in § 6.3. It is also known as the 'circuit magnification factor', since from equation (9.18) we see that it equals the ratio of the voltage across the capacitor to the voltage across the whole circuit. Thus the tuned circuit acts as a transformer; since the current through the capacitor is a maximum at resonance, the ratio of the voltages $V_C/V$ is also a maximum at this point. The voltage across the inductance $L$ is equal to that across the inductance at resonance, but in general $R$ is associated with $L$ and only the voltage across the combination $(R+j\omega L)$ can be measured in practice.

The behaviour of the circuit at frequencies near resonance is of particular interest. The reactance of the circuit changes rather rapidly in this region, passing through zero at the resonant frequency because two rather large quantities, $\omega L$ and $1/(\omega C)$, cancel at this point. For frequencies near resonance we may write $\omega = \omega_0 + \delta\omega$ and then the impedance operator becomes

$$\mathbf{Z} = R + j\left(\omega_0 L + \delta\omega L - \frac{1}{\omega_0 C} + \frac{\delta\omega}{\omega_0^2 C}\right) = R + 2j\,\delta\omega\,L, \qquad (9.19)$$

since $1/(\omega_0^2 C) = L$. On introducing $Q$, this may be written

$$\mathbf{Z} = R\{1 + 2j(\delta\omega/\omega_0)Q\} \qquad (9.20)$$

and the impedance is

$$Z = R\left\{1 + 4Q^2\left(\frac{\delta\omega}{\omega_0}\right)^2\right\}^{\frac{1}{2}}, \qquad (9.21)$$

showing that if a given current flows through the circuit, the voltage across the circuit rises by a factor $\sqrt{2}$ when the frequency deviates from the resonant frequency by a fraction $\delta\omega/\omega_0 = \pm 1/(2Q)$. Similarly, if a given voltage is applied to the circuit, the current through it falls to $1/\sqrt{2}$ of its maximum value when the frequency deviates by this amount; the power dissipated in the circuit falls to one-half of the maximum, and these points are therefore often referred to as the 'half-power' points. The form of equation (9.21) shows that the variation of impedance with frequency gives a curve of universal shape but whose spread in frequency is determined by the value of $Q$. Since in general the ratio of $|V_C|$ to $|V|$ is $(\omega C Z)^{-1}$, the voltage step-up obtained falls sharply away on either side of the resonance point. Thus the circuit is selective in its response to signals of different frequency; its 'selectivity' is determined by the value of $Q$ since $Q$ is the ratio of the resonant frequency to the difference of frequency between the two half-power points:

$$Q = \omega_0/(2\delta\omega) = f_0/(2\delta f).$$

A plot of the amplitude of the current in a series resonant circuit when a signal of given voltage but varying frequency is applied to it is shown in Fig. 9.5. Since the voltage across the capacitance $V_C = I/(\omega C)$, and

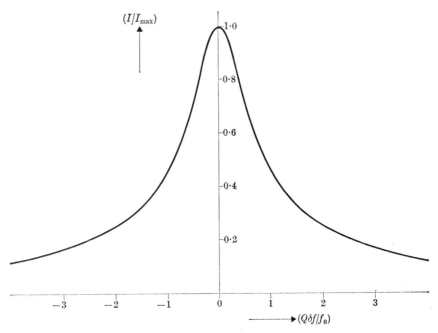

FIG. 9.5. Variation of current in series tuned circuit near resonance.

near resonance the variation in $I$ is very much more rapid (if $Q$ is large) than that of $\omega$, the voltage step-up obtained is also given to a good approximation by a curve of the same shape as in Fig. 9.5.

The approximation used in the deduction of equation (9.20) is that $\delta\omega/\omega_0 \ll 1$. At frequencies where this approximation is not valid, the variation of $\mathbf{Z}$ still follows a universal curve, since we may write

$$\mathbf{Z} = R\left\{1 + jQ\left(x - \frac{1}{x}\right)\right\},\tag{9.22}$$

where $x = (\omega/\omega_0) = (f/f_0)$. Since the reactive part of the impedance varies as $2Q(\delta\omega/\omega_0)$ near resonance, the current falls to quite small values before the approximation $\delta\omega/\omega_0 \ll 1$ becomes invalid, provided that $Q$ is fairly high. In an ordinary tuned circuit the resistance is that of the wire used in winding the inductance coil; if we use a larger inductance in order to increase the value of $Q$ at a given frequency, the resistance goes up and so does the self-capacitance between the different parts of the coil. The latter sets up an upper limit to the size of the coil since at some point the coil will resonate at the desired frequency without any external capacitance, because of its self-capacitance. As a rough guide one may take the $Q$ of a coil designed to resonate at an audiofrequency as about 20; at frequencies of the order of 1 Mc/s a $Q$ of 100–200 may be obtained; at frequencies of $10^9$ and $10^{10}$ c/s where tuned

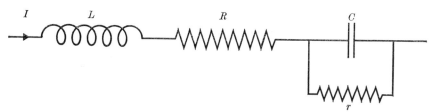

FIG. 9.6. Series resonant circuit with lossy capacitor.

transmission lines and waveguide cavities (see Chapters 11, 14, and 15) are used instead of lumped circuits, values of 1000 to 10 000 are obtained for $Q$. Thus in most radio work with tuned circuits equation (9.20) is a good approximation.

Hitherto we have assumed no loss in the capacitor; if we include some loss the circuit becomes that shown in Fig. 9.6. The impedance operator is now

$$\mathbf{Z} = R+j\omega L+\frac{1}{j\omega C+1/r} = R+j\omega L+(r-j\omega Cr^2)/(1+\omega^2 C^2 r^2).$$

If the power factor of the capacitor is small, $\omega Cr \gg 1$, and the impedance operator is approximately (cf. Problem 9.3)

$$\mathbf{Z} = R+j\omega L+(\omega^2 C^2 r)^{-1}-j/(\omega C). \tag{9.23}$$

Thus the resonance frequency is unaltered in the first approximation, but the resistance of the circuit is increased. The value of $Q$ is now given by

$$1/Q = \{R+(\omega_0^2 C^2 r)^{-1}\}/(\omega_0 L) = \frac{R}{\omega_0 L}+\frac{1}{\omega_0 Cr} = 1/Q_L+\tan\delta,$$

where $Q_L = \omega_0 L/R$ is the $Q$ of the circuit due to the loss in the inductance alone. Since for a good capacitor $\tan\delta < 10^{-3}$, while for lumped circuits with inductive coils (as distinct from transmission line circuits) $1/Q_L \approx 10^{-2}$, loss in the capacitor can generally be neglected.

*Parallel resonant circuits*

A parallel resonant circuit consists of a capacitance shunted across an inductance+resistance, as in Fig. 9.7. The admittance operator for the circuit is

$$\mathbf{Y} = j\omega C + \frac{1}{R+j\omega L} = j\omega C + \frac{R-j\omega L}{R^2+\omega^2 L^2}.$$  (9.24)

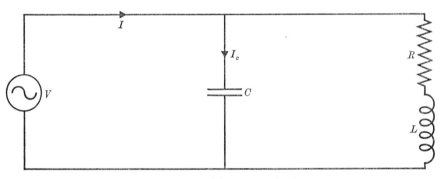

Fig. 9.7.  Parallel resonant circuit.

We will define the resonance point for this circuit as the point at which the admittance is real. Then, equating the imaginary terms to zero gives

$$R^2+\omega_0^2 L^2 = L/C$$  (9.25 a)

and hence

$$\omega_0 = \left(\frac{1}{LC}\right)^{\frac{1}{2}}\left(1-\frac{R^2 C}{L}\right)^{\frac{1}{2}} = \left(\frac{1}{LC}\right)^{\frac{1}{2}}\left(1-\frac{1}{Q^2}\right)^{\frac{1}{2}},$$  (9.25 b)

while the admittance at this point is

$$\mathbf{Y} = R/(R^2+\omega_0^2 L^2) = RC/L = 1/(Q^2 R).$$  (9.26)

We see that the resonance frequency is not quite the same as in the series tuned circuit, but the difference is small and can usually be neglected if $Q$ is large (if $Q = 100$, the fractional difference in $\omega_0$ is $\frac{1}{2} 10^{-4}$). Because of this difference, the alternative formulae $\omega_0 L/R$ and $1/(\omega_0 CR)$ for $Q$ are not exactly equivalent to $(L/C)^{\frac{1}{2}}/R$, but they are a good approximation if $Q$ is large. The reciprocal of the admittance at resonance is called the 'parallel resistance' of the circuit, and is equal to $Q^2 R$ without any approximation.

The definition of resonance as the point at which the admittance is real is to a certain extent arbitrary, but is very convenient to use; it has the further advantage of being unique. The admittance of the circuit at this point is very small, but is not necessarily a minimum. If resonance is defined as the point at which $Y$ is a minimum, then the resonance condition depends on what is being adjusted to make $Y$ a minimum. If the capacitance is altered, and other quantities are kept fixed, then, by differentiating $Y = |\mathbf{Y}|$ with respect to $C$, it can readily be shown that $Y$ is a minimum when the value of the capacitance satisfies equation (9.25 a). On the other hand, if $L$ or the applied frequency is altered, slightly different resonance conditions are obtained; the fractional difference is, however, only of order $1/Q^2$, and so can be neglected if $Q$ is large. The calculation involved in finding these resonance conditions by differentiation is very tedious in comparison with the simple device of setting the imaginary part of $\mathbf{Y}$ equal to zero, and the simple definition of resonance as the point at which the circuit has unity power factor (i.e. the admittance is real) has many advantages.

It is useful to have an approximate expression for $\mathbf{Y}$ near resonance similar to equations (9.19–21) for the series resonance circuit. Writing $\omega = \omega_0 + \delta\omega$, we have from equation (9.24)

$$\mathbf{Y} = \frac{R}{R^2 + \omega_0^2 L^2}\left(1 - \frac{2\omega_0\,\delta\omega L^2}{R^2 + \omega_0^2 L^2}\right) + j\left\{\delta\omega C - \frac{\delta\omega L}{R^2 + \omega_0^2 L^2}\left(1 - \frac{2\omega_0^2 L^2}{R^2 + \omega_0^2 L^2}\right)\right\}$$

$$= \frac{RC}{L}\{1 - 2\delta\omega(\omega_0\,CL)\} + 2j\,\delta\omega\,C^2 L\omega_0^2,$$

where we have used equation (9.25 a). In the term of order $\delta\omega$ we may put $\omega_0^2 LC = 1$, giving

$$\mathbf{Y} = \frac{RC}{L}\left\{1 - \frac{2\delta\omega}{\omega_0}\right\} + 2j\,\delta\omega\,C.$$

In general the small change in the conductance can be neglected, so that

$$\mathbf{Y} = (RC/L) + 2j\delta\omega C = (RC/L)\{1 + 2jQ(\delta\omega/\omega_0)\}, \qquad (9.27)$$

showing that the behaviour of the admittance near resonance for the parallel resonant circuit is similar to that of the impedance of the series tuned circuit. The selectivity is the same in that $Y$ rises by a factor $\sqrt{2}$ when the fractional deviation of the frequency is

$$(\delta f/f_0) = (\delta\omega/\omega_0) = \pm 1/(2Q).$$

Thus the current drawn from the voltage generator is a minimum at resonance (apart from the small corrections which can be neglected when $Q$ is large). The current in each of the arms is larger than that drawn from the source by a factor nearly equal to $Q$. Thus the ratio of the current through the capacitance to that drawn from the generator is

$$|I_C/I| = (\omega_0\,CV)/(RCV/L) = \omega_0 L/R = Q \qquad (9.28)$$

in our approximation; this relation is complementary to that given by equation (9.18). That equation showed that the series resonant circuit can be used as a tuned transformer where the output voltage across the condenser is larger by a factor $Q$ than that injected in series with the inductance. The impedance measured at the output (e.g. by finding the current drawn from a generator applied across the capacitance as in Fig. 9.7) is $Q^2 R$ at resonance (by equation (9.26)) whereas the impedance of the series tuned circuit is $R$. Thus the ratio of the impedances is $Q^2$, the square of the voltage ratio. This, which is a characteristic of all transformers, can be seen as follows: if we apply a generator of voltage $V$ to the series tuned circuit, the current drawn from it is $I$; to have the same current flowing through the capacitance in the parallel resonant circuit formed from the same elements, we must apply a generator of voltage $QV$ across the capacitance, and the current drawn from it will be $I/Q$. The power dissipated in the circuit is $VI$, the same in each case.

The importance of the quality factor $Q$ in determining the properties of a resonant circuit can be readily appreciated from the following summary. For a simple resonant circuit as considered hitherto:

(a) $Q = (L/C)^{\frac{1}{2}}/R \approx \omega_0 L/R \approx (\omega_0 C R)^{-1}$;

(b) $Q$ is equal to the voltage step-up obtained by using the circuit as a tuned transformer;

(c) the parallel resistance is $Q^2$ times the series resistance;

(d) the fractional frequency difference $(2\delta f/f_0)$ between the points at which the impedance or admittance changes by a factor $\sqrt{2}$ is $1/Q$;

(e) $Q = \pi/\lambda$, where $\lambda$ is the logarithmic decrement of free oscillations in the circuit (see § 6.3);

(f) in forced resonance,

$$Q = \frac{\omega_0 \times (\text{stored energy})}{\text{rate of energy dissipation}}.$$

This last relation can be used to define $Q$ in more complicated resonant circuits, and in other resonant systems such as waveguide cavities (see Chapter 11) where the values of $L$, $C$, $R$ cannot be specified. For the series resonant circuit of Fig. 9.2 it is readily shown that this definition agrees with that in (a) above. For the stored energy at any instant is

$$\tfrac{1}{2}LI^2 + \tfrac{1}{2}q^2/C = \tfrac{1}{2}LI_0^2 \cos^2\omega_0 t + \tfrac{1}{2}\{I_0^2/(\omega_0^2 C)\}\sin^2\omega_0 t$$

$$= \tfrac{1}{2}LI_0^2 \quad \text{at resonance,}$$

while the mean rate of energy dissipation is $\tfrac{1}{2}RI_0^2$. Hence

$$Q = \omega_0(\tfrac{1}{2}LI_0^2)/(\tfrac{1}{2}RI_0^2) = \omega_0 L/R.$$

## 9.4. Coupled resonant circuits

Two circuits are said to be coupled together if they have a common impedance. The impedance may be a resistance, inductance, or capacitance, and may be a part of each circuit, as in the example shown in Fig. 9.8 (*a*), or connected between the two circuits as in Fig. 9.8 (*b*).

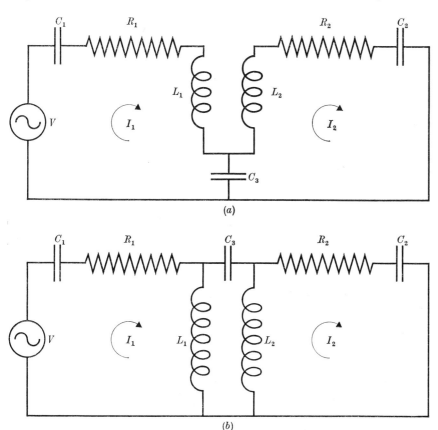

*(a)*

*(b)*

FIG. 9.8. Types of coupled circuits: (*a*) with common impedance ($C_3$); (*b*) with impedance ($C_3$) connected between them.

Two circuits may also be coupled together if one of them is in an electric or magnetic field set up by the other; for example, the oscillating magnetic flux due to a coil in one circuit may induce a voltage in a coil in the second circuit, so that there is a mutual inductance between the two circuits.

In Fig. 9.9 two resonant circuits 1 and 2 are coupled together by a mutual inductance $M$ between the coils $L_1$ and $L_2$. The voltage $V_1$

applied to the first circuit produces a current $I_1$, and this induces a voltage $M(dI_1/dt)$ in the secondary circuit. For a simple sinusoidal wave form this voltage may be written as $j\omega M I_1$, where $j\omega M$ is the impedance operator for the mutual inductance. Similarly, if $I_2$ is the current in the

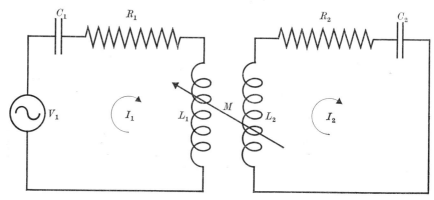

FIG. 9.9. Two resonant circuits coupled by mutual inductance $M$.

secondary, a voltage $j\omega M I_2$ will be induced in the primary. Thus for the two circuits we have

$$\left.\begin{array}{l} V_1 = I_1 Z_1 + j\omega M I_2 \\ 0 = I_2 Z_2 + j\omega M I_1 \end{array}\right\}, \tag{9.29}$$

where $Z_1$, $Z_2$ are the impedance operators for the primary and secondary circuits in the absence of the mutual inductance. On eliminating $I_2$ we have

$$V_1 = I_1\left(Z_1 + \frac{\omega^2 M^2}{Z_2}\right). \tag{9.30}$$

The quantity $(\omega^2 M^2/Z_2)$ is called the impedance 'reflected into the primary circuit'. For the secondary circuit, elimination of $I_1$ gives

$$-\frac{j\omega M}{Z_1}V_1 = I_2\left(Z_2 + \frac{\omega^2 M^2}{Z_1}\right), \tag{9.31}$$

showing that the current flow is that produced by an apparent voltage $-(j\omega M/Z_1)V_1$ working into $Z_2$ plus the impedance 'reflected into the secondary circuit' $(\omega^2 M^2/Z_1)$.

To investigate the behaviour of the primary circuit impedance in more detail we write $Z_1 = R_1 + jX_1$, $Z_2 = R_2 + jX_2$. Then

$$\begin{aligned} V_1/I_1 &= R_1 + jX_1 + \omega^2 M^2/(R_2 + jX_2) \\ &= R_1 + R_2\omega^2 M^2/(R_2^2 + X_2^2) + j\{X_1 - X_2\omega^2 M^2/(R_2^2 + X_2^2)\} \\ &= R_p + jX_p. \end{aligned} \tag{9.32}$$

The current and voltage in the primary are in phase if $X_p$ is zero. This requirement is satisfied if $X_1 = X_2 = 0$, and in the following analysis we shall assume that the elements of the primary and secondary circuits are the same, so that $R_1 = R_2$, $X_1 = X_2$ at all frequencies (the latter implies $L_1 = L_2$, $C_1 = C_2$). Then $X_p$ is zero when either

$$X = 0 \quad \text{or} \quad X^2 = \omega^2 M^2 - R^2. \tag{9.33}$$

The second of these conditions can be fulfilled only if $\omega M > R$. If $\omega M = R$, the three roots are identical, and if $\omega M < R$ only one real root exists.

The significance of these three roots becomes apparent when we examine the behaviour of the secondary current. When

$$X_1 = X_2 = X = 0,$$

from equation (9.31) we have

$$I_2 = \frac{-j\omega_0 M V_1}{R^2 + \omega_0^2 M^2}, \tag{9.34}$$

where $\omega_0 = (LC)^{-\frac{1}{2}}$ is the resonance frequency of either circuit by itself. If we can vary the mutual inductance $M$, then the value of $I_2$ at this frequency rises as $M$ is increased from zero, passes through a maximum value of $-jV_1/2R$ when $\omega_0 M = R$, and then falls again. At the maximum the impedance reflected into the primary from the secondary is just equal to $R$, so that the secondary circuit is 'matched' to the primary circuit, and the power dissipated in the secondary circuit is a maximum at this point. From equations (9.30) and (9.34) it can be seen that the currents in the primary and secondary circuits are both equal to $V_1/2R$ at this point, but they differ in phase by $\frac{1}{2}\pi$.

At the second two points given by equation (9.33) where the effective primary impedance is real, the secondary current is

$$I_2 = \frac{-j\omega M V_1}{Z^2 + \omega^2 M^2} = \frac{-j\omega M V_1}{R^2 - X^2 + \omega^2 M^2 + 2jRX}$$

$$= \frac{-j\omega M V_1}{2R^2 + 2jRX} = \frac{-j\omega M V_1}{2R(R + jX)},$$

where we have used the condition given by equation (9.33). Hence

$$|I_2| = \frac{\omega M V_1}{2R(R^2 + X^2)^{\frac{1}{2}}} = \frac{V_1}{2R}.$$

These results show that when the circuits are 'over-coupled' ($\omega M > R$) the secondary current rises to ($V_1/2R$) at the second two points given by equation (9.33), while it has fallen below this value at the point

$X = 0$. The primary circuit impedance is purely resistive at all three points, but only at the second two points is it equal to $2R$, as can be seen by substituting in equation (9.32). Thus the secondary current is a maximum at these two points because the secondary circuit is again 'matched' to the primary circuit.

The general behaviour of the secondary current is shown in Fig. 9.10, where the degree of coupling is specified in terms of the 'coefficient of coupling' defined by equation (6.14) as

$$k = M/(L_1 L_2)^{\frac{1}{2}} = M/L \qquad (9.35)$$

when the two circuits are identical.

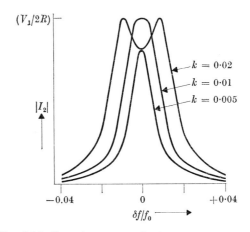

FIG. 9.10. Secondary current in the circuit of Fig. 9.9
for two identical circuits each with $Q = 100$. Critical
coupling occurs at $k = 0.01$.

The critical condition $\omega_0 M = R$ then occurs when the coefficient of coupling has the value

$$k_0 = R/(\omega_0 L) = 1/Q. \qquad (9.36)$$

The curves in Fig. 9.10 are drawn for $Q = 100$, and coefficients of coupling of $k = \frac{1}{2}k_0$, $k_0$, and $2k_0$ respectively. The first curve is similar to an ordinary resonance curve, but the current is always less than the maximum possible value $V_1/2R$. The second curve has a single peak in the centre, but the peak is decidedly flattened because of the three coincident roots. As soon as $k > k_0$ we have two side maxima in the current with a central minimum. As $k/k_0$ increases these peaks move outwards and the trough in the middle deepens. When $Q$ is large and the frequency is close to resonance we may write $X = 2\delta\omega L$, and equation (9.33) gives for the separation $2\delta f$ of the peaks

$$(2\delta f/f_0) = (2\delta\omega/\omega_0) \approx \left\{\frac{M^2}{L^2} - \frac{R^2}{\omega_0^2 L^2}\right\}^{\frac{1}{2}} = (k^2 - 1/Q^2)^{\frac{1}{2}} = (k^2 - k_0^2)^{\frac{1}{2}}.$$

(9.37)

Although identical circuits have been assumed in this analysis, the behaviour of any pair of coupled circuits whose natural resonant frequencies are the same is similar. Thus for two circuits with the same $X$ but different $R_1$, $R_2$, optimum coupling occurs (for $X = 0$) when

$$\omega_0 M = (R_1 R_2)^{\frac{1}{2}} \quad \{k = 1/(Q_1 Q_2)^{\frac{1}{2}}\}$$

and the secondary current is then $V_1/2(R_1 R_2)^{\frac{1}{2}}$. Side peaks occur when the coupling is greater than this value, and the secondary current at these peaks is $V_1/(R_1 + R_2)$, which is less than the optimum. The values of the effective primary impedance are $2R_1$ when the coupling is optimum and $X = 0$, and $(R_1 + R_2)$ at the side peaks when the circuits are over-coupled.

Coupled circuits have an important application in the reception of radio signals when it is desired to accept a narrow band of frequencies and reject frequencies outside this band. Thus in broadcast reception of sound a uniform response over a band of about 9 kc/s width is required with total rejection outside, so that the ideal response curve would be rectangular in shape. By the use of tuned circuits with rather more than critical coupling a response curve with steep sides is obtained, and the slight dip in the middle can be compensated by the use of somewhat under-coupled circuits (with a central peak) elsewhere in the receiver. In a tunable receiver of this kind a constant bandwidth is required independent of the central frequency. This cannot be achieved by mutual inductance coupling alone, for equation (9.37) shows that the bandwidth is then proportional to the central frequency. A combination of mutual inductance coupling together with capacitance coupling as in Fig. 9.8 (a) may be used to give a more or less constant bandwidth, for the coupling through the capacitance decreases with frequency, because of the fall in the impedance common to the two circuits.

## 9.5. Low-frequency transformers

The coupled resonant circuits discussed in the last section may be regarded as a tuned transformer; they are used as such at radio frequencies where the effects of stray capacitance can be reduced by making it part of the tuning capacitance. At low frequencies (such as those of power supplies) effects of stray capacitance are small, and transfer of power can be made very efficiently by use of the transformer whose principle was mentioned in § 6.2. It consists of two coils, the primary or input coil of $n_1$ turns, and the secondary or output coil of $n_2$ turns, which are closely wound together on an iron core so that all the flux due to one coil passes through the other. In practice there is always a small leakage of flux, so that not all the flux of one circuit passes through the other. Then the transformer may be represented by the circuit of Fig. 9.11, where $L_1$, $L_2$ are the self-inductances of the primary

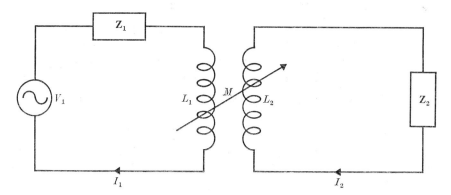

FIG. 9.11. Circuit diagram of transformer with load $Z_2$.

and secondary windings, and $M$ is the mutual inductance between them. An alternating voltage $V_1$ of angular frequency $\omega$ is applied to the primary in series with an impedance $Z_1$, and the secondary is connected to a load impedance $Z_2$. Then, if the primary and secondary currents are $I_1$, $I_2$, the equations for the primary and secondary circuits are

$$\left.\begin{aligned} V_1 &= (Z_1 + j\omega L_1)I_1 + j\omega M I_2 \\ 0 &= (Z_2 + j\omega L_2)I_2 + j\omega M I_1 \end{aligned}\right\}. \tag{9.38}$$

These equations differ from (9.29) in that the self-inductances $L_1$, $L_2$ are not included in the impedances $Z_1$, $Z_2$ because their reactances are normally very much larger than any other impedances in the circuits. Alternate elimination of $I_2$ and $I_1$ between these equations gives the following formulae for the primary and secondary circuits

$$V_1/I_1 = Z_1 + j\omega L_1 + \omega^2 M^2/(Z_2 + j\omega L_2) \tag{9.39}$$

and

$$-(M/L_1)V_1/I_2 = Z_2 + Z_1(L_2/L_1) + j\omega(L_2 - M^2/L_1), \tag{9.40}$$

where in the second equation a term $Z_1 Z_2/(j\omega L_1)$ has been omitted since it is an order of magnitude smaller than $Z_2$.

For a perfect transformer, there is complete coupling between the two coils, so that $M^2 = L_1 L_2$. Since the self-inductances are proportional to the squares of the number of turns, the turns ratio $n = (L_2/L_1)^{\frac{1}{2}}$, and with complete coupling we have also $n = M/L_1 = L_2/M$. Hence, assuming $Z_2 \ll \omega L_2$, from equation (9.39) the primary impedance $Z_p$ may be written

$$V_1/I_1 = Z_p = Z_1 + j\omega L_1 + \omega^2 M^2 (Z_2 - j\omega L_2)/(Z_2^2 + \omega^2 L_2^2)$$
$$\approx Z_1 + Z_2(M^2/L_2^2) + j\omega(L_1 - M^2/L_2) = Z_1 + Z_2/n^2. \quad (9.41)$$

The current in the secondary circuit is the same as that due to an e.m.f. $-(M/L_1)V_1 = -nV_1$ working into an impedance $Z_s$, where

$$Z_s = Z_2 + Z_1 n^2. \quad (9.42)$$

These equations show that for a perfect transformer on load ($Z_2 \ll \omega L_2$) the inductive terms such as $j\omega(L_1 - M^2/L_2)$ are exactly zero when there is complete coupling between the two coils. The effect of the secondary circuit on the current in the primary is represented by the additional impedance $Z_2/n^2$, known as the 'reflected impedance'. In the secondary circuit the effective e.m.f. is $-nV_1$, with an apparent internal impedance $Z_1 n^2$. Hence the impedances are transformed by $n^2$ while the voltages are transformed by $n$; the current transformation ratio is $1/n$, so that the power on the two sides is the same ($V_1 I_1 = V_2 I_2$), as we should expect for a perfect transformer with no losses.

In practice $M^2$ is slightly less than $L_1 L_2$ because not all the flux from one circuit passes through the other, and we write $M = k(L_1 L_2)^{\frac{1}{2}}$, where $k$ is the coupling coefficient defined by equation (6.14). It is useful to derive an equivalent circuit for the transformer, and in order to include the case where $Z_2$ is of the same order of magnitude as $\omega L_2$, we rewrite the expression for the primary impedance (equation (9.39)) in the following way

$$Z_p = Z_1 + j\omega L_1(1-k) + \frac{\omega^2 k^2 L_1 L_2 + j\omega L_1 k(Z_2 + j\omega L_2)}{Z_2 + j\omega L_2}.$$

The last term may be written in the form

$$\frac{j\omega k L_1 \{Z_2 + j\omega(1-k)L_2\}}{\{Z_2 + j\omega(1-k)L_2\} + j\omega k L_1 n^2},$$

since in the denominator $j\omega k L_1 n^2 - j\omega k L_2 = 0$. The last term is now

$$\left\{ \frac{1}{j\omega k L_1} + \frac{n^2}{Z_2 + j\omega(1-k)L_2} \right\}^{-1},$$

which is equivalent to two impedances in parallel. Hence the primary circuit may be represented by Fig. 9.12. Here $(1-k)L_1$ is the 'leakage inductance' due to the imperfect coupling, and the impedance on the extreme right is the reflected impedance of the secondary, which is in parallel with the remainder of the primary inductance.

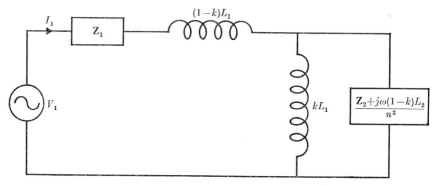

FIG. 9.12. Equivalent circuit of primary of imperfect transformer.
$$n^2 = L_2/L_1; \quad k = M/(L_1 L_2)^{\frac{1}{2}}.$$

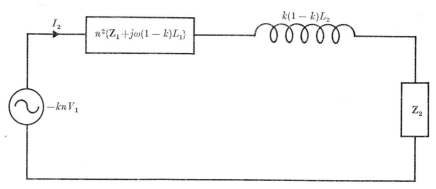

FIG. 9.13. Equivalent circuit for secondary of imperfect transformer.

For the secondary circuit, since $M/L_1 = k(L_2/L_1)^{\frac{1}{2}} = kn$, we have, from equation (9.40),

$$-knV_1/I_2 = Z_2+n^2Z_1+j\omega L_2(1-k)+j\omega(kL_2-M^2/L_1)$$
$$= Z_2+n^2\{Z_1+j\omega L_1(1-k)\}+j\omega L_2 k(1-k),$$

which is represented by Fig. 9.13. The reflected impedance is the transformed value of $Z_1$ plus the primary leakage inductance $L_1(1-k)$, while the secondary leakage inductance is, apart from a factor $k$, just that which appears in series with $Z_2$ in the impedance reflected in the primary. If $k$ is close to unity, this approximation is a good one, for the leakage inductance will be small compared with $Z_2$ except for very small values of $Z_2$. The equivalent circuit of the transformer can be drawn as in Fig. 9.14, where the centre portion enclosed in the dotted rectangle is regarded as a perfect transformer. The resistances $r_1$ and $r_2$ are the resistances of the windings, which previously we have regarded as part of $Z_1$ and $Z_2$. The resistance $R$ in parallel with $kL_1$ allows for the dissipation of energy through hysteresis and eddy currents in the iron core.

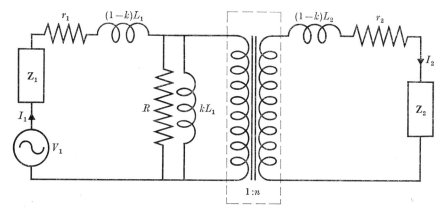

FIG. 9.14. Approximate equivalent circuit of imperfect transformer.
$r_1$, $r_2$, resistances of primary and secondary windings.
$R$, resistance equivalent to hysteresis and eddy current losses in iron core.
The portion within the dotted rectangle is regarded as a perfect transformer
of turns ratio $n$.

The prime requirements in a transformer are therefore a high primary inductance, to keep the 'magnetizing current' through $kL_1$ in Fig. 9.14 small, and the smallest possible leakage of flux between primary and secondary. These requirements are fulfilled by winding the primary and secondary round an iron core whose magnetic circuit is completed by a yoke, as in Fig. 9.15. If the two coils are interwound the leakage is reduced to a minimum, but if good insulation between primary and secondary is required they may be wound side by side.

In transformers the magnetic material is subject to an alternating magnetic field so that the hysteresis loop is traversed once every period of the alternation. From equation (8.26) this requires the expenditure of energy, the amount per cycle being just equal to the area enclosed by the hysteresis loop. This loop should therefore be as thin as possible (or, roughly speaking, the coercive force must be small). A soft magnetic material is therefore required (see § 8.4), and ideally the permeability should be high and constant, with the area of the hysteresis loop zero, so that the **B–H** curve is a straight line of high slope through the origin. Alloys of iron with a few per cent of silicon approach this ideal

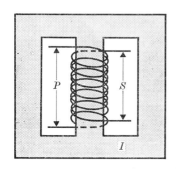

FIG. 9.15.  Construction of iron-cored
        transformer.

*I*   laminated iron core and yoke.
*P*   primary winding.
*S*   secondary winding.

more closely than pure iron, and are used in power transformers for supply frequencies. For small transformers and other uses at higher frequencies, more expensive alloys requiring lengthy heat treatment give improved performance. For example, an alloy of about 78 per cent nickel and 22 per cent iron (permalloy), if slowly cooled from 900° C and then rapidly cooled from 600° C, gives an initial permeability of nearly $10^4$ and a maximum permeability of nearly $10^5$. Another alloy (supermalloy) with the composition 80 per cent nickel, 15 per cent iron, 5 per cent molybdenum, after heating in very pure hydrogen at 1200° to 1300° C, gives initial and maximum permeabilities some ten times higher. These high permeabilities are accompanied by very low values of the coercive force, $\sim$ 4 A/metre for permalloy and 0·3 A/metre for supermalloy.

Another effect of the alternating magnetic flux in the core is to set up induced voltages and produce power loss through eddy currents. The core is therefore constructed of very thin laminations, insulated from each other, and oriented so that the insulation lies across the path of the eddy current. This is therefore constrained to flow within the lamination, and the losses are reduced (see Problem 9.14). In this respect the special magnetic alloys mentioned above have the further advantage of a high electrical resistivity. At radio-frequencies ($10^5$–$10^8$ c/s) the use of magnetic cores also reduces the size of inductors and improves the coupling between the coils of transformers; such cores are made either from fine metallic powders mixed with insulating binders or from magnetic oxides ('ferrites') which are themselves electrical insulators.

## PROBLEMS

9.1. A resistance $R$, inductance $L$, and capacitance $C$ are connected all in parallel. Show that the admittance of the circuit at frequencies near resonance is

$$Y = 1/R + 2j\delta\omega C.$$

If $R = 3 \times 10^5$ ohms, $L = 10^{-3}$ henries, $C = 100\ \mu\mu\text{F}$, calculate the current in each arm when a voltage of 10 V r.m.s. at a frequency of 0·5 Mc/s is applied, and the phase of the total current drawn from the generator.

(*Answers*: 0·033, 3·18, and 3·14 mA; 51°.)

9.2. A circuit is required to accept a signal of frequency 1·1 Mc/s and to reject a signal of frequency 1·2 Mc/s. A coil of self-inductance 200 $\mu$H and resistance 10 ohms is tuned to parallel resonance at 1·2 Mc/s by a capacitance $C_1$. A capacitance $C_2$ is then placed in series with the combination, so that the whole is in series resonance at 1·1 Mc/s. Find the values of $C_1$ and $C_2$.

(*Answers*: 88 and 16 $\mu\mu$F.)

9.3. Show that a capacitance $C$ shunted by a resistance $r$ is equivalent to a capacitance $C'$ in series with a resistance $R$ at any given frequency. If $\omega Cr \gg 1$, show that approximately $R = (\omega^2 C^2 r)^{-1}$, and $C' = C$.

9.4. Four impedances $Z_1$, $Z_2$, $Z_3$, $Z_4$, in that order, are placed in the arms of a 'generalized' Wheatstone's bridge using alternating current. Show that the balance condition is

$$Z_1/Z_2 = Z_4/Z_3.$$

Note that this is really a double balance condition, since the real and imaginary parts of this equation must be separately satisfied. This is because a null reading is obtained on the detector only if the voltages at each of its terminals are equal both in amplitude and phase.

9.5. The four arms of a Wheatstone's bridge, taken in cyclic order round the bridge, are $a, b, c, d$. $a$ and $b$ are equal resistances $R$; $c$ is a resistance $R$ in series with a capacitance $C$; $d$ is a resistance $R$ shunted by a capacitance $C$. Show that such a bridge will not be balanced at any frequency, but that if the resistance in arm $b$ is doubled, a balance will be obtained at a frequency

$$f = (2\pi RC)^{-1}.$$

9.6. A capacitor of capacitance $C$, a resistance $r$, and a coil whose inductance is $L$ and resistance is $R$, are connected all three in parallel. An e.m.f. of variable frequency is applied across the capacitor. Show that the frequency of parallel resonance is independent of the value of $r$, and prove that the parallel resistance of the combination is $rL/(L + RrC)$.

If the $Q$ of the circuit is high, show that it is given approximately by

$$\frac{1}{Q} = \frac{1}{r}\sqrt{\frac{L}{C}} + R\sqrt{\frac{C}{L}}.$$

9.7. A series resonant circuit is connected across a constant voltage generator operating at 6·50 Mc/s. As the capacitance is varied, the current is observed to fall to $1/\sqrt{2}$ of its maximum value when the capacitance is 12·47 $\mu\mu$F, and again when the capacitance is 12·64 $\mu\mu$F. Find the values of $Q$, $L$, $R$ for the circuit.

(*Answer*: $\approx 150$; 48 $\mu$H; 13 ohms.)

9.8. An alternating voltage is applied to the terminals $A$, $B$ of the network shown in Fig. 9.16. Show that, as $R$ is varied, the amplitude of the potential difference between the terminals $X$, $Y$ remains constant, but its phase is shifted by $\pi$ radians. Explain your results by means of a vector diagram. (This network is commonly used for producing a variable phase shift without change of the output amplitude.)

9.9. A high frequency transformer has primary inductance 100 $\mu$H and primary resistance 5 ohms, secondary inductance $2 \cdot 5 \times 10^3$ $\mu$H, and secondary resistance 100 ohms. If the coefficient of coupling $M/(L_1 L_2)^{\frac{1}{2}}$ is 0·9, show that at high frequencies the voltage across the secondary is approximately 4·5 times that applied to the primary.

If primary and secondary are each separately tuned by capacitors to resonance at 50 kc/s, show that the high frequency power required to produce an r.m.s. voltage of 2000 V across the capacitance in the secondary circuit is approximately 650 W.

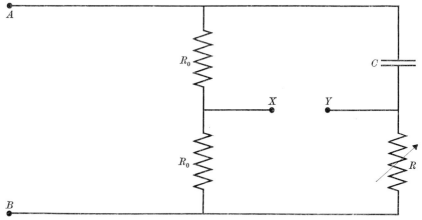

FIG. 9.16. Phase shift network (see Problem 9.8).

9.10. A wire-wound resistance has a small inductance and self-capacitance which may be represented by placing an inductance $L$ in series with the resistance $R$, and shunting the combination by a capacitance $C$. Show that the reactance at low frequencies is zero in the first approximation if the wire is wound so that $L/C = R^2$. Show also that under these conditions the apparent resistance is (to the second approximation)

$$R(1 + \omega^2 LC).$$

9.11. An inductance $L$ with small resistance $r$ has self-capacitance which can be represented approximately by a capacitance $C$ shunted across the series combination of $L$ and $r$. Show that as the frequency increases the apparent self-inductance of the coil is increased by the factor $(1 + \omega^2 LC)$ while the apparent series resistance increases by the factor $(1 + 2\omega^2 LC)$, in the region where $\omega^2 LC \ll 1$.

9.12. A parallel plate capacitor is filled with a medium which has a dielectric constant $\epsilon$ and a conductivity $\sigma$. Show that at a frequency $f = \omega/2\pi$ the power factor of the capacitor is $\cos\phi = \sin\delta$, where the loss tangent of the dielectric medium is given by the relation $\tan\delta = \sigma/\omega\epsilon\epsilon_0$.

Note that this is independent of the shape of the capacitor, as would be expected from equation (3.11).

**9.13.** A 100 V dynamo is connected to a magnet whose resistance is 10 ohm and self-inductance 0·1 henry. Show that the percentage increase in the heating of the magnet caused by the presence of a 100 c/s ripple voltage of 5 V amplitude in the output of the dynamo is 0·0031 per cent.

**9.14.** The iron core of a transformer has laminations of thickness $a$ and resistivity $\rho$; it is subject to a sinusoidally varying induction with a maximum value $B$ and frequency $f$. Show that the power loss per unit volume (neglecting skin effects, see Problem 10.13) due to eddy currents is approximately $\pi^2 B^2 a^2 f^2/6\rho$. If $a = 0·1$ mm, $\rho = 4 \times 10^{-7}$ ohm-metre, $B = 0·5$ weber/metre$^2$, and $f = 50$ c/s, show that the power loss is approximately $2·6 \times 10^{-5}$ W/cm$^3$. Compare this with the power loss through hysteresis, if the energy dissipated per cycle for permalloy at this induction is 200 ergs/cm$^3$.

(*Answer*: Hysteresis loss $= 10^{-3}$ W/cm$^3$.)

## ELECTROMAGNETIC WAVES

### 10.1. Maxwell's equations of the electromagnetic field

So far we have considered the propagation of electrical currents in material conductors. The possibility of the propagation of an electromagnetic wave through space was first suggested by Faraday, and this suggestion was confirmed by the work of Maxwell. Maxwell was able to show that the laws of electromagnetism could be expressed in the form of some fundamental equations which, with an important modification, lead to a differential equation whose solutions represent transverse waves travelling through free space with the velocity of light. Further work showed that the properties of these waves—reflection, refraction, diffraction—are the same as those established experimentally for light waves, and we are therefore justified in assuming that they are identical, and that light waves are a form of electromagnetic radiation.

The theory of Maxwell deals entirely with macroscopic phenomena, making the assumption that matter is continuous and has no atomistic structure. This assumption places certain limitations on the theory; thus it offers no explanation of the phenomenon of dispersion—the change of refractive index with frequency. This phenomenon will be discussed in Chapter 17; it arises from the change in the dielectric constant and magnetic permeability of a medium with frequency. These changes can be related to the effect of electromagnetic waves on the individual electrons in an atom, but for the present we shall regard the dielectric constant and magnetic permeability as macroscopic quantities whose values are obtained by experiment.

The fundamental laws of electromagnetism which have already been derived may be summarized as follows:

(a) the theorem of Gauss applied to electrostatics (equation (1.20)):

$$\operatorname{div} \mathbf{D} = \rho; \tag{10.1}$$

(b) the corresponding result for magnetic fields (equation (5.24)):

$$\operatorname{div} \mathbf{B} = 0; \tag{10.2}$$

(c) Faraday's and Lenz's law of electromagnetic induction (equation (6.3)):

$$\operatorname{curl} \mathbf{E} = -\frac{\partial \mathbf{B}}{\partial t}; \tag{10.3}$$

(*d*) Ampère's law for magnetomotive force (equation (5.21)):

$$\operatorname{curl} \mathbf{H} = \mathbf{J}'. \tag{10.4}$$

The reason for writing $\mathbf{J}'$ rather than the ordinary current density $\mathbf{J}$ in this last equation is as follows. Since (div curl) of any vector is identically zero, it follows that equation (10.4) implies that div $\mathbf{J}'$ is zero. If we had written $\mathbf{J}$ instead of $\mathbf{J}'$, we should have had div $\mathbf{J} = 0$, and this conflicts with the equation of continuity (3.3) which gives

$$\operatorname{div} \mathbf{J} = -\frac{\partial \rho}{\partial t}. \tag{10.5}$$

This equation represents the law of conservation of charge, and is confirmed by all experiments. Maxwell realized that the difficulty arose from an incomplete definition of the total current density in equation (10.4), which is not entirely given by the current flow due to the motion of electric charges. By using equation (10.1) we may write (10.5) in the form

$$\operatorname{div} \mathbf{J} = -\frac{\partial}{\partial t} (\operatorname{div} \mathbf{D}) = \operatorname{div}(-\partial \mathbf{D}/\partial t),$$

or

$$\operatorname{div}\!\left(\mathbf{J} + \frac{\partial \mathbf{D}}{\partial t}\right) = 0.$$

Hence if we define $\mathbf{J}'$ as 
$$\mathbf{J}' = \mathbf{J} + \frac{\partial \mathbf{D}}{\partial t}, \tag{10.6}$$

then div $\mathbf{J}' = 0$, and Ampère's law takes the form

$$\operatorname{curl} \mathbf{H} = \mathbf{J} + \frac{\partial \mathbf{D}}{\partial t} = \sigma \mathbf{E} + \frac{\partial \mathbf{D}}{\partial t}. \tag{10.7}$$

The term $\mathbf{J}$ is generally called the 'conduction current' and the second term $(\partial \mathbf{D}/\partial t)$ the 'displacement current', since it arises when the electric displacement $\mathbf{D}$ is changing with time. We may obtain some physical picture of what is implied by the displacement current by considering a simple circuit such as in Fig. 10.1, where a current $I$ is flowing from a battery to charge a capacitor $C$. If we apply Ampère's law to a closed circuit such as $LMNL$ which encircles the wire we find that $\int \mathbf{H}.\mathbf{ds}$ round this circuit is just equal to $I$. In defining the current which threads the circuit we must take some surface bounded by the circuit, and integrate the normal component of the current density crossing this surface. If we take a surface intersecting the wire, this clearly gives just $I$, the current in the wire. But if we take a surface which passes between the two plates of the capacitor, then $\int \mathbf{J}.\mathbf{dS} = 0$, since no conduction current flows through the surface. The value of this integral should be independent of what surface we choose, since $\int \mathbf{H}.\mathbf{ds}$ depends only on the circuit bounding this surface; thus it is clear that we have omitted some contribution. If for simplicity we take a parallel plate capacitor with plates of area $A$, surrounded by a guard ring, the field in between the plates is uniform, and the displacement **D** has the value

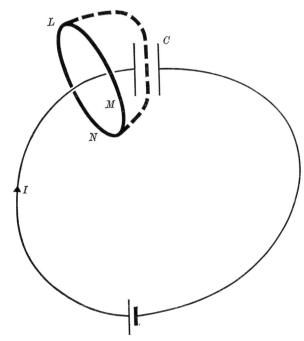

Fig. 10.1. Application of Ampère's law to calculate the magneto-motive force $\int \mathbf{H}.\mathbf{ds}$ round the circuit $LMNL$ for the case of a current $I$ charging a capacitor $C$.

$D = q/A$, where $q$ is the total charge on the positive plate. Then the total displacement current between the plates is

$$A(\partial D/\partial t) = \partial q/\partial t = I$$

and our difficulties with the surface integral of the current density disappear if we include the displacement current.

For the case of an infinite homogeneous medium of dielectric constant $\epsilon$ and magnetic permeability $\mu$, containing no free charges ($\rho = 0$) and having zero conductivity ($\sigma = 0$), our equations become

$$\text{div}\,\mathbf{D} = \text{div}(\epsilon\epsilon_0\,\mathbf{E}) = \epsilon\epsilon_0\,\text{div}\,\mathbf{E} = 0, \qquad (10.8)$$

$$\text{div}\,\mathbf{B} = \text{div}(\mu\mu_0\,\mathbf{H}) = \mu\mu_0\,\text{div}\,\mathbf{H} = 0, \qquad (10.9)$$

$$\text{curl}\,\mathbf{E} = -\partial\mathbf{B}/\partial t = -\mu\mu_0(\partial\mathbf{H}/\partial t), \qquad (10.10)$$

$$\text{curl}\,\mathbf{H} = \partial\mathbf{D}/\partial t = \epsilon\epsilon_0(\partial\mathbf{E}/\partial t). \qquad (10.11)$$

These form a set of simultaneous partial differential equations whose solutions can be found by eliminating one of the dependent variables, **E** or **H**. This can be done by means of the vector identity

$$\text{curl}(\text{curl}\,\mathbf{E}) = \text{grad}(\text{div}\,\mathbf{E}) - \nabla^2\mathbf{E} = -\nabla^2\mathbf{E} \quad \text{(using equation (10.8))}.$$

Then
$$\nabla^2\mathbf{E} = -\text{curl}(\text{curl}\,\mathbf{E}) = \text{curl}(\mu\mu_0\,\partial\mathbf{H}/\partial t)$$

$$= \mu\mu_0\frac{\partial}{\partial t}(\text{curl}\,\mathbf{H}) = \mu\mu_0\,\epsilon\epsilon_0(\partial^2\mathbf{E}/\partial t^2). \tag{10.12}$$

Similarly it may be shown that

$$\nabla^2\mathbf{H} = \mu\mu_0\,\epsilon\epsilon_0(\partial^2\mathbf{H}/\partial t^2). \tag{10.13}$$

These two equations are each of the general form for a wave motion in three dimensions; if the velocity with which the waves are propagated is $v$, the general wave equation is

$$\nabla^2\mathbf{X} = \frac{1}{v^2}\frac{\partial^2\mathbf{X}}{\partial t^2},$$

where **X** is some scalar or vector quantity. Comparison with our case shows that the wave velocity must be

$$v = (\mu\mu_0\,\epsilon\epsilon_0)^{-\frac{1}{2}} \tag{10.14}$$

with the particular value in free space ($\mu = 1$, $\epsilon = 1$) of

$$c = (\mu_0\,\epsilon_0)^{-\frac{1}{2}}. \tag{10.15}$$

Now the value of $\mu_0$ has been defined as $4\pi\,10^{-7}$, while the best value of $\epsilon_0$ is that of Rosa and Dorsey (see § 7.4): this leads to a wave velocity of our electromagnetic waves in free space (see Birge, 1941) of

$$299\ 784 \pm 10 \text{ km/sec}.$$

Within the experimental error this is the same as the velocity of light determined by direct measurement, and it is now accepted that light is a form of electromagnetic radiation, of the same form as radio waves, heat waves, X-rays, and $\gamma$-rays, which differ from light waves and from each other only in frequency and wavelength. The frequency range is from $10^4$ to $10^{11}$ c/s for radio waves to $10^{20}$ c/s and over for $\gamma$-rays. Maxwell's theory does not give an adequate account of the interaction of electromagnetic radiation with atoms, and it has been found necessary (for example, in the photoelectric effect) to consider the electromagnetic energy as travelling about in 'packets' or 'quanta', which are indivisible. The size of a quantum for radiation of frequency $\nu$ is $h\nu$, where $h$ is a universal constant known as Planck's constant. For radio waves such quantum effects are too small to affect the interaction with matter seriously, and we shall not consider them further at present.

If we accept the identification of our electromagnetic waves with light and radio waves, then we may use one of the accurate methods of determining their velocity (see § 15.6) to infer the value of the constant $\epsilon_0$, since this gives a more accurate value than the direct comparison of a capacitance and resistance. The value thus obtained is given in Appendix B.

Equation (10.14) shows that the velocity of the waves in a material medium is less than in free space, since

$$v = c/(\mu\epsilon)^{\frac{1}{2}}.$$

For a light wave the velocity in a medium is $v = c/n$, where $n$ is the refractive index of the medium. Hence we have

$$n = (\mu\epsilon)^{\frac{1}{2}}. \tag{10.16}$$

In using this equation we must remember that it applies only if we determine the values of $n$, $\mu$, and $\epsilon$ at the same frequency, and nonsensical results may be obtained if we use values determined at different frequencies. Thus, for water the optical refractive index is 1·33, but the static values of $\epsilon$ and $\mu$ are 81 and 1, leading to a refractive index (for very low frequencies only) of 9! This is one of the more glaring examples of the misuse of equation (10.16) to compare values determined at different frequencies, to which we shall return in Chapter 17.

## 10.2. Plane waves in isotropic dielectrics

In order to examine the behaviour of the electric and magnetic fields in more detail we shall consider the case of a plane wave. For simplicity we assume that this is moving in the direction of the $x$-axis of a set of right-handed Cartesian axes, $x, y, z$. Then the definition of a plane wave is one in which the quantities have the same value over any plane normal to the direction of propagation; mathematically this is expressed by setting all partial differentials with respect to the $y$- and $z$-coordinates (i.e. $\partial/\partial y$ and $\partial/\partial z$) equal to zero. If these conditions are put into the equations (10.8) and (10.9) we find that

$$\partial E_x/\partial x = \partial H_x/\partial x = 0,$$

and from the $x$-components of the curl equations ((10.10) and (10.11)) we have
$$\partial E_x/\partial t = \partial H_x/\partial t = 0.$$

This shows that apart from a uniform steady field in the $x$-direction, which is not part of any wave motion, both $E_x$ and $H_x$ must be zero. The wave is therefore purely transverse in that no components of the electric or magnetic fields exist in the direction of propagation. The remaining components of the curl equations are, taking the $x$-components of **E** and **H** to be zero, and $\partial/\partial y = \partial/\partial z = 0$,

$$-\partial E_z/\partial x = -\mu\mu_0\,\partial H_y/\partial t, \quad -\partial H_z/\partial x = \epsilon\epsilon_0\,\partial E_y/\partial t,$$

$$\partial E_y/\partial x = -\mu\mu_0\,\partial H_z/\partial t, \quad \partial H_y/\partial x = \epsilon\epsilon_0\,\partial E_z/\partial t.$$

These equations show that the $z$-component of $E$ is associated with the $y$-component of $H$, while the $y$-component of $E$ is associated with the $z$-component of $H$. The two components of **E** or **H** correspond to waves which are plane polarized in directions normal to one another and normal to the direction of propagation. Thus we have two linearly independent solutions, in each of which the magnetic field is normal to the electric field. They differ only in the plane of polarization, which we shall take to be that of the electric vector; this differs from the convention accepted in light before the electromagnetic nature of the radiation was understood, which adopted the plane now known to be that of the magnetic vector. The electric vector is more important in the theory of dispersion (Chapter 17) as it determines the force on an electron in an atom.

Since we need consider only one state of polarization, we shall take the solution where the electric vector is parallel to the $y$-axis; it then follows that the magnetic vector has only a component parallel to the $z$-axis. The wave equation for $E_y$ (equation (10.12)) becomes

$$\frac{\partial^2 E_y}{\partial x^2} - \mu\mu_0\,\epsilon\epsilon_0 \frac{\partial^2 E_y}{\partial t^2} = 0, \tag{10.17}$$

which has a general solution of the form

$$E_y = F_1(x-vt) + F_2(x+vt), \tag{10.18}$$

where $F_1$, $F_2$ may be functions of any form. The two functions represent waves travelling with velocity $v$, whose value is given by equation (10.14). $F_1$ represents a wave travelling in the direction of $x$ increasing, since any given point in the wave moves according to the equation

$$x = vt + \text{constant},$$

while $F_2$ is a wave travelling in the opposite direction, a given point moving as $x = -vt + \text{constant}$.

We may find the value of $H_z$ by using one of the remaining components of our curl equations. For

$$\partial H_z/\partial x = -\epsilon\epsilon_0\,\partial E_y/\partial t = \epsilon\epsilon_0\,v\{F_1'(x-vt) - F_2'(x+vt)\},$$

where $F'$ is the differential of $F$. Hence, since $v = (\epsilon\epsilon_0\mu\mu_0)^{-\frac{1}{2}}$, we find on integration

$$H_z = (\epsilon\epsilon_0/\mu\mu_0)^{\frac{1}{2}}\{F_1(x-vt) - F_2(x+vt)\}. \tag{10.19}$$

This shows that the value of $H_z$ bears a constant ratio to $E_y$ in each of the travelling waves, but has the opposite sign for a wave travelling to the left. The ratio of $E_y$ to $H_z$ in a plane wave is often useful, and it has been called the 'intrinsic impedance' $Z_0$ of the medium. In our case of a non-conducting medium, where the wave velocity is $v$,

$$Z_0 = E_y/H_z = (\mu\mu_0/\epsilon\epsilon_0)^{\frac{1}{2}} = \mu\mu_0 v. \tag{10.20}$$

For a plane wave in free space $Z_0 = (\mu_0/\epsilon_0)^{\frac{1}{2}} = \mu_0 c = (\epsilon_0 c)^{-1}$, and its value is approximately 376·7 ohms. The fact that the dimensions of $Z_0$ are the same as those of the impedance discussed in earlier chapters is readily seen from the relations

$$\int \mathbf{H}.\mathbf{ds} = I, \qquad \int \mathbf{E}.\mathbf{ds} = V,$$

where $V$ is the potential drop in a conductor; it appears also from the fact that $E$ is measured in volts/metre and $H$ in amperes/metre. The fact that the intrinsic impedance is a real quantity independent of $x$ or $t$ shows that the wave form of $H_z$ is everywhere the same as that of $E_y$, without any phase difference, in a travelling wave. This is true only of a non-conducting medium. Another important restriction is that the wave velocity must be independent of frequency if the wave form is to remain the same as the wave progresses. If it is not (i.e. if we have a dispersive medium) we must perform a Fourier analysis of the initial wave form and treat each component of a given frequency separately. In the remainder of this chapter we shall assume that we are dealing with waves of one frequency only, and our field components are the real or imaginary parts of the exponential functions of the form

$$\exp\{j\omega(t\pm x/v)\}.$$

Then the general solution for waves travelling both to the right and to the left will be

$$\left.\begin{aligned}E_y &= A \exp\{j\omega(t-x/v)\}+A' \exp\{j\omega(t+x/v)\} \\ Z_0 H_z &= A \exp\{j\omega(t-x/v)\}-A' \exp\{j\omega(t+x/v)\}\end{aligned}\right\}. \tag{10.21}$$

The exponentials are sometimes written in the forms $\exp\{j\omega(t\pm nx/c)\}$ or $\exp j(\omega t\pm\beta x)$; $\beta$ is called the 'phase constant', and is equal to $2\pi/\lambda$, where $\lambda$ is the wavelength in the medium. The phase velocity $v$ is given by the relation

$$v = \omega/\beta. \tag{10.22}$$

It might be thought that a phase constant $\delta$ should be included in one of the waves in equation (10.21), since otherwise some particular choice of zero is implied for either $x$ or $t$ which makes $\delta = 0$. We shall, however, allow $A'$ (or $A$) to be complex, and of the form $A'' \exp(j\delta)$, and thus include the phase constant in $A'$ rather than in the complex exponential.

## 10.3. The Poynting vector of energy flow

Since an electromagnetic wave consists of electric and magnetic fields, we may expect that stored energy is associated with these fields. If the energy density for which we now use the symbol $U$ is given by the equations derived for static fields, then for a plane wave in an isotropic dielectric it will be

$$U = \tfrac{1}{2}(\mathbf{D}.\mathbf{E}+\mathbf{B}.\mathbf{H}) = \tfrac{1}{2}(\epsilon\epsilon_0\,\mathbf{E}^2+\mu\mu_0\,\mathbf{H}^2).$$

For a wave propagated in the positive $x$-direction, the energy crossing unit area per second will just be the velocity times the energy density. This is

$$vU = \tfrac{1}{2}\left\{\sqrt{\left(\frac{\epsilon\epsilon_0}{\mu\mu_0}\right)}E_y^2+\sqrt{\left(\frac{\mu\mu_0}{\epsilon\epsilon_0}\right)}H_z^2\right\}$$

$$= \tfrac{1}{2}(E_y^2/Z_0+Z_0\,H_z^2) = E_y\,H_z = E_y^2/Z_0 = Z_0\,H_z^2.$$

These various relations show that the energy stored in the magnetic field is just equal to that in the electric field. If we denote the rate of energy flow by a vector $\mathbf{N}$ whose direction is that of the energy flow, then for this case we may write

$$N_x = E_y\,H_z,$$

or in vector form, since $E_y$, $H_z$, and $N_x$ form a right-handed triad of axes (Fig. 10.2),

$$\mathbf{N} = \mathbf{E}\wedge\mathbf{H}. \qquad (10.23)$$

The vector $\mathbf{N}$ is known as the Poynting vector, and we see that the direction of energy flow is reversed for a wave travelling in the opposite direction because the phase of $\mathbf{H}$ relative to $\mathbf{E}$ is reversed (see equations (10.21)). The value of $\mathbf{N}$ gives the

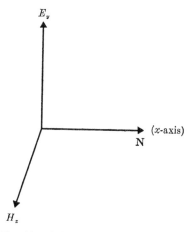

FIG. 10.2. Directions of the electric and magnetic fields $\mathbf{E}$ and $\mathbf{H}$ and the Poynting vector $\mathbf{N}$ for a plane wave propagated in the $x$-direction.

instantaneous rate of energy flow. In a periodic wave the values of $\mathbf{E}$ and $\mathbf{H}$ at any point are oscillating functions of the time, and the mean rate of energy flow is found by averaging $\mathbf{N}$ over a complete period. If $\mathbf{E}$ and $\mathbf{H}$ are given as root mean square values, then $\mathbf{N}$ as computed from (10.23) gives the mean energy flow.

The Poynting vector is of greater significance than might be thought from the way in which it has been introduced above, and we shall now derive it for the general case. Suppose there is a region of space where an electric field $\mathbf{E}$ causes a current flow of density $\mathbf{J}$. Then the power dissipated per unit volume is $\mathbf{E}.\mathbf{J}$, and the total power dissipated will be

$$\int \mathbf{E}.\mathbf{J}\, d\tau = \int (\mathbf{E}.\operatorname{curl}\mathbf{H})\, d\tau - \int \mathbf{E}.(\partial \mathbf{D}/\partial t)\, d\tau,$$

where we have substituted for $\mathbf{J}$ the expression given by equation (10.7). Now, using the vector identity

$$\operatorname{div}(\mathbf{E}\wedge\mathbf{H}) = \mathbf{H}.\operatorname{curl}\mathbf{E} - \mathbf{E}.\operatorname{curl}\mathbf{H}$$

and the expression for curl $\mathbf{E}$ given by equation (10.3), we find that the power dissipated is

$$-\int \mathbf{E}.(\partial \mathbf{D}/\partial t)\, d\tau - \int \mathbf{H}.(\partial \mathbf{B}/\partial t)\, d\tau - \int \operatorname{div}(\mathbf{E}\wedge\mathbf{H})\, d\tau.$$

Normally the permeability $\mu$ and dielectric constant $\epsilon$ do not vary with time, and the first two terms may be written as

$$-\frac{1}{2}\frac{\partial}{\partial t}\int (\mathbf{D}.\mathbf{E}+\mathbf{B}.\mathbf{H})\, d\tau$$

while the last term may be transformed into the surface integral

$$-\int (\mathbf{E}\wedge\mathbf{H}).\mathbf{dS}$$

taken over the surface bounding the volume under consideration. Hence the rate at which the field does work may be equated to the sum of two terms, the first of which we interpret as the rate at which the energy stored in the electromagnetic field diminishes, and the second as the rate at which energy flows into the volume under consideration. Thus we take
$$\tfrac{1}{2}(\mathbf{D}.\mathbf{E}+\mathbf{B}.\mathbf{H})$$

as the density of the electromagnetic energy, in agreement with our earlier results, and the vector

$$\mathbf{N} = \mathbf{E}\wedge\mathbf{H}$$

as the rate at which energy flows across unit area of the boundary. Strictly speaking, only the integral of $\mathbf{N}$ over a closed surface has been shown to represent the energy flow, but in most cases $\mathbf{N}$ does represent the flow of energy per unit area at each point. An obvious exception to this would be the case of a region with an electrostatic and a static magnetic field arising from different sources, but Problem 10.12 shows that the Poynting vector can be used in the case of a steady current flowing in a circular wire, where both electric and magnetic fields are associated with the current flow.

## 10.4. Plane waves in conducting media

In a medium with a finite conductivity $\sigma$ the field equations are the same as (10.8–11) except for the additional term $+\sigma E$ on the right-hand side of equation (10.11). These equations may be solved quite generally in the same way as in § 10.1, and elimination of $H$ gives the differential equation

$$\nabla^2 E = \frac{\mu\epsilon}{c^2}\frac{\partial^2 E}{\partial t^2} + \mu\mu_0\,\sigma\,\frac{\partial E}{\partial t}. \tag{10.24}$$

An exactly similar equation holds for $H$, and it may be shown that each of these equations represents a damped wave motion where the amplitude decays as the wave progresses owing to the extra term in $\partial E/\partial t$ or $\partial H/\partial t$. We shall not pursue this general solution, but specialize to the case of a plane wave travelling parallel to the $x$-axis. Then all partial derivatives $(\partial/\partial y)$ and $(\partial/\partial z)$ vanish, and the same methods as used in § 10.2 show that both $E_x$ and $H_x$ are zero, so that we again have a purely transverse wave. If we assume that we have a plane polarized wave with a single component of $E$ parallel to the $y$-axis, the field equations reduce to

$$\left.\begin{array}{l} \partial E_y/\partial x = -\mu\mu_0(\partial H_z/\partial t) \\ -\partial H_z/\partial x = \epsilon\epsilon_0(\partial E_y/\partial t) + \sigma E_y \end{array}\right\}. \tag{10.25}$$

These equations show that, as before, $E_y$ is associated with $H_z$. (There is an independent solution, polarized in the perpendicular direction, where $E_z$ is associated with $H_y$.) Elimination of $H_z$ would give a wave equation for $E_y$ of the same type as the general equation above, but a simpler method of solution is available on assuming that we are dealing with waves of a single frequency. It will appear that the velocity of propagation is now dependent on the frequency, so that it is necessary to consider each frequency separately in any case; we therefore introduce this restriction at the beginning, and take $E_y$ and $H_z$ to vary in time as $\exp(j\omega t)$. We will also try a solution where the variation with $x$ takes the form of a complex exponential, so that both $E_y$ and $H_z$ vary as

$$\exp\{j\omega(t - nx/c)\},$$

where $n$ is a complex refractive index. Then our equations become

$$\left.\begin{array}{l} j\omega(n/c)E_y = j\omega\mu\mu_0 H_z \\ j\omega(n/c)H_z = (j\omega\epsilon\epsilon_0 + \sigma)E_y \end{array}\right\}. \tag{10.25 a}$$

Elimination of $E_y$ or $H_z$ shows that these equations are satisfied provided that

$$\mathbf{n}^2 = \mu\epsilon - j(\sigma\mu/\omega\epsilon_0), \qquad (10.26)$$

where we have substituted $(\mu_0\epsilon_0)$ for $1/c^2$.

To separate the real and imaginary parts of $\mathbf{n}$ we write it as

$$\mathbf{n} = n - jk, \qquad (10.27)$$

giving
$$\left.\begin{array}{l} n^2 - k^2 = \mu\epsilon \\ nk = (\sigma\mu/2\omega\epsilon_0) \end{array}\right\}. \qquad (10.28)$$

To understand the significance of $n$ and $k$ we note that the wave is propagated as

$$\exp\{j\omega(t - \mathbf{n}x/c)\} = \exp(-\omega kx/c)\exp\{j\omega(t - nx/c)\},$$

showing that the value of $k$ determines the rate at which the amplitude of the wave decays ($k$ appears in the argument of the real exponential) while $n$ determines the wave velocity in the medium. Thus a complex refractive index $\mathbf{n}$ means that the wave is being absorbed as it proceeds, because the finite conductivity of the medium gives rise to a power loss through the Joule heating. The solutions we have given above apply to a wave proceeding in the positive $x$-direction; for a wave in the reverse direction we reverse the sign of $\mathbf{n}$, and hence of both $n$ and $k$.

The intrinsic impedance of our medium is defined as $E_y/H_z$, so that

$$\mathbf{Z}_0 = c\mu\mu_0/\mathbf{n} = \left\{\frac{\mu\mu_0}{\epsilon\epsilon_0 - j\sigma/\omega}\right\}^{\frac{1}{2}}. \qquad (10.29)$$

Thus the impedance is a complex quantity, but is independent of $x$ or $t$. This means that the ratio of the amplitudes of $E_y$ and $H_z$ is everywhere the same, but there is a phase difference between them. Since also

$$\mathbf{Z}_0 = \frac{c\mu\mu_0(n + jk)}{(n^2 + k^2)}$$

we see that the phase difference $\phi$ is given by the relation $\tan\phi = k/n$.

The full solution of equations (10.28) to find $n$ and $k$ gives rather complicated expressions, but these simplify greatly for the case of a good conductor. For a metal the conduction current is enormously greater than the displacement current at all frequencies up to those of ultraviolet light, as will be seen by comparing the values of $\sigma$ and $(\omega\epsilon\epsilon_0)$ which occur in the second of equations (10.25 a). For most metals $\sigma$ is $10^7$ (ohm-metre)$^{-1}$ or greater, while for light of wavelength 5000 Å $(\omega\epsilon\epsilon_0) \approx (4 \times 10^{15} \times 8 \cdot 85 \times 10^{-12} \times \epsilon) \approx 3 \cdot 5 \times 10^4\epsilon$. We do not know what $\epsilon$ is for a metal, but provided it is not very much greater than the ordinary values found in dielectric substances, the displacement current even for visible light will be much smaller than the conduction current. For lower frequencies the inequality increases, and a good approximation is obtained by omitting the displacement current. This is equivalent to setting $\epsilon = 0$, and equations (10.28) then give

$$n = k = (\sigma\mu/2\omega\epsilon_0)^{\frac{1}{2}}.$$

If we introduce a quantity $\delta$ such that $n = k = (c/\omega\delta)$, the field components in the metal are propagated as

$$\exp(-x/\delta)\exp j(\omega t - x/\delta), \tag{10.30}$$

from which it can be seen that $\delta$ has the dimensions of a length. $\delta$ is known as the 'skin depth', and the amplitude of the wave falls to $1/e$ of its initial value in a distance $\delta$, while the apparent wavelength in the metal is $2\pi\delta$. The equation for $\delta$ is (writing $\omega = 2\pi f$)

$$\delta = (\tfrac{1}{2}\sigma\omega\mu\mu_0)^{-\frac{1}{2}} = (\pi\sigma f\mu\mu_0)^{-\frac{1}{2}} \tag{10.31}$$

and the intrinsic impedance of our metal can be written as

$$\mathbf{Z_0} = (1+j)/(\sigma\delta) = (1+j)(\rho/\delta), \tag{10.32}$$

where $\rho$ is the resistivity. The magnitude of the skin depth decreases with the inverse half-power of the frequency, and of the permeability and conductivity of the metal. An idea of its order of magnitude is obtained from the fact that for copper it has the approximate values: $6\cdot6\times10^{-3}$ cm at a frequency of 1 Mc/s, $6\cdot6\times10^{-5}$ cm at $10^4$ Mc/s (a wavelength of 3 cm), and $2\cdot7\times10^{-7}$ cm at $6\times10^8$ Mc/s (green light). Thus the wavelength of the radiation in the metal is very small compared with the wavelength in free space; and $Z_0$ is also much smaller than the value for free space (for copper it is about $0\cdot026(1+j)$ ohms at $10^4$ Mc/s).

## 10.5. The skin effect

Since an electromagnetic wave varies in phase very rapidly inside a metal, one must ask whether this affects the distribution of alternating current inside a conductor. An electromagnetic field is associated with such a current, and Problem 10.1 shows that there is a flow of energy into the surface of a conductor which is just equal to the energy dissipated as Joule heat. This implies that an electromagnetic wave is passing through the surface, and from what has been found about the behaviour of such a wave we should expect it to be very rapidly attenuated inside. The current associated with it would therefore flow only in a thin skin of thickness of the order of $\delta$, a phenomenon known as the 'skin effect'. For steady currents $\omega = 0$ and $\delta = \infty$, so that the current distribution would be uniform, but as the frequency rises $\delta$ decreases and the current is increasingly confined to the surface. For this reason thin tubes are just as good conductors of high frequency currents as solid rods, but the resistance is of course higher than for a steady current in a solid rod owing to the smaller effective cross-section. We will now compute the high frequency resistance of a wire. Neglecting displacement currents, and writing $\mathbf{J}$ for $\sigma\mathbf{E}$ in equation (10.24), we have

$$\nabla^2\mathbf{J} = \mu\mu_0\,\sigma(\partial\mathbf{J}/\partial t) = j\omega\mu\mu_0\,\sigma\mathbf{J} \qquad (10.33)$$

for a current oscillating with frequency $(\omega/2\pi)$. For a cylindrical wire we should express the operator $\nabla^2$ in cylindrical coordinates and the general solution involves Bessel functions with a complex argument. The values we have found for $\delta$ in copper show that at high frequencies it will ordinarily be small compared with the radius $a$ of the wire. In this case we may obtain an approximate solution by neglecting the curvature of the surface of the wire and regarding it as a thin tube which can be split and unrolled to form an infinite flat strip of width $b = 2\pi a$, in which a current flows parallel to the surface of the strip in the long direction. If (as in Fig. 10.3) we take this direction as the $y$-axis and the normal to the surface of the strip as the $x$-axis, then the current density has a component $\sigma E_y$ in the

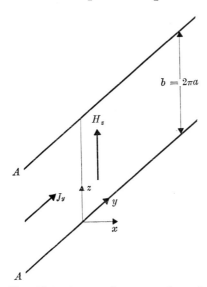

FIG. 10.3. Current flow at surface of cylindrical strip opened out to flat strip of width $b = 2\pi a$.

$y$-direction which varies with $x$ and $t$ as given by equation (10.30), so that

$$J_y = J_0\exp(-x/\delta)\exp j(\omega t - x/\delta),$$

where $J_0$ is the current density at the surface of the wire $(x = 0)$. This equation shows that the current changes phase as we move into the wire as well as decreasing rapidly in amplitude.

To find the effective resistance $R$ per unit length of the wire we must calculate the total current $I$ flowing in the strip at any instant and the power dissipation per unit length $W$, and set $W = \frac{1}{2}|I^2|R$. Now

$$I = b \int_0^\infty J_y \, dx = bJ_0 \exp(j\omega t) \int_0^\infty \exp\{-(1+j)x/\delta\} \, dx$$

$$= \left(\frac{b\delta J_0}{1+j}\right)\exp(j\omega t) = \frac{1}{\sqrt{2}} b\delta J_0 \exp j(\omega t - \tfrac{1}{4}\pi).$$

This expression shows that the total current has a different phase from $J_0$; we require to know only the amplitude of the total current whose square is

$$|I^2| = \tfrac{1}{2}(b\delta J_0)^2.$$

The instantaneous power dissipation per unit volume of the metal is $\rho J_y^2$, and hence the total average dissipation per unit length of the wire is

$$W = b \int_0^\infty \tfrac{1}{2}\rho|J_y^2| \, dx = \tfrac{1}{2}b\rho J_0^2 \int_0^\infty \exp(-2x/\delta) \, dx = \tfrac{1}{4}b\rho\delta J_0^2,$$

where $\rho$ is the resistivity of the wire. Hence the effective resistance per unit length of the wire is

$$R = 2W/|I^2| = \rho/(b\delta) = \rho/(2\pi a\delta). \tag{10.34}$$

This equation shows that the resistance is the same as if there were a current $I$ of uniform density flowing in a thin tube of radius $a$ and thickness equal to $\delta$, and the reason for the name 'skin depth' is thus apparent. The high frequency resistance of such a wire is thus greater than the d.c. resistance by a factor $(a/2\delta)$, when $\delta \ll a$.

This type of calculation may be applied to the more general problem of the power dissipated per unit area of a plane metallic surface when there is a tangential magnetic field $H_z = H_0 \cos\omega t$ at the surface. At any point in the metal the current density is

$$J_y = \sigma E_y = \sigma Z_0 H_z = (1+j)H_z/\delta \quad \text{(from equation (10.32))},$$

and hence $J_0 = \sqrt{2}H_0/\delta$. From the above it is readily seen that the mean power dissipation per unit area is

$$W = \tfrac{1}{4}\rho\delta J_0^2 = \tfrac{1}{2}\rho H_0^2/\delta. \tag{10.34a}$$

This is just equal to the average value of Poynting's vector at the surface (see Problem 10.1).

## 10.6. Reflection and refraction of plane waves at the boundary of two dielectrics

The reflection and refraction of light waves at the surface separating two media of different refractive indices is a familiar phenomenon and we must now inquire whether electromagnetic theory offers a simple explanation of it. We assume two non-conducting dielectric media, separated by a plane boundary which we take to be the $xy$-plane (the plane $z = 0$). We also choose the direction of the $x$-axis to be in the plane of incidence, i.e. the incident ray lies in the plane $y = 0$, as in Fig. 10.4, making an angle $\theta$ with the normal to the boundary. $\theta$ is known as the 'angle of incidence'. Then all field components of the incident wave vary with the space and time coordinates as

$$\exp[\,j\omega\{t - n_1(x\sin\theta + z\cos\theta)/c\}],$$

where $c/n_1$ is the velocity of the wave in the first medium, and $\omega/2\pi$ is its frequency of oscillation.

When the incident wave falls on the boundary there will in general be both a reflected wave and a transmitted wave. We know nothing about these waves, either as to their frequency or their direction. We have, however, boundary conditions for the components of $E$ and $H$ at the surface, and we assume that the behaviour of $E$ and $H$ must be the same as derived earlier in Chapters 1 and 5. Hence the tangential components of $E$ and $H$ must be continuous on the two sides of the boundary at all times and for all values of $x$ and $y$. The first of these conditions shows that the reflected and transmitted waves must have the same frequency as the incident wave. Secondly, at all points in the boundary plane along a line for which $x$ is constant the field components of the incident wave are constant in amplitude and phase. Our boundary conditions can only be satisfied everywhere if this is true also of the reflected and transmitted waves as well, and they must therefore also travel in the plane of incidence. The corresponding rays are shown in Fig. 10.4, making angles $\theta'$ and $\theta''$ with the normal respectively, known as the 'angle of reflection' and the 'angle of refraction'. The field components of the two waves must be propagated as

(reflected wave)          $\exp[\,j\omega\{t - n_1(x\sin\theta' - z\cos\theta')/c\}],$

(transmitted wave)     $\exp[\,j\omega\{t - n_2(x\sin\theta'' + z\cos\theta'')/c\}],$

where $c/n_2$ is the velocity in the second medium. At the boundary plane ($z = 0$), the boundary conditions can only be satisfied everywhere if the arguments of the exponentials for the incident, reflected, and transmitted waves are all identical. Hence

$$n_1 x\sin\theta = n_1 x\sin\theta' = n_2 x\sin\theta'',$$

which gives                              $\theta = \theta',$

so that the angles of incidence and reflection are equal, and

$$n_1\sin\theta = n_2\sin\theta'', \tag{10.35}$$

which is Snell's law for refraction.

These laws of reflection and refraction are true not only for electro-magnetic waves but for all kinds of wave motion, since they depend only on the assumption that the characteristic quantities involved in the wave motion (in this case the electric and magnetic fields) shall be continuous at the boundary.

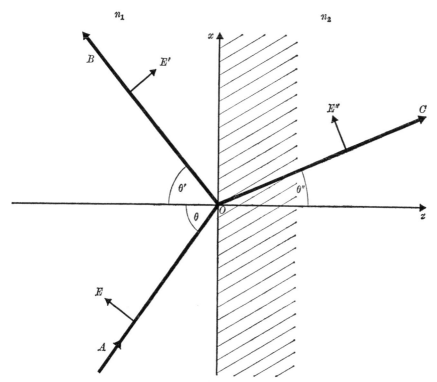

FIG. 10.4. Reflected wave $OB$ and refracted wave $OC$ at the boundary ($z = 0$) between two media. $AO$ is the incident wave, and the electric vectors are in the plane of incidence as shown. The magnetic vector is parallel to the $y$-axis, and hence normal to the plane of the paper. If $n_2 > n_1$, and the permeability of both media is unity, then the direction of $E'$ is as shown when the angle of incidence is greater than the Brewster angle $\tan^{-1}(n_2/n_1)$, but in the opposite direction when it is less than the Brewster angle.

*Intensity relations*

In order to obtain the amplitudes of the reflected and refracted waves we must examine the problem in more detail, and match the amplitudes of the tangential components of the electric and magnetic fields on the two sides of the boundary. To do this we must consider the two principal directions of polarization of the incident wave separately. These direc-tions are with the electric field in the plane of incidence and normal to the plane of incidence respectively. For the former of these there are components of **E** parallel to the $x$- and $z$-axes, but $E_y = 0$; the only component of **H** is parallel to the $y$-axis. These statements hold for all the three waves, so that we have (see Fig. 10.4):

Incident wave:

$$
\left.
\begin{aligned}
E_x &= A\cos\theta\exp[\,j\omega\{t-n_1(x\sin\theta+z\cos\theta)/c\}] \\
E_z &= -A\sin\theta\exp[\,j\omega\{t-n_1(x\sin\theta+z\cos\theta)/c\}] \\
H_y &= (A/Z_1)\exp[\,j\omega\{t-n_1(x\sin\theta+z\cos\theta)/c\}]
\end{aligned}
\right\}
\quad (10.36)
$$

Reflected wave:

$$
\left.
\begin{aligned}
E'_x &= A'\cos\theta\exp[\,j\omega\{t-n_1(x\sin\theta-z\cos\theta)/c\}] \\
E'_z &= A'\sin\theta\exp[\,j\omega\{t-n_1(x\sin\theta-z\cos\theta)/c\}] \\
H'_y &= -(A'/Z_1)\exp[\,j\omega\{t-n_1(x\sin\theta-z\cos\theta)/c\}]
\end{aligned}
\right\}
\quad (10.37)
$$

Refracted wave:

$$
\left.
\begin{aligned}
E''_x &= A''\cos\theta''\exp[\,j\omega\{t-n_2(x\sin\theta''+z\cos\theta'')/c\}] \\
E''_z &= -A''\sin\theta''\exp[\,j\omega\{t-n_2(x\sin\theta''+z\cos\theta'')/c\}] \\
H''_y &= (A''/Z_2)\exp[\,j\omega\{t-n_2(x\sin\theta''+z\cos\theta'')/c\}]
\end{aligned}
\right\}
\quad (10.38)
$$

where $Z_1$, $Z_2$ are the intrinsic impedances of the two media respectively.

On making the tangential components of **E** and **H** (i.e. $E_x$ and $H_y$) continuous at the plane $z = 0$, we obtain the relations

$$
A\cos\theta+A'\cos\theta = A''\cos\theta''
\quad (10.39)
$$

and
$$
(A-A')/Z_1 = A''/Z_2,
\quad (10.40)
$$

which give
$$
\frac{A'}{A} = \frac{Z_2\cos\theta''-Z_1\cos\theta}{Z_2\cos\theta''+Z_1\cos\theta}
\quad (10.41)
$$

and
$$
\frac{A''}{A} = \frac{2Z_2\cos\theta}{Z_2\cos\theta''+Z_1\cos\theta}.
\quad (10.42)
$$

If the media are such that $\mu_1 = \mu_2 = 1$, as is the case for light of visible wavelengths, $Z_1/Z_2 = n_2/n_1 = \sin\theta/\sin\theta''$, and these formulae can be written in the form

$$
\frac{A'}{A} = \frac{\sin 2\theta''-\sin 2\theta}{\sin 2\theta''+\sin 2\theta},
\quad (10.43)
$$

$$
\frac{A''}{A} = \frac{4\sin\theta''\cos\theta}{\sin 2\theta''+\sin 2\theta}.
\quad (10.44)
$$

The condition that there shall be no reflection ($A = 0$) is that

$$
\sin 2\theta = \sin 2\theta'',
$$

which is satisfied if $2\theta$ and $2\theta''$ are supplementary angles; that is

$$\theta + \theta'' = \tfrac{1}{2}\pi,$$

so that the reflected and refracted rays are normal to one another. Using Snell's law, we find that this occurs when

$$\tan\theta = n_2/n_1. \tag{10.45}$$

The angle which satisfies this relation is known as the Brewster angle.

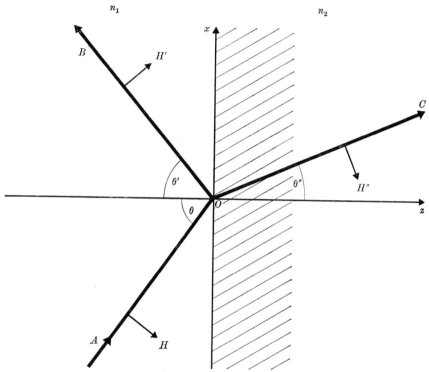

Fig. 10.5. Incident wave $AO$, reflected wave $OB$, and refracted wave $OC$ at the boundary between two media. The electric vector is normal to the plane of incidence and hence normal to the plane of the paper; the magnetic vector is in the plane of incidence. The theory shows that if $n_2 > n_1$, and the permeability of both media is unity, the actual direction of $H'$ is opposite to that given in the figure for all values of $\theta$.

The field components of the wave which is plane polarized with its electric vector normal to the plane of incidence are as follows (see Fig. 10.5).

Incident wave:

$$\left.\begin{aligned}
E_y &= BF_1 \\
H_x &= -(B/Z_1)\cos\theta\, F_1 \\
H_z &= (B/Z_1)\sin\theta\, F_1
\end{aligned}\right\} \tag{10.46}$$

T

Reflected wave:

$$E'_y = B'F_2$$
$$H'_x = (B'/Z_1)\cos\theta\, F_2$$
$$H'_z = (B'/Z_1)\sin\theta\, F_2$$

$$(10.47)$$

Refracted wave:

$$E''_y = B''F_3$$
$$H''_x = -(B''/Z_2)\cos\theta''\, F_3$$
$$H''_z = (B''/Z_2)\sin\theta''\, F_3$$

$$(10.48)$$

where for simplicity we have written $F_1$, $F_2$, $F_3$ for the three complex exponentials representing the propagation of the waves, which are the same as in equations (10.36), (10.37), and (10.38) respectively.

The boundary conditions for $E_y$ and $H_x$ now give

$$B + B' = B'',$$

$$(B - B')\cos\theta/Z_1 = B''\cos\theta''/Z_2,$$

the solutions of which are

$$\frac{B'}{B} = \frac{Z_2\cos\theta - Z_1\cos\theta''}{Z_2\cos\theta + Z_1\cos\theta''}$$

$$(10.49)$$

and

$$\frac{B''}{B} = \frac{2Z_2\cos\theta}{Z_2\cos\theta + Z_1\cos\theta''}.$$

$$(10.50)$$

These equations are similar to those obtained for the other direction of polarization but not identical, so that the magnitudes of the reflected and refracted waves are different. This is still true when we specialize to the case of $\mu_1 = \mu_2 = 1$, when the formulae become

$$\frac{B'}{B} = \frac{\sin(\theta'' - \theta)}{\sin(\theta'' + \theta)},$$

$$(10.51)$$

$$\frac{B''}{B} = \frac{2\sin\theta''\cos\theta}{\sin(\theta'' + \theta)}.$$

$$(10.52)$$

Since in general $\theta''$ is not equal to $\theta$, equation (10.51) shows that there is no angle at which the reflected wave for this direction of polarization has zero amplitude. If therefore we start with unpolarized light, which consists of light containing a superposition of many components with their electric vectors in random orientations, and reflect it from a dielectric such as glass at the Brewster angle, the reflected wave will only contain one direction of polarization, that with the electric vector normal to the plane of incidence. This phenomenon can therefore be used to produce plane polarized light, and originally it was used to define the plane of polarization of the reflected light at the Brewster angle as being the plane of the reflected ray. Our treatment shows that this is in fact the plane of the magnetic vector in the reflected light, not of the electric vector.

The fact that the expressions for $(A'/A)$ and $(A''/A)$ are real shows that the phase changes at the boundary between two perfect dielectrics are always 0 or $\pi$. Inspection of the equations shows that for a wave with the electric vector in the plane of incidence, passing from a medium of lower refractive index to one of higher refractive index, there is a change of sign in the tangential component $E_x$ (but not in $E_z$, $H_y$) of the reflected wave when the angle of incidence is less than the Brewster angle, whereas the reverse is the case when it is greater than this angle. For the wave with the electric vector normal to the plane of incidence, there is a change of phase in $E_y$ and $H_z$ in the reflected wave (assuming $n_2 > n_1$), but not in $H_x$, whatever the angle of incidence.

Equations (10.43), (10.44), (10.51), and (10.52) are known as Fresnel's formulae, after their discoverer. For normal incidence they give indeterminate results, but it is readily seen from equations (10.41) and (10.42) (or (10.49) and (10.50)) that we have then

$$\frac{A'}{A} = \frac{Z_2 - Z_1}{Z_2 + Z_1} = \frac{n_1 - n_2}{n_1 + n_2} \qquad (10.53)$$

and

$$\frac{A''}{A} = \frac{2Z_2}{Z_2 + Z_1} = \frac{2n_1}{n_1 + n_2}, \qquad (10.54)$$

where the expressions on the extreme right apply only when

$$\mu_2 = \mu_1 = 1.$$

The 'reflecting power' of the surface is equal to $(A'/A)^2$, since the power in the incident and reflected waves is proportional to the square of the amplitude. If $Z_2 > Z_1$, $A'' > A$ so that the amplitude of the electric vector is greater in the transmitted wave than the incident wave. Since the power varies as (amplitude of electric vector)$^2$/impedance, the transmitted power is less than the incident power, and it is readily verified that the difference is equal to the reflected power.

*Total internal reflection*

When the refractive index $n_2$ of the second medium is less than $n_1$, application of Snell's law (equation (10.35))

$$\sin \theta'' = (n_1/n_2)\sin \theta$$

to find the angle of refraction leads to values of $\sin \theta''$ greater than unity when $\sin \theta$ is greater than $n_2/n_1$. Since there is no real angle for which the sine is greater than one, we conclude that there is no refracted wave and that all the energy is reflected. This is confirmed by inspection of equations (10.41) and (10.49), for when $\sin\theta'' > 1$, $\cos\theta'' = (1-\sin^2\theta'')^{\frac{1}{2}}$ is a purely imaginary quantity, and the expressions for $(A'/A)$ and $(B'/B)$ are each of the form $(a-jb)/(a+jb)$ whose modulus is unity. Thus the reflection is total, but there is a change of phase on reflection which is different for the two directions of polarization. If the incident wave is plane polarized in a direction which is not in or normal to the plane of incidence, the two components in these planes of the reflected wave will not be in phase and the wave will therefore be elliptically polarized.

The fact that there is no 'refracted wave' does not mean that there is no disturbance in the second medium, for equations (10.42) and (10.50) show that $(A''/A)$ and $(B''/B)$ are finite. In order to find what kind of wave is propagated in the second medium, we write $\sin\theta'' = \cosh\gamma$ (since $\cosh\gamma$ is always greater than one), and then

$$\cos\theta'' = (1-\sin^2\theta'')^{\frac{1}{2}} = j(\cosh^2\gamma-1)^{\frac{1}{2}} = \pm j\sinh\gamma.$$

Hence the field components in the second medium are propagated as

$$\exp[j\omega\{t-n_2(x\cosh\gamma-jz\sinh\gamma)/c\}]$$
$$= \exp\{(-\omega n_2 z\sinh\gamma)/c\}\exp[j\omega\{t-(n_2 x\cosh\gamma)/c\}]$$
$$= \exp\{(-2\pi z\sinh\gamma)/\lambda_2\}\exp[j\omega\{t-(n_1 x\sin\theta)/c\}], \qquad (10.55)$$

where $\lambda_2$ is the wavelength of the radiation in the second medium. Equation (10.55) shows that the wave is rapidly attenuated on the far side of the boundary, since at a distance $z = \lambda_2$ its amplitude falls by

$$\exp(-2\pi\sinh\gamma).$$

For a given value of $x$, there is no phase change as we proceed in the $z$-direction, but there is a phase change as we move along the boundary in the $x$-direction. This is because a wave front obliquely incident on the boundary arrives at points of greater $x$ at a later time.

If all the incident energy is reflected, no energy can be transmitted in the second medium. If we compute the value of Poynting's vector for a direction normal to the boundary (i.e the value of $N_z = E_x H_y$ or $-E_y H_x$, according to the direction of polarization) in the second medium, we find that it has a purely imaginary value, because $H_y$ is $\frac{1}{2}\pi$ out of phase with $E_x$. This means that the real part of $N_z$ is zero, and no energy is transported away from the boundary on the average. Energy does flow into the second medium, since the stored energy must be finite if the field components are finite, but the flow is in the opposite direction during a later part of the cycle and the stored energy is returned to the first medium.

## 10.7. Reflection from the surface of a metal

When an electromagnetic wave is incident on the plane surface of a conducting medium, the amplitudes of the reflected and transmitted waves can be calculated in a manner essentially similar to that used for dielectrics. The refractive index and intrinsic impedance of a conducting medium are now complex numbers, and the formulae deduced for dielectrics may be taken over as they stand by use of a complex value for $n_2$ and $Z_2$. From equations (10.41) and (10.49) it is then apparent that the phase change on reflection is not in general 0 or $\pi$, so that a plane polarized wave will become elliptically polarized after reflection. Here we shall only calculate the reflecting power of a metal for a wave falling on it from free space at normal incidence, using equation (10.53). For a good conductor

$$Z_2 = (1+j)/(\sigma\delta) \quad \text{from equation (10.32),}$$

while for free space          $$Z_1 = \mu_0 c,$$

where $\delta$ is the skin depth in the metal and $c$ is the velocity of light in free space. Thus the reflection coefficient is

$$\frac{A'}{A} = \frac{Z_2-Z_1}{Z_2+Z_1} = \frac{(1+j)-\mu_0\,\sigma c\delta}{(1+j)+\mu_0\,\sigma c\delta},$$

where the complex value shows that there is a phase change even at normal incidence, and the reflecting power is

$$\left|\frac{A'}{A}\right|^2 = \left|\frac{(1-t)+j}{(1+t)+j}\right|^2 = \frac{2+t^2-2t}{2+t^2+2t},$$

where we have written $t$ for the quantity $(\mu_0\,\sigma c\delta)$. For a metal, where $\sigma \approx 10^7$ (ohm-metre)$^{-1}$, $t \approx (4\times10^9\delta)$, and is thus much greater than unity at all frequencies up to that of visible light ($f \approx 10^{15}$ c/s). Hence approximately

$$|(A'/A)|^2 = 1-4/t = 1-2\cdot1\times10^{-5}(\mu f/\sigma)^{\frac{1}{2}}. \tag{10.56}$$

This formula shows that metals should be almost perfect reflectors of electromagnetic radiation for all frequencies up to those of visible light. For copper at a frequency of $10^{10}$ c/s (a wavelength of 3 cm), the reflecting power differs from unity by about $2\cdot7\times10^{-4}$, and this formula would lead us to expect that it should only fall below unity by about $0\cdot09$ at a frequency of $10^{15}$ c/s (a wavelength of 3000 Å). The fact that copper appears strongly coloured shows that this formula fails for optical frequencies, when electrons in the atom other than those responsible for the conductivity begin to play a role. In addition, the effective conductivity of a metal at high frequencies is less than the low frequency value (see Problems 18.2 and 18.5).

The high reflection coefficient of a metal arises from the fact that its intrinsic impedance is very much smaller than that of free space. For copper at $10^{10}$ c/s, $Z_2$ is $0 \cdot 026(1+j)$ ohms, while for free space

$$Z_1 = 376 \cdot 7 \text{ ohms.}$$

Thus to satisfy the boundary conditions the wave must be almost totally reflected with a phase change in the electric vector but not in the magnetic vector, making **E** almost zero at the metal surface, and **H** almost twice the amplitude due to the incident wave alone.

## 10.8. The pressure due to radiation

When a plane electromagnetic wave travels through a conducting medium in the $x$-direction, a conduction current flows of density $J_y = \sigma E_y$ (assuming the wave to be linearly polarized parallel to the $y$-axis). Associated with the wave is a flux of magnetic induction $B_z$, which will exert a force on the current whose magnitude on a volume element $d\tau$ is

$$dF_x = (\mathbf{J} \wedge \mathbf{B})_x d\tau = J_y B_z d\tau$$

in the positive $x$-direction. This force is in the direction in which the energy is travelling, and gives rise to a 'radiation pressure'. From equation (10.7), $J_y = -\partial H_z/\partial x - \partial D_y/\partial t$, since all other components vanish in a plane wave, and hence

$$dF_x/d\tau = (-\partial H_z/\partial x - \partial D_y/\partial t)B_z$$
$$= -(\partial H_z/\partial x)B_z - \partial(D_y B_z)/\partial t + (\partial B_z/\partial t)D_y.$$

But from equation (10.3), $\partial B_z/\partial t = -\partial E_y/\partial x$, so that

$$dF_x/d\tau = -\left(D_y \frac{\partial E_y}{\partial x} + B_z \frac{\partial H_z}{\partial x}\right) - \frac{\partial}{\partial t}(D_y B_z)$$
$$= -(\partial U/\partial x) - \epsilon\epsilon_0 \mu\mu_0(\partial N_x/\partial t)$$

in a medium where $D$, $B$ are linearly proportional to $E$, $H$. In the steady state the second term $(\partial N_x/\partial t)$ vanishes when averaged over a cycle, and the significance of the minus sign before $(\partial U/\partial x)$ is that the force is in the forward direction provided that $U$ diminishes as the wave travels onwards, as it necessarily will in a conducting medium. We can interpret the volume force as due to the gradient of a pressure $P$, and, from the geometry shown in Fig. 10.6,

$$dF_x = -(\partial P/\partial x)\,dx dy dz = -(\partial P/\partial x)\,d\tau.$$

Hence $\qquad\qquad P = U \quad$ (normal incidence). $\qquad\qquad$ (10.57)

The pressure is exerted in the direction of Poynting's vector $\mathbf{N}$, and can be attributed to a momentum $G$ per unit volume which flows across unit area at the rate

$$U = vG = \mathbf{N}/v. \qquad\qquad (10.58)$$

This result is consistent with quantum and relativity theory by which radiation consists of photons of energy $h\nu$, whose momentum *in vacuo*

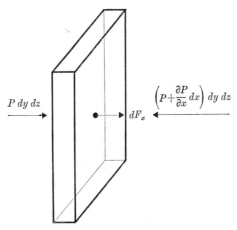

FIG. 10.6. Interpretation of volume force as gradient of a pressure.

is $h\nu/c$. For diffuse radiation, consisting of waves travelling in all directions, only one-third of the total energy density will on average be associated with waves travelling normal to the surface, so that we have

$$P = \tfrac{1}{3}U \quad \text{(diffuse radiation)}. \qquad\qquad (10.59)$$

When a wave is totally reflected, its momentum is reversed so that the pressure is doubled; however the energy density is also doubled so that the equation $P = U$ for normal incidence and equation (10.59) for diffuse radiation still hold. These results are easily obtained from the concept of momentum flow in the electromagnetic wave; other methods are much more complex, as is illustrated by considering the radiation pressure on a good conductor (such as a metal) on which a plane wave falls at normal incidence. Let the surface of the metal be the plane $x = 0$, with metal at $x > 0$, and vacuum at $x < 0$, as in Fig. 10.7. Within the metal there will be a force on the conduction current, which, from above, is $J_y \, \mu\mu_0 \, H_z \, dx$ per unit area in any thickness $dx$. Now from the equation curl $\mathbf{H} = \mathbf{J}$, where we have neglected the displacement current because it is very small in comparison with the conduction current in

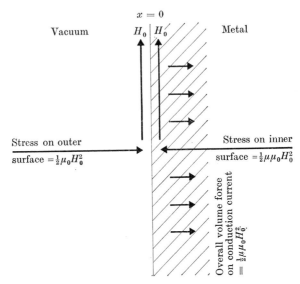

FIG. 10.7. Pressure on a totally reflecting magnetic metal, arising from stress at the surface and the volume force on the conduction current.

a metal, we have $J_y = -\partial H_z/\partial x$. Hence the overall pressure due to the force on the conduction current is

$$\mu\mu_0 \int_0^\infty J_y \, H_z \, dx = -\mu\mu_0 \int_0^\infty H_z (\partial H_z/\partial x) \, dx = \tfrac{1}{2}\mu\mu_0 \, H_0^2,$$

where $H_0$ is the instantaneous value of $H_z$ at the surface and we have used the fact that $H_z = 0$ at $x = \infty$.

In addition to this volume force, we must include the possibility of stresses at the boundary due to the electric and magnetic fields. In general such stresses take a tensor form (the 'Maxwell stress tensor'; see § 1.7 and Problem 8.9), but in the present case the fields are parallel to the boundary, and give rise to a pressure $\tfrac{1}{2}(\epsilon_0 E_y^2 + \mu_0 H_z^2)$ from the vacuum side, and $\tfrac{1}{2}(\epsilon\epsilon_0 E_y^2 + \mu\mu_0 H_z^2)$ on the metal side. For a good conductor the reflection coefficient is practically unity, and since the fields are tangential and continuous across the boundary,

$$E_y = 0, \qquad H_z = H_0 = 2H,$$

where $H$ is the amplitude in the incident wave alone. Hence the net pressure on the metal is

(stress on vacuum side)$-$(stress on metal side)$+$

$+$(force on conduction current)

$$= \tfrac{1}{2}\mu_0 H_0^2 - \tfrac{1}{2}\mu\mu_0 H_0^2 + \tfrac{1}{2}\mu\mu_0 H_0^2 = \tfrac{1}{2}\mu_0 H_0^2$$
$$= 2\mu_0 H^2.$$

Since the energy density in the incident wave is

$$U = \tfrac{1}{2}(\epsilon_0 E^2 + \mu_0 H^2) = \mu_0 H^2,$$

the net pressure is just twice the energy density in the incident wave alone; that is, it equals the sum of the energy densities in the incident and reflected waves.

This example shows that in general we must include both the stresses at a boundary and the volume force on the conduction current. In the derivation of equation (10.57) we considered a case with no change of medium so that the boundary stresses were absent, and we obtained the correct answer from the volume force alone. On the other hand, when an electromagnetic wave is partially reflected at the boundary between two non-conducting dielectrics there is no force on any conduction current and the pressure at the boundary arises entirely from the difference in the Maxwell stress tensor on either side of the boundary. It can again be calculated much more easily from the momentum balance by considering the energy densities in the incident, reflected, and transmitted waves; that the two approaches give the same answer in the case of normal incidence is verified in Problem 10.14.

## 10.9. Radiation from an oscillating dipole

In Chapter 5 the concept of a vector potential $\mathbf{A}$, such that

$$\mathbf{B} = \operatorname{curl}\mathbf{A}, \tag{10.60}$$

was introduced. The vector potential is not of great use in elementary problems, but is of considerable assistance in calculating the radiation from an aerial. The fundamental equations of the electromagnetic field are

$$\operatorname{div}\mathbf{D} = \rho, \tag{10.1}$$

$$\operatorname{div}\mathbf{B} = 0, \tag{10.2}$$

$$\operatorname{curl}\mathbf{E} = -\frac{\partial\mathbf{B}}{\partial t}, \tag{10.3}$$

$$\operatorname{curl}\mathbf{H} = \mathbf{J} + \frac{\partial\mathbf{D}}{\partial t}. \tag{10.7}$$

On substituting from equation (10.60) into (10.3) we have, as in § 6.1,

$$\operatorname{curl}\left(\mathbf{E} + \frac{\partial \mathbf{A}}{\partial t}\right) = 0,$$

the solution of which is

$$\mathbf{E} = -\frac{\partial \mathbf{A}}{\partial t} - \operatorname{grad} V, \tag{10.61}$$

where grad $V$ is the 'constant of integration', $V$ being some scalar function. Since curl grad of a scalar function is zero, any such function satisfies equation (10.3). In a static problem, where $\mathbf{A}$ is constant, equation (10.61) reduces to $\mathbf{E} = -\operatorname{grad} V$, where $V$ is the ordinary scalar electrostatic potential, as defined in equation (1.6).

Equation (10.60) does not define the vector potential $\mathbf{A}$ completely, since $\mathbf{A}$ is the solution of a differential equation and we can add to this solution any vector whose curl is zero. In equation (5.43) we added the condition div $\mathbf{A} = 0$, but for our present problem it is more convenient to generalize this condition in the form

$$\operatorname{div} \mathbf{A} = -\mu\mu_0 \,\epsilon\epsilon_0 \frac{\partial V}{\partial t} = -\frac{1}{v^2}\frac{\partial V}{\partial t}, \tag{10.62}$$

where $v = (\mu\mu_0\,\epsilon\epsilon_0)^{-\frac{1}{2}}$ is the velocity of electromagnetic waves in the medium. This definition reduces to that used previously when $V$ is constant, and has the advantage that it enables us to separate the variables $V$ and $\mathbf{A}$. From equation (10.61) we have (using equation (10.1))

$$-\nabla^2 V = -\operatorname{div} \operatorname{grad} V = \operatorname{div}\left(\mathbf{E} + \frac{\partial \mathbf{A}}{\partial t}\right)$$

$$= \operatorname{div} \mathbf{E} + \frac{\partial}{\partial t}\operatorname{div} \mathbf{A} = \frac{\rho}{\epsilon\epsilon_0} - \frac{1}{v^2}\frac{\partial^2 V}{\partial t^2},$$

so that

$$-\nabla^2 V + \frac{1}{v^2}\frac{\partial^2 V}{\partial t^2} = \frac{\rho}{\epsilon\epsilon_0}. \tag{10.63}$$

Again,

$$\operatorname{curl} \mathbf{B} = \operatorname{curl}(\operatorname{curl} \mathbf{A}) = \operatorname{grad} \operatorname{div} \mathbf{A} - \nabla^2 \mathbf{A} = -\frac{1}{v^2}\operatorname{grad}\frac{\partial V}{\partial t} - \nabla^2 \mathbf{A},$$

while from equations (10.7) and (10.61)

$$\operatorname{curl} \mathbf{B} = \mu\mu_0 \operatorname{curl} \mathbf{H} = \mu\mu_0\left(\mathbf{J} + \frac{\partial \mathbf{D}}{\partial t}\right) = \mu\mu_0\mathbf{J} + \mu\mu_0\,\epsilon\epsilon_0\frac{\partial \mathbf{E}}{\partial t}$$

$$= \mu\mu_0\mathbf{J} - \frac{1}{v^2}\left\{\frac{\partial^2 \mathbf{A}}{\partial t^2} + \operatorname{grad}\frac{\partial V}{\partial t}\right\}.$$

Identifying these two equations for curl $\mathbf{B}$ gives

$$-\nabla^2 \mathbf{A} + \frac{1}{v^2}\frac{\partial^2 \mathbf{A}}{\partial t^2} = \mu\mu_0\mathbf{J}. \tag{10.64}$$

For static systems, or systems which vary with time only slowly, equations (10.63) and (10.64) reduce to the equations (2.1) and (5.46) obtained earlier. The general solutions of our new equations are also similar to those of the earlier equations, and may be written as

$$V = \frac{1}{4\pi\epsilon\epsilon_0} \int \frac{[\rho]\,d\tau}{r}, \tag{10.65}$$

$$\mathbf{A} = \frac{\mu\mu_0}{4\pi} \int \frac{[\mathbf{J}]\,d\tau}{r}, \tag{10.66}$$

where the square brackets round $\rho$ and $\mathbf{J}$ have the following significance. The values of $V$ and $\mathbf{A}$ at a time $t$ and at a point distance $r$ from the element of volume containing $\rho$ and $\mathbf{J}$ are related, not to the values of $\rho$ and $\mathbf{J}$ at the origin at the same time, but to those values which obtained at a time $(t-r/v)$. In other words, the disturbance set up by the values of $\rho$ and $\mathbf{J}$ at the origin is propagated with the velocity $v$ and reaches a point distance $r$ away at a time later by $r/v$. Thus the disturbance at this point is related to what happened at the origin a time $r/v$ earlier, just as the light reaching the earth from a star tells us what was happening on the star, not at the same instant, but at the time when the light left the star. The values of $V$ and $\mathbf{A}$ given by equations (10.65) and (10.66) are known as 'retarded potentials'.

These equations will now be applied to the case of a short length of wire $\mathbf{s}$ at the origin of coordinates, carrying a current

$$I = I_0 \cos \omega t.$$

Then, since $\mathbf{J}\,d\tau = I\,d\mathbf{s}$, the retarded value $[\mathbf{J}]\,d\tau = [I]\,d\mathbf{s}$, and if $\mathbf{s}$ is very short compared with $r$, so that $r$ does not change significantly during the integration, we may write

$$\mathbf{A} = \frac{\mu_0}{4\pi r} \int [I]\,d\mathbf{s} = \frac{\mu_0}{4\pi r}[I]\mathbf{s}, \tag{10.67}$$

where we have assumed that the wire is *in vacuo* and have set $\mu = 1$. Then we can also write $v = c$, the velocity of light *in vacuo*. Equation (10.67) shows that the vector potential $\mathbf{A}$ is everywhere parallel to $\mathbf{s}$, as shown in Fig. 10.8.

The magnetic field $\mathbf{H}$ can now be found at any point, for

$$\mathbf{H} = \mathbf{B}/\mu_0 = (1/\mu_0)\text{curl}\,\mathbf{A}$$
$$= (1/4\pi)\text{curl}([I]\mathbf{s}/r)$$
$$= (1/4\pi)\left\{\frac{[I]}{r}\text{curl}\,\mathbf{s} - \mathbf{s} \wedge \text{grad}\frac{[I]}{r}\right\}$$
$$= -(1/4\pi)\{\mathbf{s} \wedge \text{grad}([I]/r)\}$$

since curl $\mathbf{s} = 0$. Now grad$([I]/r) = \mathbf{r}_1 \, \partial([I]/r)/\partial r$, where $\mathbf{r}_1$ is a unit vector in the direction of $r$, since $[I]$ varies in space only with $r$. Hence

$$\mathbf{H} = -(1/4\pi)\{\mathbf{s} \wedge \mathbf{r}_1\}\frac{\partial}{\partial r}\{[I]/r\},$$

showing that $\mathbf{H}$ is normal to $\mathbf{s}$ and to $\mathbf{r}_1$, and it has thus only one component, $H_\phi$ in spherical polar coordinates.

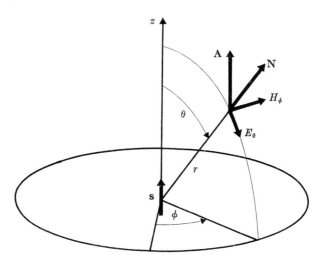

FIG. 10.8. Radiation from a short dipole $\mathbf{s}$; at the point $(r, \theta, \phi)$ the magnetic vector potential $\mathbf{A}$ is parallel to $\mathbf{s}$; Poynting's vector $\mathbf{N}$ is along the radius vector $r$, and the field components are $E_\theta$ (along a line of longitude) and $H_\phi$ (along a line of latitude).

The retarded value $[I] = I_0 \cos \omega(t-r/c)$, and hence

$$\frac{\partial}{\partial r}\{[I]/r\} = -\frac{I_0}{r^2}\cos \omega(t-r/c) + \frac{\omega I_0}{cr}\sin \omega(t-r/c)$$

$$= -\frac{I_0}{r^2}\cos \omega(t-r/c) + \frac{2\pi I_0}{r\lambda}\sin \omega(t-r/c),$$

where $\lambda$ is the wavelength of the radiation. The magnetic field is then given by the sole component

$$H_\phi = \frac{sI_0 \sin \theta}{4\pi r^2}\cos \omega(t-r/c) - \frac{sI_0 \sin \theta}{2r\lambda}\sin \omega(t-r/c). \quad (10.68)$$

The first term predominates at short distances ($r \ll \lambda$) from the origin, and will be recognized as just the field given by the law of Biot and Savart (equation (5.37)). It is known as the 'induction field'. At large distances of many wavelengths from the origin only the second term is significant; it falls off as $(\lambda r)^{-1}$ instead of $r^{-2}$ and is known as the 'radiation field'.

The electric field may be found by using equation (10.3), or it may be found from equation (10.61) if the scalar potential $V$ is first computed by means of equation (10.62). We are interested only in its value at a large distance from the origin, when our spherical wave front has very small curvature and over a small region may be taken as a plane wave. As we would expect, $\mathbf{E}$ is then normal both to $\mathbf{H}$ and to the direction of propagation, and its only component is

$$E_\theta = Z_0 H_\phi = (\mu_0/\epsilon_0)^{\frac{1}{2}} H_\phi.$$

The energy crossing unit area per second is given by Poynting's vector

$$N = E_\theta H_\phi = Z_0 H_\phi^2,$$

showing that the energy flow is radially outwards. The mean value of $N$ averaged over a cycle of oscillation is

$$\bar{N} = \tfrac{1}{8} Z_0 (I_0 s/r\lambda)^2 \sin^2\theta \tag{10.69}$$

and the total energy radiated in all directions per second is

$$W = \int_0^\pi 2\pi r^2 \bar{N} \sin\theta \, d\theta = \frac{\pi Z_0 I_0^2 s^2}{3\lambda^2}. \tag{10.70}$$

The power radiated may be expressed in terms of a resistance $R_r$, called the 'radiation resistance', obtained by writing $W = \tfrac{1}{2} R_r I_0^2$, since this is just the mean power which would be dissipated in a real resistance $R_r$. For our current element equation (10.70) gives

$$R_r = \frac{2\pi Z_0}{3}\left(\frac{s}{\lambda}\right)^2 = 789(s/\lambda)^2 \text{ ohms}, \tag{10.71}$$

showing that the radiation resistance depends only on the square of the ratio of the length of the wire to the wavelength.

We may imagine our oscillating current element to be due to two oscillating charges $\pm q_0 \sin\omega t$, separated by a short distance $\mathbf{s}$. This is an oscillating electric dipole of moment $\mathbf{p}_0 \sin\omega t = \mathbf{s} q_0 \sin\omega t$, and the current is

$$I = dq/dt = \omega q_0 \cos\omega t,$$

giving

$$\mathbf{s} I = \omega \mathbf{p}_0 \cos\omega t \quad \text{or} \quad \mathbf{s} I_0 = \omega \mathbf{p}_0.$$

The total radiated power may then be written as

$$W = \frac{\pi Z_0 \omega^2 p_0^2}{3\lambda^2} = \frac{4\pi^3 c p_0^2}{3\epsilon_0 \lambda^4} = \frac{Z_0 \omega^4 p_0^2}{12\pi c^2} = \frac{\mu_0 \omega^4 p_0^2}{12\pi c} \tag{10.72}$$

(using $Z_0 = (\epsilon_0 c)^{-1} = \mu_0 c$), showing that $W$ is proportional to the square of the oscillating dipole moment and the fourth power of the frequency.

Since the oscillating current element can be regarded as an oscillating electric dipole, it is interesting to calculate the scalar potential and compare it with our earlier results for a static dipole. Since A has a component only parallel to the polar axis (which we will call the $z$-axis), $\text{div}\,\mathbf{A} = \partial A_z/\partial z$. In the differentiation $x$, $y$ are constant and

$$(\partial/\partial z)_{x,y} = (z/r)(\partial/\partial r) = \cos\theta(\partial/\partial r) \quad (\text{cf. § 2.2}).$$

Hence, using equations (10.62) and (10.67),

$$\partial V/\partial t = -c^2\,\text{div}\,\mathbf{A} = -\frac{c^2\mu_0 I_0 s\cos\theta}{4\pi}\frac{\partial}{\partial r}\{r^{-1}\cos\omega(t-r/c)\}.$$

Since $r$ and $t$ are independent variables we may integrate with respect to $t$ inside the differential, giving

$$V = -\frac{c^2\mu_0 I_0 s\cos\theta}{4\pi\omega}\frac{\partial}{\partial r}\{r^{-1}\sin\omega(t-r/c)\}$$

$$= -\frac{p_0\cos\theta}{4\pi\epsilon_0}\frac{\partial}{\partial r}\{r^{-1}\sin\omega(t-r/c)\}$$

$$= -\frac{1}{4\pi\epsilon_0}[\mathbf{p}_0\cdot\text{grad}\{r^{-1}\sin\omega(t-r/c)\}]. \qquad (10.73)$$

Comparison with equation (1.11 a) shows that this is of the same form except that allowance must be made for the retardation in taking the gradient.

It must be emphasized that the equations we have derived apply only when the length of the oscillating dipole is small compared with the wavelength. Most of the radiation emitted by atoms is due to oscillations of electrons, and is therefore 'electric dipole' radiation. The size of the electric dipole will be of the order of the electronic charge times an atomic dimension, and the effective length of the dipole is thus about $10^{-8}$ cm; since the wavelength of visible light is about $10^{-5}$ cm, our theory could be applied to this case if the restrictions due to quantum theory could be neglected. Thus classical theory predicts that an electron moving in an orbit round the nucleus would behave as a two-dimensional oscillator and lose energy continuously by radiation until it finally spirals into the nucleus. This difficulty could not be overcome in attempts to find a satisfactory model of the atom until Bohr introduced the concept of stationary orbits in which the electron did not radiate. Thus the difficulty arose from the use of classical theory, which is a good approximation for macroscopic oscillators, in an atomic problem where it was not applicable. Nevertheless, the classical theory gives a good explanation of the phenomena of dispersion and scattering (see Chapter 17), and most of the qualitative results which it provides, such as the polarization of the radiation and the absence of radiation in the direction in which the dipole is pointing, are valid for atomic systems.

At radio frequencies the aerial or antenna used for the reception or transmission of broadcast signals is not in general short compared with the wavelength. Its radiative properties may be calculated by methods similar to those used above, the value of **A** being obtained by the use of equation (10.66). For a single straight wire this gives

$$\mathbf{A} = \frac{\mu\mu_0}{4\pi} \int \frac{[I]}{r} \, \mathbf{ds}, \tag{10.74}$$

where the integration is along the wire and $I$ is the current in the element **ds**. Two points must be noted in performing the integration: (a) the current is not in general constant along the wire, since it must fall to zero at the ends; (b) in evaluating the retarded potential, allowance must be made for the phase difference in signals coming from different parts of the wire owing to the change in the distance. The problem is similar to that of the diffraction pattern of a single slit where the amplitude varies over the aperture. The interference concepts used for light waves may be applied in finding the radiation pattern produced by an aerial array consisting of many elements; the problem is essentially similar to that of a diffraction grating.

## REFERENCE

BIRGE, R. T., 1941, *Ann. Rep. Progr. Phys.* (Physical Society, London), **8**, 90.

## PROBLEMS

10.1. A metallic sheet is bounded by the plane $x = 0$ and a tangential oscillating magnetic field $H_y = H_0 \cos \omega t$ exists at the surface. Show that the total current $I$ per unit width of the surface flowing in the metal has an instantaneous value equal to $H_y$ and that its direction is normal to $H_y$. Verify that this conforms with equation (5.22), if the $\int \mathbf{H} . \mathbf{ds}$ is taken round a suitable rectangular circuit with two sides parallel to the $x$-axis and two parallel to the $y$-axis, one of the latter being just outside the metal and the other inside at a depth much greater than the skin depth.

Compute the magnitude of Poynting's vector just inside the surface of the metal and show that its mean value (averaged over a period of oscillation) is just equal to the power per unit area dissipated in heating the metal as given by equation (10.34 a).

10.2. Show that the superposition of two waves of equal amplitude, one with angular frequency $\omega + d\omega$ and phase constant $\beta + d\beta$, the other with $\omega - d\omega$ and $\beta - d\beta$, gives a wave of frequency $\omega$ and phase constant $\beta$, whose amplitude varies as $\binom{\sin}{\cos}(t\,d\omega - x\,d\beta)$. Hence a point of maximum amplitude moves as

$$(t\,d\omega - x\,d\beta) = \text{constant},$$

or with velocity $u = (d\omega/d\beta)$. Since the energy is proportional to the square of the amplitude, $u$ gives the rate at which energy is propagated, known as the 'group velocity'.

Show that in a good conductor, such as a metal, where the displacement current can be neglected, the phase velocity $v$ $(= \omega/\beta)$ is $\omega\delta$, and the group velocity $u$ $(= d\omega/d\beta)$ is $2\omega\delta$, where $\delta$ is the skin depth.

10.3. Show from equation (10.41) that the condition for there to be no reflected wave at the boundary between two insulators $(\epsilon_1, \mu_1; \epsilon_2, \mu_2)$ when the electric vector is in the plane of incidence requires that

$$\epsilon_1 \tan \theta = \epsilon_2 \tan \theta''.$$

This equation shows that at this particular angle the lines of electric field are refracted as in the electrostatic case (cf. Fig. 1.13) so that the boundary conditions are satisfied without any reflected wave. Similarly, when the magnetic vector is in the plane of incidence, the condition for no reflection is

$$\mu_1 \tan \theta = \mu_2 \tan \theta''$$

so that the lines of magnetic field are refracted as in the magnetostatic case.

Verify that in general the boundary conditions for the normal components of **D** and **B** are automatically satisfied in the theory of § 10.6 when the conditions for the tangential components of **E** and **H** are satisfied.

10.4. The rate at which solar energy falls on the earth's surface is approximately 2 cal/cm²/minute. Calculate the r.m.s. values of the electric and magnetic fields at the earth's surface, and the pressure exerted on it, assuming it to behave as a perfect absorber.

(*Answer:* $E = 730$ V/metre; $H = 1\cdot 9$ A/metre; pressure, $4\cdot 7 \times 10^{-6}$ newton/m².)

10.5. Show that by the introduction of a complex dielectric constant $\epsilon = \epsilon' - j\epsilon''$, where $\epsilon'' = (\sigma/\omega\epsilon_0)$, the equations (10.25 a) may be written in the same form as for a non-conducting dielectric. Show that this leads to the relation $\mathbf{n}^2 = \mu\epsilon$, and that $\epsilon''/\epsilon' = \tan \delta$, where $\tan \delta$ is the loss tangent of the dielectric (see Problem 9.12).

10.6. A slightly imperfect dielectric has a small loss tangent. Show that in the first approximation the velocity of electromagnetic waves is the same as if $\tan \delta$ were zero, but the power falls as $\exp(-\sigma Z_0 x)$ in travelling a distance $x$, where $Z_0$ is the intrinsic impedance of the medium neglecting the conductivity $\sigma$. This result has the simple interpretation: in a thickness $dx$ the power dissipated per unit cross-section is $\sigma E^2 \, dx$, while the incident power $W = E^2/Z_0$. Hence

$$-dW/dx = \sigma Z_0 \, W.$$

Show also that

$$\sigma Z_0 = 2\pi(\text{loss tangent of the dielectric})/\lambda,$$

where $\lambda$ is the wavelength of the radiation in the dielectric.

10.7. When a plane wave is incident on a conducting wire the electric field set up in the wire is equal to the tangential component of the electric field strength in the wave. Show that in a short straight wire the power picked up is proportional to $\sin^2\theta$, where $\theta$ is the angle between the wire and the direction of travel of the wave. This shows that the directional properties of the wire are the same for receiving as for transmitting (cf. equation (10.69)).

10.8. When a plane wave falls on a small plane loop of wire, the e.m.f. induced in the loop is determined by the rate of change of magnetic flux through it. Show that the directional properties of the loop are the same as those of the short wire, if $\theta$ is measured from the normal to the plane of the loop, but the planes of the electric and magnetic vectors in the wave must be interchanged. This is consistent with the fact that a loop carrying an alternating current behaves as an oscillating magnetic dipole.

Show that the ratio of the e.m.f. set up in a short wire of length $s$ to that in a small loop of area $A$ is $(\lambda s/2\pi A)$, where $\lambda$ is the wavelength of the radiation. If the linear dimensions of the loop are roughly the same as those of the wire ($A \approx s^2$), this shows that the loop is a much poorer aerial when $s \ll \lambda$.

10.9. A transmitter radiates a power $W$ from a short dipole aerial. Show that the r.m.s. electric field at a distance $D$ in the equatorial plane of the dipole aerial is

$$E = (3Z_0 W/8\pi D^2)^{\frac{1}{2}},$$

where $Z_0$ is the intrinsic impedance of free space.

If $W = 1$ kW, show that the field strength at a distance of 10 km is about 0·021 V/metre.

10.10. A transmitter radiates a power $W$ from a short horizontal dipole aerial located at a height $H$ above the sea. Show that the signal received at a target whose distance is $D$ and height above the sea is $h$ ($D \gg H, h$) is a maximum when $h = D\lambda/4H$, where $\lambda$ is the wavelength of the transmitter. The sea may be assumed to act as a flat, perfectly reflecting (conducting) surface.

Show that if the height of the target is very much smaller than this value, the power incident on unit area of it (assuming it to lie in the equatorial plane of the dipole) is $6\pi WH^2h^2/D^4\lambda^2$. This equation shows that the effect of the sea is to make the power fall off with the inverse fourth power of the distance instead of the inverse square; it shows also the improvement gained by using short wavelengths.

If $W = 1$ kW, $D = 10$ km, $H = h = \lambda = 10$ metres, show that the r.m.s. electric field strength at the target is about $2·7 \times 10^{-4}$ V/metre.

10.11. Obtain equation (10.56) by the use of equation (10.34a) and the Law of Conservation of Energy.

10.12. A cylindrical conductor of finite resistance carries a current $I$. Calculate the value of Poynting's vector at the surface of the wire, and show that the energy flowing into the wire is just equal to that dissipated in heating the wire.

10.13. At high frequencies the magnetic field falls inside each lamination of a transformer owing to the skin effect; the effective permeability at high frequencies is found by calculating the total flux in a lamination in phase with that at each surface of the lamination. Show that the effective r.f. permeability is less than the static value by a factor $\delta/a$ when the skin depth $\delta$ is very much smaller than the thickness $a$ of the lamination.

What thickness of lamination is required to make $\delta = a$ for a material of permeability $10^5$ and resistivity $5 \times 10^{-7}$ ohm-metre at a frequency of 50 c/s?

*(Answer: 0·16 mm.)*

**10.14.** A plane wave falls at normal incidence on the boundary $(z = 0)$ between two media with constants $(\epsilon_1, \mu_1)$ and $(\epsilon_2, \mu_2)$ respectively. If the field components at the boundary are $E_x$, $H_y$, show that the stress is

$$\tfrac{1}{2}\{(\epsilon_1 - \epsilon_2)\epsilon_0 E_x^2 + (\mu_1 - \mu_2)\mu_0 H_y^2\}$$

and that this is equal to the sum of the momentum flows in the incident and reflected waves less that in the transmitted wave; i.e. to

$$\frac{E^2 + E'^2}{Z_1 v_1} - \frac{E''^2}{Z_2 v_2},$$

where $E$, $E'$, $E''$ are the electric intensities in the incident, reflected, and transmitted waves respectively, and $Z_1$, $v_1$; $Z_2$, $v_2$ are the impedance of and phase velocity in the two media.

*Hint:* Note that $E_x = E''$, $H_y = E''/Z_2$ and show that both expressions can be reduced to

$$\tfrac{1}{2} E''^2 \left( \frac{1}{Z_1 v_1} + \frac{Z_1}{Z_2^2 v_1} - \frac{2}{Z_2 v_2} \right).$$

**10.15.** In a region of space containing $\bar{n}$ particles per unit volume of charge $q$ and mass $m$, where the pressure is so low that collisions may be neglected, equations (10.3) and (10.7) may be written

$$\text{curl } \mathbf{E} = -\mu_0(\partial \mathbf{H}/\partial t); \qquad \text{curl } \mathbf{H} = \bar{n}q\mathbf{v} + \epsilon_0(\partial \mathbf{E}/\partial t).$$

Show that by using the equation of motion $q\mathbf{E} = m(\partial \mathbf{v}/\partial t)$, and eliminating $\mathbf{v}$ between these equations (taking grad div $\epsilon_0 \mathbf{E} = \text{grad}(\bar{n}q) = 0$), one can obtain the equation

$$\frac{\partial^2 \mathbf{E}}{\partial t^2} + \frac{\bar{n}q^2}{\epsilon_0 m} \mathbf{E} = c^2 \nabla^2 \mathbf{E}.$$

This is the equation of Tonks and Langmuir for propagation of waves in an ionized medium. Show, by assuming $\mathbf{E}$ to vary sinusoidally with frequency $f$ and wavelength $\lambda$, that

$$f^2 = (\bar{n}q^2/4\pi^2\epsilon_0 m) + (c^2/\lambda^2).$$

For very long wavelengths this reduces to the equation for plasma oscillations, equation (4.47).

# FILTERS, TRANSMISSION LINES,
# AND WAVEGUIDES

## 11.1. Elements of filter theory

A FREQUENT requirement in radio and telephony is the separation of two signals of different frequencies. Any circuit whose impedance varies with frequency can be used for this purpose, a simple example already considered being the tuned circuit, which can be employed to accept or reject a narrow band of frequencies centred on its natural resonant frequency. This acts as a 'band pass' or 'band stop' filter. Another type of filter may be required to pass all frequencies up to a certain

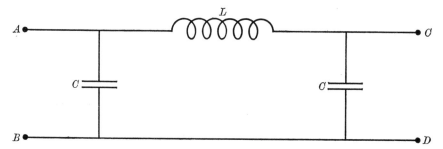

FIG. 11.1. Simple low-pass filter section.

value, and stop all higher frequencies; this is a 'low-pass' filter. The reverse case is a 'high-pass' filter, which rejects all low frequencies up to a certain value, and passes all higher frequencies.

The action of a filter can be understood by considering a simple example, the low-pass filter shown in Fig. 11.1. A common use of such a filter is to remove the ripple voltage from the output of a rectifier unit which is converting an a.c. voltage to a steady voltage. The output is applied to the terminals $AB$ of the filter, which is required to pass the steady voltage component on to the terminals $CD$, but not the alternating component. If the latter has a frequency of, say, 100 c/s, and the capacitance $C$ is chosen to have a low impedance at 100 c/s while the inductance $L$ has a high impedance, only a small fraction of the input voltage at this frequency will appear at the terminals $CD$, because the inductance and second capacitance act as a voltage divider. The fraction is approximately $X_C/X_L = (1/\omega C)/\omega L = 1/(\omega^2 LC)$, and if $C = 10\ \mu\mathrm{F}$, $L = 25$ henries, the fraction is about $1/100$. On the other hand, if there is no leakage in the capacitor, the full steady voltage component will be passed on to $CD$. Thus the filter accepts the signal of zero frequency,

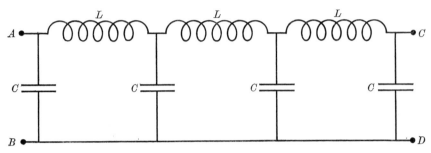

FIG. 11.2. Chain of low-pass filter sections.

and partially rejects the signal at 100 c/s frequency. Better rejection is obtained by adding more sections of this kind, as in Fig. 11.2. This arrangement is called a step- or ladder-type filter. It is clear that evaluation of the currents and voltages in the different elements by

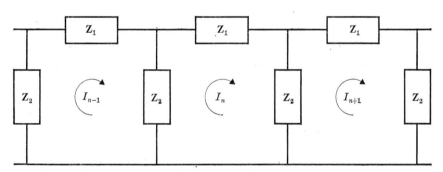

FIG. 11.3. Generalized type of uniform ladder filter.

application of Kirchhoff's laws would be very laborious, and it is preferable to proceed in a different way, making use of the recurrent nature of the elements.

We shall begin by considering a uniform filter, consisting of a chain of similar sections, as in Fig. 11.3, which are repeated indefinitely, forming an infinite chain. If a generator is applied at some point earlier in the chain, currents will flow in the various sections; let the currents in successive sections be $I_{n-1}$, $I_n$, $I_{n+1}$. Application of Kirchhoff's law to the central section gives

$$Z_2(I_n-I_{n-1})+Z_1 I_n+Z_2(I_n-I_{n+1}) = 0$$

or

$$-Z_2 I_{n-1}+(Z_1+2Z_2)I_n-Z_2 I_{n+1} = 0. \qquad (11.1)$$

We may write $I_n = aI_{n-1}$, where $a$ is a real or complex number; then in an infinite chain where we cannot distinguish between sections we must also have $I_{n+1} = aI_n$. Equation (11.1) then gives

$$\tfrac{1}{2}(a+1/a) = 1+Z_1/2Z_2. \qquad (11.2)$$

This equation determines the attenuation constant $a$. We shall confine our attention to the case where $Z_1/Z_2$ is real, which corresponds to $Z_1$ and $Z_2$ being both pure resistances or pure reactances. Then $a$ can be either real or complex, but not a purely imaginary quantity. The real roots arise when the right-hand side of equation (11.2) lies outside the range $+1$ to $-1$, i.e. $Z_1/4Z_2$ lies outside the range $0$ to $-1$. We consider separately the three cases where it is greater than $0$, between $0$ and $-1$, and less than $-1$.

(i) $(Z_1/4Z_2) > 0$

$a$ is real and positive. Since the network is 'passive' (i.e. it contains no power-generating elements), the currents must decrease as we move away from the generator attached to one end of the filter. Thus we take $a < 1$ for a wave travelling towards the right (i.e. generator attached to the left-hand end of the filter) and $a > 1$ for a wave travelling towards the left. This interpretation is consistent with the fact that the roots of equation (11.2) are reciprocal; thus the wave is attenuated by the same amount per section in the direction in which it progresses, whichever way it is going. The significance of the positive sign of $a$ is that the wave is attenuated without change of phase. If we write $a = e^{-\alpha}$, where $\alpha$ is the attenuation constant per section, equation (11.2) becomes

$$\cosh \alpha = 1+Z_1/2Z_2. \qquad (11.3)$$

(ii) $0 > (Z_1/4Z_2) > -1$

$a$ is complex, with modulus unity, so that we may write $a = e^{-i\beta}$. The wave is not attenuated at all, but suffers a phase change by an angle $\beta$ in each section, where

$$\cos \beta = 1+Z_1/2Z_2. \qquad (11.4)$$

(iii) $(Z_1/4Z_2) < -1$

$a$ is then real and negative, so that the wave is attenuated with a phase change of $\pi$ in successive sections. If we write $a = -e^{-\alpha}$, equation (11.2) becomes

$$-\cosh \alpha = 1+Z_1/2Z_2. \qquad (11.5)$$

Here we have already spoken of the current as part of a 'wave' and this terminology needs some justification. If the current in one section alternates at a given frequency, so that we can write $I_n = I_n^0 \exp(j\omega t)$, then the current in a later section $(n+m)$ will be

$$I_{n+m} = a^m I_n^0 \exp(j\omega t).$$

If we write $a = \exp(-h)$, the current in the section $n+m$ will be

$$I_{n+m} = I_n^0 \exp(-hm)\exp(j\omega t) = I_n^0 \exp(j\omega t - hm),$$

which is similar to the expression for a wave motion in a continuous medium except that $m$, the number of sections, which can only be an integer, replaces $x$, the distance travelled in the medium. If $h$ is real, we write it as $\alpha$, and we have an attenuated wave, but if $h$ is a pure imaginary quantity $j\beta$ we have an unattenuated wave with a phase change $\beta$ per section. The values of $\alpha$ and $\beta$ are given by equations (11.3–5). The reciprocal roots are obtained by changing the sign of $h$, corresponding to a wave travelling in the opposite direction. The third case (iii) above, where the attenuated wave changes sign in successive sections, could not arise in a continuous medium. The behaviour of the filter is determined immediately from the value of $(Z_1/4Z_2)$. If it lies within the range 0 to $-1$, we have a 'pass band' with no attenuation; outside this range we have a 'stop band'.

The word 'section' has been used so far without any precise definition of its meaning. The uniform chain can be regarded as made up of similar sections joined together, but two types of section can be obtained by cutting the chain in different ways. These two types are shown in Figs. 11.4 and 11.5 and for obvious reasons are known as $T$-sections and $\pi$-sections respectively. It is clear that a succession of either type of section joined together gives the same chain filter (see Fig. 11.6), so that the transmission characteristics derived earlier apply to either type of section.

If a generator of voltage $V$ is connected to a semi-infinite chain and the current $I$ drawn from it is measured, a definite value of the ratio $(V/I)$ is obtained, known as the 'characteristic' or 'iterative' impedance of the chain. It is obvious that the same value would be obtained if a number of sections were removed and the impedance of the semi-infinite chain measured at a later point. Again, the chain may be severed at some point and the infinite tail replaced by an impedance equal to the iterative impedance without altering the impedance measured at the input terminals. This gives us a method of calculating the iterative impedance. Fig. 11.4 shows a $T$-section terminated by an impedance $Z_T$;

the impedance measured at the input terminals $AB$ can be calculated by standard methods, and on equating this to $\mathbf{Z}_T$ we have

$$\mathbf{Z}_T = \tfrac{1}{2}\mathbf{Z}_1 + \left(\frac{1}{\mathbf{Z}_2} + \frac{1}{\tfrac{1}{2}\mathbf{Z}_1 + \mathbf{Z}_T}\right)^{-1}.$$

Solution of this equation gives

$$\mathbf{Z}_T = (\mathbf{Z}_1\mathbf{Z}_2 + \tfrac{1}{4}\mathbf{Z}_1^2)^{\frac{1}{2}} = (\mathbf{Z}_1\mathbf{Z}_2)^{\frac{1}{2}}(1 + \mathbf{Z}_1/4\mathbf{Z}_2)^{\frac{1}{2}}. \qquad (11.6)$$

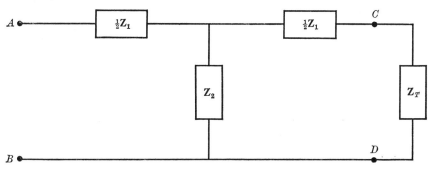

FIG. 11.4. $T$-section $ABCD$ terminated by its iterative impedance.

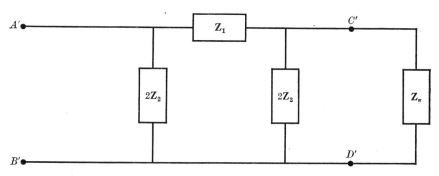

FIG. 11.5. $\pi$-section $A'B'C'D'$ terminated by its iterative impedance.

This is the value of the iterative impedance $\mathbf{Z}_T$ for a $T$-section. By applying the same method to a $\pi$-section, as shown in Fig. 11.5, we find the iterative impedance of a $\pi$-section to be

$$\mathbf{Z}_\pi = (\mathbf{Z}_1\mathbf{Z}_2)^{\frac{1}{2}}(1 + \mathbf{Z}_1/4\mathbf{Z}_2)^{-\frac{1}{2}}. \qquad (11.7)$$

Thus $\qquad\qquad\qquad\qquad \mathbf{Z}_T\mathbf{Z}_\pi = \mathbf{Z}_1\mathbf{Z}_2. \qquad\qquad\qquad (11.8)$

The importance of the iterative impedance lies in the fact that sections of different kinds may be joined together to form a non-uniform filter, without disturbing a wave travelling down the filter, provided that they have the same iterative impedance. If sections with different iterative impedances are used a 'reflection' of the wave occurs at the junction and the simple filter theory is no longer applicable. Similarly, the filter must be terminated by a load equal to its iterative impedance in order to avoid a reflection at the output terminals. Any such reflection will diminish the power dissipated in the load, since part of the incident energy will be reflected.

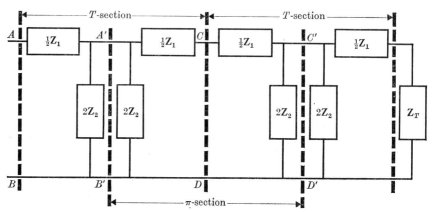

FIG. 11.6. Filter of $T$-sections such as $ABCD$ terminated by the iterative impedance $\mathbf{Z}_T$. It may also be divided into $\pi$-sections terminated by the network to the right of $C'D'$.

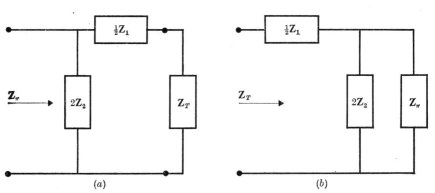

FIG. 11.7. Half-sections used as transformers (a) converting $\mathbf{Z}_T$ to $\mathbf{Z}_\pi$; (b) $\mathbf{Z}_\pi$ to $\mathbf{Z}_T$.

A filter correctly terminated by the iterative impedance $\mathbf{Z}_T$ is shown in Fig. 11.6, where it is regarded as made up of $T$-sections ($ABCD$). Alternatively, we may regard it as made up of $\pi$-sections ($A'B'C'D'$), which must still be correctly terminated. Thus the impedance of the portion to the right of $C'D'$, shown separately in Fig. 11.7 (a), must be $\mathbf{Z}_\pi$. Hence the half-section acts as a transformer from the impedance $\mathbf{Z}_T$ to $\mathbf{Z}_\pi$, as may also be verified by direct calculation. Similarly, the other half-section shown in Fig. 11.7 ($b$) transforms the impedance $Z_\pi$ to $Z_T$. To a limited extent such half-sections can be used to match a load to a filter, but their especial importance comes in the design of composite filters (see Problem 11.4).

## 11.2. Some simple types of filter

*Low-pass filter*

The simplest type of low-pass filter is that shown in Fig. 11.2 with capacitances in the shunt arms and inductances in the series arms. Then $Z_1 = j\omega L$ and $Z_2 = 1/(j\omega C)$, giving

$$Z_1/4Z_2 = -\omega^2 LC/4.$$

The cut-off frequency $\omega_0$ is obtained by setting this equal to $-1$, giving $\omega_0 = 2(LC)^{-\frac{1}{2}}$. Frequencies below this are passed without attenuation,

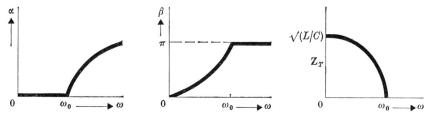

Fig. 11.8. Variation of $\alpha$, $\beta$ and the real part of $Z_T$ for a simple low-pass filter.

while higher frequencies are attenuated. In the pass band the phase change is given by

$$\cos\beta = 1 - \omega^2 LC/2 = 1 - 2(\omega/\omega_0)^2,$$

showing that $\beta$ changes from 0 to $\pi$ as the frequency increases from zero to the cut-off value. The characteristic impedance of a $T$-section is

$$Z_T = \left(\frac{L}{C} - \frac{\omega^2 L^2}{4}\right)^{\frac{1}{2}} = \left(\frac{L}{C}\right)^{\frac{1}{2}}\left(1 - \frac{\omega^2}{\omega_0^2}\right)^{\frac{1}{2}},$$

which is resistive in the pass band, but varies from $(L/C)^{\frac{1}{2}}$ to zero at the cut-off frequency. In the stop band $Z_T$ is a pure reactance and the attenuation is given by

$$-\cosh\alpha = 1 - \omega^2 LC/2,$$

which rises with frequency from zero at $\omega = \omega_0$. The negative sign shows that currents in successive sections are reversed in direction.

The general behaviour of $\alpha$, $\beta$, and $Z_T$ is illustrated in Fig. 11.8. The variation of $Z_\pi$ is easily found from the relation

$$Z_\pi = Z_1 Z_2/Z_T = L/(CZ_T).$$

As an example, we may take the problem of smoothing the output of a rectifier considered at the beginning of this chapter. Then $C = 10\ \mu\mathrm{F}$, $L = 25$ henries, and the ripple frequency is 100 c/s. The attenuation per section at this frequency is given by

$$-\cosh\alpha = -\frac{e^{\alpha}+e^{-\alpha}}{2} = 1-\tfrac{1}{2}\omega^2 LC = (1-49\cdot3).$$

Hence $e^{\alpha} \approx 100$, or the attenuation in power is approximately $10^4$ per section. If we have $n$ such inductances and capacitances, it is very

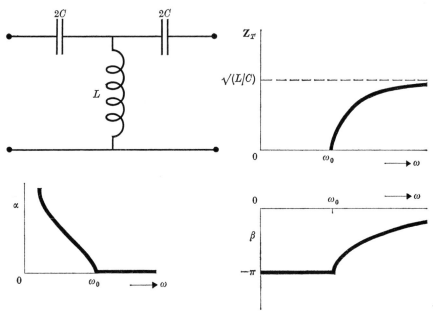

FIG. 11.9. $T$-section of simple high-pass filter, with variation of real part of $\mathbf{Z}_T$, $\alpha$, and $\beta$.

much better to join them as a ladder filter of $n$ sections than to lump them all into one section. The latter would reduce the ripple voltage by a factor $e^{\alpha'} \approx (\omega^2 n^2 LC) = 100n^2$ approximately, while the ladder type filter will reduce it by $e^{n\alpha} \approx (100)^n$. Thus three sections would reduce the ripple voltage by $10^6$, while the single section with three inductances in series and three capacitances in parallel gives only a factor 900.

### The high-pass filter

As would be expected, the simplest high-pass filter is formed by putting capacitances in the series arms and inductances in the shunt arms, and a typical $T$-section is shown in Fig. 11.9.

Then $\mathbf{Z_1} = 1/j\omega C$, $\mathbf{Z_2} = j\omega L$, and

$$\mathbf{Z_1}/4\mathbf{Z_2} = -1/4\omega^2 LC.$$

This lies between zero and $-1$ for $\omega \geqslant \frac{1}{2}(LC)^{-\frac{1}{2}}$, the latter being the critical frequency $\omega_0$. The phase change per section in the pass band is given by

$$\cos\beta = 1-1/(2\omega^2 LC) = 1-2\left(\frac{\omega_0}{\omega}\right)^2,$$

and the modulus of this expression gives also the value of $\cosh\alpha$ in the stop band.

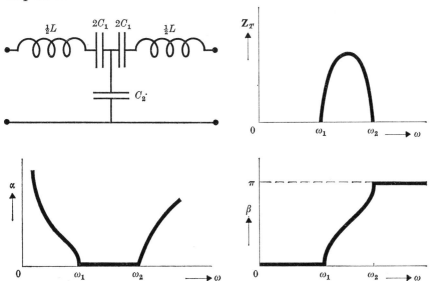

FIG. 11.10. Simple type of band-pass filter, showing $T$-section, and real part of $\mathbf{Z}_T$, $\alpha$, and $\beta$ as functions of frequency.

The iterative impedance is

$$\mathbf{Z}_T = \left(\frac{L}{C} - \frac{1}{4\omega^2 C^2}\right)^{\frac{1}{2}} = \left(\frac{L}{C}\right)^{\frac{1}{2}}\left(1 - \frac{\omega_0^2}{\omega^2}\right)^{\frac{1}{2}},$$

which is imaginary in the stop band, and rises from zero at the critical frequency to a limiting value of $(L/C)^{\frac{1}{2}}$ in the pass band. The behaviour of $\alpha$, $\beta$, and $\mathbf{Z}_T$ is illustrated in Fig. 11.9.

*Band-pass filters*

A simple type of band-pass filter is shown in Fig. 11.10. Qualitatively its behaviour can be seen as follows. At very low frequencies the impedance in the series arm will be dominated by the capacitance, so that the section will act as a simple capacitance-type attenuator (see Problem 11.1). At frequencies higher than the resonant frequency of the combination $L$ and $C_1$, $\omega L > (\omega C_1)^{-1}$ and the impedance of the series arm is inductive; then the section behaves as a low-pass filter, the highest frequencies again being stopped. Quantitatively, the analysis is

$$\mathbf{Z}_1 = j\omega L + 1/(j\omega C_1),$$

$$\mathbf{Z}_2 = 1/(j\omega C_2),$$

$$\mathbf{Z}_1/4\mathbf{Z}_2 = \frac{1}{4}\left[\frac{C_2}{C_1} - \omega^2 L C_2\right],$$

which is positive at zero frequency, but tends to $-\infty$ as $\omega \to \infty$. When it lies between 0 and $-1$, we have a pass band whose lowest frequency is

$$\omega_1 = (LC_1)^{-\frac{1}{2}}, \quad \text{where } \mathbf{Z}_1/4\mathbf{Z}_2 = 0,$$

and highest frequency is

$$\omega_2 = \left(\frac{C_2+4C_1}{LC_1C_2}\right)^{\frac{1}{2}}, \quad \text{where } \frac{\mathbf{Z}_1}{4\mathbf{Z}_2} = -1.$$

The behaviour of $\alpha$, $\beta$, and $\mathbf{Z}_T$ is shown in Fig. 11.10.

*Disadvantages of the simple filter*

A simple filter, consisting of a chain of similar sections, suffers from two principal disadvantages:

(a) the iterative impedance varies with frequency in the pass band, making it impossible to terminate the filter correctly throughout the pass band;

(b) the attenuation in the stop band varies with frequency, being low near the cut-off frequencies.

These drawbacks can be reduced by using a composite filter, containing sections of different types, instead of a uniform filter. For example, the attenuation just above the cut-off frequency of a low-pass filter can be made high by using a section with a parallel tuned circuit in the series arm, or one with a series tuned circuit in the shunt arm (as in Fig. 11.11), adjusted to resonate at a frequency just above the cut-off frequency. If there were no resistive loss in the components, this would give infinite attenuation at the resonant frequency. Such a section will have low attenuation at the high frequencies, but it can be combined with a simple low-pass section so that the composite filter has a sufficiently high attenuation throughout the stop band. In such a composite filter each section must have the same iterative impedance at all frequencies, or reflections will occur at the junctions between sections. This can be achieved by the use of '$m$-derived' filters, an example of which is given in Problem 11.3. Half-sections may also be used to make the impedance

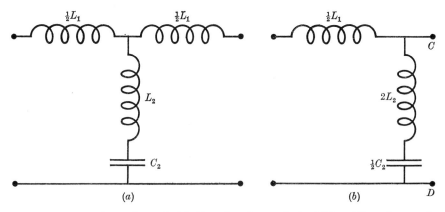

FIG. 11.11. $T$-section and terminal half-section of an $m$-derived filter. The values must obey the equations $L_1 = mL$, $C_2 = mC$, $L_2 = L(1-m^2)/4m$.

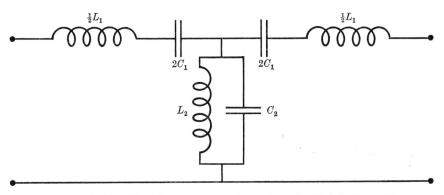

FIG. 11.12. $T$-section of constant $k$ band-pass filter ($L_2/C_1 = L_1/C_2 = k^2$).

more constant in the pass band (see Problem 11.4). The simple low-pass and high-pass filters considered earlier belong to the class of '$k$-derived' or 'constant $k$' filters, since their impedances obey the relation

$$\mathbf{Z_1 Z_2 = k^2},$$

where $k$ is a constant independent of frequency. The band-pass filter considered earlier is not of this type, but the $T$-section shown in Fig. 11.12 does obey this relation provided that $L_2/C_1 = L_1/C_2 = k^2$ (see Problem 11.2).

### 11.3. Travelling waves on transmission lines

In the electrical circuits considered hitherto we have been able to identify the circuit elements as inductances, resistances, capacitances, or combinations thereof, known as 'lumped impedances'. These elements are connected together and to generators and detectors by lengths of wire whose effect is assumed to be negligible. This is true only when the lengths of wire involved are very small compared with the wavelength

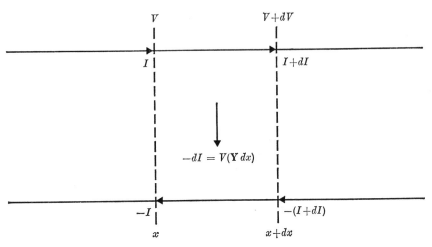

Fig. 11.13. Infinitesimal section of transmission line, showing current and voltage (the lower conductor is assumed to be earthed, so that $V$ is the voltage between the two conductors).

of the radiation flowing along them. When this condition is not fulfilled, the signal changes phase as it flows along the wires, in much the same way as in the pass band of a filter. In fact we may regard the wires as a limiting case of a low-pass filter where the elements are made infinitesimally small, but there are an infinite number of sections per unit length so that the 'distributed impedance' per unit length remains finite. Normally two wires are required to complete the circuit between any two pieces of apparatus, and we shall assume that these take the form either of two parallel wires, or two coaxial cylinders. In an element $dx$ of two such conductors, as shown in Fig. 11.13, the voltage and current will be linearly related to one another, so that the voltage drop in a length $dx$ will be

$$V-(V+dV) = -dV = I(\mathbf{Z}\, dx),$$

where $\mathbf{Z}$ is the series impedance associated with unit length of the two wires. Similarly, the current flowing across between the two wires in the element $dx$ may be written

$$-dI = V(\mathbf{Y}\,dx),$$

where $\mathbf{Y}$ is the shunt admittance between the two conductors per unit length. Since charge is conserved, $(+dI)$ is the change in the current flowing in the wires when we move the distance $dx$. In general $\mathbf{Z}$ and $\mathbf{Y}$ will be complex; both the series resistance and the inductance of the wires contribute to $\mathbf{Z}$, and the leakage conductance and capacitance between the conductors to $\mathbf{Y}$. Thus, if we assign a resistance $R$ and inductance $L$, a conductance $G$ and capacitance $C$, all per unit length, to the two conductors, our basic equations become

$$-(\partial V/\partial x) = IR+L(\partial I/\partial t), \qquad -(\partial I/\partial x) = GV+C(\partial V/\partial t). \quad (11.9)$$

These form a pair of simultaneous differential equations which may be solved by eliminating either $I$ or $V$, when a second-order differential equation similar to equation (10.24) for a one-dimensional wave motion is obtained. We may anticipate this result by assuming that equations (11.9) possess a solution in which both voltage and current vary with $t$ and $x$ exponentially, so that they change as $\exp(j\omega t-hx)$. Then the partial differentials $(\partial/\partial t)$ and $(\partial/\partial x)$ may be replaced by multiplication by $j\omega$ and $-h$ respectively, so that the equations become

$$hV = I(R+j\omega L), \qquad hI = V(G+j\omega C). \quad (11.10)$$

Elimination of $I$ and $V$ between these two equations gives

$$-h^2 = LC\omega^2-j\omega(RC+GL)-RG. \quad (11.11)$$

Since this equation is quadratic in $h$, it always has two solutions of opposite sign. These correspond to waves propagated in opposite directions, just as in the filter there were two solutions, $a$ and $1/a$, corresponding to $\exp(-hx)$ and $\exp(+hx)$ in our present nomenclature.

The general solution of equation (11.11) gives a complex value of $h$, indicating that the wave is propagated with attenuation, as we should expect when there is resistance and conductance present. To obtain a clearer picture of the wave motion we shall first consider the case when both $R$ and $G$ are zero; that is, a loss-free line. This is generally a good approximation for short, non-resonant lines (see § 11.5). Equation (11.11) then reduces to

$$-h^2 = LC\omega^2. \quad (11.12)$$

Hence $h$ is a purely imaginary quantity, which may be written $h = j\beta$. Then $\beta = \omega\sqrt{(LC)}$, and the wave velocity is $\omega/\beta = 1/\sqrt{(LC)}$.

For a pair of coaxial cylinders, radii $a$ and $b$ ($b > a$), we have

$$C = 2\pi\epsilon\epsilon_0/\log_e(b/a) \qquad \text{(Problem 1.8)},$$

$$L = (2\pi)^{-1}\mu\mu_0 \log_e(b/a) \qquad \text{(equation (6.18))},$$

while for a pair of parallel cylinders radius $a$, separation $2d$ ($2d \gg a$)

$$C = \pi\epsilon\epsilon_0/\log_e(2d/a) \qquad \text{(equation (2.51))},$$

$$L = (\pi)^{-1}\mu\mu_0 \log_e(2d/a) \qquad \text{(Problem 6.2)},$$

where the units are farad/metre and henry/metre respectively, and $\epsilon$, $\mu$ refer to the medium between the cylinders. It is readily seen that the product $(LC)$ is independent of the geometry of the cylinders, and the wave velocity is

$$v = (LC)^{-\frac{1}{2}} = (\epsilon\epsilon_0 \mu\mu_0)^{-\frac{1}{2}} = c/(\epsilon\mu)^{\frac{1}{2}}.$$

This is the same as for an electromagnetic wave travelling in the unbounded medium, and it can be shown that this is the case whatever the shape or size of the parallel conductors. The reason for this only becomes apparent if the problem is solved rigorously by starting from Maxwell's equations, when it is found that a purely transverse wave (that is, with the electric and magnetic fields both normal to the direction of propagation) is possible if the conductivity of the cylinders is infinite. This treatment shows also that the assumptions of our method, expressed in equations (11.9), are valid for perfect conductors but not for imperfect ones. The approximation is quite a good one, however, so long as $R \ll \omega L$ and $G \ll \omega C$, conditions that are generally fulfilled in practice (see § 11.5).

Since the wave velocity is independent of frequency on a loss-free line, we need not confine ourselves to sinusoidal waves, and the general solution of equations (11.9) (with $R = G = 0$) is

$$V = F_1(x-vt)+F_2(x+vt), \qquad (11.13)$$

with $v = (LC)^{-\frac{1}{2}}$. $F_1$ and $F_2$ represent waves of arbitrary wave form travelling in opposite directions with velocity $\pm v$. Further application of equations (11.9) shows that the corresponding expression for the current is

$$Z_0 I = F_1(x-vt)-F_2(x+vt), \qquad (11.14)$$

where

$$Z_0 = (L/C)^{\frac{1}{2}}. \qquad (11.15)$$

The derivation of these equations is similar to that of equations (10.18–19), and $Z_0$ is known as the 'characteristic impedance' of the line. It plays a similar role to the intrinsic impedance of a medium for electromagnetic waves, or the iterative impedance of a filter (it is equal to the limiting values of $Z_T$ and $Z_\pi$ for a low-pass filter, if the inductance and capacitance per section are allowed to go to zero keeping their ratio constant). In a wave travelling towards positive values of $x$, the ratio of the voltage to the current is $Z_0$, while for a wave in the opposite direction the ratio is $-Z_0$.

From the values of $L$ and $C$ for our two special types of line, we have:

$$\text{coaxial line:}\quad Z_0 = \frac{1}{2\pi}\left(\frac{\mu\mu_0}{\epsilon\epsilon_0}\right)^{\frac{1}{2}} \log_e(b/a),$$

$$\text{parallel wire line:}\quad Z_0 = \frac{1}{\pi}\left(\frac{\mu\mu_0}{\epsilon\epsilon_0}\right)^{\frac{1}{2}} \log_e(2d/a).$$

Typical values of $Z_0$ are: for an air-spaced coaxial line with $b \approx 3a$, $Z_0 \approx 70$ ohms; for a parallel wire line, $2d/a \approx 20$, and $Z_0 \approx 400$ ohms. In a coaxial cable a continuous dielectric is used to support the inner conductor, and the ratio $b/a$ is adjusted to make $Z_0$ some standard value, usually either 70 or 50 ohms.

An important quantity is the power flowing along the line. If we confine ourselves to a wave travelling along towards positive $x$, the energy flowing past any plane normal to the $x$-axis is, at any instant,

$$W = v(\tfrac{1}{2}LI^2 + \tfrac{1}{2}CV^2) = (\tfrac{1}{2}LI^2 + \tfrac{1}{2}CV^2)/\sqrt{(LC)}$$

$$= \tfrac{1}{2}I^2 Z_0 + \tfrac{1}{2}V^2/Z_0 = I^2 Z_0 = V^2/Z_0 = IV. \qquad (11.16)$$

Here we have given all the equivalent expressions for $W$, and we see that $Z_0$ behaves like a pure resistance, except that $W$ represents the energy flowing along the line per second rather than the energy dissipated as Joule heating of a real resistance. In a sense the energy stored in a section of the line is being dissipated, since it flows away from that section, and the stored energy would therefore diminish unless it were continually replaced by the energy flowing into it from the previous section. $W$ represents the energy crossing a given point in the line at any instant; the average flow of energy is found by using the root mean square values $\tilde{I}$ and $\tilde{V}$ in equation (11.16). The fact that $Z_0$ is real shows that the phase difference between $V$ and $I$ is 0 or $\pi$, according to whether the wave is travelling towards positive or negative $x$. From equation (11.16), $W$ has the same sign as $Z_0$, showing that the energy flows in opposite directions in the two waves, as we should expect. This result follows also from the direction of Poynting's vector (see Problem 11.5), since $V$ and $I$ are linearly related to the electric and magnetic fields $E$ and $H$.

## 11.4. Terminated loss-free lines

Hitherto we have regarded the two waves travelling in opposite directions along a line as two quite independent solutions of the wave equation. Usually, however, there is only one generator attached to the line, producing a wave travelling, say, towards positive $x$. If the line is infinite in this direction, there will be no return wave. If the line is terminated in some way, a reflection may occur at the termination and this

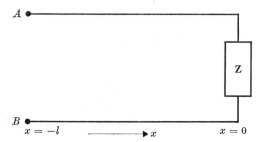

FIG. 11.14. Line terminated by impedance $Z$ at $x = 0$.

will generate a return wave, which will not be independent of the incident wave. If the latter has a given frequency, the return wave must have the same frequency in order that the ratio of current to voltage at the termination (assumed to consist of some constant impedance) shall be independent of the time. If $Z$ is the terminating impedance (as in Fig. 11.14), the fact that $V/I$ must equal $Z$ at this point for all values of the time constitutes the boundary condition, from which one can calculate the magnitude and phase of the reflected wave relative to the incident wave.

If the terminating impedance is not a pure resistance, its value depends on the frequency, and so also will the reflection coefficient. We must therefore assume a wave of a given angular frequency $\omega$. (If the wave is not purely sinusoidal, we must perform a Fourier analysis and treat each harmonic separately.) The equations for current and voltage may then be written as complex exponentials, where, as always, the real or imaginary part must be extracted at the end, according to whether the input voltage is a cosine or sine function. Equations (11.13) and (11.14) become

$$\left. \begin{aligned} V &= A \exp\{j\omega(t-x/v)\} + A' \exp\{j\omega(t+x/v)\} \\ Z_0 I &= A \exp\{j\omega(t-x/v)\} - A' \exp\{j\omega(t+x/v)\} \end{aligned} \right\}. \qquad (11.17)$$

For simplicity we shall take the termination to be at the origin of coordinates $x = 0$, noting that all points on the line will then have negative values of $x$. Inserting the boundary condition, we have

$$(V/Z_0 I)_{x=0} = Z/Z_0 = \frac{Ae^{j\omega t} + A'e^{j\omega t}}{Ae^{j\omega t} - A'e^{j\omega t}} = (A+A')/(A-A').$$

Hence
$$A'/A = (Z-Z_0)/(Z+Z_0), \tag{11.18}$$

which defines the reflection coefficient $A'/A$. If $Z$ is complex, $A'$ will be complex (assuming $A$ real, which can always be made true by choosing the zero of the time scale correctly), showing that there is a phase change in the reflected wave. If $Z$ is a pure resistance, $A'$ is real and there is no phase change (we may exclude a phase change of $\pi$ by allowing negative values of $A'$).

If the line is open-circuited, the voltage at the end is $2A$, since $A' = A$. If $Z$ is finite, the voltage across it is $A+A' = 2AZ/(Z+Z_0)$, showing that the line behaves as a generator of voltage $2A$, with an internal resistance $Z_0$. The power transferred to the load, if $Z$ is a pure resistance $R$, is $W = \bar{V}^2/R = 2A^2R/(R+Z_0)^2$. If $Z = R = Z_0$, the power transferred to the load is a maximum; that is, the load is matched to the generator. Reference to equation (11.18) above shows that under this condition $A' = 0$. Thus maximum power transfer to the load corresponds to no reflected wave; hence the matching condition has a simple physical meaning, since any reflected wave would carry energy away from the load and reduce the power dissipated in it. The power in the incident wave is $\frac{1}{2}A^2/Z_0$, and that in the reflected wave is $\frac{1}{2}A'^2/Z_0$. The difference will be found to equal the power dissipated in the load, as calculated above.

Examination of the formula for $A'/A$, when $Z$ is a pure resistance $R$, shows that as $R$ goes from zero to infinity, $A'/A$ changes continuously from $-1$ to $+1$. When $R < Z_0$, the reflected voltage wave has opposite sign from the incident wave, while the reflected current wave has the same sign. The voltage across $R$ is then less than $A$, and the current through it greater than $A/Z_0$. The reverse is true if $R > Z_0$.

When $Z$ is a pure reactance $jX$, $A'/A$ is complex and its modulus is unity. This is to be expected, since no energy is dissipated in a pure reactance, and the amplitude of the reflected wave must therefore equal that of the incident wave. We may write the reflection coefficient $A'/A$ in this case as $e^{j\delta}$, and an algebraic reduction shows that

$$e^{j\delta} = (X^2 - Z_0^2 + 2jXZ_0)/(X^2 + Z_0^2).$$

Hence $\tan \delta = 2XZ_0/(X^2 - Z_0^2)$, which may be written in the more convenient form $\tan \frac{1}{2}\delta = Z_0/X$.

In the general case, when $\mathbf{Z}$ is complex, the formulae are rather cumbersome, but may be reduced somewhat by writing $\mathbf{Z} = Z_1 e^{j\phi}$, $A' = A_1 e^{j\delta}$. Then, on clearing imaginary terms from the denominator, one finds

$$\frac{A_1}{A} e^{j\delta} = \frac{Z_1^2 - Z_0^2 + 2j Z_1 Z_0 \sin\phi}{Z_1^2 + Z_0^2 + 2 Z_1 Z_0 \cos\phi},$$

giving

$$\left.\frac{A_1}{A} = \sqrt{\left(\frac{Z_1^2 + Z_0^2 - 2 Z_1 Z_0 \cos\phi}{Z_1^2 + Z_0^2 + 2 Z_1 Z_0 \cos\phi}\right)}\right|.$$

and

$$\tan\delta = \frac{2 Z_1 Z_0 \sin\phi}{Z_1^2 - Z_0^2} \qquad \qquad (11.19)$$

The maximum voltage on the line is $(A + A_1)$, and occurs at a voltage antinode where the incident and reflected voltages are in phase; the minimum is $(A - A_1)$ at a node where they are in anti-phase. The ratio $(A + A_1)/(A - A_1)$ is called the voltage standing wave ratio (v.s.w.r.), and measurement of it together with the position of the node (which is related to $\delta$) form the basis of a method of measuring an unknown impedance $\mathbf{Z}$ at short wavelengths (see § 15.3).

### Transmission line terminated by another line of different impedance

A special case of a terminated line is one with impedance $Z_1$ joined on to another line of different characteristic impedance $Z_2$. In this case there will be an incident and a reflected wave on the first line, and a transmitted wave on the second line. Our equations are then:

first line:
$$V_1 = A \exp j\omega(t - x/v_1) + A' \exp j\omega(t + x/v_1),$$
$$Z_1 I_1 = A \exp j\omega(t - x/v_1) - A' \exp j\omega(t + x/v_1);$$

second line:
$$V_2 = A'' \exp j\omega(t - x/v_2),$$
$$Z_2 I_2 = A'' \exp j\omega(t - x/v_2),$$

where $v_1$, $v_2$ are the wave velocities on the first and second lines respectively. If the junction is at $x = 0$, the voltage and current at this point must be the same on the two lines, so that

$$A + A' = A'',$$
$$(A - A')/Z_1 = A''/Z_2,$$

the solutions of which are

$$A'/A = (Z_2 - Z_1)/(Z_2 + Z_1), \qquad A''/A = 2Z_2/(Z_2 + Z_1). \quad (11.20)$$

The former of these is the same as for a line terminated by a resistance $Z_2$, as we should expect. The reflected power is the same as in the case of a real resistance $Z_2$, and the transmitted power the same as would be dissipated in a real resistance. Note that if $Z_2 > Z_1$, the voltage on the second line is greater than that in the incident wave. The power is less, however, since the characteristic impedance is higher.

Equations (11.20) are identical with the formulae for reflection and transmission of a plane electromagnetic wave at normal incidence at the boundary of two media (equations (10.41), (10.42), (10.49), and (10.50)). This shows that there is a close analogy between the characteristic impedance of a transmission line and the intrinsic impedance of a medium transmitting an electromagnetic wave. The similarity appears also in the expressions for the power transmitted: in a plane wave we have (power transmitted across unit area) $= N = E_y^2/Z_0 = Z_0 H_z^2$ (see § 10.3), while for a transmission line $W = V^2/Z_0 = Z_0 I^2$ (equation (11.16)). The analogous behaviour makes it possible to adapt many of the formulae derived below to the case of plane waves.

*Input impedance of terminated lines*

When the reflection coefficient due to the load **Z** used to terminate a line is known, it is a simple matter to calculate the current and voltage, and hence the effective impedance, at any point in the line. This can be done for an arbitrary load **Z**, but we shall limit ourselves to a few of the simpler and more interesting cases.

For a short-circuited line, $\mathbf{Z} = 0$ and $A' = -A$ in equations (11.18), so that at a point $x = -l$ on the line (i.e. at the terminals $A$, $B$ in Fig. 11.14)

$$V = A[\exp\{j\omega(t+l/v)\} - \exp\{j\omega(t-l/v)\}]$$
$$= j2A \exp j\omega t \sin \omega l/v$$
$$= j2A \exp j\omega t \sin 2\pi l/\lambda$$

and
$$Z_0 I = 2A \exp j\omega t \cos 2\pi l/\lambda.$$

The impedance at this point is then

$$V/I = jZ_0 \tan 2\pi l/\lambda. \tag{11.21}$$

This formula shows that a section of short-circuited line behaves as a pure reactance. If $l$ is less than a quarter of a wavelength, then $\tan 2\pi l/\lambda$ is positive and the line behaves like an inductance. If $l$ lies between a quarter- and a half-wavelength, the tangent is negative and the line behaves like a capacitance. These statements hold also if we increase $l$ by an integral number of half-wavelengths.

If the line is open-circuited, $A' = +A$, and the equations for $V$ and $Z_0 I$ are just interchanged. The impedance at $x = -l$ is therefore

$$V/I = -jZ_0 \cot 2\pi l/\lambda. \tag{11.22}$$

An open-circuited line, less than a quarter-wavelength long, therefore behaves like a capacitance; if its length lies between a quarter- and a half-wavelength, it behaves like an inductance. If its length is exactly a quarter-wavelength its impedance is zero. Thus if we have an open-circuited line we can cut off a quarter-wavelength and replace it by a short circuit without affecting the conditions earlier on the line. For we then have a short-circuited line of length $(l-\frac{1}{4}\lambda)$, so the impedance at the input terminals becomes $+jZ_0 \tan(2\pi l/\lambda-\frac{1}{2}\pi) = -jZ_0 \cot(2\pi l/\lambda)$, in agreement with the value found directly from equation (11.22).

These results show that a lumped reactance $X$ at the end of a line can be replaced by a suitable additional length of line, either open- or short-circuited. We found earlier that the wave reflected by a reactance has the same amplitude as the incident wave, but a phase change $\delta$, where $\tan \frac{1}{2}\delta = Z_0/X$. If the reactance is replaced by an open- or short-circuited length of line, then the wave reflected from the far end will have the same amplitude as the incident wave, but the phase change arises from the time taken by the wave to travel the extra distance to the end of the line and back. At metre wavelengths, suitable lengths of either coaxial or parallel wire lines are commonly used as inductances because they have a lower resistance than a coil of wire of the same 'nominal' r.f. resistance. By 'nominal' r.f. resistance is meant the value which would be calculated from the skin depth for a straight wire. In a closely wound coil there is an additional energy loss because of eddy currents induced by the oscillatory currents in neighbouring turns; this is known as the 'proximity effect', and increases the effective r.f. resistance. Its effect is minimized by using straight wires, as in a section of a transmission line.

### The transmission line as a transformer

Since the voltage and current are in different ratio at the input terminals of a line from the ratio they bear at the output terminals, it follows that a line can be used as an impedance transformer. The case of greatest interest is that of a line one-quarter wavelength long. If the terminating impedance $\mathbf{Z}$ is at $x = 0$, then at the point $x = -\frac{1}{4}\lambda$, the voltage and current are

$$V = A \exp j(\omega t+\tfrac{1}{2}\pi)+A' \exp j(\omega t-\tfrac{1}{2}\pi) = j(A-A')\exp j\omega t,$$

$$Z_0 I = j(A+A')\exp j\omega t,$$

and $$V/I = Z_0(A-A')/(A+A') = Z_0^2/\mathbf{Z}, \qquad (11.23)$$

showing that the terminating impedance has been transformed to $Z_0^2/\mathbf{Z}$.

In this respect a quarter-wave line behaves like a tuned circuit, which transforms a series resistance $R$ into a parallel resistance $L/CR$. Since $Z_0^2 = L/C$, the formulae are similar in the two cases.

The quarter-wave transformer may be used to match a load $Z$ to a transmission line of impedance $Z_0$ by inserting immediately before the load a $\frac{1}{4}\lambda$ section of line whose impedance $Z_1$ is such that $Z_1^2/Z = Z_0$. If $Z$ and $Z_1$ are lines of the same dimensions but in different dielectric media, the situation is exactly analogous to the 'blooming' of optical lenses. The fraction of the incident intensity reflected from an air-glass surface is about 4 per cent, and the loss of light in an optical system with ten or twenty surfaces is serious. The reflection may be reduced by depositing on the surface a quarter-wave thick layer of material of low refractive index, ideally equal to the square root of the refractive index of the glass. The thickness is adjusted to be correct for the middle of the optical region, and is thus not quite correct for the ends of this region. 'Bloomed' surfaces appear slightly purple, therefore, owing to reflection of the red and blue rays. Quarter-wave films have also been used to produce highly reflecting layers. If the film is of characteristic impedance $Z_1$, and the initial and final media are the same (impedance $Z_0$), the film acts as a medium of impedance $Z_1^2/Z_0$, or refractive index $n^2$, where $n$ is the actual index of the film, assumed to be in air. A film of glass ($n = 1\cdot5$) will then reflect 38 per cent of the incident intensity. Further details of these optical applications are given by Kuhn (1951).

The half-wave transformer is also of interest. It may be regarded as two consecutive quarter-wave transformers, giving an impedance

$$Z_0^2/(Z_0^2/\mathbf{Z}) = \mathbf{Z}.$$

Alternatively, this result may be obtained directly, since if we move one half-wave along a line, all voltages and currents are the same except for their reversed sign. The half-wave line is therefore a 1:1 transformer  A typical use is that of a connecting link between two pieces of apparatus, which makes the impedance of either appear unchanged. This is often useful at very short wavelengths where connecting wires sufficiently short to give no impedance transformation are not practicable.

## 11.5. Attenuation on lossy lines, and resonant lines

When there is loss present on a transmission line ($R$, $G$ not zero), the velocity of a wave is altered, and it is attenuated. Writing $h$ as $\alpha + j\beta$, equation (11.11) can be separated into real and imaginary parts, giving

$$\alpha^2 - \beta^2 = RG - LC\omega^2, \qquad 2\alpha\beta = (GL + RC)\omega.$$

These equations may be solved exactly for $\alpha$ and $\beta$, but it is more instructive to solve them approximately, assuming $R$, $G$ to be small. Then

$$\beta = \omega\sqrt{(LC)}\left\{1 + \frac{1}{8\omega^2}\left(\frac{G}{C} - \frac{R}{L}\right)^2\right\}, \qquad \alpha = \frac{1}{2}\left\{R\sqrt{\frac{C}{L}} + G\sqrt{\frac{L}{C}}\right\}. \qquad (11.24)$$

The velocity is approximately

$$\omega/\beta = \frac{1}{\sqrt{(LC)}}\left\{1 - \frac{1}{8\omega^2}\left(\frac{G}{C} - \frac{R}{L}\right)^2\right\}, \qquad (11.25)$$

showing that it is altered only in the second order. The power flowing along the line decays as it travels along as (using $Z_0 = \sqrt{(L/C)}$)

$$\exp(-2\alpha x) = \exp\{-(R/Z_0 + GZ_0)x\}.$$

The two terms in the exponential represent just the fraction of the stored energy which is dissipated per unit length in the resistance and conductance respectively. We see that if $R/Z_0$ and $GZ_0$ are both small, the line is distortionless in the first approximation, since neither the velocity of the wave nor its attenuation depend on the frequency to this order. In the next approximation, distortion arises from the change in velocity with frequency and this is most serious at low frequencies. At high frequencies (owing to skin effect) the resistance rises, increasing $\alpha$. If $G$ is negligible, distortion may be reduced by increasing $L$. On telephone land lines this is accomplished by introducing inductances in series with the line at regular intervals. This also reduces the attenuation, since it increases $Z_0$, but gives the line a periodic structure so that it behaves like a low-pass filter. The cut-off frequency must be kept above the audio-frequency range, and to do this the spacing of the inductances must be small compared with the shortest wavelength which it is required to transmit. The distortion can also be greatly reduced by transmitting a voice-modulated signal of, say, 100 000 c/s frequency, instead of the actual voice frequency range of 100 to 10 000 c/s. Although the band-width required is the same, the fractional change in frequency involved is very much smaller.

In the laboratory, the lengths of line used are so short that attenuation is negligible except at the highest frequencies, where $R$ rises owing to the skin effect. To obtain a numerical value, let us take an air-spaced coaxial line at a frequency of $3 \times 10^9$ c/s ($\lambda = 10$ cm). Then for copper the skin depth $\delta$ is about $1 \cdot 2 \times 10^{-4}$ cm. If the conductor dimensions are $a = 2 \cdot 5$ mm, $b = 8$ mm (giving a 70-ohm line),

$$R = \rho\left(\frac{1}{2\pi a\delta} + \frac{1}{2\pi b\delta}\right) = 1 \cdot 2 \text{ ohm/metre.}$$

Then $\alpha = 8 \times 10^{-3}$ per metre, and the power transmitted along the line will fall by a factor of $1/e$ in a distance of 60 metres.

If the space between the conductors is filled with a dielectric, the attenuation due to dielectric loss will be important unless the dielectric is of the highest quality. If its loss tangent is $\tan \delta$, then $G = \omega C \tan \delta$, and

$$2\alpha = GZ_0 = \omega (LC)^{\frac{1}{2}} \tan \delta = (\omega/v)\tan \delta = (2\pi/\lambda_1)\tan \delta,$$

where $\lambda_1$ is the wavelength in the dielectric. If its dielectric constant is 2·2, and $\tan \delta = 2 \times 10^{-4}$, $\alpha = 9 \times 10^{-3}$ per metre at $\lambda = 10$ cm, which is as large as that due to the resistance. For this reason high-frequency cables are often made with some device such as an open spiral of poly-thene string supporting the centre conductor in order to reduce the amount of dielectric in the position of maximum electric field.

In calculating the loss on the line we have taken no account of energy lost by radiation, though we might expect each element of the conductors to radiate since it carries an alternating current. A transmission line has two conductors carrying equal and opposite currents, however, and in computing the radiation we must allow for the destructive inter-ference between their two radiation patterns. For a parallel wire line this does not give an exact null, but the maximum phase difference between the signals from the two wires in any direction will differ from $\pi$ at most by $2\pi(2d)/\lambda$, where $2d$ is the separation between the two con-ductors. Hence the radiated energy is less than that from a single wire by a factor of the order $(d/\lambda)^2$, and is small if $d \ll \lambda$. The coaxial line gives an exact null because the one current entirely encloses the other, and the magnetic field at any external point is zero. For this reason coaxial lines are to be preferred at wavelengths less than about a metre.

*Transmission lines as tuned circuits*

If we have a quarter-wave section of loss-free line, short-circuited at one end, then the impedance measured at the other end is infinite. Similarly, if it is open-circuited at one end, then the input impedance at the other end is zero. We have already seen that if a resistance $R$ is connected across one end, the impedance at the other end is

$$Z_0^2/R = L/CR.$$

Thus in all respects the section behaves like a tuned circuit. If $R$ is zero or infinity, the input impedance will only be infinity or zero so long as the line is completely loss-free. This, of course, will never occur in practice, and to assess the properties of the section as a tuned circuit we must include the effect of distributed losses. We can do this by bringing in the attenuation constant $\alpha$.

We will assume that the section is open-circuited at the far end, so that $A' = A$. Then the voltage and current at a point $x = -l$ are (since $A$ is the incident voltage amplitude at $x = 0$)

$$V = A\left[\exp\left\{j\left(\omega t + \frac{2\pi l}{\lambda}\right) + \alpha l\right\} + \exp\left\{j\left(\omega t - \frac{2\pi l}{\lambda}\right) - \alpha l\right\}\right],$$

$$Z_0 I = A\left[\exp\left\{j\left(\omega t + \frac{2\pi l}{\lambda}\right) + \alpha l\right\} - \exp\left\{j\left(\omega t - \frac{2\pi l}{\lambda}\right) - \alpha l\right\}\right].$$

The impedance $\mathbf{Z}$ at this point is then given by

$$\frac{\mathbf{Z}}{Z_0} = \frac{1 + \exp\{-j\,4\pi l/\lambda - 2\alpha l\}}{1 - \exp\{-j\,4\pi l/\lambda - 2\alpha l\}}. \tag{11.26}$$

We now assume that the length of the line $l$ is close to an odd multiple of a quarter-wavelength, and examine how the impedance changes in the neighbourhood of this point. In the complex exponentials of equation (11.26) the imaginary part of the argument gives a rapid variation and the real part (which is assumed to be small) a slow variation. We therefore treat them separately, and write $l = \{(2n+1)\lambda/4\} + \Delta l$ in the imaginary part only. Then the exponential becomes

$$\exp\{-j(2n+1)\pi - j\,4\pi\Delta l/\lambda - 2\alpha l\} = -\exp(-j\,4\pi\Delta l/\lambda - 2\alpha l)$$

$$\approx -(1 - j\,4\pi\Delta l/\lambda - 2\alpha l),$$

where we have assumed that both $\Delta l/\lambda$ and $\alpha l$ are small. Thus the impedance becomes

$$\mathbf{Z} = Z_0\frac{1 - (1 - j\,4\pi\Delta l/\lambda - 2\alpha l)}{1 + (1 - j\,4\pi\Delta l/\lambda - 2\alpha l)} \approx Z_0(\alpha l + j\,2\pi\Delta l/\lambda) = Z_0\,\alpha l\left(1 + j\frac{2\pi}{\alpha\lambda}\frac{\Delta l}{l}\right), \tag{11.27}$$

where only small quantities of the first order have been retained. This equation is of the same form as equation (9.20) for a series tuned circuit near resonance, which is

$$\mathbf{Z} = r(1 + j\,2Q\Delta\omega/\omega_0)$$

since $\Delta l/l = -\Delta\lambda/\lambda = \Delta\omega/\omega_0$ (here the minus sign is introduced in relating $\Delta l/l$ to $\Delta\lambda/\lambda$ because increasing the length of the line has the same effect as shortening the wavelength of the applied radiation). Hence at resonance the quarter-wavelength line (or a line an odd multiple of this length) behaves as a series tuned circuit with a resistance $Z_0\,\alpha l$ and a quality factor $Q = \pi/\alpha\lambda$.

In making measurements at short wavelengths it is always advisable to keep the generator frequency constant, if possible, and vary the element under test, since this avoids errors due to detectors, connecting lines, etc., being frequency sensitive. Equation (11.27) shows that we may conveniently measure $Q$ by finding the fractional change in length of the line ($\Delta l/l$) required to move between the points at which the impedance rises to $\sqrt{2}$ of its minimum value.

To find a numerical value for $Q$ we take the value $\alpha = 8 \times 10^{-3}$ per metre found earlier for an air-spaced coaxial line at 10 cm wavelength. This gives $Q = 4000$, which is very much higher than can be obtained normally with a lumped circuit at medium radio-frequencies. $Q$ is independent of the number of quarter-wavelengths in the section, but the series resistance $r = Z_0 \alpha l = 1 \cdot 4 \times 10^{-2}(2n+1)$ ohms. Thus $r$ increases when we make $n$ larger, but $Q$ does not change. This is because $Q$ depends on the ratio of the stored energy to the energy dissipated, and both of these increase as the length of the line increases.

The impedance of a short-circuited quarter-wave line can readily be calculated from the above, since in this case $A' = -A$, and the formulae are the same, if we interchange $V$ and $Z_0 I$. This gives

$$\frac{Z_0 I}{V} = Z_0 Y = \alpha l \left(1 + j\frac{2\pi}{\alpha\lambda}\frac{\Delta l}{l}\right), \tag{11.28}$$

showing that at resonance the impedance is $Z_0/\alpha l = Z_0^2/r = L/Cr$, the same expression as for a parallel tuned circuit. For a single quarter-wavelength of the coaxial line considered previously, the parallel impedance is 350 000 ohms, showing that the line makes a good anode load for an oscillator or amplifier. In practice the line would be rather shorter than a quarter-wavelength, when it behaves as an inductance which can be adjusted to resonate with the anode capacitance of the vacuum tube (see Chapter 14).

## 11.6. Guided waves—propagation between two parallel conducting planes

When an electromagnetic wave is launched from an aerial into free space (or a non-conducting medium) its amplitude falls off inversely with the distance owing to the spreading out of the wave in a spherical wave front. There is no dissipation of energy, but the power flowing through unit area normal to the wave front falls off according to the inverse square law. On the other hand, a wave sent along a coaxial line suffers no diminution in amplitude, apart from that due to resistive losses, because it is confined to the space between the conductors and does not spread out. Such a wave is a guided wave, and a more rigorous approach than that adopted in the preceding sections would be to solve Maxwell's equations with the boundary conditions that the tangential components of the electric field must be zero at the conductors (assuming these to be perfect conductors). Such an approach would

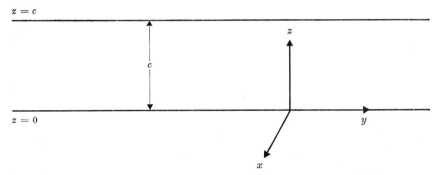

$z = c$

$z = 0$

FIG. 11.15. Coordinate system for propagation between two parallel planes.

have shown that with two parallel conductors a solution can be found giving a purely transverse wave (no components of $E$ or $H$ in the direction of propagation) which is freely propagated at all frequencies with the same velocity as a wave in the unbounded medium. With a single hollow conductor this is no longer the case, though the fact that it is possible to see down a metal tube shows that some form of electromagnetic wave can be propagated through it. Such a wave is again a guided wave, since it must move in the direction of the tube. As a preliminary to studying propagation through such a tube (known as a 'waveguide'), we shall investigate the problem of propagation between two parallel infinite perfectly conducting planes, separated by a distance $c$, as shown in Fig. 11.15.

A Cartesian coordinate system may be defined by taking the conductors to be the planes $z = 0$ and $z = c$, and assuming that the wave is propagated parallel to the $x$-axis, which is normal to the plane of the paper. The boundary conditions now demand that any components of the electric field ($E_x$ or $E_y$) tangential to the planes must vanish at the planes $z = 0$ and $z = c$. We try to find the simplest possible solution of Maxwell's equations consistent with these demands, and begin by assuming a purely transverse plane wave in which both $E_x$ and $H_x$ are zero, such as we would have in the absence of the conductors. If this wave is polarized with its electric vector normal to the planes (i.e.

$E_y = 0$) it is readily seen that the boundary conditions are satisfied automatically, and a wave of this polarization is possible. The solutions are of the same form as for a wave in the unbounded medium, and the velocity is also the same. On the other hand, a plane wave in which the field components do not vary with $z$ is obviously impossible if the electric vector is parallel to the planes, since $E_y$ must be zero at $z = 0$ and $z = c$ and will be zero everywhere unless we allow it to vary with $z$. We must therefore examine whether it is possible to have a wave in which $E_y$ is finite, but $E_z$ and $E_x$ are both zero, so that the electric field is purely transverse. The field components of **H** can then be computed from Maxwell's equations. We shall assume that the wave is propagated as $\exp(j\omega t - hx)$, so that we can replace differentiation with respect to $t$ and $x$ by multiplication by $j\omega$ and $-h$ respectively. Then, if the medium between the planes has dielectric constant $\epsilon$, magnetic permeability $\mu$, and zero conductivity, the curl equations (10.3) and (10.7) give the following components:

$$\left.\begin{aligned} -j\omega\mu\mu_0 H_x &= -\partial E_y/\partial z \\ -j\omega\mu\mu_0 H_y &= 0 \\ -j\omega\mu\mu_0 H_z &= -hE_y \end{aligned}\right\}, \tag{11.29}$$

$$\left.\begin{aligned} 0 &= \partial H_z/\partial y - \partial H_y/\partial z \\ j\omega\epsilon\epsilon_0 E_y &= \partial H_x/\partial z + hH_z \\ 0 &= -hH_y - \partial H_x/\partial y \end{aligned}\right\}, \tag{11.30}$$

where we have already assumed $E_x = E_z = 0$. Equations (11.29) show immediately that $H_y = 0$, but $H_x$ cannot be zero unless $\partial E_y/\partial z$ is zero, and this is not allowed by the boundary conditions. Hence the wave will not be purely transverse, but will have a component of **H** in the direction of propagation. On putting $H_y = 0$ in equations (11.30), we see that $\partial H_z/\partial y$ and $\partial H_x/\partial y$ are both zero, so that there is no variation in the $y$-direction, and examination of the components of $\text{div } \mathbf{E} = 0$ shows this to be true also of $E_y$. The remaining components of equations (11.29) and (11.30) therefore reduce to

$$\left.\begin{aligned} j\omega\mu\mu_0 H_x &= \partial E_y/\partial z \\ j\omega\mu\mu_0 H_z &= hE_y \\ j\omega\epsilon\epsilon_0 E_y &= \partial H_x/\partial z + hH_z \end{aligned}\right\}. \tag{11.31}$$

Elimination of $H_x$ and $H_z$ between these three equations gives

$$-\omega^2\mu\mu_0\,\epsilon\epsilon_0\,E_y = \partial^2 E_y/\partial z^2 + h^2 E_y$$

or

$$\partial^2 E_y/\partial z^2 = -(h^2 + \omega^2/v^2)E_y, \tag{11.32}$$

where $v = (\mu\mu_0\,\epsilon\epsilon_0)^{-\frac{1}{2}}$ is the velocity of an electromagnetic wave in the unbounded medium (in the absence of the conducting planes we could put $\partial/\partial z = 0$ and obtain this result directly from equation (11.32), since $h$ must then be an imaginary quantity $j\beta$, and $v = \omega/\beta$). The solution of equation (11.32) can be written in the form

$$E_y = A \sin(\pi n z/c) + B \cos(\pi n z/c)$$

and the boundary conditions $E_y = 0$ at $z = 0$ and $z = c$ require that $B = 0$ and $n$ must be an integer. To satisfy equation (11.32) we must have

$$(n\pi/c)^2 = h^2 + \omega^2/v^2$$

and hence

$$h = \left\{ \left( \frac{n\pi}{c} \right)^2 - \left( \frac{\omega}{v} \right)^2 \right\}^{\frac{1}{2}}. \tag{11.33}$$

Hence $h$ is either real or purely imaginary according to whether the quantity inside the square root is positive or negative. It is clear that at low frequencies $h$ will be real, and the wave will then be attenuated. At sufficiently high frequencies $h$ will be imaginary, and waves will be freely transmitted without attenuation; thus the system acts as a high-pass filter. The condition for free transmission of waves is that

$$\omega/v > n\pi/c.$$

Since $\omega/v = 2\pi/\lambda_0$, where $\lambda_0$ is the wavelength of the radiation in the unbounded medium, this condition may be written in the form

$$\lambda_0 < 2c/n.$$

Hence $2c/n$ is the cut-off wavelength $\lambda_c$, and only radiation of shorter wavelength is freely transmitted. In the pass band we may write $h = j\beta = j(2\pi/\lambda_g)$, where $\lambda_g$ is the apparent wavelength of the radiation in the guide; that is, it is the distance between points along the $x$-axis where the phase differs by $2\pi$. Equation (11.33) then reduces to

$$\frac{f^2}{v^2} = \frac{1}{\lambda_0^2} = \frac{1}{\lambda_g^2} + \frac{1}{\lambda_c^2}. \tag{11.34}$$

This is known as the 'waveguide equation', and it is found to hold for any shape of waveguide, although it has here been deduced only for a simple special case. The cut-off wavelength $\lambda_c$ depends on the shape and dimensions of the waveguide, and on the mode of propagation (i.e. in the present case, on the values of $c$ and $n$ respectively).

Equation (11.34) shows that the wavelength in the guide is always greater than that in the unbounded medium $\lambda_0$. When $\lambda_0 \ll \lambda_c$, $\lambda_g$ approaches $\lambda_0$, while when $\lambda_0 \rightarrow \lambda_c$, $\lambda_g$ tends to infinity. The phase velocity in the guide behaves in the same way as $\lambda_g$, since

$$v_g = \omega/\beta = f\lambda_g, \tag{11.35}$$

showing that $v_g$ is always greater than the velocity in the unbounded medium. If the guide contains no material medium, the phase velocity will be greater than the velocity of light $(f\lambda_0)$ in free space, since $\lambda_g > \lambda_0$. This does not mean that energy is transmitted with a velocity greater than that of light, since we have dispersion: the phase velocity depends

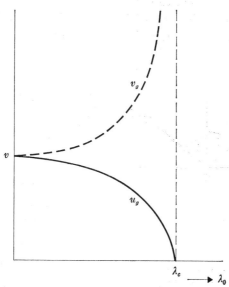

FIG. 11.16. Variation of the phase velocity $v_g$ (broken line) and group velocity $u_g$ (full line) in a waveguide.

on the frequency, and does not equal the group velocity $u_g = d\omega/d\beta$. From equation (11.33)

$$-h^2 = \beta^2 = \left(\frac{\omega}{v}\right)^2 - \left(\frac{n\pi}{c}\right)^2,$$

and hence
$$2\beta(d\beta/d\omega) = 2\omega/v^2,$$

giving
$$(\omega/\beta)(d\omega/d\beta) = v_g u_g = v^2. \tag{11.36}$$

Since $v_g$ is always greater than $v$, it follows that $u_g$ is always less than $v$, and is thus always less than the velocity of light. The behaviour of $u_g$ and $v_g$ is illustrated in Fig. 11.16; these relations hold for all waveguides, since they depend only on the waveguide equation (11.34).

The propagation of waves between two parallel conducting planes may be considered in another way which is illuminating, particularly in respect of the group and phase velocity. The wave motion may be regarded as consisting of an ordinary plane wave, with the same properties as a wave in the unbounded medium, which is multiply reflected

from the two planes. The normal to the wave front is assumed to make
an angle $\theta$ with the normal to the conducting planes, as in Fig. 11.17.
From Figs. 10.4, 10.5, if we replace $\theta$ by $\pi-\theta$, the components of such
incident and reflected waves are given by equations (10.36) and (10.37),
if the electric vector is in the plane of incidence, or equations (10.46)
and (10.47) if it is normal to the plane of incidence. In either case we
must satisfy the boundary conditions, that the tangential components
of $\mathbf{E}$ must be zero all over the planes $z = 0$ and $z = c$. For the former

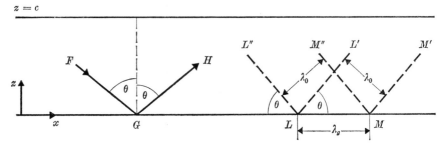

Fig. 11.17. Reflection of ordinary plane waves between two parallel planes. $FG$, $GH$ normals to wave fronts incident and reflected at plane $z = 0$. $LL'$, $MM'$ incident wave fronts; $LL''$, $MM''$ reflected wave fronts, differing in phase by $2\pi$. $LM$ gives the guide wavelength $\lambda_g$.

case (electric vector in plane of incidence) the first of these conditions
gives $A' = -A$ in order to make the $x$-component of $\mathbf{E}$ zero at $z = 0$;
the same condition is obtained at $z = c$ if we take $\cos\theta = 0$ ($\theta = \frac{1}{2}\pi$).
This makes the $x$-component of $\mathbf{E}$ zero everywhere, but $E_z$ and $H_y$ are
finite, so that we have a simple plane wave moving in the $x$-direction;
this wave is purely transverse, and moves with the same velocity as in
the unbounded medium.

When the electric vector is normal to the plane of incidence, to make
the $y$-component of $\mathbf{E}$ zero at $z = 0$, we must take $B' = -B$ in equations (10.46) and (10.47). At other points the amplitude of the $y$-com-
ponent of $\mathbf{E}$ is then (replacing $\theta$ by $\pi-\theta$)

$$E_y = B(F_1 - F_2)$$
$$= B\exp\{j\omega(t - x\sin\theta/v)\}\{\exp(j\omega z\cos\theta/v) - \exp(-j\omega z\cos\theta/v)\}$$
$$= 2jB\sin(\omega z\cos\theta/v)\exp\{j\omega(t - x\sin\theta/v)\}, \qquad (11.37)$$

where we have written $v$ for the velocity in the unbounded medium. At
the plane $z = c$ the field component given by equation (11.37) is zero
provided that
$$\omega c\cos\theta/v = 2\pi c\cos\theta/\lambda_0 = n\pi$$
or
$$\cos\theta = \lambda_0(n/2c) = \lambda_0/\lambda_c, \qquad (11.38)$$

where $\lambda_c$ is the cut-off wavelength as previously defined, and $\lambda_0$ is the wavelength in the unbounded medium. This equation shows clearly that no wave is possible for $\lambda_0 > \lambda_c$, for then there is no real value of $\theta$ which satisfies it.

The wavelength $\lambda_0$ is defined as the normal distance between two wave fronts such as $LL'$ and $MM'$ in the plane waves where the phase differs by $2\pi$; these wave fronts have an intercept $LM$ on the plane $z = 0$, and the length of this intercept, which gives the apparent wavelength $\lambda_g$ of a wave propagated in the $x$-direction, is $\lambda_0/\sin\theta$. Hence

$$\sin\theta = \lambda_0/\lambda_g, \tag{11.39}$$

and on combining this with equation (11.38) we have

$$1/\lambda_0^2 = (\sin^2\theta + \cos^2\theta)/\lambda_0^2 = 1/\lambda_g^2 + 1/\lambda_c^2,$$

which is the 'waveguide equation' already derived (equation (11.34)). We see that it follows from the fact that only one angle $\theta$ is possible for the direction of our multiply reflected plane wave in order to satisfy both the boundary conditions. The energy flow travels with velocity $v$ in the plane wave in a direction normal to the plane wave front (that is, along $FG$ or $GH$); the component of this velocity in the $x$-direction is $v\sin\theta$, and this is the speed $u_g$ at which the energy flows in the guided wave. On the other hand, the phase velocity $v_g$ of the guided wave, from equation (11.37), is $v/\sin\theta$; hence $u_g v_g = v^2$, as shown earlier (equation (11.36)). (It should be noted that the possibility of $v_g$ being greater than $v$ is not peculiar to electromagnetic waves; the effect can be observed by watching the movement parallel to a reflecting boundary of a crest in any wave motion, as, for example, in water waves being reflected at an angle from a breakwater.) The behaviour of our guided wave when $\lambda_0$ is equal to the cut-off wavelength $\lambda_c$ can be understood if we remember that this requires $\theta = 0$; that is, the wave motion is an ordinary plane wave being reflected at normal incidence between the two planes. Then no energy is propagated in the $x$-direction, so that $u_g = 0$; but the phase at a given value of $z$ is independent of $x$, so that the apparent phase velocity $v_g$ in the $x$-direction is infinite.

## 11.7. Waveguides

The type of wave we have been considering, propagated between two parallel planes, has the following components:

$$\left.\begin{array}{l} E_y = A\sin(2\pi z/\lambda_c)\sin(\omega t - 2\pi x/\lambda_g) \\ H_x = -A(\lambda_0/Z_1\lambda_c)\cos(2\pi z/\lambda_c)\cos(\omega t - 2\pi x/\lambda_g) \\ H_z = A(\lambda_0/Z_1\lambda_g)\sin(2\pi z/\lambda_c)\sin(\omega t - 2\pi x/\lambda_g) \end{array}\right\}. \tag{11.40}$$

These components may either be obtained from equations (10.46) and (10.47) (e.g. $E_y$ is found by taking the real part of equation (11.37) and writing $2B = -A$), or by taking $E_y$ as the appropriate solution of equation (11.32) and using equations (11.31); $Z_1$ is the intrinsic impedance of the medium between the conducting planes. These equations show that for a given value of $\lambda_c$, the component $H_x$ in the direction of propagation diminishes in amplitude as $\lambda_0$ is decreased, so that the wave

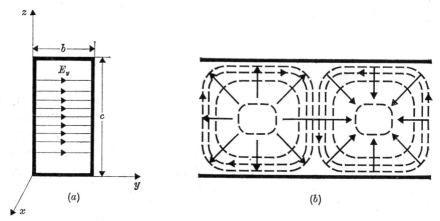

FIG. 11.18. Rectangular waveguide with $TE_{01}$ mode.
(a) Lines of electric field ———.
(b) Lines of magnetic field – – – – and current flow ——→.

approaches a purely transverse wave travelling along the $x$-axis. As $\lambda_0 \to \lambda_c$, $H_z \to 0$ since $\lambda_0/\lambda_g \to 0$, giving in the limit a transverse wave travelling along the $z$-axis.

Since the only electric field component is in the $y$-direction, it is possible to insert conducting planes normal to the $y$-axis without introducing any new boundary conditions. We have then a closed rectangular waveguide, as shown in Fig. 11.18 (a), bounded by the perfectly conducting planes $z = 0$, $z = c$; $y = 0$, $y = b$. The field components within the guide are given by equations (11.40), and are zero outside. This type of wave is designated $TE_{0n}$ (or $H_{0n}$); $TE$ means 'transverse electric', indicating that there is no electric field component in the direction of propagation; the subscripts 0, $n$ mean that there is no variation in the $y$-direction of any field component, while in the $z$-direction they vary as sin or cos $(\pi n z/c)$. The simplest wave ($n = 1$) is shown in Fig. 11.18, and this is also the mode with the largest cut-off wavelength $\lambda_c = 2c$. It is therefore used as the standard mode for waveguide propagation, and the guide dimensions are chosen so that $2c > \lambda_0 > c$ for the wavelength it is desired to propagate. No higher mode (with $n = 2$ or more) can then be propagated; this has the advantage that waves of higher modes, set up by a local disturbance of the field (due to discontinuities or changes in the guide dimensions), decay exponentially along the guide. By making the dimension $b$ less than $\lambda_0/2$, no $TE$ mode can be propagated with the electric vector polarized in the $z$-direction; and it can be shown that all other modes have still smaller cut-off wavelengths, and so cannot be propagated.

The field components in the $TE_{01}$ mode are shown in Fig. 11.18. $E_y$ is a maximum in the centre of the guide, and zero at the planes $z = 0$ and $z = c$; it varies sinusoidally with $z$, with just one half-period of variation (modes with higher values of $n$ make $n$ half-periods of variation, and so require a correspondingly larger value of $c$ for a given $\lambda_0$). The components of the magnetic field are everywhere tangential to the boundaries, and the lines of magnetic field are shown in Fig. 11.18 (b), where the guide is viewed looking down on the broad face. The lines of magnetic field encircle the points at which $\partial E_y/\partial t$ is greatest; that is, the points where the displacement current is greatest. This corresponds to Maxwell's equation $\mathrm{curl\,H} = \partial\mathbf{D}/\partial t$, which implies that a displacement current (a changing electric displacement) is encircled by lines of magnetic field. The lines of displacement current flow are completed by conduction current flowing in the conducting walls; such current flow is always normal to the magnetic field at the surface of the wall. The direction of conduction current flow is also shown in Fig. 11.18 (b). The lines of current flow (displacement plus conduction) encircle the regions of changing magnetic flux, corresponding thus to $\mathrm{curl\,E} = -\partial\mathbf{B}/\partial t$.

We may form a physical picture of the propagation of the wave in this way, since an oscillating electric field sets up and is encircled by an oscillating magnetic field, which in turn sets up and is encircled by an oscillating electric field; this has a component further on, a half-wavelength from the original disturbance. The lines of $E$ and $\partial B/\partial t$ are in perpendicular planes (similarly $H$ and $\partial D/\partial t$), and may be crudely represented by the links of a chain. In an ordinary plane wave in free space the lines of force go to infinity, and may be considered to join up there.

Study of the propagation characteristics of waves in guides of other than rectangular shape involves the use of more complex mathematics, and we mention only the cylindrical waveguide. This involves the solution of the wave equation or Maxwell's equations in cylindrical coordinates, and requires the use of Bessel functions. Waves may be designated as $TM_{mn}$ or $TE_{mn}$, according as there is no magnetic or no

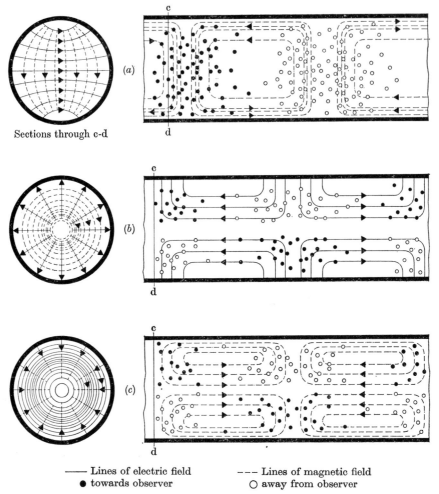

Sections through c-d

—— Lines of electric field     --- Lines of magnetic field
    ● towards observer         ○ away from observer

Fig. 11.19. Approximate configurations of electric and magnetic fields in a cylindrical
waveguide. Propagation is directed away from the observer or to the right.

(a) $TE_{11}$ or $H_{11}$ mode; (b) $TM_{01}$ or $E_{01}$ mode; (c) $TE_{01}$ or $H_{01}$ mode (after Southworth,
1936, Bell System Technical Journal, **15**, 287 (by courtesy of Bell Telephone Laboratories);
or see Proc. I.R.E. 1937, p. 237).

electric field in the direction of propagation; the first subscript indicates
that the field components vary as cos or sin $m\phi$, where $\phi$ is the azimuthal
angle, while the second gives the number of values of the radius at which
the electric field components other than the radial component $E_r$ are
zero. The simplest modes are $TE_{11}$, which is rather similar to the $TE_{01}$
mode in rectangular guide; the electric field is purely transverse, and
distributed as shown in Fig. 11.19 (a); the cut-off wavelength is $1{\cdot}707d$,

where $d$ is the diameter of the guide. The $TM_{01}$ mode has a transverse magnetic field whose lines of force are circular; the cut-off wavelength is $1 \cdot 308 d$, and the mode is similar to that in a coaxial line except that the conduction current in the centre conductor is replaced by displacement current, with lines of $E$ running down the centre and turning outwards to terminate on the wall as in Fig. 11.19 (b). The $TE_{01}$ mode is rather similar, but with the lines of electric field and magnetic field interchanged; the electric field has closed circular lines of force and is purely transverse, while the magnetic field is greatest down the axis (see Fig. 11.19 (c)); the cut-off wavelength is $0 \cdot 820 d$.

*Cavity resonators*

If a length of waveguide is closed by conducting walls at each end, it will resonate at wavelengths such that the distance between the end walls is a multiple of half a guide wavelength. In the case of a rectangular guide closed by conducting walls normal to the $x$-axis a distance $a$ apart, the distance $a$ must be $\frac{1}{2} l \lambda_g$ where $l$ is an integer, in order that the electric field (which is tangential to the end walls) may be zero at the two ends. From equation (11.34) the wavelength $\lambda_0$ in the unbounded medium at which the rectangular cavity will resonate in a $TE_{0n}$ mode is thus given by

$$\frac{1}{\lambda_0^2} = \left(\frac{l}{2a}\right)^2 + \left(\frac{n}{2c}\right)^2. \tag{11.41}$$

This is a special case of the more general formula for a $TE_{mn}$ mode, for which

$$\frac{1}{\lambda_0^2} = \left(\frac{l}{2a}\right)^2 + \left(\frac{m}{2b}\right)^2 + \left(\frac{n}{2c}\right)^2 \tag{11.42}$$

for a rectangular cavity of dimensions $a$, $b$, $c$; this formula may be recognized as that used in the theory of heat radiation in computing the resonant modes of a hollow rectangular cavity (see Problem 11.12).

The most important quantity for any resonant system is its quality factor, $Q$; this may be found for a waveguide cavity by using the relation (see § 9.3)

$$Q = \omega(\text{energy stored})/(\text{energy dissipated per sec}).$$

The total stored energy may be computed by integrating the energy density in the cavity, while the total energy dissipated in the metallic walls (owing to their finite resistivity) can be found by using equation (10.34 a). The order of magnitude of $Q$ can readily be found without carrying through the details of the integration in the following way. If the amplitude of the oscillating magnetic field in the cavity is $H_0$, the stored energy $\approx \frac{1}{2}\mu_0 H_0^2 V$, where $V$ is the volume of the cavity (assumed to be evacuated), while the energy lost at the walls $\approx \frac{1}{2}\rho H_0^2 A/\delta$, where $A$ is the total wall area, $\rho$ and $\delta$ the resistivity and skin depth in the wall. Hence

$$Q \approx \omega(\tfrac{1}{2}\mu_0 H_0^2 V)/(\tfrac{1}{2}\rho H_0^2 A/\delta) = (V/A)(\omega\delta\mu_0/\rho) \approx V/(A\delta) \quad (11.43)$$

assuming the magnetic permeability of the wall to be unity, and using equation (10.31). This result shows that at a given wavelength the value of $Q$ increases with the linear dimensions of the resonator; while at different wavelengths, if the linear dimensions are scaled in proportion to the wavelength, $Q$ varies as $\lambda_0^{\frac{1}{2}}$, since $\delta$ varies as $\lambda_0^{\frac{1}{2}}$, and $V/A$ as $\lambda_0$. For a given wavelength and size of cavity $Q$ does not vary greatly with the mode of resonance, with one exception. The $TE_{01}$ mode in a cylindrical cavity has rather a high $Q$, and there is no radial flow of current on the end walls; for this reason it is used in wavemeters (see § 15.4) where one end is a movable plunger. A good contact between this and the cylindrical wall is not essential to a high $Q$, since there is no current flow across the contact. A value of 10 000 may be obtained for $Q$ at centimetre wavelengths, and the sharpness of resonance is thus rather higher than for a resonant coaxial line, mainly because there is no centre conductor with its rather high current density to contribute to the dissipation of energy.

## REFERENCE

KUHN, H., 1951, *Ann. Rep. Progr. Phys.* (Physical Society, London), **14**, 64.

## PROBLEMS

11.1. Show that if $Z_1$ and $Z_2$ in a simple filter are both pure resistances or pure capacitances the filter acts as an attenuator at all frequencies. Calculate the attenuation per section when both $Z_1$ and $Z_2$ are pure resistances of 100 ohms, and find the iterative impedance of a $T$-section.

(*Answers*: Power falls by factor 6·8 per section; $Z_T = 112$ ohms.)

11.2. A filter where $Z_1 Z_2 = k^2$, a constant independent of frequency, is called a constant-$k$ filter. Show that the simple low-pass and high-pass filters of § 11.2 are of this type, but the band-pass filter of Fig. 11.10 is not.

Show that the filter section of Fig. 11.12 is a band-pass section of the constant-$k$ type provided that $L_1 C_1 = L_2 C_2$, when $k^2 = L_2/C_1 = L_1/C_2$. If $f_1, f_2$ are the lower and upper frequency limits of the pass band, show that they satisfy the relations

$$\pi(f_2-f_1) = k/L_1 = (kC_2)^{-1}; \qquad \frac{1}{4\pi}\left(\frac{1}{f_1}-\frac{1}{f_2}\right) = L_2/k = kC_1.$$

**11.3.** The values of the components in the $m$-derived $T$-section shown in Fig. 11.11 $(a)$ obey the relations $(m < 1)$

$$L_1 = mL, \qquad C_2 = mC, \qquad L_2 = L(1-m^2)/4m.$$

Show that the section behaves as a low-pass filter with the following properties: $(a)$ the cut-off frequency $f_0$ is independent of $m$; $(b)$ the iterative impedance is $\mathbf{Z}_T = (L/C - \omega^2 L^2/4)^{\frac{1}{2}}$, and is thus the same as that of a simple low-pass filter section in § 11.2; $(c)$ the attenuation in the stop band is infinite at a frequency $f = f_0/(1-m^2)^{\frac{1}{2}}$.

**11.4.** A chain of the $T$-sections of Fig. 11.11 $(a)$ is terminated by the half-section shown in Fig. 11.11 $(b)$, where the values of the components obey the same relations as in the preceding problem. Prove that the impedance at the terminals $CD$ is

$$\mathbf{Z} = \left(\frac{L}{C}\right)^{\frac{1}{2}} \frac{\{1-(1-m^2)f^2/f_0^2\}}{(1-f^2/f_0^2)^{\frac{1}{2}}}.$$

If $m = 0\cdot6$, show that this does not depart by more than 4 per cent from the value $(L/C)^{\frac{1}{2}}$ for frequencies up to 85 per cent of the cut-off frequency $f_0$. Thus the use of a half-section as a transformer gives a more uniform impedance in the pass band.

**11.5.** Find expressions for the electric and magnetic fields in a coaxial transmission line carrying a current $I$ and a voltage $V$, and show by integrating Poynting's vector over the cross-section between the two conductors that the power flowing along the line is $IV$.

If the conductors have a finite resistivity, compute the power flowing into them per unit length by means of equation (10.34 a), and show that this gives the same attenuation as calculated in § 11.5.

**11.6.** In an infinite transmission line a leak develops at one point whose resistance is just equal to the characteristic impedance of the line. Show that of the power in the incident wave one-ninth is reflected, four-ninths is transmitted, and four-ninths is dissipated in the leak.

**11.7.** A length of loss-less transmission line is first short-circuited at one end and then open-circuited; the impedance measured at the other end is $\mathbf{Z}_1$ in the first case and $\mathbf{Z}_2$ in the second. Show that $\mathbf{Z}_1 \mathbf{Z}_2 = Z_0^2$, where $Z_0$ is the characteristic impedance of the line. This is a convenient way of measuring $Z_0$ for a cable of unknown electrical length.

**11.8.** A film of cryolite (refractive index $1\cdot35$) one-quarter wavelength thick is deposited on a glass surface $(n = 1\cdot50)$. Show that the reflected intensity is reduced to about 1 per cent.

A reflecting film is made up of a layer of cryolite $(n_2 = 1\cdot35)$ placed between two layers of $TiO_2$ $(n_1 = 2\cdot45)$. Each layer is one-quarter of a wavelength thick. Show that the ratio of the reflected to the incident amplitude is $(n_2^2 - n_1^4)/(n_2^2 + n_1^4)$, and that the reflected intensity is about 81 per cent of the incident intensity (assume normal incidence).

**11.9.** A quarter-wavelength, air-spaced, parallel wire transmission line is found to be in resonance with an oscillator when its length is 25 cm. When a capacitance of 1 $\mu\mu$F is connected across the open end, it is found that the length of the line must be reduced to 12·5 cm to obtain resonance. Show that the characteristic impedance of the line is approximately 530 ohms.

11.10. Show, either by the use of equations similar to (11.29) and (11.30) but with the assumptions $H_x = H_z = 0$, or by the use of equations (10.36) and (10.37), that a wave can be propagated between two parallel conducting planes with the following field components:

$$H_y = (A/Z_1)\cos(2\pi z/\lambda_c)\cos(\omega t - 2\pi x/\lambda_g),$$
$$E_x = (A\lambda_0/\lambda_c)\sin(2\pi z/\lambda_c)\sin(\omega t - 2\pi x/\lambda_g),$$
$$E_z = -(A\lambda_0/\lambda_g)\cos(2\pi z/\lambda_c)\cos(\omega t - 2\pi x/\lambda_g),$$

where $\lambda_c$ and $\lambda_g$ have the same values as for the transverse electric wave derived in § 11.6. This wave is a transverse magnetic wave, and may be designated as $TM_{0n}$; note that it cannot exist in a closed rectangular guide because the tangential components of $\mathbf{E}$ must then vanish at the walls $y = 0$ and $y = b$. The lowest transverse magnetic wave then possible would be $TM_{11}$, with components $H_y$, $H_z$, $E_x$, $E_z$ each varying sinusoidally in both the $y$- and $z$-directions.

11.11. A hollow cubical box of side $a$ resonates in the $TE_{101}$ mode (that is $l = n = 1$ in equation (11.41)). Calculate the energy stored and energy dissipated per second, and show that the value of $Q = a/2\delta$, where $\delta$ is the skin depth in the metal walls at the resonant frequency.

11.12. A hollow rectangular box is bounded by perfectly conducting planes at $x = 0$, $x = a$; $y = 0$, $y = b$; $z = 0$, $z = c$. Show that the standing wave system

$$E_x = A_x \cos\alpha x \sin\beta y \sin\gamma z \exp(j\omega t),$$
$$E_y = A_y \sin\alpha x \cos\beta y \sin\gamma z \exp(j\omega t),$$
$$E_z = A_z \sin\alpha x \sin\beta y \cos\gamma z \exp(j\omega t)$$

satisfies the boundary conditions provided that $\alpha a = l\pi$, $\beta b = m\pi$, $\gamma c = n\pi$, and that the wave equation is satisfied if

$$\frac{1}{4\pi^2}(\alpha^2 + \beta^2 + \gamma^2) = \left(\frac{l}{2a}\right)^2 + \left(\frac{m}{2b}\right)^2 + \left(\frac{n}{2c}\right)^2 = \left(\frac{\omega}{2\pi v}\right)^2 = \frac{1}{\lambda_0^2}.$$

Show also that, to satisfy $\operatorname{div} \mathbf{D} = 0$,

$$\alpha A_x + \beta A_y + \gamma A_z = 0.$$

(In general there can be only two independent amplitudes, corresponding to the two possible polarizations of an electromagnetic wave.)

# THERMIONIC VACUUM TUBES

IF a tungsten wire is heated *in vacuo* to a temperature of about 2500° K, it is found that electrons are emitted from the surface of the metal. Other metals and some metallic oxides show the same effect, known as thermionic emission (§ 4.4). If a second electrode is placed in the same evacuated envelope, and held at a positive potential with respect to the first, then the emitted electrons will be attracted to the second electrode, and a current will flow. This phenomenon is the basis of the radio tube, and the device just described is known as a diode. The surface emitting electrons is called the cathode, and that receiving them the anode. If the anode is cold, and emits no electrons, then no current will flow if it is made negative with respect to the cathode; the device acts as a valve, permitting only a unidirectional flow of current. The diode may thus be used to 'rectify'; that is, to convert an alternating current into a direct current. If a third electrode in the form of a grid is inserted between the cathode and the anode, a 'triode' tube is formed, which may be used to amplify an alternating voltage, or to sustain an alternating current in a tuned circuit; that is, to act as a generator of oscillations. In these two operations the tube is converting energy from a d.c. source into a.c. energy while, in rectification, a.c. energy is transformed into d.c. energy. The generic name for the diode, triode, and similar devices utilizing the flow of electrons from a hot surface is the thermionic vacuum tube, and it is one of the fundamental tools of modern physics and of modern technology. In this chapter an outline is given of the mode of action of the thermionic vacuum tube and its chief uses.

## 12.1. Construction of the thermionic vacuum tube

The number of materials available for use as cathodes is severely limited by the requirement of high electron emission at temperatures where the material does not disintegrate. The emission current per unit area of a cathode surface at absolute temperature $T$ is given by equation (4.21)

$$J = AT^2 e^{-\phi/kT},$$

where the constants $A$ and $\phi$ depend on the material, a few values being given in Table 4.1. The temperature at which adequate emission is obtained is determined primarily by the value of the work function, $\phi$. Of the materials listed in Table 4.1 those in most general use are tungsten, thoriated tungsten, and a barium oxide–strontium oxide mixture. The temperatures required are approximately 2500°, 1900°, and 1100° K respectively for current densities of the order of 1 A/cm².

Tungsten and thoriated tungsten (often known as 'bright emitter' and 'dull emitter' respectively) are used in the form of fine filaments heated by the passage of electric current through them, this being the only practical method of maintaining the high temperatures required. Pure tungsten is very resistant to 'poisoning' by residual gas and will give long life in transmitting tubes where the anode potential may be 10 000 V or more. Thoriated tungsten is less good in these respects, but the lower operating temperature is a considerable advantage. One to two per cent of thorium oxide is added to the tungsten during manufacture, and after the tube has been evacuated the filament is 'activated' by temporarily running it at a very high temperature. Some of the thorium oxide is thereby decomposed, the thorium atoms migrating to the surface where they form a monatomic layer with a lower work function.

The oxide-coated cathode, owing to its low working temperature, has the great advantage that it can be heated indirectly, thus making it possible to have an equipotential cathode. In small receiving triodes the voltage drop along a directly heated filament is comparable with the voltage difference between grid and cathode, so that this voltage difference cannot everywhere be the optimum. In addition, the filament cannot be heated with a.c., since the alternating voltage difference between various parts of the filament and the grid would be amplified and cause an intolerable hum. The indirectly-heated cathode is generally made of a nickel tube, of circular or rectangular cross-section, with an internal heater of tungsten wire coated with a refractory insulator such as alumina. For cathode ray and other tubes where a flat cathode is required, a hollow disk is used with the heater in the form of a flat spiral. Since the barium–strontium oxide mixture is unstable in air, the material is deposited in the form of carbonate, usually by spraying on a suspension of it in a volatile organic solvent. On heating *in vacuo* carbon dioxide is evolved and pumped away, and in some cases the cathode surface has to be activated by drawing current from it at an elevated temperature. It is generally believed that the emission takes place from particles of free metal (barium) at the surface of the oxide coating. The free metal gradually evaporates and has to be replaced by reduction of the oxide; this is caused partly by positive ion bombardment, partly by electrolysis through the potential gradient in the coating, and partly by reaction with the surface on which the oxide is deposited.

As in the case of the thoriated tungsten filament, the oxide-coated cathode is easily 'poisoned' by the presence of gas, especially oxygen. It is therefore essential to maintain a high vacuum for the whole life of the tube. Most metallic surfaces contain occluded gas, which is very gradually evolved if the surfaces are maintained *in vacuo* at room temperature, but is rapidly evolved at high temperatures. Nickel is commonly used for the anode and other electrodes, and is 'out-gassed' by heating to about 1300° K *in vacuo* or in hydrogen before the tube is assembled. Grids are generally wound of tungsten wire, owing to its stiffness and high melting-point. After the tube has been assembled, it is evacuated and, while still on the pump, is heated to just below the softening point of the glass envelope to remove occluded gas from the glass. The metallic electrodes are then outgassed at red heat by inducing eddy currents in them with a high frequency oscillator. The advantage of this method is that the glass is not heated directly, and the electrodes can therefore be raised to a temperature well above the melting-point of glass. The cathode is then activated, and immediately before the tube is sealed off a film of an active metal such as barium is deposited by evaporation over part of the inside of the glass envelope. The purpose of this 'getter' is to absorb residual oxygen and nitrogen by chemical action.

## 12.2. The diode

The simplest type of thermionic vacuum tube is the diode, and we shall discuss first the way in which the current flow to the anode depends on the anode voltage.

If the electrons were emitted from the cathode with zero velocity, and there were no contact potential difference between anode and cathode, we should expect the current flow to be zero when the anode voltage is negative, and to rise immediately to a constant value, equal to the total emission from the cathode, as soon as the anode is made positive. In fact the electrons are emitted with finite velocities, corresponding to a Maxwellian distribution. The number with an energy between $W$ and $(W+dW)$ is then $C \exp(-W/kT) dW$, and, if a negative potential $V$ is applied to the anode, only those electrons with energy $W$ greater than $(-e)V$ will reach the anode. Hence the current is

$$I = C \int_{W=-eV}^{W=\infty} \exp(-W/kT) dW = CkT \exp(eV/kT) = I_0 \exp(eV/kT)$$
$$(12.1)$$

and the rate of change of $I$ with $V$, known as the slope of the characteristic, or tube conductance, is

$$(dI/dV) = (e/kT)I_0\exp(eV/kT) = (e/kT)I. \tag{12.2}$$

For a diode with an oxide-coated cathode whose temperature is about $1100°$ K, the value of $(dI/dV)/I$ is approximately $10$ V$^{-1}$. In practice this slope is not attained because the flow of current to the anode is limited, not by the velocity of emission, but by the mutual repulsion of the electrons in the space between cathode and anode. These electrons are known as the 'space charge', and the current flow under these conditions is called 'space-charge limited'. Only at very low current density, when the space charge is small, is the current 'temperature limited'. The origin of the latter term arises from the fact that both the maximum current, and the shape of the characteristic, are determined by the temperature of the cathode. In general tubes are operated under 'space-charge limited' conditions and it is possible for most purposes to neglect the finite velocity of emission and its spread. Similarly, any contact potential difference between anode and cathode, which has the effect of shifting the characteristic up or down by a few volts, will be neglected.

## 12.3. The three-halves power law

To examine the effect of space charge on the flow of current, we shall consider the case of a diode where the cathode and anode form parts of parallel planes denoted respectively by the equations $x = 0$ and $x = d$. We shall further assume that the potential of the cathode is zero, while that of the anode is $V_a$. The potential between the electrodes can be determined by solving Poisson's equation

$$\frac{d^2V}{dx^2} = -\frac{\rho}{\epsilon_0} = \frac{ne}{\epsilon_0}, \tag{12.3}$$

where $-e$ is the electronic charge, and $n$ the number of electrons per cubic metre. If the mass of an electron is $m$, and its velocity $u$ at the point $x$ where the potential is $V$, then the energy equation gives

$$\tfrac{1}{2}mu^2 = eV, \tag{12.4}$$

while the current density is

$$J = neu. \tag{12.5}$$

(Here the flow is unidirectional and it is not necessary to treat $J$ as a vector quantity; we have omitted the negative sign which denotes that the direction of positive current flow is from anode to cathode.) The velocity can be eliminated between these equations, giving

$$ne = J\bigg/\sqrt{\left(\frac{m}{2eV}\right)}.$$

Substitution of this in Poisson's equation gives

$$d^2V/dx^2 = aV^{-\frac{1}{2}},$$

where $a = (J/\epsilon_0)\sqrt{(m/2e)}$. This equation may be integrated if both sides are multiplied by $2(dV/dx)$, giving

$$\left(\frac{dV}{dx}\right)^2 - \left(\frac{dV}{dx}\right)_0^2 = 4aV^{\frac{1}{2}}.$$

$(dV/dx)_0$ is the electric field at the cathode, where $V$ and $x$ are zero. Since the constant $a$ is proportional to $J$, it is evident that the maximum current density is attained when $(dV/dx)_0 = 0$. Then we may write

$$dV/dx = 2a^{\frac{1}{2}}V^{\frac{1}{4}},$$

integration of which gives

$$V^{\frac{3}{4}} = \tfrac{3}{2}a^{\frac{1}{2}}x, \qquad (12.6)$$

where the constant of integration is zero because $V = 0$ at $x = 0$. Since at the anode $x = d$ and $V = V_a$, we have

$$V_a^{\frac{3}{2}} = 9ad^2/4 = (9/4\epsilon_0)\sqrt{(m/2e)}d^2J, \qquad (12.7)$$

showing that the current density $J$ is proportional to the three-halves power of the anode voltage, and inversely proportional to the square of the separation between cathode and anode. This relation was first derived by Child, and is sometimes known as Child's law.

Since the current density is independent of $x$, it follows from equation (12.5) that the density of electrons is greatest where their velocity is smallest; that is, near the cathode. It is this concentration of electrons which reduces the electric field at the cathode, since their electric field is oppositely directed at this point to that due to the positive potential on the anode. The electron concentration cannot rise to a greater value than that required to make $dV/dx$ zero at the cathode, since no electrons could then leave the cathode, and the space charge would fall as electrons move away to the anode, without their being replenished from the cathode. Near the anode the electric field is greater than that due to the anode potential alone, because the field is here increased by the repulsive force due to the negative space charge near the cathode. The potential variation is shown in Fig. 12.1. Curve $A$ shows the linear potential gradient which would exist in the absence of space charge, while curve $B$ is that calculated above, on the assumption that the electrons are emitted from the cathode with zero velocity. It is easily seen from equation (12.6) that the equation of curve $B$ may be written in the form $V/V_a = (x/d)^{\frac{4}{3}}$. Owing to the finite velocity of emission, electrons can leave the cathode even when there is a small reverse electric field, and the space charge can then increase to the extent of setting up a potential

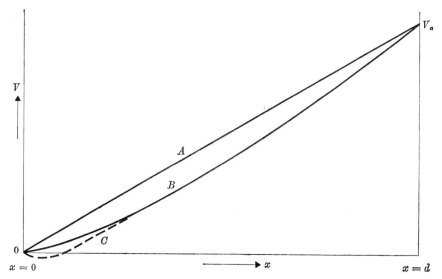

Fig. 12.1. Potential distribution in a diode with plane parallel electrodes.
Curve $A$    no space charge.
Curve $B$    space charge limited, electrons emitted with zero velocity.
Curve $C$    space charge limited, electrons emitted with finite velocity.

minimum, as shown by curve $C$. The depth of this minimum is of the order $W/e$, where $W$ is the average energy of the emitted electrons, since only those electrons with sufficient energy to penetrate the potential minimum will eventually reach the anode.

On inserting numerical values, the equation for the current density may be written
$$J = 2{\cdot}34 \times 10^{-6} V_a^{\frac{3}{2}}/d^2, \tag{12.8}$$
where $J$ is in A/cm$^2$, $V_a$ in volts, and $d$ in cm. Obviously this equation cannot hold indefinitely as $V_a$ is increased, since the current density will eventually be limited by the emission from the cathode, and will then reach a constant value. The current will depart from the three-halves power law as soon as the space charge is no longer sufficiently dense to nullify the electric field at the cathode. The form of the current–anode potential curve will therefore be as in Fig. 12.2. At low anode voltages, the current is limited by the space charge, and its magnitude is inde-

pendent of the cathode temperature. At high potentials the size of the current is limited only by the cathode emission, and thus, in the first approximation, depends only on the cathode temperature. In practice it will be found that the saturation current does increase slightly with $V_a$, owing to field emission (§ 4.4). This increase is more noticeable with oxide-coated cathodes than with pure tungsten cathodes.

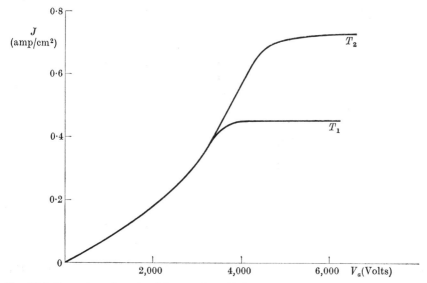

FIG. 12.2. Current-anode potential curve for a diode with plane parallel electrodes, 1 cm apart, for two different cathode temperatures $T_1$ and $T_2$ ($T_2 > T_1$).

Although the derivation of the three-halves power law has been given here only for the case of the diode with plane-parallel electrodes, it has been shown to hold also for electrodes in the shape of coaxial circular cylinders and of concentric spheres. By a dimensional argument it may be shown to hold for any electrode geometry, assuming always that the electrons are emitted with zero velocity. Most vacuum tubes for low frequency applications are constructed with electrodes in the form of coaxial cylinders, sometimes, but by no means always, with circular cross-section. At very high frequencies, where the clearance between the electrodes must be made very small, the plane-parallel arrangement is used for special tubes.

## 12.4. Uses of the diode

The primary use of the diode is as a rectifier, converting an alternating voltage into a steady voltage. The basic circuit for this purpose is shown in Fig. 12.3. The diode is connected in series with a load resistance $R$ to a source of alternating voltage such as a transformer, and a capacitor $C$ is placed in parallel with $R$. To understand the mode of action, consider first the case where $R$ is infinite. On applying the alternating voltage, current will flow round the circuit through the diode only when the anode of the diode is at a positive voltage with respect to the cathode. While the capacitor is uncharged this occurs every other half-cycle. Since the cathode loses electrons to the anode during this half-cycle, and

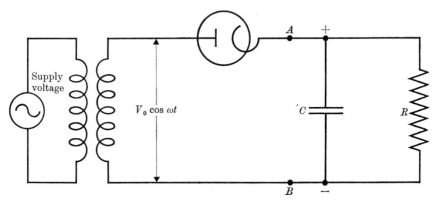

FIG. 12.3. The diode as a half-wave rectifier.

cannot regain them during the reverse half-cycle, the cathode and the plate of the capacitor connected to it will become positively charged. The flow of electrons from cathode to anode will continue so long as the anode reaches a positive voltage with respect to the cathode at any point during the cycle. The charge on the capacitor will thus continue to rise, the limit being reached when the voltage across the capacitor is equal to the peak value $V_0$ of the alternating voltage $V_0 \cos \omega t$. At this point the voltage across the diode is $-V_0 + V_0 \cos \omega t$, showing that the anode never becomes more positive than the cathode, and hence no current flows. At one point in the cycle the anode-cathode voltage difference is $-2V_0$. This is known as the 'inverse peak voltage', and the diode must be constructed so that it can withstand the inverse peak voltage without failure.

If a voltmeter is placed across the capacitor, it will register a voltage equal to the peak value $V_0$ of the alternating voltage. This is the basic circuit for the use of the diode as a 'peak' vacuum tube voltmeter. If the capacitor has no leakage, it will remain charged to the greatest peak voltage ever applied to the system, but if the voltmeter has a finite resistance $R$, it will be able to follow changes in the peak voltage so long as they do not occur within a time of order $RC$, the time constant of the $R$–$C$ combination.

In general the circuit of Fig. 12.3 is used to deliver direct current into a load $R$. Under these conditions the capacitor will discharge slightly through the resistance during that part of the cycle when the diode is not conducting, being recharged to the peak voltage when the diode conducts. The voltage across $R$ is therefore not constant, but contains

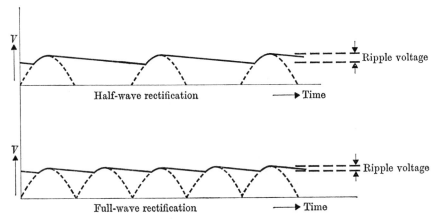

FIG. 12.4. Half-wave and full-wave rectification. $V$ = voltage across $R$.

a component fluctuating at the frequency of the applied alternating voltage, as in Fig. 12.4. This component is not sinusoidal, owing to the asymmetrical nature of the capacitor charge–discharge system. The 'ripple voltage', as the fluctuating component is generally called, becomes larger if $R$ is reduced, since the time constant of the $R$–$C$ combination is then smaller, and the capacitor discharges to a lower voltage before being recharged. The ripple voltage is therefore more serious when the diode is on load. The ripple voltage must be eliminated or very considerably reduced if the system is used to supply d.c. power for an amplifier or other electronic device, since any alternating voltage applied to the early stages will be greatly magnified at the output. Reduction of the ripple is effected either by using a very large capacitance $C$, so that the time constant $RC$ is very long compared with the period of the alternating supply, or by the use of a simple low-pass filter circuit. Either of these may be used with a full-wave rectifier, whose circuit, with a filter section, is shown in Fig. 12.5.

The advantage of full-wave rectification over half-wave rectification

can be seen from a comparison of the two without the filter section, that
is with a circuit consisting of the capacitor $C$ in parallel with a load
resistance $R$ connected across the terminals $AB$ in each case. With the
full-wave rectification the capacitor is charged to the peak voltage by
the passage of current through one diode during the first half of the
cycle, and is then again charged during the second half-cycle by current

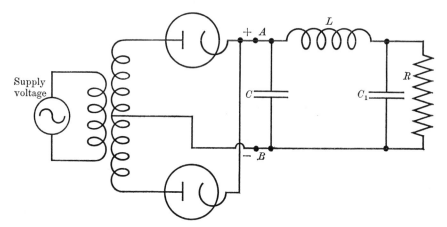

Fig. 12.5. A full-wave rectifier with filter circuit.

flowing through the second diode. If the time constant of the $C$–$R$
combination is long compared with the period of the supply voltage, so
that the voltage drop during the discharge period is only a small fraction
of the initial peak voltage, then the voltage on $C$ will fall nearly linearly
with time during the discharge interval. With full-wave rectification,
this interval is only half a cycle, and the size of the ripple is thus only
half as great as with half-wave rectification (see Fig. 12.4). In addition
its fundamental frequency is now twice the supply frequency, making
the filtering problem easier. The simplest type of filter, as shown in
Fig. 12.5, consists of the capacitance $C$ with a series inductance $L$ and
a second shunt capacitance $C_1$. These must be of such a magnitude that
the impedance of $C_1$ at the ripple frequency is very small compared
with $R$, while the impedance of $L$ is very high compared with that of $C_1$.
This arrangement acts as a potentiometer which delivers the full steady
voltage output across $R$, but reduces the ripple voltage roughly in the
ratio $(1/\omega C_1)/(\omega L) = 1/\omega^2 LC_1$, where $\omega$ is the ripple frequency. For a
full-wave system delivering about 100 mA at 300 V (i.e. $R \approx 3000$ ohms)
from a supply frequency of 50 c/s, the conditions laid down above are
amply fulfilled for most purposes if $L$ is about 25 henries, and $C$ and $C_1$

about 10 $\mu$F. If the reduction of ripple is insufficient, further filter sections may be added (see Chapter 11).

The system described in the last paragraph is known as 'capacitor input', since a capacitor is connected immediately across the terminals $AB$. If the impedance of this capacitor at the mains frequency is small, then the whole of the transformer output voltage is applied across the diode and, on no load, the capacitor charges up to the peak voltage developed between the centre tap and either end of the transformer secondary winding. On load, the current through the diode consists of short pulses centred on the instant when the secondary voltage reaches its peak value. The peak current is therefore much higher than the steady current drawn by the load, and if the latter is many amperes, the peak diode current may be so high as to damage the tube. This is avoided by omitting the first capacitor $C$, so that an 'inductive input' system is used. Since the action of the inductance is to oppose any change in the current flowing through it, the current through each diode is substantially constant during the half-cycle when it conducts, the current being switched to the other diode in the second half-cycle. The voltage output is lower than with capacitor input, and the percentage ripple is higher. On the other hand, the 'regulation' (the change of output voltage with output current) is improved. Where the load current is fairly constant, and not more than a few hundred milliamperes (e.g. in a radio receiver), capacitor input is generally used for the power supply unit.

## 12.5. The triode

In the triode tube a third electrode, known as the grid, is interposed between the cathode and the anode. If the electrodes are planar, the grid takes the form of a coarse wire mesh; if the electrodes are cylindrical the grid is wound in the form of a helix. The total current drawn from the cathode will now depend on the potentials of both grid and anode, since both control the field at the cathode. In the absence of space charge, the charge on the cathode, assumed to be at zero potential, is equal to

$$-(C_{cg}V_g + C_{ca}V_a) = -C_{cg}\left(V_g + \frac{V_a}{C_{cg}/C_{ca}}\right) = -C_{cg}\left(V_g + \frac{V_a}{\mu}\right),$$

where $C_{cg}$, $C_{ca}$ are the coefficients of capacitance between cathode and grid (at potential $V_g$) and anode (at potential $V_a$) respectively. These capacitances are in the same ratio as the division of lines of force from the cathode between the grid and the anode when $V_a = V_g$. The ratio

$\mu = C_{cg}/C_{ca}$ is known as the 'amplification factor' of the tube (however, the values of $C_{cg}$, $C_{ca}$ given in tube manuals do not normally fit this relation because they include the capacitances of the leads). If the current from the cathode is limited by space charge, so that the field at the cathode (as in the assumption made in deriving Child's law) is zero, then no lines of force will reach the cathode, but all will terminate on the space charge. Since the latter is mainly located very close to the cathode, it is affected equally by lines of force from the grid and from the anode, and it follows that the current leaving the cathode depends on the equivalent voltage $V'_a = (V_g + V_a/\mu)$. Experimentally it is found that the current depends very nearly on the three-halves power of this equivalent voltage in the region of complete space charge limitation, corresponding to the fact that near the cathode the potential distribution is the same as in an 'equivalent diode'. We may therefore write

$$J = b(V_g + V_a/\mu)^{\frac{3}{2}}/d^2, \tag{12.9}$$

where $d$ is known as the 'equivalent diode spacing'; for tubes with fairly high values of $\mu$ (i.e. when nearly all the lines of force terminating on the space charge come from the grid) $d$ is nearly equal to the cathode-grid spacing in a plane triode. The constant $b$ has the same numerical value as for the diode. In general the triode is used with the grid voltage negative, so that no current flows to it, and the total current leaving the cathode (to which equation (12.9) applies) is also the anode current. It is obvious that current will leave the cathode so long as the equivalent voltage $(V_g + V_a/\mu)$ is positive, and a small negative grid voltage must be combined with a large positive anode voltage. This has the advantage that a source of voltage applied to the grid will influence the anode current without any current being drawn from the source by the grid.

### 12.6. Characteristics of the triode

Characteristic curves may be drawn for the negative grid triode showing the anode current as a function of the grid voltage for various values of the anode voltage. A typical set of curves is given in Fig. 12.6. Since the anode current depends on the expression $(V_g + V_a/\mu)$, it is obvious that all the curves will be similar, but will be displaced to more negative values of $V_g$ as $V_a$ is increased, the shift in $V_g$ being $-(1/\mu)$ of that in $V_a$.

A second set of characteristic curves may be formed by plotting the anode current as a function of the anode voltage for various values of the grid voltage, as shown in Fig. 12.7. A third set of characteristics may be obtained by plotting the grid voltage against the anode voltage at various constant values of the anode current.

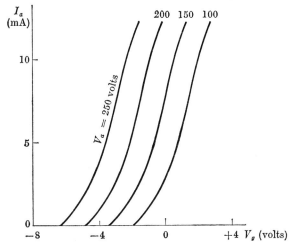

FIG. 12.6. $I_a$-$V_g$ curves for a small triode tube.
$g_m \sim 4$ mA/V, $\mu \sim 30$.

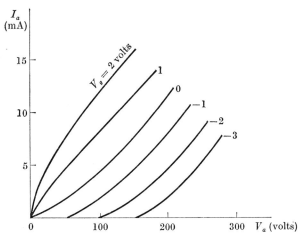

FIG. 12.7. $I_a$-$V_a$ curves for a small triode tube.
$g_m \sim 4$ mA/V, $\mu \sim 30$.

In order to carry out calculations on the performance of a triode tube in various applications, it is convenient to have some simple method of specifying the tube characteristics. The three-halves power law of equation (12.9) is clumsy to handle and not amenable to calculation, as well as being only approximately true. For most applications, we are interested in small changes in $I_a$ resulting from the application of an alternating grid voltage. For this purpose the anode current may be expanded in the form of a Taylor's series, for small changes about its mean value. We have then, for small changes $v_g$, $v_a$ in the grid and anode voltages respectively,

$$I = I_0 + v_g\left(\frac{\partial I_a}{\partial V_g}\right)_{V_a} + v_a\left(\frac{\partial I_a}{\partial V_a}\right)_{V_g} +$$

$$+ \left\{\tfrac{1}{2}v_g^2\left(\frac{\partial^2 I_a}{\partial V_g^2}\right)_{V_a} + v_g v_a\left(\frac{\partial^2 I_a}{\partial V_g \partial V_a}\right)_{V_a, V_g} + \tfrac{1}{2}v_a^2\left(\frac{\partial^2 I_a}{\partial V_a^2}\right)_{V_g}\right\} + \dots . \quad (12.10)$$

The presence of the second-order terms results in the change of anode current not being linear with the change in the applied voltages. This is generally undesirable, since it causes 'distortion' of the applied signal. It can be avoided by keeping the magnitude of $v_g$ and $v_a$ small, when the second-order terms become relatively less important. If we adopt the convention of using lower-case symbols for small changes (e.g. we write $i_a$ for $I - I_0$), we may simplify the notation and, on omitting the second-order terms, equation (12.10) becomes

$$i_a = g_m v_g + (1/\rho)v_a. \quad (12.11)$$

Here $g_m = (\partial I_a/\partial V_g)_{V_a}$ is known as the mutual conductance of the tube, and $\rho = (\partial V_a/\partial I_a)_{V_g}$ is called the anode slope resistance (or often just the anode resistance of the tube. If $i_a$ is zero, then

$$\mu = -\left(\frac{\partial V_a}{\partial V_g}\right)_{I_a} = -\left(\frac{v_a}{v_g}\right)_{i_a=0} = g_m \rho, \quad (12.12)$$

which gives a simple relation between the three constants of the tube. These 'constants' will vary with the working conditions of the tube, and are constants only in so far as the approximations we have made are justified. These approximations are equivalent to considering the characteristics of the tube as straight lines in the neighbourhood of the working point.

When the three-halves law (equation (12.9)) is a good approximation, the value of $g_m$ is
$$g_m = \tfrac{3}{2}(b^2 J/d^4)^{\frac{1}{3}} = cI_a^{\frac{1}{3}},$$

showing that $g_m$ increases with the one-third power of the anode current Since $\mu = C_{cg}/C_{ca}$, it is substantially independent of the working conditions, being determined by the geometry of the tube. It follows from equation (12.12) that $\rho$ will decrease as the inverse one-third power of the anode current.

Typical values of the tube constants for small triodes are as follows. $g_m$ varies from 1 to 10 mA/V, which is sometimes expressed as 1000 to 10 000 micromhos. $\mu$ varies from 20 to 100, and $\rho$ from 5000 to 100 000 ohms. The working voltages are about —3 V on the grid, and +100 to

$+250$ V on the anode. The value of $\mu$ is controlled by the closeness of the winding of the grid, and the relative distances of grid and anode from the cathode. If the number of lines of force reaching the cathode from the anode is very small compared with the number from the grid (as is the case with a closely wound grid), the magnification factor $\mu$ is high. If the grid is fairly openly wound, $\mu$ is low.

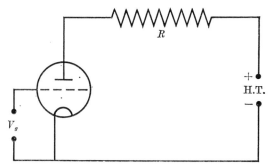

FIG. 12.8. Triode tube with resistance in anode circuit

## 12.7. Equivalent circuit of the triode

The most important use of the triode is as an amplifier. If the voltage applied to the grid is changed by a small amount, there will be a corresponding change in the anode current. If the anode is connected to its high tension source through a resistance $R$, as in Fig. 12.8, the change in anode current will cause a change in the potential drop across $R$. The ratio of the change in this voltage to the change in the grid voltage is known as the voltage amplification. The change in the potential drop across the load resistance $R$ will cause a corresponding change in the anode voltage, which will fall if the grid voltage rises. This fall reduces the anode current, and hence to calculate the voltage amplification we proceed as follows.

If $i_a$, $v_a$ represent the changes in anode current and voltage due to a change $v_g$ in the grid voltage,

$$i_a = g_m v_g + v_a/\rho.$$

But $v_a = -i_a R$, and hence the voltage amplification is

$$A = \frac{v_a}{v_g} = -\frac{i_a R}{v_g} = -\frac{g_m \rho R}{(R+\rho)} = -\frac{\mu R}{(R+\rho)}. \tag{12.13}$$

This result is the same as would be obtained from a generator of voltage $-\mu v_g$ with an internal resistance $\rho$, as can be seen from the circuit of Fig. 12.9 $(a)$. This is known as the equivalent circuit of the triode, and its use greatly facilitates calculation. For example, the anode load is often not a pure resistance $R$ but a complex impedance $\mathbf{Z} = R+jX$. The voltage amplification is then

$$A = -\frac{i_a \mathbf{Z}}{v_g} = -\frac{\mu \mathbf{Z}}{\mathbf{Z}+\rho} = -\frac{\mu(R+jX)}{(\rho+R)+jX}. \qquad (12.14)$$

In this expression the presence of a complex number shows that the anode voltage change is not in phase with the grid voltage change, whereas with a pure resistive load they are exactly in anti-phase. Usually the

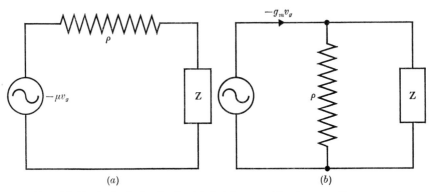

Fig. 12.9. (a) Equivalent circuit of a triode tube, considered as a voltage generator.
(b) Equivalent circuit of a triode tube, considered as a current generator.

phase shift between anode and grid voltage is of no significance, and the useful amplification is given by taking the modulus of equation (12.14). If the reactance $X$ is a function of frequency, as is usually the case, the voltage amplification will also vary with frequency unless $\mathbf{Z} \gg \rho$ over the whole range of frequencies which it is desired to amplify. For this reason, resistive loads are generally used for wide band amplifiers

An alternative equivalent circuit for the triode which is often useful is shown in Fig. 12.9 (b). The tube is replaced by a current generator of magnitude $-g_m v_g$, which has infinite internal impedance, across which is the anode resistance $\rho$ of the tube. The external load $\mathbf{Z}$ is connected in parallel with $\rho$, and a fraction $\rho/(\mathbf{Z}+\rho)$ of the current from the generator flows through $\mathbf{Z}$. The voltage across $\mathbf{Z}$ is thus $-g_m v_g \mathbf{Z}\rho/(\mathbf{Z}+\rho)$, giving the same result as in equation (12.14).

## 12.8. Input impedance of the triode

At radio frequencies ($10^5$ c/s and upwards) the effects of the finite capacitances between the various electrodes of a tube become important. The full treatment of this problem is complicated, since the grid-cathode, grid-anode, and cathode-anode capacitances form a network together with the anode resistance and load as in Fig. 12.10. A simplified treatment is given below, where $C_{ca}$ is deemed to be part of the load $\mathbf{Z}$, and the currents through the other electrode capacitances are assumed to be small compared with the anode current through the tube.

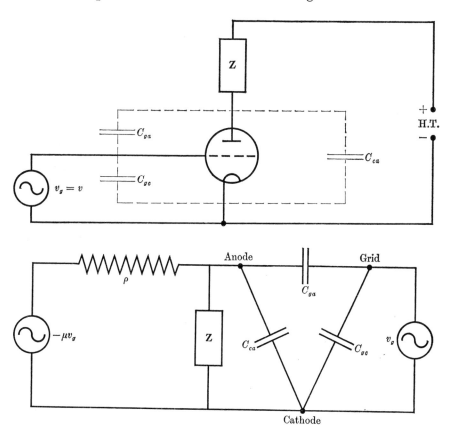

FIG. 12.10. The triode with its electrode capacitances (above) and its full equivalent circuit (below).

The principal effect of the capacitances from the grid to the other electrodes is to draw a finite current from the source of the voltage applied to the grid. If this voltage is $v$ relative to the cathode (taken as the zero of voltage) then the current flowing from grid to cathode is $j\omega C_{gc} v$. In addition, there is the current flowing through the grid-anode capacitance, which also completes its return path through the signal source. To compute this we note that the anode voltage is $Av$, where $A = -\mu\mathbf{Z}/(\mathbf{Z}+\rho)$ is the amplification produced by the tube working into an anode load $\mathbf{Z}$. Thus the total voltage across the grid-anode capacitance is

$$v - v_a = v(1 - A),$$

and the resulting current flow is $j\omega C_{ga}(1 - A)v$. Thus the total admittance associated with the grid is

$$\mathbf{Y}_g = 1/\mathbf{Z}_g = j\omega C_{gc} + j\omega C_{ga}[1 + \mu \mathbf{Z}/(\mathbf{Z} + \rho)]. \tag{12.15}$$

If $\mathbf{Z}$ is a pure resistance $R$, then the input impedance of the grid is that of a pure capacitance $C_g$ of magnitude

$$C_g = C_{gc} + C_{ga}[1 + \mu R/(R + \rho)]. \tag{12.16}$$

If $\mathbf{Z}$ is complex $= R + jX$, then

$$\frac{1}{\mathbf{Z}_g} = j\omega\left[C_{gc} + C_{ga}\left\{1 + \frac{\mu(R\rho + R^2 + X^2)}{(\rho + R)^2 + X^2}\right\}\right] - \frac{\mu\omega X\rho C_{ga}}{(\rho + R)^2 + X^2}. \tag{12.17}$$

Thus $1/\mathbf{Z}_g$ contains a resistive component whose value is negative if $X$ is positive, i.e. if the anode load is inductive. This negative resistance means that power is flowing back to the grid through the grid-anode capacitance, and if this power is more than is required to supply the power dissipated in any positive resistance in the source of the grid voltage, oscillations will result (see Chapter 13). This is one of the chief difficulties in the use of triodes as amplifiers at radio frequencies. On the other hand, if the anode load is capacitative, the resistive component of the grid input impedance is always positive.

In this treatment we have neglected the fact that the current through the grid-anode capacitance flows also through the anode load, thereby altering the anode voltage slightly. A more accurate treatment shows that $C_{ga}$ in equation (12.15) should be replaced by

$$C_{ga}\left\{1 + \left(\frac{\mathbf{Z}\rho}{\mathbf{Z} + \rho}\right)j\omega C_{ga}\right\}^{-1}.$$

This introduces a resistive component to the grid input impedance even when the load $\mathbf{Z}$ is a pure resistance $R$. Its value is then approximately

$$1/R_g = \omega^2 C_{ga}^2\left[1 + \frac{\mu R}{R + \rho}\right]\left(\frac{\rho R}{R + \rho}\right), \tag{12.18}$$

and it is in parallel with the grid input capacitance. When the anode load is inductive, this reduces the negative conductance effect at the grid.

To estimate the magnitude of these effects we take $\mu = 30$, $\rho = 10^4$ ohms, $R = 2\cdot5 \times 10^4$ ohms, $\omega = 10^6$, $C_{gc} = C_{ga} = 5\ \mu\mu\mathrm{F}$. Then

$$R_g \approx 2\cdot5 \times 10^5\ \text{ohms}, \qquad C_g \approx 120\ \mu\mu\mathrm{F}.$$

At this frequency $C_g$ corresponds to a reactance of only 8000 ohms, so that the input impedance of the triode is very low, and almost wholly capacitative. The bulk of this capacitance is due to the grid-anode capacitance, which is magnified because it has the amplified signal voltage across it. The input impedance will be greatly increased if $C_{ga}$ can be diminished, and for this purpose the screen-grid tetrode tube was introduced.

## 12.9. The screen-grid tetrode

In the screen-grid tetrode a fourth electrode is inserted in the form of an extra grid between the control grid and the anode of the tube. This extra electrode, the screen grid, is maintained at a fixed positive potential with respect to the cathode, so that the voltage on it does not change when a signal is applied to the control grid. The screen grid is wound so that most of the lines of force from the control grid terminate on the screen grid, and comparatively few reach the anode. In this way the grid-anode capacitance is reduced to about $10^{-9}$ F, and although the capacitance between the control grid and screen grid is of the same order as that between grid and anode in the triode, the alternating voltage across this capacitance is the same as that across the grid-cathode capacitance and is not magnified by the action of the tube. Thus the capacitance between the two grids is just added directly to the grid-cathode capacitance.

Since the screen grid is at a positive potential with respect to the cathode, it will collect electrons which would otherwise have gone to the anode. Most of the lines of force which penetrate through the control grid to the space charge round the cathode will come from the screen grid rather than the anode, and the former will exercise much more control over the current than the anode. Thus the anode resistance of the tube will be high since $(\partial I_a/\partial V_a)_{V_g}$ is small, and so will be the amplification factor, which depends on the ratio of the number of lines of force reaching the space charge from the grid to the number from the anode.

The screen current and anode current in a tetrode for given voltages on the screen and control grids are shown as functions of the anode voltage in Fig. 12.11. As the anode voltage is increased from zero, the anode current shows initially a steep rise, followed by a fall and a second rise when the anode voltage becomes of the same order as the screen voltage. The screen current shows the inverse behaviour, and the sum of screen and anode currents is substantially constant since the total current leaving the cathode depends practically only on the control and screen-grid voltages, which are both constant. The fall in the anode current and rise in the screen current are due to secondary emission of electrons by the anode. This is negligible at very low anode voltages, but appreciable when the anode voltage rises above 10 V or so. The ratio of the number of secondary electrons to the number of incident primary electrons may be high when a composite surface (see § 4.4) is formed on the anode by barium evaporated from the cathode. In the

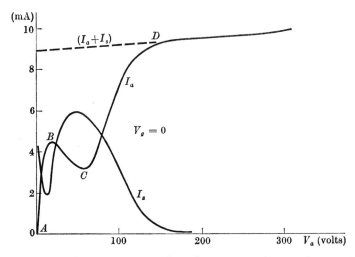

Fig. 12.11. Curves of screen current and anode current against anode potential, with zero control grid voltage, for a tetrode tube. (Screen voltage ∼ 60 V.)

Initial rise of $I_a$ in region $AB$ occurs when anode voltage is too low to give appreciable secondary emission. The latter sets in at $V_a \sim 10$ V and increases over range $BC$, causing net anode current to fall. It rises again in region $CD$ when $V_a$ becomes greater than screen voltage $V_s$, since secondary electrons are then attracted back to the anode.

triode, secondary electrons are emitted by the anode with low velocities, but they find themselves in a strong potential gradient which returns them to the anode, so that there is no net effect on the anode current. In the tetrode, however, the field at the anode is reversed when the screen is at a higher potential than the anode, and secondary electrons emitted by the latter will therefore travel to the screen. This causes a reduction in the net current flowing to the anode, and an increase in that flowing to the screen. The resulting kink in the anode current characteristic is a considerable drawback, since strong distortion of the amplified signal will occur unless the tube is worked so that the anode voltage is always greater than the screen-grid voltage. This is possible with small signals, but not with large signals.

## 12.10. The pentode

The undesirable kink in the characteristic of the tetrode is eliminated in the pentode, where an extra electrode is inserted between the screen grid and the anode. This electrode, a grid of coarse mesh or an open helix, is known as the suppressor grid, and is maintained at cathode potential (in many tubes it is internally connected to the cathode). Its

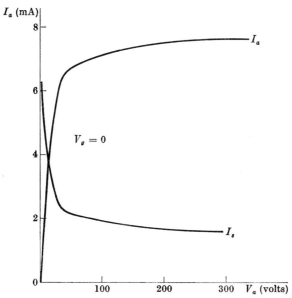

Fig. 12.12. Curves of screen current and anode current against anode potential, at zero grid voltage, for a pentode.

function is to maintain the field at the anode always in a direction such that the force on any secondary electrons emitted by the anode will return them to the anode, and they will not reach the screen. As would be expected, the anode current is practically independent of the anode potential, so that the anode slope resistance is very high, and so also is the amplification factor $\mu$, since hardly any lines of force from the anode penetrate to the space charge near the cathode. The voltage amplification obtained from a pentode with a resistance $R$ as the anode load may, from equation (12.13), be written in the form

$$A = -g_m R/(1+R/\rho),$$

which is approximately $-g_m R$ if $\rho \gg R$. It is obvious that the amplification is greater than that obtained from a triode which has the same mutual conductance $g_m$, but a lower value of $\rho$.

The anode current and screen current of a typical pentode are shown as functions of the anode voltage in Fig. 12.12. The current drawn from the cathode is virtually independent of the anode voltage, which affects only the division of current between screen and anode. The capacitance between the control grid and the anode in the pentode is usually of the order of a few thousandths of a micromicrofarad, and its contribution to the input capacitance is negligible.

The kinkless characteristic of the pentode may also be achieved in special tetrodes known as 'beam-power' tetrodes. In these tubes the space charge formed by the electrons in the region between screen grid and anode produces a potential minimum in front of the anode which, like that due to the suppressor grid in the pentode, returns to the anode any secondary electrons emitted by it. The effect of the space charge is enhanced by using a rather large spacing between screen grid and anode, and by making the screen grid of the same pitch as the control grid (ordinarily it is much coarser). The screen-grid wires are in the 'shadow' of the control grid wires, so that the electrons flow in beams between them and the screen current is smaller than in an ordinary tetrode. The beam action (enhanced by the use of side plates at cathode potential which limit the area over which current flows) increases the electron density and the space charge effect near the anode.

### GENERAL REFERENCE

ROLLIN, B. V., 1964, *An Introduction to Electronics* (O.U.P.).

### PROBLEMS

12.1. Calculate the anode voltage $V'_a$ of the equivalent diode for a triode with plane parallel electrodes in which the grid–cathode spacing is 0·03 cm and the current density is 0·02 A/cm², assuming that the 'equivalent diode spacing' is the same as the actual grid–cathode spacing.

If $V_g = -3$ V, $V_a = +150$ V on the triode, what must be the value of $\mu$?

(*Answer*: $V'_a = 3·9$ V; $\mu = 22$.)

12.2. Prove that in a plane-parallel diode the transit time of an electron is 3/2 times as long under space charge limited conditions as it would be in the absence of space charge.

What will be the transit time between cathode and grid in the triode of Problem 12.1?

(*Answer*: $7·7 \times 10^{-10}$ sec.)

12.3. In the arrangement of Fig. 12.3, assume that the capacitor charges instantaneously to $V_0$ when the diode conducts just at the peak of the applied voltage $V_0 \cos \omega t$, and that the time constant $RC = \tau$ of the capacitor–resistor combination is so long that the voltage on the capacitor falls linearly during the discharge period. Show by Fourier analysis that the amplitude of the component $\sin(n\omega t)$ of the voltage on the capacitor is $(2V_0/n\omega\tau)$.

# APPLICATIONS OF THERMIONIC
# VACUUM TUBES

In the previous chapter the chief characteristics of the basic types of thermionic vacuum tubes were outlined. In this chapter their main uses as amplifiers, oscillators, and detectors will be considered in more detail.

## 13.1. Audio-frequency voltage amplifiers

Amplifiers may be classed under various headings, and we shall deal first with small-signal amplifiers, where the magnitude of the alternating voltage applied to the grid of the tube is such that the resulting changes in the anode current are only a small fraction of the mean anode current. The fundamental circuit for the use of the triode as an amplifier was discussed in § 12.7. If more amplification is required than can be obtained from a single tube, several stages may be used in cascade. Some form of coupling is then required to transfer the amplified voltage appearing at the anode of one tube to the grid of the next tube, while preserving the correct steady potentials on these electrodes. The most common method employs $RC$-coupling. A capacitor $C$ is connected from the anode of the previous stage to the grid of the next, as in Fig. 13.1, and the grid is connected to earth (or to its bias battery) through a large resistance $R_1$. It is important that the capacitor $C$ (known as the blocking capacitor) have a very small leakage current under the steady voltage which it has to sustain, since otherwise this leakage current will flow also through the grid resistance $R_1$ and change the grid voltage from its optimum. The size of the capacitor must be such that its impedance is small compared with $R_1$ at the signal frequency, since then all the amplified voltage at the anode will be impressed on the grid of the next tube.

The equivalent circuit of an $RC$-coupled amplifier is shown in Fig. 13.2. Since the high tension supply must form a low impedance for the signal frequency, both terminals are at earth potential as far as signal voltages are concerned. The resistances $R$ and $R_1$ have therefore a common terminal, as also has $C_g$, which represents the input capacitance of the following tube. At low audio-frequencies the impedance of $C_g$ is large compared with $R_1$, and may be neglected. If the impedance of $C$ is small compared with $R_1$, as should be the case, then it will be seen that the grid resistor $R_1$ is effectively in parallel with $R$, and the combination forms the load for the first tube. It is usual to make $R_1$ large compared with $R$, so that the effective load is not materially smaller than $R$.

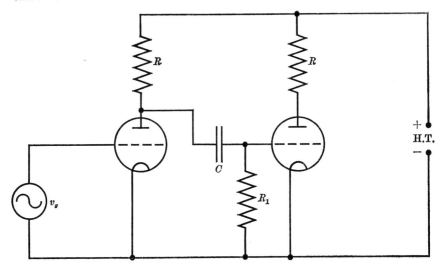

FIG. 13.1. *RC*-coupled amplifier.

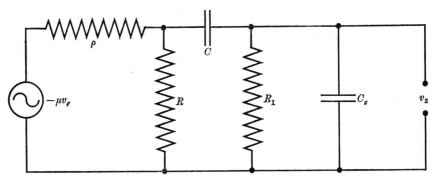

FIG. 13.2. Equivalent circuit for Fig. 13.1.

The effect of the capacitances $C$ and $C_g$ can readily be seen from consideration of a common requirement, an audio-frequency amplifier to cover the range of 50 to 10 000 c/s with constant amplification. We shall assume that the triode constants are $\mu = 30$, $\rho = 10\,000$ ohms; then, with $R = 25\,000$ ohms, the input capacitance of the triode $C_g$ is approximately 120 $\mu\mu$F (see § 12.8). $R_1$ may be made 1 megohm, so that its shunting effect on $R$ is negligible. At the low frequency limit the effect of $C_g$ is negligible and the ratio of the voltage across $R_1$ to that across $R$ is

$$\left|\frac{R_1}{R_1+1/j\omega C}\right| = \left(1+\frac{1}{\omega^2C^2R_1^2}\right)^{-\frac{1}{2}}.$$

Thus the required condition is $(1/\omega C) \ll R_1$, which is amply satisfied by making $C = 0\cdot1$ $\mu$F, when the ratio differs from unity by just over 1 per cent at 10 c/s. At the high frequency end, the shunting effect of the input capacity of the next triode must be considered. (Reference to § 12.8 shows that the input resistance of the triode will be about 60 megohms at a frequency of 10 kc/s, and its shunting effect may therefore be neglected.) The capacitance $C_g$ is in parallel with both $R$ and $R_1$, and its presence becomes noticeable only when its impedance becomes comparable with the lower of these, $R$. The effective load for the tube is then $C_g$ and $R$ in parallel, and the amplification becomes

$$\left|\frac{\mu}{1+\rho/\mathbf{Z}}\right| = \left|\frac{\mu}{1+\rho/R+j\omega C_g\rho}\right| = \frac{\mu}{\{(1+\rho/R)^2+\omega^2C_g^2\rho^2\}^{\frac{1}{2}}}, \qquad (13.1)$$

showing that the amplification is affected only when $\omega C_g\rho$ becomes comparable with $1+\rho/R$. The values of these two quantities are respectively $0\cdot075$ and $1\cdot4$ at 10 kc/s, so that the effect of $C_g$ is negligible. At 100 kc/s the amplification would be reduced by 13 per cent, and falls rapidly as the frequency is increased still further. Phase shifts in the amplifier may also be important (see Problem 13.7).

In certain applications, such as pulsed radar, the amplification of short pulses of the order of microsecond duration is required, and if the output is to be undistorted the amplifier must have a uniform magnification from very low frequencies up to several megacycles per second. It is clear that triodes cannot be used in such an amplifier, owing to their large input capacitance, and pentodes must be used instead. The second point is that the anode load is shunted by small capacitances from several sources: (a) a capacitance of 5 to 10 $\mu\mu$F between the anode and the suppressor- and screen-grids, (b) the input capacitance of the next stage, again from 5 to 10 $\mu\mu$F, and (c) stray capacitance from the wiring. The total capacitance may be as much as 15 $\mu\mu$F and its effect may be analysed as follows. Since the anode resistance of the pentode is very high, it is convenient to use the constant current generator for the equivalent circuit, as shown in Fig. 13.3. Here $R$ is the load resistance and $C$ the total capacitance shunted across it. The voltage across the load is

$$-g_m v_g|\mathbf{Z}| = -g_m v_g R/(1+\omega^2C^2R^2)^{\frac{1}{2}},$$

showing that the magnification per stage will fall by a factor $\sqrt{2}$ when

A a

$\omega CR = 1$. If $C = 15\ \mu\mu\text{F}$ and $R = 10\,000$ ohms, this point is reached at a frequency of 1·1 Mc/s. If the amplifier has altogether $n$ stages, each with magnification $A$, then the overall magnification is $A^n$, and at 1·1 Mc/s the overall amplification will be down by $2^{n/2}$. If $n$ is 5 or 6, this is far too much distortion. A more uniform magnification per stage can be secured by reducing $R$, which reduces the stage gain in proportion.

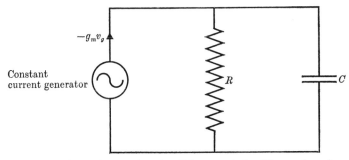

FIG. 13.3. Current-generator circuit for a pentode. The anode resistance of the tube would be shunted across $R$, but it is so high it can be neglected.

$R = $ load resistance. $C = $ total capacitance shunted across load.

More stages must be added, but the overall magnification will be more uniform because the distortion depends on the $R^2$ term in the denominator. A second method of maintaining the stage gain at the high frequency limit is to introduce a small inductance in series with the resistance, which, shunted by the capacitance, forms a low $Q$ resonant circuit. The values of $R$ and $L$ should be chosen so that their impedance is about the same as that of the capacitance $C$ at the highest frequency it is desired to amplify.

## 13.2. Negative feed-back amplifiers

In a negative feed-back amplifier, a fraction of the output voltage is fed back to the input in such phase as to reduce the net input voltage. A schematic diagram is shown in Fig. 13.4. The gain of the amplifier in the absence of feed-back is $A$, and $\beta$ is the fraction of the output returned to the input. The output voltage $v_0$ is then

$$v_0 = A(v_i + \beta v_0),$$

giving
$$v_0 = Av_i/(1 - A\beta). \tag{13.2}$$

The gain is now $A/(1 - A\beta)$, and it is therefore reduced if $\beta$ is negative, i.e. if the feed-back voltage opposes the input voltage. This drawback is offset by several advantages, in particular the reduction of distortion.

Any distortion voltage which would appear at the output is fed back to the input and reduced in the same ratio as the amplification. If now the input voltage is increased by means of a preceding amplifier until the overall output is restored to its former level, the distortion voltage will remain at the reduced level provided the preceding amplifier does not introduce distortion. This condition is generally fulfilled because the signal is at a low level in the preceding amplifier, and distortion arises only when the signal is high, as in the last stages of an amplifier.

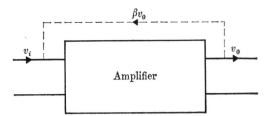

Fig. 13.4. Amplifier with feed-back.

If $(-A\beta)$ is made large compared with unity, then the voltage amplification becomes simply $1/\beta$. Thus it depends only on the feed-back ratio and not at all on the actual amplification factor of the receiver. It is therefore independent of any variations in $A$ due to fluctuations in the h.t. voltage, etc. If the feed-back ratio is independent of frequency, a wide-band amplifier with a very uniform frequency response is obtained. For these conditions to be satisfied in a receiver with considerable net gain, $\beta$ must be small and $A$, the amplification in the absence of feed-back, large. Great care is then required in the design, for if the feed-back $\beta$ becomes positive at any frequency where $A$ is sufficiently large to make $(1-A\beta)$ zero or negative, oscillation will set in. To avoid this, the feed-back must be negative over a wider range of frequency than the receiver will amplify.

## 13.3. Audio-frequency power amplifiers

The discussion so far has been concerned with 'voltage amplifiers', where an amplified voltage output is required working into such a high impedance that no power is drawn. This is true for the intermediate stages of low-frequency amplifiers, but the last stage is generally required to supply power to a finite load. If this load is a pure resistance $R$, then use of the equivalent circuit of the triode (Fig. 12.9 $(a)$) shows that the mean power developed in the load will be

$$\overline{i_a^2}\,R = \mu^2\overline{v_g^2}\,R/(\rho+R)^2. \tag{13.3}$$

If $R$ can be varied, then maximum power will be developed in $R$ if it is made equal to $\rho$, as can be shown either by use of the maximum power theorem (§ 3.3) or by direct differentiation of equation (13.3) with regard to $R$. For most triodes this means that the optimum value of $R$ is in the region of 10 000 ohms or more. Since the power output under the optimum condition $R = \rho$ can be written as $\mu^2 v_g^2/4\rho$, it is obvious that for a fixed value of $\mu v_g$, more power can be obtained by reducing $\rho$. For this reason low impedance triodes, with $\rho$ of the order of a few thousand ohms, are used for output stages. In practice the allowable value of $\mu v_g$ is fixed by the size of the h.t. voltage, for the voltage swing on the load will be $\frac{1}{2}\mu v_g$, and this cannot approach the h.t. voltage too closely without causing considerable distortion (see below). Low impedance triodes have low values of $\mu$, since $g_m$ is fixed by the cathode emission, so that to obtain the desired power output larger values of $v_g$ are required. Typical values for an output triode are $g_m = 2\cdot5$ mA/V, $\rho = 1500$ ohms, $\mu = 3\cdot75$.

*Push-pull amplifiers*

In order to reduce distortion in the output, a method of working using two identical tubes in 'push-pull' is commonly employed. The circuit is shown in Fig. 13.5, the grids being excited in antiphase by means of a transformer with centre tapped secondary winding. The anodes of the two tubes are connected to the h.t. supply through the two halves of the centre-tapped primary of a transformer whose secondary winding is connected to the load. Since the change in the grid voltage of one tube is $+v_g$ while that on the other is $-v_g$, the anode currents of the two tubes can be expressed as series expansions

$$\left.\begin{array}{l} b_0+b_1 v_g+b_2 v_g^2+b_3 v_g^3+b_4 v_g^4+\dots \\ b_0-b_1 v_g+b_2 v_g^2-b_3 v_g^3+b_4 v_g^4-\dots \end{array}\right\} \qquad (13.4)$$

and

These flow in opposite directions through the two halves of the output transformer, so that it is their difference

$$2(b_1 v_g+b_3 v_g^3+b_5 v_g^5+\dots) \qquad (13.5)$$

which forms the magnetizing current for the transformer, and which induces a voltage in the secondary winding. Thus, if the two halves of the circuit are equally matched, all the even harmonics disappear from the output. So also do the steady components $b_0$ of the anode currents since they flow in opposite directions through the two halves of the primary. This has the advantage that saturation of the transformer core by the steady components of the anode currents is avoided.

Use of a transformer has two further advantages: (*a*) if the turns ratio is $n:1$, the load seen by the tube is $n^2$ times greater than the actual load (see equation 9.41), and $n$ can be chosen to match the load to the tube; (*b*) the d.c. resistance of its primary winding is low so that the mean voltage on the anode is almost equal to the h.t. voltage.

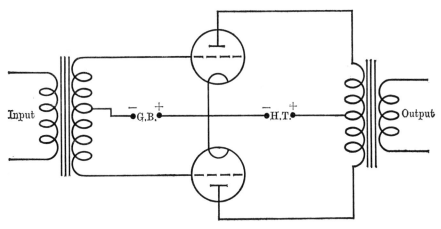

FIG. 13.5. Push-pull amplifier.

*Efficiency of power amplifiers*

We consider now the source of the a.c. power which an amplifier delivers into a load. It clearly cannot come from the signal source applied to the grid, for the power drawn from this source is practically zero because of the high input impedance of the valve. The ultimate source of the output power is the h.t. supply, though this is not immediately obvious, for the current drawn from the h.t. supply does not change when a signal is being amplified if there is no distortion. For simplicity, we shall analyse the case of a triode whose anode is connected through a resistance $R$ to a h.t. supply of $V_0$ volts. If the anode current is $I_a$, the power drawn from the h.t. is $I_a V_0$, of which a part $I_a^2 R = I_a(V_0 - V_a)$, where $V_a$ is the anode voltage, is dissipated in the load resistance. The remainder, $I_a V_a$, is dissipated in the tube and appears as heat at the anode. The electrons forming the current $I_a$ through the tube gain kinetic energy $I_a V_a$ as they move through the potential difference $V_a$ between cathode and anode, and this kinetic energy is destroyed when they collide with the anode, being turned into heat. When a signal is applied to the grid, an alternating component is added to the anode current, which becomes $I_a + i_a \sin \omega t$, while the anode voltage becomes

$V_0 - R(I_a + i_a \sin \omega t)$. The mean power dissipated on the anode is now the mean value of the product of these two expressions. On multiplying out, it is seen that the product contains terms in $\sin \omega t$ whose average value is zero, and the remainder is

$$(V_0 - RI_a)I_a - Ri_a^2 \sin^2 \omega t.$$

The first term is the same as the anode heating in the absence of a signal, but the presence of the second term shows that there is a reduction in the mean power dissipated on the anode of $\frac{1}{2}Ri_a^2$. This is just equal to the a.c. power dissipated in the load $R$. The physical reason for the reduction in the anode heating arises from the fact that the anode potential falls as the anode current rises. Thus more current reaches the anode while its potential is lower than the average value, and less current while it is higher than the average, with a consequent reduction in the mean power dissipated at the anode.

Since the source of the a.c. power is the h.t. supply, we define the efficiency of the power amplifier as the ratio of the a.c. power output to the power drawn from the h.t. supply. Thus in the above example, the efficiency is
$$\frac{1}{2}Ri_a^2/I_aV_0.$$

To find the theoretical efficiency we take an idealized case where the characteristics of the tube are straight lines passing through the point $I_a = 0$ at $V_a = 0$. We assume the load resistance $R$ to be connected through a 1:1 transformer with zero resistance in its primary winding so that no voltage drop across the primary occurs in the absence of a signal. Then the mean anode voltage is $V_0$ and its instantaneous value is $V_0 - v_a \sin \omega t$, where $v_a$ is the amplitude of the alternating voltage developed across the load. If the characteristics are straight down to $V_a = 0$, we can increase $v_a$ without introducing distortion up to the value $V_0$, when the instantaneous anode voltage becomes zero at one point in the cycle. The a.c. power is then $\frac{1}{2}V_0^2/R$, while the power drawn from the h.t. is $I_aV_0 = (V_0^2/\rho)$, where $\rho$ is the anode slope resistance of the tube. As was shown earlier, $R$ should be made equal to $\rho$ for optimum output, and the theoretical efficiency is then 50 per cent.

Practical values of the efficiency are much less because the curvature of the characteristics prevents large voltage swings being employed. In the push-pull amplifier, with its cancellation of the even harmonics, bigger swings can be tolerated. It is then possible to depart from the type of working (known as Class A) we have considered hitherto, and to use Class B working, where the tubes are biased to the cut-off point on the grid. Current flows in each valve of the push-pull pair only during the half-cycle when the alternating voltage applied to its grid is positive. During this half-cycle the anode voltage is low, and no current flows in the other half-cycle when the anode voltage is high. This makes the efficiency high, the theoretical value being 78 per cent (see Problem 13.5). In practice, values of 50 to 60 per cent are realized.

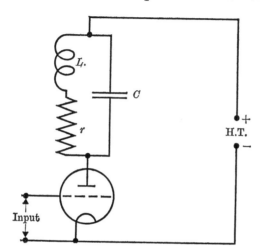

FIG. 13.6. Amplifier with tuned circuit as load. For radio frequencies a screen grid or pentode tube would be used.

## 13.4. Radio-frequency amplifiers

At radio frequencies (by which is meant frequencies of the order of 1 Mc/s and higher) it is usual to employ a tuned circuit for the anode load. Resistive loads are unsatisfactory because they are shunted by low reactances formed by the input capacitance of the next tube, the anode to earth capacitance, and stray capacitance in the wiring. A parallel tuned circuit is employed, as in Fig. 13.6, to obtain a high impedance for the anode load; these various capacitances are then shunted across the tuned circuit, and form part of the total capacitance $C$ required to tune the coil to the desired resonant frequency. Since the impedance of a parallel tuned circuit is high only near the resonant frequency, such an amplifier is selective, the magnification falling rapidly on either side of resonance. Near resonance the impedance of the parallel tuned circuit may be written approximately as (see Problem 9.1)

$$\frac{1}{\mathbf{Z}} = \frac{1}{R} + 2j\Delta\omega C,$$

where $R = L/(Cr)$, and $\Delta\omega$ is the departure of $\omega$ from the resonant value $\omega_0 = 1/(LC)^{\frac{1}{2}}$. Hence the amplified voltage across the tuned circuit is

$$\frac{-\mu v_g}{1+\rho/\mathbf{Z}} = \frac{-\mu v_g}{1+\rho/R+2j\Delta\omega C\rho} = \frac{-g_m v_g}{1/\rho+1/R+2j\Delta\omega C}. \qquad (13.6)$$

At the resonant frequency the magnification is $\mu/(1+\rho/R)$ and it falls by a factor $\sqrt{2}$ at frequencies deviating from the resonant value such that

$$\pm 2\Delta\omega C = (1/\rho+1/R).$$

If the selectivity is defined as $f/(2\Delta f) = \omega/(2\Delta\omega)$, so that it is analogous to the $Q$ of a resonant circuit, we see that the selectivity is the same as that of our tuned circuit shunted by the anode resistance $\rho$ of the tube. Reference to the equivalent current generator circuit of Fig. 12.9 (b) shows that $\rho$ is effectively in parallel with the load $\mathbf{Z}$.

The values of inductance and capacitance for the tuned circuit are determined as follows. The desired resonant frequency is usually fixed, so that $LC = 1/\omega_0^2$. For high voltage amplification, $R$ should be as high as possible, say about $10^5$ ohms. Now $R = Q\sqrt{(L/C)}$, and a good working rule is that $Q$ is of the order of 100 at frequencies of a few megacycles per second. Thus at a frequency of 1·6 Mc/s ($\omega_0 = 10^7$), we have $\sqrt{(LC)} = 10^{-7}$, $\sqrt{(L/C)} = R/Q = 10^3$, giving $L = 100 \,\mu\text{H}$, $C = 100 \,\mu\mu\text{F}$.

Transformer coupling is often employed in r.f. amplifiers, the secondary winding being tuned as in Fig. 13.7. The input capacitance of the following stage then forms part of the tuning capacitance. The magnification at resonance (the ratio of the voltage across the tuned circuit to the voltage applied to the grid) is then (see Problem 13.2)

$$A = g_m \frac{\omega_0 MQ}{1+(\omega_0 M)^2/r\rho}, \qquad (13.7)$$

which is a maximum when the coupling is adjusted so that $(\omega_0 M)^2 = r\rho$. Here $Q$ is the magnification factor of the tuned circuit in the absence of any coupling. In many applications the primary of the transformer is tuned by a parallel capacitance as well, and the coupling is adjusted to give the 'band-pass' tuning obtainable with coupled circuits (see § 9.4).

Triodes are seldom used for r.f. voltage amplifiers because of the feedback through the grid-anode capacitance. It was shown in § 12.8 that this feed-back gives a finite value for the input admittance of the tube. This admittance consists of two parts, one primarily capacitative which can be tuned out if it is not too great (in the example of § 12.8 the input capacitance was found to be 120 $\mu\mu\text{F}$, which is of the same order as the tuning capacitance required above at 1·6 Mc/s.) The second term is resistive, but may have either sign, being negative if the anode load is inductive. Since a parallel tuned circuit will be inductive at frequencies below its resonant frequency, the amplifier will break into oscillation if the negative conductance resulting at the input is greater than any positive conductance in the source with which it is in parallel. To avoid such instability in the amplifier, screen-grid or pentode tubes are generally used, since their low grid-anode capacitance makes the feed-back very

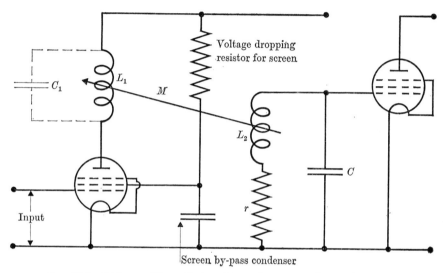

Fig. 13.7. R.F. amplifier with tuned transformer coupling and pentode tubes. The capacitor $C_1$ is used if coupled tuned circuits are needed to obtain bandpass tuning.

small. With high gain amplifiers using several stages each stage must be screened by enclosure in an earthed metal box to prevent feed-back from one stage to another through stray capacitances or inductances. Such a box is an effective screen provided that its thickness is greater than the skin depth for r.f. currents induced on the inside of the walls, since such currents are then highly attenuated before they reach the outside.

If triode tubes are used, as is generally the case in power amplifiers, the feed-back through the grid-anode capacitance must be 'neutralized' by the provision of a second feed-back path of opposite phase. This can be done by a number of methods, one of which, the 'neutrodyne circuit', is shown in Fig. 13.8. The anode coil is split into two halves, the h.t. supply being connected to the centre point. The two ends of the coil are then at equal and opposite potentials with respect to earth as far as the amplified signal is concerned. The feed-back to the grid through the grid-anode capacitance from one end of the coil is then balanced out by that through the neutralizing capacitor $C_n$ from the other end of the coil. The arrangement is effectively a bridge circuit as shown in Fig. 13.9. At balance, for which the condition is $L_2 C_n = L_1 C_{ga}$, none of the output voltage appears across the input terminals. So long as inductance

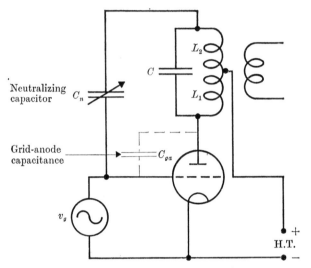

FIG. 13.8. The neutrodyne circuit.

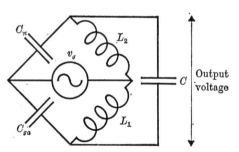

FIG. 13.9. Equivalent circuit of the neutrodyne.

in the leads and other stray reactances are negligible, the balance and hence the neutralization is independent of frequency.

For high efficiency, r.f. power amplifiers may be run under Class C conditions. The grid of the tube is then biased back well beyond cut-off, so that current flows through the tube only for a small fraction of a cycle near the positive peak of the alternating potential applied to the grid. The amplitude of the grid swing must be of the same order as the negative bias on the grid in order to carry the tube into the conducting region. The relations between grid voltage and anode current are illustrated in Fig. 13.10. The characteristic plotted here is a 'dynamic characteristic', the variation of the anode current with grid bias being shown not at constant anode voltage, as in a 'static characteristic', but under working conditions with a resistive load in the anode circuit. The anode current is highly distorted, consisting of short pulses, but a tuned circuit is used as the anode load so that a high impedance is presented

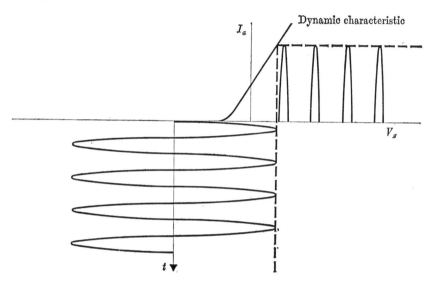

Fig. 13.10. The relation between grid voltage and anode current in a Class C amplifier. The grid has a large negative d.c. bias, and the applied alternating voltage has a large amplitude. Anode current only flows for a fraction of the positive half of the cycle.

to the anode current only at the fundamental frequency. This eliminates the harmonics from the output voltage across the tuned circuit. The theoretical efficiency of Class C operation is 100 per cent, since under idealized conditions the anode current flows only in pulses of infinitesimal duration which coincide with the point in the cycle at which the anode voltage is zero (we assume that the anode voltage swing is equal in amplitude to the h.t. voltage). In practice efficiencies of 60 to 80 per cent are obtained.

Class C operation may also be used for the purpose of frequency multiplication. The form of the anode current makes it very rich in harmonics. If a tuned circuit tuned to one of the harmonics is used as the anode load, the oscillatory voltage across the load will have a frequency which is an exact multiple of that applied to the grid. Frequency multiplication of this type is used in frequency measuring equipment where an unknown frequency is to be determined by comparison with a standard of much lower frequency (see § 15.4).

## 13.5. Tuned anode and tuned grid oscillators

In the discussion of power amplifiers it was shown that the tube acts as a converter which transforms d.c. power from the h.t. supply into a.c. power in the load. For this purpose the signal applied to the grid of the tube acts merely as a trigger, little or no power being drawn from the signal source so long as the grid does not go positive in any part of the cycle. If a small fraction of the a.c. power in the load is used as a source of the signal applied to the grid, the conversion of d.c. power into a.c. power may be made automatic, and no external 'trigger' is required. The tube then acts as a self-sustained oscillator. For this to occur, certain conditions must be fulfilled by the size and phase of the voltage feed-back to the grid. Reference to equation (13.2) shows that the output voltage $v_0$ is

$$v_0 = Av_i/(1-A\beta),$$

where $A$ is the gain of the amplifier without feed-back, and $\beta$ is the fraction of the output voltage fed back to the input. If $v_0$ is to be finite when the input voltage $v_i$ from an independent source is made zero, then the denominator must be zero. In other words, the product $A\beta$ must be positive and equal to unity. This imposes conditions on both the phase and the magnitude of the feed-back, whose nature can be more clearly understood by reference to a simple case.

*The tuned anode oscillator*

A circuit diagram for a 'tuned anode' oscillator is shown in Fig. 13.11. A parallel tuned circuit forms the anode load of a triode tube, and a voltage is fed back to the grid by means of a mutual inductance. We shall analyse the circuit starting from first principles. If $V = V_0 - V_a$ is the voltage across the tuned circuit and $I$ the current through the inductance $L$, we have the relations

$$I_a = I_0 + g_m V_g + V_a/\rho = I_0 + g_m V_g + (V_0 - V)/\rho,$$
$$V_g = M\,dI/dt,$$
$$V = rI + L\,dI/dt,$$
$$I_a = I + C\,dV/dt.$$

From this set of simultaneous equations, all variables but one may be eliminated. It is simplest to retain $I$ as the dependent variable, and the resulting equation is

$$LC\, d^2I/dt^2 + (Cr + L/\rho - g_m M)dI/dt + (1 + r/\rho)I = I_0 + V_0/\rho. \quad (13.8)$$

The right-hand side is independent of the time, and the differential equation is that of a damped harmonic oscillation. The damping will be zero if conditions are chosen so that the coefficient of $dI/dt$ is made zero, i.e.

$$Cr + L/\rho - g_m M = 0. \quad (13.9)$$

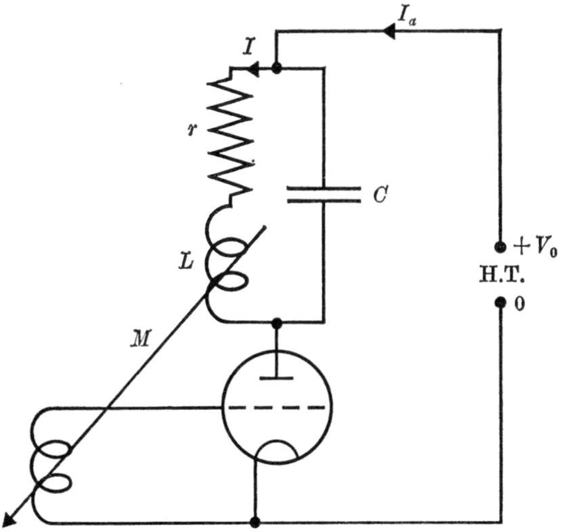

FIG. 13.11. The tuned-anode oscillator.

The frequency of natural oscillation of the circuit is then given by the relation

$$LC\omega^2 = (1 + r/\rho), \quad (13.10)$$

and any oscillation of this frequency which exists will continue with the same amplitude. Equation (13.9) is the condition for the maintenance of oscillation, and it can be shown that it corresponds to the condition $A\beta = 1$ (see Problem 13.3).

In practice the feed-back is not adjusted so as to make the coefficient of $dI/dt$ in equation (13.8) exactly zero, since this would not give stable oscillations (a small change in the conditions leading to a reduction in $g_m$, for example, would make the coefficient of $dI/dt$ positive, and the oscillations would die away). The feed-back is therefore made so large that the coefficient of $dI/dt$ is negative, and the solution of equation (13.8) is then of the form

$$I = (I_0 + V_0/\rho) + e^{-bt}(Ae^{(b^2-c^2)^{\frac{1}{2}}t} + Be^{-(b^2-c^2)^{\frac{1}{2}}t}), \quad (13.11)$$

where $b = (Cr+L/\rho-g_m M)/2LC$, and $c^2 = (1+r/\rho)/LC$. If $c^2 > b^2$, the oscillatory part of the current may be written

$$I = e^{-bt}(A' \cos \omega t + B' \sin \omega t),$$

where $\omega = \sqrt{(c^2-b^2)}$. This represents an oscillation which decays away if $b$ is positive, is just maintained if $b$ is zero, and increases in amplitude if $b$ is negative. The condition for the latter is

$$g_m M > (Cr+L/\rho) \quad \text{or} \quad M > \frac{(L+\rho Cr)}{\mu},$$

showing that there is a minimum value of $M$ required to give oscillations. When $b$ is negative, any transient oscillation in the anode circuit (such as would be caused by switching on the h.t. voltage, or by noise (see Chapter 16)) builds up in amplitude instead of dying away. Our equations suggest that the amplitude would increase indefinitely, but this is not so, because the 'constants' $g_m$, $\rho$ of the tube are truly constant only for small amplitudes of oscillation, limited to the straight portion of the tube characteristic. When the amplitude is so great that the peaks of the oscillation carry the tube on to the flat portions of the characteristic at saturation and cut-off, the effective value of $g_m$ falls, and the amplitude will reach a steady point where its effective value is such as to make $b = 0$. In general this point is reached when the amplitude of the voltage swing across the tuned circuit is of the same order as the h.t. voltage $V_0$.

The coefficient $b$ may be written in the form

$$b = \frac{r}{2L} + \frac{1}{2\rho C} - \frac{g_m M}{2LC}. \tag{13.12}$$

Here the first term gives the rate at which oscillations would decay in the anode circuit if the tube were not connected, or not switched on; the second term represents the extra damping caused by the anode resistance of the tube $\rho$, which is effectively shunted across the tuned circuit when the tube is running; and the last term shows the effect of the tube and the feed-back in reducing the damping of the tuned circuit even when $M$ is not large enough to maintain oscillations. This effect is known as 'regeneration'. It is important to remember that the sign of $M$ can be negative if the connexions to the mutual inductance are reversed. The damping of the tuned circuit is then increased by the action of the tube, an effect known as 'degeneration'. The $Q$ and selectivity of the circuit are thereby decreased, whereas they are increased by regeneration. The latter has the effect of creating a 'negative resistance' in the tuned circuit, and spontaneous oscillation occurs when the negative resistance is large enough to outweigh the positive resistance. A positive resistance is one in which power is dissipated, a negative resistance one in which power is generated.

### The tuned grid oscillator

A second important type of oscillator is obtained by attaching the tuned circuit to the grid of the tube, and feeding back a voltage into this circuit by mutual inductance coupling from a coil in the anode lead. This is known as the 'tuned grid' oscillator and is shown in Fig. 13.12.

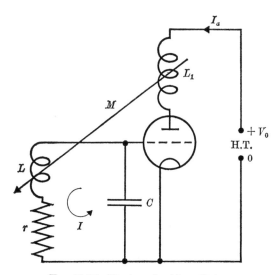

FIG. 13.12. The tuned-grid oscillator.

The analysis of this circuit is similar to that used for the tuned anode oscillator. Let $I$ be the circulating current in the grid circuit, $V$ be the voltage developed between grid and cathode, $V_a$ the anode voltage, and $I_a$ the anode current. Then the equations for the grid circuit are

$$V = M(dI_a/dt)+rI+L(dI/dt), \qquad I = -C(dV/dt),$$

while for the anode circuit we have

$$I_a = I_0+g_m V+V_a/\rho, \qquad V_0 = V_a+\left(L_1\frac{dI_a}{dt}+M\frac{dI}{dt}\right).$$

A simple solution of these equations is possible if we assume that the effect of the terms in the last bracket is small, so that effectively $V_a$ is constant and equal to $V_0$. This is usually true in practice. Then elimination of $I$ and $I_a$ between the first three equations leads to the expression

$$LC\frac{d^2V}{dt^2} + (rC - g_m M)\frac{dV}{dt} + V = 0. \tag{13.13}$$

This represents an oscillatory motion, and is similar to equation (13.8). Oscillations will be maintained or will build up if $M \geqslant rC/g_m$.

When the oscillator is running steadily, the coefficient of the term $dV/dt$ in the oscillatory equation (13.13) is zero, and the frequency of oscillation is given by the relation $\omega = (LC)^{-\frac{1}{2}}$, showing that it is determined by the natural resonance frequency of the tuned circuit. If we return to the corresponding equation (13.8) for the tuned anode oscillator, the angular frequency is found to be $\omega = \{(1+r/\rho)/LC\}^{\frac{1}{2}}$ showing that it depends slightly on the anode impedance $\rho$ of the tube. Since the latter may change with the running conditions, the frequency will also vary, and when good frequency stability is desired, the tuned grid oscillator is generally preferred, since here the tube constants do not enter directly into the equation for the frequency. In practice the frequency will depend to some extent on the tube, for the input capacitance of the latter is shunted across the tuning capacitor of the grid circuit of the tuned grid oscillator, and the input capacitance varies with the running conditions (see § 12.8). Another cause of frequency drift is change in the temperature of the components, with consequent changes in their electrical constants. As a rough guide it may be said that the frequency of an ordinary small oscillator, following the initial warming up period after switching on, is stable to the order of a part in 1000. If higher stability is required quartz crystal oscillators are used (see § 15.4). These are low power oscillators (a few watts at most), which are then followed by r.f. power amplifiers to supply the required output. For the highest efficiency, such amplifiers are run as 'Class C' (see § 13.4).

### 13.6. Power oscillators

When a large power output is required, but it is not essential to have the highest frequency stability, an oscillator run under 'Class C' conditions is used. This is similar to the Class C amplifier (see § 13.4), and gives high efficiency; it may be regarded as a Class C amplifier with regeneration to supply the grid excitation voltage. The mean potential of the grid is well beyond the cut-off value for the tube, and the excitation voltage must therefore have sufficient amplitude to carry the tube into the conducting region at the positive peaks. A convenient circuit giving a large grid excitation is that due to Hartley, where a tapped inductance is used as an auto-transformer to supply the required feed-

back. The basic circuit is shown in Fig. 13.13. The cathode is connected
to the mid-point of the inductance, and the grid and anode through their
respective voltage supplies to the opposite ends of the inductance, where

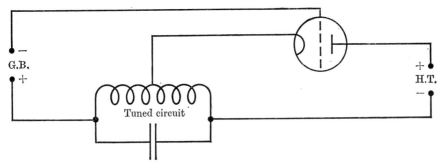

FIG. 13.13. Basic circuit of Hartley oscillator.

the alternating potentials are in opposite phase with respect to the
cathode, thus giving the right sign in the feed-back for oscillation.

An alternative form of the Hartley circuit is shown in Fig. 13.14.
This is known as the 'shunt-feed' type of circuit, the h.t. voltage being
connected to the anode in parallel with the tuned circuit, instead of in

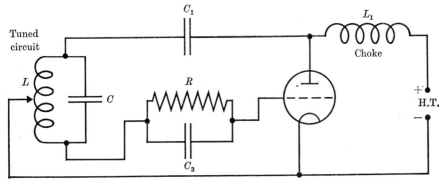

FIG. 13.14. Shunt-feed Hartley oscillator with automatic grid-bias. Appropriate values
of the circuit elements for a frequency of 1 Mc/s: $L = 125\,\mu\mathrm{H}$, $L_1 = 0\cdot1\,\mathrm{H}$; $R = 10\,000$
ohms; $C = 200\,\mu\mu\mathrm{F}$; $C_1 = 0\cdot01\,\mu\mathrm{F}$, $C_3 = 0\cdot001\,\mu\mathrm{F}$.

series with it, as in Fig. 13.13. This requires a choke $L_1$ in the h.t. lead
to prevent oscillatory currents flowing to the h.t., and a blocking capacitor $C_1$ to isolate the tuned circuit, whose mean potential is that of the
cathode, from the h.t. The values of $L_1$ and $C_1$ must be sufficiently large
at the frequency of oscillation that their impedances are respectively
large and small compared with that of the tuned circuit.

For Class C operation of an oscillator, a special type of grid bias circuit is required, for the following reason. If a large steady negative bias, such as that provided by a battery, is applied to the grid, oscillations cannot start because no current can flow through the tube when the amplitude of oscillation is small, though oscillations can be maintained at a high level sufficient to swing the grid into the conducting region. To overcome this difficulty, an automatic form of grid bias is required which is initially zero, and increases with the level of oscillation. This is provided by the $RC_3$ combination shown in Fig. 13.14. As the oscillations increase in amplitude, the grid is swung positive for part of the cycle, and collects electrons. This gives a grid current which, flowing through $R$ on its return path, makes the mean potential of the grid negative provided that the size of the capacitor $C_3$ is such as to make the time constant of the $RC_3$ combination long compared with the period of oscillation. Then the short pulse of electron current to the grid when it swings positive charges up $C_3$, and the slow discharge of $C_3$ through $R$ creates the mean negative potential required for the grid bias. In practice the optimum value of $R$ is usually around 10 000 ohms; lower values give insufficient bias, and much higher values are dangerous. For, if the voltage swing becomes too large, and the anode potential falls too low while the grid potential is positive, the grid may start to emit more secondary electrons than it receives primaries. This reverses the mean grid current, and the bias becomes positive instead of negative; the excessive current which results may destroy the tube.

The capacitor $C_3$ should be chosen to make the $RC_3$ time constant about 10 periods of oscillation. If the time constant is made too long, intermittent operation known as 'squegging' may be caused, for the grid bias cannot adjust itself quickly enough to follow random changes in the amplitude of oscillation. If the latter starts to fall, but the bias is not reduced, current ceases to flow through the tube, and the oscillations will die away; they cannot restart until $C_3$ has discharged through $R$ so that anode current can flow again. Thus oscillations may be interrupted periodically at a frequency determined by the $RC_3$ combination.

Typical values of the circuit constants for a Hartley oscillator at a frequency of about 1 Mc/s are given above in Fig. 13.14. The resistance of the inductance is omitted from the diagram, but its value can be found if the $Q$ of the coil is known.

## 13.7. The Kipp relay and the multivibrator

The oscillators which have been considered so far produce sinusoidal oscillations whose frequency is controlled almost entirely by the constants of a tuned circuit. This is true even of the Class C type, where the anode current is very far from sinusoidal, for the tuned circuit offers an appreciable impedance only to the fundamental frequency, and the voltage developed across it is almost sinusoidal (in this respect the oscillator is similar to the Class C amplifier). The question arises, what will happen if we take an untuned amplifier, and introduce feed-back of the right sign to produce instability? Such a device is shown in Fig. 13.15, where the circuit consists of a two-stage aperiodic amplifier,

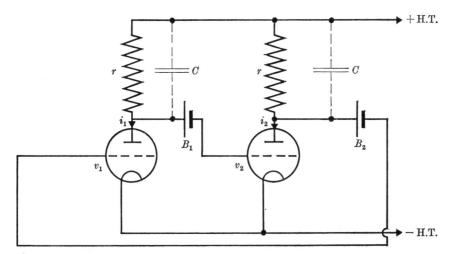

FIG. 13.15. The Kipp relay. $B_1$, $B_2$ are batteries to supply grid-bias voltage.

with feed-back from the anode of the second tube to the grid of the first tube. The purpose of the batteries $B_1$, $B_2$ is to provide direct coupling from anode to grid while preserving the correct steady voltages on these electrodes. If the voltage amplification of each stage is $A$, where $A$ is negative to allow for the change of phase between grid and anode voltages, then the overall amplification is $A^2$. The feed-back factor $\beta$ is practically unity, so that if $A^2 > 1$, the device should be unstable.

In the analysis of this system we must take account of the electrode capacitance of the anode and other stray capacitance between anode and earth; this is represented by the small capacitance $C$ which shunts the anode load $r$ of each tube. The anode current of the first tube is

$$i_1 = g_m v_1 + v_2/\rho,$$

where lower-case symbols are used, since we shall deal only with the fluctuating components. Here $v_1$ is the voltage change applied to the grid of tube 1, and $v_2$ is its anode voltage change, which is the same as the grid voltage change of the second tube. Since the anode current $i_1$ flows through $r$ and $C$ in parallel, we have also

$$-i_1 = C(dv_2/dt) + v_2/r.$$

Elimination of $i_1$ gives the following relation between $v_1$ and $v_2$, together with an exactly similar relation with $v_1$ and $v_2$ interchanged, obtained by applying the same analysis to the second tube:

$$\left.\begin{aligned} -g_m v_1 &= C(dv_2/dt) + v_2(r+\rho)/r\rho \\ -g_m v_2 &= C(dv_1/dt) + v_1(r+\rho)/r\rho \end{aligned}\right\}. \tag{13.14}$$

Since $-g_m \rho r/(r+\rho) = A$, the amplification of each tube, we may write these equations in the form

$$\left.\begin{aligned} Av_1 &= \tau(dv_2/dt) + v_2 \\ Av_2 &= \tau(dv_1/dt) + v_1 \end{aligned}\right\}, \tag{13.15}$$

where $\tau = Cr\rho/(r+\rho)$ is the time constant of the capacitance $C$ in parallel with $r$ and $\rho$. The solution of these equations is

$$v_1 = -v_2 = v_0 \exp\{-(A+1)t/\tau\}. \tag{13.16}$$

If the value of $-A$ for each tube is greater than unity, this solution shows that a situation with each tube conducting will not be stable, since any disturbance of the grid potential of one tube due to noise, etc., will increase exponentially. The grid of one tube will rise in potential while the other goes negative at the same rate. The first tube will therefore conduct at an increasing rate until it saturates, while the second will conduct at a decreasing rate until it is cut off; or vice versa. This situation will remain until a short pulse applied to the grid of the tube which is cut off brings it into the conducting region; then the exponential increase of its grid voltage will carry it to saturation while the other tube will change from saturation to cut-off. The time required for this voltage 'landslide' is very short. If $-A \gg 1$, the effective time constant of the exponential is approximately $\tau/(-A) = C/g_m$, and typical values are $C = 50 \ \mu\mu\text{F}$, $g_m = 5 \times 10^{-3}$ A/V, giving $C/g_m = 10^{-8}$ sec. Hence the time required for an initial disturbance (which might be of the order of a microvolt) to increase to 100 V is

$$t = 10^{-8}\{2 \cdot 3 \log_{10}(10^2/10^{-6})\} = 0 \cdot 2 \times 10^{-6} \text{ sec.}$$

This result of less than a microsecond gives a rather optimistic value for the duration of the voltage landslide, however, for two reasons: (a) when saturation sets in the value of $g_m$ is lower than that assumed, and (b) when the grid of the second tube is swung negative beyond the cut-off point, the discharge of its anode capacitance is incomplete and can continue only through the anode load resistance $r$, which is usually much greater in value than $1/g_m$. This makes the landslide of longer duration for the tube which is being cut off than for the other tube.

The device which has just been considered is known as the Kipp relay. It will respond to a very short voltage pulse, and once switched over will remain so until a pulse of the opposite polarity is applied. The anode current of the tube which is caused to conduct by the pulse may be

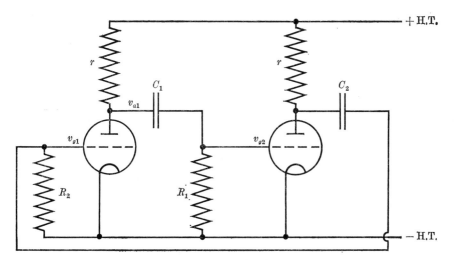

Fig. 13.16. The multivibrator.

used to operate a mechanical relay. In practice the bias batteries $B_1$, $B_2$ may be eliminated by a suitable automatic biasing arrangement.

If the direct coupling between stages of the Kipp relay provided by the batteries $B_1$, $B_2$ is replaced by $RC$ coupling, as in Fig. 13.16, a system is produced in which a periodic change over from (tube 1 saturated, tube 2 cut off) to (tube 1 cut off, tube 2 saturated), and vice versa, is produced automatically. This is known as the multivibrator. Its action can be understood as follows. Suppose at some instant tube 1 is saturated, and tube 2 is cut off. Then the voltage on grid 2 is negative, but the charge on capacitor $C_1$ which is holding it negative is gradually returning to its equilibrium value and the voltage across the grid resistance $R_1$ is returning to zero. When it becomes sufficiently small to allow anode current to start flowing in the second tube, the exponential voltage landslide will take place. The anode voltage of this tube will drop suddenly, and this drop will be transferred through $C_2 R_2$ to the grid of tube 1, which will therefore be cut off. The voltage across $R_2$ will then decay as $C_2$ recharges to its equilibrium value, and the reverse landslide will occur when it has fallen sufficiently for conduction to begin in tube 1. The cycle is now complete, and the wave forms of grid and anode voltage for tube 1, and grid voltage of tube 2 are shown in Fig. 13.17. The positive kicks of grid voltage which occur at the change-over points are cut off at a small positive voltage by the flow of electrons to the grid. The anode of each tube is alternately at the h.t. voltage (during cut-off)

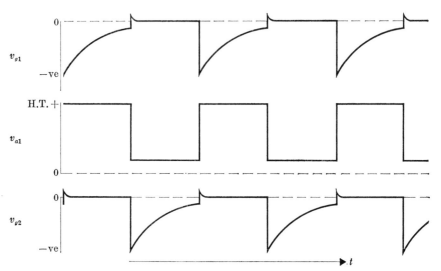

Fig. 13.17. Voltage changes in the multivibrator on the grid and anode of tube 1, and the grid of tube 2.

and at a low voltage determined by $r$ and the saturation current of the tube. It has therefore a rectangular wave form, the steepness of the sides depending on the rapidity of the voltage landslides, which are controlled mainly by the stray anode capacitance. As already noted for the Kipp relay, the change over from conduction to cut-off takes rather longer than the reverse change, so that the two sides of the square wave are not equally steep.

The period of a complete cycle is mainly determined by the charging of $C_1$ through $R_1$, and $C_2$ through $R_2$. At saturation the voltage drop across the tube is small, so that the sudden change of anode voltage when the tube conducts is practically equal in amplitude to the h.t. voltage; so is the negative voltage kick applied to the grid of the next tube. This voltage must decay to the cut-off point of the grid characteristic, which is nearly equal to the h.t. voltage divided by $\mu$, the amplification factor of the tube. The time of decay for the circuit of Fig. 13.16 will therefore be nearly $R_1 C_1 \log \mu$ for one tube, and $R_2 C_2 \log \mu$ for the other, the time required for a complete cycle being

$$(R_1 C_1 + R_2 C_2)\log \mu.$$

A more accurate analysis shows that each $R$ should be replaced by

$$R + \frac{r\rho}{(r+\rho)}$$

in each case, since $C$ really charges through $R$ in series with ($r$ and $\rho$ in parallel).

The multivibrator, with its rectangular wave form, is of great use in generating square voltage pulses, and harmonics of a standard frequency. It is readily synchronized with an injected sinusoidal signal, applied to the grid of one tube, if its natural period is close to that of the signal. The effect of such a signal is to delay the return of the grid voltage to the conducting point if it would be early, and to speed it up if its natural period is such that it would return too late. This property of synchronizing with an applied signal is of use in frequency measurement, since the harmonics generated by the multivibrator are then exact multiples of the standard frequency, and an unknown frequency may be compared with the nearest harmonic. The multivibrator may also be used for frequency division, for it will synchronize with a signal whose period is close to an exact fraction of its own, i.e. a frequency up to 5 or 10 times its own.

## 13.8. Amplitude modulation and detection

In Chapter 12 the use of vacuum tubes for rectification was outlined; that is, the conversion of an alternating voltage into a steady voltage. A process similar to this is employed in the reception of radio signals, and is generally known as detection. The difference lies in the fact that the radio signal is modulated in some way in order to convey information, such as speech or music, whose characteristic frequencies lie in the audio range, while the signal itself is at a much higher frequency, known as the carrier frequency. One system used for this purpose is called amplitude modulation, since the amplitude of the carrier signal is made to vary with the period of the audio frequency, and by an amount which is proportional to the strength of the audio-frequency information. For simplicity we shall consider only a single audio frequency of constant strength. The amplitude-modulated radio signal may then be written in the form

$$V = A(1 + m \cos pt)\cos \omega t. \qquad (13.17)$$

Here $A$ is the amplitude of the carrier signal in the absence of modulation, and $\omega/2\pi$ its frequency. The constant $m$ is known as the depth of modulation, and cannot be greater than unity, and $p/2\pi$ is the audio frequency.

The nature of an amplitude-modulated signal can be seen from Fig. 13.18 (a), which shows the variation of the voltage $V$ with time. Its

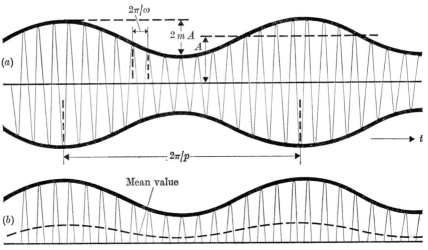

FIG. 13.18.  (a) Amplitude-modulated signal, before detection.
(b) Amplitude-modulated signal, after detection.

Normally $\omega$ is much greater than $p$.

amplitude fluctuates slowly between a maximum value of $A(1+m)$ and a minimum of $A(1-m)$, the period of a complete cycle of this fluctuation being $2\pi/p$. Manipulation of equation (13.17) shows that it may be rewritten as

$$V = A \cos \omega t + \tfrac{1}{2}mA \cos(\omega+p)t + \tfrac{1}{2}mA \cos(\omega-p)t. \qquad (13.18)$$

This indicates that the modulated signal may also be regarded as composed of the carrier signal $A \cos \omega t$, together with two other frequencies, higher and lower by $p/2\pi$, which are known as side-bands, and whose amplitude is proportional to the product of the carrier strength and the depth of modulation. The presence of these side-bands shows that any receiver with r.f. circuits must be designed to have a pass band which will accept the frequencies $(\omega \pm p)/2\pi$ as well as the carrier frequency $\omega/2\pi$, as otherwise the audio-frequency modulation will be cut out. The presence of the side-bands may be demonstrated by applying the modulated signal to a sharply tuned frequency-meter, which will show responses at the three frequencies $(\omega-p)/2\pi$, $\omega/2\pi$, and $(\omega+p)/2\pi$.

In general the modulation will not consist of a single audio frequency, but of a whole range of frequencies. For speech or music these cover the range from about 50 c/s to several kc/s, while for television a band of several Mc/s is required. This is because the picture consists, for example, of $400 \times 400$ separate dots, scanned 25 times a second, so that $400 \times 400 \times 25 = 4 \times 10^6$ pieces of information must be transmitted per second. The pulse corresponding to a spot must therefore last less than a microsecond, and a receiver to amplify such pulses requires a bandwidth of the order of $4 \times 10^6$ c/s. By Fourier analysis any modulation can always be resolved into a set of sinusoidal oscillations, and our analysis can therefore proceed in terms of one such frequency, bearing in mind that the various parts of a receiver must then have the bandwidth required to accommodate all modulation frequencies up to the highest.

The mean value of the signal voltage $V$ is zero over any period long compared with that of the carrier frequency, and it will therefore produce no effect in a receiver designed to accept only audio frequencies. If the signal is passed through a rectifier stage so that the portions where $V$ is negative are wiped out, as in Fig. 13.18 (b), the mean value of the resultant is not zero and fluctuates at the audio-frequency rate corresponding to the modulation. This process is known as detection, since the information which is conveyed by the modulation can now be detected by the ear if the signal from the rectifier, after suitable amplification, is applied to headphones or a loudspeaker. An obvious requirement of a detector is that its output signal shall be as nearly as possible a true reproduction of the original modulation, i.e. the output voltage should be linearly proportional to the depth of modulation $m$, and the constant of proportionality should be the same for all modulation frequencies.

A circuit using a diode for the detection of amplitude modulated waves is shown in Fig. 13.19. It will be seen that it is essentially the same as that of Fig. 12.3, but certain limitations must be placed on the values of $R$ and $C$ to obtain efficient and distortionless detection. These may be summarized as follows:

(1) The load resistance $R$ should be large compared with the effective output resistance of the diode, $\rho$. The latter is approximately equal to the reciprocal of the slope of the diode characteristic, and forms a voltage divider with $R$ just as in the case of the triode tube. Since $\rho$ varies with the size of the applied signal, the condition $R \gg \rho$ not only makes the fraction of the possible output voltage appearing across $R$ nearly unity

(high efficiency) but also makes this fraction nearly independent of $\rho$ and hence of the magnitude of the applied signal (low distortion).

(2) The time constant of the $RC$ circuit should be long compared with the period of the carrier voltage, to avoid voltages of this frequency appearing in the output (i.e. $1/\omega C \ll R$).

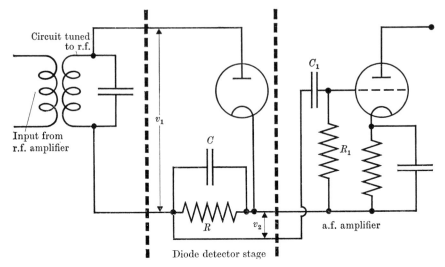

FIG. 13.19.  Diode detection circuit.

$v_1$ = modulated input voltage.
$v_2$ = output voltage.

(3) An upper limit to $RC$ is set by the requirement that the voltage across $C$ shall change sufficiently rapidly to follow the modulation. This requires $(1/pC) > R$, or more strictly, $(1/pC) \geqslant Rm/(1-m^2)^{\frac{1}{2}}$ (for proof of this relation, see E. Williams, 1952; the presence of $m$ arises because the rate of change of the carrier amplitude depends on the depth of modulation).

(4) $C$ should be several times as large as the cathode-anode capacitance $C_{ca}$ of the diode, since $C$ and $C_{ca}$ form a voltage divider for the r.f. voltage applied to the diode.

The circuit of Fig. 13.19 shows the modulated input voltage being supplied from a tuned r.f. transformer. The condition $R \gg \rho$ (see (1) above) makes it necessary for the size of the input voltage to be of the order of a volt or so, in order to work on a portion of the diode characteristic where the slope is fairly high. In the reception of broadcast signals ranging from millivolts down to microvolts, it is therefore necessary to amplify the signal before detection. At the right of Fig. 13.19

the output from the detector is shown applied to the first stage of an a.f. amplifier. The blocking capacitor $C_1$ is inserted to prevent the steady component of the rectified voltage across $R$ being applied to the grid of the first tube and so changing its bias. The size of $C_1$ should be such that $(1/pC_1) \ll R_1$ for the lowest frequency $(p/2\pi)$ present in the modulation, and $R_1$ should be of the same order or larger than $R$, since, in parallel with $R$, it forms part of the load resistance for the diode detector.

The use of the diode described above, where the applied signal is large enough to operate the diode on the straight part of its characteristic, is known as 'linear detection', since the output voltage is linearly proportional to the amplitude of the input voltage. If the input voltage is very small, as would be the case if a broadcast signal were applied to the diode directly without previous amplification, the diode is operated only over a very tiny portion of its characteristic, and detection or rectification results only from the curvature of the characteristic of this region. The output current or voltage is proportional to the square of the input voltage, and the process is known as 'square law detection'. An approximate analysis may be made by assuming the load resistance is small compared with the mean output resistance of the diode; the latter is very high when the applied signal is small. Then the current through the tube when a small signal voltage $v$ is applied may be written as

$$I = I_0 + \left(\frac{\partial I}{\partial V}\right)v + \frac{1}{2}\left(\frac{\partial^2 I}{\partial V^2}\right)v^2 + \dots = I_0 + av + bv^2 + \dots, \qquad (13.19)$$

where $I_0$ is the current flow (if any) when $v = 0$, and $a$ and $b$ are determined by the slope and curvature of the characteristic near the point $I = I_0$. If $v = v_1 \cos \omega t$, then

$$i = I - I_0 = av_1 \cos \omega t + \tfrac{1}{2}bv_1^2(1 + \cos 2\omega t) + \dots, \qquad (13.20)$$

showing that there is a change $\tfrac{1}{2}bv_1^2$ in the mean current, which is proportional to the square of the applied signal. If the latter is modulated, so that $v_1 = B(1 + m \cos pt)$, then the low frequency current change is $\tfrac{1}{2}bB^2(1 + 2m \cos pt + \tfrac{1}{2}m^2 + \tfrac{1}{2}m^2 \cos 2pt)$, showing that the detected signal will have harmonic distortion owing to the presence of the term in $\cos 2pt$. For this reason, and because of the very low efficiency, square law detection is not used in radio reception. It is used in some vacuum-tube voltmeters, but usually with a triode tube rather than a diode. The triode is worked on a curved portion of its anode current–grid voltage characteristic, and the analysis given above may be applied if $v$ is the change in grid voltage and $i$ the change in the anode current. The change in anode current may be observed on a milliammeter inserted in the anode load. This system is known as 'anode bend' detection, since it depends on the curvature of the anode current characteristic. The advantage of using a triode instead of a diode is that comparatively large changes in the output current may be obtained, while a high input impedance is offered to the source.

It should be noted that the triode can be used for linear detection if the grid is biased to cut-off, and the size of the input signal is sufficient to swing the grid on to the linear portion of the anode current–grid voltage characteristic during the positive peaks. The mean anode current will then change linearly with any change in the amplitude of the applied signal. This can be used either for detection of amplitude modulated signals, or in frequency changing, discussed in the next section.

### 13.9. Frequency changing

Since square law detection is very inefficient compared with linear detection (see Problem 13.4), it is always desirable that a signal be amplified sufficiently, before being applied to the detector, to work the latter in its linear region. Often it is undesirable, and sometimes impossible, to provide sufficient amplification for this purpose at the carrier frequency. A device known as frequency changing is then used, in which, as the name suggests, the carrier frequency is altered to another more convenient frequency, the modulation being preserved intact. In the formulae (13.17) and (13.18) above for a modulated signal, this means that $\omega$ is changed to another value, but that the terms in $m$ remain the same.

This change of frequency is accomplished by adding to the original signal an alternating voltage of another frequency ($\omega_1/2\pi$) generated locally, and passing the two into a rectifying stage known as the mixer. The output from the mixer then contains voltage components which fluctuate at, apart from the modulation frequencies, $(\omega_1-\omega)/2\pi$ and $(\omega_1+\omega)/2\pi$. If the difference frequency $(\omega_1-\omega)/2\pi$ lies in the audible range, it may be amplified and made to work headphones or a loudspeaker. This system is known as heterodyne reception and is used in telegraphy where the carrier signal is modulated only by being switched on and off in accordance with some prearranged code such as the dot-dash system of the Morse code. The dots and dashes are then heard as audible notes (usually about 1000 c/s).

In a superheterodyne system, the sum and difference frequencies are outside the audible range, and one of them is selected and amplified.

The frequency selected is known as the intermediate frequency (i.f.) and the i.f. amplifier magnifies the signal, with its original modulation, to a level at which it can be detected by a diode operating in the linear region. Since the mixing stage must incorporate a non-linear device, it is often called the 'first detector', while that following the i.f. amplifier is called the 'second detector'.

The operation of frequency changing (or 'frequency conversion') can be readily understood as follows. Suppose an alternating voltage $v_1 \cos \omega_1 t$ is supplied by a 'local oscillator', and to this is added a small signal voltage $v \cos \omega t$, where $v \ll v_1$ and $\omega_1$ is close to $\omega$. Then the total amplitude of the alternating voltage will fluctuate between $(v_1 + v)$ when the two components are in phase, and $(v_1 - v)$ when they are out of phase. The time interval between instants at which the two are in phase is $2\pi/(\omega_1 - \omega)$; the amplitude therefore fluctuates sinusoidally at a frequency equal to the difference of the two original components, and the size of the fluctuation is the same as that of the signal voltage $v$. This constitutes an amplitude modulated voltage which can be detected as described in the last section, the difference being that the 'modulation' frequency is determined by the difference between the signal and local oscillator frequencies. The amplitude of the local oscillator voltage $v_1$ may be adjusted so that the detector is worked on the linear portion of its characteristic, and the 'modulation' of the local oscillator voltage produced by the signal appears in the output as a component at the i.f. frequency whose amplitude is proportional to that of the original signal. Any slow fluctuation of the latter, such as that due to an audio-frequency amplitude modulation, is preserved, and the signal at the i.f. amplifier differs from the original only in the frequency of the carrier voltage.

For the purpose of mathematical analysis, the action of the local oscillator voltage on the detector may be assumed to produce a periodic variation of its slope conductance $dI/dV$ (or transconductance in the case of anode bend detection). This fluctuating conductance may be analysed as a Fourier series of the form

$$g = g_0 + g_1 \cos \omega_1 t + g_2 \cos 2\omega_1 t + \dots . \tag{13.21}$$

The effect of adding a small voltage $v \cos \omega t$ is to change the detector current by an amount

$$gv \cos \omega t = g_0 v \cos \omega t + g_1 v \cos \omega_1 t \cos \omega t + \dots$$

$$= g_0 v \cos \omega t + \tfrac{1}{2} g_1 v \{\cos (\omega + \omega_1) t + \cos (\omega - \omega_1) t\} + \dots, \tag{13.22}$$

showing that there are Fourier components at both the sum and difference of the signal and local oscillator frequencies. The i.f. amplifier may be tuned to accept either of these; components at $(n\omega_1 \pm \omega)$ also exist, but they are usually small because the coefficients $g_n$ decrease in magnitude as $n$ increases. This analysis shows that either the sum or the difference frequency may be used, although in the previous discussion only the difference term was considered. In work at very high frequencies the difference is generally used, since this is more convenient in building an i.f. amplifier. In addition, where selectivity is required, it is easier to get a narrow pass band from circuits at the lower frequency. For example, a $Q$ of 100 would give a pass band of about 10 kc/s in the

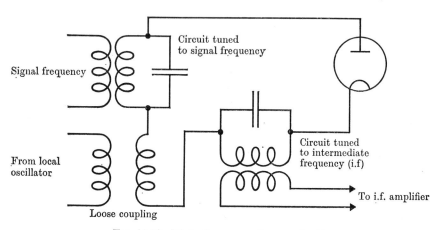

Fig. 13.20. Diode frequency changer circuit.

circuits of an i.f. amplifier at 1 Mc/s, whereas to obtain the same limited band at a r.f. of say 100 Mc/s, would require a $Q$ of $10^4$. In a superheterodyne receiver using such frequencies, the local oscillator might be at 99 or 101 Mc/s, and the r.f. circuits would have to be sufficiently sharply tuned to reject any signal at 98 or 102 Mc/s respectively, which would produce the same beat frequency. This requirement is known as 'second channel suppression'. In general it means that the tuned r.f. circuits for the signal frequency $\omega/2\pi$ must be sufficiently selective to reject any unwanted signal at the 'image frequency' $(2\omega_1 - \omega)/2\pi$, which is separated from the local oscillator frequency $\omega_1/2\pi$ by the same amount, and hence would also be accepted by the i.f. amplifier.

At frequencies of the order of a few megacycles per second or less, anode bend detection is generally used in the mixing stage, and special tubes such as the hexode and pentagrid (or heptode) are employed. The former is a screen-grid tube with two control grids, one for the signal voltage and the other for the local oscillator voltage, separated by an extra screen grid which prevents either of the two voltages being fed back into the circuits of the other section through the inter-electrode capacitance. A separate local oscillator tube is required, though this may be enclosed in the same envelope, as in the triode-hexode. In the penta-grid tube, the first two grids form the control grid and anode of a triode which is used as local oscillator. The electron stream emerging from the second grid is thus modulated at the local oscillator frequency before tra-versing the second part of the tube, again effectively a screen-grid tube.

At high frequencies diode frequency changers are used, the essential circuit being shown in Fig. 13.20. The main difference from the simple detection circuit of Fig. 13.19 is the addition of a loose coupling to the local oscillator, and the use of a tuned transformer coupling to the i.f. amplifier, instead of an $RC$ circuit coupled to an a.f. amplifier.

## 13.10. Frequency modulation

The transmission of intelligence by a radio wave requires some form of modulation, and amplitude modulation, where a carrier wave of a fixed high frequency is modulated in amplitude at a low frequency, has been outlined in § 13.8. An alternative system is 'frequency modulation', in which the signal wave has a constant amplitude, but its frequency is varied periodically in accordance with the modulating signal. The amount of frequency variation is proportional to the amplitude of the modulating voltage, and the rate of variation is proportional to the modulating frequency. The unmodulated carrier wave, for which $\omega$ is constant, may be written as

$$V = A \cos \phi(t) = A \cos \omega t,$$

where the function $\phi(t) = \int \omega \, dt$. If the frequency of this carrier wave is modulated by a single audio-frequency $(p/2\pi)$ of constant amplitude, then the instantaneous angular frequency becomes

$$\omega_i = \omega + \Delta\omega \cos pt,$$

where $\Delta\omega$ is the maximum deviation of $\omega_i$ from $\omega$, the frequency of the unmodulated carrier. Then for the frequency modulated wave

$$V = A \cos\left(\int \omega_i \, dt\right) = A \cos\left(\omega t + \frac{\Delta\omega}{p} \sin pt\right) = A \cos(\omega t + m_f \sin pt).$$

$$(13.23)$$

The quantity $m_f = (\Delta\omega/p)$ is called the modulation index. For example, if the unmodulated carrier wave has a frequency $(\omega/2\pi) = 10^8$ c/s, and the modulation is at a frequency $(p/2\pi) = 500$ c/s, and the modulation index is $m_f = 0.04$, then the modulated carrier wave will vary in frequency from $(10^8+20)$ c/s to $(10^8-20)$ c/s and back again 500 times a second. On the other hand, if the modulation index is 20, the frequency of the carrier varies from $(10^8+10^4)$ c/s to $(10^8-10^4)$ c/s and back again 500 times a second.

Since a frequency modulated wave is not a simple sine wave, it contains side-bands, which are more complicated than those for an amplitude

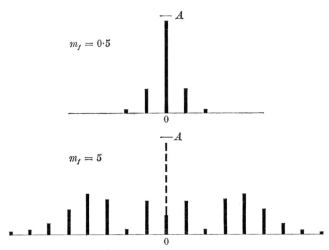

FIG. 13.21. Side bands in a frequency modulated wave with modulation index 0·5 and 5 respectively. $OA$ = amplitude of unmodulated carrier.

modulated wave. By Fourier analysis it may be shown that the voltage wave form of equation (13.23) can be written as

$$V = AJ_0(m_f)\cos \omega t + AJ_1(m_f)\{\cos(\omega+p)t - \cos(\omega-p)t\} +$$
$$+ AJ_2(m_f)\{\cos(\omega+2p)t + \cos(\omega-2p)t\} + \dots$$
$$= A[J_0(m_f)\cos \omega t + \sum_{n=1}^{\infty} J_n(m_f)\{\cos(\omega+np)t + (-1)^n \cos(\omega-np)t\}].$$
$$(13.24)$$

Here the numerical coefficients $J_n(m_f)$ can be found from tables of Bessel functions, for $J_n$ is a Bessel function of order $n$. Although the side-band frequencies stretch to infinity, the more distant side-bands have small intensity. If the modulation index $m_f = 0.5$, the first order side-bands $(\omega \pm p)$ have amplitude 0·24, and the second order side-bands $(\omega \pm 2p)$ have amplitude 0·03 relative to the unmodulated carrier; higher order side-bands are negligible. If $m_f = 5$, the amplitudes of the side-bands are larger, as shown in Fig. 13.21, the amplitude of the carrier is markedly reduced, and most of the energy is in the side-bands (the total energy is independent of $m_f$). This represents an economy in transmitter power over amplitude modulation, where the carrier wave is fixed in amplitude and carries half the energy even with 100 per cent depth of modulation. As a rough rule the width of the frequency band over which the side-bands have appreciable amplitude is approximately

$$2\left[\left(\frac{\Delta\omega}{2\pi}\right)+\left(\frac{p}{2\pi}\right)\right].$$

In a typical system for transmitting speech and music, the maximum frequency deviation ($\Delta\omega/2\pi$) is $\pm75$ kc/s, and the maximum audio-modulation frequency 15 kc/s, so the bandwidth required is

$$2(75+15) = 180 \text{ kc/s}.$$

Though the bandwidth required is thus considerably greater than for transmission of an amplitude modulated wave with the same maximum audio frequency, a frequency modulation system has the great advantage in that it cuts out all amplitude modulated disturbances caused by interference and noise, and so gives much improved reception. The carrier frequencies used for frequency modulation transmission are high ($\approx 100$ Mc/s), partly because the fractional frequency deviation ($\Delta\omega/\omega$) is then small and easier to realize in transmission, and partly because only the direct ray from the transmitter is then received. Any ray received indirectly (e.g. by reflection from the ionosphere) would be more seriously distorted by selective fading (unequal transmission of different frequencies) than in an amplitude modulated system, because of the greater bandwidth required.

In the reception of an f.m. transmission it is necessary to convert the frequency modulation into an amplitude modulation, and this is accomplished by a 'discriminator'. Several types of discriminator are in use, the essential ingredient being a circuit whose impedance depends on frequency. A simple example is a tuned circuit adjusted so that the mean signal frequency ($\omega/2\pi$) lies on the side of the resonance curve, at the point of inflexion where the change in current (see for example Fig. 9.5) varies linearly for small changes in frequency. Two such circuits, one with its natural resonance frequency tuned above the signal frequency, and the other below, can be used with a push-pull circuit to balance out distortion, as well as unwanted amplitude modulation. The latter is mainly suppressed, however, by passing the frequency modulated signal first through a 'limiter', such as a pentode run at an abnormally low anode voltage so that it can be swung from cut-off to saturation by a change of a few volts in the grid potential. The received signal is amplified to such a level before being applied to the limiter that the grid swing on the pentode is well into the cut-off region in one direction and into the saturation region in the other. Then the amplitude of the signal voltage in the tuned circuit used as anode load is determined entirely by the tube characteristics and is practically independent of the amplitude of the signal applied to the grid. Two such pentodes, one following the other, are generally used to make the removal of any amplitude modulation more complete.

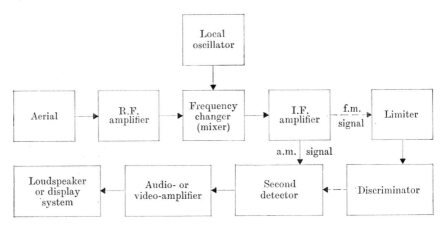

FIG. 13.22. Block diagram of a radio receiver. The two stages on the extreme right are required only for the reception of a frequency modulated transmission.

## 13.11. Radio receivers

We are now in a position to outline briefly the component parts of a typical receiver, as exemplified in the block diagram in Fig. 13.22. The signal from the aerial is fed into an r.f. amplifier which must be tuned to the signal frequency. If the latter is variable then all the tuned circuits in the amplifier must be adjusted each time a signal of different frequency is received. This is cumbersome and expensive and the stages of r.f. amplification are therefore kept to a minimum, or even omitted. In the latter case the only tuning required is that of the local oscillator resonant circuit together with the circuit into which the aerial signal is fed. The latter is tuned not only to achieve a voltage step-up but also to suppress the second channel at the image frequency which would otherwise be passed into the mixer. This suppression is of course improved by the use of an r.f. amplifier, and so also is the sensitivity, since the amplifier can be designed to give low noise (see Chapter 16).

The local oscillator is generally a simple tuned anode oscillator with a triode tube, and a power output of a few watts is sufficient to drive the mixing stage in the linear detection region without using tight coupling from the local oscillator. Tight coupling makes it difficult to tune the signal circuits and local oscillator circuits independently, and may also result in loss of signal into the local oscillator circuits.

The presence of side-bands in a modulated signal means that all circuits in the receiver must have sufficient bandwidth to pass the side-bands if the modulation is to be preserved. In the r.f. stages, simple tuned circuits will generally suffice, but in the i.f. amplifier some form of band-pass tuning, such as can be obtained by the use of coupled resonant circuits (see § 9.4), may be required. It is then convenient to place one tuned circuit in the anode lead of the amplifier tube, and couple it by a mutual inductance or capacitance (or both) to another resonant circuit connected to the grid of the next tube, as in Fig. 13.7.

In a receiver for amplitude modulated signals the purpose of the i.f. amplifier is to magnify the signal until it is large enough to work a detector (the second detector) in the linear region. In a receiver for frequency modulation the i.f. amplifier magnifies the signals before they are applied to the limiter and discriminator detector. It is readily seen that it is more convenient to perform these operations at a constant frequency than at a variable one, so that the superheterodyne system is a considerable advantage in a receiver designed to cover a range of frequencies. In all receivers the final amplification is by an aperiodic amplifier designed to pass all frequencies up to a few kilocycles per second for sound or a few megacycles per second for vision. Thus the only substantial difference between a receiver for a.m. and one for f.m. is that the latter requires two extra stages, a limiter and a discriminator.

REFERENCES

ROLLIN, B. V., 1964, *An Introduction to Electronics* (O.U.P.).
WILLIAMS, E., 1952, *Thermionic Valve Circuits* (Pitman).

## PROBLEMS

**13.1.** A 'cathode-follower' circuit is shown in Fig. 13.23. Show that the amplification is

$$A = \frac{v_c}{v_g} = \frac{g_m}{g_m + (1/\rho) + (1/\mathbf{Z})}$$

and that the equivalent circuit consists of a constant current generator $g_m v_g$, shunted by a conductance $g_m$, working into a load consisting of impedances $\rho$, $\mathbf{Z}$ in parallel.

**13.2.** In the circuit of Fig. 13.7, the amplification may be defined as the ratio (voltage across capacitor $C$)/(input voltage at grid of first tube). Show that

$$A = \frac{M g_m}{C\{\omega^2 M^2/\rho + \mathbf{Z}_2(1 + j\omega L_1/\rho)\}},$$

where $\mathbf{Z}_2$ = series impedance of the tuned circuit $L_2$, $C$, $r$ by itself. If the circuit is tuned to an angular frequency $\omega_0$ which makes the denominator of this equation purely resistive, show that $A$ can be written as

$$A = g_m \frac{\omega_0 M Q}{\{1 + \omega_0^2 M^2/(r\rho) + \omega_0^2 L_1^2/\rho^2\}},$$

where $Q = (\omega_0 Cr)^{-1}$. In general $(\omega_0 L_1/\rho)^2 \ll 1$, typical values being $\omega_0 = 10^7$ sec$^{-1}$, $L_1 = 10^{-4}$ henry, $\rho = 10^5$ ohms, and the expression for $A$ then reduces to that given by equation (13.7).

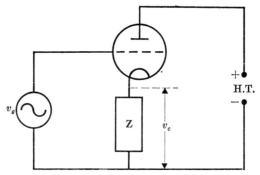

Fig. 13.23. The 'cathode-follower' circuit.

**13.3.** In the tuned anode oscillator circuit of Fig. 13.11, show that the fraction of the voltage output which is fed back to the input is

$$\beta = -j\omega M/(r + j\omega L).$$

By means of equation (12.14) calculate the amplification $A$ which the triode with its tuned circuit would give at the oscillation frequency given by equation (13.10), and show that

$$A\beta = g_m M/(Cr + L/\rho).$$

Hence the condition $A\beta \geqslant 1$ gives the same condition for oscillation as equation (13.9).

**13.4.** An amplitude-modulated voltage signal $v = B(1 + m\cos pt)\cos \omega t$ is applied to two different receivers: (1) a diode detector with the characteristic given by equation (13.19), working in the square law region, followed by an audio-frequency amplifier with overall amplification $A$; (2) a signal frequency amplifier with overall amplification $A$, followed by the same diode working in the linear region.

Show that the output voltages (assuming that the diode works into a resistance $R$ in each case) from the two systems are in the ratio $bB:a$, and show that if $B = 10^{-5}$ V, $a = 10^{-3}$ A/V, $b = 10^{-5}$ A/V$^2$ the ratio is $10^{-7}$. This illustrates the inefficiency of square law detection.

**13.5.** In a push-pull Class B amplifier the anode current wave form in each tube consists of a half-period of a sine wave, the current being zero in the other half-period. Assuming that the amplitude of the anode voltage swing cannot be greater than the h.t. voltage, show that the greatest efficiency is $\frac{1}{4}\pi$.

**13.6.** The 'flip-flop' circuit is a hybrid of the Kipp relay and the multivibrator, in which the battery $B_1$ of Fig. 13.15 is retained but the battery $B_2$ is replaced by capacitor and resistance (e.g. $C_2$ and $R_2$ of Fig. 13.16). Show that this arrangement has a stable position with tube 1 conducting and tube 2 cut off, but if a short positive pulse is applied to grid 2 (or a short negative pulse to grid 1) the circuit executes one cycle of oscillation (similar to the multivibrator), returning to its stable position.

**13.7.** In the circuit of Fig. 13.2 the voltage $v_2$ is not exactly in phase with $(-v_g)$ showing that the amplification $A = v_2/v_g$ is complex. Writing $A = -|A|\exp(j\theta)$, show that the phase angle $\theta$ is given by the expression

$$\tan\theta = \frac{(1+\rho/R)(\omega CR_1)^{-1}-\rho\omega C_g}{\rho/R_1+(1+\rho/R)(1+C_g/C)}.$$

This shows that the phase delay varies with frequency, and if it is appreciable it will cause distortion. Thus a square wave will not appear square after amplification because the phase of the higher frequency components is altered relative to the lower frequency components; the ear is, however, insensitive to distortion of this kind.

# THERMIONIC VACUUM TUBES AT
# VERY HIGH FREQUENCIES

AT frequencies above about 50 Mc/s the performance of thermionic vacuum tubes begins to fall off for a number of reasons. These may be briefly classed as follows:

(a) Effects of electrode impedance, which make the voltage appearing at the actual electrode differ from that applied to the lead outside the tube.

(b) Effect of the finite time taken by the electrons in travelling from one electrode to another, causing the current flow not to be exactly in phase with the applied voltage at the various electrodes.

(c) Increased power loss in the external circuits, due to skin effect in conductors (and proximity effect in coils), dielectric loss in imperfect dielectrics such as tube bases, and radiation.

It is convenient to discuss these effects separately, and then show how the design of tube and circuit is modified in order to improve their performance.

## 14.1. Effects of electrode impedance

At very low frequencies the effects of stray inductance and capacitances associated with the various electrodes of a thermionic vacuum tube may be neglected. As the frequency is raised, the interelectrode and other capacitances become important, as discussed in § 12.8, where it was shown that the effect of the grid-anode capacitance in a triode is to reduce the input impedance. This difficulty is eliminated in the pentode tube, which is therefore generally used for amplification at frequencies between about 100 kc/s and 100 Mc/s. At the high frequency end of this range the inductance of the cathode lead becomes important, for this inductance is common to the grid and anode circuits, and it therefore introduces feed-back, as in the cathode follower circuit of Problem 13.1. In particular the performance is adversely affected because the flow of current through the grid-cathode capacitance and the cathode lead inductance results in a low input resistance. This resistance is shunted across the tuned circuit which is normally used for the input

at high frequencies, and may seriously reduce the voltage magnification
which this circuit would otherwise give. The size of the input resistance
may be estimated as follows, using the circuit of Fig. 14.1.

Let $v$ be the external voltage applied, and $v_g$ the actual voltage existing
between grid and cathode. These differ because of the voltage developed
across the inductance $L$ through the flow of anode current through it.

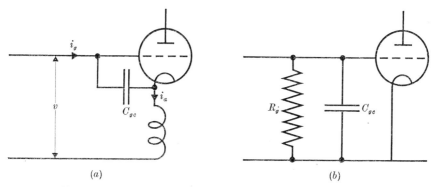

FIG. 14.1. Effect of cathode lead inductance at high frequencies.
$$R_g = (g_m \omega^2 L C_{gc})^{-1}.$$

If the anode load is small compared with the anode impedance of the
tube, as is usually true in the pentodes used in r.f. amplifiers, the anode
current is approximately equal to $g_m v_g$, and we have
$$v = v_g + g_m v_g (j\omega L).$$
Now the presence of the grid-cathode capacitance will cause grid current
to flow, of magnitude $i_g = v_g(j\omega C_{gc})$. Hence the grid admittance $\mathbf{Y}$
will be
$$\begin{aligned}
\mathbf{Y} = i_g/v &= j\omega C_{gc}/(1 + g_m j\omega L) \\
&\approx j\omega C_{gc}(1 - g_m j\omega L) \quad \text{(since } g_m \omega L \text{ is small)} \\
&= j\omega C_{gc} + g_m \omega^2 L C_{gc}.
\end{aligned} \qquad (14.1)$$

From this equation it is seen that the input capacitance of the tube
is shunted by a conductance whose value is proportional to the cathode
lead inductance, the cathode-grid capacitance, and the square of the
frequency. To estimate the magnitude of the effect, we shall take
$$g_m = 5 \text{ mA/V}, \qquad C_{gc} = 5 \ \mu\mu\text{F}, \qquad L = 5 \times 10^{-8} \text{ henries,}$$
where the value of the inductance is of the right order for a straight
wire 5 cm long and 1 mm in diameter. Then at a frequency $f$ the input
conductance is approximately $5 \times 10^{-20} f^2$ mhos; at 50 Mc/s, this corresponds to a resistance $R_g$ of 8000 ohms, and at 500 Mc/s, of only 80 ohms.

This resistance is shunted across any parallel tuned circuit which may be attached to the input, and will therefore lower its $Q$, with resulting loss of magnification of the signal voltage in the input circuit. The figures given above show that this effect will be serious at 50 Mc/s, while the power drawn from a signal source applied between grid and cathode at 500 Mc/s would be intolerable.

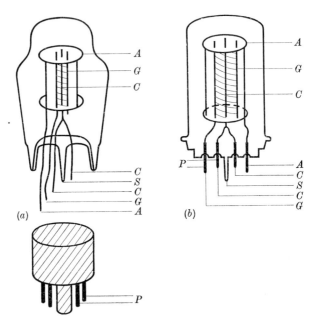

FIG. 14.2. (a) Tube with leads brought out of glass, through bakelite base (shown detached below) to pins $P$.
(b) Tube with pressed glass base has much shorter leads, as the pins are sealed into the glass.

$A$   anode, front portion removed to show inside.
$G$   grid.                              $P$   pins.
$C$   cathode.                         $S$   sealing-off point.

Reduction of the input conductance of a tube at high frequency can be achieved by a design in which both the grid-cathode capacitance and the cathode lead inductance are kept as small as possible. Since the grid-cathode separation cannot be increased, owing to transit time limitations, the electrodes must be made with the smallest possible area, and the leads to grid and cathode must be kept well apart. The cathode lead must be kept as short as possible, since its inductance increases with its length. For this reason, a pressed glass base is used as in Fig. 14.2, since a separate base entails greater lead length, but the length of lead inside the tube is fixed by the necessity of providing adequate heat insulation between the hot cathode and the point where the cathode lead is sealed into the glass envelope. One method of reducing the inductance is to bring out several leads from the cathode; the inductance of each lead is in parallel with that of the others, and the net inductance is therefore reduced by a factor equal to the number of leads. A reduction in the input conductance by a factor of about 10 below the values given above can be achieved by modifications of this sort in the design. An additional advantage of using a tube requiring no separate base is that dielectric losses in the material of the base are avoided. To avoid such losses in the material of the tube holder it must be a good dielectric, and special insulating materials with low power factor have been developed for this purpose.

## 14.2. Effect of transit time on input conductance

While an electron is leaving one electrode of a tube and approaching another it induces a charge on each of these electrodes. As it moves, the induced charge on the electrode which it has left diminishes, while that on the electrode which it is approaching increases. This can be seen quite simply by considering two plane parallel electrodes which are maintained at voltages 0 and $V_a$ respectively by means of a battery. Suppose a charge $-q$ is emitted from the plane of zero voltage. It will be accelerated towards the other plane, and when it has moved through a potential $V$ the work done on the electron will be $qV$. This work must be supplied by the battery, whence it follows that a charge $q(V/V_a)$ must have flowed through the battery. The direction of flow is such that the plane at potential $V_a$ will have acquired a charge $+q(V/V_a)$, while the charge on the other plane, which was $+q$ at the moment after the electron was emitted, is reduced to $+q(1-V/V_a)$. Thus the movement of the charge is accompanied by changes in the induced charges on the two planes, corresponding to the change in the number of lines of field from the electron which terminate on either plane (see Fig. 14.3). The duration of these changes is equal to the transit time of the charge between the two planes, and a current pulse flows for this length of time.

Similar arguments hold if one plane is replaced by a grid, and the passage of a charge through a grid therefore causes a momentary flow of charge to the grid which reverses in sign as the charge passes through. It is not necessary for the charge to hit the grid to create an induced charge, and the current flow accompanying the passage of the charge is shown in Fig. 14.4. The area under the curve up to any point represents the charge induced at that moment. The total area (i.e. the net accumulated charge) is zero, since the positive and negative sections annul one another provided that all the charge flows through the grid and none is

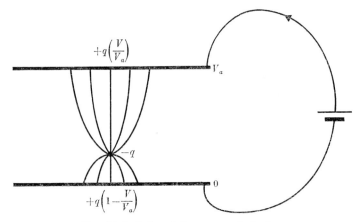

Fig. 14.3. Induced charges on electrodes.

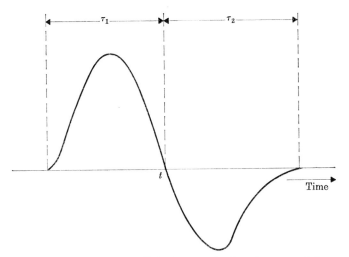

Fig. 14.4. Current flow to grid during transit of an electron. $t$ is instant at which electron passes through grid. Transit time is $\tau_1 + \tau_2$.

intercepted. The low frequency components of the induced current are negligible provided the period is much longer than the transit time. This is about $10^{-9}$ sec for electrons in a normal tube, and at frequencies up to 10 Mc/s the induced current is virtually zero. At higher frequencies, where the transit time is an appreciable fraction of an r.f. cycle, the effect of the passage of the electrons in inducing an r.f. current to flow to the grid is appreciable. Full analysis of the effect is complicated, but an estimate of its order of magnitude can be obtained by the following method.

At a time $t$, let the voltage applied to the grid be $V = V_0 \sin \omega t$. Let the transit time from cathode to grid be $\tau_1$, and that from grid to anode be $\tau_2$. Then the current induced in the grid by the electrons approaching it will be approximately

$$I_1 = g_m V_0 \sin \omega(t-\tau_1)$$

since the size of the current is determined by the value of the grid voltage at the time $(t-\tau_1)$ when the electrons left the cathode (or, more strictly, the space charge region). Similarly the current induced in the grid by the electrons leaving for the anode may be written

$$I_2 = -g_m V_0 \sin \omega(t-\tau_1-\tau_2),$$

the minus sign arising from the reversal of the current for departing electrons. The net current is therefore

$$\begin{aligned}
I_1+I_2 &= 2g_m V_0 \cos \omega\{t-(\tau_1+\tfrac{1}{2}\tau_2)\}\sin \tfrac{1}{2}\omega\tau_2 \\
&= 2g_m V_0 \sin \tfrac{1}{2}\omega\tau_2\{\cos \omega t \cos \omega(\tau_1+\tfrac{1}{2}\tau_2)+\sin \omega t \sin \omega(\tau_1+\tfrac{1}{2}\tau_2)\} \\
&= 2g_m \sin \tfrac{1}{2}\omega\tau_2\left\{\frac{dV}{dt}\frac{\cos \omega(\tau_1+\tfrac{1}{2}\tau_2)}{\omega}+V \sin \omega(\tau_1+\tfrac{1}{2}\tau_2)\right\}.
\end{aligned}$$

This contains both a capacitative and a resistive component. The latter is more important since it causes a loading of the input circuit. If both $\omega\tau_1$ and $\omega\tau_2 \ll 1$ the input conductance may be written

$$G = g_m \omega^2(\tau_1\tau_2+\tfrac{1}{2}\tau_2^2). \tag{14.2}$$

A full analysis by North shows that for tubes of common size the input conductance $G$ is approximately equal to $g_m \omega^2\tau_1^2/10$.

If we take our standard value of 5 mA/V for $g_m$, and $\tfrac{1}{2}\times 10^{-9}$ sec for $\tau_1$, the value of $G$ is found to be about $5\times 10^{-21}f^2$ mhos at a frequency $f$. It is therefore of the same order as the input conductance due to cathode lead inductance in the improved vacuum tubes mentioned in § 14.1.

## 14.3. Modified circuits and tubes for metre and decimetre wavelengths

A third cause of lowered efficiency of operation of vacuum tubes at very high frequencies is increased power loss in the external circuits. At a frequency of 100 Mc/s the skin depth in copper (cf. § 10.4) is only $\approx 0\cdot007$ mm, and the current flow is therefore confined to a very small part of the cross-section of any conductor, with consequent increase in the effective resistance. In a closely wound coil there is a further loss

of power and increase of resistance due to eddy currents induced by the
alternating currents in neighbouring parts of the coil (principally in the
nearby turns). This proximity effect can be reduced to a minimum, and
so also is the self-capacitance, by using straight conductors rather than
coils. It was shown in § 11.4 that a short-circuited length of a transmission line behaves as a reactance, and in § 11.5 that lengths which are

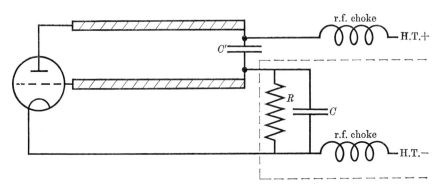

FIG. 14.5. Lecher-wire oscillator. The *RC*-combination enclosed by broken lines is an
automatic bias circuit for Class C operation.

odd multiples of quarter-wavelengths behave as parallel tuned circuits
of high impedance. At metre wavelengths (frequencies $\sim$ 30–300 Mc/s)
short lengths of parallel wire lines may be used for the tuned circuits,
a typical circuit for a triode oscillator being shown in Fig. 14.5. This is
the equivalent of the Hartley oscillator discussed in § 13.6. The blocking
capacitor $C'$ serves only to separate the steady voltages on anode and
grid, and its impedance should be low so that it is effectively a short
circuit for the r.f. currents. Then this forms the closed end of the transmission line, and the two wires at the open end, where the voltages
are greatest and of opposite phase, are connected to anode and grid
respectively. This gives feed-back of the correct sign for oscillation, as
in the Hartley circuit. The actual line length required will be rather less
than one-quarter of a wavelength, since the electrode capacitances must
be tuned to resonance by an inductive length of line. Since the anode
and grid electrodes have somewhat different capacitances to earth, the
currents flowing in the Lecher wires will not be quite equal and opposite.
This increases the loss of energy by radiation, which is small if the
currents are exactly balanced and the distance apart of the wires is
made small compared with a quarter-wavelength.

This difficulty may be avoided by using a pair of tubes working in
push-pull. The circuit shown in Fig. 14.6 is of this type, being a tuned

grid-tuned anode oscillator with feed-back through the grid-anode capacitance. The latter gives a negative input resistance at the grid (see § 12.8), provided that the anode circuit is tuned to be inductive at the

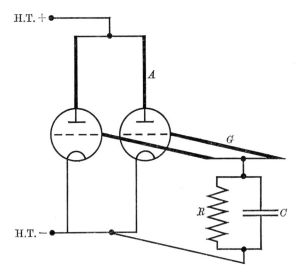

FIG. 14.6. Push-pull Lecher-wire oscillator.
   *A*   anode line.        *G*   grid line.

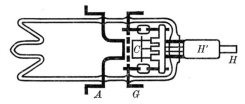

FIG. 14.7. CV273 triode with grounded grid.
*A, G*   anode and grid, on copper disks sealed through glass envelope.
*C*       cathode.
*H*       heater connexion.
*H′*      (cathode and heater) connexion.
Grid-cathode separation 0·07 mm.
Grid-anode separation 0·25 mm.
$\mu = 30.$ $g_m = 7$ mA/V. Maximum frequency, 3700 Mc/s.

frequency of oscillation. To avoid magnetic coupling between the anode and grid lines, they are usually brought out at right angles to one another. In both the circuits of Figs. 14.5 and 14.6 it may be necessary to use r.f. chokes in the supply leads to prevent the flow of unwanted r.f. currents. The *RC*-combination shown provides automatic grid bias for Class C operation.

At decimetre wavelengths (frequencies between 300 and 3000 Mc/s) considerable modifications in the design of vacuum tubes are required. To reduce transit time effects, triodes are used with small clearances between the electrodes. Lead inductance is cut to a minimum by avoiding thin wire leads and bringing large diameter metal disks through the glass envelope (a logical development from the practice of putting in several leads of thin wire to the cathode to reduce inductance). Such disks give

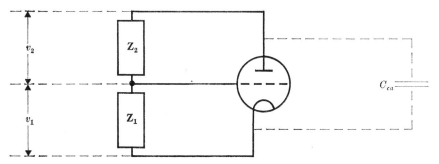

FIG. 14.8. The grounded-grid triode connexion.

good electrical connexion to the external circuits, which are in the form of coaxial lines to avoid loss of energy by radiation; the diameter of the conductors is usually from 1 to 5 cm to reduce resistive losses. A common form of tube construction uses a copper disk seal to carry the grid, as in Fig. 14.7, and anode and cathode are also plane structures. The disk seal reduces the anode-cathode capacitance to a very small value, an important point since the tube is normally used in the 'grounded grid' connexion, whose equivalent circuit is shown in Fig. 14.8. It has the important advantage that feed-back to the grid circuit through the grid-anode capacitance is avoided, since the current through this capacitance does not have to flow through the source of signal voltage applied between grid and cathode, as is the case in the ordinary 'grounded cathode' connexion (see § 12.8). This greatly increases the stability of the system when used as an amplifier, and this is further increased by the presence of negative feed-back due to the flow of anode current through the input circuit. In the latter respect the circuit is similar to the 'cathode follower' or 'grounded anode' connexion (see Problem 13.1).

The analysis of the circuit of Fig. 14.8, neglecting the cathode-anode capacitance $C_{ca}$, is as follows. The usual equation for the anode current takes the form

$$i_a = g_m v_1 + (-i_a Z_2 + v_1)/\rho,$$

or

$$i_a(\rho + Z_2) = v_1(1 + \mu).$$

The voltage magnification is

$$A = v_2/v_1 = i_a \mathbf{Z}_2/v_1 = (1+\mu)\mathbf{Z}_2/(\rho+\mathbf{Z}_2), \qquad (14.3)$$

while the input impedance is

$$\mathbf{Z}_1 = v_1/i_a = (\rho+\mathbf{Z}_2)/(1+\mu). \qquad (14.4)$$

These formulae show that the circuit is equivalent to a voltage generator of magnitude $(1+\mu)v_1$, with internal impedance $\rho$ working into a load $\mathbf{Z}_2$.

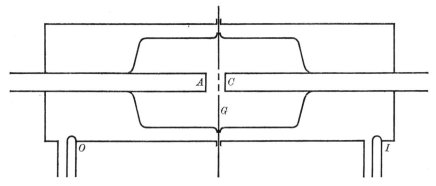

FIG. 14.9. Disk-seal triode with quarter-wave coaxial-line circuits.

A anode; C cathode; G grid.

I, O input and output coaxial lines with loop coupling.

The grid-anode capacitance must be included in $\mathbf{Z}_2$ and will be tuned out by the inductance of the attached coaxial line at resonance. The cathode-anode capacitance, on the other hand, acts as a bypass for r.f. current and must be kept small. Since the anode current flows through the signal source, the input impedance is finite. This is not serious as the effects discussed in §§ 14.1 and 14.2 would limit the input impedance in any case. Inspection of the equations given above shows that the voltage magnification is just equal to $\mathbf{Z}_2/\mathbf{Z}_1$, a result which could have been obtained directly since the anode current flows in series through both of them.

　　A schematic diagram of a triode with its coaxial line circuits is shown in Fig. 14.9. As an amplifier it is useful down to about 20-cm wavelength, one such stage being used before a superheterodyne mixing stage. Oscillation at a usable efficiency (a few per cent) is obtained in low power tubes (suitable as local oscillators for a superheterodyne receiver) down to 10-cm wavelength, but much higher efficiencies are obtained at longer wavelengths.

## 14.4. The klystron

We have seen already that the finite time which an electron takes to pass from cathode to anode causes difficulty in the operation of conventional tubes at metre and decimetre wavelengths. At centimetre wavelengths the problem of reducing the cathode-grid clearance so as to keep the transit time down to a small fraction of a cycle becomes practically insuperable. It is therefore necessary to look for some other means of reducing the transit time. One obvious solution is to shoot the electrons at a large velocity through a grid which then acts as an effective cathode. For example, if electrons are accelerated by a potential of 2500 V, their velocity is about $3 \times 10^9$ cm/sec, and they will traverse a distance of 1 mm in $3 \times 10^{-11}$ sec, which is only one-tenth of a period at a wavelength of 10 cm. Thus, if the cathode-grid system is replaced by two grids, between which the high-frequency voltage is imposed, and the electrons are shot through these grids at a high velocity, the transit time can be kept short.

Such an arrangement must depend on some different principle for its working from that of a conventional tube. In the latter case the grid voltage influences the space charge in the potential minimum just in front of the cathode, and thus causes a change in the number of electrons flowing to the anode. When an alternating voltage is applied between grid and cathode a periodic 'density modulation' is set up in the electron stream flowing to the anode. If, now, the cathode, which emits electrons with an average energy corresponding to about one-tenth eV, is replaced by a grid through which electrons are injected at high voltage, there will be practically no space charge between this pseudo-cathode and second grid. It is obvious that application of a small r.f. voltage between the two grids will not then cause any change in the density of electrons leaving this space. It will cause a 'velocity modulation', for some of the electrons will be accelerated by the r.f. field, while others which go through this field half a period later, when it is reversed in sign, will be retarded.

The principle of 'velocity modulation' rather than 'space charge modulation' is fundamental in the working of the klystron and other centimetre wave tubes. Velocity modulation is not of itself sufficient to produce amplification or oscillation, since for this we require a density modulation of the electron beam. However, if a velocity modulated beam is allowed to 'drift' along in a field-free space, a density modulation will be set up in the following way. The electrons which were accelerated by the r.f. field will gradually overtake the slower electrons in front of them, which were retarded by the field. In this way 'bunching' of the electrons will occur, as illustrated in Fig. 14.10. Here the distance covered by a number of electrons, initially uniformly spaced in the beam, is plotted against time. Lines corresponding to fast electrons overtaking slow electrons converge, while at points appropriate to half a period earlier or later in the r.f. field, the lines diverge. The former gives a 'bunch' since the convergence of the lines means that more electrons occupy a given volume, while the latter gives a 'rarefaction'. If now the beam traverses a second pair of grids, between which an r.f. field of the same frequency is applied in such a phase that a bunch is retarded by the field, while a rarefaction is accelerated, energy will be transferred from the beam to the field because more electrons are slowed down than are speeded up. This constitutes a conversion of energy from the h.t. supply used for the initial acceleration of the beam into energy in the alternating electromagnetic field, in a similar manner to that in a conventional radio tube. There, in an ordinary ampli-

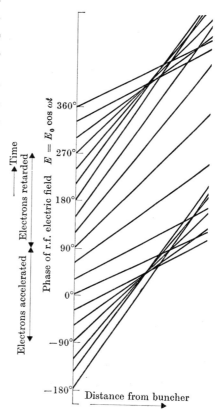

FIG. 14.10. Bunching of electrons after velocity modulation.

fier or oscillator, the denser current flow to the anode coincides with the moments at which the anode potential is low, so that these electrons are slowed up by the alternating component of the electric field in front of the anode, thus doing work against this field.

A schematic diagram of a klystron is shown in Fig. 14.11. Electrons accelerated and formed into a beam by a suitable gun pass through a resonator $B$ where a velocity modulation is imposed on them by the r.f. field. They then travel through the field-free 'drift-space' in which bunching occurs, and enter a second resonator $C$ called the 'catcher', tuned to the same frequency as $B$. Finally, the electrons are collected

on an electrode at h.t. potential, which plays no essential role in the
action of the tube, but prevents the beam from striking the glass envelope. If some of the r.f. signal in the catcher is fed back through a
coaxial line to the buncher, oscillations will be set up if the phase is correctly adjusted, and if more energy is extracted from the beam by the
catcher than is dissipated in the combined resistances of the catcher and

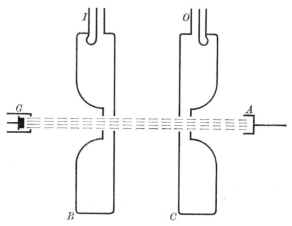

FIG. 14.11.  Schematic diagram of klystron oscillator.

$G$   electron gun.                    $B$   buncher.     $C$   catcher.
$A$   anode to collect electrons.     $I, O$   input and output coupling loops.
$A, B, C$ at h.t. positive, $G$ at h.t. negative potential.

buncher. In this connexion it should be noted that the velocity modulation of the beam by the r.f. field in the buncher requires no net power
if the transit time is short, for as many electrons are slowed down as
are speeded up. For high efficiency, it is necessary to develop the greatest
r.f. electric field in the resonator at the point where the beam traverses
it, with the smallest dissipation of power in the resistive walls. The
cavity resonator gives the best type of circuit in this respect, and its
shape is determined primarily by the requirement of a short transit time
for the electrons. If the latter travel with one-tenth of the velocity of
light, and their transit time is to be not more than one-tenth of the
period of oscillation, the gap which they traverse must be about one-
hundredth of a wavelength. This requires an indented cavity of the
shape shown in Fig. 14.11. It may be regarded either as a short section
of coaxial line, slightly less than a quarter-wavelength long so that its
inductance resonates with the capacitance across the gap, or as an indented waveguide resonant cavity.

As with most oscillators, the full mathematical theory is rather complex, but it is possible to derive the starting condition for oscillations from elementary considerations as follows. We assume that the electrons leave the gun with potential $V_0$, and the path they traverse in the resonant cavity $B$ has a potential difference $V \cos \omega t_0$ across it at the instant $t_0$. Then if $V \ll V_0$, as will be the case for small amplitudes of oscillation, we may use the differential relation $\delta v/v = \frac{1}{2}(\delta V/V)$ to find the fractional change in their velocity after traversing the cavity; their final velocity may then be written as

$$v = v_0(1 + V \cos \omega t_0/2V_0), \qquad (14.5)$$

where $v_0 = (2eV_0/m)^{\frac{1}{2}}$ is the velocity with which an electron leaves the gun. An electron which leaves $A$ at time $t_0$ reaches the second resonator $B$, at a distance $x$ away, at a time

$$t = t_0 + x/v = t_0 + (x/v_0)(1 + V \cos \omega t_0/2V_0)^{-1}$$
$$\approx t_0 + (x/v_0)(1 - V \cos \omega t_0/2V_0), \qquad (14.6)$$

where we have again used the approximation $V/V_0 \ll 1$.

Now the current at any point is equal to $dq/dt$, the rate at which charge passes that point. To find the current, we shall consider a small section of the beam containing charge $dq$, and follow it along the beam. Owing to the velocity modulation, the front and rear portions of this section travel at different speeds, and the time $dt$ which the section takes to pass a given point therefore changes with the distance it has travelled. The beam current at the time $t$ is therefore

$$I = dq/dt = (dq/dt_0)(dt_0/dt) = I_0(1 + \omega x V \sin \omega t_0/2v_0 V_0)^{-1}$$
$$\approx I_0\{1 - (\omega x V/2v_0 V_0)\sin \omega(t - x/v_0)\}, \qquad (14.7)$$

where we have used the relations $(dq/dt_0) = I_0$, the initial beam current, and

$$(dt_0/dt) = (dt/dt_0)^{-1} = (1 + \omega x V \sin \omega t_0/2v_0 V_0)^{-1}$$

obtained by differentiation of equation (14.6).

Equation (14.7) shows that we have now a density modulated current, whose amplitude of modulation increases linearly with $x$, the distance travelled, so long as we restrict ourselves to small velocity modulation. If this current now passes through a second resonator, with a potential difference $V_2 \cos \omega t$, the mean power extracted from the beam will be

$$\overline{-IV_2 \cos \omega t} = -\frac{\omega}{2\pi} \int_0^{2\pi/\omega} I_0 V_2 \cos \omega t \left\{1 - (\omega x V/2v_0 V_0)\sin \omega\left(t - \frac{x}{v_0}\right)\right\} dt$$

$$= \frac{I_0 VV_2 \omega x}{2v_0 V_0} \frac{\omega}{2\pi} \int_0^{2\pi/\omega} \cos \omega t \sin \omega\left(t - \frac{x}{v_0}\right) dt = -\frac{I_0 VV_2 \omega x}{4v_0 V_0} \sin \frac{\omega x}{v_0},$$

since only terms in $\cos^2 \omega t_0$ contribute to the mean power. The power extracted from the beam will be greatest when $-\sin \omega x/v_0 = +1$, i.e. $\omega x/v_0 = 2\pi(n+\tfrac{3}{4})$, where $n$ is an integer. In other words, if oscillations in $B$ and $C$ are in phase, the beam must take $(n+\tfrac{3}{4})$ periods to travel from $B$ to $C$. The time of travel can be adjusted by altering the initial accelerating voltage $V_0$.

So far we have considered the power extracted from the beam when r.f. signals from an external source are fed into resonators $B$ and $C$. It is clear, however, that if a little of the power that is fed from the beam into $C$ is returned to $B$ to act there as the source of signal, oscillations can be sustained so long as the power extracted from the beam is greater than that dissipated in resistive heating of resonators $B$ and $C$. We may represent this dissipation by a resistance $R$ for each resonator. The oscillations will be sustained if

$$\frac{I_0 \, V V_2 \, \omega x}{4 v_0 V_0} > \frac{V^2}{2R} + \frac{V_2^2}{2R}.$$

If $V = \alpha V_2$, where $\alpha$ is small, the power dissipated in the buncher may be neglected, and this relation may be expressed in the form

$$\text{minimum starting current } I_0 = 2V_0(v_0/\omega x)/(\alpha R)$$
$$= V_0/\{\alpha R \pi(n+\tfrac{3}{4})\}. \qquad (14.8)$$

This shows that the smallest beam current required for sustained oscillations is of the order of the beam voltage divided by the parallel impedance of the resonator. The current required is diminished if $\alpha$ is increased, or if the time of drift between the resonators $(x/v_0)$ is increased, since the density of the bunches reaching the second resonator is enhanced in either case.

With large electrode voltages and currents, the klystron is an efficient and powerful oscillator, and can be used as a transmitter, but its principal use is as a low power local oscillator, for which an output of a few milliwatts is sufficient, in a superheterodyne receiver. For this purpose the klystron must be tunable, and this is not feasible when two separate resonators of high $Q$ (several thousand) must be adjusted simultaneously. A single resonator or reflex klystron is therefore employed, as in Fig. 14.12, where the electron stream after passage through the resonator is confronted by an electrode whose potential is negative with respect to the cathode potential. The electrons are thereby halted and reflected back through the same resonator. Bunching occurs because the electrons which are speeded up in the first passage through the resonator travel further towards the reflector electrode and so return later (as in the case of a ball thrown into the air), together with the electrons which passed through the resonator half a period later and were retarded by the r.f. field. Thus the bunches occur at points in the returning beam which the faster electrons reach later rather than earlier, but as they are retarded on their return passage through the resonator when the r.f. field is directed away from the cathode instead of towards it (as in the two-resonator klystron), the required transit time for oscillation is still $(n+\frac{3}{4})$ periods. The minimum starting current is now given by equation (14.8) with $\alpha = 1$. In an early type of tube for 10-cm wavelength, $V_0 = 1200$ V, $R = 70\,000$ ohms, $(n+\frac{3}{4}) = 1\frac{3}{4}$, giving a starting current of about 3 mA. The running current is about 8 mA, and the power output of an average tube is $\approx 300$ mW corresponding to an efficiency of 3 per cent. Later types run at a beam voltage of 300 V, and a current of 20 mA, with a rather lower power output.

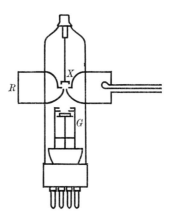

Fig. 14.12. Reflex klystron. Electrons from the gun $G$ pass through the gap in the resonator $R$, and are returned back through the gap by the reflector $X$ which is at a potential negative with respect to the cathode.

Reflex klystrons of this type have been made to oscillate at wavelengths down to about $\frac{1}{2}$ cm, which seems to be about the limit. The main difficulties in making such oscillators for shorter wavelengths arise from the smaller size of the resonant cavity, with its correspondingly lower parallel impedance $R$, which means that a higher beam current is required to start oscillations. This higher current needs to be sent through a smaller hole in the cavity, but the current density which can be obtained in the beam is limited by the mutual repulsion of the electrons.

## 14.5. The magnetron

Oscillations of high power at centimetre wavelengths are produced by the magnetron; an outline diagram of a typical tube is shown in Fig. 14.13. Electrons are emitted from a central cylindrical cathode, and are accelerated towards a coaxial cylindrical anode consisting of a solid copper block with a number of resonant cavities. These may have the shape shown in the figure, but other shapes are also possible. Essentially they form a set of quarter-wave resonant lines or cavities, the open end of the line being at the inner surface of the anode block.

Thus, when oscillations take place, a strong r.f. electric field is set up at the inner surface, the field lines running mainly in the circumferential direction across the open end of the cavity, as shown in Fig. 14.14.

The magnetron operates with a strong axial magnetic field of some few kilogauss (a few tenths of a weber/metre²), which is normally pro-

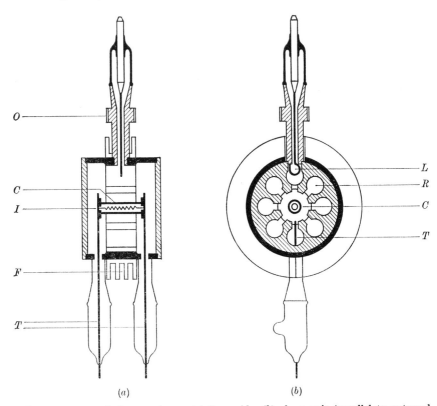

Fig. 14.13. A typical magnetron: (a) from side, (b) along axis (parallel to external magnetic field) (after Willshaw *et al.*, 1946, *J.I.E.E.* **93**, Part 3a, 985).

*O*, output side arm; *C*, oxide-coated cathode; *I*, insulated heater; *F*, cooling fins; *L*, output coupling loop; *R*, resonator system; *T*, tungsten heater and cathode leads (cathode connected to one side of heater).

vided by a permanent magnet, and a potential of 10 to 50 kV on the anode. An electron on its way from the cathode to the anode experiences a magnetic force perpendicular to its direction of motion and a radial electric force. Its trajectory under the action of these forces can best be pictured by reference to a case with simple plane geometry. Suppose a uniform electric field $-E$ (i.e. in the sense which accelerates a negative electron in the positive $y$-direction) exists between two parallel conducting planes $y = 0$ and $y = a$, with a uniform magnetic field $B$ in the $z$-direction. Then the equations of motion for an electron of charge $-e$ are

$$\ddot{x} = -\frac{eB}{m}\dot{y}, \qquad \ddot{y} = +\frac{e}{m}E + \frac{e}{m}B\dot{x}, \qquad \ddot{z} = 0.$$

If the electron starts from rest at the origin, it moves in a cycloid whose equations are

$$x = vt - \rho\sin\omega t = \rho(\omega t - \sin\omega t), \qquad y = \rho(1 - \cos\omega t),$$

where $v = E/B$, $\rho = mE/eB^2$, and $\omega = eB/m$. The cycloid is the same as the path followed by a point on the circumference of a cylinder of radius $\rho$, rolling along the plane $y = 0$ with angular velocity $\omega$; $v$ is then the linear velocity of its centre in the $x$-direction.

In the case of cylindrical geometry, the electron orbit is approximately an epicycloid generated by rolling a cylinder on the cylindrical cathode, and so is rather similar to the case of the parallel planes if we imagine the latter to be given a small curvature. The approximation arises because we are neglecting the radial decrease in the electric field which occurs with cylindrical geometry as we go from cathode to anode. In addition we are neglecting the mutual repulsions of the various electrons ('space charge') in either case. If the difference between the radius $a$ of the cathode and the radius $b$ of the anode is small compared with either, at a point midway between cathode and anode we may write the angular velocity of the electron cloud as approximately

$$\frac{v}{\frac{1}{2}(a+b)} = \frac{2E}{B(a+b)} = \left(\frac{V}{b-a}\right)\left\{\frac{2}{B(a+b)}\right\} = \frac{2V}{B(b^2-a^2)}, \qquad (14.9)$$

where $V$ is the steady voltage applied between anode and cathode. This expression shows that to give the electron cloud a certain angular velocity of rotation, we must maintain a certain linear relation between the anode voltage and the magnetic field. The importance of this angular rotation of the electron cloud arises from the necessity of synchronizing the movements of the electrons with the alternation of the r.f. electric fields in the resonators, in order to preserve the right phase relationships. This is essential for the efficient transfer of energy from the electron cloud to the r.f. field, the basis of any oscillator.

Before considering the mechanism of this transfer, it is necessary to discuss the resonator system. Each resonant cavity behaves like a tuned circuit but the system is more complicated than that of a simple oscillator because of the presence of $N$ such circuits, all coupled together. This coupling is partly electrostatic, lines of electric field originating from one

cavity terminating in another, but it is predominantly magnetic; the
lines of r.f. magnetic field going down through one cavity are completed
by returning up through another cavity. With a system of $N$ circuits
all tuned to the same frequency, and strongly coupled together, the

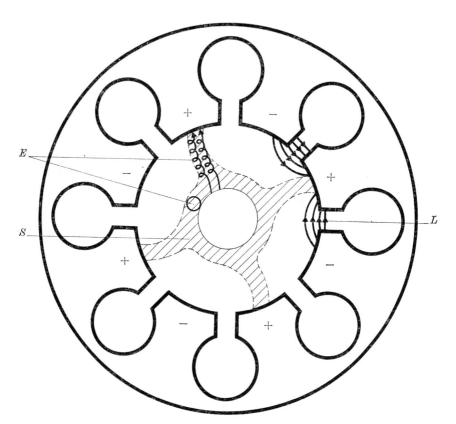

Fig. 14.14.  Electron trajectories ($E$) and lines of r.f. electric field ($L$) (arrows show
direction of force on electrons) in the '$\pi$ mode' magnetron.

$S$   space charge cloud, enclosed by broken lines.

natural frequencies of oscillation are split apart in the same way as with
two circuits (see § 9.4), but analysis of the system is much more complex.
The different resonant frequencies correspond to oscillations with varying change of phase between successive resonators; they can be analysed
into systems of standing waves, or of travelling waves, or a mixture of the
two. The simplest system is a standing wave where the phase difference
between successive cavities is $\pi$ (the so-called '$\pi$ mode'), and this is also
one of the most efficient modes of operation of the magnetron. At any

instant the direction of the lines of force in successive cavities is exactly reversed, as would arise from a simple potential distribution where alternate segments are just plus and minus in the r.f. voltage (see Fig. 14.14).

The interaction between the electrons and the r.f. field must now be considered. Under normal conditions of operation, but in the absence of oscillation, the electrons would travel (approximately) in circles such that their farthest point from the cathode is about half-way across the cathode-anode space. At the moment when they return to the cathode, their velocity would be zero, since the magnetic field does no work on them, and that done by the electrostatic field as they move initially away from the cathode is all regained on the return path. Suppose now that an electron is just moving tangentially at the farthest point in its trajectory from the cathode. Then the force exerted on it by the magnetic field is towards the cathode, while that exerted by the electrostatic field is towards the anode. If the tangential velocity of the electron is increased at this moment through being accelerated by the fringing field of one of the cavities, the magnetic force on it (which is proportional to its velocity) will be increased, while the electrostatic force is unchanged, so that the effect is to return it towards the cathode. If, on the other hand, the electron is retarded by the r.f. field, the magnetic force is decreased and the electron will move in a path which brings it closer to the anode than it would have got in the absence of the r.f. field. If now it arrives opposite another cavity at the moment when it is again retarded, it again gives up energy to the r.f. field, and moves still closer to the anode. Note that as it does so, it moves into positions where the r.f. field is stronger and so a greater proportion of the kinetic energy of the electron is transferred to the r.f. field. On the other hand, an electron which is speeded up returns towards the cathode where its interaction with the r.f. field is smaller. Thus, if the right phase relationship can be maintained, some of the electrons will give up energy to several cavities in succession, and eventually reach the anode with kinetic energy much less than that corresponding to $e \times V$, while others will be returned to the cathode. On the whole, the latter take much less energy from the r.f. field than the former give to it, and the net transfer of energy will maintain oscillation.

To get the right phase relationship, the angular velocity of the electron cloud must coincide with the angular velocity of rotation of one of the Fourier components of the r.f. field system. For the $\pi$-mode, this simply means that the electron cloud must rotate through the angle $(2\pi/N)$, between successive cavities, in $n+\frac{1}{2}$ cycles (where $n$ is an integer). Its angular velocity must therefore be $(2\pi/N)/(n+\frac{1}{2})\tau = 2\pi f/N(n+\frac{1}{2})$, where $f = 1/\tau$ is the frequency of the oscillations. Equating this to (14.9) gives

$$V = \frac{\pi f}{k} b^2 B \left(1 - \frac{a^2}{b^2}\right), \qquad (14.10)$$

where $k = N(n+\frac{1}{2})$. Assuming the ratio $a:b$ is roughly constant, it will be seen that to maintain operation at a given frequency $f$ in a given mode $k$, at a fixed field $B$, the anode voltage must be increased with the square of the anode diameter. If it is desired to keep the voltage fixed and to construct a magnetron of higher frequency (shorter wavelength) but with equivalent operating conditions, then the resonator system and anode diameter must be scaled in proportion to the wavelength ($b \propto 1/f$), and $B$ must be increased in proportion to $f$.

High power output from the magnetron can be achieved only if high anode voltages and high anode currents are used. By running the tube in short pulses roughly of 1 $\mu$sec duration, with a repetition rate of about 1000/sec, the power in the pulse can be made over 1000 times as great as can be obtained under continuous operation. These high powers are mainly due to three factors:

($a$) the electronic conditions are such that high efficiency is attained at high level;

($b$) oxide-coated cathodes can give very high currents per unit area, 100 times greater under pulsed conditions than under continuous running;

($c$) the mean power dissipated on the anode is reduced, and is easily removed by conduction through the solid copper anode.

An important factor under ($a$) is focusing action by the r.f. field, which helps to concentrate the space charge into a number of narrow spokes (see Fig. 14.14). Each spoke then passes through the r.f. field at the moment when it is a maximum, giving the equivalent of Class C operation in ordinary triodes. The main technical difficulties have been the construction of rugged cathode surfaces, which can withstand the heavy bombardment by the returning electrons accelerated by the r.f. field, and avoiding 'mode jumping', where the frequency changes as the tube jumps from one value of $k$ to another. Power is extracted by means of a loop coupling in one of the resonators, or through a waveguide slit in one resonator.

Typical operating conditions for a medium high power magnetron operating at 10-cm wavelength are: magnetic field, $B = 0\cdot28$ weber/

metre², anode voltage 31 kV, anode current during pulse 35 A, output power in pulse 750 kW. In this tube the cathode diameter is 6·0 mm, and the inside diameter of the anode is 16·1 mm; the length of the anode block is 2 cm, and the overall length of the tube is 3·2 cm. The dimensions of the tube are thus comparatively small, and the high power obtainable in the pulse is due to the high efficiency (70 per cent), which also reduces the dissipation on the anode block to only 30 per cent of the input power. At 10-cm wavelength, output pulse powers of a few megawatts can be achieved, but the power decreases rapidly as the wavelength is reduced, owing to a number of factors. Experimental tubes have been made to operate at wavelengths of a few millimetres, and the short wavelength limit is about the same as or a little lower than that of the klystron. Most cavity magnetrons are fixed frequency tubes, but some magnetrons tunable over a range of 10–20 per cent in frequency have been constructed, the variation being obtained by plungers moving into the resonators from one end.

### 14.6. Crystal diodes

At centimetre wavelengths the most common type of receiver uses a frequency-changing system (§ 13.9), with a reflex klystron as the local oscillator. The thermionic vacuum tube diode is unsatisfactory as a detector or mixer, because, to make the transit time sufficiently short, a very small clearance between cathode and anode is required. This increases the inter-electrode capacitance, and since the oxide coating of the cathode acts as a lossy dielectric, the capacitance is effectively shunted by a comparatively low resistance; thus when the diode is made part of a tuned circuit, the r.f. voltage across it is rather low. For this reason a crystal diode is used instead, consisting of a small piece of silicon on which a point contact is made by means of a fine tungsten 'whisker'. Silicon is a semi-conductor, and electrons can flow across the contact with the tungsten very much more easily in one direction (towards the silicon) than in the other (see Chapter 19). Hence the current-voltage characteristic is asymmetrical as shown in Fig. 14.15. The characteristic is rather similar to that of a thermionic diode, with a somewhat higher slope in the forward direction, but with a small current flow in the reverse direction. It is clear that it will act as a detector or mixer in the same way as an ordinary diode. The transit time of the electrons and the capacitance across the point contact are both very much smaller than in a thermionic diode, and the silicon crystal diode can be used up to much higher frequencies. Two typical mountings are shown in Fig. 14.16:

a capsule type, for wavelengths of 10 cm and longer (an alternative
coaxial construction is preferred for wavelengths of 1–10 cm), and a
waveguide mounting for millimetre wavelengths.

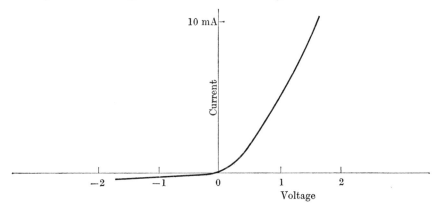

Fig. 14.15. Current-voltage characteristic of silicon–tungsten crystal diode.

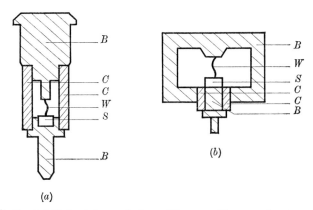

Fig. 14.16. Crystal diodes (a) capsule type, (b) waveguide mounting for millimetre
wavelengths.

| | | | |
|---|---|---|---|
| B | brass. | W | tungsten whisker. |
| S | silicon | C | insulator. |

## 14.7 Travelling wave tubes

An important class of electronic tubes for centimetre wavelengths,
which we shall not discuss in detail, is that of the 'travelling wave' tube.
This is a velocity modulation device in which the beam interacts continuously with the electromagnetic wave, instead of only locally, as in
the klystron. To make this possible the wave velocity must be reduced
to coincide with the beam velocity; this is accomplished by a 'slow-wave
structure', such as a wire helix surrounding the beam, which behaves as

an artificial transmission line with wave velocity $1/\sqrt{(LC)}$ (see § 11.3). Travelling wave tubes can be used as oscillators or amplifiers, an important application being as amplifiers in communication repeater stations, where the large bandwidth which can be amplified makes them of considerable commercial importance.

## GENERAL REFERENCE

ROLLIN, B. V., 1964, *An Introduction to Electronics* (O.U.P.).

# ALTERNATING CURRENT MEASUREMENTS

## 15.1. Measurement of voltage, current, and power

IF an alternating voltage is applied to the terminals of a d.c. instrument such as a moving-coil galvanometer, the reading observed is usually zero. The movement of the galvanometer is too sluggish to follow the alternations of the applied voltage if these occur at more than a few cycles per second. The instrument therefore records only the mean value of the current over many cycles, which is zero for a symmetrical waveform. Thus the measurement of alternating currents and voltages requires the use of special instruments which may be divided into three classes according to the principle involved in their construction. In the first class are instruments with very rapid responses so that they can follow the alternating wave form; second, 'square law' instruments, so called because they respond to the square of the current or voltage applied; and third, rectifier instruments, where the alternating voltage is converted to a steady voltage which can be measured on a d.c. instrument. In practice the most widely used instruments are those with the greatest frequency range, and Fig. 15.1 shows that these are the thermoammeter, a square law instrument, for current; the vacuum tube voltmeter, a rectifier instrument, for voltage; and the cathode ray oscillograph, a short time constant instrument for the display of wave form and measurement of voltage. Of more restricted use are moving iron instruments and the dynamometer. The latter is one of the few instruments which measures power directly, but its use is confined to supply frequencies. At radio frequencies power is normally determined from the voltage developed across a known resistance, or the current flow through it. Thus in general current and voltage are the primary quantities measured. The chief types of instrument are described below.

*The cathode-ray oscillograph*

The cathode ray oscillograph is an instrument whereby the wave form of an alternating voltage may be displayed on a screen. A diagram of the instrument is shown in Fig. 15.2, the various parts being contained in an evacuated glass envelope. An electron gun consisting of a cathode $C$, a grid $G$, and anodes $A_1$ and $A_2$ is used to form a narrow beam of electrons

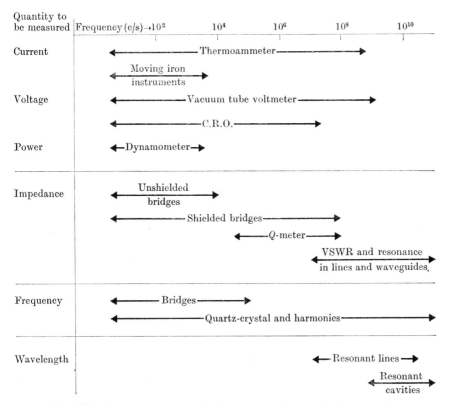

FIG. 15.1. Frequency ranges of various types of measuring instruments.

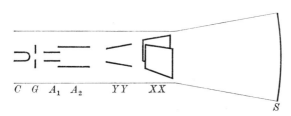

FIG. 15.2. The cathode-ray oscillograph (not to scale).

| $C$ | cathode. | $YY$ | $y$-deflecting plates. |
|---|---|---|---|
| $G$ | grid. | $XX$ | $x$-deflecting plates. |
| $A_1$ | first anode. | $S$ | screen. |
| $A_2$ | second anode. | | |

travelling parallel to the axis of the tube. $XX$ and $YY$ are two pairs of plates oriented at right angles to one another, and various voltages may be applied across the plates of either pair to deflect the electron beam. These deflexions in the $x$- and $y$-directions are normal to the axis of the tube and proportional to the voltages applied to the $X$- and $Y$-plates.

The beam finally strikes a screen $S$, coated on the inside with a fluorescent substance such as zinc sulphide so that the position of arrival of the beam is shown by a small luminous spot. The brightness depends on the beam current, which is controlled by the grid $G$ and the accelerating voltage on anode $A_2$. This voltage ranges from 2000 V or more on large tubes (6-in. diameter face or greater) to 500 V on smaller tubes. The magnitude of the deflexion, and hence the sensitivity (defined as the deflexion per unit voltage applied to the $X$- or $Y$-plates), is inversely proportional to the accelerating voltage (see Problem 15.1). The sensitivity is increased by reducing the separation between the two members of a pair of deflecting plates, and they are therefore splayed as in Fig. 15.2 in order that they shall not intercept the beam at large deflexions. Electrostatic deflexion, as this system is called, causes a certain amount of distortion, and magnetic deflexion, using fields generated by small coils placed outside the tube, is more common for television tubes, where very large deflexion angles are employed. Electrostatic deflexion is used for most laboratory work, and the pattern observed on the screen is then determined by the voltages applied to the two sets of deflecting plates. It is usual to apply a known voltage wave form to the $X$-plates (the 'time-base'), while the unknown voltage is applied to the $Y$-plates. The most useful type of time-base is one where the spot moves to the right across the screen in the $x$-direction at constant velocity, followed by a rapid 'fly-back' to the left-hand side. This is called a linear time-base, and requires a saw-tooth voltage wave form as shown in Fig. 15.3. To obtain a stationary picture, the repetition frequency of the time-base must be an exact submultiple of the basic frequency of the wave form applied to the $Y$-plates. Thus the time-base frequency must be adjustable, and synchronization is usually obtained by applying a little of the voltage from the $Y$-plates to the time-base circuit, so that the time-base is 'locked in'.

The basic method of generating a saw-toothed wave form is also shown in Fig. 15.3. A capacitor $C$ is charged up through a resistance $R$ from an h.t. supply, and is then periodically discharged through another resistance $r$ by a switch $S$. If $r \ll R$, the discharge occupies a very short period compared with the charging, and so provides the fly-back, while the increasing voltage across $C$ during the charging period provides the forward sweep. This will not be exactly linear since the capacitor charges exponentially, but if the switch $S$ is arranged to operate before the voltage across $C$ has risen to more than a small fraction of the h.t. voltage, the departure from a constant rate of charging will be small.

The linearity is further improved by charging the capacitor not through a resistance, but through a constant current device such as a pentode, where the current is almost independent of the anode voltage provided the latter does not fall too low. The rate of charging is controlled by the

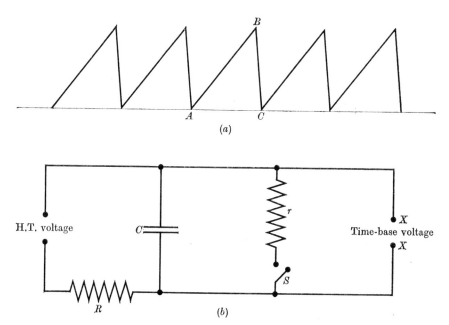

Fig. 15.3. (a) Saw-tooth voltage wave form. $AB$ gives linear forward sweep, $BC$ gives rapid fly-back.

(b) Basic circuit for generating saw-tooth voltage.

screen voltage of the pentode, which serves as a fine frequency control, coarse control being provided by choice of a number of capacitors $C$ of different values. Other types of time-base include the single sweep for observing transient phenomena (which must be triggered by the onset of the transient) and circular or elliptical time-bases, obtained by applying sinusoidal voltages differing in phase by $\frac{1}{2}\pi$ to the $X$- and $Y$-plates. These are useful in the measurement of frequency (see below).

The oscillograph may be used to determine the amplitude of an alternating voltage by measurement of the deflexion on the screen from peak to peak. For this purpose it must be calibrated using a known d.c. or low frequency a.c. voltage. The sensitivity of a 6-in. diameter tube is usually of the order of a few tenths of a millimetre deflexion per volt. The range may be extended by the use of an amplifier of known gain, and signals of the order of microvolts can be made to give an observable deflexion. This technique may also be used for current wave form, by passing the current through a low resistance and amplifying the voltage developed across it.

Other applications of the C.R.O. are comparison of phase and frequency. The phase difference between two voltages of the same frequency may be found by applying one to the $X$-plates and the other to the $Y$-plates. If the amplitudes are equal, and the phase difference is 90°,

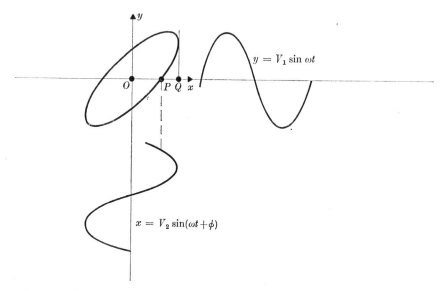

FIG. 15.4. Determination of phase angle from the phase ellipse (see Problem 15.2).

the resultant of the two waves is a circle, but for any other phase difference, or unequal amplitudes, the pattern on the screen is an ellipse (as in Fig. 15.4), or a straight line if the phase difference is zero or $\pi$. If a double-beam oscillograph is available, where each beam has a linear time-base of the same frequency, the two voltages to be compared may be displayed one above the other on the screen, and the phase difference is measured directly.

Double-beam tubes are also useful for frequency comparisons. The second beam is deflected with a standard frequency, and if the time-base is such that five or six complete wave forms are shown on the screen, a small difference between the frequencies on the beams is easily seen. On a single-beam tube, the best method is to use a circular time-base, produced by applying voltages of equal amplitude, but differing in phase by 90°, to the two pairs of plates. The unknown frequency is applied to the anode, modulating the sensitivity, and if its frequency is $n$ times the time-base frequency, a stationary picture with $n$ loops is obtained (Fig. 15.5 $a$). Alternatively, the unknown frequency may be applied to the grid of the tube, thus modulating the intensity. The pattern on the screen is broken up (as in Fig. 15.5 $b$) into dots whose number gives the frequency ratio. Grid modulation is more sensitive than anode modulation, an amplitude of a few volts being sufficient for the unknown frequency.

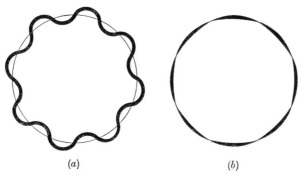

(a)                              (b)

FIG. 15.5. Comparison of frequency with circular time-base.
Time-base frequency $= \frac{1}{8}$ (unknown frequency).

(a) Anode modulation.          (b) Grid modulation.

If the ratio of the frequencies is not exactly an integer, the
pattern is not stationary but rotates.

The great advantage of the cathode ray oscillograph is its ability to portray the wave form of an alternating voltage up to frequencies of a few hundred megacycles per second. At this point limitations arise from the difficulty of making suitable time-bases and amplifiers, as well as from inherent drawbacks in the tube itself (see Problem 15.3).

*Square law instruments*

Any d.c. instrument whose deflexion depends on the square of the current or voltage can be used for a.c. measurements, and the reading obtained by calibration with d.c. will give the root mean square value. Thus the electrostatic voltmeter can be used for alternating voltages and currents; so can the dynamometer (§ 7.1), though it is confined to audio frequencies. The thermoammeter has a greater frequency range; the current passes through a resistive coil which heats a copper disk; this is soldered to a thermojunction, the current from which is read on a moving-coil galvanometer. The instrument can be calibrated by d.c. or low frequency a.c., and is used for currents of the order of milliamps.

The readings are independent of frequency up to about 1 Mc/s, but above that there is coupling between the coil and the thermocouple due to stray capacitance. The sensitivity can be increased by mounting the thermojunction in an evacuated glass envelope to improve the thermal insulation; the copper disk is sometimes joined to the junction by a small glass bead, which provides thermal contact but insulates the r.f. circuit from the galvanometer. The heater is very thin, to avoid any change of resistance with frequency due to skin-effect, and the deflexion is very nearly proportional to (current)² over a large range of frequencies. The frequency range may be greatly extended by using a separate thermo-junction which may be inserted in the circuit quite apart from the instrument used to measure its d.c. output voltage. Leads to the latter instrument must be carefully decoupled.

The dynamometer wattmeter can be used for measuring power, by connecting it as in Fig. 7.5. The scale reading is then proportional to the average value of $V_0 I_0 \sin \omega t \sin(\omega t + \alpha)$ over a cycle, where $V_0 \sin \omega t$ is the voltage across the load, and $I_0 \sin(\omega t + \alpha)$ is the current through it. The scale reading gives $\frac{1}{2}(V_0 I_0)\cos \alpha$ and this is the power consumed by the load, so that the instrument can be calibrated to read power directly, and no determination of the phase angle or power factor is required.

The dynamometer is suitable only for audio frequencies up to about 1000 c/s. At radio frequencies power is normally measured by determining the voltage across, or the current through, a known resistance. This method can be used at all frequencies where the calibration of the voltmeter or ammeter is reliable, but at centimetre wavelengths it is replaced by a direct measurement of power. For low powers (1 W down to a microwatt or so) a 'bolometer' may be used, consisting of a thin wire such as tungsten of 0·01 mm diameter and a few centimetres long, enclosed in an evacuated envelope. The thin wire is welded to stout leads, which are collinear with the wire. The bolometer can then be made the centre conductor of a coaxial line, which is tuned to resonance (half a wavelength long) as in Fig. 15.6. The input power is fed in from a coaxial line, which is tapped on to the centre conductor at such a point that the resonant section is matched to the line. The dissipation of r.f. power in the thin wire of the bolometer causes its temperature and hence its resistance to rise, the change in the latter being determined by including the bolometer as one arm of a Wheatstone's bridge. If the bridge is balanced with the r.f. power on, and the direct current through the bridge arms is increased so as to return to the same balance point when the r.f. is switched off, then the r.f. power can be calculated from the change in d.c. power dissipated in the bolometer lamp. An alternative bolometer element is the thermistor, consisting of a tiny bead of various semi-conducting oxides whose resistance falls steeply with increasing temperature and hence with power input. Such elements have the advantage of small size, and their resistance can be adjusted in manufacture to be of the order of a hundred ohms, which is convenient for matching to a coaxial line whose characteristic impedance is of this order.

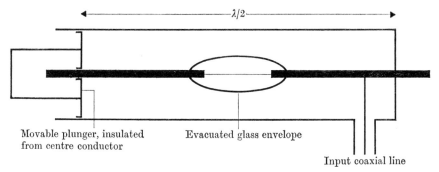

Movable plunger, insulated    Evacuated glass envelope
from centre conductor

Input coaxial line

FIG. 15.6. Resistance variation bolometer for use at short wavelengths. The position of the input tapping must be adjusted for correct termination of the input line. (Waveguide input can also be used.)

Powers of more than a few watts are measured by dissipating the power in water, whose high absorption coefficient at centimetre wavelengths is convenient for this purpose (see § 17.7). The temperature rise is measured, usually with a continuous flow method.

### Rectifier instruments

Since rectification is the process of turning an a.c. voltage into a d.c. voltage, it is obvious that this may be used as the basis of a method of measuring an a.c. voltage. When a thermionic vacuum tube is used as the rectifying device the instrument is known as a vacuum tube or valve voltmeter. The detector circuit of Fig. 12.3 may be used for this purpose, the d.c. voltage being measured directly by a voltmeter placed across the load resistance $R$. When more sensitivity is required the output voltage may be applied to the grid of a triode, as in Fig. 13.19, but without the blocking capacitor $C_1$. The rectified voltage then causes a change in the anode current of the triode which may be read on a meter in the anode circuit.

The prime requirement of a voltmeter is a very high impedance, and it is therefore more common to use a triode employing anode bend rectification than a diode because of its higher input impedance. It also has the advantage of producing a certain amount of amplification of the input voltage. A typical circuit is shown in Fig. 15.7, the purpose of the second triode being to balance out the meter reading due to the steady anode current flow in the first triode in the absence of an applied signal. The instrument may be used in various ways. If the grid is biased so as to work on a curved portion of the characteristic, then the

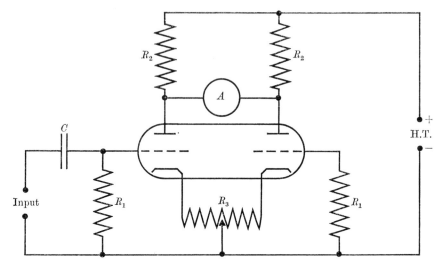

FIG. 15.7. Vacuum tube voltmeter, using double triode.

$R_1, R_1$   grid leaks.                    $A$   microammeter.
$R_2, R_2$   anode loads.
      $R_3$   cathode bias resistance with variable tapping to adjust meter reading to zero in the absence of any input voltage to the first triode.

change in anode current will be proportional to the mean square value of the input voltage (see equation (13.20)) provided the amplitude of the latter is not too high. This is called full-wave square law action. Half-wave action is achieved if the grid is biased just to cut-off, so that only the positive half-cycles of the input voltage cause current to flow to the anode. If the applied voltage is small, the anode current will be proportional to the square of the input voltage, but larger signals will swing the grid on to the linear portion of the characteristic, giving linear rectification. If the grid is biased well back beyond cut-off so that only the positive peaks of the input signal will cause current flow, the device can be used as a peak voltmeter.

The chief advantages of the triode voltmeter are its high input impedance (especially when used as a half-wave or peak instrument), and its large frequency range. Once calibrated at the supply frequency, it will give correct readings at frequencies up to 30 Mc/s or more, the limit being set by the effects of transit time and cathode lead inductance discussed in Chapter 14. With careful design these may be reduced so that the error is small up to about 200 Mc/s. In addition the meter in the anode circuit is protected by saturation of the anode current from the effects of accidental overloads. The sensitivity is limited by the stability of the tube characteristics, since these affect the zero balance of the meter. It should be noted also that the reading may be dependent on the wave form, since sharp positive peaks are more effective in causing anode current flow, owing to the curvature of the characteristic.

It is often needed to measure a voltage of a particular frequency separate from other frequencies which may simultaneously be present. This can be done by means of a 'phase-sensitive detector', a simple design being a modification of the circuit of Fig. 15.7 in which the signal voltage is fed equally to the grids of both triodes, instead of just one, while a larger alternating voltage of the desired frequency is impressed across $R_3$ between the two cathodes. In the absence of a signal the cathodes are thus oscillating in voltage in anti-phase. If a signal voltage of the same frequency is fed to both grids, this will be in phase with the cathode oscillation on one tube, and out of phase on the other; the mean current through the two tubes will alter, and the ammeter $A$ will register a current. Since it is a direct-current instrument, it can respond only to currents which do not fluctuate within its response time; thus the device is sensitive only to signals which lie very close in frequency to the voltage impressed on $R_3$. In addition, the sign of the current through $A$ depends on the relative phase of the signal and the voltage across $R_3$, making the device 'phase-sensitive'. Many other circuits can be used, the basic principle being observation of the d.c. (zero frequency) voltage obtained by heterodyning the signal against a local oscillation of the same frequency; the device is sometimes called a 'homodyne'. When interfering signals or noise are large compared with the desired signal, they may overload the triodes and in such cases diodes, which have a linear response up to larger voltages, are preferable; a suitable circuit is given by Rollin (1964).

## 15.2. Measurement of impedance at low frequencies

The measurement of resistance using direct current is usually accomplished most precisely by means of a bridge, either Wheatstone's bridge or one of its modifications. At audio frequencies the measurement of a complex impedance is also readily achieved with high precision by means of an a.c. bridge. To determine a complex impedance fully, two quantities must be measured—its real and imaginary parts. At first sight this might seem to require two separate experiments, but in fact the balancing of an a.c. bridge requires that two separate conditions be

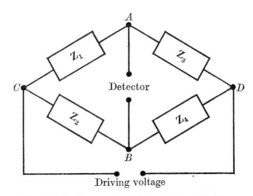

FIG. 15.8. Generalized Wheatstone's bridge.

satisfied simultaneously. These two conditions involve the real and imaginary components of the unknown impedance, and thus both are determined when both conditions are fulfilled. The reason for this extra complexity in the balancing of an a.c. bridge can readily be seen from consideration of a simple network such as the generalized Wheatstone's bridge shown in Fig. 15.8, with complex impedances in each of the arms. For a balance the voltage applied to the detector must be zero. This voltage is equal to the difference of voltage between the points $A$ and $B$, which is truly zero only if the voltage at these points has not only the same amplitude but also the same phase. In other words, the voltage at each of these points must be represented by a vector with two components, and for the vectors at the two points to be identical, their components must be individually the same.

The presence of two balance conditions which must be fulfilled simultaneously has an important effect on the design of a.c. bridges. In order to avoid disturbing one balance condition when adjusting the other, it is essential that the two balance conditions shall be independent of one another. This can be achieved by choosing a bridge where each balance condition can be met by adjusting a variable impedance which does not appear in the other balance condition. The final balance can be obtained relatively quickly by first adjusting one variable until a minimum detector reading is obtained, and then the other. On returning to the first a finer balance is obtained, and so on. A second highly desirable quality is that the balance conditions shall be independent of frequency. The reason for this is that the source of power employed for the bridge never produces a pure sine wave, but contains some distortion which can be represented in a Fourier analysis of the wave form by harmonics of the fundamental frequency. The presence of quite a small harmonic content will be important if the balance conditions depend on frequency, because the sensitivity of the bridge depends on the ability to detect a small fraction of the applied voltage, and this will be obscured by the harmonic content unless this is balanced out simultaneously. In practice it is often found that the harmonics do not vanish even in a bridge where the balance conditions are independent of frequency, because the impedances used may vary with frequency, usually because of stray reactances (see Problems 9.10 and 9.11). In this case it is advantageous to use either a tuned detector, such as a phase-sensitive detector with phase shifts of 0 and $\frac{1}{2}\pi$ so that signals can be observed both in phase and quadrature, or to insert a filter at the input to the detector to eliminate the harmonics.

The driving voltage for the bridge is usually provided by a small audio-frequency oscillator, a few volts being sufficient for most purposes. The detector consists either of ear-phones or, for greater sensitivity, a small audio-frequency amplifier followed by a detector or by a C.R.O. The latter has the advantage that it shows the wave form reaching the detector, and the presence of harmonics near the balance point is readily observed. To some extent it is possible to separate visually the fundamental and harmonics and to reduce the former to one-fifth or so of the harmonic. The amplifier gain must be variable at the input stage (a potentiometer before the grid of the first tube is sufficient) in order to avoid saturation of the later stages when the bridge is far from balance. The gain is increased as the balance is approached and the amplifier has the advantage that it is not readily damaged by an overload.

When a vacuum tube generator and amplifier are both used it may happen that one terminal of each is earthed, or has a large capacitance to the mains supply which is common to both. This would throw either a short circuit or a large capacitance across one arm of the bridge, and an isolating transformer (preferably one with an electrostatic screen between primary and secondary) should be used between the bridge and either the generator or the detector-amplifier.

Variable impedances are required to balance the bridge, and for this purpose resistances and capacitances are much preferred to inductances.

A variable self-inductance requires an adjustable contact, and has an appreciable resistance; at audio frequencies the $Q$ is generally not better than about 30, while the loss tangent ($= 1/Q$) of a good mica capacitor is about $10^{-4}$. The ratio of reactance to resistance in a standard resistance is normally much less than this at frequencies at least up to 10 kc/s. A good general rule is that the impedances of all arms should be of the same order for optimum operation of the bridge.

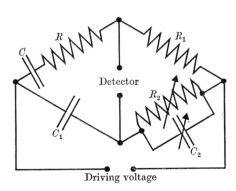

FIG. 15.9. Schering bridge for the measurement of capacitance.

The generalized Wheatstone's bridge shown in Fig. 15.8 is the basis of most bridge circuits, and the balance condition is similar to that for the d.c. bridge:
$$\mathbf{Z}_1/\mathbf{Z}_2 = \mathbf{Z}_3/\mathbf{Z}_4. \tag{15.1}$$

The two balance conditions are contained in this complex equation, since the real and imaginary parts must be satisfied simultaneously. This will be seen in the following application to the Schering bridge, which is commonly used for the determination of capacitance.

The circuit diagram of the Schering bridge is shown in Fig. 15.9. The unknown (lossy) capacitor is represented by the series combination of $C$ and $R$. $C_1$ is a good standard capacitor, whose magnitude should be of the same order as that of the capacitor under test. $R_1$ is a fixed resistance, and $R_2$ is a variable resistance shunted by a variable capacitor $C_2$. The balance condition is
$$j\omega C_1\left(R+\frac{1}{j\omega C}\right) = R_1\left(\frac{1}{R_2}+j\omega C_2\right).$$

The real and imaginary parts of this give
$$C = C_1(R_2/R_1) \Big\}$$
and
$$R = R_1(C_2/C_1) \Big\} \tag{15.2}$$

These conditions fulfil the requirements for an a.c. bridge outlined earlier. They are independent of each other, provided that $R_2$ and $C_2$ only are varied, and they are independent of frequency. In addition the capacitance of the unknown capacitor is obtained in terms of a known standard capacitor and the ratio of two resistances, and the variable capacitance $C_2$ enters only into the equation for the apparent series resistance of the unknown capacitor. With a good capacitor this will be small, and high accuracy in the determination of $R$ is seldom required. A small variable air capacitor usually suffices for $C_2$, and its leakage resistance under normal conditions will be so high that it does not affect $R_2$, with which it is in parallel.

Owing to the difficulty of constructing a standard variable inductance, it is generally preferable to determine an unknown self-inductance in terms of standard capacitances and resistances. In Maxwell's $L/C$ bridge (see Problem 15.5) a network of the Wheatstone bridge type is used, but to make the two balance conditions independent of each other a standard variable capacitance is required. A modification of this bridge, which is commonly used, is due to Anderson and has the advantage that only variable resistances are required, together with a standard fixed capacitance. The circuit is shown in Fig. 15.10. The unknown self-inductance is $L$, with resistance $r$, which forms one arm of the bridge when placed in series with a variable resistance $S$. The fixed capacitor $C$ is in series with a variable resistance $T$, the combination being shunted by a resistance $P$. The detector is connected from $B$ to the junction of $C$ and $T$, instead of to the point $A$. The balance condition is most readily found by calculating the voltages across $FE$ and $FB$ as fractions of the driving voltage $V$. The voltage across $FE$ is a fraction $1/(1+j\omega CT)$ of that across $FA$, while that across $FA = V\mathbf{Z}/(\mathbf{Z}+Q) = V/(1+Q/\mathbf{Z})$, where $\mathbf{Z}$ is the total impedance between $F$ and $A$. Since

$$1/\mathbf{Z} = 1/P + j\omega C/(1+j\omega CT),$$

the voltage across $FE$ is

$$V/\{(1+j\omega CT)(1+Q/\mathbf{Z})\} = V/\{(1+j\omega CT)(1+Q/P)+j\omega CQ\},$$

while the voltage across $FB$ is $VR/(R+j\omega L+r+S)$. Equating these voltages gives

$$1+(j\omega L+r+S)/R = (1+j\omega CT)(1+Q/P)+j\omega CQ.$$

The real and imaginary parts of this equation give separately

$$(r+S)/R = Q/P$$

and

$$L/R = CT(1+Q/P)+CQ.$$

It is generally convenient to make $Q = P$, in which case the balance conditions reduce to

$$\left. \begin{array}{l} r = R - S \\ L = CR(2T + P) \end{array} \right\}. \qquad (15.3)$$

It is obvious from this that no balance is possible unless $CRP < L$; if this condition is being violated it will be indicated by the fact that the nearest approach to balance is obtained when $T$ is zero. Inspection of the balance conditions shows also that they are independent of frequency, and of each other if $S$ and $T$ are made the variables.

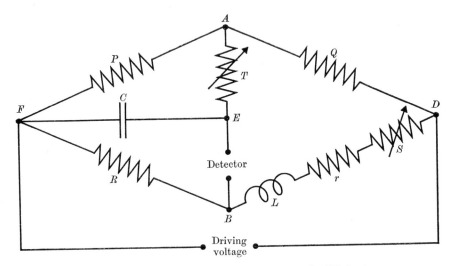

Fig. 15.10. Anderson's bridge for measurement of self-inductance.

The simplest method of measuring mutual inductance is by means of a direct comparison with a variable standard mutual inductance. The primary windings of the inductance under test and the standard are connected in series to a generator, and the secondary windings are connected in series to a detector. If the secondary connexions are made so that the induced voltages oppose one another, a null reading is obtained in the detector when the variable mutual inductance is equal to that under test. In practice it is generally impossible to get a good balance because the voltage induced in the secondary of each inductance contains a component in phase with the primary current, arising from effects such as self and mutual capacitance in the coils. This may be represented by writing the secondary voltage as $V_s = (\rho + j\omega M)i_p$. Hartshorn has shown that this difficulty may be overcome by the inclusion of a variable resistance which is common to both the primary and secondary circuits, as shown in Fig. 15.11. The equation for a balance at the detector $D$ is now

$$ri_p \pm (\rho_1 + j\omega M_1)i_p \mp (\rho_2 + j\omega M_2)i_p = 0$$

which separates to

$$\left.\begin{array}{c} M_1 = M_2 \\ r = \pm(\rho_1 - \rho_2) \end{array}\right\}. \tag{15.4}$$

The second of these equations can only be satisfied if the connexions are made so as to give the right signs; we have already assumed that the secondaries are connected in antiphase with respect to one another.

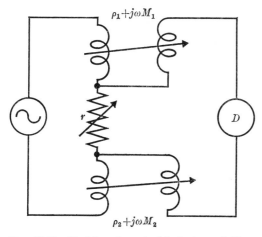

FIG. 15.11. Hartshorn's mutual inductance bridge.

## 15.3. Measurement of impedance at radio frequencies

As the frequency is increased the difficulties associated with the use of bridges for the determination of impedance rise rapidly. Each arm of the bridge must be enclosed in its own shield, and each connexion must be shielded. The generator and detector should also be shielded and care must be taken to avoid any direct pick-up from generator to detector which would give a false zero-setting for the bridge. The capacitance between each arm and its shield must be included in the analysis of the network. It is usual to make two arms identical, with equal resistance and equal capacitance between the resistance and its shield. This gives an equal ratio in two arms in spite of the shielding capacitances. It is also common to use a 'substitution' method, the bridge being balanced first with the unknown impedance in parallel with the variable standard impedance (usually resistance plus capacitance) and then without it. No general account of r.f. bridges can be given here, but it may be said that their construction requires expert and specialized knowledge if accurate results are to be obtained.

A general purpose instrument which is commonly used at radio frequencies is the 'Q-meter'. The basic circuit of this instrument is shown in Fig. 15.12. A small current $I$ from an oscillator is read on a milliammeter $A$ and then flows to a known low resistance $r$. A series tuned circuit is connected in parallel with $r$, and the voltage $V$ developed across the capacitor $C$ is read on a vacuum tube voltmeter when the capacitor

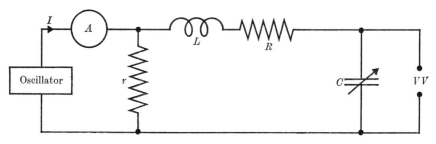

Fig. 15.12. $Q$-meter circuit.
$A$  thermoammeter.   $L$  inductance under test.   $VV$  vacuum tube voltmeter.

is adjusted for resonance. The latter is indicated by a maximum reading of the voltmeter. The $Q$ of the circuit under test is then equal to the ratio $V/Ir$, since $Ir$ is the voltage introduced in series with the tuned circuit. It is necessary that the resistance $r$ shall be small compared with the series resistance $R$ of the tuned circuit, in order that substantially all the current registered by the milliammeter shall flow through $r$. This requirement may be stated in another way—$r$ must be small compared with $R$ in order not to load the circuit under test. (It is easy to show that the measured $Q$ is that for a circuit whose total series resistance is the sum of $r$ and $R$.) In a commercial instrument an internal oscillator of calibrated variable frequency is provided, and the current from it may be adjusted to bring the milliammeter reading always to a fixed mark. An internal vacuum tube voltmeter may then be calibrated directly to read the $Q$ of an unknown coil. The variable capacitor $C$ is included in the instrument, and is calibrated so that the inductance of the unknown coil may be calculated from the known oscillator frequency and the tuning capacitance. An unknown capacitance may also be measured by the substitution method: a suitable coil $L$ is inserted and the reading of $C$ required to tune it to resonance with and without the unknown capacitor in parallel with $C$ is found. An unknown resistance can be measured by finding the effect on the $Q$ of a circuit when it is placed in series with the circuit.

At frequencies above about 100 Mc/s (wavelengths of 3 metres and less) the leads to the impedance under test are not negligible in length compared with the wavelength and errors may be introduced because the current and voltage at the measuring instrument are not the same as those at the unknown impedance. These errors may be eliminated by making the leads part of a transmission line of known and constant impedance, the unknown impedance being placed at the end of this line and acting as its termination. The impedance $Z_0$ of the transmission line may be calculated from its dimensions (see § 11.3) and the unknown impedance is determined as a ratio to $Z_0$. This may be carried out either by determining the voltage standing wave ratio (v.s.w.r.) on the line, or by a resonance method.

The first of these methods has the advantage that the results do not depend on the generator impedance, and the generator may therefore be connected directly to the line. From the theory of transmission lines (Chapter 11) it follows that the voltage at any point on the line may be regarded as due to an incident wave of amplitude $A$ and a wave reflected from the terminating impedance of amplitude $A_1$. The resultant voltage amplitude is a maximum $(A+A_1)$ at an antinode where the incident and reflected waves are in phase, and a minimum $(A-A_1)$ where they are 180° out of phase, these points being a quarter of a wavelength apart. From a measurement of the voltage standing wave ratio

$$(A+A_1)/(A-A_1),$$

and the position of the nodes or antinodes, the ratio of the terminating impedance $\mathbf{Z}$ to the characteristic impedance $Z_0$ may be found using equations (11.19):

$$\left.\begin{aligned}\frac{A_1}{A} &= \sqrt{\left(\frac{Z_1^2+Z_0^2-2Z_1 Z_0 \cos\phi}{Z_1^2+Z_0^2+2Z_1 Z_0 \cos\phi}\right)}\\[2mm]\tan\delta &= \frac{2Z_1 Z_0 \sin\phi}{Z_1^2-Z_0^2}\,.\end{aligned}\right\} \qquad (11.19)$$

where $\mathbf{Z} = Z_1 e^{j\phi}$, and $\delta$ is the difference in phase between the reflected and incident waves at the point of reflection (the termination of the line). This phase constant can be found from the position of a voltage node, this being generally more accurate than the location of an antinode (especially if the v.s.w.r. is high) because the sensitivity of the detector can be increased as the node is approached. If the end of the line is at $x = 0$, and the voltage node at a point $x = -l$, then the phase of the incident wave at this point is $-\omega(-l/v) = 2\pi l/\lambda$, and that of the reflected wave is $\delta+\omega(-l/v) = \delta-2\pi l/\lambda$. For a node these must differ by $\pi$, whence $\delta = \left(\dfrac{4\pi l}{\lambda}+\pi\right)$. To determine $l$ accurately, it is best to replace the unknown impedance $\mathbf{Z}$ by a short circuit and find the distance between the previous node and the new one; the latter is (electrically) exactly an integral number of half-wavelengths from the end of the line.

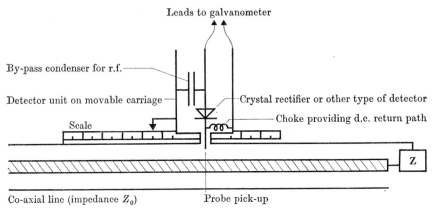

Fig. 15.13. Standing wave detector on coaxial line.

The voltage standing wave ratio can be measured by moving any loosely coupled voltage detector along the line. Since only a ratio of the maximum and minimum readings is required, the absolute calibration of the indicator is unnecessary, and a knowledge of the rectifying characteristic (d.c. current or voltage output against r.f. voltage input) is sufficient. With a coaxial line, a section of air-spaced line is made up with known dimensions, and a narrow slot is cut lengthwise along the outer conductor. Since this slot is parallel to the direction of current flow in the line, it does not disturb conditions on the line materially. In this slot (see Fig. 15.13) is inserted a small radial probe, which is parallel to the lines of electric field inside the coaxial line; it picks up a small fraction of the voltage on the line and feeds it to a detector. The intrusion of the probe is made as small as possible to minimize disturbance on the line, and for this purpose a sensitive detector is required to obtain adequate sensitivity. The probe is mounted on a movable carriage, carefully machined so that the intrusion of the probe does not change as it moves along. This may be checked by observing the constancy of the detector reading when the line is terminated by its characteristic impedance, when the v.s.w.r. should be unity. With a parallel wire line a similar arrangement may be used with a probe near the wires, but the indicator and its leads must be shielded and kept well away from the line since the electric and magnetic fields around the line are not now rigorously confined as they are in the coaxial line.

From the measurement of the v.s.w.r. and of $\delta$, the ratio of the real and imaginary parts of $\mathbf{Z}$ to $Z_0$ can be found by using equations (11.19), but these are algebraically so clumsy to handle that graphical methods are normally employed. 'Impedance diagrams' can be obtained from which the real and imaginary parts of $\mathbf{Z}/Z_0$ can be read off at once.

When the impedance to be measured has only a small dissipative component the standing wave ratio becomes very large and is difficult to measure accurately, principally because the detector law must be known over a wide range. It is often then more convenient to use a resonance method. The unknown impedance is connected across the end of a line as in Fig. 15.14, and an oscillator and detector are loosely coupled to it. A movable bridge, which should make such good contact as to be essentially a short circuit, is adjusted until resonance is indicated by maximum deflexion of the detector. If the load $\mathbf{Z}$ is represented by a resistance $R$ in parallel with a reactance $jX$, then resonance occurs when this reactance is equal and opposite to the line reactance. If the length of the line at this point is $l$, then the line reactance is

$$jX' = -jX = jZ_0 \tan 2\pi l/\lambda,$$

which may be positive or negative according to the value of $l/\lambda$. Thus the value of $X$ is determined from the resonant length. The value of $R$ may be found by measuring the sharpness of resonance. This is most conveniently done by varying the length of the line until the detector reading shows that the voltage (or current) on the line has fallen to $1/\sqrt{2}$ of the maximum. At this point the susceptance formed by $X^{-1}$ in parallel with $Z_0^{-1} \cot 2\pi(l \pm \delta l)/\lambda$ has risen from zero to be just equal to $1/R$ (cf. the theory of the parallel tuned circuit in § 9.3). If the change in length is $\delta l$, then the value of the susceptance is

$$|-X^{-1} + Z_0^{-1} \cot 2\pi(l \pm \delta l)/\lambda| = Z_0^{-1}(2\pi \delta l/\lambda)\mathrm{cosec}^2(2\pi l/\lambda) = 1/R,$$

whence $R$ can be determined. If loss in the line cannot be neglected, as has been assumed above, then it can be found by a separate measurement with the line short-circuited at both ends (or open-circuited at one end) and a correction applied. The calculation is rather complicated, but from equation (11.28) it can be seen that the length of line can be represented by a complex admittance $\mathbf{Y}'$ which is in parallel with $1/\mathbf{Z}$. If $\mathbf{Y}'$ is separated into its real and imaginary parts $G'$ and $S'$, then the calculation proceeds as before. As the resonant lengths of line unloaded and terminated by **Z** will be different, the loss on the line must be expressed in terms of the attenuation coefficient $\alpha$ (equation (11.24)).

The advantage of the resonance method over the s.w.r. method is that the detector law need only be known over a small range, the other

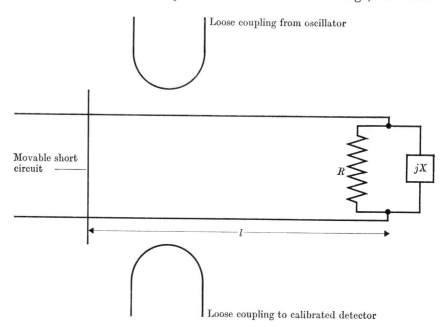

Loose coupling from oscillator

Movable short circuit

Loose coupling to calibrated detector

FIG. 15.14. Measurement of impedance using resonance method on transmission line.

measurements being those of lengths. Both types of measurements may also be used with waveguides at centimetre wavelengths, though here the concept of a lumped impedance loses most of its meaning. A few examples of such measurements will be given later in this book, but for a full discussion reference should be made to Barlow and Cullen, *Microwave Measurements* (Constable).

## 15.4. Measurement of frequency and wavelength

The measurement of the frequency of an audio oscillation can be made in terms of known impedances by the use of a bridge whose balance is dependent on frequency. It is obvious that the oscillation to be measured must be constant in frequency and free from harmonics, since the latter would be out of balance in the bridge (two uses of a frequency bridge are the suppression of a given frequency such as a troublesome harmonic and the analysis of harmonic content). A large number of bridges have been devised which satisfy the desiderata that the balance conditions should be mutually independent and only one of them should depend on the frequency. A simple bridge using only resistances and capacitances is due to Wien and is shown in Fig. 15.15. The balance conditions are

$$
\left.
\begin{aligned}
\omega^2 &= \frac{1}{RSC_1 C_2} \\
\frac{C_2}{C_1} &= \frac{Q}{P} - \frac{R}{S}
\end{aligned}
\right\}, \tag{15.5}
$$

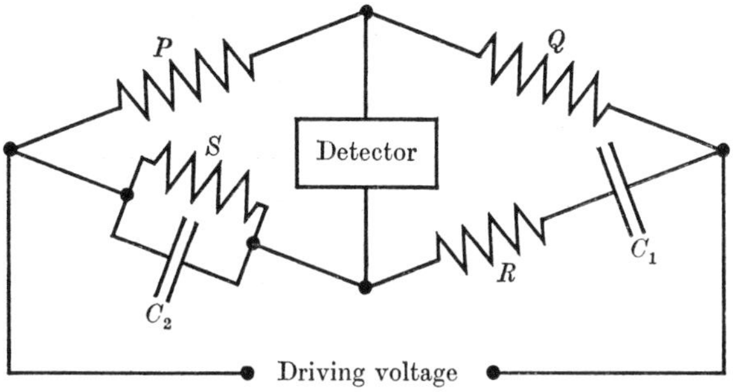

FIG. 15.15. Wien's bridge for frequency measurement.

which are mutually independent if the variables $R$ and $S$ or $C_1$ and $C_2$ are ganged so that their ratio is kept constant. Then the second condition will remain satisfied once it has been set up and measurement of a wide range of frequencies is obtained by a single adjustment.

At wavelengths less than 1 or 2 metres the measurement of wavelength directly becomes quite convenient, and high accuracy may be attained because of the high $Q$ of resonant transmission lines and waveguide cavities. Parallel wire lines may be used for the longer wavelengths, but coaxial lines are better at decimetre wavelengths, and cavity resonators at centimetre wavelengths. A simple type of coaxial line wave-meter is shown in Fig. 15.16. The centre conductor is variable in length, and moves through a spring contact which forms the closed end of the line. Power is introduced by means of a small loop which intersects some of the magnetic lines of force at the closed end, and a second loop takes power to a detector (usually a crystal rectifier). These loops must be kept small to give loose coupling, and to avoid pulling the oscillator whose wavelength is to be measured through coupled circuit effects. The equivalent circuit of the wave-meter is shown in Fig. 15.16, from which it can be seen that the detector reading is a maximum when the line is resonant. With a high $Q$ it is usually undetectably small away

from resonance. Since the loops introduce small impedances which alter
the electrical length of the line, it is preferable to measure successive
points of resonance, which are exactly half-wavelength apart. The wave-
meter then needs no calibration, the wavelength being found directly

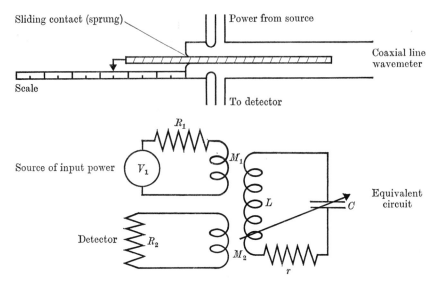

FIG. 15.16. Coaxial line wave-meter and equivalent circuit.

from a scale and vernier attached to the moving part. The accuracy is
usually about 1 part in $10^3$, the main difficulty being in making a good
contact between the moving conductor and the stationary end.

A basic type of cavity wave-meter is shown in Fig. 15.17. A section
of circular waveguide is closed at one end, the other end being formed
by a plunger driven by a micrometer head. Power is fed into the cavity
from a waveguide through a small hole, and resonance is detected by
coupling a little power out through a second hole to a detector. The
holes should be kept as small as possible, subject to getting a finite
detector reading, in order to avoid lowering the natural $Q$ of the resonator,
which may be of the order of 10 000. The wavelength in the cavity is
found from the distance $(\lambda_g/2)$ between successive resonance points. The
wavelength in free space may then be found from the diameter of the
cavity, and the mode of resonance. To avoid the difficulty of making
a good contact between the moving plunger and the walls, a particular
waveguide mode ($TE_{01}$ or $H_{01}$) is often used, where there is no current
flow across this contact (see § 11.7). Other modes of resonance may then
also be present, since the $TE_{01}$ mode needs rather a large cavity diameter

(the cut-off wavelength is equal to 0·82 times the diameter). These may be avoided by using special arrangements of the coupling holes (see Bleaney, Loubser, and Penrose, 1947). An accuracy of one or two parts in $10^4$ may be attained, but a correction is then needed for the dielectric constant (1·0006) of the air in the cavity.

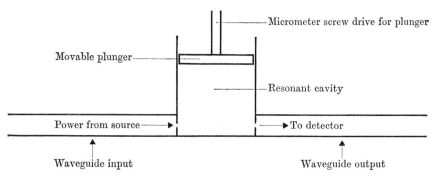

FIG. 15.17. Resonant cavity wave-meter.

### The quartz crystal oscillator

Where high accuracy of frequency control or measurement is required, use is made of the properties of a piezo-electric crystal, quartz being the most satisfactory for this purpose. A quartz crystal grows in the form of a hexagonal prism with pointed ends, the cross-section of the prism being as shown in Fig. 15.18 (a). If an electric field is applied to the crystal

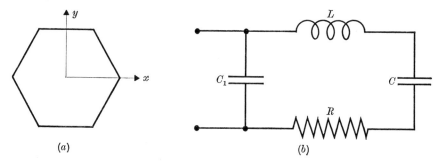

FIG. 15.18. (a) Quartz crystal ($x$, $y$ are one of the three pairs of $X$, $Y$ axes). (b) Equivalent circuit of crystal and its electrodes.

in the $X$-direction, the crystal contracts or elongates in the $Y$-direction according to the sign of the electric field. Similarly, if a mechanical stress is applied in the $Y$-direction, an electric polarization is set up in the $X$-direction and charges appear on the faces of the crystal. These effects are reversible and very nearly linearly related, and their importance lies in the fact that they couple together an electrical and a mechanical system. If an alternating voltage is applied in the $X$-direction, an alternating stress appears in the $Y$-direction and the amplitude of the resulting mechanical vibrations is large if the frequency of alternation coincides with a natural mechanical vibration of the crystal. A number of different modes of oscillation exist, but those most commonly used are longitudinal and shear vibrations. The damping of the mechanical vibrations is very low, and the sharpness of the resonance makes them very suitable for use as frequency standards. The desirable properties for this purpose are:

(a) Zero temperature coefficient of frequency of oscillation.

(b) High piezo-electric effect.

(c) A single mode of mechanical resonance well separated in frequency from other modes, so that there is no tendency to jump from one mode to another.

The greatest piezo-electric effect is obtained when the electrical and mechanical stresses are applied along the electrical or $X$-axis and mechanical or $Y$-axis respectively, but oscillations can be excited by any stress which has a component parallel to these axes. (Note that, owing to the high symmetry of the crystal, there are three sets of $X$- and $Y$-axes, related to one another by rotations of $120°$ and $240°$ about the $Z$-axis, the optic axis of the crystal.) An $X$-cut crystal consists of a thin slab with faces parallel to the $YZ$-plane, and the temperature coefficient of the frequency of oscillation is negative, about $-22 \times 10^{-6}$ per °C. A $Y$-cut crystal is a thin slab with its faces parallel to the $XZ$-plane, and the temperature coefficient is positive with a number of discontinuities due to couplings between different modes of oscillation. In general it is more important to obtain zero temperature coefficient than high piezo-electric activity, and intermediate cuts are used such as the $AT$-cut, a thin plate whose faces contain the $X$-axis and a line in the $YZ$-plane making an angle of about $35 \cdot 5°$ with the $Z$-axis. When a voltage is applied between the large faces, a shear vibration is set up whose frequency in megacycles per second is $0 \cdot 1675/$(thickness in centimetres). This is suitable for frequencies from roughly $\frac{1}{2}$ to 10 Mc/s. Lower frequencies may be obtained from modes where the frequency is determined by one of the long dimensions of the slab, the full range of quartz crystals being roughly from 25 kc/s to 15 Mc/s. To apply the alternating voltage the slab is mounted between the plates of a capacitor; these are generally formed by sputtering a metallic film on to the large faces. This reduces the loading on the mechanical vibrations, which is further reduced by mounting the crystal *in vacuo* between light supports touching the crystal at a mechanical node. For the highest frequency stability the crystal is kept in an oven thermostatically controlled to $0 \cdot 1^\circ$ or better, because the temperature coefficient is zero only over a narrow range of temperature.

The mechanical system of a quartz crystal may be represented by the equivalent electrical circuit shown in Fig. 15.18 (b). The mechanical resonance is equivalent to a series tuned circuit and this is shunted by the capacitance $C_1$ of the electrodes. Typical values are:

*X-cut quartz* (lengthwise vibration)
    *Dimensions*: rectangular bar,

$$X = 1 \cdot 4 \text{ mm}, \ Y = 30 \cdot 7 \text{ mm}, \ Z = 4 \cdot 1 \text{ mm}$$

| | |
|---|---|
| $R = 15\,000$ ohms | $C_1 = 3 \cdot 54$ pF |
| $L = 137$ henries | $Q = 5150$ |
| $C = 0 \cdot 0228$ pF | $f_0 = 89 \cdot 87$ kc/s |

*AT-cut quartz*
    *Dimensions*: disk, 25 mm diameter, thickness $1 \cdot 10$ mm.

| | |
|---|---|
| $R = 24 \cdot 2$ ohms | $C_1 = 17 \cdot 9$ pF |
| $L = 0 \cdot 119$ henries | $Q = 46\,500$ |
| $C = 0 \cdot 0945$ pF | $f_0 = 1500$ kc/s |

(From W. G. Cady, *Piezoelectricity* (McGraw-Hill, 1946).)

The presence of $C_1$ causes the circuit to behave as a parallel tuned circuit at a frequency just above that of the series resonance (see Problem 15.8). The difference between these two frequencies is very small so that the phase angle of the circuit varies very rapidly. A simple one-tube circuit for maintaining the crystal in oscillation is shown in Fig. 15.19. Feedback of energy to the grid circuit takes place through the grid-anode capacitance $C_{ga}$, and to obtain the right phase the anode circuit must be tuned to a frequency higher than the parallel resonance frequency of the crystal in its mount, so that the impedance of the anode circuit is inductive at this frequency (see § 12.8). The crystal oscillation will be damped if the amplitude of oscillation is so high that grid current flows in the tube, and various arrangements for controlling the feed-back are used, such as a bridge system where one arm is a lamp or thermistor whose resistance varies with the amplitude of oscillation. The frequency of oscillation can be adjusted over a very narrow range by a small variable capacitance in parallel with $C_1$ and this is used for fine adjustment.

*Comparison of unknown frequency with standard frequency*

The high frequency stability of the quartz crystal oscillator makes it extremely useful as a frequency standard, and the accurate measurement of an unknown frequency is invariably made by means of a comparison

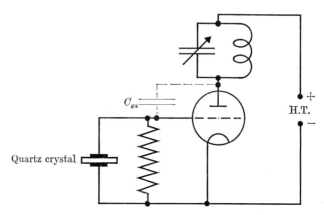

Fɪɢ. 15.19. Quartz crystal oscillator.

with such a standard. The block diagram of a frequency standard suitable for ordinary laboratory purposes is shown in Fig. 15.20. The fundamental frequency generated is 100 kc/s, using a quartz crystal contained in a thermostat. Although long-term frequency stability of the order of one part in $10^8$ is possible, it is unnecessary to build the complex system that this requires. Instead, the frequency of the standard may be adjusted immediately before use, and checked during operation, against one of the accurate frequencies originated at a standardizing laboratory and radiated by station MSF, Rugby, England, and station WWV, Washington, U.S.A. The working quartz crystal standards at the national standards laboratories are calibrated in terms of the frequency of an atomic transition of the caesium atom, and an international committee has decided (1964) that the unit of time should be thus defined, making the caesium frequency

$$9\ 192\ 631\ 770\ \text{c/s.}$$

This is a more convenient and a more precise standard than previous ones based on the mean length of the solar day or year, because the motion of the earth is known to be subject to fluctuations (see § 23.6).

In order to measure frequencies other than those close to the 100 kc/s fundamental it is necessary to generate higher and lower frequencies by multiplication and division of the fundamental. Higher harmonics are generated by feeding the fundamental into a Class C amplifier stage, where the short pulse of anode current has a high harmonic content. This excites a circuit tuned to the desired harmonic which acts as the anode load, and this harmonic is then amplified to the desired extent.

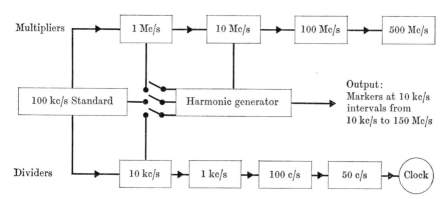

FIG. 15.20. Frequency measuring equipment.

It is convenient to work with harmonics rising by factors of 10 (usually achieved by multiplying first by five, and then by two). By repetition of this process frequencies up to a few hundred megacycles may be generated with the same accuracy as the fundamental, and harmonics of such frequencies have been generated up to $\sim 10^{11}$ c/s (wavelengths of a few millimetres). Frequency division may be achieved by a number of methods, such as use of the multivibrator (see § 13.7). A better system is illustrated by the following method of producing 10 kc/s from 100 kc/s: the output of an amplifier for 10 kc/s is multiplied to 90 kc/s, which is heterodyned with the 100 kc/s to produce a 10 kc/s signal which is fed back to the input of the 10 kc/s amplifier. This causes it to oscillate at a frequency precisely one-tenth of the standard 100 kc/s, since only then is the feed-back signal of the same frequency. This process may be repeated down to 50 c/s if it is desired to run a clock which can be checked against radio time signals in order to monitor the long-term stability of the system.

Comparison of an unknown frequency with the standard requires the use of an adjustable oscillator which can be heterodyned against both the harmonics of the standard and the unknown. Suppose the latter is known (by resonance with a calibrated tuned circuit) to be approximately 13 Mc/s. The adjustable oscillator is first tuned to zero beat with the 10 Mc/s standard, and the 1 Mc/s output is then also switched into the mixer stage, which now generates every harmonic of 1 Mc/s. The variable oscillator is now increased in frequency, and the number of zero beat notes with the 1 Mc/s harmonics passed before zero beat with the unknown is reached are counted. Suppose there are three; then the unknown frequency lies between 13 and 14 Mc/s. The variable oscillator is then returned to 13 Mc/s, and the 100 kc/s signal from the standard added to the mixer. The variable oscillator is now again increased in frequency, and the zero beats every 100 kc/s counted until the unknown is reached. This shows that the unknown lies, say, between 13·1 and 13·2 Mc/s, and the process is repeated with the 10 kc/s standard to establish that the unknown lies between, say, 13·16 and 13·17 Mc/s. The ultimate heterodyne difference frequency between the unknown and the nearest harmonic of the 10 kc/s standard lies in the audio-frequency range and may be measured by a frequency bridge, or by comparison with a calibrated audio-frequency oscillator, etc., according to the accuracy required.

## 15.5. Measurement of dielectric constant

The dielectric constant of a substance affords some valuable information as to the structure of its constituent molecules (see Chapter 17), and accurate measurement of the dielectric constant is therefore of some importance. Since the dielectric constant is defined by the ratio of the capacitance of a capacitor filled with the substance under test to that of the empty capacitor, it is obvious that in general two measurements of capacitance will suffice. For solids and liquids the dielectric constant varies from about 2 to 100, and any of the bridges designed to measure capacitance may be used to give accurate results. For the higher dielectric constants care must be taken to avoid stray capacitance which may seriously affect the reading obtained with the empty capacitor, if this has a rather small capacitance.

In the case of gases the dielectric constant differs from unity only by about 0·001 and special methods must be used. One such method (see, for example, Hector and Woernley, 1946) makes use of the high accuracy which can be obtained in the measurement of frequency, by incorporating a specially designed capacitor in the resonant circuit of a tuned anode oscillator. The frequency of this oscillator is then compared with a standard frequency from a quartz crystal oscillator, first with the capacitor evacuated, and then filled with gas. The change in frequency may either be measured directly, or the frequency may be restored to its original value by adjustment of a small standard variable capacitor in parallel with the capacitor containing the gas. The accuracy of this latter method is usually limited by that of the variable capacitor, and the former method is to be preferred.

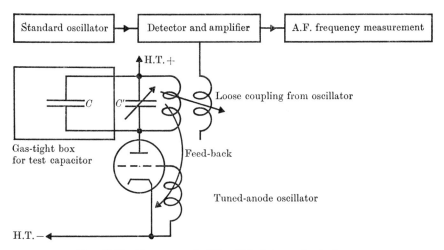

FIG. 15.21. Measurement of the dielectric constant of a gas.

A block diagram of the apparatus is shown in Fig. 15.21. To avoid dimensional changes when the gas is introduced, the capacitor $C$ is surrounded, first by a perforated case, and then by a heavy steel gas-tight container. The surfaces of the capacitor are gold-plated to maintain high conductivity and avoid tarnishing. If measurements are made over a range of temperature, in order to determine the electric dipole moment of a molecule (see § 17.3), a correction must be made for thermal expansion. A correction is also required for stray capacitance which is not altered by the introduction of the gas. If a frequency measuring equipment is not available, a small tuning capacitor $C'$ is adjusted when $C$ is evacuated so that a zero beat note is obtained between the tuned anode oscillator and a standard oscillator, preferably controlled by a quartz crystal. If this frequency $f'$ is about 1 Mc/s, then on introducing the gas an audio-frequency beat note is produced between the new frequency $f''$ and the standard $f'$, which may be measured by a Wien's bridge or by comparison with a tuning fork. Then since $f' = 1/2\pi\sqrt{(LC)}$, and $f'' = 1/2\pi\sqrt{(L\epsilon C)}$, we have $\epsilon = (f'/f'')^2$.

Lovering and Wiltshire (1951) have criticized the above method on the ground that long-term stability is not attained, and it is therefore necessary to measure the frequency change fairly quickly after introduction or removal of the gas. This introduces errors because of adiabatic temperature changes. They used a simple capacitance bridge at 0·11 Mc/s, and determined the capacitance change by means of a variable cylindrical capacitor whose inner conductor was advanced by a micrometer screw.

The most accurate measurements appear to be those of Essen and Froome (1951), using a cavity resonator and working at a frequency of 24 000 Mc/s. The cavity was cylindrical, with a diameter of about 5 cm, and resonated in the $TE_{01}$ mode. The frequency of resonance was determined first with the cavity evacuated, and then filled with gas, by plotting out the resonance curve using a klystron oscillator whose frequency could be determined to 1 part in $10^8$ by comparison with the N.P.L. frequency standard. The frequency of resonance is given by equation (11.34):

$$\frac{f^2}{v^2} = \frac{\mu\epsilon f^2}{c^2} = \frac{1}{\lambda_c^2} + \frac{1}{\lambda_g^2}, \tag{11.34}$$

where $\mu$ and $\epsilon$ are the magnetic permeability and dielectric constant of the gas filling the resonator and $\lambda_c$, $\lambda_g$ are fixed by the diameter and length of the cavity respectively. Thus if $f'$ is the resonant frequency of the empty cavity, and $f''$ that of the gas-filled cavity, $(f'/f'')^2 = \mu\epsilon$. Hence the ratio of the two frequencies determines $n = \sqrt{(\mu\epsilon)}$, the refractive index of the gas. A correction must be applied for the permeability, which differs slightly from unity for air and oxygen, since the latter is paramagnetic. A comparison of the measurements of $\epsilon$ of a number of workers at different frequencies, together with the square of the optical refractive index, is given in Table 17.4.

The cavity resonance method may also be used for measurement of the dielectric constant of liquids and solids, provided that their loss tangent is fairly small (see Faraday Society Conference on Dielectrics, 1946). A partly filled cavity must be used for solids or liquids of high loss tangent, but for non-polar liquids a filled cavity was employed by Bleaney, Loubser, and Penrose (1947). A tunable cavity resonant in the $TE_{01}$ mode of the same type as described earlier (§ 15.4) was adjusted to resonance with a klystron oscillator of fixed frequency, first with the cavity empty, and then filled with liquid. By measuring a number of successive resonant points, the wavelength in the guide was found in each case, and the dielectric constant calculated from the equations

$$\frac{\epsilon_a}{\lambda^2} = \frac{1}{\lambda_a^2} + \frac{1}{\lambda_c^2}, \qquad \frac{\epsilon}{\lambda^2} = \frac{1}{\lambda_d^2} + \frac{1}{\lambda_c^2}, \tag{15.6}$$

where $\epsilon_a$ is the dielectric constant of air and $\epsilon$ that of the liquid, $\lambda$ the wavelength in free space, and $\lambda_a$, $\lambda_d$ the wavelengths in the air- and liquid-filled cavity respectively. The loss tangent of the liquid was found from the width of the resonance curve determined by detuning the cavity. Thus only measurements of length, depending on a micrometer thread, were involved. Typical results at a temperature of 20° C are given in Table 15.1. When two measurements are given at 1·35-cm wavelength, they were made with cavities of different diameter.

TABLE 15.1

| | Dielectric constant $\epsilon$ | | Loss tangent (tan δ) | |
| | $\lambda = 3\cdot2$ cm | $\lambda = 1\cdot35$ cm | $\lambda = 3\cdot2$ cm | $\lambda = 1\cdot35$ cm |
|---|---|---|---|---|
| Cyclo-hexane . | 2·0244 | 2·0246, 2·0251 | 0·00005 | 0·00019 |
| n-Heptane . . | 1·9220 | 1·9223 | 0·00037 | 0·00076 |
| n-Hexane . . | 1·9016 | 1·9016 | 0·00034 | 0·00076 |
| CS$_2$ . . . | 2·6476 | 2·6477 | 0·00024 | 0·00072 |
| CCl$_4$ . . . | 2·2386 | 2·2390 | 0·00031 | 0·00078 |

All the samples except those of n-hexane and CCl$_4$ were specially purified. The loss tangent is considerably affected by small traces of polar impurities, but it is not certain that such impurities would account for all the dielectric loss.

## 15.6. Measurement of the velocity of radio waves

The velocity of electromagnetic radiation has long been regarded as one of the fundamental constants of physics, and much effort has been devoted to its accurate determination. Apart from one measurement of the velocity of radio waves on a transmission line by Mercier (1924), most of the early work has used light waves. The results showed a good deal of scatter, but in a review by Birge (1941) the mean value of 299 776±4 km/sec was adopted. From 1945 onwards a number of new determinations have been made, of greater accuracy, which suggest that the true value is nearly 299 793 km/sec (see Table 15.2). These methods have made use of radio techniques to improve the accuracy, and in some cases the wavelength of radiation used has been a few centimetres. A brief description is given below.

In § 15.4 it was pointed out that both frequency and wavelength can be measured at centimetre wavelengths. The product of these two quantities gives the wave velocity, and this has been the basis of one type of measurement at the National Physical Laboratory. It involves the construction of a cavity resonator whose resonant wavelength can be calculated from the inner dimensions and whose resonant frequency can be determined by comparison with a frequency standard. The dimensions were measured in the Metrology Department of the N.P.L. In the earlier work of Essen and Gordon-Smith (1948) a cavity of fixed length was employed, consisting of a copper cylinder of diameter 7·4 cm and length 8·5 cm. The resonant frequencies for a number of different modes were measured with the evacuated resonator in a temperature controlled room, the frequencies lying between about 3000 and 5000 Mc/s (wavelengths of 10 cm and 6 cm). The velocity $c$ may be found from the formula

$$\frac{f'(1+1/2Q)}{c} = \left\{\left(\frac{x}{\pi D}\right)^2 + \left(\frac{n}{2L}\right)^2\right\}^{\frac{1}{2}}, \qquad (15.7)$$

where $f'$ is the observed frequency of resonance, $L$ and $D$ the internal length and diameter, $x$ is a constant for a particular mode (the root of a Bessel function), $n$ the number of half-wavelengths in the resonator, and $Q$ the quality factor. The value of $Q$ was about 15 000 and it appears as a small correction for the finite electrical conductivity of the copper walls. The effect of this may be regarded as an effective increase in the dimensions of the order of the skin depth of the radiation in copper. The use of several modes of resonance is a check on 'end-effects', and the change in the resonant frequency caused by the intrusion of the coupling probes $A$, $B$ (see Fig. 15.22) was determined. The length of these probes was finally reduced beyond the point at which any such change could be observed. The measured values of the length $L$ and diameter $D$ were accurate to 3 parts in $10^6$. Four measurements of $c$ lay between 299 796 and 299 789 km/sec, the average value being 299 792±9 km/sec with a rather liberal estimate of the error.

In a second determination Essen (1950) used a cavity resonator of variable length and measured the distance required to move between successive resonances. The scatter in these distances (which are each half a guide wavelength) was about $\pm 5 \times 10^{-5}$ cm with a total travel of about 12 cm. This scatter is partly due to variations in the diameter (though no systematic variation was detected) but also includes errors arising from temperature changes, frequency measurement, and setting to resonance, giving a proportional error in $c$ of $3 \times 10^{-6}$. Measurements were made at $\sim$ 6000, 9000 and 11 000 Mc/s, and showed a systematic decrease in the apparent value of $c$ when the resonant conditions were such that the diameter of the cavity played a greater part in determining the guide wavelength. Since the measured $Q$ was lower than the theoretical $Q$, it was assumed that a surface film of poorly conducting tarnished silver (detectable by eye) caused the effective diameter to be greater than the measured diameter, since the r.f. current runs beneath this film. The measurements at different frequencies made it possible to apply a correction for this, and the final value of the velocity *in vacuo* was found to be 299 792·5 km/sec, with a maximum error of $\pm 3$ km/sec.

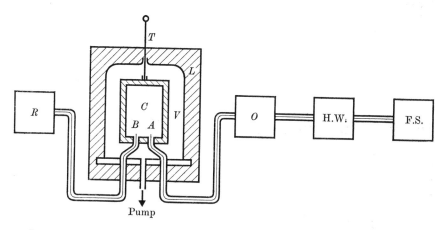

FIG. 15.22. Apparatus of Essen and Gordon-Smith for measuring the velocity of electromagnetic waves.

| | | | |
|---|---|---|---|
| $A, B$ | probes. | $V$ | vacuum. |
| $R$ | receiver. | $O$ | klystron oscillator. |
| $T$ | thermometer. | H.W. | heterodyne wavemeter. |
| $C$ | cavity resonator. | F.S. | frequency standard. |
| $L$ | lagging. | | |

These difficulties in the cavity resonator method led Froome (1952) at the N.P.L. to devise an interferometer experiment at 1·25 cm wavelength which approximates closely to a free space method. This uses a microwave analogue of the Michelson interferometer, as shown in Fig. 15.23. Power from a stabilized klystron oscillator flowing along a waveguide was divided into two portions at a hybrid junction $B$ (the analogue of a half-silvered plate). One half traversed a short length of waveguide and was reflected from a shorting piston. The other was fed to a horn and launched as a wave in space. Part of this radiation was reflected back to the horn by a 6-in. square metal plate $M$ which could be placed at points from $6\frac{1}{2}$ to $21\frac{1}{2}$ metres away. This reflected wave on returning to the hybrid junction interferes with that reflected from the shorting piston in the second arm, and the vector sum of the two amplitudes is passed along the fourth arm to a detector (a superheterodyne receiver). The latter is used to detect when the two reflected waves are exactly in anti-phase and so give a null at the detector. The metal plate *M* is then moved through successive null points, which occur every half-wavelength. The total distance moved was 1·62 metres, and this could be measured with an accuracy of $\pm 0\cdot003$ mm. At the same time the frequency of the klystron oscillator was measured against the quartz crystal standard with an accuracy of 1 part in $10^8$. Thus the wavelength

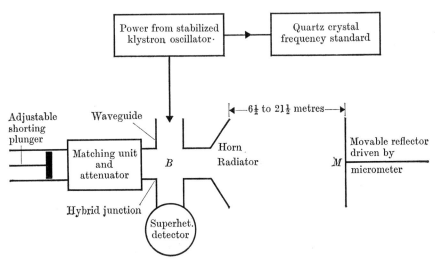

FIG. 15.23.  Froome's microwave Michelson interferometer.

in air and the frequency were determined simultaneously. In the former case two important corrections must be applied to find the wavelength *in vacuo*.

(a) a correction for the refractive index of the air, based on the measurements of Essen and Froome (see § 15.5);

(b) a correction for the fact that the wave front reaching the mirror is not a plane, but has a small curvature, and similarly for the reflected wave; this correction was calculated from diffraction theory, using data from different mirror distances.

The final value obtained for the velocity *in vacuo* was $299\,792\cdot6 \pm 0\cdot7$ km/sec. In later experiments (Froome, 1954, 1958) has used a four-horn interferometer of symmetrical design, first at a wavelength of 1·25 cm, then at 4 mm. The final results are

$$299\,792\cdot75 \pm 0\cdot3 \text{ km/sec}\quad \text{(frequency } 24\,000 \text{ Mc/s)},$$
$$299\,792\cdot5 \pm 0\cdot1 \text{ km/sec}\quad \text{(frequency } 72\,000 \text{ Mc/s)}.$$

These agree very closely with the best optical method as can be seen from Table 15.2. A description of Bergstrand's optical 'geodimeter' and of Froome's later interferometer can be found in J. H. Sanders, *The Fundamental Atomic Constants* (Oxford University Press, 1961).

TABLE 15.2

*Velocity of electromagnetic waves*

| Date | Author | Published result (km/sec) | Method |
|------|--------|---------------------------|--------|
| 1941 | Birge | 299 776 ± 4 | Statistical survey of earlier work |
| 1949 | Aslakson | 299 792·4 ± 2·4 | Radar, 300 Mc/s |
| 1950 | Essen | 299 792·5 ± 3 | Cavity resonator |
| 1952 | Froome | 299 792·6 ± 0·7 | Microwave interferometer |
| 1958 | Froome | 299 792·75 ± 0·3 | Ditto, 24 000 Mc/s |
|  |  | 299 792·5 ± 0·1 | Ditto, 72 000 Mc/s |
| 1950 | Bergstrand | 299 792·9 ± 0·25 | Optical geodimeter |
| 1957 | Bergstrand | 299 792·75 ± 0·34 | Ditto, average with earlier instrument |
|  |  | 299 792·85 ± 0·16 | Ditto, average with later instrument |

Selected values, based on Froome (1952) and Dumond (1959).

REFERENCES

ASLAKSON, C. I., 1949, *Nature, Lond.* **164**, 711.
—— 1951, ibid. **168**, 505.
BERGSTRAND, E., 1950, *Archiv für Fysik*, **2**, 119.
—— 1957, *Ann. franc. Chronom.* **2**, 97.
BIRGE, R. T., 1941, *Ann. Rep. Progr. Phys.*, London, Physical Society, **8**, 90.
BLEANEY, B., LOUBSER, J. H. N., and PENROSE, R. P., 1947, *Proc. Phys. Soc. Lond.* **59**, 185.
DUMOND, J. W. M., 1959, *Ann. Phys.* **7**, 365.
ESSEN, L., 1950, *Proc. Roy. Soc. A*, **204**, 260.
—— and FROOME, K. D., 1951, *Proc. Phys. Soc. B*, **64**, 862.
—— and GORDON-SMITH, A. C., 1948, *Proc. Roy. Soc. A*, **194**, 348.
Faraday Society Conference on Dielectrics, 1946, *Trans. Faraday Society*, 42 A.
FROOME, K. D., 1952, *Proc. Roy. Soc. A*, **213**, 123.
—— 1954, ibid. **223**, 195.
—— 1958, ibid. **247**, 109.
HECTOR, L. G., and WOERNLEY, D. L., 1946, *Phys. Rev.* **69**, 101.
LOVERING, W. F., and WILTSHIRE, L., 1951, *Proc. I.E.E.* **98**, Part II, 557.
MERCIER, J., 1924, *J. Phys. Radium*, **5**, 168.
ROLLIN, B. V., 1964, *An Introduction to Electronics* (O.U.P.).

## PROBLEMS

15.1. A cathode-ray tube has plane parallel deflecting plates of separation $a$ and length $b$ parallel to the axis of the tube; the distance from the centre of the plates to the screen is $L$. If the electrons are initially accelerated by a voltage $V_0$, show that their deflexion on the screen due to a voltage $V_1$ on the deflector plates is

$$s = \tfrac{1}{2}(LbV_1/aV_0),$$

assuming that $L \gg b$, that the field is uniform between the plates, and that edge effects can be neglected.

If $a = 0 \cdot 5$ cm, $b = 4$ cm, $L = 30$ cm, and $V_0 = 1300$ V, show that the deflexion sensitivity is $0 \cdot 92$ mm/V.

15.2. Referring to Fig. 15.4, show that the phase angle $\phi$ is given by the relation $\sin \phi = OP/OQ$.

15.3. If the frequency limit of the cathode-ray tube of Problem 15.1 were set by the finite transit time of the electrons through the deflector plates, show that the deflexion would fall to zero at about 540 Mc/s.

15.4. If in the bolometer of Fig. 15.6 all the heat is lost by conduction to the leads, which remain at room temperature, show that the fractional change in resistance $(\Delta R/R)$ when a d.c. power $W$ is dissipated in the thin wire is given by

$$(\Delta R/R) = \alpha WL/(12KA),$$

where $\alpha$ is the temperature coefficient of resistivity, $L$ the length, $K$ the thermal conductivity, and $A$ the cross-section of the wire.

15.5. Maxwell's bridge for comparing an inductance and a condenser has the circuit of Fig. 15.8, with the following impedances:

$\mathbf{Z}_1$     an inductance $L$ in series with a resistance $R_1$,

$\mathbf{Z}_2$     a resistance $R_2$,

$\mathbf{Z}_3$     a resistance $R_3$,

$\mathbf{Z}_4$     a capacitance $C$ in parallel with a resistance $R_4$.

Show that the balance conditions are

$$R_1/R_3 = R_2/R_4, \qquad L = R_2 R_3 C.$$

To make the two balance conditions independent, $R_4$ and $C$ must be varied.

15.6. At higher audio frequencies resistances may possess a small inductive component; in Anderson's bridge this may be allowed for by writing the components as $\mathbf{P} = P + jP'$, $\mathbf{Q} = Q + jQ'$, $\mathbf{R} = R + jR'$, $\mathbf{T} = T + jT'$ (we neglect any inductive component in $S$ as this will be added to $L$ at all frequencies). If $\mathbf{P}$ and $\mathbf{Q}$ are identical impedances, show that the balance conditions are

$$r + S = R - \omega C(2RT' + 2R'T + RQ' + R'Q),$$
$$L = C(2RT + QR - 2R'T' - Q'R') + R'/\omega.$$

These equations show that it is important to make $R'$ as small as possible. If $R' = 0$, the error in the determination of $L$ is zero, while that in the resistance $r$ of the inductance is $\omega CR(2T' + Q')$.

15.7. In the equivalent circuit (Fig. 15.16) of the coaxial line wavemeter, the source is taken to be a generator of voltage $V_1$ with internal resistance $R_1$, and the detector has a resistance $R_2$. If the series impedance of the tuned circuit by itself is $Z$, show that the ratio of the voltage $V_2$ across the detector to the input voltage is

$$\frac{V_2}{V_1} = -\frac{\omega^2 M_1 M_2}{R_1(Z+\omega^2 M_1^2/R_1+\omega^2 M_2^2/R_2)}.$$

This equation shows that $V_2$ is a maximum when $Z$ is a minimum, i.e. when the wave-meter is on tune and $Z$ is just the resistance $r$. It shows also that the coupled impedances $\omega^2 M_1^2/R_1$ and $\omega^2 M_2^2/R_2$ lower the effective $Q$; by writing $Z = r+2j\delta\omega L$ near resonance, show that the 'loaded $Q$' $= \sqrt{L}/\{\sqrt{C}(r+\omega^2 M_1^2/R_1+\omega^2 M_2^2/R_2)\}$, and that it may be measured by finding the fractional change in the frequency required to reduce $V_2$ to $1/\sqrt{2}$ of its maximum value (neglect changes in the coupled impedance when varying $\omega$).

15.8. In the equivalent circuit (Fig. 15.18 b) of a quartz crystal, the components for a particular crystal are $L = 3.3$ henrys, $C = 0\cdot042$ $\mu\mu$F, $R = 4500$ ohms, $C_1 = 5\cdot8$ $\mu\mu$F. Show that it behaves as a parallel resonant circuit at a frequency approximately 8 cycles above the series resonance frequency (the natural mechanical resonance frequency).

# 16

## FLUCTUATIONS AND NOISE

### 16.1. Brownian motion and fluctuations

THE irregular motion of small particles suspended in a fluid was first observed by Brown in 1828. This 'Brownian motion' never ceases and is a result of the random motion of the molecules both of the particles themselves and of the fluid. If the motion is observed over a long time, it is found that the average component of the velocity in any direction is zero, since positive and negative values occur with equal probability. The mean square value of the velocity is not zero, and from classical statistical mechanics it may be shown that the average value of each of the terms $\frac{1}{2}m\dot{x}^2$, $\frac{1}{2}m\dot{y}^2$, $\frac{1}{2}m\dot{z}^2$ of the translational kinetic energy is $\frac{1}{2}kT$, where $k$ is Boltzmann's constant (approximately $1 \cdot 38 \times 10^{-16}$ ergs/deg) and $T$ is the absolute temperature. This is a special case of the theorem of equipartition of energy: if the energy of a system can be written as the sum of a number of terms each containing only the square of a variable, then the average energy of each of these terms is $\frac{1}{2}kT$. This theorem applies just as much to macroscopic objects as to microscopic ones or molecules, but the magnitude of the fluctuations in the dynamical variable become smaller as the inertia of the object increases, since the average energy is independent of size. Given sufficient magnification, the motion can always be observed, and it sets a limit to the sensitivity of any measuring instrument, since the fluctuations give a random signal which masks any applied signal of smaller magnitude.

If this theorem is applied to a suspension galvanometer, the following result is obtained. The suspension has one degree of freedom, a rotation measured by the angle $\theta$. The total energy may be written as the sum of two terms, the potential energy of the suspension due to work done against the restoring torque, and the kinetic energy, so that

$$W = \tfrac{1}{2}c\theta^2 + \tfrac{1}{2}\Im\dot{\theta}^2, \tag{16.1}$$

where $c$ is the restoring torque per unit angle of twist and $\Im$ is the moment of inertia of the system. To each of these terms we must assign an average energy $\frac{1}{2}kT$, so that fluctuations in the angle $\theta$ and the angular velocity $\dot{\theta}$ will occur whose mean square values are given by

$$\tfrac{1}{2}c\overline{\theta^2} = \tfrac{1}{2}\Im\overline{\dot{\theta}^2} = \tfrac{1}{2}kT. \tag{16.2}$$

A system which is mathematically similar is the electrical tuned circuit, consisting of an inductance, capacitance, and resistance connected together. The total electrical energy of such a system, where $I$ is the instantaneous current and $q$ the instantaneous charge on the capacitor, is

$$W = \tfrac{1}{2}q^2/C + \tfrac{1}{2}LI^2. \qquad (16.3)$$

If the theorem of equipartition of energy applies also to electrical systems, as we would expect in view of its general nature, then the mean square values of the fluctuating charge and current will be given by

$$\tfrac{1}{2}\overline{q^2}/C = \tfrac{1}{2}L\overline{I^2} = \tfrac{1}{2}kT. \qquad (16.4)$$

These relations give only the mean square values of the total fluctuations, and tell us nothing about the frequency distribution of the fluctuations. If we imagine that we perform a Fourier analysis of the fluctuations, and postulate that they are due to some random force acting on the system, then for the electrical tuned circuit we write

$$L(d^2q/dt^2) + R(dq/dt) + q/C = V_f\exp(j\omega t), \qquad (16.5)$$

where $V_f$ is the amplitude of the component of the random e.m.f. causing the fluctuations at the frequency $f = \omega/2\pi$. We now make the following assumptions about $V_f$: its mean square value $\overline{V_f^2}$ is independent of frequency, but voltages of different frequency are entirely uncorrelated, so that the average value of the product $\overline{V_f V_{f'}}$ is zero. The justification for these assumptions will not be discussed here, but it is obvious that they are plausible in view of the random nature of the fluctuations. On solving equation (16.5) to find the mean square amplitude $\overline{q_f^2}$ of the fluctuating charge at the frequency $f$, we have

$$d(\overline{q_f^2}) = \frac{d(\overline{V_f^2})}{(L\omega^2 - 1/C)^2 + R^2\omega^2}. \qquad (16.6)$$

The frequencies are continuously distributed, and the differentials are used since this expression gives the mean square amplitude of the fluctuations in the frequency range between $f$ and $f + df$. The total mean square fluctuation must be given by equation (16.4), and hence, integrating over all frequencies, we must have

$$\tfrac{1}{2}kT = \tfrac{1}{2}\overline{q^2}/C = \frac{1}{2C}\int d(\overline{q_f^2}) = \frac{1}{4\pi C}\frac{d(\overline{V_f^2})}{df}\int_0^\infty \frac{d\omega}{(L\omega^2 - 1/C)^2 + R^2\omega^2}.$$

This integral may be evaluated as follows. On making the substitution $\omega = x(LC)^{-\frac{1}{2}}$, it becomes

$$(C^3/L)^{\frac{1}{2}}\int_0^\infty \frac{-d(1/x)}{(x - 1/x)^2 + R^2C/L} = (C^3/L)^{\frac{1}{2}}\int_0^\infty \frac{dx}{(x - 1/x)^2 + R^2C/L},$$

where the second form is obtained by replacing $x$ by $1/x$. Hence the integral may be written as

$$\tfrac{1}{2}(C^3/L)^{\frac{1}{2}} \int_0^\infty \frac{d(x-1/x)}{(x-1/x)^2+R^2C/L} = \tfrac{1}{2}(C^3/L)^{\frac{1}{2}} \int_{-\infty}^\infty \frac{dz}{z^2+R^2C/L} = \pi C/(2R).$$

Hence $$\tfrac{1}{2}kT = \tfrac{1}{2}\overline{q^2}/C = \frac{1}{8R}\frac{d(\overline{V_f^2})}{df},$$

or $$d(\overline{V_f^2}) = 4kTR\,df, \qquad (16.7)$$

and $$d(\overline{q_f^2}) = \frac{4kTR\,df}{(L\omega^2-1/C)^2+R^2\omega^2}. \qquad (16.8)$$

It is easily verified (see Problem 16.1) from these results that $\tfrac{1}{2}L\overline{i^2} = \tfrac{1}{2}kT$ in accordance with equation (16.4). The equations lead to the interesting result that, whereas the total mean square values of the fluctuations depend only on $L$ and $C$, the expression for the distribution of the voltage fluctuations with frequency involves only $R$. The result given by equation (16.7) may be expressed by saying that the mean square voltage $d(V_f^2)$ of the fluctuations in the frequency range $df$ is $4kTR\,df$, and is thus proportional to the bandwidth $df$. The existence of such fluctuations was first verified by Johnson, and they are known as resistance or 'Johnson' noise. They will be considered in more detail in § 16.3.

## 16.2. Fluctuations in galvanometers

We return now to the case of the galvanometer, and consider first a moving-coil suspension galvanometer when the coil is on open circuit. Then the equation of motion is

$$\Im(d^2\theta/dt^2)+b(d\theta/dt)+c\theta = F_f\exp(j\omega t), \qquad (16.9)$$

where $\Im$ is the moment of inertia, $b$ the mechanical damping constant, and $c$ the restoring torque per unit angle of twist. We assume that the fluctuations are caused by a random torque, whose Fourier component at the frequency $f = \omega/2\pi$ has the amplitude $F_f$. Our further postulates about the nature of $F$ are similar to those made about $V$ in the last section. Then the analysis is exactly similar to the previous case of the electrical tuned circuit, so that by comparison we obtain at once

$$d(\overline{F_f^2}) = 4kTb\,df \qquad (16.10)$$

and $$d(\overline{\theta_f^2}) = \frac{4kTb\,df}{(\Im\omega^2-c)^2+b^2\omega^2}. \qquad (16.11)$$

By integration it may be shown that these expressions satisfy equation (16.2).

In general the galvanometer will be used for observing a current and will therefore be connected to a circuit whose total resistance (including the galvanometer coil) is $R$. Then we have two equations

$$\Im(d^2\theta/dt^2)+b(d\theta/dt)+c\theta = NI+F_f\exp(j\omega t)\\ RI = -N(d\theta/dt)+V_f\exp(j\omega t+j\delta)\Bigg\}, \qquad (16.12)$$

where $N = nAB$, and $I$ is the instantaneous current through the circuit. Two sources of fluctuations have been included; a random torque due to Brownian motion of the suspended coil, and a random voltage associated with the electrical circuit. In equations (16.12) the Fourier components of these two sources of fluctuations at the frequency $f = \omega/2\pi$ have been used, with a phase difference $\delta$ between them. Since the two sources are independent, we do not expect any correlation in phase, and for different frequencies the phase difference $\delta$ will have random values. Elimination of the current $I$ between the two equations gives

$$\Im(d^2\theta/dt^2)+(b+N^2/R)(d\theta/dt)+c\theta = (N/R)V_f\exp(j\omega t+j\delta)+F_f\exp(j\omega t),$$

and the square of the amplitude of the fluctuations at the frequency $f$ is found to be

$$\theta_f^2 = \frac{(N/R)^2V_f^2+F_f^2+2(N/R)V_fF_f\cos\delta}{(\Im\omega^2-c)^2+(b+N^2/R)^2\omega^2}.$$

On summing over a range of frequencies, $\delta$ takes all values between 0 and $2\pi$ and the mean value of $\cos\delta$ is therefore zero. Hence the mean square angular amplitude in the frequency range $f$ to $f+df$ is

$$d(\theta_f^2) = \frac{\{(N/R)^2d(V_f^2)\}+d(F_f^2)}{(\Im\omega^2-c)^2+(b+N^2/R)^2\omega^2}. \qquad (16.13)$$

On substituting the expressions for $d(V_f^2)$ and $d(F_f^2)$ given by equations (16.7) and (16.10), we find

$$d(\theta_f^2) = \frac{4kT(b+N^2/R)\,df}{(\Im\omega^2-c)^2+(b+N^2/R)^2\omega^2}. \qquad (16.14)$$

This equation is similar to that obtained for the galvanometer on open circuit except that the total damping constant $(b+N^2/R)$ appears instead of just the mechanical damping $b$. Integration of equation (16.14) over all frequencies will obviously give the same result, $\frac{1}{2}c\overline{\theta^2} = \frac{1}{2}kT$, as for the galvanometer on open circuit, since the result is independent of the magnitude of the damping. Thus, although there are now two independent sources of random fluctuations, and these add in the squares as shown by the numerator of equation (16.13), each is associated with a damping term so that the total mean energy $\frac{1}{2}c\overline{\theta^2}$ stored in the suspension remains unaltered, provided that each source is at the same temperature. This argument could be extended by separating the mechanical damping $b$ into two parts, one due to imperfect elasticity of the suspension and the other to damping by the viscosity of the air. Then it follows that the total mean square angular fluctuations have the same value whether the galvanometer is evacuated or not; the admission of air provides an extra source of fluctuations owing to the molecular bombardment whose tendency to increase the mean square deflexion is just counterbalanced by the viscous air damping which accompanies it. The frequency distribution of the fluctuations is of course changed because of the increase in the damping, but it is important to realize that the Brownian motion is inherent in the suspended coil and is not caused by the bombardment by the gas molecules. If it were, and the suspension had an imperfect elasticity, then the molecular bombardment would result in the suspension being heated, through the dissipation of energy in it, and the gas would be cooled, even though both were originally at the same temperature. This is contrary to the second law of thermodynamics.

The processes which we regard as 'damping' in the galvanometer represent a degradation of mechanical energy into heat energy; in viscous damping, into kinetic energy of the gas molecules; in electromagnetic damping, ultimately into the vibrational energy of the lattice of the resistance in the external circuit (the coil moving in the magnetic field acts as a transducer, converting mechanical motion into electrical voltage). At the level of the molecular fluctuations, the damping processes are just the mechanisms by which thermal equilibrium is established; without them, an individual component of the system (galvanometer suspension, gas molecules, lattice of the resistor) would have no means of knowing what the temperatures are of the other components. In the electrical case, resistance arises from the conversion of electrical energy into heat energy, and at the fluctuation level is the mechanism by which the electrical fluctuations reach thermal equilibrium with the lattice fluctuations. The nature of the carriers of the electric current is no more important in this process than that of the molecules of the gas causing viscous damping.

It is convenient to define the minimum observable current for a galvanometer as that current which would produce a deflexion equal to the root mean square value of the total Brownian angular motion. For a steady current $I$ the deflexion $\theta = I(nAB)/c = IN/c$, and hence the minimum observable current $I_m$ would be

$$I_m = (ckT)^{\frac{1}{2}}/N. \qquad (16.15)$$

In general the electromagnetic damping term $(N^2/R)$ is much larger than the mechanical damping term $b$, and the critical damping resistance $R_c$ is given by equation (7.5),

$$R_c = \tfrac{1}{2}N^2/(\Im c)^{\frac{1}{2}},$$

while the period $\tau = 2\pi(\Im/c)^{\frac{1}{2}}$. Using these two relations the minimum observable current and voltage are conveniently expressed in the form

$$I_m = (\pi kT/R_c\tau)^{\frac{1}{2}}, \qquad V_m = (\pi kTR_c/\tau)^{\frac{1}{2}}, \qquad (16.16)$$

since $V_m = R_c I_m$ if the galvanometer is critically damped. Taking room temperature as $290°$ K, so that $kT = 4 \times 10^{-21}$ joules, for a galvanometer of period 2 sec and critical damping resistance 100 ohms, we find that the minimum observable current and voltage are approximately $8 \times 10^{-12}$ A and $8 \times 10^{-10}$ V.

The correctness of the expressions derived above has been verified experimentally by Jones and McCombie (1952). The deflexions of an ordinary galvanometer of about 2 sec period (sensitivity 1 mm deflexion at 1 metre distance for $10^{-8}$ A) were magnified by an optical lever. The beam of light reflected from the galvanometer mirror fell on a split photocell, so that rotation of the mirror transferred light from one cell to the other. The difference in the currents from the two photocells was observed on a second galvanometer; a deflexion of 15 mm on this instrument corresponded to a voltage of about $10^{-9}$ V (or a current of $10^{-11}$ A) applied to the first galvanometer. To make use of this amplification, all external sources of disturbance such as vibration had to be eliminated. Typical traces obtained were similar to those shown in Fig. 16.1. With the first galvanometer on open circuit the damping is small, and the frequency distribution of the angular deflexions is large only in the region around the normal frequency of the suspension. Consequently the fluctuations resemble bursts of oscillation at the natural frequency, the number of oscillations in each being in inverse ratio to the damping (and roughly equal to the '$Q$' of the suspension). When the galvanometer is just critically damped, $(b+N^2/R)^2 = 4\Im c$ and the denominator of equation (16.14) can be written as $(\Im\omega^2+c)^2$, showing that the frequency distribution of the fluctuations now has its maximum value at zero frequency. The appearance of the fluctuations is now that of a random disturbance without any sinusoidal character (Fig. 16.1 (b)). The voltage sensitivity of the system was found by applying a voltage of about $10^{-8}$ V, obtained by attenuating a known voltage $\approx 1$ V through a resistance chain, and a thorough statistical analysis of the results showed that the magnitude of the fluctuations agreed with the theoretical value within 1 per cent.

(a)

(b)

FIG. 16.1. Fluctuations of a galvanometer (after Jones and McCombie, 1952).
(a) On open circuit.          (b) Nearly critically damped.

### 16.3. The relation between resistance noise and thermal radiation

In an evacuated enclosure containing thermal radiation at an absolute temperature $T$ the energy density in the frequency range $f$ to $f+df$ is given by Planck's law

$$dU = \frac{8\pi h f^3\,df}{c^3\{\exp(hf/kT)-1\}},\tag{16.17}$$

where $h$ is Planck's constant and $k$ is Boltzmann's constant. For all radio frequencies $hf \ll kT$ at room temperature, since $290k$ corresponds to a quantum of energy for a wavelength of approximately $\frac{1}{200}$ cm. We may therefore expand the exponential, obtaining

$$dU = 8\pi f^2 kT\,df/c^3,\tag{16.18}$$

which is simply the Rayleigh–Jeans law of classical theory. Since the polarization of the radiation is random, on the average only one-third of this energy corresponds to radiation whose electric vector is parallel to a given direction (say the $y$-axis), and only such radiation will induce a voltage in a short dipole aerial inserted in the enclosure parallel to the $y$-axis. From § 10.3 the mean square electric field component is then given by $E_y^2 = cZ_0(\tfrac{1}{3}U)$, where $Z_0 = (\mu_0/\epsilon_0)^{\frac{1}{2}}$ is the intrinsic impedance of free space. Hence the mean square voltage induced in an aerial of length $s$ will be

$$d(V_r^2) = s^2 d(E_y^2) = 8\pi f^2 s^2 kT Z_0\,df/(3c^2).\tag{16.19}$$

Even if the aerial consists of a perfectly conducting wire, the resulting current which flows will be finite, since energy will be re-radiated by this oscillatory current, and this energy must just be equal to that picked up by the aerial. The radiation must therefore behave as a generator of open-circuit voltage $V_r$ with an internal impedance $R_r$, as in the equivalent circuit of Fig. 16.2 $(a)$. This drives a current $I_r$ when short-circuited, and the power dissipated is $V_r^2/R_r = I_r^2 R_r$; this power is lost by re-radiation, and from § 10.9 it follows that $R_r$ is just the radiation resistance given by equation (10.71) as

$$R_r = 2\pi Z_0 f^2 s^2/(3c^2). \tag{16.20}$$

If the aerial is not a perfectly conducting wire, and has a real ohmic resistance $R$, the equivalent circuit will be as shown in Fig. 16.2 $(b)$, and

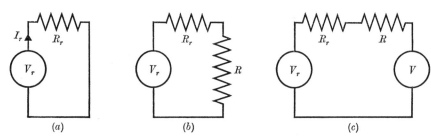

FIG. 16.2. Equivalent circuit of an aerial. $V_r$, voltage induced by thermal radiation; $R_r$, radiation resistance of aerial.

(a) Aerial short-circuited at centre.
(b) Aerial with resistance $R$ at centre.
(c) As (b) but showing noise voltage due to $R$.

the energy dissipated in the load $R$ will be $V_r^2 R/(R_r+R)^2$. This will heat the resistance $R$, while less energy is re-radiated to the enclosure. If $R$ is initially at the same temperature $T$ as the radiation in the enclosure, the apparent result will be that $R$ is heated and the enclosure cooled, which is contrary to the second law of thermodynamics. In order that the net exchange of energy between $R$ and the enclosure be zero, we must postulate that there is a fluctuation voltage associated with $R$, as in Fig. 16.2 $(c)$, of mean square voltage $V^2$ and internal resistance $R$. This will send a power $V^2R_r/(R_r+R)^2$ back into the aerial which must just equal that drawn from the enclosure and dissipated in $R$. Thus $V_r^2 R = V^2 R_r$, and in the frequency range from $f$ to $f+df$

$$d(\overline{V^2})/R = d(\overline{V_r^2})/R_r = \frac{8\pi f^2 s^2 k T Z_0\, df}{3c^2} \times \frac{3c^2}{2\pi Z_0 f^2 s^2} = 4kT\, df.$$
$$\tag{16.21}$$

This result is identical with that obtained earlier (equation (16.7)) by considering a simple tuned circuit. The voltage fluctuations have a constant distribution with frequency so long as the energy quantum $hf \ll kT$; this limitation corresponds to our use of the classical expression (Rayleigh–Jeans law) for the energy density in the enclosure. The fluctuations associated with a resistance $R$ can be represented by inserting a voltage generator $V$, whose mean square open-circuit voltage is given by equation (16.21), for which $R$ acts as the internal impedance as in Fig. 16.2 (c). The equivalent current generator will have a mean square current

$$d(\overline{I^2}) = 4kT\,df/R \qquad (16.22)$$

and it will be shunted by the resistance $R$.

Let us suppose that we are able to connect to our aerial a load of resistance $R$ which itself produces no noise (e.g. a resistance kept at a temperature very close to $0°$ K). Then the maximum power which can be drawn from the enclosure and dissipated in $R$, obtained by making $R$ equal to $R_r$, is $d(V_r^2)/(4R_r) = kT\,df$; this is the 'available noise power'. If $R$ is in fact a radio receiver, this power drawn from the thermal radiation incident on the aerial forms a source of 'noise', and can be heard as a hiss from a loudspeaker, or viewed on a cathode-ray oscillograph. It will obscure any signal which it is desired to receive unless the signal power in the aerial is larger than that picked up from the radiation background. This difficulty cannot be overcome by increasing the overall amplification of the receiver, since both noise and signal will be amplified together. Thus the radiation noise sets a limit to the useful sensitivity of a receiver. If a theoretically perfect receiver is defined as one which itself introduces no noise, then the amplified noise output will be $AkT\,df$, where $A$ is the overall amplification. The amplified signal output will be $AP$, where $P$ is the signal power incident on the aerial. Then the minimum detectable input signal may be defined as that which gives a signal output equal to the noise output, from which

minimum detectable signal power $P_0 = kT\,df \qquad (16.23)$

for a perfect receiver. It is clear that the only variable at our disposal here is the bandwidth $df$, and the reduction in noise obtained on narrowing the bandwidth can be seen in Fig. 16.3. This shows the noise output from a receiver covering a band from 0 to 2 Mc/s, before and after the insertion of a low-pass filter cutting out frequencies above 0·1 Mc/s. The change in character of the noise when the high frequency components are absent can be seen as well as the reduction in amplitude. In general, however, the bandwidth cannot be reduced beyond a certain limit without impairing the quality of the reception, since the higher modulation frequencies will be cut out. If only audio-frequency modulation is involved, the bandwidth will be about $10^4$ c/s and the minimum detectable signal power will be $4 \times 10^{-17}$ W. In a television receiver it is necessary to have a bandwidth of $\approx 4$ Mc/s to include all the information necessary to form the picture, and the minimum signal power to equal noise in a perfect receiver is $1 \cdot 6 \times 10^{-14}$ W.

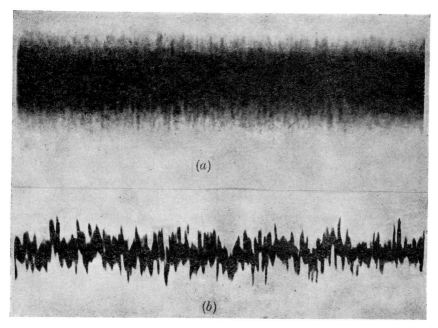

(*Photograph by L. J. Arundel.*)

FIG. 16.3. Noise output from an aperiodic amplifier.
(*a*) Covering the band from 0 to 2 Mc/s.
(*b*) After insertion of a low-pass filter reducing the band to 0 to 0·1 Mc/s.

In practice, all receivers generate a certain amount of internal noise, with the result that the noise output is greater than for a perfect receiver. The signal input $P_1$ required to give a signal output equal to the noise output is therefore greater than $P_0$. The quantity $P_1 - P_0$ is a measure of the internal noise generated in the receiver, and by writing

$$P_1 - P_0 = kT_e \, df$$

it may be expressed in terms of the 'excess noise temperature' $T_e$ of the receiver. In an ideal receiver $T_e = 0$, but in practice little is gained by making it smaller than about $T/10$, where $T$ is the temperature of the thermal radiation being received in the application for which the receiver is designed. In laboratory applications the source to which the receiver is connected is generally at room temperature, and it is then convenient to take a value of $T = 290°$ K to define $P_0$, making it equal to $4 \times 10^{-21} \, df$ (watts). The ratio of $P_1$ to this value of $P_0$ is then defined as the 'noise figure' of the receiver, and denoted by $F$. Since $F$ is a ratio of two powers, it is often expressed in decibels.

### 16.4. Shot noise

For most purposes it is sufficient to consider the electron current in a tube as consisting of a uniform flow of charge to the anode. Since the current consists in fact of the arrival of a finite number of electrons per second, this cannot be true. The flow of electrons is a random process, and we may expect that there will be a fluctuation in the number arriving in a given time interval, if we measure over a number of such intervals. If the arrival of the electrons consists of a succession of completely random events, then the mean square deviation from the average number $N$ per second is proportional to $N$. These fluctuations give rise to noise in the anode circuit of the tube, known as shot noise from the obvious analogy with the random patter of shot on a target.

In general we are interested not in the total deviation from the mean, but in the frequency distribution of the fluctuations. To find this it is necessary to carry out a Fourier analysis of the pulse of current due to the arrival of a single electron of charge $e$. We will assume that this pulse, occurring at time $t = 0$, has some irregular shape but is entirely confined within the time interval $-\tau/2$ to $+\tau/2$. Since the total charge arriving is $e$, we have

$$e = \int_{-\tau/2}^{+\tau/2} I \, dt.$$

We do not specify anything about the duration of the pulse $\tau$ except that it is very short ($\sim$ the transit time, see § 14.2). The Fourier series representing the frequency distribution of the current due to the arrival of $e$ is written

$$I = a_0 + \sum_{n=1}^{\infty} a_n \cos \frac{2\pi n t}{T} + \sum_{n=1}^{\infty} b_n \sin \frac{2\pi n t}{T}.$$

Here $a_0$, $a_n$, and $b_n$ are coefficients to be determined, and $T$ is an undefined large interval of time. In effect we regard all the frequencies we are interested in as multiples of the fundamental frequency $1/T$. To obtain a continuous frequency distribution we should make $T$ infinite, and replace the summations in the series by integrations. As the student is likely to be more familiar with a Fourier series than a Fourier integral we shall use the former, and by making $T$ large we can obtain a good approximation to a continuous frequency distribution.

From the ordinary formulae of Fourier analysis

$$a_0 = \frac{1}{T} \int\limits_{-T/2}^{+T/2} I \, dt; \qquad a_n = \frac{2}{T} \int\limits_{-T/2}^{+T/2} I \cos(2\pi nt/T) \, dt;$$

$$b_n = \frac{2}{T} \int\limits_{-T/2}^{+T/2} I \sin(2\pi nt/T) \, dt.$$

To evaluate the coefficients we restrict ourselves to frequencies small compared with $1/\tau$. Then, since the current is finite only in the range $-\tau/2$ to $+\tau/2$, and zero outside this range, we can write $\cos(2\pi nt/T) = 1$ and $\sin(2\pi nt/T) = 0$ over the range of integration for which the current is finite. Hence $b_n$ is zero, while

$$2a_0 = a_n = \frac{2}{T} \int\limits_{-T/2}^{+T/2} I \, dt = 2e/T.$$

Thus we have
$$I = \frac{e}{T} + \sum_{n=1}^{\infty} \frac{2e}{T} \cos(2\pi nt/T)$$

and the mean square value of the $n$th component is
$$\overline{I_n^2} = \tfrac{1}{2}(2e/T)^2 = 2e^2/T^2.$$

If $N$ electrons arrive in time $T$, then each will contribute an equal amount to the value of $I_n^2$. (The electrons arrive at random times, and their contributions to the Fourier series will all differ slightly in phase. Thus we must add intensities, and not amplitudes.) Then

$$\overline{I_n^2} = 2e^2N/T^2 = 2eI_0/T,$$

where $I_0 = Ne/T$ is the mean value of the current. Now the number of Fourier components whose frequencies lie within a range between $f$ and $f+df$ is $T \, df$, since the components are equally spaced in frequency by amounts $(1/T)$. Adding together the mean square values of these components gives

$$d(\overline{I^2}) = 2eI_0 \, df \qquad\qquad (16.24)$$

for the mean square current fluctuation in the frequency range $f$ to $f+df$.

*Influence of space charge*

In this derivation of the formula for shot noise the arrival of an electron is considered as a random event, completely independent of the arrival of any other electron. We expect that the emission of electrons from the cathode has this property of complete randomness, but this is not necessarily true of their arrival at another electrode. In practice it is found that the value of the shot noise is materially lower than that given by the above equation unless the current to the anode is limited only by the rate of emission from the cathode. In general the anode current is only a fraction of the emission current because of the formation of 'space charge' outside the cathode which causes a large number of electrons emitted from the cathode to be turned back to the cathode. Since this is due to the mutual interaction of the electrons, we may expect that the flow of electrons to the anode is not now a succession of completely random events. The value of the fluctuations is greatest for random events, and falls as soon as they become not completely random. Physically, the action of the space charge may be envisaged as follows. Suppose that at some instant the number of electrons emitted from the cathode rises momentarily above the average. This will cause a temporary increase in the space charge, and a number of electrons greater than average will leave the space charge region for the anode. This number is smaller than the surge from the cathode because the space charge acts as a reservoir; the effect of the increased space charge is to turn some of the excess electrons back to the cathode. Similarly, at instants when the cathode emission falls momentarily below the average, the space charge also drops and less electrons are turned back. To allow for this 'space charge smoothing', as it is called, a factor is inserted in the equation for the shot noise. Thus

$$d(\overline{I^2}) = 2\beta e I_0 \, df. \qquad (16.25)$$

$\beta$ is called the space charge smoothing factor, and may be as low as $0\cdot03$, showing that the smoothing effect is very considerable.

### Noise in multi-electrode tubes

The presence of grids in a tube does not affect the validity of the equations given above for shot noise so long as they do not intercept any of the current on its way to the anode. Thus equation (16.25) is still valid for a negative-grid triode, but this is not so for a screen-grid tube or a pentode, for then the positive screen grid intercepts a considerable portion of the anode current. Since the chance of an electron hitting the wire of the screen grid is purely random, the screen current will have the full shot noise appropriate to its magnitude. It is obvious that similar fluctuations, though of opposite sign, must be imposed on the current that goes through the screen grid to the anode. Assuming that less than half of the total current goes to the screen, we may write approximately for the anode current

$$d(\overline{I^2}) = 2\beta e I_a\, df + 2e I_s\, df. \qquad (16.26)$$

Since $\beta$ may be less than $0\cdot1$, while the screen current $I_s$ is $0\cdot2$ or $0\cdot3$ of $I_a$, the second term is often more important than the first. Hence screen-grid tubes and pentodes are generally more noisy than triodes. The additional noise is called 'partition noise'. In some high frequency pentodes an attempt is made to reduce partition noise by incorporating an extra grid, carefully wound and placed so that its wires are exactly in front of the screen-grid wires. This extra grid is kept at a potential negative with respect to the cathode, so that electrons on their way to the anode must go through the holes in this grid and it collects no current. Since these holes are exactly in front of those in the screen grid, the electrons shoot through the screen grid also, and the screen current is materially reduced, with a corresponding reduction in partition noise.

It is often convenient to define the amount of noise by referring it to an equivalent resistance $R_n$ (at 290° K) in the grid circuit. The fluctuating voltage at the grid due to $R_n$ has the mean square value

$$d(\overline{V^2}) = 4kTR_n\, df$$

since the grid consumes no power and the equivalent noise resistance is therefore on open circuit. This causes a fluctuating anode current whose mean square value is

$$d(\overline{I^2}) = g_m^2 d(\overline{V^2}) = g_m^2\, 4kTR_n\, df,$$

where $g_m$ is the mutual conductance of the tube. If $\overline{I^2}$ is due to the shot noise, the equivalent noise resistance may be calculated by means of this formula, $T$ being taken as room temperature. The advantage of this method of specifying the noise is that the value of $R_n$, unlike that of $d(\overline{I^2})$, is independent of the bandwidth, and it facilitates comparison of the shot noise with the resistance noise in the circuits attached to the grid. If partition noise is included by replacing equation (16.26) by (16.25) with an effective value $\beta'$ instead of $\beta$,

$$R_n = \beta' e I_0/(2g_m^2\, kT). \qquad (16.27)$$

An estimate of the relative importance of shot noise and resistance noise can be obtained from the formula for the equivalent noise resistance. For a typical triode, $g_m = 5$ mA/V, $\beta = 0\cdot03$, $I_0 = 10$ mA, $e = 1\cdot6 \times 10^{-19}$ coulombs; this gives $R_n = 240$ ohms. The value for a pentode would be somewhat higher, owing to partition noise. These figures apply at medium radio frequencies (i.e. of the order of Mc/s); at higher frequencies

(100 Mc/s and up) $R_n$ rises owing to noise voltages induced in the grid which have period of oscillation comparable with the electron transit time (cf. § 14.2). At audio frequencies the shot noise (particularly from tubes with oxide-coated cathodes) becomes abnormally large. This is known as the flicker effect, and is thought to be associated with changes in the state of the cathode surface which cause abnormal fluctuations in the anode current.

## 16.5. Design of receivers for optimum performance (minimum noise figure)

The correct design of a receiver is of great importance. If it is being used in an application where the signal strength is fixed, such as in r.f. astronomy or spectroscopy, then the limiting sensitivity attainable will depend entirely on the design of the receiver. In radio communications an improvement of a factor $n$ in signal/noise ratio can be achieved by increasing the transmitter power by a factor $n$, but a very much more economical method is to improve the receiver performance by the same factor instead. The following remarks illustrate only the basic principles, and do not go into any detail of receiver design.

In general all the stages of a receiver will contribute some noise, but if the amplification of each stage is high only the first stage or two is important. If stage $k$ gives noise power $N_k$, and the stage gain is $m$, then the signal/noise ratio after $n$ stages is

$$Sm^n/(N_1 m^n + N_2 m^{n-1} + ... + N_n) = S/(N_1 + N_2 m^{-1} + N_3 m^{-2} + ...).$$

$$(16.28)$$

With a stage gain of ten to a hundred even the second stage will contribute little to the noise output. If not, the design of the second stage should follow the same principles as that of the first stage, and only the latter need be considered.

In the circuit of Fig. 16.4 $(a)$ $S$ represents a signal source of voltage $S$ with output resistance $R_1$. $R_1$ is assumed to be noisy, at temperature $T$, and its equivalent noise voltage is represented by $V_{n1}$, in series with $S$. The source $S$ may be a signal induced in an aerial, in which case $R_1$ is the radiation resistance of the aerial and $T$ is the ambient temperature which we take to be 290° K. The source is connected to the grid of the tube, and $R_2$ is the grid-bias resistance, or the first tuned circuit, in which case $R_2$ is its parallel impedance. In general $R_2$ will also generate resistance noise, which is represented by the insertion of a voltage source $V_{n2}$ in series with $R_2$. In the first instance we shall assume that the tube contributes no shot noise ($R_n = 0$), and that noise from subsequent stages is negligible. Then the signal/noise ratio will be the same at the grid of the first tube as at any later point in the receiver, and we need only compute the ratio of the mean square signal voltage on the grid to the mean square noise voltage. For simplicity $R_1$ and $R_2$ are taken to have the same temperature, which in practice will not be far from true.

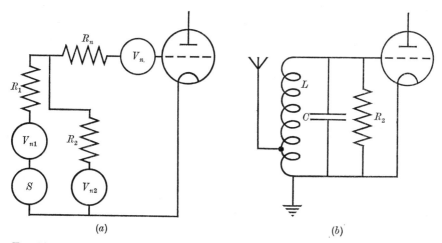

FIG. 16.4. (a) Equivalent input circuit of a receiver, showing noise voltages.
(b) Actual input circuit, showing aerial tapped on to inductance of input tuned circuit.

Since $V_{n1}^2/R_1 = V_{n2}^2/R_2 = 4kT\,df$, and $R_2$ acts as the load for the noise generator $V_{n1}$, and $R_1$ as the load for $V_{n2}$, the mean square noise voltage on the grid is

$$4kT\,df\left\{R_1\frac{R_2^2}{(R_1+R_2)^2}+R_2\frac{R_1^2}{(R_1+R_2)^2}\right\} = 4kT\,df\times\frac{R_1R_2}{R_1+R_2}.$$

$$(16.29)$$

Since $R_1$ and $R_2$ are random noise sources, the mean square voltages have been added; note that the result is the same as that for a resistance equal to $R_1$ and $R_2$ in parallel, as we should expect.

The mean square signal voltage on the grid is

$$S^2 R_2^2/(R_1+R_2)^2.$$

Hence the signal to noise ratio at the grid is

$$\frac{S^2}{4kT\,df}\frac{R_2}{R_1+R_2}\frac{1}{R_1} = \frac{P}{kT\,df}\frac{R_2}{R_1+R_2},$$

$$(16.30)$$

where $P = S^2/(4R_1)$ is the available signal power. If equation (16.30) is put equal to unity, we obtain the signal power $P_1$ required to give an output power equal to the noise output power of the receiver. The noise figure $F$ is defined as the ratio of this signal power to the value $kT\,df$ for a perfect receiver, and hence the noise figure is

$$F = P_1/kT\,df = (R_1+R_2)/R_2. \tag{16.31}$$

If the aerial is matched to the first circuit, $R_1 = R_2$, and $F = 2$. But if $R_2 > R_1$, $F$ is reduced and tends to its limiting value of unity as the ratio of $R_2$ to $R_1$ is increased indefinitely. Hence to obtain optimum sensitivity it pays to mismatch the aerial to the receiver, since the reduction in noise at the grid when $R_2$ is shunted by the lower resistance $R_1$ is greater than the loss of signal at the grid due to the mismatch. We see also that, in the absence of tube noise, it is possible to approach very closely to the theoretical limit of sensitivity. In a practical case $R_1$ (for a half-wave dipole aerial) would be 80 ohms, while $R_2$ could be of the order of 100 000 ohms, giving $F = 1{\cdot}001$.

This optimum can no longer be attained if tube noise is appreciable. In this case it is not sufficient to compute the signal/noise ratio at the first grid, since there is a later source of noise. Since this source of noise can be represented as a mean square current fluctuation in the tube, the analysis need only be carried one step further by transforming any fluctuating voltage at the grid into a fluctuating anode current. The effect of the anode load on the anode current need not be included since it affects all fluctuations in this current equally, whatever their source. We have:

mean square signal current $= g_m^2\, S^2 R_2^2/(R_1+R_2)^2$,

mean square noise current $= 2\beta'eI\,df + g_m^2\,4kT\,df\,R_1 R_2/(R_1+R_2)$

$$= g_m^2\,4kT df\left(R_n + \frac{R_1 R_2}{R_1+R_2}\right),$$

on substituting the equivalent noise resistance of the tube. The signal to noise ratio at this stage is now

$$\frac{P}{kT\,df}\frac{R_1 R_2^2}{(R_1+R_2)^2}\left[R_n + \frac{R_1 R_2}{R_1+R_2}\right]^{-1},$$

where the available signal power has been introduced as before. Putting the signal to noise ratio equal to unity, we find the noise figure $F$ is (after some reduction)

$$F = \frac{P_1}{kT\,df} = \left(\frac{R_1}{R_2}+1\right)\left\{\left(\frac{1}{R_1}+\frac{1}{R_2}\right)R_n+1\right\}. \tag{16.32}$$

If $R_1$ is fixed and $R_2$ is the only variable, then the smallest value for $F$ is obtained by making $R_2$ very large, when $F = 1+R_n/R_1$. For a typical

pentode, $R_n$ is of the order of 800 ohms, and if $R_1$ is 80 ohms, we have
a noise factor of 11, which is very poor in comparison with that obtained
in the absence of tube noise. Clearly the trouble is due to the small value
of $R_1$ compared with $R_n$, and this suggests that we should use a transformer between the aerial and the grid in order to step up the value
of $R_1$ as seen from the grid. This will, however, reduce the ratio of $R_2$
to $R_1$, so that there will be some optimum transformer ratio. In practice,
the grid circuit will probably be a parallel tuned circuit, with the aerial
tapped into the inductance as in Fig. 16.4 (b). If this tapping point is
variable, then at the grid the equivalent circuit is as assumed, with a
generator of the same available power but with a variable internal
impedance depending on the position of the tapping. This means that
our variable is $R_1$, while $R_2$ is fixed as the parallel impedance of the tuned
circuit without the aerial being attached. Differentiating the expression
for $F$ with respect to $R_1$ we find that the optimum value occurs when

$$\frac{R_2}{R_1^2} = \frac{1}{R_n} + \frac{1}{R_2}. \tag{16.33}$$

If $R_2$ is much larger than $R_n$, this reduces to $R_1 = \sqrt{(R_n R_2)}$. With the
values assumed previously ($R_n = 800$ ohms, $R_2 = 100\,000$ ohms), this
gives $R_1 = 9000$ ohms, and the optimum value of $F$ is now $1\cdot19$. Though
slightly worse than in the case of no tube noise, it will be seen that this
value of $F$ is very much better than that obtained previously by tapping
the aerial right across the tuned circuit ($R_2$). If the tapping had been
adjusted to obtain the maximum signal voltage on the grid by matching
the aerial to the tuned circuit ($R_1 = R_2$), the value of $F$ would have
been $2\cdot03$. Hence we have gained a factor of nearly 2 by over-coupling
the aerial, just as in the case of no tube noise. The chief difference
when tube noise is present is that the over-coupling must not be carried
so far that the net impedance of aerial+tuned circuit becomes lower
than the equivalent noise resistance. Note that, in the equivalent circuit,
$R_n$ is effectively in series with ($R_1$ in parallel with $R_2$). Since no grid
current flows, $R_n$ may be inserted in the lead immediately attached to
the grid as shown in Fig. 16.4 (a), without affecting any of the other
voltages imposed on the grid.

The noise figures derived in this section apply to receivers at ordinary
radio frequencies using vacuum tubes; transistors (discussed in § 19.8)
also show shot noise due to the random motion of the charge carriers,
and the noise problems involved are basically similar. At higher
frequencies the noise properties of vacuum tubes deteriorate, though

travelling wave tubes can give noise figures as low as 6 dB at centimetre wavelengths. Wavelengths of this order are used in radar and satellite communication in order to obtain highly directional antennae; these point at the open sky and the background thermal radiation corresponds to a temperature of a few degrees absolute. This makes it worth while to use receivers of very low noise; this is achieved in special devices where shot noise has been eliminated, and resistive elements are absent or at a very low temperature. The parametric amplifier makes use of a non-linear reactance, and the solid state maser of a paramagnetic material in which a negative resistance is produced at liquid helium temperatures. In each case sufficient amplification must be produced to make noise from the later (conventional) stages unimportant.

## 16.6. Measurement of receiver noise

Although it is in principle possible to calculate the conditions for optimum noise figure, it is always necessary in practice to have some method of measuring the noise figure in order to be sure of the performance of a receiver. A vacuum tube may deteriorate in use, so that it produces excessive noise, or it may lose its gain, so that noise from the second stage becomes important. At high frequencies the performance of a tube may not be sufficiently well established, particularly in the experimental or development stage, for the necessary data to be known with sufficient accuracy.

The most straightforward method of measurement of noise figure is to replace the aerial by a calibrated signal generator, and find the amount of signal power which must be applied to the receiver in order to produce an output equal to the noise output. By definition of the noise figure, this signal power, divided by $kT\,df$, gives the noise figure $F$ directly. This method needs careful design of the signal generator. The most obvious necessity is that the signal generator output must simulate the antenna; that is, it must behave as a generator whose output impedance is the same as that of the antenna, so that when the latter is disconnected and replaced by the signal generator, conditions at the input of the receiver are unaltered. Adjustment of the generator output impedance may be achieved by some simple transformer circuit.

The most difficult technical requirement in a signal generator is that it must produce accurately known outputs of the order of $10^{-14}$ W or less. Since powers of this order of magnitude can only be detected by a radio receiver, it is not practicable to measure the output directly. Instead, the power is measured at a high level (e.g. $10^{-3}$ to $10^{-6}$ W) and then attenuated down by known amounts using a resistance or capacitance network. A schematic diagram of a typical signal generator is shown in Fig. 16.5.

Power is generated by a small oscillator producing about 1 W. The oscillator is tunable, and a given frequency may be selected by adjustment of a calibrated dial. The accuracy of the frequency calibration is

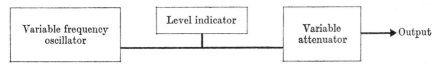

FIG. 16.5. Block diagram of signal generator.

usually of the order of 1 or 2 per cent, which is sufficient for most purposes. A small fraction of the power is fed to a resistance, which forms the input to the attenuator. The voltage across this resistance is read on a built-in vacuum tube voltmeter; usually the amount of power is adjusted by an external control until the voltmeter reads some standard value, such as 1 V. The various steps on the attenuator are calibrated by the maker and labelled with the voltage output across the output terminals either on open circuit or across a load equal to the output impedance at these terminals, which is fixed at some value independent of the attenuator setting. The output impedance is always marked on the signal generator.

Since the oscillator generates about 1 W of power, and this must be attenuated in a known way by a factor of $10^{14}$ or so, all components carrying radio-frequency currents at high level must be very carefully shielded. This is especially true at short wavelengths, where a few centimetres of exposed wire would be an efficient radiator. At wavelengths below a few metres, the typical layout of a signal generator is as follows. The oscillator is in its own screened box, and a fraction of its output is fed to a bolometer (cf. § 15.1), also screened, whose reading shows when the power level is adjusted to its standard value. The attenuator is a circular tube forming a waveguide which is beyond cut-off for the frequency used. The field components of any wave launched in such a tube are attenuated exponentially as $\exp(-hx)$, where $h$ is given by the generalized form of equation (11.33),

$$h = \left\{ \left( \frac{2\pi}{\lambda_c} \right)^2 - \left( \frac{\omega}{v} \right)^2 \right\}^{\frac{1}{2}}, \tag{16.34}$$

where $\lambda_c$ is the cut-off wavelength for the particular mode launched in the tube, and may be calculated from the diameter. At frequencies considerably below cut-off the second term in equation (16.34) may be neglected and the attenuation is then independent of frequency. In general several modes will be launched at the input to the tube, which should be designed to keep the number of modes to a minimum; the higher modes, with smaller values of $\lambda_c$, are attenuated much more rapidly and

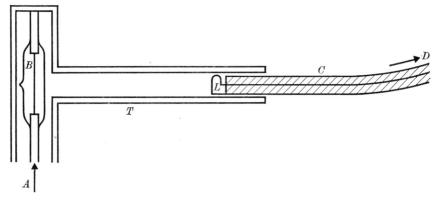

FIG. 16.6. Signal generator output with piston attenuator.

A   input from oscillator.
B   bolometer in screened housing.
T   accurately machined tube of known diameter.
L   loop to pick up wave in tube.
C   coaxial line, driven along tube by micrometer movement.
D   output.

At centimetre wavelengths it is sometimes preferable to launch the wave in the tube from the end of a waveguide, instead of from a bolometer lamp acting as the centre conductor of a coaxial line.

only the lowest mode need be considered except very close to the input. A design where the bolometer lamp launches a $TE_{11}$ mode is shown in Fig. 16.6; this has a magnetic field component, normal to the plane of the diagram, which is picked up by a loop connected to a coaxial line which slides along the tube. Such a 'piston attenuator' gives complete screening, and the output can be adjusted over a very wide range. Since the attenuator law is not known accurately over the initial range where higher modes are present, the best procedure is to measure the power output (of the order of $10^{-6}$ W) by a bolometer when the attenuation is adjusted to the smallest value possible consistent with its following the correct exponential law. A known smaller output is then obtained by the use of equation (16.34).

The maintenance and use of standard signal generators for the measurement of noise figure are rather cumbersome, as the instruments require constant checking. In addition the bandwidth of the receiver must be known in order to deduce the noise figure. For these reasons it is generally simpler to use a source of noise of known power rather than a signal generator. This type of source is already roughly at the level required, so obviating the necessity of careful screening and attenuation of signal by large known amounts required in a signal generator. So long as the bandwidth of the noise source is larger than that of the receiver, the bandwidth of the latter drops out of the calculation, since the input noise power is known per unit bandwidth. Thus measurement of the receiver bandwidth is unnecessary.

A simple type of noise source is the resistance noise from a known resistance whose temperature may be varied. The available noise power is $kT\,df$, and for this to give a signal output equal to the ordinary noise output of a receiver of noise figure $F$ we must have $kT\,df = F\,k(290)\,df$, or $F = T/290$. Thus if $F$ is high, a high temperature filament is required, so high that only tungsten can be used. The principal difficulties of this method are measurement of the temperature, and the change in resistance with temperature of the tungsten, which affects the matching to the receiver.

The commonest type of noise source is a diode operated under temperature-limited conditions; that is, at saturation anode current. This is achieved by maintaining a constant anode potential of 100 to 200 V, the anode current being controlled by the temperature of the filament. For this purpose a pure tungsten filament must be used, as an oxide-coated cathode would quickly deteriorate when under-run in temperature, as well as giving flicker effect and considerable drift in the anode current. If the anode load is a resistance $R$ whose value is small compared with the anode impedance of the diode, the available noise power is $2eIR\,df$, where $I$ is the anode current. Equating this to $F\,kT\,df$, we have $F = 80IR$, where $I$ is in amperes and $R$ in ohms. If $R$ is made equal to 80 ohms to simulate a half-wave dipole aerial, then for a noise figure of 10, a diode current of $1\cdot6$ mA is required. This is easy to produce under temperature-limited conditions.

To determine when the signal output from the receiver is equal to the noise output, they should be fed into a square law device such as a thermo-junction milliammeter. The noise output from the receiver alone is measured first, and then the signal or noise source input is adjusted until the mean square current read by the thermo-junction is doubled, when

$$(\text{signal}+\text{noise output}) = 2(\text{noise output}).$$

The thermo-junction method is more satisfactory than display of the output on an oscilloscope, since the eye can detect signals well down into the noise, and is not a good judge of the signal/noise ratio.

## REFERENCES

JONES, R. V., and MCCOMBIE, C. W., 1952, *Phil. Trans.* **244**, 205.
LAWSON, J. L., and UHLENBECK, G. E., 1949, *Threshold Signals* (M.I.T. Radiation Laboratory Series, McGraw-Hill Book Co.).
ROBINSON, F. N. H., 1962, *Noise in Electrical Circuits* (O.U.P.).

## PROBLEMS

**16.1.** Show, by differentiation of equation (16.5) to obtain the differential equation for the current $I = dq/dt$, and following through an analysis similar to that of § 16.1, that $\frac{1}{2}L\overline{I^2} = \frac{1}{2}kT$.

**16.2.** A signal generator whose output impedance is 500 ohms is calibrated in terms of the power it will deliver into a matched load (i.e. the available signal power). It is connected to a receiver whose bandwidth is 10 kc/s, and whose first stage consists of a triode whose shot noise is negligible, with a 1000-ohm resistance connected between cathode and grid. What will the signal generator reading be when it is adjusted so that the signal output from the receiver is equal to the noise output?

(*Answer*: $6 \times 10^{-17}$ W.)

**16.3.** Referring to Problem 10.10, assume that the target is low over the sea and intercepts the power incident on an area $A_1$. This power is scattered with the same angular distribution as that of the radiation from a short horizontal dipole parallel to the transmitter dipole. Some of this scattered power falls on an aerial of effective area $A_2$ located at the transmitter, and is detected by a receiver of noise figure $F$ and bandwidth $df$. Show that the signal/noise ratio, for the signal returned from the target, is unity for a target distance

$$D = \left(\frac{36\pi^2 W A_1 A_2}{FkT\,df}\right)^{\frac{1}{4}}\left(\frac{Hh}{\lambda}\right)^{\frac{1}{2}}.$$

(This formula shows how difficult it is to increase the range by increasing the transmitter power $W$, and how much better it is to reduce the wavelength.)

**16.4.** By following the treatment of § 16.3 using Planck's law instead of the Rayleigh–Jeans law, show that the quantum-mechanical formula for resistance noise is

$$\frac{d(\overline{V^2})}{R} = \frac{4hf\,df}{\exp(hf/kT)-1}.$$

Verify from this formula that the transition from classical region to quantum-mechanical region occurs when the number of quanta per unit bandwidth in the noise power is of the order of unity.

# THEORY OF THE DIELECTRIC CONSTANT

## 17.1. Molecular structure and the dielectric constant

FROM the standpoint of electromagnetic theory, a dielectric may be regarded as a continuous medium which becomes polarized under the action of an electric field. The ratio of the polarization to the electric field producing it is proportional to the electric susceptibility, and is substantially independent of the field strength. The volume susceptibility $\chi$ is related to the dielectric constant $\epsilon$ by the formula

$$\epsilon = 1 + \chi.$$

The dielectric constant varies not only from substance to substance, but also with the physical state of any one substance. Hitherto it has been taken as a constant, experimentally determined, and no inquiry was made as to the origin of the polarization which gives rise to the susceptibility.

The concept of a continuous medium is alien to modern atomic theory, by which any substance is regarded as an assembly of atoms or molecules. Each atom consists of a heavy, positively-charged nucleus with negatively-charged electrons surrounding it. The atom is electrically neutral, having equal amounts of positive and negative charge. The same is true of a molecule, formed by several atoms joined together, with either a sharing or a transfer of electrons. The distribution of electronic charge in an atom is symmetrical about the nucleus, and, as discussed in § 2.3, no atom possesses a permanent electric dipole moment. This is not true of molecules, which may be divided into two classes—polar molecules, which possess a permanent electric dipole moment, and non-polar molecules, which do not. Homonuclear diatomic molecules such as $H_2$, $N_2$, $O_2$ have a symmetrical charge distribution and are non-polar, but asymmetrical molecules such as KCl and HCl are polar, since there is a net transfer of electronic charge from one atom to the other. A simple picture of the KCl molecule is that of two ions $K^+$ and $Cl^-$, and on this basis we should expect the dipole moment to be just equal to the product of the electronic charge and the internuclear distance. Measured dipole moments are generally smaller than but of the same order of magnitude as suggested by this crude model, and are expressed in terms of the

Debye unit, defined as

$$1 \text{ Debye} = 10^{-18} \text{ e.s.u.} = 3 \cdot 336 \times 10^{-30} \text{ coulomb-metre.}$$

A number of electric dipole moments and internuclear distances for diatomic molecules are given in Table. 17.1. The alkali halides come near to having the moments expected on the picture of two ions, but are somewhat smaller because the field of each ion polarizes the other ion (see Fig. 17.1), producing induced moments $\mathbf{p}_i$ in the opposite sense to the main moment. The ionic approximation is much worse for the

TABLE 17.1

*Internuclear distances and electric dipole moments*
*of some diatomic molecules*

| Molecule | Internuclear distance r (Å) | Electronic charge × r (Debye units) | Observed dipole moment (Debye units) |
|---|---|---|---|
| CsF  | 2·345 | 11·2 | 7·88  |
| CsCl | 2·906 | 14·0 | 10·46 |
| CsI  | 3·315 | 15·9 | 12·1  |
| KF   | 2·55  | 12·2 | 7·33  |
| KCl  | 2·667 | 12·8 | 10·48 |
| KBr  | 2·821 | 13·5 | 10·41 |
| KI   | 3·048 | 14·6 | 11·05 |
| HCl  | 1·27  | 6·1  | 1·03  |
| HBr  | 1·42  | 6·8  | 0·78  |
| HI   | 1·62  | 7·8  | 0·38  |

hydrogen halides, HCl, HBr, HI, where the dipole moments actually decrease while the internuclear distances increase in this progression. This, together with the fact that the moments are much smaller than the product of the electronic charge and the internuclear distance, shows that our picture of these molecules as two ions is an over-simplification. In fact most of the electronic charge resides between the two nuclei. This tendency increases as we go from HCl to HI, and we speak of a progressive change from ionic binding towards covalent binding, where the valence electrons are shared between the two atoms.

The question of whether a more complicated molecule will have a permanent dipole moment or not depends on its symmetry; the problem may be illustrated by reference to three triatomic molecules. Water, $H_2O$, has a large moment, 1·84 Debyes, and this shows that it cannot be linear; for then it must either be symmetrical, like carbon dioxide, O—C—O, which has no dipole moment, or asymmetrical, like nitrous oxide, N—N—O, which has the small dipole moment 0·17 Debyes. The latter possibility is unlikely for valence reasons. $H_2O$ must be therefore a bent, triangular molecule, with the negatively-charged oxygen at the apex and the positively-charged hydrogens at the foot of the triangle. Thus the absence of a dipole moment, or its magnitude, if it is present, is an important guide to the structure of a molecule. It is also intimately connected with the dielectric constant of a substance, the theory of which will now be outlined. Since each dipole interacts with the neighbouring

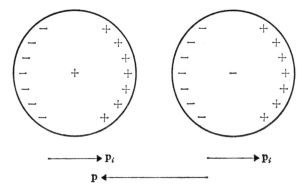

FIG. 17.1. The induced dipoles $p_i$ on each ion are in the opposite direction to the main dipole $p$ formed by the charges on the two ions, so that the total dipole moment is less than $p$.

dipoles through the local electric field which it possesses, the theory for dense substances, where the dipoles are close together, is more complicated than that for rarefied substances. We shall therefore consider first the dielectric constants of gases.

## 17.2. Dielectric constant of non-polar gases

In a molecule which possesses no permanent electric dipole moment, the electron distribution is symmetrical about the centre. When a uniform electric field is applied, no translational force acts on the molecule as a whole, since it is electrically neutral, and the centre of mass remains fixed (or moving with uniform velocity). The electrons and nuclei are, however, subjected to forces of opposite sign, and they will therefore be displaced a little in opposite directions until the internal forces balance those due to the external field. The molecule thereby acquires an induced moment when the field is applied. The forces exerted on the charged constituents of the molecule are parallel to the field and proportional to it, and the induced moment is also parallel to the field, and proportional to it at static field strengths used in the laboratory. (Non-linear effects have been observed at the abnormal field strengths encountered when the light from a high-powered laser is brought to a focus.) Since the electrons are so much lighter than the nucleus, their displacement is correspondingly greater, as the position of the centre of mass is unaltered. In general we shall refer only to the electron displacement relative to the nucleus, since this determines the induced moment.

The statements in the last paragraph may be summed up in the mathematical equation

$$\mathbf{p}_i = \alpha \mathbf{E}, \tag{17.1}$$

where $\mathbf{p}_i$ is the induced moment, $\mathbf{E}$ the field acting on the molecule, and $\alpha$ is a constant known as the molecular (or atomic, if we are dealing with atoms rather than molecules) polarizability. The value of $\alpha$ is typical of each different type of atom or molecule. The field $\mathbf{E}$ is known as the local field, since it is the actual field acting on each molecule. This is not necessarily the same as the external field $\mathbf{E}_0$, applied for instance by maintaining a voltage difference between two capacitor plates and calculated therefrom, since each molecule is subjected also to the electric fields of neighbouring molecules which, like it, have acquired dipole moments under the influence of the field. The local field $\mathbf{E}$ is equal to the vector sum of $\mathbf{E}_0$ and the fields due to neighbouring molecules; approximately (see below), $\mathbf{E}$ can be replaced by the sum of $\mathbf{E}_0$ and an average field due to the neighbours which is parallel to $\mathbf{E}_0$. Thus we shall find an average local field $\mathbf{E}$ which is also parallel to $\mathbf{E}_0$.

The general relation between the electric displacement $\mathbf{D}$, the external field $\mathbf{E}_0$, the polarization $\mathbf{P}$, and the dielectric constant $\epsilon$ is

$$\mathbf{D} = \epsilon_0 \mathbf{E}_0 + \mathbf{P} = \epsilon \epsilon_0 \mathbf{E}_0. \tag{17.2}$$

Here $\mathbf{P}$ is the induced electric moment $\mathbf{P}_i$ per unit volume, and it is related to the average local field $\mathbf{E}$ by the equation

$$\mathbf{P} = n_0 \alpha \mathbf{E}, \tag{17.3}$$

where $n_0$ is the number of molecules per unit volume (assumed to be all of the same type). From equation (17.2) we have also

$$\mathbf{P} = (\epsilon - 1)\epsilon_0 \mathbf{E}_0. \tag{17.4}$$

In order to relate the macroscopic dielectric constant $\epsilon$ to the molecular polarizability $\alpha$, we require to know the relation between $\mathbf{E}$ and $\mathbf{E}_0$. The following approximate solution of this problem is due to Lorentz.

The substance is imagined to be divided into two parts, and the contribution of each is considered separately. One part consists of a sphere whose size is so large that when considering the local field acting

on a molecule at the centre of the sphere, the effect of the molecules in
the region outside the sphere may be evaluated by regarding the region
outside as a continuum. This is obviously a satisfactory approximation
if the radius of the sphere is large compared with the intermolecular
distance, so that the sphere contains many molecules. Then the local
field is $\mathbf{E} = \mathbf{E_0} + \mathbf{E_1} + \mathbf{E_2}$, where $\mathbf{E_1}$ is the field due to the molecules
outside the sphere, and $\mathbf{E_2}$ that due to the molecules inside. The field
$\mathbf{E_1}$ is the same as that due to the polarization charge $P_n$ over the surface
of the sphere, where $P_n$ is the outward component of the polarization
normal to the surface. From the result of Problem 2.1, we have

$$\mathbf{E_1} = \mathbf{P}/3\epsilon_0. \tag{17.5}$$

Here $\mathbf{P}$ is the ordinary polarization of the medium (we do not have to
allow for any distortion of the field, as in Problem 2.1, because we have
not excavated a real cavity in the dielectric).

The value of $\mathbf{E_2}$ is more difficult to calculate, since it depends on how
the molecules are arranged within the sphere. Lorentz showed that for
a cubical array of molecules (as in a simple type of crystal) $\mathbf{E_2} = 0$, and
this is also true of gases and non-associated liquids where the molecules
are moving at random, independently of one another. We have therefore
$\mathbf{E} = \mathbf{E_0} + \mathbf{E_1}$, whence from equation (17.3) $\mathbf{P} = n_0 \alpha \mathbf{E} = n_0 \alpha \{\mathbf{E_0} + \mathbf{P}/3\epsilon_0\}$.
Elimination of $\mathbf{P}$ using equation (17.4) yields the equation, first derived
by Clausius and Mossotti, and generally known by their names,

$$\frac{\epsilon - 1}{\epsilon + 2} = \frac{n_0 \alpha}{3\epsilon_0}. \tag{17.6}$$

If each molecule could be regarded as a perfectly conducting sphere of
radius $a$, the moment acquired by such a sphere (see § 2.4) in a field $\mathbf{E}$
is $4\pi\epsilon_0 a^3 \mathbf{E}$. This suggests that the value of $\alpha$ will be close to $4\pi\epsilon_0 a^3$,
where $a$ is the molecular radius, and the right-hand side of equation
(17.6) is then seen to be equal to the actual volume occupied by all the
molecules in unit volume. If the values of the molecular volume calculated in this way are compared with those derived from kinetic theory
(e.g. from measurements of viscosity), it is found that they are of the
same order, being generally rather smaller, as is illustrated by the
examples given in Problem 17.1.

If both sides of equation (17.6) are multiplied by $M/\rho$, where $M$ is
the molecular weight and $\rho$ the density, it becomes

$$\frac{\epsilon - 1}{\epsilon + 2}\frac{M}{\rho} = \frac{N\alpha}{3\epsilon_0}, \tag{17.7}$$

where $N = Mn_0/\rho$ is Avogadro's number. The quantity $N\alpha/3\epsilon_0$ is sometimes called the molar polarizability.

The values of the dielectric constants of a number of common gases at normal temperature and atmospheric pressure are given in Table 17.2. It will be seen that the difference between $\epsilon$ and unity is of the order of $10^{-3}$, and for non-polar gases it increases with the complexity and hence with the size of the molecule. The values of $\epsilon-1$ for gases whose molecules have permanent dipole moments are markedly higher, but at ordinary pressures it is obvious that it is sufficient to write $\epsilon+2$ as 3 in the denominator of equation (17.7) above. This is tantamount to ignoring the difference between $\mathbf{E}_0$ and $\mathbf{E} = (\epsilon+2)\mathbf{E}_0/3$, and the value of $\epsilon-1$ with this approximation could have been obtained immediately from equations (17.3) and (17.4). At high pressures this approximation ceases to hold, and the validity of the Clausius–Mossotti relation (17.6) has been verified by various experimenters using pressures up to 1000 atm. The constancy of the value of $N\alpha/3\epsilon_0$ as calculated using equation (17.7) is shown in Table 17.3, while the values calculated using the approximation $\epsilon+2 = 3$ deviate appreciably at higher pressures.

## 17.3. Static dielectric constant of polar gases

The theory developed in the last section holds not only for non-polar gases, but for all gases, since the application of an electric field will always cause a distortion of the molecule and thus give an induced dipole moment. In the case of polar gases, however, there is an additional effect arising from the presence of the permanent dipole moments. In the absence of an applied field these point in random directions, and there is no net polarization of the gas. When a field is applied, there is a small excess in the number of dipoles pointing with the field over those pointing against the field, and so there is a contribution to the net polarization. The excess number is determined by the Boltzmann distribution, since a dipole pointing with the field has a slightly lower energy than one pointing against the field, and so is slightly more favoured in the distribution. This problem has already been treated by classical methods for the corresponding magnetic case in § 8.3, and the results obtained there may be applied immediately to the electrical case if we write $\mathbf{p}$ and $\mathbf{E}$ for the electric dipole moment and field instead of the magnetic quantities $\mathfrak{m}$ and $\mathbf{B}$. The contribution to the polarization is therefore (cf. equation (8.13))

$$\mathbf{P}_d = \frac{n_0 \mathbf{p}^2}{3kT}\mathbf{E}, \tag{17.8}$$

## TABLE 17.2

*Dielectric constants of some common gases
at atmospheric pressure and 0° C*

| Gas | $(\epsilon-1)10^3$ | Dipole moment Debye units |
|---|---|---|
| He | 0·071 | 0 |
| $H_2$ | 0·270 | 0 |
| $O_2$ | 0·531 | 0 |
| $N_2$ | 0·588 | 0 |
| $CO_2$ | 0·988 | 0 |
| $CH_4$ | 0·948 | 0 |
| $C_2H_4$ | 1·38 | 0 |
| CO | 0·692 | 0·10 |
| $N_2O$ | 1·08 | 0·17 |
| $NH_3$ | 8·34 | 1·45 |
| $SO_2$ | 9·93 | 1·59 |

## TABLE 17.3

*Dielectric constant of $CO_2$ and the
Clausius–Mossotti relation*

| Experimenters | Pressure (atm.) | Dielectric constant (at 100° C) | $\dfrac{\epsilon-1}{\epsilon+2}\dfrac{M}{\rho}$ (cm³) |
|---|---|---|---|
| K. and K. | 10 | 1·00753 | 7·49 |
| | 30 | 1·0240 | 7·53 |
| | 50 | 1·0431 | 7·57 |
| | 70 | 1·0645 | 7·60 |
| | 100 | 1·1041 | 7·69 |
| | 151 | 1·1912 | 7·73 |
| M. and M. | 103·2 | 1·1086 | 7·71 |
| | 194·5 | 1·2695 | 7·75 |
| | 295·4 | 1·3895 | 7·70 |
| | 365·0 | 1·4375 | 7·68 |
| | 476·6 | 1·4900 | 7·67 |
| | 588·3 | 1·5274 | 7·66 |
| | 700·2 | 1·5570 | 7·66 |
| | 812·3 | 1·5812 | 7·65 |
| | 970·6 | 1·6097 | 7·62 |

The value of $\dfrac{\epsilon-1}{\epsilon+2}\dfrac{M}{\rho}$ at N.T.P. is 7·33 cm³ for 1 g-mole.

The data indicate a slight rise in the molar polarizability with pressure, followed by a small decrease at the highest pressures.

*References*:

K. and K., F. G. Keyes and J. G. Kirkwood, 1930, *Phys. Rev.* **36**, 754.
M. and M., A. Michels and C. Michels, 1932, *Phil. Trans.* A, **231**, 409.

where $k$ is Boltzmann's constant and $T$ the absolute temperature. Here **E** is again the local field, and the relation between the local field and the external field $\mathbf{E}_0$ is more complicated than for induced dipoles because the permanent dipoles are not all oriented parallel to the field (this problem will be considered further in § 17.6). For gases at such low densities that the difference between **E** and $\mathbf{E}_0$ can be neglected, the static dielectric constant $\epsilon_s$ is given by the relation

$$\epsilon_s - \epsilon_i = \mathbf{P}_d/\epsilon_0\,\mathbf{E}_0 = \frac{n_0 p^2}{3\epsilon_0 kT}, \qquad (17.9)$$

where $\epsilon_i$ is that part of the dielectric constant due to the induced dipoles alone; in the low density limit $\epsilon_i - 1 = n_0\alpha/\epsilon_0$. It will be noticed that we have used the formula appropriate to the case of $pE/kT \ll 1$, a condition which is well fulfilled at ordinary field strengths. At room temperature $kT$ is $4\times10^{-21}$ joules, so that even with a dipole moment of 4 Debyes a field of $3\times10^7$ V/metre would be required to make $pE/kT = 0.1$. A slight decrease in the dielectric constant has been observed in some liquids at very high field strengths, but one cannot approach saturation as in the case of magnetic dipoles by going to very low temperatures (see § 20.5), since all polar gases tend to have high liquefaction and freezing-points owing to the large intermolecular forces between their permanent dipoles. In the solid state these are so large that the electric dipoles cannot rotate when an electric field is applied, whereas magnetic dipoles in suitable paramagnetic salts are relatively free to orient themselves in a magnetic field.

The derivation of the contribution to the polarization from the permanent dipoles which we have given is a purely classical one, and the reader may wonder to what extent it is confirmed by wave mechanics. The answer to this is that exactly the same result is obtained, but in a surprisingly different way. This may be illustrated by reference to a diatomic molecule. The rotational states of such a molecule are distinguished by having quantized values of the angular momentum equal to $J(h/2\pi)$, where $J$ is zero or a positive integer, and $h$ is Planck's constant. The calculation shows that in small fields the states for which $J \neq 0$ contribute nothing to the polarization in respect of the permanent dipole moment of the molecule. This is reasonable because when the molecule is turning end over end, the average projection of the dipole moment on any direction in space is zero. In the state $J = 0$, however, the molecule is not rotating, and the whole of the contribution comes from this state. At high temperatures a large number of rotational states are occupied, and the fraction of molecules which are in the state $J = 0$ is proportional to $1/T$. This gives the same temperature variation as the classical theory, and detailed calculation shows that the numerical constant is also the same (see Pauling and Wilson, 1935).

The molecular polarizability constant $\alpha$ is not of great theoretical interest except in the case of a very simple atom such as helium, where a wave-mechanical calculation of its magnitude is possible. The size of the permanent dipole moment is, however, a valuable clue to the structure of a molecule, as pointed out in § 17.1, and gives some quantitative information about the nature of the chemical binding. It is obvious from equation (17.9) that the size of the dipole moment may be obtained from measurements of the dielectric constant of the gas, experimental methods for which were discussed in § 15.5. In order to separate out the contributions from the induced polarization and the permanent dipoles, measurements may be made over a wide temperature range. If the molar polarizability is then plotted against $1/T$, a straight line is obtained from the slope of which the dipole moment can be calculated using equation (17.9). The intercept at $1/T = 0$ gives also the value of $\alpha$, the molecular polarizability.

## 17.4. Dispersion in gases

The theory of electromagnetic waves (Chapter 10) shows that the refractive index of a substance should be equal to the square root of its dielectric constant, if the magnetic permeability can be taken as unity, as is usually the case. A comparison of the dielectric constants measured at low frequencies with the refractive indices measured in the optical region (i.e. at frequencies of the order of $10^{14}$) gives very poor agreement with this relation except in the case of simple non-polar gases. Values of the dielectric constant of a few such gases measured over a wide range of frequencies are given in Table 17.4 together with the square of the optical refractive index. The latter is extrapolated to 'infinite wavelengths' to correct for dispersion in the optical region. The agreement is seen to be excellent in the cases quoted.

In the optical region, variation of the refractive index with wavelength has been known for a very long time, and is called dispersion. In general the refractive index increases as the wavelength decreases, and this is known as 'normal dispersion'. The reverse case, where the refractive index decreases with decreasing wavelength, occurs only in the vicinity of an absorption line, and is difficult to observe because of the absorption. This is known as 'anomalous dispersion', but both types have a simple explanation in terms of classical theory, based on the assumption that an atom contains electrons vibrating at certain natural frequencies characteristic of the type of atom, and that the application of an alternating electric field sets such electrons into forced vibration.

TABLE 17.4

| Gas | $(\epsilon-1)10^6$ at N.T.P. | | | | |
|---|---|---|---|---|---|
| | 0·1 Mc/s | 1 Mc/s | 9000 Mc/s | 24 000 Mc/s | Optical |
| Air     .     .     . | 570 ±0·7 | 567·0 ±1·0 | 575·4 ±1·4 | 576·0 ±0·2 | 575·7 ±0·2 |
| Nitrogen     .     . | 578 ±0·7 | 579·6 ±1·0 | 586·9 ±2·9 | 588·3 ±0·2 | 581·3 |
| Oxygen .     .     . | 528 ±1 | 523·3 ±1 | 530·0 ±1·9 | 531·0 ±0·4 | 532·7 |
| Argon     .     .     . | 545 ±1 | 545·1 ±0·5 | — | 555·7 ±0·4 | 554·7 |
| Carbon dioxide     . | 987 ±1 | 987·5 ±2 | 985·5 ±3 | 988 ±2 | — |
| Hydrogen     .     . | 270 ±1 | 272 | — | — | 272 |
| | A | B | C | D | E |

References:
   A. Lovering and Wiltshire, 1951, Proc. I.E.E. 98, Part II, 557.
   B. Hector and Woernley, 1946, Phys. Rev. 69, 101.
   C. Birnbaum, Kryder, and Lyons, 1951, J. Appl. Phys. 22, 95.
   D. Essen and Froome, 1951, Proc. Phys. Soc. B, 64, 862.
   E. $(n^2-1)10^6$ (various authors), extrapolated to infinite wavelength.

Let us take the simplest possible case of a gas of dielectric constant $\epsilon$ subjected to an oscillating electric field $\mathbf{E} = \mathbf{E}' \exp(j\omega t)$. We shall assume that the wavelength of the incident radiation is very large compared with atomic dimensions (which is true up to the region of hard X-rays), so that the field acting on an electron in a given atom is independent of its position with respect to the nucleus, which is assumed to be stationary. Each electron in the molecule is displaced a distance $\mathbf{s}$ by the field, and the restoring force is written as $-m\omega_p^2\,\mathbf{s}$, where $\omega_p/2\pi$ is the natural frequency of oscillation of the electron and $m$ its mass. In addition there will be damping due to collisions, radiation of energy, etc., which may be represented by a term $-m\gamma(d\mathbf{s}/dt)$. Hence we have

$$m\left(\frac{d^2\mathbf{s}}{dt^2}+\gamma\frac{d\mathbf{s}}{dt}+\omega_p^2\mathbf{s}\right) = -e\mathbf{E}'e^{j\omega t}. \qquad (17.10)$$

The solution of this is

$$\mathbf{s} = -\frac{e\mathbf{E}}{m\{(\omega_p^2-\omega^2)+j\gamma\omega\}} + e^{-\frac{1}{2}\gamma t}\{\mathbf{A}\cos[(\omega_p^2-\tfrac{1}{4}\gamma^2)^{\frac{1}{2}}t]+\mathbf{B}\sin[(\omega_p^2-\tfrac{1}{4}\gamma^2)^{\frac{1}{2}}t]\}.$$

The terms in **A** and **B** average to zero over many atoms since **A** and **B** depend on the initial conditions and are as often positive as negative. The instantaneous electric dipole moment due to the displacement of the electron is $\mathbf{p} = -e\mathbf{s}$, and, if there are $n_0$ molecules per unit volume, the polarization **P** is

$$\mathbf{P} = n_0\mathbf{p} = \frac{n_0 e^2 \mathbf{E}}{m} \frac{1}{(\omega_p^2 - \omega^2) + j\gamma\omega}. \tag{17.11}$$

For gases at higher density a correction for the difference between the local field and the external field may be applied in the same way as in § 17.2, leading to the formula

$$\frac{\epsilon-1}{\epsilon+2} = \frac{n^2-1}{n^2+2} = \frac{n_0 e^2}{3m\epsilon_0} \frac{1}{(\omega_p^2 - \omega^2) + j\gamma\omega}. \tag{17.12}$$

This formula shows that both $\epsilon$ and $n$ must be regarded as complex. Writing $\epsilon = \epsilon' - j\epsilon'' = (n - jk)^2$, where $n$ is the real part of the refractive index and $k$ is the absorption coefficient, we may separate the real and imaginary parts of equation (17.12). The formula is clumsy to handle, however, and we shall assume that we are dealing only with gases at such low pressures that we can neglect the Lorentz correction. Since the value of $k$ is small, and negligible except near an absorption line, we may also make the approximation, if the line is narrow, of writing

$$(\omega_p^2 - \omega^2) = (\omega_p + \omega)(\omega_p - \omega) \approx 2\omega(\omega_p - \omega).$$

Then we obtain the formulae

$$\left.\begin{aligned}
\epsilon' &= n^2 - k^2 \approx n^2 = 1 + \frac{n_0 e^2}{2m\omega\epsilon_0}\left\{\frac{\omega_p - \omega}{(\omega_p - \omega)^2 + \Delta\omega^2}\right\} \\
\epsilon'' &= 2nk \approx 2k = \frac{n_0 e^2}{2m\omega\epsilon_0}\left\{\frac{\Delta\omega}{(\omega_p - \omega)^2 + \Delta\omega^2}\right\}
\end{aligned}\right\}, \tag{17.13}$$

where the symbol $\Delta\omega$ has been used for $\gamma/2$, and we have assumed $n \approx 1$, $k \ll n$.

The variation of $n$ and $k$ in the neighbourhood of a weak absorption line is shown in Fig. 17.2. The absorption coefficient reaches a maximum at the resonant frequency where $\omega = \omega_p$, and falls to half its maximum value at $\omega_p - \omega = \pm\Delta\omega$. In optical usage, the quantity $2\Delta\nu = \Delta\omega/\pi$ is called the 'half-width' of the line, meaning the frequency difference between the points at which the absorption has dropped to half the maximum value. Microwave spectroscopists, however, prefer to call $\Delta\nu$ the half-width.

In general, each atom or molecule possesses a number of characteristic resonant frequencies, and the expressions given above for the refractive index and absorption coefficient should be replaced by others with summations over the various values of $\omega_p$. If the number of electrons per molecule which have a resonant frequency $\omega_p$ is denoted by $f_p$, we may write equation (17.12) in the form

$$\frac{\epsilon-1}{\epsilon+2} = \frac{n^2-1}{n^2+2} = \frac{n_0 e^2}{3m\epsilon_0} \sum_p \frac{f_p}{(\omega_p^2-\omega^2)+j\gamma\omega}. \tag{17.14}$$

The value of $f_p$ is known as the 'oscillator strength' of an absorption line, and on classical theory we should expect it to be unity. In practice

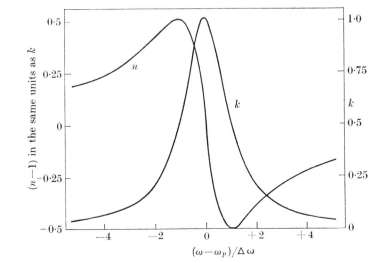

FIG. 17.2. Variation of $n$ and $k$ near a narrow absorption line (from equation (17.13)). $n-1$ and $k$ are in units of $n_0 e^2/4m\omega\epsilon_0\Delta\omega$.

it generally has values less than unity, and the quantum mechanical explanation shows that this corresponds to the fact that each electron possesses a number of possible frequencies of oscillation, and its total oscillator strength is divided between them. We have then $\sum_p (f_p) = 1$ for each electron.

At frequencies far from resonance the absorption coefficient is negligible. At very low frequencies, where $\omega \ll$ any value of $\omega_p$, we have

$$\frac{\epsilon-1}{\epsilon+2} = \frac{n^2-1}{n^2+2} = \frac{n_0 e^2}{3m\epsilon_0} \sum_p \frac{f_p}{\omega_p^2} = \frac{n_0 \alpha}{3\epsilon_0} \tag{17.15}$$

by comparison with (17.6). This shows that the molecular polarizability $\alpha$ is intimately connected with the oscillator strengths and absorption lines. In fact, as the frequency is raised and we pass through an absorption line at $\omega_p/2\pi$, the refractive index goes through the anomalous variation shown in Fig. 17.2 and approaches a smaller limiting value on the high frequency side than it had on the low frequency side. When there are a number of absorption lines, the behaviour is as shown in Fig. 17.3, and finally, when $\omega$ is greater than all values of $\omega_p$, $n$ approaches

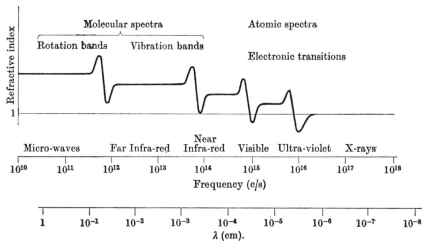

Fig. 17.3. Schematic diagram showing variation of refractive index with frequency.

unity, but the value of $(n-1)$ is slightly negative. This is the well-known anomaly in the refractive index in the X-ray region, and the value of $n$ is then generally calculated by assuming that the electrons are free, so that equation (17.10) reduces to

$$m\frac{d^2\mathbf{s}}{dt^2} = -e\mathbf{E}'e^{j\omega t}. \tag{17.16}$$

This is equivalent to the assumption that $\omega \gg \omega_p, \gamma$.

If a molecule has a permanent electric dipole moment, its static dielectric constant contains an additional term involving the dipole moment (see equation (17.9)). From the discussion of dispersion in this section, we should expect that this term would also be related to some absorption lines. This is the case, for such molecules have a 'pure rotational' spectrum in the far infra-red, due to transitions between the different rotational levels of the molecule. Such transitions can be observed only if the molecule has a permanent dipole moment, since then an alternating electric field exerts a couple on the molecule which changes the state of rotation. In the optical region we are far on the high frequency side of such absorption lines, so that they give no contribution to the optical refractive index. If the molecule has no other absorption lines in the infra-red, the square of the optical refractive index would (by equation (17.15)) be equal to that part of the low frequency dielectric constant which arises from the molecular polarizability. In general, however, molecules show absorption lines due to molecular vibrations, since the distorted molecule may have a dipole moment. Under the action of the vibration this gives the molecule an oscillating dipole moment, which can emit or absorb radiation.

## 17.5. Static dielectric constants of liquids and solids

The static dielectric constants of liquids and solids are related to absorption lines (or bands) at higher frequencies in a similar way to that outlined in the preceding section for gases. In simple atomic substances, such as the condensed phases of the rare gases of the atmosphere, there are no absorption bands in the infra-red, and the low-frequency dielectric constant does not differ greatly from that deduced from the Clausius–Mossotti formula, using the molecular polarizability measured for the gas phase. For example, at its boiling-point liquid helium has a dielectric constant of 1·048, and a density of 0·125 g/cm³. This gives a molar polarizability of $(N\alpha/3\epsilon_0) = 0·12$, while that deduced from the optical refractive index of the gas at 0° C (after allowing for dispersion by extrapolating to infinite wavelength), or from the static dielectric constant of the gas, is 0·123.

On a broad classification, a second class of substances contains those which consist of agglomerations of molecules held together by the van der Waals forces between the molecules; such forces are relatively small (though larger than those between atoms), and these substances have fairly low melting- and boiling-points. Most organic substances belong to this class. The static dielectric constant corresponds to a molar polarizability considerably higher than that calculated from the optical refractive index, the difference being associated with internal vibrations within the molecules. These give rise to absorption bands in the infra-red, provided that the vibration sets up an oscillating electric dipole moment. From equation (17.15) it follows that their effect is largest when the oscillator strength $f_p$ is high and the resonant frequency $\omega_p$ is low. These vibrations are characteristic of the molecule, and occur at frequencies which are not greatly different in the solid or liquid from those in the gas. The characteristic rotational frequencies are absent in the condensed phase, however, because of the intermolecular forces. In the solid such rotations are completely inhibited in most cases, but in liquids where the molecules carry permanent electric dipole moments a dispersion band is observed at radio-frequencies (see § 17.7).

The third class of substances contains the ionic solids, consisting of lattices of positively and negatively charged ions; these give rise to strong binding forces, and the substances have rather high melting-points. In ionic crystals an electric field exerts a force on each ion, causing a displacement of the whole positive ion lattice with respect to the negative ion lattice. This gives a rather large polarization, and a high dielectric constant. In the light of equation (17.15) this can be interpreted in terms of the rather low (far infra-red) vibrational frequencies associated with displacements of the positive ion lattice relative to the negative ion lattice. Some of these have been measured spectroscopically, but the calculation of the dielectric constant is complicated because (*a*) of local field corrections and (*b*) the charge clouds of the ions partly overlap one another, producing short-range forces which are not adequately represented by the Lorentz local field, which is essentially a dipolar or long-range force. Szigeti (1949) has derived the formula

$$\epsilon - n^2 = \left(\frac{n^2+2}{3}\right)^2 \frac{n_0\, q^2}{M_r\, \omega_t^2\, \epsilon_0}, \tag{17.17}$$

where $n^2$ is the square of the optical refractive index (extrapolated to infinite wavelength, $q$ is the effective charge on each ion, $\omega_t$ the characteristic frequency for transverse elastic waves, and $M_r$ the reduced mass, which for a solid containing two types of ion of mass $M_1$, $M_2$ is given by

$$\frac{1}{M_r} = \frac{1}{M_1} + \frac{1}{M_2}. \tag{17.18}$$

The effective charge $q = s(ze)$, where $z$ is the valency of the ion, $e$ the electronic charge, and $s$ a factor close to unity which is introduced to allow for the charge overlap mentioned above. Some typical values of $s$ are given in Table 17.5. In cubic crystals the dielectric constant is isotropic, but this is not necessarily true of non-cubic crystals. In the ionic case anisotropy arises when the vibrational frequency $\omega_t$ depends on the direction of vibration, and, correspondingly, the displacement of an ion (involving the same restoring forces) depends on the direction of the applied field.

In general the dielectric constant of a solid is not greatly dependent on temperature, but there are some notable exceptions. In barium titanate, $BaTiO_3$, for example, the dielectric constant varies at high temperatures as $(T-T_c)^{-1}$, and rises as high as $10^4$ just above 120° K. Below this temperature spontaneous polarization is observed, which can be reversed by an electric field of sufficient strength, with hysteresis effects. This is a co-operative transition, showing many resemblances to ferromagnetism, and substances showing such effects (other examples

TABLE 17.5

*Dielectric constants of some ionic solids*

| Substance | Lattice type | $\epsilon$ | $n^2$ | $\left(\dfrac{n^2+2}{3}\right)^2$ | $s$ |
|---|---|---|---|---|---|
| TlCl    .    .    .    . | Cubic (CsCl) | 31·9 | 5·10 | 5·6 | 1·08 |
| SrO.    .    .    .    . | Cubic (NaCl) | 13·2 | 3·31 | 3·14 | 0·6 |
| TiO$_2$ (parallel to axis)    . | Tetragonal | 173 | 8·42 | 12·1 | 0·79, 0·65 |
| TiO$_2$ (perpendicular to axis) |  | 89 | 6·82 | 8·7 | 0·88, 0·65 |

Two values of $s$ are given for TiO$_2$ because of an ambiguity in the interpretation of the infra-red absorption bands (after Szigeti, 1949).

are Rochelle salt, $T_c = 24°$ C; and potassium dihydrogen tartrate, $T_c = -150°$ C) are known as 'ferro-electrics'. However, a ferro-electric (unlike a ferromagnetic) does not contain permanent dipoles which become spontaneously oriented below the transition temperature. The properties below this transition temperature are due to a spontaneous lattice distortion in which ions of one type undergo a small displacement relative to the rest of the lattice. This is accompanied by a change in crystal symmetry; in BaTiO$_3$ the symmetry is cubic above the transition temperature of 120° C, changing to tetragonal symmetry below this temperature. There are further structural changes to orthorhombic symmetry below 0° C, and to rhombohedral symmetry below $-90°$ C, these changes being accompanied by changes in the direction of the spontaneous polarization. Cochran (1960) has shown that the apparent Curie–Weiss law (cf. equation 8.14) above the transition temperature results from a temperature dependence of one vibrational mode, such that in an equation of the form (17.17) $\omega_t^2$ varies as $(T-T_c)$. The latter has been verified experimentally by Cowley (1962) for strontium titanate. This frequency falls to zero at $T = T_c$, where the lattice becomes unstable in respect of this one mode and a spontaneous distortion takes place.

The possibility of anti-ferro-electrics, where no net polarization exists below the transition temperature because equal numbers of ions are shifted in opposite directions, was pointed out by Kittel (1951), the first such substance to be identified being lead zirconate, PbZrO$_3$ ($T_c = 230°$ C).

### 17.6. Static dielectric constants of polar liquids

In polar liquids the local field is very large, and its representation by the Lorentz field leads to the result that such liquids should become ferro-electrics. If we consider only that part of the polarization $\mathbf{P}_d$ arising from the permanent dipole moments, we have from equations (17.5), (17.8)

$$\frac{\mathbf{P}_d}{\mathbf{E}_0} = \frac{\mathbf{P}_d}{\mathbf{E}-(\mathbf{P}_d/3\epsilon_0)} = \frac{n_0\mathbf{p}^2}{3kT\{1-(n_0\mathbf{p}^2/9kT\epsilon_0)\}} = \frac{n_0\mathbf{p}^2}{3k(T-T_c)}, \quad (17.19)$$

where $T_c = n_0p^2/9\epsilon_0$. For water $T_c$ would be about $1000°$ K, so that water should be spontaneously electrified at ordinary temperatures, as in the corresponding ferromagnetic case (Chapter 21). In fact the known examples of ferro-electrics arise from spontaneous ionic displacements rather than spontaneous orientation of dipoles (see § 17.5). The nonsensical result of equation (17.19) is due to the fact that the Lorentz method for the local field assumes that each dipole has a moment equal to the average moment and parallel to the applied field. This is true for induced dipoles, but electric fields of ordinary magnitudes cause only a slight departure from random orientation of the permanent dipoles. The induced dipoles must be treated separately from the permanent dipoles, and Onsager (1936) has suggested an alternative method of treating the local field in which each dipole is regarded as being at the centre of a spherical cavity whose size is equal to the average volume occupied by each molecule. In the absence of any permanent dipoles it gives the same result as the Lorentz method, as can be verified by putting $p = 0$, $\epsilon_s = \epsilon_i$ in equations (17.22)–(17.24) below; the equivalent local field $E$ is then $E_c/(1-\alpha g) = (\epsilon_i+2)E_0/3$, which is the same as in § 17.2.

Each permanent dipole $\mathbf{p}$ polarizes the dielectric outside the spherical cavity containing it, and this produces a reaction field (see Problem 2.2) which will react back on the dipole. The reaction field $\mathbf{E}_r$ is parallel to $\mathbf{p}$, and produces an extra moment $\alpha\mathbf{E}_r$ through polarization of the molecule making the net moment $\mathbf{p}'$. Since the reaction field is proportional to $\mathbf{p}'$, the net moment, we have

$$\mathbf{p}' = \mathbf{p}+\alpha\mathbf{E}_r = \mathbf{p}+\alpha g\mathbf{p}',$$

where $g$ is the factor relating $\mathbf{E}_r$ to $\mathbf{p}'$. Hence

$$\mathbf{p}' = \frac{\mathbf{p}}{1-\alpha g}. \quad (17.20)$$

A similar effect occurs with the induced moment $\mathbf{p}_i$, changing it to

$$\mathbf{p}'_i = \frac{\mathbf{p}_i}{1-\alpha g}. \quad (17.21)$$

These are then the effective moments, which interact with the field in the cavity $\mathbf{E}_c$. From equations (17.3) and (17.8) we have then (since $\mathbf{p}_i = \alpha \mathbf{E}_i$)

$$\mathbf{P} = n_0 \mathbf{p}_i' + \frac{n_0 p'^2}{3kT} \mathbf{E}_c = \left\{ \frac{n_0 \alpha}{1-\alpha g} + \frac{n_0 p^2}{3kT(1-\alpha g)^2} \right\} \mathbf{E}_c. \qquad (17.22)$$

This gives us the result, using some formulae from electrostatics. If $\epsilon_s$ is the actual dielectric constant of the medium,

$$\mathbf{E}_c = \frac{3\epsilon_s}{2\epsilon_s + 1} \mathbf{E}_0 \quad \text{(from equation (2.43))} \qquad (17.23)$$

and

$$g = \frac{2(\epsilon_s - 1)}{2\epsilon_s + 1} \frac{1}{4\pi\epsilon_0 a^3} \quad \text{(from Problem 2.2)}$$

$$= \frac{2(\epsilon_s - 1)}{2\epsilon_s + 1} \frac{n_0}{3\epsilon_0}, \qquad (17.24)$$

since the average volume occupied by one molecule is $4\pi a^3/3 = 1/n_0$. The polarizability $\alpha$, from equation (17.6), is given by

$$\frac{\epsilon_i - 1}{\epsilon_i + 2} = \frac{n_0 \alpha}{3\epsilon_0}, \qquad (17.25)$$

where $\epsilon_i$ is that part of the dielectric constant associated with the induced dipoles only. On substituting these relations into equation (17.22), using $\mathbf{P} = (\epsilon_s - 1)\epsilon_0 \mathbf{E}_0$ from equation (17.4), and carrying out a tedious algebraic reduction, we find

$$\frac{(\epsilon_s - \epsilon_i)(2\epsilon_s + \epsilon_i)}{\epsilon_s(\epsilon_i + 2)^2} = \frac{n_0 p^2}{9\epsilon_0 kT}. \qquad (17.26)$$

For water, using $\epsilon_i = 4{\cdot}9$ (see § 17.7) and $p = 1{\cdot}94$ Debyes, the formula gives $\epsilon_s \approx 100$, which, although higher than the actual value of 80, corresponds much better to reality than the Lorentz prediction. The discrepancy is partly due to the fact that we can only expect it to hold for spherical molecules (since we assumed a spherical cavity), while $H_2O$ is triangular, and partly because only dipolar (long range) forces have been included, short-range forces which act only between neighbouring molecules being neglected. In a gas the molecules are so far apart that only the long-range forces need be considered, and Onsager's formula, equation (17.26), should be used at high densities; at low densities it reduces to equation (17.9).

In very dilute solutions of polar molecules in non-polar solvents, the dipoles are sufficiently far apart that their mutual interactions can be neglected. Thus we would expect to be able to apply equation (17.9), if we replace $p$ by the effective value of the dipole moment after allowing for interaction effects with the solvent. For spherical molecules this can be done by an extension of Onsager's theory, and this gives a method of finding the molecular dipole moment. The dielectric constant of the solution can be determined by one of the standard methods (see § 15.5); the solvents normally employed are carefully purified benzene and carbon tetrachloride. Measurements over a range of concentrations are used, followed by extrapolation to infinite dilution. The dipole moments measured in this way agree fairly well with those found using the gaseous method (§ 17.3), but discrepancies would be expected due to short-range forces and non-spherical molecules. The gaseous method is more satisfactory when it can be used, but the solvent method is employed for substances whose vapour pressure is very low. For a number of simple molecules (such as those in Table 17.1) accurate values of the dipole moments have been obtained from microwave spectroscopy (see Townes and Schawlow, 1955) or electric resonance in molecular beams (see Ramsey, 1956), by measurements of the splitting of the rotational lines in an electric field.

## 17.7. Radio-frequency dispersion in polar liquids

In the discussion of polar gases it was pointed out that the static dielectric constant is higher than the square of the optical refractive index, the difference being mainly due to dispersion in the infra-red, associated with the pure rotational spectrum of the molecules. In the liquid state this difference is even more marked; the well-known case being liquid water, whose static dielectric constant is 80, while the refractive index in the optical region is $1 \cdot 33$. Since the large dielectric constant is due to orientation of the molecular dipoles when a field is applied, it will clearly be much lower if orientation is inhibited for some reason. If a high frequency field is applied, the dipoles must be able to re-orient themselves sufficiently quickly to follow the reversal of the field, in order to make their full contribution to the polarization. If this re-orientation takes a finite time $\tau$, the dipoles will not be able to follow a field whose angular frequency is such that $\omega\tau \gg 1$. In the region where $\omega\tau \approx 1$, the dielectric constant will fall, and absorption of energy will take place from the alternating field into the dielectric.

To form an estimate of $\tau$, we must consider the mechanism inhibiting re-orientation. In a liquid this is simply the bombardment of the molecule by other molecules; that is, the Brownian motion. If a spherical particle of radius $a$ is suspended in a liquid of viscosity $\eta$, then the mean square value of the rotational angle $\theta$ in a time $t$ is

$$\overline{\theta^2} = \frac{kT}{4\pi\eta a^3} t = t/\tau, \tag{17.27}$$

where $\tau = 4\pi\eta a^3/kT$ is a characteristic time for the Brownian motion. If we apply this to the molecules of a liquid such as water, taking $a = 2 \cdot 3 \times 10^{-8}$ cm, the value found from the viscosity of the vapour, and $\eta = 0 \cdot 010$ c.g.s. units $= 0 \cdot 001$ m.k.s. units at $20°$ C, we find $\tau = 3 \cdot 7 \times 10^{-11}$ sec. Since this time is longer than any of the characteristic periodic times of rotation of the free water molecule, it follows that the molecule cannot rotate at any of its natural frequencies in the liquid state. Instead, the dispersion associated with the permanent dipoles will take place at frequencies such that $\omega \approx 1/\tau$, that is at a wavelength of the order of 1 cm.

In order to introduce $\tau$ into our treatment of the dielectric constant, we consider the effect of maintaining a steady field on a polar liquid, and then suddenly removing it. Under the influence of the Brownian motion, the preferred orientations of the dipoles will gradually disappear. It is reasonable to suppose that the rate of decay of the polarization is proportional to the instantaneous value of the polarization, and we write

$$d\mathbf{P}/dt = -\mathbf{P}/\tau,$$

giving
$$\mathbf{P} = \mathbf{P_0}\exp(-t/\tau),$$

where $\tau$ is a characteristic 'relaxation time' which we would expect to be of the same order as that found above for the Brownian motion. Here $\mathbf{P}$ is, of course, only that part of the polarization associated with the permanent dipoles. If the field is not switched off, but changed suddenly to a value for which the equilibrium polarization is $\mathbf{P_0}$, then the rate of change of $\mathbf{P}$ is given by the equation

$$d\mathbf{P}/dt = (\mathbf{P_0}-\mathbf{P})/\tau, \quad \text{or} \quad \mathbf{P}+\tau\frac{d\mathbf{P}}{dt} = \mathbf{P_0},$$

When an alternating field $\mathbf{E}'\exp(j\omega t)$ is applied, we may write our equation for the polarization in the form (cf. equation (17.8))

$$\mathbf{P}+\tau\frac{d\mathbf{P}}{dt} = \mathbf{P_0} = \frac{n_0\mathbf{p}^2}{3kT}\mathbf{E}'\exp(j\omega t),$$

giving
$$\mathbf{P} = \frac{n_0\mathbf{p}^2}{3kT}\frac{\mathbf{E}'\exp(j\omega t)}{1+j\omega\tau}. \tag{17.28}$$

Here $\mathbf{E}'$ is the amplitude of the local alternating field, and $\mathbf{P}$ is that part of the polarization due only to the permanent dipoles. Allowing for these effects, we find for the dielectric constant the expression

$$\frac{\epsilon-\epsilon_i}{\epsilon_s-\epsilon_i} = \frac{1}{1+j\omega\tau} \tag{17.29}$$

where $\epsilon_i$ is that part of the dielectric constant due to induced polarization, and $\epsilon_s$ is the static dielectric constant. This result holds for the Onsager treatment for the local field, but it can be shown that the formula is similar if the Lorentz correction is used, except that we must use a

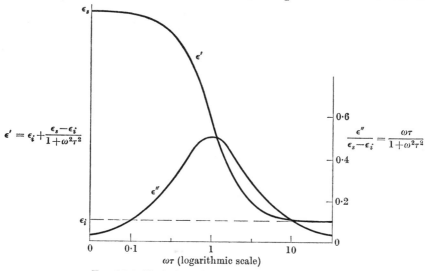

FIG. 17.4. Variation of $\epsilon'$ and $\epsilon''$ for a polar liquid.

modified relaxation time $\tau' = \tau(\epsilon_s+2)/(\epsilon_i+2)$. This difference is signifi-cant only in a comparison of the relaxation time determined from the dispersion of the dielectric constant with that from the Brownian motion.

Equation (17.28) above shows that $\mathbf{P}$, and hence $\epsilon$, is complex, and we may either write $\epsilon = \epsilon'-j\epsilon''$, or $\epsilon = (n-jk)^2$, where $n$ is the refrac-tive index and $k$ the absorption coefficient. Then

$$n^2-k^2 = \epsilon' = \frac{\epsilon_s-\epsilon_i}{1+\omega^2\tau^2}+\epsilon_i, \tag{17.30}$$

$$2nk = \epsilon'' = \frac{(\epsilon_s-\epsilon_i)\omega\tau}{1+\omega^2\tau^2}. \tag{17.31}$$

The variation of these quantities with frequency is easily seen from Fig. 17.4. $\epsilon'$ falls from $\epsilon_s$ at low frequencies to $\epsilon_i$ at high frequencies, the transition taking place near $\omega = 1/\tau$. $\epsilon''$ has a maximum in this region at $\omega = 1/\tau$, and falls to zero at both low and high frequencies.

The theory of the dispersion of the dielectric constant of polar liquids was first given by Debye (1929), and that given above is a simplified version of his treatment. It was first verified for glycerine and a number of alcohols, for which $\tau$ is much greater than for water owing to their higher viscosity and larger molecular radius. For example, at 22° C the values of $\epsilon'$ and $\epsilon''$ for glycerine at a wavelength of 9·5 metres are 42 and 8·6 respectively, showing that we are already well into the region of anomalous dispersion at this wavelength. Vacuum tube oscillators and detectors were available for such wavelengths, but the dispersion in water could not be measured accurately until centimetre wave technique was established, owing to the small value of $\tau$. We shall here describe the measurements of Collie, Hasted, and Ritson (1948).

An accurate method of determining the dielectric constant of low loss liquids, using resonant cavities, was described in § 15.5. This method cannot be used with water, since the absorption is so great if the cavity is filled with water that no resonance can be observed. This difficulty can be surmounted by using a cavity partly filled with water, the degree of filling being adjusted to give a measurable change in the resonant frequency and $Q$ of the cavity.

An alternative method, used by the same workers, is to determine the propagation constant in a waveguide filled with water. This constant depends on both the real and imaginary parts of the dielectric constant, and on the linear dimensions of the guide. By using two guides of different sizes, the values of $\epsilon'$ and $\epsilon''$ can be found separately, since their relative contributions to the propagation constant depend on the size of the guide. From equation (16.34) the field in the guide varies as

$$\exp(-hx) = \exp\{-(\alpha+j\beta)x\},$$

where ($\lambda_0 = $ wavelength in free space)

$$h = 2\pi\left\{\frac{1}{\lambda_c^2} - \frac{f^2}{v^2}\right\}^{\frac{1}{2}} = 2\pi\left\{\frac{1}{\lambda_c^2} - \frac{\epsilon}{\lambda_0^2}\right\}^{\frac{1}{2}} = 2\pi\left\{\frac{1}{\lambda_c^2} - \frac{\epsilon'-j\epsilon''}{\lambda_0^2}\right\}^{\frac{1}{2}}.$$

Hence

$$\left.\begin{aligned} \alpha^2-\beta^2 &= 4\pi^2\left\{\frac{1}{\lambda_c^2} - \frac{\epsilon'}{\lambda_0^2}\right\} \\ \alpha\beta &= 2\pi^2\frac{\epsilon''}{\lambda_0^2} \end{aligned}\right\} \qquad (17.32)$$

Thus two separate measurements of $\alpha$, with different values of $\lambda_c$, suffice to determine $\epsilon'$ and $\epsilon''$. The value of $\alpha$ can be found by moving a detector through the liquid, and the measurement of phase (i.e. $\beta$), which is very difficult when large attenuation is present, is avoided. Essentially the method adopted was to use two piston attenuators (similar to that described in § 16.6) in series, one being filled with water and the other not. The two attenuators are adjusted, one moving in and the other out, so as to keep the power reaching a receiver constant; thus no calibration of the receiver is required. The attenuation in the water is calculated from the known law of the air-filled attenuator.

The results obtained may be fitted accurately to the theory using a value of $\tau = 1{\cdot}01 \times 10^{-11}$ sec, as shown in Fig. 17.5, where both the calculated curves and the experimental points are given. The great intensity of the absorption is illustrated by the fact that at a wavelength of

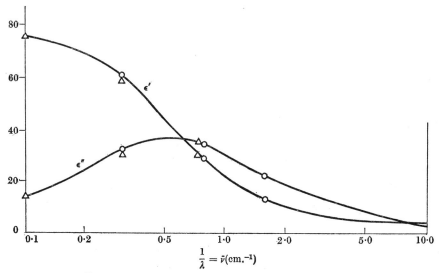

FIG. 17.5. Complex dielectric constant of water at 20° C.
△   Collie, C. H., Hasted, J. B., and Ritson, D. M., 1948, *Proc. Phys. Soc.* **60**, 145.
○   Lane, J. A., and Saxton, J. A., 1952, *Proc. Roy. Soc.* A, **213**, 400.
$$\omega\tau_0 = 1{\cdot}90\bar{\nu}. \qquad \tau_0 = 1{\cdot}01 \times 10^{-11}\text{ sec.}$$

1·24 cm, the power in an incident wave would be diminished by a factor of $e^{-2(2\pi k)} = e^{-36}$ or about $10^{-15.5}$ in passing through a thickness of 1·24 cm. Thus water is quite 'black' at such wavelengths. It should be noted that in fitting these results, the best value of $\epsilon_i$, that part of the dielectric constant due to induced polarization, is found to be 4·9. This is appreciably higher than the square of the optical refractive index ($n = 1{\cdot}33$), showing that there must be other strong absorption bands in liquid water in the infra-red; these are associated with internal vibrations of the $H_2O$ molecule. Rather similar results have been obtained by Lane and Saxton (1952) for methyl and ethyl alcohols.

It has been found that the values of $\epsilon'$ and $\epsilon''$ in the region of dispersion vary quite rapidly with temperature, corresponding to a variation in the relaxation time $\tau$. Saxton (1952) has shown that $\lambda$ varies from about $27 \times 10^{-12}$ sec at $-10°$ C (in supercooled water) to only $4\cdot7 \times 10^{-12}$ sec at $+50°$ C. This variation is very closely parallel to that of the viscosity, and indeed the value of $\tau$ is surprisingly close to that which would be obtained using the simple formula $\tau = 4\pi\eta a^3/kT$.

In the solid state rotation of the permanent dipoles is generally so restricted that they make practically no contribution to the dielectric constant. Thus the dielectric constant of ice at 3-cm wavelength is about 3. At temperatures just below the melting-point, however, ice exhibits some dispersion at low frequencies (of the order of $10^6$ c/s) and the dielectric constant falls from about 80 at zero frequency to the value quoted above at high frequencies. These changes are connected with residual rotation of the dipole moments similar to that in liquid water, but with a very much longer relaxation time, corresponding to very high effective viscosity.

## 17.8. Scattering

When electromagnetic radiation is incident on any substance, the intensity and angular distribution of the emergent radiation are determined by two distinct phenomena which are both present in varying degree. These two phenomena are collision damping and scattering, and both result in a loss of energy from the primary wave, which thus suffers absorption in its passage through the medium. When an electron is set into vibration by the electromagnetic field of the radiation, it gains energy which may be lost if the molecule containing it makes an inelastic collision with another molecule. The energy lost serves to increase the kinetic energy of the molecules, and so appears as heat. Scattering arises from the fact that when an electron is set into vibration, it radiates energy in all directions. The amplitude of the radiation from each electron can be computed using the formula for an oscillating dipole (§ 10.9). In general the loss of energy by scattering is small compared with that lost by collisions.

The angular distribution of the scattered radiation depends on the relative phases of the oscillating electrons, and their distribution in space. The phase of the incident wave is constant over any wave front, and so also is the displacement of the electron relative to the nucleus due to the action of the incident wave. The vibrating atoms therefore form an array of oscillating dipoles, which are all in phase across a wave front of the incident wave. The total amplitude of the radiation from these dipoles in any given direction is found by summing the amplitudes from the individual dipoles, and in forming this sum we must allow for the phase delay in the waves coming from the various dipoles. The new wave front may be found by using Huyghens' principle. It is obvious that it will be parallel to the old wave front so that there is no bending of the wave. We must, however, allow for the phase difference between the 'real' secondary wavelets radiated from the oscillating dipoles and the 'virtual' wavelets from intermediate points (that is, those 'virtual' wavelets used to generate the new wave front *in vacuo*). The result of this is to modify the phase at the wave front, so that the phase velocity is different from that in free space, i.e. the medium has a refractive index different from unity.

In order to compute the scattering at an angle to the incident wave, it is necessary to have some information about the distribution of oscillating dipoles over the wave front. If this distribution is uniform, as in a crystal, then the scattered waves may reinforce strongly in certain directions, forming a diffraction pattern. This is possible only at wavelengths of the same order as the distance between the dipoles; that is, for a crystal, where the spacing is of the order of $10^{-8}$ cm, at X-ray wavelengths. For much longer (optical) wavelengths there is no direction of strong reinforcement except the forward direction, and the scattering (diffraction) is practically zero. Scattering will occur, however, when the crystal contains imperfections where the atoms are not uniformly spaced. In a gas the molecules are randomly spaced, and there will be a random phase difference between the individual scattered waves in all directions except that parallel to the incident wave. The total scattered amplitude in any arbitrary direction will contain a sum of the form

$$\sum_i a \cos(\omega t - \delta_i) = \sum_i a \cos \omega t \cos \delta_i + \sum_i a \sin \omega t \sin \delta_i,$$

where $a$ is the amplitude due to an individual dipole. In taking the sum the terms $\cos \delta_i$ and $\sin \delta_i$ will be nearly as often positive as negative, and the sum will be very much smaller than $aN$, where $N$ is the total number of dipoles. In fact we shall get just the statistical deviation from zero, which is $a\sqrt{N}$. This corresponds to adding the intensities rather than the amplitudes, for the total intensity is

$$\left\{ \sum_i a \cos(\omega t - \delta_i) \right\}^2 = \sum_i a^2 \cos^2 \omega t \cos^2 \delta_i + \sum_i a^2 \sin^2 \omega t \sin^2 \delta_i +$$
$$+ 2 \sum_i a^2 \cos \omega t \sin \omega t \cos \delta_i \sin \delta_i +$$
$$+ \sum_i \sum_{\substack{j \\ i \neq j}} \{ a^2 \cos^2 \omega t \cos \delta_i \cos \delta_j + a^2 \sin^2 \omega t \sin \delta_i \sin \delta_j +$$
$$+ 2a^2 \cos \omega t \sin \omega t \cos \delta_i \sin \delta_j \}.$$

For a very large number of dipoles, the sums over the various phases may be replaced by integrals, since there will be a uniform distribution of the phases over the range 0 to $2\pi$. The only non-zero terms will be the averages over $\cos^2\delta_i$ and $\sin^2\delta_i$ which are each $\frac{1}{2}$. The total intensity is thus

$$\tfrac{1}{2}a^2 N \cos^2\omega t + \tfrac{1}{2}a^2 N \sin^2\omega t = N(\tfrac{1}{2}a^2),$$

where $\frac{1}{2}a^2$ is the mean square value of the scattered intensity from each dipole.

The fraction of the incident intensity lost by scattering may be found as follows. From equation (10.72) the energy scattered by an oscillating dipole of amplitude $p_0$ is (per unit time)

$$W = \frac{Z_0 \omega^4 p_0^2}{12\pi c^2}$$

Now the mean incident power per unit area is $N = \frac{1}{2}E_0^2/Z_0$, where $E_0$ is the amplitude of the electric field and $Z_0$ is the intrinsic impedance of free space. Hence, writing $p_0 = \alpha E_0$, we have

$$W/N = \sigma = \left(\frac{Z_0^2 \omega^4}{6\pi c^2}\right)\alpha^2. \tag{17.33}$$

Since $W$ has the dimensions of power, and $N$ of power/unit area, $\sigma$ is an area, known as the 'scattering cross-section'.

For X-rays, $\omega \gg \omega_p$, $\gamma$, and from equation (17.11) we have then $\alpha = e^2/m\omega^2$. Hence the scattering cross-section is independent of frequency, and has the classical value derived by Thomson

$$\sigma_0 = \frac{Z_0^2 e^4}{6\pi m^2 c^2} = 6\cdot 65 \times 10^{-25} \text{ cm}^2. \tag{17.34}$$

For visible wavelengths and substances such as the molecules of the air we have $\omega \ll \omega_p$, and hence $\alpha = e^2/m\omega_p^2$ if we assume only one resonant frequency per molecule, giving

$$\sigma = \sigma_0(\omega/\omega_p)^4. \tag{17.35}$$

This is the well-known formula, originally derived by Rayleigh in a different way, which shows that the scattering should vary with the inverse fourth power of the wavelength. Hence shorter wavelengths are scattered to a much greater extent than longer wavelengths. The blue colour of the sky is due to scattered sunlight; the transmitted light is complementary in colour, and the rising and setting sun therefore appear red. Macroscopic particles such as raindrops, whose dimensions are large compared with the wavelength, scatter all wavelengths equally, and hence clouds appear white.

If the frequency of the incident radiation coincides with one of the natural frequencies of a molecule, the induced dipole moment is very large and the scattered radiation is abnormally intense. This is known as 'resonant scattering', and may readily be observed, for example, if a bulb containing sodium vapour is illuminated with the sodium $D$-lines.

In all such scattering phenomena, the induced dipoles do not radiate parallel to the direction of oscillation of the electric charge. Hence if the incident radiation is plane polarized, there will be no scattered radiation in the direction of the electric vector. This fact is used to determine the plane of polarization of X-rays and $\gamma$-rays. If the incident radiation is unpolarized, the scattered radiation will be partly polarized, as can be observed by looking at the blue of the sky through polarizing sun glasses.

## REFERENCES

COCHRAN, W., 1960, *Adv. Phys.* **9**, 387.
COLLIE, C. H., HASTED, J. B., and RITSON, D. M., 1948, *Proc. Phys. Soc.* **60**, 145.
COWLEY, R. A., 1962, *Phys. Rev. Letters*, **9**, 159.
DEBYE, P., 1929, *Polar Molecules* (Dover Publications, New York).
TOWNES, C. H., and SCHAWLOW, A. L., 1955, *Microwave Spectroscopy* (McGraw-Hill, New York).
KITTEL, C., 1951, *Phys. Rev.* **82**, 729.
LANE, J. A., and SAXTON, J. A., 1952, *Proc. Roy. Soc.* A, **213**, 400.
ONSAGER, L., 1936, *J. Amer. Chem. Soc.* **58**, 1486.
PAULING, L., and WILSON, E. B., 1935, *Introduction to Quantum Mechanics* (McGraw-Hill, New York).
RAMSEY, N. F., 1956, *Molecular Beams* (O.U.P.).
SAXTON, J. A., 1952, *Proc. Roy. Soc.* A, **213**, 473.
SZIGETI, C., 1949, *Trans. Faraday Soc.* **45**, 155.

## PROBLEMS

17.1. The static dielectric constants of $CO_2$ and $NH_3$ are measured at $0°$ C and $100°$ C at a pressure of 1 atm and the values of $10^3(\epsilon-1)$ are found to be:

|        | $CO_2$ | $NH_3$ |
|--------|--------|--------|
| $0°$ C | 0·988  | 8·34   |
| $100°$ C | 0·723 | 4·87   |

Calculate the permanent electric dipole moment for each gas, and also the radius of the molecule, assuming the polarizability to be the same as that of a conducting sphere.

(*Answer*: $p = 0$ and 1·45 Debyes; radius = 1·4 and 1·8 Å; from viscosity data the radii are 2·3 and 2·2 Å respectively.)

17.2. The dielectric constant of liquid helium at its boiling-point is 1·048, and its density is 0·125 g/cm³. Calculate the refractive index of the gas at N.T.P., and estimate the radius of the helium atom, assuming it to behave like a conducting sphere. Compare the radius with (a) that given by the Bohr theory for an atom with a nuclear charge of two units in its ground state, (b) with that calculated from the diamagnetic susceptibility (see Problem 8.1).

(*Answer*: $n = 1·000034$; radius $= 0·59$ Å; Bohr theory radius $= 0·26$ Å.)

17.3. In the upper regions of the atmosphere (the ionosphere) the gas molecules are ionized, mostly through the effects of ultraviolet radiation from the sun. Show that in a region where the number of free electrons per m³ is $n_0$, the refractive index for waves of frequency $f$ (c/s) is

$$\left(1 - \frac{n_0 e^2}{m\omega^2\epsilon_0}\right)^{\frac{1}{2}} = \left(1 - \frac{\omega_p^2}{\omega^2}\right)^{\frac{1}{2}} \approx \left(1 - \frac{81n_0}{f^2}\right)^{\frac{1}{2}},$$

where $\omega_p/2\pi$ is the plasma frequency.

At this frequency, the refractive index falls to zero, and the ionosphere is totally reflecting even at normal incidence. The frequency at which this occurs is called the critical frequency and at midday is about 4 Mc/s for the E-layer at latitude 40° N. Estimate the maximum value of $n_0$ in the E-layer from this figure.

(*Answer*: $n_0 = 2 \times 10^{11}$/m³. Neglect the Lorentz field.)

17.4. Show that in an ionized region such as that in the previous question the product of the group velocity and the phase velocity is equal to the square of the velocity in free space.

17.5. A particle of charge $-e$ and mass $m$ performs a simple harmonic motion $s = s_0 \cos \omega t$ under the action of a restoring force. Show that through the radiation of energy (given by equation (10.72)) the total energy of the particle falls as $W = W_0 \exp(-\gamma t)$, where

$$\gamma = (Z_0 e^2 \omega^2/6\pi mc^2) = (2\pi Z_0 e^2 f^2/3mc^2).$$

Here $Z_0 = $ intrinsic impedance of free space, and $f = \omega/2\pi$. On the quantum theory, the chance that an atom spends a time $t$ in an excited state has the probability of the order $\exp(-\gamma t)$; hence show that the mean lifetime $\tau = (1/\gamma)$ of a sodium atom in an excited state before emitting one of the sodium D-lines ($\lambda = 5900$ Å) is roughly $1·6 \times 10^{-8}$ sec.

17.6. By the uncertainty principle, the width $\Delta E$ of the upper energy level of the previous question is given by the relation $\tau \Delta E = (h/2\pi)$, where $h$ is Planck's constant. Use the relation $\Delta E = h(\Delta f)$ to show that this gives a line width of $\Delta f = (\gamma/2\pi)$. This is called the natural or radiation breadth of the line, and the same result is obtained on classical theory by a Fourier analysis of the spectrum of an oscillator whose energy is decaying exponentially as $W = W_0 \exp(-\gamma t)$.

Estimate the line widths due to the Doppler effect and to collisions in a gas at 1000° K and $10^{-3}$ atm pressure, and show that (a) at $f = 10^{10}$ c/s ($\lambda = 3·0$ cm) collision broadening is dominant, (b) at $f = 10^{15}$ c/s ($\lambda = 3000$ Å) Doppler effect is dominant, (c) at $f = 10^{18}$ c/s ($\lambda = 3·0$ Å) natural line breadth is dominant.

17.7. For a vibrating molecule, the polarizability $\alpha$ varies as $\alpha = \alpha_0(1 + bx^2)$, where $x = a \cos pt$ is the change in the normal dimensions of the molecule due to the vibration. Show that if incident light of frequency $\omega/2\pi$ falls on the molecule, the scattered radiation will contain light of frequencies $(\omega \pm 2p)/2\pi$. (This is the classical explanation of the Raman effect.)

**17.8.** Show that for a narrow absorption line the maximum and minimum of the refractive index in the region of anomalous dispersion occur at the frequencies where the absorption coefficient has fallen to half its maximum value.

**17.9.** The conductivity of sea-water at 20° C is about 2 (ohm-metre)$^{-1}$. Show that the absorption at 1-cm wavelength due to this conductivity is small compared with the Debye absorption, but the two are roughly equal at a wavelength of about 10 cm. (Use the data given for pure water in Fig. 17.5; in fact the Debye relaxation time is somewhat altered by the salts dissolved.)

**17.10.** Discuss the propagation in and reflection from the surface of the sea of radio waves in the light of the data given in the previous question.

## ELECTRONS IN METALS

### 18.1. Kinetics of free electrons in metals

IN Chapter 4 an outline of Drude's theory of metallic conduction was given, and it was shown that this classical model gives a plausible explanation of the mechanism of conductivity and is also successful in accounting for the ratio of the thermal to the electrical conductivity. The classical theory predicts a large specific heat of $3R/2$ per mole for the conduction electrons, however, which is not observed experimentally; this difficulty was overcome only when it was realized that quantum statistics must be used rather than classical statistics when dealing with electrons in metals. This requires the use of the Fermi–Dirac distribution function equation (4.17) instead of the Maxwell-Boltzmann function constant $\times \exp(-W/kT)$, to which equation (4.17) approximates when

$$(W-W_F)/kT \gg 1.$$

It is also necessary to take account of the wave-like properties of the electrons, and in § 4.2 an elementary account of this was given using the de Broglie relation and the analogy with waves in a box. In a real solid the wave-like nature is important for yet another reason: the wavelength is comparable with the inter-atomic distance, giving rise to diffraction effects. Before considering these, we shall discuss the simpler problem of the wave equation for free electrons.

The wave equation for a free electron of total energy $W$ in an unbounded region where the potential is $V$ is

$$\frac{\hbar^2}{2m}\nabla^2\psi+(W-V)\psi = 0. \tag{18.1}$$

For simplicity we consider first the one-dimensional case, for which the wave equation is

$$\frac{\hbar^2}{2m}\frac{\partial^2\psi}{\partial x^2}+(W-V)\psi = 0, \tag{18.2}$$

and for convenience we further assume $V = 0$ everywhere. Then the solutions of this equation are of the form

$$\psi = A\exp(jk_x x). \tag{18.3}$$

The momentum of the particle $p_x$ is given by

$$p_x = -j\hbar \int_{-\infty}^{+\infty} \psi^* \frac{\partial \psi}{\partial x} dx = -j\hbar(jk_x) \int_{-\infty}^{+\infty} \psi^* \psi \, dx = \hbar k_x \quad (18.4)$$

since the normalization of the wave function requires $\int_{-\infty}^{+\infty} \psi^* \psi \, dx = 1$.

In order to satisfy equation (18.2) we must have $(\hbar^2/2m)k_x^2 = W$, or

$$W = (\hbar^2/2m)k_x^2 = p_x^2/2m \quad (18.5)$$

so that $W$ corresponds to that part of the kinetic energy of the electron associated with its momentum $p_x$ in the $x$-direction.

The three-dimensional equation (18.1) also has a simple solution in Cartesian coordinates, corresponding to the product of three functions of the type (18.3). This solution is

$$\psi = A \exp(jk_x x)\exp(jk_y y)\exp(jk_z z)$$
$$= A \exp j(k_x x + k_y y + k_z z) = A \exp j(\mathbf{k}.\mathbf{r}) \quad (18.6)$$

since $(x, y, z)$ are the components of the vector $\mathbf{r}$, and we can similarly regard $(k_x, k_y, k_z)$ as the components of a vector $\mathbf{k}$, known as the wave vector. In order to satisfy equation (18.1) we have

$$W = (\hbar^2/2m)(k_x^2 + k_y^2 + k_z^2) = (p_x^2 + p_y^2 + p_z^2)/2m = \mathbf{p}^2/2m, \quad (18.7)$$

where $\mathbf{p}$ is the momentum vector, with components $(p_x, p_y, p_z)$. These components of $\mathbf{p}$ are just $\hbar$ times those of $\mathbf{k}$; that is, we have the de Broglie relation     $$\mathbf{k} = \mathbf{p}/\hbar \quad (18.8)$$

which was used in § 4.2. The wavelength associated with the electron is $2\pi/k = h/p$.

In applying the free electron model to a metal, we assume that the electrons move in a region of constant potential, with a sharp rise in the potential at the boundaries of the metal. Since the electrons do not have enough energy to surmount this barrier, they are confined within the metal (we neglect phenomena such as thermionic emission, which are insignificant, affecting only a minute proportion of the electrons). Our model thus assumes a rectangular potential well, such as is shown in Fig. 18.1 (a) for one dimension. Taking the floor of the well to be at $V = 0$, the solutions of the wave equation are of the form (18.6) inside the well. Outside the well, where the potential $V_0 \gg W$, so that $(W - V_0)$ is negative, the solutions are real exponentials, showing that the chance of finding an electron outside, which is proportional to

$$\psi^* \psi = \exp\left[\left\{\frac{8m(V_0 - W)}{\hbar^2}\right\}^{\frac{1}{2}} x\right],$$

falls off very rapidly with distance. A proper solution of the problem requires that the wave functions and their derivatives be continuous at the boundary, but if we make the approximation of taking $V_0$ to be infinite this reduces to making $\psi$ vanish at the boundary. Then the problem is similar to that of electromagnetic waves in a perfectly conducting box; if the latter is rectangular with dimensions $(a, b, c)$, the

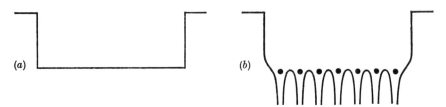

FIG. 18.1. (a) Rectangular potential well assumed in free electron model of a metal. (b) Actual potential variation, showing sharp fall near each positively-charged ion.

allowed solutions (cf. Problem 11.12) are a set of standing waves where $\psi$ is a product of terms such as

$$\frac{\sin}{\cos}(\pi l x/a)\frac{\sin}{\cos}(\pi m y/b)\frac{\sin}{\cos}(\pi n z/c)$$

and the wavelength is given by equation (11.42)

$$\left(\frac{1}{\lambda}\right)^2 = \left(\frac{l}{2a}\right)^2 + \left(\frac{m}{2b}\right)^2 + \left(\frac{n}{2c}\right)^2.$$

For electrons at the top of the Fermi distribution the wavelengths involved are of order $10^{-7}$ cm or less, which are very small compared with the dimensions of a metal of ordinary size. The spacing of the allowed wavelengths is therefore very close, and the number in a given wavelength range can be computed using the approximations adopted in the theory of heat radiation, as in § 4.2.

## 18.2. The energy band approximation

At this stage we are still making the arbitrary assumption that in a metal some of the electrons are detached from their parent atoms and are merely bound to the metal as a whole by a potential well inside which they move quite freely. However, many solids are very good electrical insulators in which we must assume there are no such free electrons. There is also the intermediate class of solids, the semiconductors, which are much poorer conductors than metals and which generally possess a negative rather than a positive coefficient of resistivity. To understand why these different types of solids exist we must consider the interaction between the electrons and nuclei when they are closely packed in a solid, where the interatomic distance is of the same order as the atomic radius. The potential energy of an electron then varies rather as shown in Fig. 18.1 (b), falling steeply when the electron approaches a positively-charged nucleus. Obviously the motion of the electrons in such a potential is a very complicated problem and cannot be solved exactly. Approximate methods must be used, whose nature is illustrated by approaching the problem from two different standpoints.

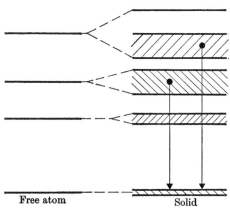

Fig. 18.2. Sharp energy levels in a free atom and the corresponding bands in a solid (the top band is shown only partly full). The arrows indicate allowed transitions giving X-ray emission bands when an electron has been ionized out of the lowest energy band.

In an isolated atom the electrons are tightly bound and have discrete, sharp energy levels. When two identical atoms are brought together, the energy levels of each atom, which are initially the same, are split into two, one higher and one lower than the corresponding levels of the separated atoms. The splitting only becomes appreciable when the wave functions of the electrons on different atoms begin to overlap considerably; at a given distance it is therefore greatest for the outermost electrons and least for the inner electrons. If more atoms are brought together, more levels are formed, and for a solid of $N$ atoms (where $N$ is a very large number) the levels are so close together that they form an almost continuous band. The width of this band depends on the degree of overlap of electrons on adjacent atoms, and is again largest for the outermost atomic electrons. Fig. 18.2 is a rough diagram showing how the atomic levels develop into bands as the atoms are brought closer together.

The problem may be approached from the opposite viewpoint by considering how the motion of the electrons, previously assumed to be moving freely in the flat-bottomed potential well of Fig. 18.1 (a), is modified when we allow for the drop of the potential near each atomic nucleus shown in Fig. 18.1 (b). In a crystal the atoms form a regular array, and the potential has therefore a periodic variation in three dimensions.

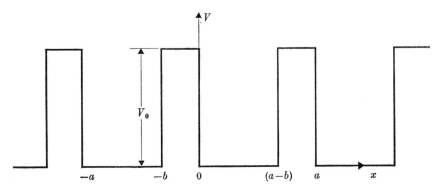

Fig. 18.3. Periodic rectangular potential well assumed in the one-dimensional model of Kronig and Penney (1931).

The effect of this periodicity in the potential can be understood by considering a simple one-dimensional case. The electric fields of other electrons will be neglected, and the potential assumed to have the form of a rectangular wave as in Fig. 18.3, where

$$V = 0 \quad \text{when } 0 < x < (a-b); \qquad V = V_0 \quad \text{when } -b < x < 0.$$

It may be shown that the solutions of the wave equation (18.2) in this case are of the form

$$\psi = u(x)\exp(jk_x x),$$

where $u(x)$ is a periodic function of $x$ such that $u(x+a) = u(x)$, i.e. $u$ repeats itself with the same periodicity as the potential. We take two different functions

$$u_1 = [A \exp(jqx) + B \exp(-jqx)]\exp(-jk_x x) \quad \text{where } V = 0$$

and $\quad u_2 = [C \exp(rx) + D \exp(-rx)]\exp(-jk_x x) \quad \text{where } V = V_0.$

Here $q$ and $r$ must satisfy the relations

$$q = (2mW/\hbar^2)^{\frac{1}{2}} \quad \text{and} \quad r = \{2m(V_0 - W)/\hbar^2\}^{\frac{1}{2}},$$

and in addition the solutions for the two regions must join smoothly at the boundaries so that we must have $u_1 = u_2$ and $(\partial u_1/\partial x) = (\partial u_2/\partial x)$ both at $x = 0$ and $x = (a-b)$. This gives four equations from which the constants $A, B, C, D$ can be eliminated, yielding a complicated relation between $k$ and $W$. Considerable simplification is obtained by allowing $b \to 0$ and $V_0 \to \infty$ in such a way that the product $(bV_0)$ remains finite. Then, if $c$ is the limiting value of $(2mV_0 ab/\hbar^2)$, one obtains

$$\cos k_x a = c \frac{\sin qa}{qa} + \cos qa. \tag{18.9}$$

The r.h.s. of this equation is plotted as a function of $(qa)$ in Fig. 18.4 for a value of $c = 2\pi$: allowed values of $k_x$ are obtained only when the function lies between 1 and $-1$, and hence only certain ranges of values of $q$

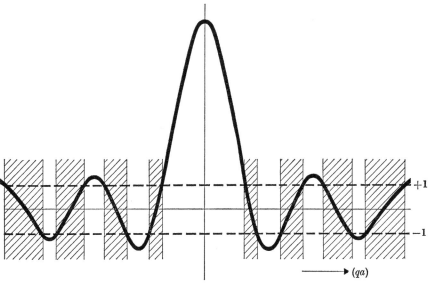

FIG. 18.4. Plot of the function given by equation (18.9) when $c = 2\pi$ as a function of $(qa)$. The ranges which give real values of $k$ are shaded.

are allowed. Since $q = (2mW/\hbar^2)^{\frac{1}{2}}$, this means that the energy $W$ is restricted to lie within certain ranges, which form the allowed energy bands. The allowed bands are narrowest for small values of $q$ (low values of the energy $W$), and become broader as $W$ increases, the unallowed bands getting narrower, just as in Fig. 18.2.

This treatment of a simple model, due to Kronig and Penney (1931), illustrates how allowed and forbidden energy bands arise in a solid. Their occurrence is associated with the periodic structure of the crystal lattice, and two analogies may help in understanding this point: (a) X-rays whose wavelength satisfies the condition for interference between successive Bragg planes in a crystal are strongly diffracted, while others are transmitted. The electron wavelengths in a solid are of the same order as X-ray wavelengths, and the strong diffraction corresponds to the forbidden wavelengths (values of $k_x$ which are not allowed); (b) a continuous transmission line transmits all wavelengths freely, whereas the periodic structure of a filter restricts free transmission to certain bands of wavelength. In fact the Kronig–Penney model corresponds to a continuous transmission line in which identical lumped impedances have been inserted at regular intervals, a distance $a$ apart. Wavelengths which are long compared with $a$ are freely transmitted, but as the wavelength $\lambda$ is reduced dispersion sets in as in a filter, and when $a = \lambda/2$ the reflections from each lumped impedance are in phase and we enter a stop band.

*Particle aspects*

The foregoing treatment of electrons in a solid considers them as waves occupying the whole volume of the solid; these waves are the stationary states, solutions of the time-independent wave equation. We need to know how the electrons behave under the influence of a force (electric or magnetic); this is essentially a particle description, which must be related to the wave aspect of the electron. As shown in books on elementary quantum mechanics, a free electron must be considered as a wave packet, where the group velocity corresponds to the particle velocity. The $x$-component of the group velocity is given by the relation

$$v_x = \frac{\partial}{\partial k_x}\left(\frac{W}{\hbar}\right) = \frac{1}{\hbar}\frac{\partial W}{\partial k_x} \tag{18.10}$$

which is analogous to the formula $d\omega/d\beta$ used for the group velocity in § 11.6; the energy $W$ corresponds to $\hbar\omega$ and $k_x$ to the phase constant $\beta$. A rigorous analysis shows that equation (18.10) is valid for an electron moving in the periodic potential of a crystal lattice, and also that $dp_x/dt = F_x$, where $p_x = \hbar k_x$ and $F_x$ is the component of an external force. Differentiation of equation (18.10) then gives

$$\frac{dv_x}{dt} = \frac{d}{dt}\left(\frac{1}{\hbar}\frac{\partial W}{\partial k_x}\right) = \frac{1}{\hbar}\frac{\partial^2 W}{\partial k_x^2}\frac{dk_x}{dt} = \frac{1}{\hbar^2}\frac{\partial^2 W}{\partial k_x^2}\frac{dp_x}{dt} = \frac{1}{m^*}F_x, \tag{18.11}$$

where

$$\frac{1}{m^*} = \frac{1}{\hbar^2}\frac{\partial^2 W}{\partial k_x^2}. \tag{18.12}$$

This last equation defines the quantity $m^*$, which in equation (18.11) clearly has the dimensions of mass, and is known as the 'effective mass'. It follows also from (18.11) that $p_x = m^*v_x$.

The value of $W$ for a free particle is given by equation (18.5), and it can easily be verified that equations (18.10)–(18.12) satisfy (18.5) with

$m^* = m$, so that the effective mass is equal to the true mass for a free particle. For an electron in a periodic potential the effective mass may depart markedly from the true mass. The advantage of the concept of effective mass is that the dynamic behaviour of an electron in a periodic potential can be treated as if it were a particle of mass $m^*$. The difference between $m^*$ and the true mass $m$ represents the effect on the motion of the electron which results from the electric potential of the ions forming the crystal lattice; when a force is applied to the electron, its change in momentum is different from that of a free electron, and $\mathbf{p} = \hbar \mathbf{k}$ is often referred to as the 'crystal momentum'. The fact that $p_x = m^* v_x$ and not $m v_x$ does not represent a breakdown of Newton's laws of motion, since the residual momentum is taken up by the lattice. Experiments to determine the ratio of current to momentum, similar to those of Kettering and Scott described in § 3.1, have been carried out by Scott (1951) and Brown and Barnett (1951). They find that even in the case of substances where the current is carried by 'positive holes' (see below), the ratio of current to net momentum has the same sign and is numerically the same as for free electrons.

The relation between the energy $W$ and $k_x$, as derived from the Kronig–Penney model or otherwise, has the form shown in Fig. 18.5. It does not differ greatly from that for a free electron except near the edges of the allowed band. At the points where $\cos k_x a = \pm 1$, of which the first is at $k_x = \pm \pi/a$, there is a discontinuity in the relation between $W$ and $k_x$; differentiation of equation (18.9) shows that $dq/dk_x$ is proportional to $\sin k_x a$, and hence is zero at such points. Since $W \propto q^2$, it follows that $\partial W/\partial k_x$ is then also zero, and from equation (18.10) this means that the electron velocity is zero at the edge of an allowed zone. This is the point at which the wavelength is such that the electron waves are strongly diffracted (in one dimension this means reflected) and form a set of standing waves, no travelling waves being allowed.

It can be seen that the shape of the curve of $W$ against $k_x$ in Fig. 18.5 means that the effective mass $m^*$ becomes negative near the top of an allowed band, because $\partial^2 W/\partial k_x^2$ becomes negative. Application of a force $+F_x$ will increase $k_x$, but as $k_x$ approaches $+\pi/a$ the slope $\partial W/\partial k_x$ diminishes, so that by equation (18.10) the velocity $v_x$ decreases, as we should expect if the mass were negative. Just below $W_0$, the top of the band, we have approximately, since $\partial W/\partial k_x = 0$ at $k_x = \pi/a$, and $m^*$ is negative,

$$W = W_0 - dk_x \frac{\partial W}{\partial k_x} + \tfrac{1}{2}(dk_x)^2 \frac{\partial^2 W}{\partial k_x^2} = W_0 + \hbar^2 \frac{(dk_x)^2}{2m^*} = W_0 + \frac{(dp_x)^2}{2m^*}.$$

An important property of a full band (an allowed band where all the states are occupied) is that it can carry no electric current, since for every electron with a positive value of $k_x$ there is another with the value $-k_x$. Suppose we have a band which is full except for one state at the top. Since $\hbar\,(d\mathbf{k}/dt) = \mathbf{F}$, under the influence of an electric field the whole state distribution moves, giving a current $\mathbf{I}$. But this must be just the

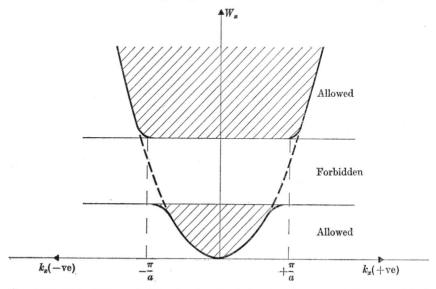

FIG. 18.5. Plot of $W_x$ against $k_x$ showing band structure due to periodic potential of lattice. - - - $W_x$ against $k_x$ in the absence of the periodic structure.

negative of the current corresponding to the one empty state, so that $\mathbf{I} = -(-e\mathbf{v}) = e\mathbf{v}$, as for a positively charged particle. Again, for the empty state, $\hbar\,(dk_x/dt) = F_x = -eE_x$, so that the net effect of $E_x$ is $dI_x/dt = e\,(dv_x/dt) = (e/m^*)F_x = e^2E_x/(-m^*)$, where we have used (18.11). Since $m^*$ for the empty state is negative, we have

$$dI_x/dt = e^2E_x/|m^*|,$$

and the net effect of all the filled states is equivalent to that of a particle whose dynamic properties correspond to its having positive charge and positive mass. Such a particle is called a 'positive hole'; it is analogous to the hole in the filled bands of electrons in Dirac's theory of the positron. The advantage of the concept of positive holes is that the momentum and current in a nearly filled band can be attributed to the presence of entities which behave like ordinary particles with positive charge and positive effective mass $|m^*|$; the energy near the top of a band can then be written as

$$W = W_0 - (dp_x)^2/2\,|m^*|.$$

*Three dimensions*

Treatment of a three-dimensional lattice corresponding to a real solid, even with simplified models of the potential variation, is very complex and will not be discussed here. The wave function of an electron associated with a wave vector $\mathbf{k}$ is of the form

$$\psi = u(\mathbf{r})\exp j(\mathbf{k}.\mathbf{r}), \tag{18.13}$$

where
$$u(\mathbf{r}+\mathbf{a}_n) = u(\mathbf{r}).$$

Here $\mathbf{a}_n$ is a translation vector representing the repetitive property of the lattice; in particular, that the potential energy is periodic, obeying the rule that $V$ at the point $(\mathbf{r}+\mathbf{a}_n)$ is the same as at $\mathbf{r}$. From the analogy with X-rays it is clear that the values of $\mathbf{k}$ at which strong diffraction occurs will depend on the direction of $\mathbf{k}$; that is, the value of $\mathbf{k}$ at which there is a discontinuity in the energy (the boundary of a zone) is a function of direction. If we draw a vector $\mathbf{k}$ in 'k-space' whose length corresponds to this value, and repeat this process for all possible directions, the ends of the vectors will map out a three-dimensional figure, known as a 'Brillouin zone'. Its construction involves only geometry, and its symmetry is related to the symmetry of the crystal lattice.

Values of $\mathbf{k}$ whose vectors end on points inside the zone correspond to allowed energies; those which terminate at the zone boundary correspond to discontinuities in the energy. Higher zones corresponding to higher allowed energy bands exist, but it is possible to bring all wave vectors into the first zone (in the one-dimensional case this procedure corresponds to taking values of $k_x a$ in equation (18.9) only between $-\pi$ and $+\pi$). Values of $\mathbf{k}$ in the first zone then correspond to more than one allowed energy, but in general we are concerned only with the one band which is partly filled with electrons. At the absolute zero of temperature electrons fill this up to a certain energy, the Fermi energy, and it is therefore of interest to draw plots of constant $W$, or 'energy surfaces' in k-space. Calculation of the energy surfaces is very complex: the results obtained by one method are shown in Fig. 18.6 for a simple cubic lattice. Energy surfaces well within the zone are spherical in shape, but this is by no means true near the zone boundary; in general at the boundary $\partial W/\partial \mathbf{k} = 0$ and the energy surfaces must end normal to the boundary. The boundary in k-space between the filled and empty states at $0°$ K follows the energy surface corresponding to the Fermi energy, and is known as the 'Fermi surface'. Only electrons near the Fermi surface (see § 18.3) can take part in conduction processes, and many details of their behaviour are determined by the exact shape of the Fermi surface. An important property is the effective mass, which in general is a function of direction. Near the top or bottom of a band the energy may be expanded in a power series in **k**, the lowest terms being quadratic; they can be reduced by a suitable choice of axes to the form

$$W = W_0 \pm \tfrac{1}{2}\hbar^2 \left\{ \frac{k_x^2}{m_x^*} + \frac{k_y^2}{m_y^*} + \frac{k_z^2}{m_z^*} \right\}. \qquad (18.14)$$

Here the upper sign must be taken for electrons near the bottom of a band, and $W_0$ is then the energy at the bottom; while the lower sign

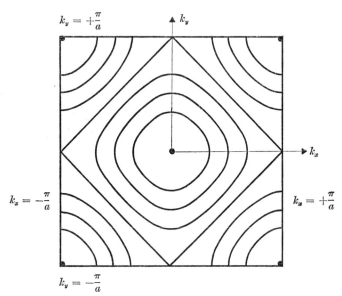

$$k_y = +\frac{\pi}{a}$$

$$k_x = -\frac{\pi}{a}$$

$$k_x = +\frac{\pi}{a}$$

$$k_y = -\frac{\pi}{a}$$

FIG. 18.6. Section through the constant energy surfaces for a simple cubic lattice obtained by one method of calculation (the 'tight-binding' approximation). The energy surfaces end normally to the zone boundary except where two end at the same point.

should be used for holes near the top of a band, and $W_0$ is then the energy at the top. Thus for holes the energy appears to be measured downwards from the top of the band, a point which we shall return to in considering semiconductors (Chapter 19).

*Correlation energy*

An important effect which has been neglected in our treatment is the electrostatic repulsion of the conduction electrons. This tends to keep the electrons apart, and the chance of finding two electrons close together is less than it would be on our assumption that their motion is completely independent of each other; in other words, there is a *correlation* between their motions. There is a further effect due to the fact that the overall wave function for the assembly of electrons must be antisymmetric, which is similar in nature to the 'exchange interaction' discussed in Chapter 21. These two effects contribute to the 'correlation energy' and are important in calculating the cohesive energy of a metal. The electrostatic repulsion is a long-range interaction which gives rise to 'plasma oscillations' (see § 4.9), for which the characteristic frequency in a metal is of order $10^{15}$ c/s. At low frequencies the dynamical properties of the electrons are not greatly altered, a fortunate circumstance which makes a simple treatment neglecting the correlation energy more accurate than might have been expected.

## 18.3. Conductors and insulators on the band theory

In older theories the fact that some solids are electrical conductors while others are insulators was explained by assuming that in the insulators all the electrons belonging to each atom were firmly bound to that atom, while in conductors some of the outer electrons were detached from their parent atoms and able to move freely throughout the whole volume of the solid. On the band theory there is no such distinction between 'bound' and 'free' electrons; the electronic wave functions spread out through the whole volume of the solid, though the states of lower energy (corresponding to the inner electrons of a single atom) have the electronic density ($\psi\psi^*$ of the wave function) greatest near each nucleus. How then does the band theory explain the occurrence of both conductors and insulators?

At the absolute zero of temperature the electrons in a solid will have the lowest possible energy consistent with the Pauli exclusion principle, and they will fill the energy bands from the bottom upwards. The lowest energy bands will be fully occupied, but the highest occupied level may occur in the middle of an allowed band. The state of lowest energy is one in which as many electrons have positive values of $\mathbf{k}$ as have negative values, so that the net current is zero. To establish a current flow some electrons must be transferred from negative values of $\mathbf{k}$ to positive values, but because of the exclusion principle this is possible only if they make transitions to unoccupied states of higher energy, the energy being gained by acceleration through the application of an electric field. In weak fields this can occur only if adjacent levels are unoccupied; i.e. if the top of the Fermi distribution comes in the middle of a band. If, on the other hand, the highest occupied band is completely full, an electron must gain sufficient energy from a movement in the applied electric field to raise it into the next higher band. This requires enormous electric fields, and for ordinary field strengths the substance is an insulator.

On this picture it is readily seen that the alkali metals such as lithium, sodium, potassium, etc., will be good conductors, for their atoms possess only one valence electron in an $s$-state, whereas the energy band in the solid corresponding to this atomic state requires two electrons per atom to fill it. The alkaline earth elements, magnesium, calcium, etc., have two such electrons, which we would expect to fill the band, making these substances insulators. They are in fact quite good conductors, and the

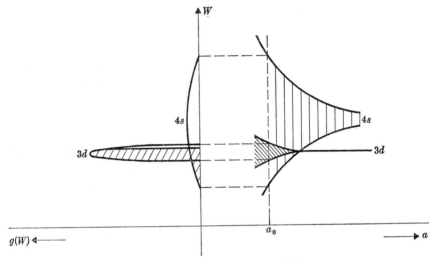

FIG. 18.7.  Energy bands for nickel.

To the right is shown the bandwidth of $4s$ and $3d$ states as a function of interatomic distance $a$ ($a_0$ is the value for solid nickel). To the left is shown $g(W)$, the shaded area indicating the filled parts of the bands.

reason for this is that the energy bands corresponding to the $s$- and $p$-states in the atom are so broad in the solid that they overlap appreciably. The state of lowest energy is then one where the electrons partially fill both the $s$- and $p$-bands, and conduction is possible. In transition elements the situation is more complex because of the energy bands corresponding to $d$-electron states. In copper the $3d$ band is completely filled and there is one electron per atom in the $4s$ band, making it a good conductor. In iron, cobalt, and nickel the $3d$ band is not completely filled; it is a rather narrow band, since $d$-electron wave functions do not spread as far out as $s$-electron wave functions, and interactions between $d$-electrons on adjacent atoms are smaller than interactions between $s$-electrons. The narrow $3d$ band is overlapped by a broad $4s$ band,

and the $3d$ band (which can contain 10 electrons per atom) gives an abnormally high value of $g(W)$ as shown in Fig. 18.7.

Information about the widths of energy bands in the solid state can be obtained directly from soft X-ray emission spectra (see, for example, Skinner, 1938). If an electron is excited out of an inner shell, then electrons in outer shells make transitions to the inner shell, emitting X-rays. For a free atom X-rays of discrete wavelengths are obtained, since we have sharp energy levels. In a solid a band of wavelengths is obtained whose width is the sum of the widths of the bands which the electron leaves and enters; if the latter band corresponds to an inner electron shell, its width is small and the observed width is practically entirely that of the initial band (compare Fig. 18.2). Since the electrons come only from the filled part of the band, the observed width is that only of the filled part, not the whole width.

## 18.4. Specific heat of the conduction electrons

The specific heat of free electrons can be found from the energy distribution function equation (4.18) derived from Fermi–Dirac statistics. The energy is given by

$$U = \int_0^\infty W g(W) \, dW$$

and the specific heat $C = dU/dT$. Since the integration must be carried out by approximate methods, we quote the result for the internal energy at a temperature $T$, which is (for $n$ electrons)

$$U = U_0 + \frac{\pi^2}{6}(kT)^2 \{g(W)\}_F. \tag{18.15}$$

Here the difference between $U$ and $U_0$ is the first term of a power series in ascending powers of $T$, but further terms are negligible at ordinary temperatures. The specific heat of the electrons (per unit volume) is

$$C_V = dU/dT = \frac{\pi^2}{3} k^2 T \{g(W)\}_F, \tag{18.16}$$

where $\{g(W)\}_F$ is the density of states at $W = W_F$; on substituting from equation (4.13) we obtain

$$C_V = n\frac{\pi^2 k^2 T}{2W_F}. \tag{18.16a}$$

Comparison with the classical value, $C_V = \frac{3}{2}nk$, shows that the quantum statistical value is smaller by a factor of the order $(kT/W_F)$. The reason for this is that only a small fraction $\approx (kT/W_F)$ of the electrons at the top of the energy distribution curve are able to increase their kinetic energy, as illustrated by the distribution curve of Fig. 4.3. The increase in energy of these electrons is $\approx kT$, and so the total internal energy increases by an amount $\approx n(kT)^2/W_F$. Electrons in the middle of the band cannot be raised to higher energies unless they can reach energy levels above $W_F$, since all the available energy levels in the middle of the band are already occupied by electrons.

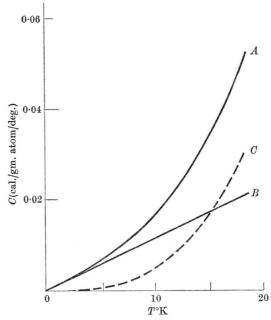

FIG. 18.8. Specific heat of cobalt at low temperatures (after Duyckaerts, 1939).

A    experimental curve.
B    electronic contribution; $C_v = 12 \cdot 0 \times 10^{-4} T$.
C    lattice contribution; $C_v = 465(T/443)^3$, where 443 is the Debye $\theta$ for cobalt.

The units are cal/g atom/deg.

Since $kT \ll W_F$ at ordinary temperatures, the electronic specific heat will be only a small fraction of that predicted by classical theory, and the difficulty of the large excess specific heat predicted by that theory for metals is removed. An experimental test of equation (18.16) is possible only at low temperatures, where the specific heat associated with the lattice vibrations of a solid falls very rapidly. According to the theory of Debye, the specific heat from this cause is proportional to $T^3$ at sufficiently low temperatures, and eventually this will become small compared with the electronic specific heat, which falls only with $T$. The specific heats of a number of metals have been measured, and below about 20° K they are found to follow a law of the form

$$C_V = aT^3 + bT. \qquad (18.17)$$

Figure 18.8 shows the relative magnitudes of the two contributions to the specific heat of cobalt at temperatures below 20° K. This metal is ferromagnetic, and like a number of other transition group metals,

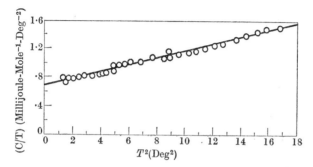

FIG. 18.9. Plot of $C/T$ against $T^2$ for copper (Corak, Garfunkel, Satterthwaite, and Wexler, 1955). The intercept at $T^2 = 0$ gives the coefficient $b$ of the electronic specific heat.

shows an abnormally high electronic specific heat. In many metals the electronic specific heat is predominant only below about 5° K, and rather precise measurements are required to determine it accurately. Rearrangement of equation (18.17) shows it may be written in the form

$$C_V/T = aT^2 + b \qquad (18.17\,a)$$

and by plotting the quantity $C_V/T$ against $T^2$ a straight-line graph should be obtained whose intercept gives the value of $b$. Figure 18.9 shows a typical graph for copper.

The measured values of the electronic specific heats of a number of representative metals are shown in Table 18.1. To compare them with values calculated from equation (18.16) we need to know the value of $n$, the number of conduction electrons per unit volume, and of $W_F$, which by equation (4.11) is again dependent on $n$. It is simplest to discuss $n$ in terms of the number of conduction electrons per atom. For metals such as copper and silver, we may reasonably expect one conduction electron per atom, and for beryllium and magnesium two. With the transition metals nickel, palladium, and platinum, which belong to the 3d, 4d, and 5d transition groups respectively, the energy bands are nearly filled, and the number of free 'particles' is determined by the number of 'holes' in the band; from magnetic evidence these amount to about 0·6 holes per atom. Using these values of the number of carriers per atom, we can compute the electronic specific heat from equation (18.16), and in each case some deviation is found. The last column of Table 18.1 gives the ratio of the observed to the calculated electronic specific heat for free electrons.

TABLE 18.1

*Electronic specific heats of some metals*

| Metal | $C_V/T$ (*in units of* $10^{-4}$ *cal/deg*$^2$*/g atom*) | *Number of conduction electrons per atom* | *Ratio of observed value of electronic spec. ht. to that given by equation* (18.16 a) |
|---|---|---|---|
| Cu | 1·80 | 1 | 1·5 |
| Ag | 1·54 | 1 | 0·95 |
| Be | 0·54 | 2 | 0·46 |
| Mg | 3·25 | 2 | 1·33 |
| Ni | 17·4 | 0·6† | 28 |
| Pd | 31 | 0·55† | 27 |
| Pt | 16 | 0·6† | 13 |

The observed values are given in column 2; column 4 gives the ratio of these values to those calculated from equations (18.16 a) and (4.11) assuming the number of conduction electrons (or holes) per atom given in column 3. This ratio is interpreted as the ratio of the effective mass $m^*$ to the free electron mass $m$.

† No. of holes per atom, based on magnetic evidence.

The reason for these discrepancies is that we are using formulae derived for free electrons, whereas we know that in a solid their motion is modified by the periodic potential. It was pointed out in § 18.2 that this modification can be allowed for by using the effective mass $m^*$ instead of the true $m$ in many of the formulae derived for free electrons. Thus equation (4.11) for the Fermi energy becomes

$$W_F = \frac{\hbar^2}{2m^*}(3\pi^2 n)^{\frac{2}{3}},\tag{18.18}$$

while the density of states $g(W)$ becomes

$$g(W) = \frac{1}{2\pi^2}\left(\frac{2m^*}{\hbar^2}\right)^{\frac{3}{2}} W^{\frac{1}{2}}\tag{18.19}$$

$$= 3n W^{\frac{1}{2}}/2W_F^{\frac{3}{2}},\tag{18.20}$$

the last relation being in form the same as for free electrons. These relations show that $\{g(W)\}_F^{\frac{1}{2}}$ is proportional to $m^*$, and inversely proportional to $W_F$. Thus for copper (see Table 18.1) the observed specific heat is about 1·5 times larger than the value calculated on the basis of free electrons, from which we conclude that $m^*/m = 1\cdot5$ in this case, and that the Fermi energy $W_F$ should be about $4\cdot7$ eV instead of the value $7\cdot0$ eV given in Table 4.1.

This effect on the specific heat can be seen in another way which does not involve the concept of effective mass. The Pauli exclusion principle restricts the number of points in momentum space to two (including the electron spin) per elementary volume $(h^3/V)$, and so fixes the number of states in a given range of wave vector $k$ to $k+dk$. The effect of band structure is to alter the relation between $W$ and $k$, so that the value of $g(W)$ is changed. From equation (18.16) the specific heat is proportional to $g(W)$, since doubling the value of the density of states means that twice as many electrons can increase their energy for a given temperature increase. Narrow bands have exceptionally large values of $g(W)$, as shown in Fig. 18.7, thus giving rise to abnormally large values of the electronic specific heat in transition elements.

## 18.5. Electrical and thermal conductivity of metals

On the classical theory of free electrons, the electrical conductivity of a metal is given by equation (4.3). For electrons in a periodic potential this formula holds provided we replace the true electron mass $m$ by the effective mass $m^*$, so that we have

$$\sigma = n(e^2/m^*)\tau = ne^2l/m^*v, \qquad (18.21)$$

where $n$ is the number of electrons per unit volume and $\tau$ is the relaxation time defined in § 4.1. $l$ is the mean path length between collisions, here taken as $v\tau$, where $v$ is the mean electron velocity. Since only electrons at the Fermi surface can be accelerated and gain energy, the value of the velocity required is that corresponding to $W_F$; this velocity is about $10^8$ cm/sec for most metals, and since $\tau \approx 10^{-14}$ sec at room temperature, the mean free path is of the order of $10^{-6}$ cm, or about 100 times the atomic spacing in a solid.

Classical physics gives us no method of calculating the mean path length, nor does it suggest in what manner it might vary with temperature. Since the number and the energy of the electrons at the top of the Fermi band varies insignificantly with temperature, equation (18.21) shows that any change in the resistance must be associated with a change in the mean path length. Most metals show a resistance which is roughly proportional to the absolute temperature at room temperature and above, but at low temperatures the resistance falls markedly below the value given by this law. Any theoretical approach to this problem must be made through the wave theory, and is extremely complicated. Here we shall attempt to give only an outline of the results.

It was first pointed out by Houston that the mean path length of an electron in a perfectly regular lattice of atoms should be infinite. If an electron is in an allowed energy state, then that is a stationary state, and in the absence of perturbations, the electron will continue in that state of fixed energy, and hence fixed velocity, indefinitely. Real metals do not have perfect lattices for two reasons: (1) the lattice contains foreign atoms (impurities) or atoms displaced from their normal position (point defects and dislocations), and (2) the atoms deviate from their mean positions because of the thermal vibrations. Each of these imperfections causes scattering of the electron waves in the same way that a defective insulating crystal scatters a light wave, whereas a perfect crystal does not. An alloy is an example of a disordered lattice, and we would therefore expect its resistance to be higher than that of a pure metal. The scattering in such a case (or from any of the causes listed in (1) above) should be independent of temperature, giving rise to the constant resistance which is characteristic of alloys.

The thermal vibrations of the atoms can be analysed into normal modes of vibration of the crystal as a whole. In the long wavelength limit these are identical with the standing waves composed of elastic waves (longitudinal and transverse) propagated through a continuous solid, but at shorter wavelengths comparable with the inter-atomic spacing they must be treated by methods (similar to those used for electron waves) which allow for the periodic structure of the lattice. Each mode has wave-vector $\mathbf{q}$ and angular frequency $\omega$. The energy is quantized, and at temperatures where $\hbar\omega \approx kT$ quantum effects must be included in computing the mean energy of each mode; this treatment gives the well-known Debye theory of the lattice specific heat. Just as the electrons have both a wave and a particle aspect, so do the lattice modes; they are known as 'phonons', a name which emphasizes their resemblance to the photons of the electromagnetic field and to sound waves in a solid. The free paths of the phonons are limited by 'collisions' with other phonons, and scattering by point defects, dislocations and ultimately by the boundaries of crystallites. In metals there is a further scattering mechanism due to collisions between the phonons and the conduction electrons. Such collisions also limit the free paths of the conduction electrons, and are the main cause of the electrical resistance at ordinary temperatures. At low temperatures, where the lattice vibrations die out, we would expect the scattering to fall and the conductivity to increase rapidly as the temperature approaches the absolute zero. This is found to be the case, but the conductivity reaches an upper limit which depends on the previous history of the specimen. This is due to the lattice defects, which can be reduced by careful annealing. Then, in general, the purer the specimen the higher the limiting conductivity, showing that the impurities are responsible for the residual scattering. A semi-empirical formula, due to Gruneisen, which represents the resistance variation of many pure metals well, is

$$\frac{\rho}{T} = A\left(\frac{T}{\theta}\right)^4 \int_0^{\theta/T} \frac{x^5 \, dx}{(e^x - 1)(1 - e^{-x})}, \tag{18.22}$$

where the constants $A$ and $\theta$ are chosen to obtain the best fit with experiment. This formula gives a variation of $(\rho/T)$ with temperature which is not unlike the variation of the lattice specific heat of a solid as given by Debye's theory, and the value of $\theta$ is close to the Debye characteristic temperature. At high temperatures $(\rho/T)$ approaches the constant value $\frac{1}{4}(A/\theta)$, but at low temperatures the resistivity varies as $125 A T (T/\theta)^4$; this latter relation was deduced theoretically by Bloch.

The electrical resistance of many metals has been measured over a wide temperature range: the resistivity of three specimens of sodium at low temperatures is shown in Fig. 18.10. If the constant residual resistance observed at low temperatures, which is due to impurities, is subtracted from each curve, an identical remainder is obtained at higher temperatures which we may take to be the resistance of ideally pure sodium (the fact that the resistance contributions due to electron scattering by impurities and by phonons are additive is known as 'Matthiesen's rule'). The close agreement with the Gruneisen formula is shown in Table 18.2.

In a solid, heat can be transported both by the phonons and by the conduction electrons, the thermal conductivity in each case increasing with the mean path length of the carriers. In a metal the phonons are scattered by collisions with electrons, and their mean path length is smaller than it would be in an insulator where there is no such scattering process. Hence the heat transport by the phonons should be smaller in a metal than in an insulator, whereas experimentally the thermal conductivity is found to be much larger. We therefore conclude that the thermal transport in a metal is nearly all due to the electrons, and in fact the lattice conductivity is negligible in comparison at all temperatures except in superconductors.

At room temperature the thermal conductivity $K$ of most metals is practically independent of temperature, but at low temperatures $K$ increases, and for nearly all pure metals (see Rosenberg, 1955) its variation can be fitted to a formula of the type

$$1/K = \alpha T^2 + \beta/T. \tag{18.23}$$

The two terms in the thermal resistivity $1/K$ arise from scattering of the electrons by the phonons and by crystal imperfections (or impurities)

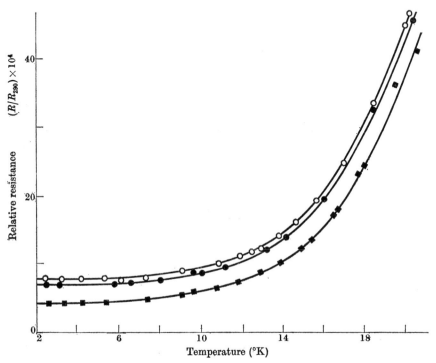

FIG. 18.10. Low temperature resistance of three specimens of sodium (from MacDonald and Mendelssohn (1950)).

respectively; for an ideally pure metal with a perfect lattice $\beta$ would be zero. The temperature variation of the thermal resistivity at low temperatures is different from that of the electrical resistivity, causing departures from the Wiedemann–Franz rule. This rule (see § 4.1) states that the quantity $L = K/\sigma T$ should be a universal constant for all metals; $L$ is known as the 'Lorenz number', and on the free electron theory (see Problem 18.1) it should have the value

$$L_0 = \frac{\pi^2}{3} \frac{k^2}{e^2} = 2 \cdot 45 \times 10^{-8} \text{ watt ohm deg}^{-2}, \tag{18.24}$$

where $k$ is Boltzmann's constant and $e$ the electronic charge. The numerical constant is different from that in equation (4.6) because the latter was based on classical statistics and the average velocity is that of all the electrons, while in equation (18.24) we have used the fact that only electrons at the Fermi surface with a substantially fixed velocity are involved. In the derivation of these formulae it is assumed that scattering of the electrons is equally effective as regards electrical and

TABLE 18.2

*Ratio of the resistance at $T^\circ K$ to that at $273 \cdot 2^\circ K$ for ideally pure sodium metal*

The calculated values are from the Gruneisen formula, equation (18.22). The experimental values are from D. K. C. MacDonald and K. Mendelssohn (1950).

| $T^\circ K$ | Calculated ratio | Observed ratio |
|---|---|---|
| 273·2 | 1·0000 | 1·0000 |
| 90·0 | 0·2600 | 0·2420 |
| 20·4 | 0·00327 | 0·00326 |
| 15·95 | 0·00100 | 0·00098 |
| 11·05 | 0·00015 | 0·00017 |
| 8·1 | 0·00004 | 0·00005 |
| 4·2 | 0·00000 | 0·00000 |

The value $\theta = 202^\circ$ K is assumed in using the Gruneisen formula to find the calculated ratio. The residual resistance due to impurity has been subtracted from the measured resistance before finding the 'observed ratio'. For the purest specimen the ratio of the residual resistance to the resistance at $273 \cdot 2^\circ$ K was $0 \cdot 0004$.

thermal transport, so that the effective mean free path is the same for both processes. This would make the quantities $\rho$ and $T/K$ vary together; the single power of $T$ occurs in the thermal case because the quantity of heat carried by the electrons is proportional to the electronic specific heat, which varies linearly with $T$. There is no corresponding term in the electrical case, so that both the electrical resistivity and $T/K$ are proportional to the reciprocal of the mean path length, i.e. to the scattering rate.

At temperatures approaching the Debye temperature $\theta$, all phonons are fully excited and we can use a classical approximation. The mean free path is inversely proportional to the mean square amplitude of thermal lattice vibrations, which is proportional to the absolute temperature. Hence $\rho$ and $T/K$ both vary as $T$ (giving a thermal conductivity independent of temperature), and the observed value of $L$ is close to $L_0$ for most metals at room temperature. At the opposite extreme of very low temperatures where the scattering of electrons is all due to impurities, the mean free path is independent of temperature, so that $\rho$ and $T/K$ are constant, and $L$ again approaches $L_0$. However, in a pure metal at low temperatures where scattering is due to phonons of long wavelengths, the mean free paths for electrical and thermal transfer are different. The number of phonons of the right wavelengths to scatter electrons is proportional to $q^2$, and the scattering cross-section for each varies as $q$, where $\mathbf{q}$ is the wave vector for a phonon. This gives us a scattering rate

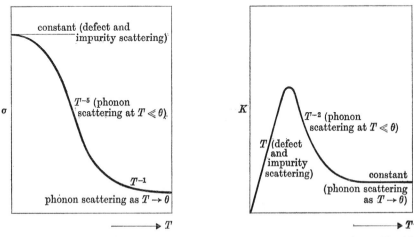

FIG. 18.11. Variation of electrical conductivity $\sigma$ and thermal conductivity $K$ with temperature in a metal. $\theta$ is the Debye temperature.

proportional to $q^3$, and hence to $\omega^3$, where $\omega = q/v$, and $\omega$ is the angular frequency of the phonon and $v$ its velocity. At any temperature the preponderant number of phonons are those for which $\hbar\omega$ is of order $kT$, and hence we get a $T^3$ dependence of the rate of scattering. All such scattering collisions are effective in energy transfer, and $T/K$ varies as $T^3$, so that $K^{-1}$ varies as $T^2$, corresponding to the first term in equation (18.23).

In considering the electrical resistivity we must allow for the fact that the long wavelength phonons carry little momentum, and scatter electrons only through small angles. The forward current carried by an electron scattered through an angle $\alpha$ is reduced only by an amount $(1-\cos\alpha)$, which varies as $\alpha^2$ for small angles, and hence with $q^2$ and with $T^2$. This extra factor of $T^2$, together with the factor of $T^3$ mentioned above, gives an overall variation of $\rho$ with $T^5$. The behaviour of $\rho$ and $K$ with temperature is illustrated in Fig. 18.11.

The difference in the effective mean free path for electrical and thermal conduction in this region makes $L$ fall below $L_0$. A typical plot of the variation of $L$ is shown in Fig. 18.12, for copper. Below about $10°$ K $L$ is close to $L_0$, but has a minimum at about $40°$ K. For ideally pure copper the electrical resistance can be found by subtracting the residual resistance observed at very low temperatures, and the thermal resistivity

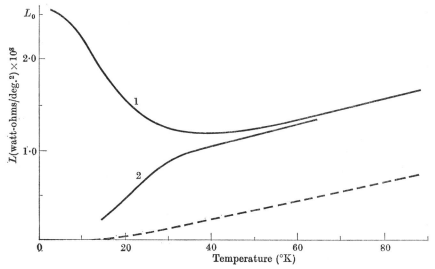

FIG. 18.12. Lorenz number for copper (Berman and MacDonald, 1952).
1   experimental curve;
2   experimental curve for ideally pure copper, obtained by subtracting contributions to the electrical and thermal resistivity from impurities.

is given by the first term of equation (18.23). From these two quantities one finds the Lorenz number $L$ for the ideally pure metal, and this is shown by curve 2, while the broken line gives the curve calculated by Sondheimer. Similar discrepancies between theory and experiment have been found for other metals.

There are a number of effects in connexion with the electrical resistance at low temperatures which we shall not discuss in detail. The most important of these is 'superconductivity': for a number of metals and compounds the resistance falls to zero below a certain temperature characteristic of each substance. At the same time all flux of magnetic induction $\mathbf{B}$ through the substance is expelled; this is not what we should expect from a straightforward application of Maxwell's equations, since a vanishing resistivity requires $\mathbf{E} = 0$, and hence $\partial\mathbf{B}/\partial t = 0$, so that any flux of $\mathbf{B}$ in the metal when it passes into the superconducting state should remain fixed, not be reduced to zero. The subject of super-conductivity is fully discussed in many books on low temperature physics.

At high frequencies the skin depth in a metal, as calculated using the conductivity measured at low frequencies, becomes smaller than the mean free path of an electron. The high frequency resistivity is then greater than is calculated from the classical formula for the skin depth, for the effective relaxation time $\tau'$ is determined by the length of time the electron spends within the skin depth (i.e. the time it is acted on by the h.f. electric field) rather than the actual time $\tau$ between 'collisions'. This is known as the 'anomalous skin effect' (see, for example, Pippard (1949); also Problem 18.5).

### 18.6. The Hall effect

When a block of metal carrying a current of density $\mathbf{j}$ parallel to the $y$-axis is placed in a field of magnetic induction $\mathbf{B}$ parallel to the $z$-axis, a potential difference appears across the metal in the direction of the $x$-axis. This effect was discovered by Hall in 1879. The magnetic induction $\mathbf{B}$ exerts a force on the charged particles carrying the current, displacing them in the $x$-direction. This sets up a non-uniform charge density which gives rise to an electric field in the $x$-direction; in equilibrium the force due to this field must just balance that due to the magnetic field, so that

$$\mathbf{F} = e\mathbf{E} + e\mathbf{v} \wedge \mathbf{B} = 0. \tag{18.25}$$

If we can identify $\mathbf{v}$ with the drift velocity of the charged particles, then $\mathbf{j} = ne\mathbf{v}$, where $n$ is the number of particles of charge $e$ per unit volume. Then we have

$$\mathbf{E} = -\mathbf{v} \wedge \mathbf{B} = -(\mathbf{j} \wedge \mathbf{B})/(ne) = -R_H(\mathbf{j} \wedge \mathbf{B}),$$

where $R_H$, the ratio of the electric field to the product (current density $\times$ magnetic induction $\mathbf{B}$), is known as the Hall coefficient. Its magnitude is

$$R_H = -1/n|e|, \tag{18.26}$$

where we have introduced the negative sign explicitly to emphasize that we would expect $R_H$ to be negative for electrons of charge $-e$. A rigorous analysis shows that equation (18.26) is correct for a metal where only the electrons at the Fermi surface take part in the conduction process, so that they all have substantially the same velocity. For a semiconductor where a Maxwellian velocity distribution is appropriate, the expression for $R$ involves a numerical factor which depends on how the mean free path varies with carrier velocity.

A comparison of the observed values of $R_H$ for various metals and semiconductors with those calculated from equation (18.26) is given in Table 18.3. The agreement is quite good for the monovalent metals, but for other metals, such as the divalent alkaline earth metals, $R_H$ is found to have a positive instead of a negative sign. This unexpected result suggests that the current is carried by positive instead of negative charges, for which there was no explanation until the band theory

TABLE 18.3

*Observed and calculated values of the Hall effect*

| Metal | $R_H$ (in units of $10^{-5}$ cm$^3$/coulomb) | |
| --- | --- | --- |
| | Observed | Calculated, assuming $q$ electrons per atom |
| Lithium   .    .    . | $-17\cdot0$ | $-13\cdot1$  ($q = 1$) |
| Sodium.   .    .    . | $-25\cdot0$ | $-24\cdot4$  ($q = 1$) |
| Copper .  .    .    . | $-\ 5\cdot5$ | $-\ 7\cdot4$  ($q = 1$) |
| Silver  .  .    .    . | $-\ 8\cdot4$ | $-10\cdot4$  ($q = 1$) |
| Zinc   .   .    .    . | $+\ 4\cdot1$ | $-\ 4\cdot6$  ($q = 2$) |
| Cadmium  .    .    . | $+\ 6\cdot0$ | $-\ 6\cdot5$  ($q = 2$) |

showed that a nearly full band of electrons behaved in a similar manner to a set of 'positive holes' (see § 18.2). The Hall effect is important in being the only simple way in which we can tell whether we have to deal with electrons or positive holes, and its magnitude gives the number of carriers $n$ per unit volume. These results cannot be obtained from the conductivity, but by combining measurements of the conductivity and the Hall effect we can find both $ne$ and the mobility $u$ (the drift velocity in unit electric field), since $\sigma = neu$. This is especially important when dealing with semiconductors.

## 18.7. Dia- and paramagnetism of conduction electrons

In most metals the bound electrons attached to the positive ions have closed electron shells with no permanent magnetic dipole moment and show only a small diamagnetism corresponding to equation (8.7). In a magnetic field the conduction electrons are affected in two ways: (1) the Lorenz force $-e(\mathbf{v} \wedge \mathbf{B})$ alters the translational motion and gives rise to a diamagnetic moment; (2) associated with the electron spin is a magnetic dipole moment (see Chapter 21), whose component is one Bohr magneton $\beta = e\hbar/2m$ parallel or anti-parallel to the magnetic field. These two components of the dipole moment are associated with the two allowed components of the electron spin (see § 4.2), and when a magnetic field is applied they have different energies, $+\beta B$ and $-\beta B$ respectively. The latter state, whose dipole moment is parallel to the field, has a lower energy than the anti-parallel state, and will have the larger probability of occupation, giving a net paramagnetism. We cannot calculate this by the methods used in § 8.3, however, for the Langevin formula derived there assumes a Boltzmann distribution function. The Fermi–Dirac distribution function must be used for free electrons, and, since this varies very little with temperature, the susceptibility turns out to be practically independent of temperature. We shall derive an expression for the paramagnetic susceptibility at the absolute zero of temperature, which can be done rather simply.

At the absolute zero, two electrons with oppositely directed spins occupy each translational energy level up to a certain energy $W_F$, the top of the Fermi distribution. When a magnetic field is applied, an electron can only reverse its spin magnetic dipole from an anti-parallel to a parallel orientation if the decrease in its magnetic energy $(2\beta B)$ is sufficient to supply the extra kinetic energy required to raise it to an empty translational energy level. This follows from the Pauli principle, which shows that two electrons with parallel spins cannot occupy the same energy level. The effect on the distribution of electrons in the energy band is shown in Fig. 18.13. This differs from the earlier diagram (Fig. 4.3) in that the band is drawn in two halves, one containing the electrons whose spin dipoles are parallel to the field **B**, the other those with their spin dipoles anti-parallel. The two half-bands are then separated in energy by $2\beta B$, the potential energy difference in the magnetic field. For the total energy, magnetic plus kinetic, of the whole system to be a minimum, the electrons must fill the two displaced half-bands up to the same level, as in Fig. 18.13. Any deviation from this would require a transfer of electrons from one half-band to higher vacant levels in the other half-band, and so increase the energy.

The total magnetic moment of the system is $2x\beta$, where $x$ is the number of electrons transferred from the anti-parallel to the parallel orientation, since the excess in the latter is then $2x$ and each electron has a spin dipole moment of one Bohr magneton $\beta$. The value of $x$ can be found in the following way. We assume that the energy difference $w$ between successive energy levels at the top of the Fermi distribution is approximately constant. To turn round the dipole of one electron then requires that its kinetic energy be increased by $w$, since we may take an electron from the topmost filled level and put it in the next level, which is vacant. To turn round a second electron requires an additional kinetic energy of $3w$, since the next two levels with parallel orientation are already filled. The third electron then must be given extra energy equal to $5w$, and for the $x$th electron the excess kinetic energy will be $(2x-1)w$. If $x$ is very large compared with unity, this may be taken as $2xw$, and at equilibrium $2xw$ will just equal $2\beta B$, so that the half-bands are filled to the same level,

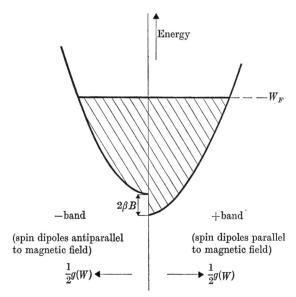

FIG. 18.13. Displacement of $+$ and $-$ bands of conduction electrons by an applied magnetic field.

The displacement is equal to the difference of energy $2\beta B$ of a spin dipole parallel and anti-parallel to the field $B$. The resultant magnetization is due to the excess of electrons in the $+$ band.

as in Fig. 18.13. Since two electrons with spins anti-parallel can occupy each kinetic energy level, the number of such levels in the range $W$ to $W+dW$ is $\frac{1}{2}g(W)$, where $g(W)$ is the density of states in this range. Hence the energy separation $w$ between successive levels at the top of the Fermi distribution is $\{\frac{1}{2}g(W)_F\}^{-1} = 2\{g(W)\}_F^{-1}$. Hence

$$2x = 2\beta B/w = \beta B\{g(W)\}_F,$$

and the susceptibility per unit volume is

$$\chi_p = \frac{2x\beta}{H} = \mu_0\,\beta^2\{g(W)\}_F. \tag{18.27}$$

For free electrons the value of $\{g(W)\}_F$ may be obtained from equation (4.13), and then

$$\chi_p = \frac{3\mu_0 n\beta^2}{2W_F}. \tag{18.28}$$

This simple expression was first derived by Pauli, and the phenomenon is sometimes called 'Pauli paramagnetism'. Since the change in the Fermi distribution with temperature is very small so long as $kT/W_F$ is small, the susceptibility is practically independent of temperature; Stoner has shown that the next term in a series expansion for the susceptibility is smaller by a factor of the order $(kT/W_F)^2$.

Comparison of equations (18.16) and (18.27) shows that both the specific heat and the paramagnetism of the conduction electrons are determined by the density of the states $\{g(W)\}_F$ at the Fermi level, and that each is smaller by a factor of order $kT/W_F$ than the corresponding quantity for a set of particles obeying classical statistics (cf. equation (8.13) or (20.16) for the susceptibility).

Calculation of the diamagnetic susceptibility arising from the translational motion of the conduction electrons in a magnetic field is considerably more complicated, and we quote only the result for free electrons, first derived by Landau:

$$\chi_d = -\frac{\mu_0 e^2}{6\pi m}\left(\frac{3n}{8\pi}\right)^{\frac{1}{3}}. \tag{18.29}$$

Substitution of the formula for $W_F$ (equation (4.11)) in equation (18.28) shows that $\chi_p$ is just three times as great as $\chi_d$ for free electrons, so the net susceptibility is positive. This expression is valid only in small fields; at high fields further terms become important which give rise to an oscillatory variation of $\chi_d$ with fundamental period $W_F/2\beta B$. This is known as the de Haas–van Alphen effect, and is observed in many metals at low temperatures.

The formulae given above are valid for free electrons; for electrons in a periodic potential the formulae are similar, provided we substitute the effective mass $m^*$ for $m$. Thus the diamagnetic susceptibility becomes

$$\chi_d = -\frac{\mu_0 e^2}{6\pi m^*}\left(\frac{3n}{8\pi}\right)^{\frac{1}{3}} \tag{18.30}$$

and so decreases when $m^*$ increases. The paramagnetic susceptibility $\chi_p$ is still correctly given by equation (18.28), but as $W_F^{-1} \propto m^*$, $\chi_p$ increases with $m^*$. Thus an increase in the effective mass makes $\chi_p$ predominate over $\chi_d$ more than by a factor 3. In addition, interaction effects between the electrons cause a further increase in $\chi_p$ (for a review, see Van Vleck (1957)).

Comparison of theoretical results with experiment is complicated by the fact that a static susceptibility determination measures only the total susceptibility $\chi = \chi_d + \chi_p + \chi_c$, where $\chi_c$ is the diamagnetic susceptibility of the electrons bound to the positive ion cores. However, this can be estimated from values for neighbouring non-metallic elements, or from calculated values of $\sum \langle r^2 \rangle$ (equation (8.7)). The susceptibility due to the electron spins alone, $\chi_p$, can be measured by electron spin resonance (see Chapter 23), and $\chi_d$ can then be found from the value of $(\chi - \chi_p - \chi_c)$. The experimental and theoretical results for lithium and sodium are summarized in Table 18.4, which is based on Van Vleck (1957). Later measurements of $\chi_p$ give slightly different values, but a satisfactory comparison with theory must await an experimental determination of $m^*/m$.

## TABLE 18.4

*Experimental and theoretical values of the volume susceptibility of lithium and sodium (after Van Vleck (1957))*

(In units of $10^{-6}$ e.m.u./cm$^3$; to convert to m.k.s./m$^3$ multiply by $4\pi$)

| | Lithium | | Sodium | |
|---|---|---|---|---|
| | experiment | theory | experiment | theory |
| $m^*/m$ | | 1·46 | | 0·985 |
| $\chi_p$ | 2·08±0·1 | 1·17† | 0·95±0·1 | 0·64† |
| | | 1·87‡ | | 0·85‡ |
| $\chi$ | 1·89±0·05 | | 0·70±0·03 | |
| $\chi_c$ | | −0·05 | | −0·18 |
| $\chi_d$ | −0·14±0·15 | −0·19§ | −0·07±0·13 | −0·22§ |

† From equation (18.28), using effective mass.
‡ Calculated by Pines, including interaction effects.
§ From equation (18.30), using effective mass.

## REFERENCES

BEATTIE, J. R., 1955, *Phil. Mag.* **46**, 235.
BERMAN, R., and MACDONALD, D. K. C., 1952, *Proc. Roy. Soc.* A, **211**, 122.
BROWN, S., and BARNETT, S. J., 1951, *Phys. Rev.* **81**, 657.
CORAK, W. S., GARFUNKEL, M. P., SATTERTHWAITE, C. B., and WEXLER, A., 1955, ibid. **98**, 1699.
DUYCKAERTS, G., 1939, *Physica*, **6**, 817.
KRONIG, R. DE L., and PENNEY, W. G., 1931, *Proc. Roy. Soc.* A, **130**, 499.
MACDONALD, D. K. C., and MENDELSSOHN, K., 1950, ibid. **202**, 103.
PIPPARD, A. B., 1949, *Physica*, **15**, 45.
ROSENBERG, H. M., 1955, *Phil. Trans.* A, **247**, 441.
SCOTT, G. G., 1951, *Phys. Rev.* **83**, 656.
SKINNER, W. B., 1938, *Rep. Progr. Phys.* **5**, 257.
VAN VLECK, J. H., 1957, *Nuovo Cim.* **6**, 857.

## GENERAL REFERENCES

DEKKER, A. J., 1958, *Solid State Physics* (Macmillan).
KITTEL, C., 1956, *Introduction to Solid State Physics* (Wiley).
ROSENBERG, H. M., 1963, *Low Temperature Solid State Physics* (O.U.P.).

## PROBLEMS

18.1. Using the kinetic theory expression $K = \frac{1}{3}lv(dU/dT)$ for the thermal conductivity $K$ of a gas, show that on the free electron model

$$K = \frac{\pi^2 nvlk^2 T}{6W_F},$$

where $n$ is the number of electrons per unit volume of velocity $v$ and mean free path $l$, $k$ is Boltzmann's constant, and $W_F$ the Fermi energy. This expression is valid at very low temperatures where $l$ is determined by the impurity scattering, and corresponds to the second term in equation (18.23).

Verify, by using equation (4.3), that this leads to the expression for

$$L_0 = K/\sigma T$$

given in equation (18.24).

18.2. The effect of scattering on the electronic motion may be represented by a damping term, as in Problem 3.9. If an alternating electric field is applied, the equation of motion becomes

$$m(d\dot{x}/dt) + m\dot{x}/\tau = eE_0 \exp(j\omega t).$$

Show that this leads to an effective conductivity $\sigma = \sigma_0/(1+j\omega\tau)$, where $\sigma_0$ is the conductivity at low frequencies. Thus the conductivity at frequencies where $\omega\tau \approx 1$ is complex; the real part gives a contribution to the conduction current, but with a reduced conductivity $\sigma' = \sigma_0/(1+\omega^2\tau^2)$, while the imaginary part is equivalent to a displacement current (but of opposite sign to the normal displacement current), so that the dielectric constant of the medium is effectively reduced from $\epsilon$ to $\epsilon - \sigma'\tau/\epsilon_0$.

18.3. Using the treatment of § 10.4, find an expression for the complex refractive index $(n-jk)$ of a metal in the region where relaxation effects in the conductivity are important, that is, where the conductivity is complex as in Problem 18.2.

If the ordinary dielectric constant of the metal is neglected, show that

$$(n^2 - k^2)/(2nk) = -\omega\tau.$$

The measurements of Beattie (1955) show that for aluminium at room temperature at wavelengths between 6 and 12 microns, the quantity $(n^2 - k^2)/(2nk)$ is roughly equal to $-11/\lambda$, where $\lambda$ is the wavelength in microns (1 micron $= 10^{-6}$ metre). Show that this gives a value of $\tau$ of about $0.6 \times 10^{-14}$ sec.

18.4. The resistivity of copper at 4° K is approximately $10^{-10}$ ohm-metre ($10^{-8}$ ohm-cm). Assuming that $m^*/m = 1.5$, and $W_F = 4.7$ eV, show that the mean free path of electrons in copper at this temperature is about $7 \times 10^{-4}$ cm, while the classical value of the skin depth (equation (10.31)) at a wavelength of 3 cm is about $5 \times 10^{-6}$ cm. Show also that at this wavelength and temperature the value of $\omega\tau$ (see Problem 18.2) is about $\frac{1}{4}$. (Assume one electron per atom for $n$.)

18.5. The anomalous skin effect makes the effective high frequency conductivity $\sigma'$ less than the d.c. value $\sigma$ by a factor $\approx (\delta/l)$, where $\delta$ is the effective skin depth and $l$ the mean free path of the electrons. Assuming that

$$\sigma'/\sigma = \beta(\delta/l),$$

where $\beta$ is a numerical factor (of the order of unity), and that the effective skin

depth is given by equation (10.31) with $\sigma'$ instead of $\sigma$, show that the effective skin depth becomes
$$\delta = (2l/\sigma\beta\mu\mu_0\omega)^{\frac{1}{4}}.$$

From equation (18.21) $(l/\sigma)$ is a constant, and hence $\delta$ becomes independent of temperature at low temperatures. (The reflecting power of pure metals in the infrared at low temperatures is principally determined by the anomalous skin effect, not the relaxation effect.)

18.6. In a simple cubic lattice the energy surfaces given by the 'tight-binding' approximation are of the form
$$W = W_1 - W_2(\cos k_x a + \cos k_y a + \cos k_z a),$$

where $a$ is the atomic separation. Show that the width of the energy band is $6W_2$, and that near the bottom ($k_x a \to 0$, etc.) the energy is approximately
$$W = (W_1 - 3W_2) + \tfrac{1}{2}W_2 k^2 a^2 + \dots,$$

while near the top ($k_x a \to \pm\pi$, etc.) it is
$$W = (W_1 + 3W_2) - \tfrac{1}{2}W_2 k^2 a^2 + \dots,$$

where $k^2 = k_x^2 + k_y^2 + k_z^2$. This shows that the energy surfaces are spheres about the centre of the zone, or the corners of the zone respectively (compare Fig. 18.6). Note that the effective mass $m^* = h^2/a^2 W_2$, and hence is inversely proportional to the bandwidth.

## SEMICONDUCTORS

### 19.1. Intrinsic and extrinsic conductivity

A SUBSTANCE in which the number of electrons is just sufficient to fill the lowest energy bands at 0° K is an insulator at very low temperatures. At a non-zero temperature a few electrons may have sufficient energy to be excited into the lowest unoccupied band (the 'conduction' band), leaving holes in the highest 'occupied' band (the 'valence' band). This gives a small electrical conductivity whose magnitude depends on the temperature and on the width of the energy gap $W_g$ between the full and empty bands. We shall find in § 19.3 that the number of electrons excited into the conduction band is proportional to $\exp(-W_g/2kT)$, and if the gap is not more than about 1 eV, which corresponds to a value of $kT$ with $T \approx 12\,000°$ K, there will be a measurable conductivity at room temperature. This phenomenon is known as 'intrinsic conductivity' and is a characteristic of pure semiconductors; it has been observed in pure silicon, germanium, indium antimonide (InSb) and some other substances.

For each electron in the conduction band, there will be a corresponding 'hole' in the filled band. Both electrons and holes contribute to the conductivity $\sigma$, so that

$$\sigma = |e|(n_e u_e + n_h u_h), \tag{19.1}$$

where the subscripts $e$, $h$ refer to electrons and holes respectively. As in § 4.6 the mobilities $u_e$, $u_h$ are taken as positive numbers and no sign is attached to $|e|$, though the holes and electrons drift in opposite directions under the influence of an electric field. For intrinsic conductivity $n_e = n_h$, since electrons and holes occur only in pairs. The equilibrium concentration rises rapidly as the temperature rises, but the mobilities vary much less rapidly with temperature; hence the increase in $n$ is the dominant factor and the conductivity rises as the temperature increases. This is the hall-mark of a semiconductor, and one of the features (together with its much smaller conductivity) which distinguishes it from a metal. Another difference is that electrons in the conduction band are in excited states, and have only a finite lifetime. An electron from the conduction band can drop down into the top of the valence band, recombining with a hole and releasing an energy $W_g$;

conversely an electron-hole pair can be created by lifting an electron
from the valence band to the conduction band. Both processes occur
repeatedly, giving a dynamic equilibrium concentration which is a
function of temperature.

The properties of a semiconductor are generally profoundly modified
by the presence of an impurity, or some other cause of irregularity in
the lattice. If these are present in not too great a concentration, they
produce discrete energy levels. The reason for this is that the levels

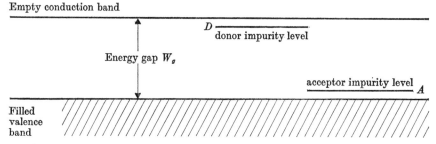

FIG. 19.1. Energy bands in a semiconductor, showing the gap between the valence band
and the conduction band. At 0° K the valence band is full and the conduction band is
empty, so that the substance behaves as an insulator. The discrete levels $D$, $A$ are due
to the presence of impurities in low concentration, where the impurity atoms are too
far apart for their electronic wave functions to overlap.

only spread out into bands when the impurity atoms are sufficiently
close for their wave functions to overlap, and at low concentrations the
impurity atoms are so far apart that any such overlap is negligible.
These discrete energy levels are important when they lie in the forbidden
band, and particularly so if they lie close to the conduction or the valence
band, as illustrated in Fig. 19.1. In the former case electrons may
occupy the impurity level $D$ at low temperatures, and are then localized
on the impurity atom and unable to partake in electrical conduction.
As the temperature rises, these electrons are excited into the empty
band. They behave then as conduction electrons, with negative charges;
the material is known as an $n$-type semiconductor, and the impurity
levels from which the electrons come are known as 'donor' levels. In
the second case, the impurity levels $A$ which lie just above the valence
band, will be unoccupied at 0° K, but as the temperature rises electrons
are excited from the valence band into these levels, which are therefore
known as 'acceptor' levels. This process leaves holes in the valence band,
which behave as positively charged carriers, and the material is known
as a $p$-type semiconductor.

If the impurity level lies close to a conduction or valence band, the temperature at which appreciable numbers of electrons or holes may be excited is relatively low, and the 'extrinsic conductivity' due to this cause may outweigh any intrinsic conductivity, even with small concentrations of impurities. In pure germanium at room temperature, for example, the number of intrinsic electrons in the conduction band is only about $10^{13}$ per $cm^3$, whereas the number of germanium atoms per $cm^3$ is $4\cdot5 \times 10^{22}$. If an impurity atom which is easily ionized at room temperature is present to a concentration of 1 part per hundred million $(4\cdot5 \times 10^{14}$ impurity atoms per $cm^3)$, it can give rise to an extrinsic conductivity which exceeds the intrinsic conductivity.

The extrinsic conductivity increases as the temperature rises until all the donor impurity atoms are fully ionized, or all the acceptor levels fully occupied. The number of extrinsic conduction electrons, or holes, then becomes substantially constant; the conductivity becomes constant, or may fall with temperature because of a decrease in the mobility. This is known as the 'exhaustion range'.

Extrinsic and intrinsic conductivity may of course be present simultaneously, but the former will depend on the impurity content while the latter is a property of the pure material. In each case conduction depends on excitation into higher levels, and the charge carriers have a finite lifetime. All substances would be expected to show intrinsic conductivity at a sufficiently high temperature; 'insulators' are substances with such large energy gaps that appreciable conductivity sets in only at temperatures outside the normal laboratory range, and which may be above the melting-point of the substance.

## 19.2. Elementary and compound semiconductors

A number of elements are known to be semiconductors in their normal allotropic form; the principal ones are silicon, germanium, boron, selenium, and tellurium. Of these the most important are silicon and germanium; they are used in many solid-state devices and their properties have been extensively investigated, so that much more reliable information is available about their properties than for any other semiconductor.

The elements carbon, silicon, germanium, tin, and lead belong to group IV of the periodic table. Silicon, germanium, and the allotrope grey tin crystallize in the diamond structure (see Fig. 19.2) in which each atom has four equidistant neighbours arranged in the form of a regular tetrahedron. Each atom forms four covalent bonds with these neighbours, donating one electron to each bond whose spin is paired off with that of the corresponding electron donated by the neighbour. These electrons can be regarded as being in a filled valence band, above which is an energy gap to the next band which is empty and forms a possible conduction band. This picture represents the position at 0° K, where the substances behave as insulators. The energy gaps are listed in Table 19.1. At a non-zero temperature some electrons may be excited

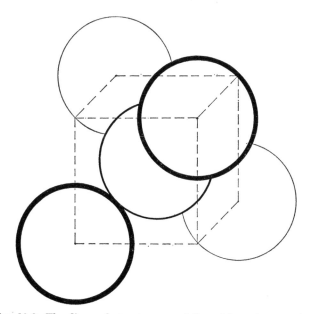

Fig. 19.2. The diamond structure, consisting of four atoms centred on alternate corners of a simple cubic lattice, bonded to one at the centre of the cube. The structure is repeated so that every atom is in identical surroundings.

from the valence band into the conduction band, making the substance an intrinsic semiconductor. On a localized electron model this corresponds to taking an electron out of a bond to behave like a 'free electron'. This leaves a 'hole' in one bond; an electron can migrate from an adjacent bond to fill this hole, thereby transferring the hole to another bond. In this way the hole can be pictured as moving in a random way through the crystal, and being mobile like the 'free' electron, though not necessarily with the same mobility.

Intrinsic conductivity is exhibited only by very pure specimens, and the properties of silicon and germanium are drastically modified by small amounts of impurity. If an impurity from group V of the periodic table, such as phosphorus, is introduced, it enters 'substitutionally', occupying the place of a silicon or germanium atom. Like the atom it replaces, it forms four covalent bonds with its four immediate neighbours. This uses up four of its valence electrons, leaving one in excess, which experiences an electrostatic attraction to the phosphorus because of the extra positive charge of its parent ion. This system of a singly charged ion and excess electron resembles a hydrogen atom, but one in which the potential due to the positively charged nucleus is modified by the presence of the surrounding silicon or germanium ions. These are electrically polarized by the excess positive charge of the phosphorus nucleus, and their effect on the electrostatic potential can be crudely approximated by the introduction of a dielectric constant, making the potential $V = e/4\pi\epsilon_0 r$. Obviously this device of using a dielectric constant is only realistic at distances large compared with the inter-atomic distance, where the electron orbit is so large that it embraces many atoms, and whose effect then resembles that of a continuous medium. For an electron of effective mass $m^*$ in an orbit of principal quantum number $n$ the energy is then found to be (see Problem 19.1)

$$W = -\frac{m^*}{m}\frac{R}{\epsilon^2 n^2} = -\frac{m^*}{m\epsilon^2 n^2} \times 13\cdot5 \text{ eV}, \qquad (19.2)$$

where 13·5 eV is the ionization potential of an electron in the $n = 1$ state of a free hydrogen atom. The bulk dielectric constant of germanium is 16, and if we use this value for $\epsilon$, and a value of $m^*/m = 0\cdot2$ (an average of values obtained from other evidence), we find $W \sim 0\cdot01$ eV for the lowest state $n = 1$. This is fairly close to that actually observed for group V donors in germanium (for phosphorus the observed value is 0·012 eV). The corresponding orbit radius is over 40 angstrom units, which is quite large compared with the inter-atomic distance of 2·45 Å. Since 0·01 eV is equivalent to a temperature of only 120° K, it is evident that such donor impurities will release nearly all their electrons into the conduction band at room temperature, a process similar to that of ionization of free hydrogen atoms at the very high temperatures in the interior of stars. For group V donors in silicon the corresponding binding energy is about 0·04 eV (see Problem 19.1).

If a group III element is added as an impurity we have a different situation. The impurity atom now has one electron too few to fill the four bonds which it should make on replacing a silicon or germanium atom, and we are therefore left with a hole in one bond. If this hole moves away from its parent impurity, all four bonds to the impurity atom become filled and it has one net negative charge. Since the hole is effectively a positive charge, it has an electrostatic attraction to the negatively charged impurity ion, and we have an 'inside-out' hydrogen atom consisting of a negatively charged 'nucleus' with the positive hole in orbit around it. This gives an 'acceptor' level just above the valence band, the height above the top of the valence band being again about 0·01 eV. At 0° K the valence band is full of electrons, and the hole occupies the impurity level; it is then localized on the impurity ion, forming a neutral atom in a bound state. At a finite temperature an electron may be excited from the valence band into the impurity level; this leaves a hole in the valence band which is free to move, and corresponds to ionization of the 'inside out' impurity atom.

This analysis shows that at 0° K the hole is in the highest level (the acceptor level) and as the temperature rises more and more holes are excited in the lower levels (the valence band). This behaviour is similar to that of electrons being excited from donor levels into the conduction band, except that for the holes energy must be measured downwards instead of upwards. In § 19.3 we shall find that holes obey similar equations to electrons provided we measure energy downwards from the top of the filled band, an example of which has already occurred in equation (18.14).

A wide range of compounds show semiconducting properties of which only a few which illustrate general classes, and for which sufficient information exists to make their properties reasonably well understood, can be mentioned here. Following the group IV compounds germanium and silicon, it is natural to discuss first the group III–group V compounds, taking as example indium antimonide, InSb, the most studied of such materials. The two elements, indium and antimony, come in the periodic table immediately before and after tin. They form a compound in which each atom is surrounded by four equidistant neighbours at the apices of a regular tetrahedron, as in the diamond structure, but with the difference that each of the four nearest neighbours is of the other type (this is known as the zinc-blende structure, after one form of the compound ZnS). These four bonds are mainly covalent in character, and link lattice sites which may be regarded as occupied by $In^-$ and $Sb^+$ ions in regular alternation. Each of these ions has the same electron configuration as tin, the group IV element, and forms covalent bonds in a similar fashion. However, the fact that we now have ions of alternate negative and positive charge gives rise to some ionic binding. Indium antimonide can be prepared in a sufficiently pure state to behave as an intrinsic semiconductor, with an energy gap of about 0·24 eV at 0° K, decreasing to 0·17 eV at room temperature.

The next binary compounds in sequence are the II–VI and I–VII compounds; these grow progressively more ionic in character, with larger

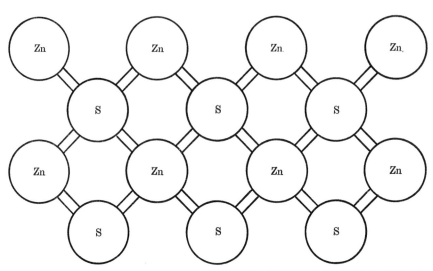

FIG. 19.3. The zinc-blende structure (two-dimensional representation). It is similar to the diamond structure, except that Zn and S ions alternate.

energy gaps. This is illustrated in the sequence formed from atoms in the seventh row of the periodic table:

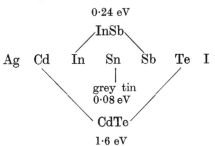

Silver iodide is a good insulator, and clearly has a large energy gap. Though probably not as pure a polar compound as NaCl, we may regard it as consisting of $Ag^+$ and $I^-$ ions, with closed shells of electrons. With a II–VI compound such as CdTe we have the dilemma of whether to regard it as a polar compound, consisting of $Cd^{++}$ and $Te^{--}$ ions, or a covalent compound formed of $Cd^{--}$ and $Te^{++}$ ions. However, the crystal structure resembles that of zinc-blende, suggesting a covalent compound; on the other hand, the group of salts PbS, PbSe, PbTe have the NaCl structure, suggesting a polar compound. These difficulties illustrate the reserve with which such extreme classification should be regarded. In fact the group of lead salts have smaller energy gaps than CdTe, and their electrical properties are more typical of semiconductors.

The energy gaps of a number of substances are given in Table 19.1. General (but not invariable) rules are that the energy gap diminishes

TABLE 19.1

*Values of the energy gap (eV)*

| Group IV elements | | III–V compounds | | II–VI compounds | |
|---|---|---|---|---|---|
| Diamond | $\sim 5\cdot3$ | BN | $\sim 10$ | | |
| Silicon | $1\cdot21$ | AlP | 3 | | |
| Germanium | $0\cdot78$ | GaAs | $1\cdot35$ | ZnSe | $\sim 5$ |
| Grey tin | $\sim 0\cdot08$ | InSb | $0\cdot24$ | CdTe | $1\cdot6$ |
| | | | | PbS | $\sim 0\cdot4$ |

the heavier the atoms involved (that is, reading downwards in the table), but increases on moving from covalent to polar compounds (that is, from left to right). Much less information is available about the polar semiconductors, owing to the difficulty of preparing them in the pure state. Apart from foreign atoms, which act as acceptors or donors according to their group in the periodic table, such crystals may be non-stoichiometric. For example, lead sulphide may have an excess of lead, producing donor levels, or of sulphur, producing acceptor levels.

The energy gap varies considerably with temperature, and most of the above are rounded values. In the case of silicon, germanium, and InSb the values given in the table are those for $0°$ K; at room temperature they are approximately $1\cdot12$, $0\cdot66$, and $0\cdot17$ eV respectively.

## 19.3. Electron distribution and the Fermi level

Under conditions of thermal equilibrium the number of electrons with energy between $W$ and $W+dW$ can be calculated by means of statistical mechanics, using of course the Fermi–Dirac statistics appropriate to particles of half-integral spin. This number is (see § 4.2)

$$dn = f(W)g(W)\,dW, \qquad (19.3)$$

where $f(W)$ is the Fermi–Dirac function

$$f(W) = \frac{1}{\exp\{(W-W_F)/kT\}+1} \qquad (19.4)$$

and $g(W)$ is the density of states. $W_F$ is the Fermi level defined as the energy at which the function $f(W) = \frac{1}{2}$. In a metal, $W_F \gg kT$ at ordinary temperatures, and the only electrons which are thermally excited or can take part in conduction processes are those very close to the Fermi level.

In a semiconductor, it is not so obvious where the Fermi level lies with respect to the conduction and valence bands. We shall consider first an intrinsic semiconductor, where at low temperatures only a few electrons are excited into the conduction band. In the limit of extremely few electrons the chance of an electron occupying a given state is very low, and the restrictions imposed by the Exclusion Principle play little role. We are thus in a situation where the classical Maxwell–Boltzmann statistics are a good approximation, so that we can write

$$f_c(W) = \exp\{-(W-W_F)/kT\} \quad \text{very nearly.} \qquad (19.5)$$

This is just the approximation of equation (19.4) in the limit where $(W-W_F) \gg kT$, so that we can neglect the second term in the denominator; this approximation is appropriate for electrons in the conduction band, which is empty of electrons at $0°$ K. At this temperature the valence band is full, and thus corresponds to energies well below the Fermi level. In the region where $(W_F - W) \gg kT$ the first term in the denominator of equation (19.4) is now very small, and we can write

$$1 - f_v(W) = \exp\{-(W_F - W)/kT\}, \quad \text{very nearly.} \qquad (19.6)$$

The quantity $1 - f_v(W)$ is relevant to the number of holes in the valence band.

We must now consider the density of states, $g(W)$. This is zero at the edge of a band and we assume that it varies as the square root of the distance from the edge of the band. That is, we can modify equation (4.16) and write

$$g_c(W) = C(m_e^*)^{\frac{3}{2}}(W-W_c)^{\frac{1}{2}} \qquad (19.7)$$

and

$$g_v(W) = C(m_h^*)^{\frac{3}{2}}(W_v-W)^{\frac{1}{2}}, \qquad (19.8)$$

where $W_c$, $W_v$ are the energies at the bottom of the conduction band and the top of the valence band respectively.

The total number of electrons in the conduction band is thus

$$n_e = \int_{W_c}^{\infty} f_c(W)g_c(W)\,dW$$

$$= C(m_e^*)^{\frac{3}{2}} \int_{W_c}^{\infty} (W-W_c)^{\frac{1}{2}} \exp\{-(W-W_F)/kT\}\,dW.$$

On writing $y = (W - W_c)/kT$, this integral becomes

$$n_e = C(m_e^* kT)^{\frac{3}{2}} \exp\{-(W_c - W_F)/kT\} \int_0^\infty y^{\frac{1}{2}} e^{-y} \, dy$$
$$= (\pi^{\frac{1}{2}}/2) C(m_e^* kT)^{\frac{3}{2}} \exp\{-(W_c - W_F)/kT\}$$
$$= N_c \exp\{-(W_c - W_F)/kT\}. \tag{19.9}$$

This result is the same as if we had a number $N_c$ of states at energy $W_c$; thus $N_c$ is the effective density of states at the bottom of the conduction band, and on substituting for $C$ from equation (4.16) we find

$$N_c = 2(2\pi m_e^* kT/h^2)^{\frac{3}{2}}. \tag{19.10}$$

Similarly for the number of holes in the valence band we find

$$n_h = \int_{-\infty}^{W_v} \{1 - f_v(W)\} g_v(W) \, dW$$
$$= N_v \exp\{-(W_F - W_v)/kT\}, \tag{19.11}$$

where

$$N_v = 2(2\pi m_h^* kT/h^2)^{\frac{3}{2}}. \tag{19.12}$$

For the product $n_e n_h$ we find

$$n_e n_h = N_c N_v \exp\{-(W_c - W_v)/kT\} = N_c N_v \exp\{-W_g/kT\} \tag{19.13}$$

and since in an intrinsic conductor we must have $n_e = n_h = n_i$ we obtain

$$n_i = n_e = n_h = (N_c N_v)^{\frac{1}{2}} \exp\{-W_g/2kT\}, \tag{19.14}$$

where $W_g = W_c - W_v$ is the width of the energy gap between the valence and conduction bands.

To find the position of the Fermi level, $W_F$, we must equate the formulae for $n_e$ and $n_h$, which yields

$$\frac{N_v}{N_c} = \exp \frac{2W_F - W_c - W_v}{kT},$$

whence, since $N_v/N_c = (m_h^*/m_e^*)^{\frac{3}{2}}$,

$$W_F = \frac{1}{2}(W_c + W_v) + \frac{3}{4}kT \ln(m_h^*/m_e^*). \tag{19.15}$$

This result shows that for most intrinsic semiconductors, where $m_h^*$, $m_e^*$ are nearly equal, the Fermi level lies in the middle of the energy gap, as shown in Fig. 19.4. In some cases, such as InSb, where $m_h^*/m_e^* \approx 20$, the level varies markedly in position with temperature, and at room temperature is shifted well towards the bottom of the conduction band.

When impurities are present, and conduction is partly intrinsic and partly extrinsic, the position is a good deal more complicated. There is, however, one important general result which holds provided the numbers of electrons in the conduction band and holes in the valence band are

N n

small compared with the density of states. In that case the relations
(19.9)–(19.13) are still valid, since they do not depend on any supposition about the position of the Fermi level. Thus we have in equation
(19.13) an important relation between the numbers of electrons and
holes, and in the light of equation (19.14) we have also $n_e n_h = n_i^2$,
where $n_i$ is the number of intrinsic electrons which would exist at the

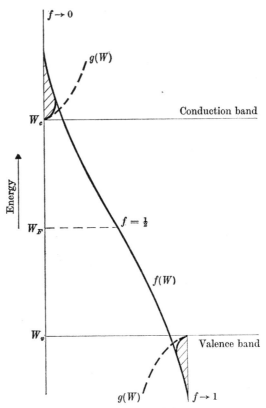

Fig. 19.4. The Fermi–Dirac distribution of electrons and holes in
an intrinsic semiconductor; the figure is drawn for a case where
$m_h^* = m_e^*$, so that the Fermi level $W_F$ is in the centre of the forbidden
band. The shaded areas indicate the numbers of electrons in the conduction band, and holes in the valence band.

same temperature. The ratio of numbers of electrons and holes depends
on the position of the Fermi level, for which we shall quote some results
only for extreme cases.

When donors or acceptors (but not both together) are present, which
produce discrete levels lying close to the conduction or valence band
respectively, the conductivity at low temperatures is dominated by the

ionization of the impurity levels. The Fermi level at $0°$ K then lies between the donor level and the conduction band, or between the acceptor level and the top of the valence band (see Fig. 19.5). As the temperature rises the Fermi level shifts because of a term similar to the second term in equation (19.15), but involving $\ln(N_d/N_c)$ or $\ln(N_a/N_v)$,

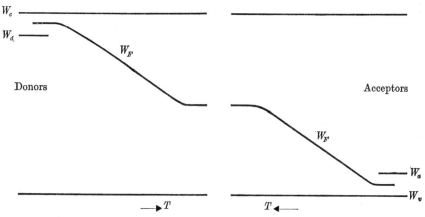

FIG. 19.5. Variation of Fermi level when *either* donors *or* acceptors are present. At very low temperatures the Fermi level lies midway betwen the impurity level and the conduction or valence band. For small impurity concentrations $(N_d < N_c$ or $N_a < N_v)$ the level moves towards the centre of the forbidden band with rising temperature. At higher temperatures the electron distribution is dominated by the intrinsic contribution, and $W_F$ is at the centre of the forbidden gap if $m_h^* = m_e^*$.

where $N_d$ and $N_a$ are the number of donor and acceptor levels per unit volume respectively. Thus for donors we have

$$W_F = \tfrac{1}{2}(W_d + W_c) + \tfrac{1}{2}kT\ln(N_d/N_c) \quad (n_e \ll N_d), \qquad (19.16)$$

showing that as the temperature rises the Fermi level will rise if $N_d > N_c$, or fall if $N_d < N_c$.

In the exhaustion range the donor levels are fully ionized and $n_e = N_d$; in this case the Fermi level is given approximately by

$$W_F = W_c + kT\ln(N_d/N_c) \quad (n_e = N_d). \qquad (19.17)$$

If $N_d < N_c$ the Fermi level lies below the conduction band, the number of electrons excited into the conduction band is small compared with the number of available states and they obey the classical statistics. This condition is called 'non-degenerate'. On the other hand, if $N_d > N_c$ the Fermi level lies in the conduction band, and since $n_e = N_d$, the number of conduction electrons is greater than the number of available states; this condition is called 'degenerate'. This situation is similar to that in a metal, where the exclusion principle limits the number of electrons in a given energy range, and the electron distribution must be treated by Fermi–Dirac statistics instead of classical statistics.

Similar results are obtained for acceptor impurities, provided we count energy as increasing downwards from the top of the valence band rather than upwards from the bottom of the conduction band (cf. Fig. 19.4).

The importance of the Fermi level lies in the fact that its value is equal to that of the thermodynamic potential $G = U - TS + eV$ of the electrons. If the electron distributions in two substances are in thermal equilibrium with each other, then the values of the thermodynamic potential in the two substances are equal, and hence so also are the Fermi levels. Thus the position of the Fermi level plays an important role in discussing the properties of junctions.

### 19.4. Optical properties

Semiconductors such as germanium and silicon look very much like metals; they are opaque to visible light and have a high reflectivity. This is because the quantum carried by a visible photon, which corresponds to an energy roughly between 1·5 and 4 eV, is sufficient to excite an electron from the valence band right across the forbidden energy gap into the conduction band. If the absorption coefficient is measured at longer wavelengths, a sharp drop in absorption would be expected when the photon energy becomes smaller than the energy gap $W_g$; that is, at wavelengths such that $h\nu < W_g$. The change in the absorption coefficient can be quite dramatic, from $10^4$ to $10^5$ cm$^{-1}$ at wavelengths shorter than the absorption edge, down to $10^{-1}$ cm$^{-1}$ at wavelengths beyond the edge, as illustrated in Fig. 19.6. The absorption beyond the edge depends on the purity of the specimen, since impurities produce levels in the forbidden band from or to which electrons can still be excited by photons of lower energy.

An optical determination of the position of the absorption edge gives, in principle, a direct measurement of the energy gap, whose accuracy is limited by the fact that the drop in absorption is spread out over a small but finite range of frequency. Careful analysis of the experimental results in the light of a detailed theory of how the absorption coefficient should vary with frequency in the vicinity of the absorption edge has given quite accurate measurements of the energy gap, and shows directly how it varies with temperature. However, care is needed in the interpretation, through the presence of selection rules connected with the conservation of linear momentum. A photon of energy $h\nu$ carries momentum $h\nu/c$, which is negligible compared with the momentum of a particle of non-zero rest mass (such as an electron) of the same energy. As a result the momentum of an electron excited into the conduction band must be the same as it was in the valence band before

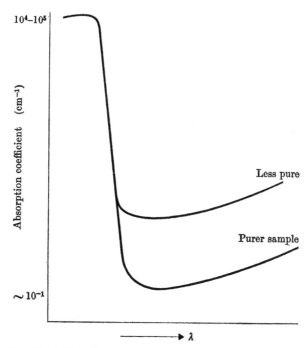

FIG. 19.6. The absorption edge in a semiconductor at low temperatures. At short wavelengths the semiconductor is quite opaque, since the light intensity falls as $\exp(-\alpha x)$; at long wavelengths the absorption is higher in impure samples because of electron excitation in and out of the impurity levels in the forbidden band. In germanium the absorption edge lies in the infra-red at about $1\cdot 6\,\mu$ (16 000 Å) at 0 °K.

the absorption of a photon. Quantum-mechanical analysis shows that it is the crystal momentum $\hbar\mathbf{k}$ which is conserved, giving a selection rule $\Delta\mathbf{k} = 0$. If the maximum of the valence band and the minimum of the conduction band both occur at $\mathbf{k} = 0$, as in Fig. 19.7, no difficulty arises. This applies to InSb, but in germanium and silicon the conduction band has only a subsidiary minimum at $\mathbf{k} = 0$, the deeper minimum occurring at a finite value of $\mathbf{k}$, as shown also in Fig. 19.7. Thus transitions in the vicinity of $\mathbf{k} = 0$ do not determine the minimum value of $W_g$, defined as the difference of energy between the top of the valence band and the bottom of the conduction band. It turns out, however, that transitions such as that marked $\Delta \mathbf{k} \neq 0$ in Fig. 19.7 are allowed (though much weaker) provided the lattice can supply or take up the momentum required to make the total momentum of lattice plus electron unchanged. This involves the creation or destruction of a phonon

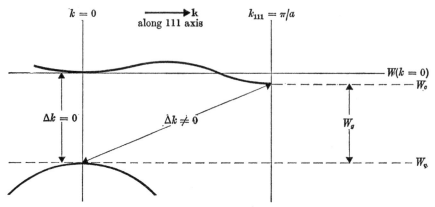

FIG. 19.7. Shape of the band edges against crystal momentum $\mathbf{k}$ for germanium. The momentum of a photon is negligible, so that there can be no net transfer of momentum on absorption. Either $\Delta \mathbf{k} = 0$ for the electron, or the difference in momentum when $\Delta \mathbf{k} \neq 0$ must be taken up by the creation or destruction of a phonon. For germanium $W_g = 0.75$ eV at 0° K, but $W(\mathbf{k} = 0) - W_c \approx 0.14$ eV, so that the $\Delta \mathbf{k} \neq 0$ transitions give a fine structure on the absorption edge.

(processes involving more than one phonon have negligible probability). Transitions in which $\Delta \mathbf{k} = 0$ are known as direct transitions, and transitions in which $\Delta \mathbf{k} \neq 0$ are called indirect transitions.

*Excitons*

When an electron is excited from the valence band into the conduction band by a direct transition, a hole is created in the valence band whose momentum must be equal and opposite to that of the electron in the conduction band in order to make $\Delta \mathbf{k} = 0$. The electron and hole therefore move apart in opposite directions. In the vicinity of $\mathbf{k} = 0$, they move apart rather slowly, and their mutual coulomb attraction begins to play a role; finally at $\mathbf{k} = 0$ itself the electron and hole stay together. Under these conditions their behaviour resembles that of an electron and proton in a hydrogen atom; a better comparison is with an electron and donor impurity atom, as discussed in § 19.2. Electron and hole may move in discrete orbits about the mutual centre of mass, giving rise to a series of energy levels

$$W = -\frac{m_r}{m} \frac{R}{\epsilon^2 n^2}, \qquad (19.18)$$

where $m_r$ is the reduced mass given by the relation

$$\frac{1}{m_r} = \frac{1}{m_e^*} + \frac{1}{m_h^*}.$$ (19.19)

$W = 0$ in equation (19.18) corresponds to separation of the electron and hole to such a large distance that their mutual attraction is negligible (i.e. to 'ionization' of the electron-hole 'atom') and thus corresponds to the bottom of the conduction band at $\mathbf{k} = 0$. A lower energy is obtained when the electron and hole are together, so that the levels of equation (19.18) lie just below the conduction band (like those of a donor impurity and bound electron), as shown in Fig. 19.8. The energy is also of the same order; if $m_e^* = m_h^* = 2m_r$, the energy levels are just half those given by equation (19.2), and lie therefore very close to the conduction band.

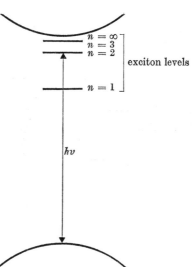

exciton levels

The electron-hole bound pair is known as an 'exciton' and has been identified through its hydrogen-like spectrum in some semiconductors with large energy gaps, together with $Cu_2O$ and Ge. In germanium excitons are associated both with the direct and indirect transitions. In

FIG. 19.8. Exciton levels lying just below the conduction band in the vicinity of $\mathbf{k} = 0$. The quantum of energy shown is that required to excite an electron from the valence band to the $n = 2$ level, and is slightly smaller than that corresponding to the absorption edge, which requires excitation to the bottom of the conduction band $(n = \infty)$.

the former case a sharp line spectrum would be expected at frequencies just short of the energy gap at $\mathbf{k} = 0$; in the indirect transitions the electron-hole pair can be formed with finite momentum and possess kinetic energy, so that the exciton levels are not sharp but broadened into bands.

*Photoconductivity*

When radiation whose wavelength is sufficiently short that the energy quantum $h\nu$ is larger than the energy gap is shone on a semiconductor, electrons are lifted into the conduction band and holes created in the valence band. The presence of this excess of carriers increases the conductivity, and the phenomenon is known as photoconductivity. For small intensities of illumination the increase in conductivity is approximately proportional to the intensity of the incident radiation, and the conductivity change is an important method of detecting infra-red radiation. Such a detector is sensitive only to wavelengths shorter than the absorption edge; PbS can be used for wavelengths up to about $4\,\mu$, and InSb to about $7\,\mu$ (these limits vary with temperature because the energy gap and hence the absorption edge are temperature dependent). Such detectors not only have a high sensitivity, but also have a

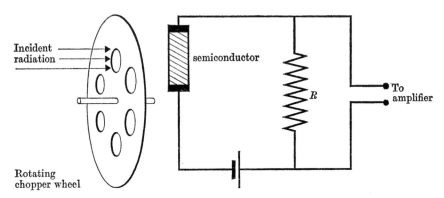

Fig. 19.9. Use of photoconductive effect in a semiconductor for the detection of radiation. The incident radiation is modulated in intensity by a mechanical 'chopper', and produces a variation in the resistance of the semiconductor at the modulation frequency. The resulting alternating voltage across the resistance $R$ is amplified by a narrow-band amplifier tuned to the modulation frequency.

short response time (varying from $10^{-4}$ to $10^{-7}$ sec) because the excess carriers quickly disappear through recombination, etc. This makes it possible to modulate the incident radiation (e.g. by a mechanical chop-ping device) and obtain an a.c. signal which can readily be amplified and detected, as illustrated in Fig. 19.9. The use of germanium doped with suitable impurities makes it possible to construct detectors which are sensitive to much longer wavelengths, the photoconductive effect then being due to electrons excited into the conduction band from donor impurity levels (or holes created by electrons being lifted into acceptor levels from the valence band). Since the smallest separation of such discrete levels from the adjacent bands is about 0·01 eV, suitably doped samples are sensitive to wavelengths up to about 100 $\mu$. Such detectors must of course be cooled to a temperature where thermal ionization of the impurity levels is unimportant.

## 19.5. Transport properties

In addition to the energy gap $W_g$, the most important quantities we require to know about a semiconductor are the numbers of charge carriers of either sign, their effective masses, and their mobilities. The best method of measuring the effective mass is by means of cyclotron resonance, which is discussed in Chapter 23. Determination of $W_g$ by optical methods is possible only on very pure specimens, and in many cases it can only be deduced indirectly, using equation (19.13). To bring out the temperature dependence explicitly we rewrite this in the form

$$n_e n_h = (2 \cdot 33 \times 10^{31})(m_e^* m_h^* / m^2)^{\frac{3}{2}} T^3 \exp(-W_g/kT), \qquad (19.20)$$

where the units are metre$^{-6}$. At first sight the simplest method of finding the number of charged particles would be measurement of the Hall coefficient $R_H$, which from equation (18.26) is inversely proportional to the number of carriers. Since this number is so much smaller in a semiconductor than in a metal, the Hall effect is much larger ($\approx 10^5$ to $10^6$ cm$^3$/coulomb for pure Si and Ge at room temperature) and correspondingly easier to measure. However, we are immediately faced with the difficulty that the Hall coefficient changes sign according to whether the current is carried by electrons or positive holes; in particular, in an intrinsic semiconductor, with equal numbers of each, we would expect the Hall coefficient to vanish. In practice this does not happen, because the electrons and holes have different mobilities, and so carry different fractions of the current. The general expression for the Hall coefficient is

$$R_H = -\frac{B}{|e|} \frac{(n_e b^2 - n_h)}{(n_e b + n_h)^2}, \qquad (19.21)$$

where $b = \mu_e/\mu_h$ is the ratio of the mobilities of electrons and holes, and $B$ is a coefficient not far from unity. The presence of $B$ arises from the fact that in a full analysis, different averages over the distributions of velocity and relaxation time are involved in calculating the conductivity and the Hall effect. For a metal or a degenerate semiconductor, $B = 1$; for a non-degenerate semiconductor with the value of B depends on how the scattering cross-section varies with carrier velocity.

Measurement of the Hall coefficient $R_H$ and the conductivity $\sigma$ makes it possible to determine both $n_e$ and $n_h$, using equations (19.1) and (19.21), provided that the value of $b$ is known. The direct measurement of mobility is discussed below, but this is possible only with certain substances such as silicon and germanium. In other cases we can proceed only by making some assumptions about $b$. In an intrinsic semiconductor, $n_e = n_h = n_i$, and we have the relations ($n_i$ per metre³)

$$n_i = (4 \cdot 8 \times 10^{15})(m_e^* m_h^*/m^2)^{\frac{3}{4}} T^{\frac{3}{2}} \exp(-W_g/2kT) \qquad (19.22)$$

and
$$R_H = -\frac{B}{n_i|e|} \frac{(b-1)}{(b+1)}. \qquad (19.23)$$

Although the mobilities $u_e$ and $u_h$ both vary with temperature, their ratio $b$ does not vary rapidly in comparison with $n_i$, which is dominated by the exponential factor in equation (19.22). Thus a plot of $\ln(R_H T^{\frac{3}{2}})$ against $1/T$ should be a straight line, and this is found to hold for silicon and germanium. The slope of the straight line yields a value of $W_g$, but since $W_g$ is itself temperature dependent, care must be exercised in the interpretation (see Problem 19.2).

Another approximate method of finding $W_g$ involves only measurement of the conductivity. For an intrinsic semiconductor (or an impurity semiconductor at high temperatures where the conductivity is dominated by the intrinsic electrons), we have

$$\sigma = |e|n_i(u_e+u_h) \qquad (19.24)$$

and from measurement of the conductivity over a range of temperature we can find the variation of $n$ and hence determine the energy gap provided we know how the mobilities vary with temperature. When the mobility is determined by scattering processes due to lattice vibrations (phonons) the mobility (see p. 557) should vary as $T^{-\frac{3}{2}}$. Since from equation (19.22) $n_i$ varies as $T^{\frac{3}{2}} \exp(-W_g/2kT)$, we should expect that the conductivity would follow the law

$$\sigma = \sigma_0 \exp(-W_g/2kT) \qquad (19.25)$$

so that the energy gap can be found from a plot of $\ln \sigma$ against $1/T$. This method was used in early work, but such plots show a slight curvature, indicating that the mobility does not follow a $T^{-\frac{3}{2}}$ law exactly.

Determination of the energy gap from the optical absorption edge needs careful experimentation and interpretation, but it is the most satisfactory method and the only one which gives directly the energy gap at a given temperature. Use of the Hall effect or the conductivity depends on assumptions about the mobility, whose experimental determination will now be discussed.

*Measurement of mobility*

The mobility of electrons and holes in semiconductors can be measured directly by a method due originally to Shockley and Haynes. The specimen is in the form of a narrow rectangular bar, about 0·05 cm square and a few cm long. A steady voltage is applied between the ends to give a field of order 10 V/cm along the bar; two electrodes $A$, $B$ are applied to the specimen, as shown in Fig. 19.10. A short voltage pulse of duration about 1 microsecond is applied to electrode $A$; if the semiconductor is $n$-type, and $A$ is made positive in the pulse, electrons are withdrawn from the semiconductor by the electrode; some of these may

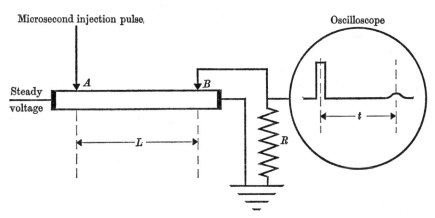

FIG. 19.10. Apparatus for direct measurement of mobility. The steady voltage applied at extreme left produces a uniform field in the semiconductor bar under whose influence a microsecond pulse of minority carriers drift from $A$ to $B$. The mean drift velocity is $L/t$, where $t$ is measured on the oscilloscope.

come from the valence band, creating an excess of holes in the semiconductor. To preserve electrical neutrality of the specimen, electrons enter at any terminals which are negative with respect to $A$. One of these is $B$, which is connected (through an amplifier) to the $Y$-plates of an oscilloscope; this registers a voltage because of the flow of such electrons through the resistance $R$. This pulse does not quite coincide in time with the pulse at $A$, but the time delay is that required by an electromagnetic wave set up by the disturbance at $A$ to travel to $B$, which is of order $10^{-10}$ seconds and quite negligible. The holes injected at $A$ are swept by the field towards $B$, and arrive a time $t = L/v$ later, where $L$ is the distance between electrodes $A$, $B$ and $v$ is the drift velocity in the steady field. On arrival at $B$ they appear as a second voltage pulse on the oscilloscope, and the time interval $t$ between the two pulses can be determined from the oscilloscope trace by calibrating the timebase. The voltage $V$ between the electrodes $A$, $B$ due to the steady field is measured independently. Since the drift velocity $v = uE = uV/L$, the time $t = L/v = L^2/uV$ and the mobility is found from the relation

$$u = L^2/Vt. \qquad (19.26)$$

In a typical experiment the value of $t$ is about 30 $\mu$sec. The second pulse at $B$ due to the arrival of holes is broader and smaller than the first for two reasons: (a) diffusion of the holes in random directions; for accurate results the holes must be swept from $A$ to $B$ in a time $t$ short enough to make diffusion effects small, and the voltage pulse applied at $A$ must be short compared with $t$; (b) holes are lost by recombination with electrons within the specimen.

To measure the mobility of electrons, all that would seem necessary at first sight would be to use $n$-type material and apply a negative pulse at $A$. This would inject electrons, creating a local excess, which is, however, dissipated in an extremely short time (see Problem 19.3), restoring the equilibrium concentration of electrons everywhere in the semiconductor. In this case only the first pulse is observed at $B$, and no second pulse. When a positive pulse is applied at $A$, with an $n$-type semiconductor, holes are created, and although electrical neutrality is restored by an inflow of electrons, we have now a non-equilibrium distribution with an excess of holes and a corresponding excess of electrons. Equilibrium is restored only when the holes flow out at $B$, or are annihilated within the semiconductor by recombination with electrons. The net result is that we can measure directly the mobility only of 'minority carriers'; i.e. of holes in an $n$-type semiconductor, or electrons in a $p$-type semiconductor. By observing the spread in the second pulse at $B$ the diffusion constant can be determined, and by observing its size as a function of $L$ or of electric field $E$ the rate of recombination can be found.

The quantity measured directly in such experiments is called the 'drift mobility', but in many semiconductors it cannot be so determined because of rapid diffusion of the carriers. In that case the mobility, when only one type of carrier is present, can be found from the conductivity and Hall effect, since then $|R_H| = B/n|e|$ and $|R_H \sigma| = Bu$. The quantity $|R_H \sigma|$ is often written $u_H$ and called the 'Hall mobility' to distinguish it from the drift mobility.

*Variation of mobility with temperature*

The mobility of electrons or holes in semiconductors is limited by scattering processes which are basically similar to those in metals, but the temperature dependence of the mobility is very different for two reasons. In a metal only electrons at the Fermi surface contribute to the conduction current, and their velocity $v$ is substantially independent of temperature; hence we do not need to take into account any velocity dependence in a scattering cross-section. Similarly the fact that the scattering cross-section determines the free path $l$, while the mobility depends on the relaxation time $\tau = l/v$, does not of itself introduce any temperature dependence. In a semiconductor, however, the average kinetic energy of the charge carriers is $\approx kT$, and the velocity variation as $T^{\frac{1}{2}}$ plays an important role.

Measurements of mobility at various temperatures and different impurity concentrations show that it is a function of both. In a pure material the charge carriers are scattered by the lattice vibrations (phonons); at all but the lowest temperatures (when impurity scattering

TABLE 19.2

*Mobilities in elemental semiconductors*

|  | Electrons | Holes |
|---|---|---|
| Silicon | $(4 \cdot 0 \times 10^9)T^{-2 \cdot 6}$ | $(2 \cdot 5 \times 10^8)T^{-2 \cdot 3}$ |
| Germanium | $(3 \cdot 5 \times 10^7)T^{-1 \cdot 6}$ | $(9 \cdot 1 \times 10^8)T^{-2 \cdot 3}$ |

The units are cm²/volt-sec, and the values are quoted from Ziman (1960), *Electrons and Phonons* (O.U.P.).

dominates in any case) the scattering cross-section is proportional to the mean square amplitude of the thermal fluctuations, and hence is proportional to $kT$. This gives a mean free path $l$ proportional to $T^{-1}$ which is the same for all carrier velocities, and the relaxation time $\tau = l/v$ and hence also the mobility should vary as $T^{-\frac{3}{2}}$. Table 19.2 shows that this law is not very well obeyed, except for electrons in germanium. The discrepancies may be due either to scattering by short wavelength lattice vibrations where adjacent atoms vibrate in anti-phase (the so-called 'optical modes'), or to the complicated band structure (see Fig. 19.7), both of which allow scattering processes with a large change in electron wave vector (ordinary lattice scattering by the long-wavelength or 'acoustic' modes allows only small changes in electron momentum because the phonon momentum is small). The observed mobilities in silicon and germanium at room temperature are found from Table 19.2 to lie between about 500 and 4000 cm²/volt-sec, and are thus considerably higher than those in metals (for copper the value is about 40 cm²/volt-sec). The high mobility is partly due to low values of the effective mass of electrons and holes in the semiconductors.

The scattering cross-section due to neutral impurities is inversely proportional to carrier velocity, giving a relaxation time independent of velocity and hence also of temperature. Charged (i.e. ionized) impurities will scatter carriers by a process analogous to Rutherford scattering of alpha particles; the cross-section is inversely proportional to the square of the carrier energy and hence varies as $T^{-2}$, so that the mean free path varies as $T^2$. Since the mean velocity varies as $T^{\frac{1}{2}}$, the relaxation time varies as $T^{\frac{3}{2}}$. A special case of scattering by charged particles is the mutual scattering of electrons and holes.

TABLE 19.3

*Summary of dependence of electron (hole) scattering on velocity v and temperature T*

| Scattering mechanism | Cross-section $\sigma$ | Free path $l \propto \sigma^{-1}$ | Relaxation time $\tau = l/v$ |
|---|---|---|---|
| Phonons (at ordinary temperatures) | $T$ | $T^{-1}$ | $T^{-\frac{3}{2}}$ |
| Neutral impurities . . . | $v^{-1}$ | $v$ | constant |
| Ionized impurities . . . | $v^{-4}$ | $v^4$ | $v^3 \equiv T^{\frac{3}{2}}$ |

The velocity and temperature dependence of these scattering mechanisms are summarized in Table 19.3. In a first approximation the rates of scattering by different processes are additive; that is, we can write

$$\frac{1}{\tau} = \sum_i \frac{1}{\tau_i}. \tag{19.27}$$

At low temperatures the lattice scattering decreases as the lattice vibrations die away, and the mobility is eventually dominated by the impurity scattering.

*Recombination and diffusion*

At any given temperature there is an equilibrium concentration of electrons and holes in a semiconductor, the two concentrations being equal in intrinsic material and generally unequal in extrinsic material. In the experiment of Shockley and Haynes we have seen that an excess of minority carriers can be injected at a contact, and to preserve electrical neutrality there will be a corresponding injection of majority carriers, possibly at another electrode. Any abnormal charge distribution caused thereby vanishes in about $10^{-11}$ sec (see Problem 19.3), so that we can write $\Delta n_h = \Delta n_e$, where $\Delta n_h$, $\Delta n_e$ are the local excesses in the number of holes and electrons respectively per unit volume. If we did not have this equality, a space charge $\rho = e(\Delta n_h - \Delta n_e)$ would be set up, which by Poisson's equation

$$\text{div } \mathbf{E} = \rho/\epsilon\epsilon_0 = (e/\epsilon\epsilon_0)(\Delta n_h - \Delta n_e)$$

would give rise to strong electric fields. These would cause currents to flow which would neutralize the space charge in the time given above. Obviously this current flow consists mainly of the more numerous majority carriers, and the controlling factor is the departure from the equilibrium value of the number of minority carriers. The fact that $\Delta n_h = \Delta n_e$ (in practice the equality is not exact, but departures from it are very small and can be neglected for present purposes) means that the *fractional* change in the number of minority carriers may be appreciably greater than the *fractional* change in majority carriers. A number of important devices described later in this chapter depend on changes in the minority carrier concentration; such changes represent departures from equilibrium, and the mechanisms by which they decay play an important role in the design of such devices.

As mentioned in § 19.1, the charge carriers in a semiconductor have a finite lifetime, but this varies widely with the purity of the crystal. Simple recombination of an electron and a hole can only take place if certain restrictions on momentum and energy are satisfied, and measurements on very pure germanium show that this process would give a lifetime greater than $10^{-2}$ sec. The observed lifetimes are generally much shorter, owing to the presence of chemical impurities which provide extra levels, known as 'traps'. In an $n$-type material, for example, electrons may drop from the conduction band into such traps; holes may then collide with these electrons to give recombination. The energy and momentum considerations involved in this 'indirect' process are much less restrictive than for the direct process of recombination, and the lifetime of the carriers is correspondingly shorter. These processes take place in the body of the semiconductor, but the discrete levels at the surface (see p. 564) may also act as traps which promote recombination through 'indirect' processes. A further loss of minority carriers will also occur at the electrodes.

The chance of a hole and an electron recombining is proportional to the concentration of each species; hence the rate of annihilation is $-an_h n_e$, where $a$ is a constant which depends on the mechanism involved. In thermal equilibrium the loss by recombination is balanced by the creation of new carriers through thermal excitation into the conduction band; if we denote the rate of creation by $c$, then clearly $c = an_h^0 n_e^0$, where $n_h^0$, $n_e^0$ are the equilibrium concentrations. When a departure from equilibrium takes place we have

$$dn_h/dt = dn_e/dt = c - an_h n_e = a(n_h^0 n_e^0 - n_h n_e).$$

As mentioned above, the *fractional* change in the majority carrier concentration is much smaller than the *fractional* change in the minority carrier concentration, and to a first approximation the former may be neglected. Hence, taking for example the holes in an $n$-type material, we may write

$$dn_h/dt \doteq an_e^0(n_h^0 - n_h) = -\Delta n_h/\tau_h, \qquad (19.28)$$

showing that the rate of decay of the minority carrier concentration is simply proportional to the excess of minority carriers. The quantity $\tau_h$ is the 'recombination lifetime' of the minority carriers.

Recombination at the surface or extraction at an electrode causes a local diminution in the excess of minority carriers; this is counteracted by the movement of carriers from regions where they are more numerous. This is a process of diffusion, and for small field strengths diffusion currents are much larger than conduction currents. For simplicity, we consider a case where the minority carrier density $n_h$ (taking again holes in $n$-type material) varies only in one dimension. Then the number crossing unit area per second is $-D_h(\partial n_h/\partial x)$, and the net rate of increase in a thickness $dx$ is $d\{-D_h(\partial n_h/\partial x)\} = -D_h(\partial^2 n_h/\partial x^2)\,dx$, where $D_h$ is the diffusion coefficient for the minority carriers. In the steady state this equals the rate of loss by recombination, which in thickness $dx$ is $\{(n_h^0 - n_h)/\tau_h\}\,dx$; hence we obtain the relation

$$\frac{\partial^2 n_h}{\partial x^2} = \frac{n_h - n_h^0}{D_h \tau_h}. \qquad (19.29)$$

This has a solution (writing $\Delta n_h$ for $(n_h - n_h^0)$)

$$\Delta n_h = (\Delta n_h)_0 \exp(-x/L_h), \qquad (19.30)$$

where $(\Delta n_h)_0$ is the excess concentration at $x = 0$, and $L_h = (D_h \tau_h)^{\frac{1}{2}}$ is a measure of the mean distance a minority carrier will move under the action of diffusion before it is lost by recombination. It is known as the 'diffusion length' and is an important quantity in transistor design. A typical value for germanium is 0·1 cm for both holes in $n$-type material and electrons in $p$-type material; typical values in silicon are smaller by a factor of about three.

## 19.6. Metal–semiconductor junctions

To investigate the electrical properties of semiconductors it is necessary to make electrical connexions to them. The behaviour of a junction between a metal electrode and a semiconductor depends on the nature and geometry of the connexion, as well as on the properties of the metal and semiconductor, making a full treatment very complex. The most important property of such a junction is that the current flow for a given voltage is quite different in opposite directions, so that it acts as a rectifier.

When contact is made between a metal and a semiconductor, a potential difference is set up between the two in a similar manner to that between two metals (the contact potential). For an $n$-type semiconductor whose Fermi level is above that of the metal, electrons pass from the semiconductor to the metal until the two Fermi levels are equal. This process is illustrated in Fig. 19.11. The excess negative charge on

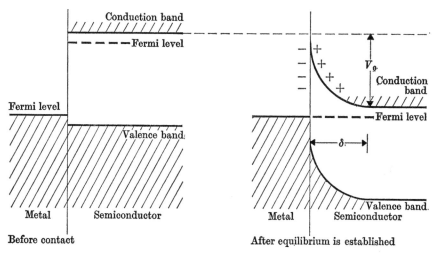

Fig. 19.11. Energy bands and Fermi levels at a metal to semiconductor contact, before and after equilibrium is established.

the metal repels electrons near the surface of the semiconductor, creating a layer which is depleted of conduction electrons and so has a higher resistance than the bulk of the semiconductor. This layer is known as the 'barrier layer' and is a region of positive space charge because it contains the ionized donor impurities without the compensating charge of the negative conduction electrons. By Poisson's equation (equation (2.1)) the potential will vary through the space charge layer, so that there will be a potential difference $V_0$ between the position of the bottom of the conduction band at the surface and in the bulk semiconductor; the energy bands are therefore distorted near the surface, as shown in Fig. 19.11.

In equilibrium there will be no net current flow across the barrier, but this is a dynamic equilibrium between a current $-I_d$ of electrons flowing out of the metal into the semiconductor, and an equal current of electrons (and, to a much lesser extent, holes) leaving the semi-conductor for the metal. The latter may be written in the form $I_0 \exp(-eV_0/kT)$, since the fraction of the electrons which have sufficient energy to surmount the barrier $V_0$ is proportional to $\exp(-eV_0/kT)$. If a voltage $V$ is now applied which makes the metal positive with respect to the semiconductor, this extra voltage appears almost entirely across the barrier since this has a much larger resistance than either

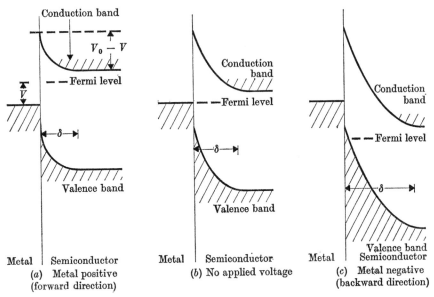

FIG. 19.12. Effect of applied voltage $V$ at metal-semiconductor junction. In (a) a forward voltage $V$ is applied, reducing the barrier height to $V_0 - V$, and giving a large current flow of electrons from the semiconductor into the metal; in (c) a reverse voltage is applied, increasing the barrier and reducing the current flow. Note the change with voltage in the effective thickness of the barrier $\left(\delta = \left\{ \dfrac{2\epsilon\epsilon_0(V_0 - V)}{eN_d} \right\}^{\frac{1}{2}}\right)$, and that the Fermi level in the metal is depressed when the metal is made positive because of the negative sign of the electronic charge.

the metal or the bulk semiconductor. The current leaving the semi-conductor then becomes $I_0 \exp\{-e(V_0 - V)/kT\}$, because the barrier height is reduced from $V_0$ to $V_0 - V$; on the other hand the current leaving the metal is still $-I_d$, since the barrier which the electrons in the metal have to surmount is unaltered (see Fig. 19.12). Since

$$I_d = I_0 \exp(-eV_0/kT),$$

the net current flow is

$$I = I_d\{\exp(eV/kT) - 1\}. \tag{19.31}$$

If $V$ is positive and greater than $(kT/e)$, large forward currents can flow, while if $V$ is negative $I$ approaches $-I_d$; the current-voltage characteristic therefore has the form shown in Fig. 14.15, and the junction is an efficient rectifier.

This treatment gives a satisfactory qualitative treatment of the rectifying properties, though agreement with experiment is by no means exact. A satisfactory feature is that it gives the right sign for the forward direction; that is, that the direction of easy flow of electrons (for an $n$-type semiconductor) is from semiconductor to metal. In an early theory the flow of electrons through the barrier was ascribed to the tunnel effect, so that the easy flow was from metal (where the electron density is high) to semiconductor. However, the tunnel effect is only appreciable when the barrier thickness is comparable with the electron wavelength in the metal; i.e. less than $10^{-7}$ cm, whereas the theory of a barrier due to a depletion layer gives a thickness of order $10^{-6}$ cm. A simple version of a theory for the barrier thickness put forward by Schottky is as follows.

We assume that all conduction electrons are removed from the barrier layer, so that the charge density $\rho = eN_d$, where $N_d$ is the number of donors per unit volume (for simplicity we take these all to carry unit charge, and all to be positively ionized; i.e. we are in the exhaustion region). Let the surface of the semiconductor be the plane $x = 0$, and the barrier extend from the surface to the plane $x = \delta$, so that the space charge becomes zero for $x \geqslant \delta$. Then the potential is constant for $x \geqslant \delta$, and the electric field vanishes at $x = \delta$. In the barrier, Poisson's equation reduces to

$$\nabla^2 V = d^2V/dx^2 = -eN_d/\epsilon\epsilon_0. \tag{19.32}$$

Integration, using the boundary conditions $dV/dx = 0$ (no electric field) at $x = \delta$, and $V = 0$ at $x = 0$, gives

$$V = -(eN_d/2\epsilon\epsilon_0)\{(x-\delta)^2-\delta^2\}. \tag{19.33}$$

Hence the difference of potential at the surface $x = 0$ from that in the interior of the semiconductor $(x \geqslant \delta)$ is

$$V_0 = eN_d\delta^2/2\epsilon\epsilon_0. \tag{19.34}$$

If we take $\epsilon \approx 12$ (as in silicon) and $N_d = 10^{18}$ cm$^{-3}$ ($10^{24}$ m$^{-3}$), $\delta$ is found to be about $3 \times 10^{-6}$ cm if $V_0$ is about 1 volt.

A difficulty in the Schottky theory is that $V_0$ should be equal to the difference in the work functions of metal and semiconductor, and hence $I_d$, which is proportional to $\exp(-eV_0/kT)$, should depend on the metal used, whereas experimentally it does not. To overcome this difficulty

Bardeen put forward the idea of 'surface states'. At the surface of the semiconductor the atomic arrangement is different because there are no atoms on the one side with which to form bonds. Thus the surface atoms have different energy levels, and these levels are discrete because bands are only formed from the levels of atoms which are identical. There may also be impurity atoms absorbed on the surface. Those surface levels which lie below the Fermi level of the semiconductor will be filled by electrons which drop into them out of the conduction band, giving a negative charge on the surface which repels electrons near the surface. This gives a depletion layer just inside the surface, which acts as the barrier. If $N_s$ is the number of surface states per unit area, and $N_d$ the number of donors per unit volume, then the thickness $\delta$ of the barrier will be determined by the relation $N_s = N_d \, \delta$ if we assume that all the conduction electrons for a distance $\delta$ are drawn into the surface states. Application of Poisson's equation to the barrier layer yields equation (19.34) as before, but on writing $\delta = N_s/N_d$ we have

$$V_0 = eN_s^2/2\epsilon\epsilon_0 N_d. \tag{19.35}$$

This equation shows that $V_0$ depends on $N_s$ and $N_d$ for the semiconductor and is independent of what metal is used to make the contact; in fact the barrier layer exists in the absence of any contact.

The discussion above has been on the basis of an $n$-type semiconductor, but similar arguments apply to a $p$-type semiconductor if holes are substituted for electrons (thereby reversing the direction of easy current flow). Thus a metal–semiconductor junction will act as a rectifier. However, in order to use it two junctions must be made to complete a circuit, and since the forward direction will be in the opposite sense at the two junctions, no rectifying action will result unless the two junctions are different in nature. At microwave frequencies one junction must be very small in cross-section, since otherwise the capacitance between the metal and bulk semiconductor across the barrier layer acts as a short circuit, the current flowing as displacement current through this capacitance instead of real current through the barrier. This small contact is made by a thin metal whisker (usually tungsten) pressed against the semiconductor (see Fig. 14.16); the other contact is soldered and of large area, so that it offers little resistance (and large capacitance) to the flow of current in what would otherwise be its 'backward' direction.

Such fine contacts have a relatively high resistance, since the current has to spread out from a fine point through the interior of the semiconductor, and they cannot carry more than a few mA of current. At power frequencies semiconductor–metal junctions of large area can be used; the second contact is soldered, in such a way that the semiconductor surface is doped to make almost an ohmic contact. In the past both $Cu_2O$ and selenium have been used for such power rectifiers, but semi-conductor–metal junctions for this purpose have now been superseded by junctions between two parts, differently doped, of a single semi-conductor crystal.

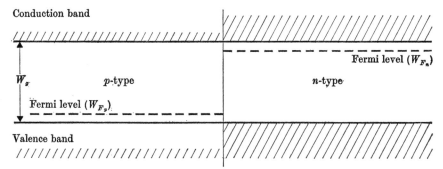

FIG. 19.13. Energy bands and Fermi levels at a $p$–$n$ junction, before equilibrium is established.

## 19.7. The $p$–$n$ junction

Single crystals of a semiconductor (usually germanium) can be prepared in which one end is doped to make it $p$-type, and the other end $n$-type, the change from $p$-type to $n$-type taking place in a region whose thickness is of order $10^{-6}$ cm. Such a unit is called a $p$–$n$ junction. The $p$-type material is made by doping with a concentration $N_a$ of acceptors, the $n$-type by doping with a concentration $N_d$ of donors; obviously there will be a narrow region at the junction where the doping concentration varies from one extreme to the other, but provided this region is small in width compared with the thickness of the barrier region estimated below, we can regard the change from $p$-type to $n$-type as discontinuous. In germanium doped with group III and group V impurities the ionization potential is so small that at room temperature we can regard the donors and acceptors as fully ionized (i.e. we are in the exhaustion region).

The energy level situation shown in Fig. 19.13 is not stable and could only exist if the $n$-type and $p$-type material were in separate crystals. There is an excess hole concentration in the $p$-type, and excess electron concentration in the $n$-type, so that when they are in the same crystal holes will diffuse to the right and electrons to the left, each giving a

positive current to the right. This gives a positive potential to the
$n$-type material, so that the energy levels of its electrons are lowered
because of their negative charge. This process continues until the Fermi
levels of the two halves are equalized, as in Fig. 19.14. The difference
of potential between the two halves means that strong electric fields
exist near the junction, and these sweep out the mobile carriers in the

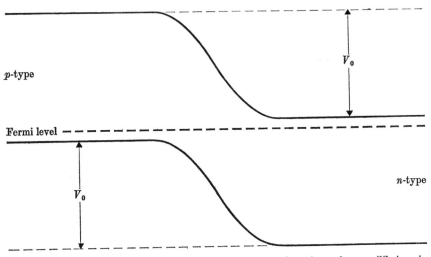

$p$-type

Fermi level

$V_0$

$n$-type

$V_0$

Fig. 19.14. Energy bands and the Fermi level at a $p$–$n$ junction, after equilibrium is
established. The $n$-type becomes positively charged, so that its electrons have lower
potential energy.

vicinity of the junction, giving a barrier layer of high resistance. The
whole of the potential drop occurs across this barrier layer; removal of
the holes in the barrier layer on the $p$-type side leaves a negative space
charge of $-eN_a$ per unit volume, and removal of electrons on the $n$-type
side leaves a positive space charge of $+eN_d$ per unit volume, as shown in
Fig. 19.15. We may apply Poisson's equation to the barrier layer, making the same kind of simplifying assumptions as in the treatment of the
metal-semiconductor junction. Let the change from $p$- to $n$-type occur
discontinuously at the plane $x = 0$, and let the barrier thickness be $\delta_p$
and $\delta_n$ on each side respectively. Then, taking $V = 0$, at $x = 0$ we have,
using the boundary conditions $dV/dx = 0$ at $x = -\delta_p$ and at $x = +\delta_n$:

$$x < 0 \qquad\qquad\qquad\qquad x > 0$$

$$\frac{d^2V}{dx^2} = +\frac{eN_a}{\epsilon\epsilon_0} \qquad\qquad\qquad \frac{d^2V}{dx^2} = -\frac{eN_d}{\epsilon\epsilon_0}$$

$$V = \frac{eN_a}{2\epsilon\epsilon_0}\{(x+\delta_p)^2 - \delta_p^2\} \qquad V = -\frac{eN_d}{2\epsilon\epsilon_0}\{(x-\delta_n)^2 - \delta_n^2\}$$

Thus the overall potential difference $V_0$ between the $n$-type material and the $p$-type material is the difference between $V_n$, the value of $V$ at $x = \delta_n$, and $V_p$ at $x = -\delta_p$. This is

$$V_0 = V_n - V_p = \frac{e}{2\epsilon\epsilon_0}\{N_d\delta_n^2 + N_a\delta_p^2\}. \qquad (19.36)$$

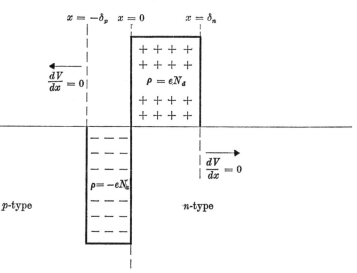

Fɪɢ. 19.15. Space charge density at a $p$–$n$ junction, on the simplified model used in the text.

From the fact that $dV/dx$ must be continuous at $x = 0$ we obtain the additional condition

$$N_a\delta_p = N_d\delta_n. \qquad (19.37)$$

Finally, comparison of Figs. 19.13 and 19.14 shows that

$$e(V_n - V_p) = W_{Fn} - W_{Fp} \approx W_g, \qquad (19.38)$$

where $W_{Fn}$, $W_{Fp}$ are the Fermi levels in $n$- and $p$-type as shown in Fig. 19.13; in the exhaustion range these lie close to the bottom of the conduction band and top of the valence band respectively, so that the energy difference is nearly equal to the energy gap. If we take

$$N_a = N_d = 10^{24} \text{ m}^{-3},$$

then for germanium the width of the barrier $(\delta_n + \delta_p)$ is found to be about $5 \times 10^{-6}$ cm.

The fact that the barrier layer has a very much higher resistivity than that of the bulk material means that any external voltage applied appears almost wholly across the barrier layer; there is little potential variation in the bulk material and currents near the barrier are due to diffusion.

Majority carriers which cross the barrier become, of course, minority carriers on the far side; for example, holes leaving the $p$-type material on the left of Fig. 19.14 become minority carriers on entering the $n$-type material on the right. This creates an excess of minority carriers at the barrier edge, giving rise to a diffusion current away from the barrier which is the controlling factor in the steady state for the net current flow across the barrier. From equation (19.30), we have for holes in the $n$-type

$$\Delta n_h = (\Delta n_h)_0 \exp\{-(x-\delta_n)/L_h\},$$

where $(\Delta n_h)_0$ is the excess concentration at $x = \delta_n$, the right-hand edge of the barrier. The diffusion hole current density is

$$j_h = -eD_h(\partial n_h/\partial x) = e(\Delta n_h)_0(D_h/L_h)\exp\{-(x-\delta_n)/L_h\}$$
$$= e(\Delta n_h)_0(D_h/L_h)$$

at the barrier edge. A detailed analysis shows that, as we might expect, the hole concentration at $x = \delta_n$ is proportional to the density of holes in the $p$-type material which have sufficient energy to surmount the barrier. If an external voltage $V$ is applied which makes the $n$-type material less positive, the voltage across the barrier becomes $(V_0-V)$ and hence $(n_h)_0 = A \exp\{-e(V_0-V)/kT\}$. In the absence of any external voltage $(n_h)_0$ is just equal to the equilibrium hole density $n_h$ in the $n$-type material, so that $n_h = A \exp(-eV_0/kT)$ and

$$(\Delta n_h)_0 = (n_h)_0 - n_h = n_h\{\exp(eV/kT)-1\}.$$

This gives
$$j_h = e(n_h D_h/L_h)\{\exp(eV/kT)-1\}$$

and a similar equation is obtained for the flow of electrons across the barrier to the left. Hence the total current density across the junction is

$$j = j_h + j_e = e\left\{\frac{n_h D_h}{L_h} + \frac{n_e D_e}{L_e}\right\}\left\{\exp\frac{eV}{kT}-1\right\}, \qquad (19.39)$$

where $n_h$, $D_h$, $L_h$ refer to holes in the $n$-type material and $n_e$, $D_e$, $L_e$ to electrons in the $p$-type. This emphasizes the role played by the minority carriers.

This equation, due originally to Shockley, is similar to that obtained in the previous section for a metal–semiconductor junction, and a $p$–$n$ junction acts as a rectifier. It can be controlled in production much better than a metal-semiconductor junction because of the absence of an external surface. The forward resistance is lower than in a thermionic vacuum tube diode because of the high density of majority carriers in a solid, but there is a small back-current, and the junction cannot withstand such high back voltages. This is because at high field strengths the carriers gain sufficient energy from the field to excite electrons from the valence band into the conduction band, producing more carriers. This is an avalanche process, and similar to the Townsend discharge in a gas, so that the back current increases very rapidly beyond a certain voltage.

Both germanium and silicon are used for $p$–$n$ junctions. Germanium has the smaller energy gap, giving a bigger carrier density. The mobility is also somewhat higher, so that the forward resistance is lower than

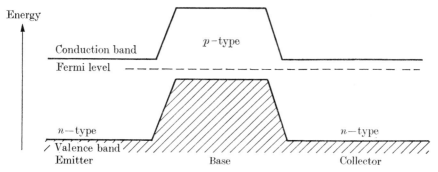

FIG. 19.16. Electron energy levels in an unbiased $n$–$p$–$n$ ($NPN$) transistor.

for silicon, but the back current is higher (in germanium the value of $I_d$ at room temperature is about $10^{-5}$ A/cm$^2$). Silicon can be operated at higher temperatures before thermal ionization across the energy gap increases the back current and drops the rectification efficiency appreciably. The absence of a heated cathode requiring its own power supply, better reliability, and longer life give solid-state rectifiers a great advantage over vacuum tube devices.

## 19.8. The junction transistor

The $NPN$ junction transistor consists of a single crystal of semiconductor, usually germanium or silicon, in which a thin $p$-type region, the base, is sandwiched between two $n$-type regions called the emitter and collector. $PNP$ devices also exist and the following discussion applies equally to them if the roles of the holes and electrons are exchanged. The transition layers are thinner than the base region whose thickness is itself less than $L$, the diffusion length (see equation (19.30)). When no external voltages are present, the energy levels are as shown in Fig. 19.16.

In normal operation, voltages are applied to give the situation shown in Fig. 19.17 where the emitter-base junction is forward biased and the collector-base junction reverse biased. Electrons from the emitter enter

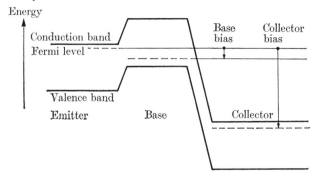

FIG. 19.17. Electron energy levels in a normally biased *NPN* transistor.

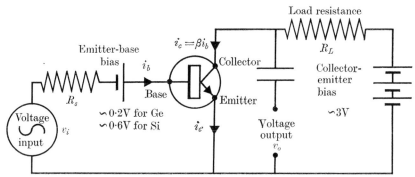

FIG. 19.18. An amplifier using an *NPN* transistor in a common-emitter circuit. $R_s$ is the internal resistance of the signal source of voltage $v_i$, and $R_L$ the load resistance. $\beta$ is the current gain (see p. 571).

the base while holes travel in the opposite direction, but as the emitter is doped more heavily, the hole contribution is small ($< 1$ per cent) and will be neglected. After crossing this junction, the electrons become minority carriers and diffuse across the base and into the collector since the potential drop is in their favour. The number of electrons flowing from emitter to collector depends on the emitter bias $V_{be}$ according to the diode law (equation (19.39)) and is found to be only weakly dependent on the voltage between collector and emitter $V_{ce}$. Following equations (12.10) and (12.11) for the triode valve we write, for small changes of the collector current $I_c$,

$$i_c = g_m v_{be} + v_{ce}/\rho, \tag{19.40}$$

where from equation (19.39) the mutual conductance

$$g_m = (\partial I_c / \partial V_{be})_{V_{ce}} \doteq e I_e / kT, \qquad (19.41)$$

giving $(g_m/I_e) = 40$ volt$^{-1}$ for transistors with abrupt junctions since $(kT/e) = \frac{1}{40}$ volt at room temperature. In the basic amplifier circuit of Fig. 19.18 (cf. Fig. 12.8) the output voltage $v_0$ is

$$v_0 = i_c R_L = g_m R_L v_{be} + (R_L/\rho) v_0, \qquad (19.42)$$

and as the output resistance $\rho$ is usually large compared with the load resistance $R_L$, the voltage amplification $v_0/v_{be}$ is given approximately by $g_m R_L$ as for a pentode vacuum tube.

The mutual conductance of thermionic vacuum tubes is nearly constant over an appreciable range of cathode current, whereas that of junction transistors is proportional to the emitter current $I_e$ (equation (19.41)). Therefore distortion will occur if the circuit of Fig. 19.18 is used to amplify voltages that cause appreciable changes in $I_e$. This difficulty is overcome as follows. In all practical devices a small current flows in the base lead, arising from recombination of a few of the injected electrons as they wander through the base, and from smaller components of the currents crossing the junctions which we have so far neglected. Both contributions are closely proportional to the collector current, so that an important parameter, the current gain $\beta = (\partial I_c / \partial I_b)$ at constant $V_{ce}$, is substantially constant in a given transistor. In spite of tight control in manufacture, $\beta$ can vary considerably (e.g. from 30 to 400) from transistor to transistor.

The input impedance $R_i$ is found from the relation

$$R_i = (\partial V_{be} / \partial I_b) = (\partial V_{be} / \partial I_c)(\partial I_c / \partial I_b) = \beta / g_m = \beta kT / eI_e, \quad (19.43)$$

where the partial differentials are all at constant $V_{ce}$, showing that $R_i$ varies with $I_e$ even when $\beta$ is constant. (In practice there are corrections to (19.43) because of the finite resistance of the bulk semiconductor in series with the base and emitter leads.) If the signal source has an open circuit voltage $v_i$ and internal resistance $R_s \gg R_i$, then using equation (19.43) we have approximately, if $R_L \ll \rho$,

$$v_0 = i_c R_L \doteq g_m R_L v_{be} = (eI_e/kT) R_L (v_i R_i / R_s) = \beta v_i (R_L / R_s). \quad (19.44)$$

Thus, under these conditions the variations of $R_i, g_m$ with $I_e$ cancel, and a linear amplification can be realized. Essentially the device behaves as a current amplifier, since the input current $i_i = v_i / R_s$ and the output current $i_0 = v_0 / R_L = \beta i_i$. The inequalities are readily satisfied since from the numerical values given earlier $R_i = \beta / g_m \approx 3 \ 10^2$ to $3 \ 10^3$ ohm for $I_e = 3$ mA, while in a small transistor $\rho \approx 2 \ 10^4$ ohm (it is lower for a power output transistor); in a cascade amplifier $R_L$ is shunted by the input impedance of the next stage (cf. § 13.1) so that there is no point in making $R_L$ much larger than $R_i$.

At high frequencies the situation becomes much more complicated, but it can be broadly understood in terms of the transit time of electrons diffusing across the base, which makes $\beta$ a frequency-dependent complex number, together with feedback through the capacitance of the reverse-biased collector-base junction (cf. § 12.8).

Transistors are smaller, consume less power, and have a longer life than thermionic vacuum tubes, and the availability of both $PNP$ and $NPN$ types is a great advantage in circuit design. They are, however, restricted in their ability to produce large power outputs at high frequencies; like $p$–$n$ junctions (see § 19.7), they are susceptible to transient overloads which produce ionization avalanches, and to temperature rises.

## GENERAL REFERENCES

Amos, S. W., 1965, *Principles of Transistor Circuits* (Iliffe).
Rollin, B. V., 1964, *An Introduction to Electronics* (O.U.P.).
Simpson, J. H., and Richards, R. S., 1962, *Physical Principles and Applications of Junction Transistors* (O.U.P.).

## PROBLEMS

19.1. Show that the energy levels of an 'atom' consisting of a positive charge equal to that of the proton, with an effective mass $m_h^*$, and a negative charge equal to that of the electron, with an effective mass $m_e^*$, moving in a medium of dielectric constant $\epsilon$, are those given by equations (19.18) and (19.19).

Show that the binding energy of a donor impurity level in silicon ($m_h^* = \infty$, $m_e^*/m = 0.4$, $\epsilon = 11.5$) is about 0.041 eV, and that the Bohr radius is about 6.5 times the inter-atomic distance (2.35 Å).

19.2. In many semiconductors the energy gap varies linearly with $T$ over a fair temperature range, though it tends to a constant value at low temperatures. Show that if $W_g = W_g^0 - aT$, then a plot of $\ln(R_H T^{\frac{3}{2}})$ against $1/T$ gives a straight line whose slope gives the value of $W_g^0$. Show also that the effect of the temperature variation of $W_g$ on equation (19.22) is to replace $W_g$ by $W_g^0$ and to increase the apparent value of the product $(m_e^* m_h^*)$ by $\exp(2a/3k)$.

19.3. By combining equations (1.20), (3.3), and (3.5) show that any abnormal charge distribution in a conductor of conductivity $\sigma$, dielectric constant $\epsilon$, vanishes in time as $\rho = \rho_0 \exp(-t/\tau)$, where $\tau = \epsilon\epsilon_0/\sigma$. Show that for germanium where $\epsilon = 16$, $\sigma = 10$ (ohm-metre)$^{-1}$, the value of $\tau$ is about $1.4 \times 10^{-11}$ sec.

A sample of germanium contains $10^{18}$ holes/m$^3$. Show that the presence of a net space charge equivalent to 1 per cent of the hole concentration would give rise to an electric field gradient of about $10^7$ V/m$^3$.

**19.4.** When an external bias voltage $V$ is applied to a $p$–$n$ junction with a high resistance barrier, the voltage across the barrier in equation (19.33) becomes $V_n - V_p = V + V_g$, where $|e| V_g = W_g$. Show that the total charge $\pm Q$ in each of the space charge regions of Fig. 19.15, when $N_a = N_d = N_I$, is given by

$$Q = (\epsilon \epsilon_0 e N_I)^{\frac{1}{2}} (V + V_g)^{\frac{1}{2}} \quad \text{per unit area.}$$

This is a function of the applied voltage, and the barrier acts as a capacitance for a.c. voltages of magnitude

$$C = (dQ/dV) = \tfrac{1}{2} (\epsilon \epsilon_0 e N_I)^{\frac{1}{2}} (V + V_g)^{-\frac{1}{2}} \quad \text{per unit area.}$$

Special junction diodes of this type are used as variable capacitors (since $C$ is a function of $V$) in the parametric amplifier (§ 16.5).

**19.5.** Verify that the capacitance derived in the previous problem is the same as that of a parallel-plate capacitor with plate separation equal to the barrier thickness and filled with dielectric of relative permittivity $\epsilon$.

**19.6.** In a crystal the velocity of a particle is given by the relation $\hbar \mathbf{v} = \text{grad}_k\, W$, where $\text{grad}_k = \mathbf{i}_x(\partial/\partial k_x) + \mathbf{i}_y(\partial/\partial k_y) + \mathbf{i}_z(\partial/\partial k_z)$, in which $\mathbf{i}_x$, etc., are unit vectors along the $x$, $y$, $z$ directions. Show that in general $\mathbf{v}$ is not parallel to $\mathbf{k}$ unless it is along one of the axes, for a particle whose energy $W$ is given by equation (18.14).

Show that with respect to axes $(x', y', z')$ which are derived from the $(x, y, z)$ axes by a rotation through an angle $\theta$ about the $y$-axis, equation (18.14) becomes

$$W = W_0 \pm \tfrac{1}{2}\hbar^2 \left\{ k_x'^2 \left( \frac{\cos^2\theta}{m_x^*} + \frac{\sin^2\theta}{m_z^*} \right) + k_y'^2/m_y^* + k_z'^2 \left( \frac{\sin^2\theta}{m_x^*} + \frac{\cos^2\theta}{m_z^*} \right) + \right.$$
$$\left. + 2k_x' k_z' \sin\theta \cos\theta \left( \frac{1}{m_x^*} - \frac{1}{m_z^*} \right) \right\}.$$

Hence show that the effective mass for a particle for which $\mathbf{k}$ is along the $z'$-axis is

$$\frac{1}{\hbar^2} \frac{\partial^2 W}{\partial k_z'^2} = \frac{\sin^2\theta}{m_x^*} + \frac{\cos^2\theta}{m_z^*}.$$

($m^{*-1}$ is a tensor quantity, and cross-product terms such as $k_x' k_z'$, etc., are absent only when a suitable choice of axes (usually dictated by the crystal symmetry) is made.)

**19.7.** For a semiconductor in the infra-red, where $\omega\tau \gg 1$, the effective conductivity (see Problem 18.2) becomes $\sigma' = \sigma_0/(1 + \omega^2\tau^2)$. Show that an electromagnetic wave will fall in intensity inside the semiconductor as $W = W_0 \exp(-\alpha x)$, where

$$\alpha \doteqdot \frac{\sigma_0}{n\epsilon_0 c(1 + \omega^2\tau^2)}$$

provided that $k \ll n$ in the complex refractive index $n - jk$. Calculate the value of $\alpha$ for a sample of germanium in which $n = 4$, $\sigma_0 = 10$ (ohm-metre)$^{-1}$, at a frequency where $\omega\tau = 100$.

(*Answer*: $\alpha = 10^{-1}$ per metre, approximately.)

# THE ATOMIC THEORY OF PARAMAGNETISM

## 20.1. A general precession theorem

IN Chapter 8 the origin of paramagnetism was discussed, and it was shown to exist in substances containing permanent magnetic dipoles. Such dipole moments are associated with moving charges, being due either to the motion of electrons in their orbits about the atomic nucleus or the spin of the electron about its own axis. From observations of hyperfine structure in atomic spectra it was inferred that the nuclei of many types of atom also possess 'spin' due to rotation about an internal axis, and that a magnetic dipole moment is associated with this spin. In all these cases the magnetic moment is associated with some units of angular momentum, and the direction of the magnetic moment $\mathbf{m}$ is parallel to that of the angular momentum vector $\mathbf{G}$, and proportional to it. Thus we may write (cf. equation (8.2))

$$\mathbf{m} = \gamma \mathbf{G}, \tag{20.1}$$

where $\gamma$ is a constant whose reciprocal $(1/\gamma)$ is known as the gyromagnetic ratio. For an electron of charge $-e$ and mass $m_0$ moving in an orbit, $\gamma$ is equal to the classical value $-e/2m_0$; the magnetic moment associated with the intrinsic spin of the electron is anomalously large, the ratio being in this case very nearly equal to $-e/m_0$. The minus sign in each of these cases arises from the fact that the charge carried by the electron is negative, and shows that the magnetic moment is oppositely directed to the angular momentum vector. In the case of the nucleus, the angular momentum is of the same order as that of an electron, being either a small half-integral or integral multiple of $\hbar$, but the magnetic moment is $\approx$ a thousand times smaller, corresponding to the greater mass of the particles (proton and neutron) in the nucleus. The value of $\gamma$ is then $g_n(e/2M)$, where $M$ is the mass of the proton, and $g_n$ is a number which is of the order of unity but is not in general an exact integer or a simple fraction.

When an atom or nucleus with a permanent magnetic dipole moment $\mathbf{m}$ is placed in a steady magnetic field $\mathbf{B}$, a couple is exerted on it which may be written in vector form as $\mathbf{m} \wedge \mathbf{B}$. The angular momentum must therefore change (either in magnitude or direction) at a rate equal to

this couple; that is
$$\dot{\mathbf{G}} = \mathbf{m} \wedge \mathbf{B}.$$
Since **m** is proportional to and parallel to **G**, we have
$$\dot{\mathbf{G}} = \gamma \mathbf{G} \wedge \mathbf{B}. \qquad (20.2)$$
This is a vector equation whose solution is easily found by writing down its components referred to Cartesian coordinates. If the magnetic field is assumed to act along the $z$-axis the components are
$$\left.\begin{array}{l} \dot{G}_x = \gamma B G_y \\ \dot{G}_y = -\gamma B G_x \\ \dot{G}_z = 0 \end{array}\right\}. \qquad (20.3)$$
Integration of the last equation shows that the component $G_z$ along the $z$-axis is a constant. It follows that the angle $\alpha$ which **G** makes with **B** is constant, and we may write $G_z = G \cos \alpha$. The equations for the $x$- and $y$-components may be solved by differentiating one of them and eliminating either $G_x$ or $G_y$. One finds
$$\ddot{G}_x = \gamma B \dot{G}_y = -(\gamma B)^2 G_x$$
with an identical equation for $G_y$. The solution is of the form
$$G_x = A \cos(-\gamma B t + \epsilon),$$
and from equation (20.3) we find
$$G_y = A \sin(-\gamma B t + \epsilon).$$
Thus it will be seen that the projection of $G$ on the $xy$-plane is of constant magnitude $A = G \sin \alpha$, but rotates with the angular velocity $-\gamma B$, which we may write as $\omega_L$. Thus our solution for the components of **G** is
$$\left.\begin{array}{l} G_x = G \sin \alpha \cos(\omega_L t + \epsilon) \\ G_y = G \sin \alpha \sin(\omega_L t + \epsilon) \\ G_z = G \cos \alpha \end{array}\right\}. \qquad (20.4)$$
The motion is such that the magnitudes of both **m** and **G** remain constant, but their directions 'precess' at a constant angle about the direction of the field **B** as in Fig. 20.1. The angular velocity of the precession depends only on the gyromagnetic ratio and the size of the magnetic field. The direction of precession is that of a right-handed screw progressing along **B** if $\gamma$ is negative, and vice versa. The angle $\alpha$ depends on the initial conditions prevailing when the magnetic field was switched on.

Although we have chosen to solve equation (20.2) by the use of a Cartesian coordinate system, we could have derived a certain amount

of information about the motion by inspection of the vector equation
(20.2) itself. Since the vector product of two vectors is a vector perpen-
dicular to both, it follows that $\dot{\mathbf{G}}$ is normal to $\mathbf{G}$ and to $\mathbf{B}$. Thus, in
Fig. 20.1, if instantaneously both $\mathbf{G}$ and $\mathbf{B}$ are in the plane of the paper,
the motion of $\mathbf{G}$ must be normal to the paper. This means that if the

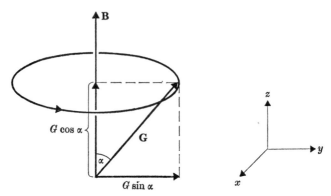

Fig. 20.1. Precession of $\mathbf{G}$ about $\mathbf{B}$. The direction of precession is that for an
electronic momentum ($\gamma$ negative).

momentum vector $\mathbf{G}$ is drawn from a fixed origin, then its tip must move
out of the paper, and since $\dot{\mathbf{G}}$ always remains normal to $\mathbf{G}$, the tip must
move in a circle around $\mathbf{B}$, i.e. the angular momentum vector precesses
around $\mathbf{B}$.

This precessional motion, originally derived in a theorem due to
Larmor, is a quite general result, depending only on the connexion
between angular momentum and magnetic dipole moment. In a quantum mechanical system, such as the atom, the angular momentum plays
an important role, as is well known from atomic theory. In the next
section we turn to consideration of the magnetic moments of single
atoms, making use of our general precession theorem. The chief difference we shall find from the classical case considered above is that the
angle $\alpha$ is now fixed by the rules of quantization, only a small number
of values being possible, instead of any value.

## 20.2. The vector model of the atom

An understanding of the origin of magnetic moments in atoms is possible only when one has a thorough knowledge of the quantum theory of
the behaviour of the electrons in the atom. A comprehensive discussion
of this theory is far beyond the scope of this book, and it is therefore
necessary to assume the reader is acquainted with atomic structure to

the extent given in most elementary textbooks of atomic physics. The outline which follows is intended only as a résumé of the theory, mainly in terms of orbits rather than wave functions. The results quoted will be those appropriate to the wave-mechanical theory, however, unless otherwise indicated.

The state of an electron in an atom is defined by four quantum numbers $n$, $l$, $m_l$, and $s$, whose significance is as follows. The principal quantum number $n$ has integral values from unity upwards, and the energy of the electron is mainly determined by the value of $n$. On the original Bohr theory the energy depended only on the value of $n$, its value being, for an atom with only one electron,

$$W_n = -\frac{RZ^2}{n^2},\tag{20.5}$$

where $R$ is a universal constant (Rydberg's number), and $Ze$ the charge on the nucleus. The same result is obtained by wave mechanics for a one-electron atom, but this result does not hold for atoms with several electrons owing to the electrostatic repulsion between the electrons. For most atoms it remains true that electrons with the lower values of $n$ have the lower energy, and the difference of energy for successive values of $n$ decreases as $n$ becomes larger (cf. Fig. 20.2).

The quantum number $l$ is defined by the value of the angular momentum which the electron possesses in its orbit around the nucleus, this being equal to $\sqrt{\{l(l+1)\}}\hbar$, where $\hbar = h/2\pi$, and $h$ is Planck's constant. The allowed values of $l$ are integral, from 0 up to $(n-1)$ for an electron whose principal quantum number has the value $n$. Since the electron is charged, its motion in an orbit is equivalent to a circulating current, and a magnetic dipole moment is associated with the orbit which has the same value as that to be expected on classical theory. That is, a moment

$$\mathfrak{m} = (-e/2m_0)\sqrt{\{l(l+1)\}}\hbar = -(e\hbar/2m_0)\sqrt{\{l(l+1)\}}.$$

If the angular momentum is represented by a vector $\mathbf{l}$ normal to the plane of the orbit of length proportional to $\sqrt{\{l(l+1)\}}$, then the dipole moment $\mathbf{m}$ is parallel to $\mathbf{l}$ and proportional to it. The minus sign shows that $\mathbf{m}$ and $\mathbf{l}$ have opposite directions, owing to the negative charge possessed by the electron. We see also that the Bohr theory gives us a natural unit of atomic dipole moment, equal to $(e\hbar/2m_0)$. This is known as the Bohr magneton, and its magnitude is

$$0.9273 \times 10^{-23}\ \text{ampere-metre}^2\ (0.9273 \times 10^{-20}\ \text{e.m.u.});$$

it will be denoted by the symbol $\beta$.

Since each orbit has a magnetic dipole moment associated with it, the precession theorem of § 20.1 shows that in the presence of a magnetic field the dipole moment, and hence, also, the angular momentum vector, will precess about the direction of the applied field. Each vector makes a constant angle with this direction, and the component of the angular

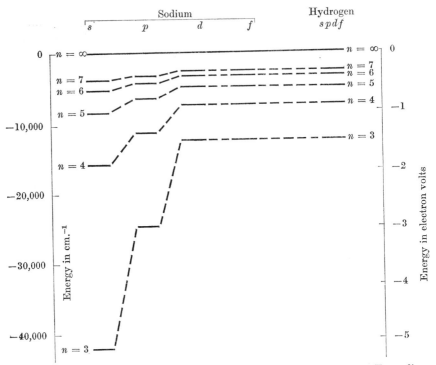

FIG. 20.2. The energy levels of sodium compared with those of hydrogen. For sodium the levels are those of the single electron outside the closed shells $1s^2$, $2s^2$, $2p^6$. For the higher values of $n$ the levels approach closely those of the hydrogen atom. This is because at large distances from the nucleus the electric field is that of the nuclear charge $+Ze$ surrounded by $(Z-1)$ electrons, and hence (by Gauss's theorem) is that of unit positive charge. Orbits with lower values of $n$ penetrate the closed electron shell and so feel a greater positive charge, giving a lower energy. This is most marked for the 'penetrating' s-orbits.

momentum in this direction is therefore constant. On quantum theory the magnitude of this component must be an integral multiple of $\hbar$, and it is written $m_l\hbar$, where $m_l$ is called the magnetic quantum number. It may take all integral values (including 0) between $+l$ and $-l$, as in Fig. 20.3. Since the magnetic moment is proportional to the angular momentum, it follows that the moment associated with the orbit has a fixed component parallel to the direction of the magnetic field of magnitude $-m_l\beta$, together with a component of magnitude $\{l(l+1)-m_l^2\}^{\frac{1}{2}}\beta$ which rotates in the plane normal to the field. The angular velocity of precession $\omega = -(e/2m_0)B$, which is the same as the classical value given by Larmor's theorem. Note that the projection of the angular momentum on the field has the value $m_l\hbar$, not $\sqrt{\{m_l(m_l+1)\}}\hbar$; it is a general feature of wave mechanics that the absolute magnitude of the angular momentum associated with any quantum number such as $l$ has the value $\sqrt{\{l(l+1)\}}\hbar$, while components of angular momentum in a given direction are of the form $m_l\hbar$, where $m_l$ is the associated magnetic quantum number.

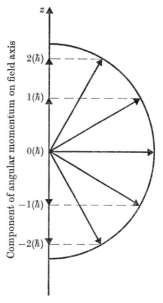

FIG. 20.3. Quantization of orbital angular momentum. The figure is drawn for the case of $l = 2$.

The electron also possesses, in addition to its orbital motion about the nucleus, a spin about its own axis, whose angular momentum is equal to $\sqrt{\{s(s+1)\}}\hbar$, where $s$ is the electronic spin quantum number and is always equal to $\frac{1}{2}$. With the rotating charge of the electron is associated a magnetic moment

$$-g_s\sqrt{\{s(s+1)\}}\times(e\hbar/2m_0)$$
$$= -g_s\beta\sqrt{\{s(s+1)\}}.$$

Here the coefficient $g_s$ is inserted because the ratio of the magnetic moment to the angular momentum differs from the classical value (corresponding to $g_s = 1$). For a long time it was thought that the value of $g_s$ for the electron spin was exactly 2, but it has now been shown both experimentally and theoretically that the value is

$$2(1{\cdot}001160\pm0{\cdot}000002):$$

for our purpose it is sufficient to omit the correction and assume that $g_s$ is 2 for electron spin. In an atom there are relativistic and diamagnetic corrections to both the orbital and spin magnetic moments (of order $10^{-6}$ to $10^{-4}$), which we shall neglect. The minus sign in the expression for the magnetic moment shows that it is oppositely directed to the angular momentum vector, owing to the negative charge of the electron, as in the orbital case. In a magnetic field both the spin angular momentum and its magnetic moment precess about the direction of the field, as in Fig.

20.4, the steady component of the angular momentum in this direction having one of the values $\pm\frac{1}{2}\hbar$, and the corresponding steady component of the magnetic moment having the values $\mp\frac{1}{2}g_s\beta \approx \mp\beta$. Note that these components amount to one Bohr magneton, though the spin is half integral.

In an atom containing a number of electrons, the total angular momentum will be the vector sum of the individual momenta, both orbit and

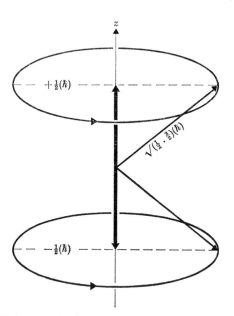

FIG. 20.4. Quantization of spin angular momentum $s = \frac{1}{2}$.

spin. In general this vector sum can be formed in a number of ways, with a number of different resultants. To know which of these is correct or, if several are allowed, which corresponds to the state of lowest energy (the ground or normal state of the atom), we need to know more about the mutual interactions between the various electrons. We shall see that these can be expressed in the form of a set of rules for coupling together the angular momenta in forming the vector resultant. These rules are subject to one overriding condition, expressed in the well-known Pauli principle: 'no two electrons in the same system can be in states with identical sets of quantum numbers'. When applied to an atom this means that no two electrons can have identical sets of values for $n$, $l$, $m_l$, and $m_s$, where $m_s$ is the magnetic quantum number associated with the electron spin. Since $m_s$ can only have the values $\pm\frac{1}{2}$, it may be omitted if we restate the rule as: not more than two electrons can have identical sets of quantum numbers $n$, $l$, $m_l$. Here it must be understood that any two such electrons must be in the states $m_s = +\frac{1}{2}$ and $-\frac{1}{2}$ respectively. The Pauli principle shows that there is a limit to the number of electrons with any given quantum number in a given shell. We have already seen that only two electrons can have identical values of $n$, $l$, $m_l$. Since $m_l$ can only have the $(2l+1)$ values $l$, $l-1$, $l-2$,..., $-(l-1)$, $-l$, only $2(2l+1)$ electrons can be in a subshell with a given value of $l$. Again, since $l$ can only have the values $(n-1)$, $(n-2)$,..., 1, 0, only

$$2\{(2n-1)+(2n-3)+...+3+1\} = 2n^2 \text{ electrons}$$

can have a given value of $n$. Whenever electrons occupy all the possible states corresponding to a given $n$, we have a 'filled shell', and similarly when all possible states for a given $n$, $l$ are occupied, we have a 'filled subshell'. The occurrence of these filled shells gives a similarity between different elements, expressed in the 'periodic table'. From the point of view of magnetism the most important property of a closed shell is that its resultant angular momentum is zero, which can be seen as follows. When we have two electrons with $m_s = +\frac{1}{2}$ and $-\frac{1}{2}$, the total projection of their spin momentum on any axis (such as that supplied by an external field) is $+\frac{1}{2}-\frac{1}{2} = 0$. The precessing components also vanish, as we should expect from the fact that the total angular momentum should be $\sqrt{\{0(0+1)\}}\hbar = 0$. Similarly, for any given value of $l$, when we have electrons occupying all the states $m_l = l$, $(l-1)$, $(l-2)$,..., $-(l-1)$, $-l$, the total projection on any axis adds to zero, and the total orbital angular momentum is also zero. Since in the case either of spin or orbit the associated magnetic moments are proportional to the angular momenta, it follows that the resultant magnetic moment is zero when we have a closed subshell $(n, l)$. Thus the magnetic moment of an atom is due only to the unfilled subshells.

Our next problem is that of how to couple together the angular momenta in a partly-filled subshell. This depends on the mutual interactions between the electrons, of which the two principal types are as follows:

(a) *Mutual repulsion between the electrons, due to their electrical charge.* When this is treated by wave mechanics an unexpected result is found. The energy of the system contains two terms, one corresponding to the classical coulomb interaction, the other known as an 'exchange energy', because it appears to be connected with an exchange of any pair of electrons between the states we assigned to them before including the effect of their mutual repulsion. These exchange forces have no analogue in classical theory, but play an important role in atomic theory. By means of the Pauli exclusion principle, their effect can be shown (see § 21.9) to correspond to a strong coupling between the electron spins, this coupling being such that within an atom the state with the spins parallel is more stable and has the lower energy. The energy of interaction of this coupling may be written in the form $W = -2\mathscr{J}_{ij}\mathbf{s}_i.\mathbf{s}_j$, where $\mathbf{s}_i$, $\mathbf{s}_j$ are the spin vectors, and $\mathscr{J}_{ij}$ is called the 'exchange energy', being positive for any pair of electrons within a given atom but varying in magnitude, depending on their orbital quantum states. Thus with a number of electrons, the primary effect of the exchange forces is to couple together the various vectors $\mathbf{s}_i$, $\mathbf{s}_j$ to form a resultant $\mathbf{S}$, which in the state of lowest energy has the largest possible value consistent with the exclusion principle. The remaining orbital momenta are then coupled together by the electrostatic forces to form a resultant $\mathbf{L}$, which in the state of lowest energy again has the largest possible value consistent with the exclusion principle. (These two rules are known as Hund's rules.) Lower values of $\mathbf{S}$ and $\mathbf{L}$ are possible, but correspond to states of higher energy. This method of coupling the angular momenta is known as Russell–Saunders coupling. On wave mechanics $S$ and $L$ are quantum numbers and the absolute magnitudes of the total angular momenta associated with them are $\sqrt{\{S(S+1)\}}\hbar$ and $\sqrt{\{L(L+1)\}}\hbar$; it is common practice to speak just of the vectors $\mathbf{s}$, $\mathbf{l}$, $\mathbf{S}$, $\mathbf{L}$, etc. (corresponding to the old quantum theory), but it must be remembered that the absolute magnitudes associated with these are $\sqrt{\{s(s+1)\}}$, $\sqrt{\{l(l+1)\}}$, etc.

(b) *Magnetic coupling between the magnetic moments of orbit and spin* (*'spin-orbit' interaction*). The motion of an electron round the charged nucleus produces a field $\mathbf{B}$ which we can estimate as follows. From the theory of relativity one finds that a charged particle moving with velocity $\mathbf{v}$ through an electric field $\mathbf{E}$ experiences a force which is equivalent to a magnetic field $\mathbf{B} = -(\mathbf{v} \wedge \mathbf{E})/c^2$, where $c$ is the velocity of electromagnetic waves. In an atom with nuclear charge $Ze$ and a single electron the field $\mathbf{E}$ at distance $r$ from the nucleus is $\mathbf{E} = \mathbf{r}(Ze/4\pi\epsilon_0 r^3)$; in an atom with many electrons the electric field is still radial to a good approximation (this is the 'central-field' approximation used in atomic theory), but the field is reduced because of the screening effect of other electrons. We can therefore write $\mathbf{E} = \mathbf{r}(Z'e/4\pi\epsilon_0 r^3)$, where $Z'e$ is the nuclear charge which would give the correct value of the field at distance $r$. Then the magnetic field $\mathbf{B}$ experienced by the electron through its motion through the field $\mathbf{E}$ is

$$\mathbf{B} = \frac{Z'e}{4\pi\epsilon_0 c^2 r^3}(\mathbf{r} \wedge \mathbf{v}) = \frac{\mu_0}{4\pi}\frac{Z'e}{m_0}\frac{\mathbf{G}}{r^3} = \frac{\mu_0}{4\pi}\frac{Z'e}{m_0 r^3}\hbar\mathbf{l} = \frac{\mu_0}{4\pi}\frac{2Z'}{r^3}\beta\mathbf{l},$$

where $\mathbf{G}$ is the orbital angular momentum whose quantized value is $l\hbar$. It was first found empirically and later shown theoretically that this formula should be multiplied by a factor $\frac{1}{2}$ (this is a relativistic effect associated with the motion of the electron in a curved path). We must also average $\mathbf{B}$ over the distribution of spin moment, giving

$$\mathbf{B} = \frac{\mu_0}{4\pi}\left\langle\frac{Z'}{r^3}\right\rangle\beta\mathbf{l}, \tag{20.6}$$

where the brackets $\langle\,\rangle$ mean that the average value must be taken. The interaction with the spin magnetic moment $\mathbf{m}_s$ is then

$$-\mathbf{m}_s.\mathbf{B} = g_s\beta(\mathbf{s}.\mathbf{B}) = g_s\frac{\mu_0}{4\pi}\left\langle\frac{Z'}{r^3}\right\rangle\beta^2(\mathbf{l}.\mathbf{s}) = \zeta(\mathbf{l}.\mathbf{s}). \tag{20.7}$$

The effect of this spin-orbit interaction is to tend to couple together the vectors $\mathbf{s}$ and $\mathbf{l}$ for each electron to form a resultant $\mathbf{j}$; the various values of $\mathbf{j}$ for the individual electrons would then be coupled together (vectorially) to form the total angular momentum vector $\mathbf{J}$. However, the spin-orbit interaction is smaller in magnitude than the exchange interactions between the spins discussed in ($a$) above, except in the heaviest elements. We shall therefore confine ourselves to Russell-Saunders coupling, where the individual spins are coupled to form a resultant $\mathbf{S}$, and the individual orbital momenta to form a resultant $\mathbf{L}$. The spin-orbit interaction then couples $\mathbf{S}$ and $\mathbf{L}$ together with an energy

$$W = \lambda\mathbf{L}.\mathbf{S}, \tag{20.8}$$

which is similar in form to equation (20.7) (it can be shown that the relation between the two constants is $\lambda = \pm\zeta/2S$, where the positive sign is required for a shell that is less than half-filled, and the negative sign for one that is more than half-filled; the spin-orbit coupling parameter $\lambda$ vanishes for a half-filled shell). This coupling of $\mathbf{S}$ and $\mathbf{L}$ gives a resultant vector $\mathbf{J}$, of angular momentum $\{J(J+1)\}^{\frac{1}{2}}\hbar$. The number of possible values of $J$ is either $(2S+1)$ or $(2L+1)$, whichever is the smaller. $L$ has only integral values, and the values of $J$ are therefore integral or half-integral according to whether the value of $S$ is integral or half-integral. The latter depends on whether the number of electrons involved is even or odd.

The nomenclature used to describe atomic energy states is mainly derived from pre-quantum attempts to analyse atomic spectra, and therefore does not possess the simple logical sequence which quantum theory could give it. Single electron states for which the orbital quantum number $l$ has the values 0, 1, 2, 3, 4, 5,... are called $s, p, d, f, g, h,...$ states, and similarly the levels of a many-electron atom for which $L = 0, 1, 2, 3, 4, 5,...$ are denoted by the symbols $S, P, D, F, G, H,....$. The value of $n$ for a single electron state is given by the number preceding the symbol, i.e. $1s, 2s, 2p, 3s, 3p, 3d$, etc. The number of electrons with given values of $n$ is denoted by a superfix; thus, 3 electrons with $n = 2, l = 1$ appear as $2p^3$. The spectroscopic state of the whole atom is defined by the values of $S$, $L$, and $J$; the value of the spin multiplicity $2S+1$ is given by a superfix preceding the symbol for $L$, and the value of $J$ by a following suffix. Thus the symbol $^4F_{\frac{3}{2}}$ means that the state has $S = \frac{3}{2}$, $L = 3$, $J = \frac{3}{2}$; the other possible values of $J$ in this case are $\frac{5}{2}, \frac{7}{2}, \frac{9}{2}$, thus ranging in all from $L-S$ to $L+S$.

The coupling scheme for a many-electron atom or ion may be illustrated by reference to the energy level diagram for the $Cr^{3+}$ ion, shown in Fig. 20.5. The triply charged chromium ion has the configuration $1s^2, 2s^2, 2p^6, 3s^2, 3p^6, 3d^3$, with three electrons in the partly filled $3d$ shell. By Hund's rules the energy is lowest when all three electrons have parallel spins, giving $S = \frac{3}{2}$. The electrons must then all have different values of $m_l$, by the Pauli principle, but since we have five possible values ($m_l = 2, 1, 0, -1, -2$) there are $(5!/3!\,2!) = 10$ possible arrangements. The largest possible value of $M_L = \sum m_l$ that we can have is $3 = 2+1+0$, and this belongs to an $L = 3$ state. This has $2L+1 = 7$ values of $M_L$, which therefore take up seven of the possible arrangements of electrons in the $m_l$ states; the other three belong to a state with $L = 1$. By Hund's rule, the $L = 3$ states will have lower energy than the $L = 1$ states. Both are shown in Fig. 20.5, the $^4P$ ($L = 1$) states being higher in energy than the $^4F$ ($L = 3$) states by about 14 000 wave numbers. States of still higher energy are formed by reversing one spin, giving $S = \frac{1}{2}$. Two electrons with opposite spin can now occupy the $m_l = 2$ state, so that the greatest possible value of $L_z = M_L$ is $5 = 2+2+1$, which belongs to a $^2H$ state. Altogether six doublet states, $^2H$, $^2G$, $^2F$, $^2D$ (twice), $^2P$ are allowed; they have energies ranging from about 14 000 cm$^{-1}$ to 37 000 cm$^{-1}$. All other states are much higher in energy, the $3d^2 4s$ configuration lying about 100 000 cm$^{-1}$ above the ground state $3d^3$, $^4F$.

The separation of the various quartet and doublet terms is determined by a combination of the exchange interaction and coulomb interaction arising from the mutual repulsion of the electrons. The spin orbit coupling splits the $^4F$ term into four levels with values of $J$ ranging from $|L-S|$ to $|L+S|$, and the $^4P$ term is similarly split, the only allowed values of $J$ in this case being $\frac{5}{2}$, $\frac{3}{2}$, and $\frac{1}{2}$. From the energy levels given in Fig. 20.5 it can be verified (see Problem 20.7) that the spin-orbit coupling constant $\lambda$ has the value 87 cm$^{-1}$ for the ground states of Cr$^{3+}$.

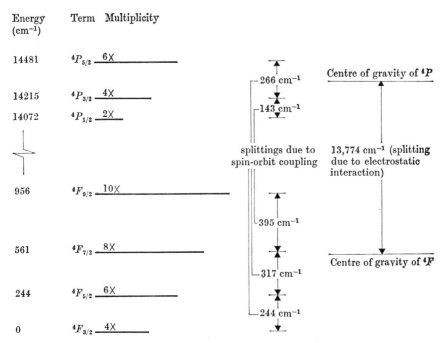

| Energy (cm$^{-1}$) | Term | Multiplicity |
|---|---|---|

FIG. 20.5. Quartet energy levels of the free triply charged chromium ion, Cr$^{3+}$, $3d^3$. These are formed from the three electrons in the $3d$ shell: the splitting between the $^4F$ and $^4P$ terms is due to electrostatic repulsion between the electrons; the splittings between levels of different $J$ within each term are due to spin-orbit coupling.

Doublet terms formed from $3d^3$ lie in the energy range 14 000–37 000 cm$^{-1}$. The next lowest levels are those belonging to the configuration $3d^24s$, and lie above 100 000 cm$^{-1}$.

It can be seen that the splittings due to the 'magnetic' spin-orbit coupling are an order of magnitude smaller than those due to 'electrostatic' interactions.

## 20.3. Magnetic moments of free atoms

When we turn to consider the magnetic properties of atoms we find that the problem is simplified by the fact that these depend only on the partly filled electron shells, since completely filled shells (and of course empty shells) have $S$, $L$, and $J = 0$. The magnetic moment associated with each electron spin can be described by a vector parallel to and proportional to the angular momentum vector **s**, and on forming the vector sum **S** for a number of electrons the magnetic moments add in a similar way, so that the total magnetic moment of the spin is parallel to **S** and has the same factor of proportionality to it. The same is true of the total orbital magnetic moment and the total orbital angular momentum **L**. When we come to make the vector addition of **S** and **L**

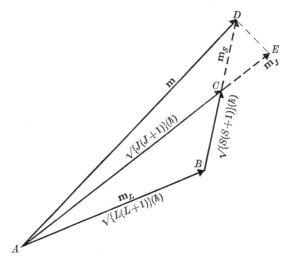

FIG. 20.6. Vector coupling of angular momentum vectors **L, S, J** (represented by $AB, BC, AC$) and the associated magnetic moments $\mathbf{m}_L$, $\mathbf{m}_S$, **m** (represented by $AB, BD = 2BC, AD$). $AE$ is the projection $\mathbf{m}_J$ of **m** on **J**.

the problem is not so simple because the factor of proportionality between the magnetic moment and the angular momentum is not the same for **S** and **L**. The vector representing the total magnetic moment will not therefore be parallel to **J**; this is illustrated by the vector diagram in Fig. 20.6. Here the magnetic moment vector associated with **L** is drawn of the same length as **L**, but on this scale the magnetic moment vector associated with **S** must be drawn twice as long as **S**. The resultant magnetic moment vector **m** is therefore at an angle to **J**.

In considering this question further we must return to the discussion of the spin-orbit coupling between **L** and **S**. This is primarily magnetic in origin, and arises from the magnetic moments of the orbit and spin. Each of these produces a magnetic field which interacts with the dipole moment of the other.

The interaction energy $\lambda \mathbf{L} . \mathbf{S}$ is equivalent to $-\mathbf{m}_S . \mathbf{B}_L$ or to $-\mathbf{m}_L . \mathbf{B}_S$; i.e. to a field $\mathbf{B}_L = -\lambda \mathbf{L}/\gamma_S \hbar$ acting on the spin moment $\mathbf{m}_S = \gamma_S \hbar \mathbf{S}$, or to a field $\mathbf{B}_S = -\lambda\mathbf{S}/\gamma_L\hbar$ acting on the orbital moment $\mathbf{m}_L = \gamma_L\hbar\mathbf{L}$. Hence from equation (20.2) the equations of motion will be

$$\left.\begin{aligned}
\dot{\mathbf{L}} &= \gamma_L\mathbf{L}\wedge\mathbf{B}_S = \gamma_L\mathbf{L}\wedge(-\lambda\mathbf{S}/\gamma_L\hbar) = -(\lambda/\hbar)(\mathbf{L}\wedge\mathbf{S}) \\
\dot{\mathbf{S}} &= \gamma_S\mathbf{S}\wedge\mathbf{B}_L = \gamma_S\mathbf{S}\wedge(-\lambda\mathbf{L}/\gamma_S\hbar) = -(\lambda/\hbar)(\mathbf{S}\wedge\mathbf{L})
\end{aligned}\right\}. \quad (20.9)$$

We note that the couples are equal and opposite, as they must be since no external couple acts on the system. Since $\mathbf{L}+\mathbf{S}=\mathbf{J}$, and

$$\mathbf{L}\wedge\mathbf{L} = \mathbf{S}\wedge\mathbf{S} = 0,$$

we have

$$\left.\begin{aligned}
\dot{\mathbf{L}} &= -(\lambda/\hbar)(\mathbf{L}\wedge\mathbf{S}+\mathbf{L}\wedge\mathbf{L}) = -(\lambda/\hbar)(\mathbf{L}\wedge\mathbf{J}) \\
\dot{\mathbf{S}} &= -(\lambda/\hbar)(\mathbf{S}\wedge\mathbf{L}+\mathbf{S}\wedge\mathbf{S}) = -(\lambda/\hbar)(\mathbf{S}\wedge\mathbf{J})
\end{aligned}\right\}, \quad (20.10)$$

showing that $\mathbf{L}$ and $\mathbf{S}$ each precess about $\mathbf{J}$ with angular velocity $\lambda/\hbar$.

Since the magnetic moments associated with $\mathbf{L}$, $\mathbf{S}$ are parallel to them, it follows that they and their resultant $\mathbf{m}$ must precess round $\mathbf{J}$ at the same rate. Thus the total magnetic moment of the atom has a fixed component, $\mathbf{m}_J$, given by the projection of $\mathbf{m}$ on $\mathbf{J}$, and a precessing component. In general we shall be interested only in the fixed component, and this may be calculated by simple algebra if we remember that the values of the squares of angular momenta associated with $\mathbf{S}$, $\mathbf{L}$, and $\mathbf{J}$ are $S(S+1)$, $L(L+1)$, $J(J+1)$ (each times $\hbar^2$). The projection of $\mathbf{m}$ on $\mathbf{J}$ may be found in the following manner, using the vector diagram of Fig. 20.6. The magnetic moment $\mathbf{m}_L$ associated with $\mathbf{L}$ is $-\beta\{L(L+1)\}^{\frac{1}{2}}$, and its component on $J$ is $\mathfrak{m}_L\cos BAC$. From the geometry of the triangle,

$$-\cos BAC = \frac{S(S+1)-L(L+1)-J(J+1)}{2\{L(L+1)J(J+1)\}^{\frac{1}{2}}}$$

and the projection of the orbital moment on $J$ is therefore

$$+\beta\left[\frac{S(S+1)-L(L+1)-J(J+1)}{2\{J(J+1)\}^{\frac{1}{2}}}\right],$$

where $\beta$ is the Bohr magneton, as before. Similarly the projection of the spin moment on $J$ has the value

$$\mathfrak{m}_S\cos ACB = -2\beta\{S(S+1)\}^{\frac{1}{2}}\cos ACB$$
$$= +2\beta\left[\frac{L(L+1)-S(S+1)-J(J+1)}{2\{J(J+1)\}^{\frac{1}{2}}}\right],$$

where the extra factor 2 appears to allow for the anomalous value of the moment associated with the spin. The sum of these two components is

$$\mathfrak{m}_J = \beta\frac{L(L+1)-S(S+1)-3J(J+1)}{2\{J(J+1)\}^{\frac{1}{2}}}.$$

By analogy with our definitions of the moments associated with $L$ and $S$, we define the magnetic moment $\mathfrak{m}$ associated with $J$ as

$$\mathfrak{m}_J = -g\beta\{J(J+1)\}^{\frac{1}{2}},$$

where $g$ is the Landé factor (named after its originator) whose value is, from comparison of the two equations for $\mathfrak{m}_J$,

$$g = \frac{3}{2} + \frac{S(S+1)-L(L+1)}{2J(J+1)}. \qquad (20.11)$$

It is easy to see that if $S$ or $L$ is zero, so that $J = L$ or $J = S$, then $g$ is 1 or 2 respectively, corresponding to the cases of 'orbit only' and 'spin only'.

When an atom such as we have been considering is placed in an external magnetic field, the behaviour of the angular momentum vectors in general will be rather complicated. The reason is that each of the magnetic moments associated with orbit and spin is acted on by the magnetic field due to the magnetic moment of the other as well as the external magnetic field. No simple description of the motion is possible when these fields are of the same order of magnitude, but when one is much larger than the other an approximate treatment is possible. We shall consider only the case when the external field is very small compared with the field due to the spin-orbit coupling. The vectors **L**, **S** then precess round **J** as in the case of zero external field, but **J** is no longer stationary in space, its motion being a precession round the external field **B**. The precession of **L**, **S** about **J** is at a much higher frequency than that of **J** about **B**, since the external field is small compared with that due to the spin-orbit coupling, and we may therefore picture the components of the magnetic moment precessing around **J** as averaging to zero, leaving only the steady component along **J**. This is acted on by the external field to give the precession of **J** about **B**, at an angular velocity $\boldsymbol{\omega} = -g(-e/2m_0)\mathbf{B}$, where $g$ is the Landé $g$-factor. This is identical with the general result of § 20.1, if we take

$$\gamma = -g(e/2m_0) = -g\beta/\hbar.$$

The quantization rule for the projection of **J** on the field **B** is similar to the previous rules for other angular momentum vectors. The projection has the value $M_J\hbar$, where $M_J$ takes the values $J$, $J-1$, $J-2$,..., $-(J-1)$, $-J$. The component of the magnetic dipole moment of the atom parallel to the field thus has the value $-M_J g\beta$, and the energy is

$$W_{M_J} = -\mathbf{m}.\mathbf{B} = M_J g\beta B. \qquad (20.12)$$

Thus the $2J+1$ levels with different values of $M_J$ are split in energy by the application of a magnetic field, but have the same energy when $B = 0$. In the latter case they are said to be 'degenerate', and the application of a field 'lifts the degeneracy'. This 'Zeeman splitting' is illustrated in Fig. 20.7 for the $^4F$ states of the $Cr^{3+}$ ion in a field $B = 10$

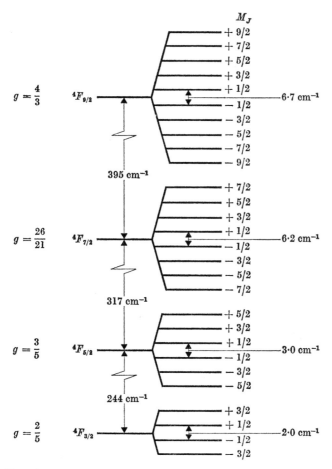

FIG. 20.7. Zeeman splitting of the $^4F$ states of the $Cr^{3+}$ ion (see Fig. 20.5) in a magnetic field $B = 10^5$ gauss (10 weber/m$^2$). Note that the Zeeman splittings are very much smaller relative to the spin–orbit splittings (separation of states of different $J$) than the figure suggests.

weber/metre$^2 = 10^5$ gauss. The value of the spin-orbit coupling parameter $\lambda$ is about 87 cm$^{-1}$ for this ion (see Problem 20.7), and the frequency of precession of $\mathbf{L}$, $\mathbf{S}$ about $\mathbf{J}$ is $\lambda/h = 2 \cdot 6 \times 10^6$ Mc/s. In contrast the frequency of precession of $\mathbf{J}$ about $\mathbf{B}$ in the $J = \frac{3}{2}$ state is only about $6 \times 10^4$ Mc/s in a field of $B = 10^5$ gauss. Thus our assumption of a very fast precession of **L**, **S** about **J**, and a much slower precession of **J** about **B**, will be valid for all fields of ordinary magnitude. In Fig. 20.7 this corresponds to the fact that the Zeeman splittings between the states of different $M_J$ (but the same $J$) are very small compared with the separation between states of different $J$. It is only when this inequality holds that the energy of a Zeeman sub-level is linearly proportional to the applied field (equation (20.12)); when the Zeeman energy ($\sim \beta B$) is comparable with $\lambda$ the behaviour of the energy levels is more complicated. In the opposite extreme when $\beta B \gg \lambda$, the coupling between **L** and **S** is broken down and each tends to precess independently about the external field; this is known as the Paschen–Back effect, and can be observed only in very high fields for light atoms where the spin-orbit coupling is small.

## 20.4. The measurement of atomic magnetic moments—the Stern–Gerlach experiment

The spatial quantization of angular momentum (that is the fact that $M_J$ can have only a discrete number of values, and not a continuous range, as in classical theory) was directly demonstrated in the celebrated atomic beam experiment of Stern and Gerlach in 1922, which also made possible the direct measurement of the magnetic moment of an atom. Though this experiment has been succeeded by more refined and accurate methods, it remains an historical landmark, and developments of this method, mainly due to Rabi and his colleagues, have made experiments with atomic and molecular beams the basis of the extremely accurate knowledge we now possess about atomic magnetic moments, and their interaction with the magnetic moment of the nucleus.

A molecular or atomic beam is a beam of molecules or atoms moving with thermal velocities in a given direction. It is formed by heating the substance in an oven until its vapour pressure is about $10^{-2}$ mm Hg, the oven being in a highly evacuated enclosure. Atoms or molecules effuse through a narrow orifice $S_1$ (see Fig. 20.8), and if the pressure is so low that the mean free path is large compared with the dimensions of $S_1$ no collisions occur in the orifice and all molecules will be moving in substantially the same direction. The angular diameter of the beam is then further limited by the slits $S_2$, $S_3$. The total path traversed by the beam in the apparatus may be up to 50 cm and the pressure must be so low ($< 10^{-6}$ mm) that very few collisions occur to scatter the molecules out of the beam.

In order to determine the magnetic moment of an atom, Stern and

Gerlach deflected the beam in an inhomogeneous magnetic field. This was obtained from a magnet with one wedge-shaped pole piece, which gives a field gradient $\partial B/\partial z$ in the $z$-direction, which is perpendicular to the path of the beam. The beam traversed the inhomogeneous field for a distance $l$ and then struck a detector, which in the early experiments was simply a target cooled in liquid air on which the molecules condensed.

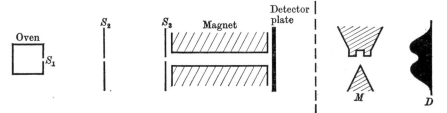

FIG. 20.8. Experimental arrangement for the Stern–Gerlach experiment.
$M$    end view of pole pieces producing inhomogeneous field.
$D$    density of trace on detector plate for atoms in doublet ground state, e.g. Ag,$^2S_{\frac{1}{2}}$.
$S_1\,S_2\,S_3$    collimating slits.

If $\mathfrak{m}_z$ is the component parallel to $\partial B/\partial z$ of the magnetic moment of the atom, then the force exerted on the atom in the $z$-direction is $\mathfrak{m}_z(\partial B/\partial z)$, and the deflexion $s$ after traversing the field gradient for a molecule of mass $M$ and velocity $v$ is

$$s = \tfrac{1}{2}(l/v)^2\mathfrak{m}_z(\partial B/\partial z)/M = l^2\mathfrak{m}_z(\partial B/\partial z)/2Mv^2. \qquad (20.13)$$

To obtain appreciable deflexions (of the order of a millimetre) fields of about $10^4$ gauss with gradients of about $10^5$ gauss/cm are required. The deflexion is inversely proportional to the thermal energy $\tfrac{1}{2}Mv^2$ of the molecules, and the traces are thus spread out owing to the distribution of velocities appropriate to the temperature of the oven. This limits the accuracy of this type of experiment, but with atoms such as sodium or silver, which are both in $^2S_{\frac{1}{2}}$ states, two distinct traces were obtained, with deflexions appropriate to values of $\mathfrak{m}_z$ equal to $\pm$one Bohr magneton. Thus both the existence of spatial quantization corresponding to $M_J = \pm\frac{1}{2}$ and the magnetic moment of one Bohr magneton associated with electron spin of $\frac{1}{2}\hbar$ were confirmed. Later modifications of these experiments gave fairly precise values of atomic magnetic moments, but much higher accuracy has been obtained by the magnetic resonance method, outlined in Chapter 23.

## 20.5. Curie's law and the approach to saturation

A theoretical derivation of Curie's law due to Langevin was given in Chapter 8. This was based on a classical approach in its use of Boltzmann statistics, but used the idea of the existence of permanent magnetic moments of fixed values. This latter assumption is not in accordance with classical theory, for we should then expect a continuous range of magnetic moments from $-\infty$ to $+\infty$. It was shown independently by Bohr and by Miss van Leeuwen that if such a continuous range is assumed, the paramagnetic and diamagnetic contributions to the susceptibility of any system should be exactly equal and opposite, and thus, in a strictly classical calculation, the susceptibility would be zero. The quantum mechanical approach outlined in § 20.2 shows that finite permanent magnetic dipoles do exist in atoms, and we must now examine how the Langevin calculation must be modified to take account of the fact that only a finite number of projections of the moment on an external field are allowed.

It was shown in § 20.3 that the potential energy $W$ of an atom in a magnetic field is $M_J g\beta B$, where $M_J$ is the magnetic quantum number, and $g$ the Landé factor appropriate to the spectroscopic state of the atom. As in classical theory, the probability of an atom being in a state with an energy $W$ is proportional to $\exp(-W/kT)$, and for a given value of $M_J$ this is therefore proportional to $\exp(-M_J g\beta B/kT)$. Thus the fraction of all atoms in this state is $\exp(-M_J g\beta B/kT)/\sum \exp(-M_J g\beta B/kT)$, where the summation is over all values of $M_J$. (We assume that all the atoms are in the same spectroscopic state $L$, $S$, $J$, this being the ground state of the atom.) The component of the atomic magnetic moment parallel to $B$ is $-M_J g\beta$, and the total magnetic moment of a system of $n$ atoms will therefore be

$$n\bar{m} = n\frac{\sum (-M_J g\beta)\exp(-M_J g\beta B/kT)}{\sum \exp(-M_J g\beta B/kT)}, \qquad (20.14)$$

where the summation in each case is over all values of $M_J$ from $+J$ to $-J$. This expression is rather clumsy to handle, but it may be shown by an algebraic reduction that it reduces to the form (see Problem 20.1)

$$n\bar{m} = ngJ\beta\left\{\frac{2J+1}{2J}\coth\left(\frac{2J+1}{2J}y\right) - \frac{1}{2J}\coth\left(\frac{y}{2J}\right)\right\}, \qquad (20.15)$$

where $y = Jg\beta B/kT$. The expression in brackets in equation (20.15) is called the Brillouin function. When $J$ becomes very large it approaches as a limit the Langevin function $\{\coth y - (1/y)\}$, as we should expect from the fact that a summation over a large number of terms can be replaced by an integration, as used in the derivation in § 8.3.

At normal field strengths and ordinary temperatures, the value of $y$ is very small; at $B = 1$ weber/m$^2$ = $10^4$ gauss and $T = 290°$ K, with

$g = 2$ and $J = \frac{1}{2}$, $y$ is about 0·002. It is then possible to make a series expansion of either equation (20.14) or (20.15). To the first order the former equation becomes

$$n\bar{\mathfrak{m}} = -ng\beta \sum_{-J}^{+J} M_J(1-M_J\,g\beta B/kT) \Big/ \sum_{-J}^{+J} (1-M_J\,g\beta B/kT)$$

$$= \frac{ng^2\beta^2 B}{(2J+1)kT} \sum_{-J}^{+J} M_J^2.$$

The summation amounts to $\frac{1}{3}J(J+1)(2J+1)$, and the susceptibility is thus

$$\chi = \frac{n\bar{\mathfrak{m}}}{H} = \frac{\mu_0\,ng^2\beta^2 J(J+1)}{3kT} = \frac{C}{T}, \qquad (20.16)$$

which is the same as the classical expression (equation (8.13)) if we write

$$\mathfrak{m}^2 = g^2\beta^2 J(J+1).$$

This is just the value of the atomic magnetic moment which we should expect on the quantum mechanical theory, but the magnetic moment of the whole system is different at higher field strengths, corresponding to the difference between the Langevin and Brillouin functions. In particular, the limiting saturation moment reached at high field strengths and low temperatures (large values of $y$) is $ng\beta J$, and not

$$n\mathfrak{m} = ng\beta\sqrt{\{J(J+1)\}}.$$

This is because the greatest component of each moment parallel to **B** is $Jg\beta$, and the actual magnetic moment always precesses at a finite angle to the field. The correctness of the Brillouin function has been verified in a number of experiments, representative results being those of Henry shown in Fig. 20.9. Note that the close approach to saturation is obtained by the combination of high field (50 kilogauss) and low temperature (4° K and lower).

## 20.6. Susceptibility of paramagnetic solids—the 4f group

The theory given above applies only to an assembly of free atoms, and the situation is rather different when one considers matter in the aggregated state, because of the large forces exerted by the atoms on each other. These are mainly electrical in origin, and are generally far stronger than the interaction between the magnetic moment of an atom and an external magnetic field. We must therefore consider the effect of the inter-atomic forces first, and we shall find that whereas most free atoms have permanent magnetic dipole moments, most bound atoms do not. This is due to the fact that the exchange forces between electrons in different atoms are nearly always of opposite sign to those between

electrons in the same atom, and they therefore tend to make the electron
spins line up anti-parallel, giving no resultant spin whenever possible.
Thus in the formation of a homo-polar molecule such as $N_2$, the binding
electrons from the nitrogen atoms are shared between the two atoms with

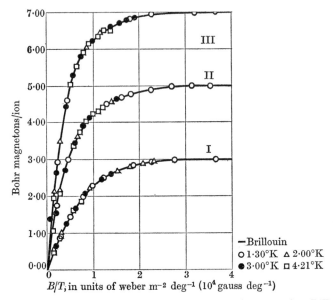

Fig. 20.9. Plot of average magnetic moment per ion $\mathfrak{m}$ against $B/T$
for (I) potassium chromium alum ($J = S = \frac{3}{2}$), (II) iron ammonium
alum ($J = S = \frac{5}{2}$), and (III) gadolinium sulphate octahydrate
($J = S = \frac{7}{2}$).

their spins anti-parallel. The orbits are also arranged so that the electrons
have no resultant orbital angular momentum; the total angular momentum is therefore zero and the molecule has no permanent magnetic
moment, though there will always be an induced negative moment when
a magnetic field is applied, giving rise to diamagnetism. In hetero-
polar binding a molecule such as NaCl is formed of the two ions $Na^+$ and
$Cl^-$, both of which have closed electron shells; thus again there is no
resultant magnetic moment. Though this picture of molecule formation
is oversimplified, and in general we have a mixture of homo-polar and
hetero-polar binding, the general result of no permanent magnetic
moment is still true. Thus the only common gases with permanent
moments are NO, which has an odd number of electrons, so that a resultant spin must remain (there is also one unit of orbital angular momentum), and $O_2$, where two electron spins are unpaired, giving oxygen gas
a paramagnetism appropriate to $S = 1$, $g = 2$.

In the solid state most substances consist of ions with closed shells of electrons and are therefore diamagnetic. The main exceptions to this rule arise in compounds of the so-called 'transition elements', where an electron shell is in process of being filled. Such elements are marked by their possession of more than one chemical valency, and some (if not all) of their ions of different valency have unclosed shells, and hence a permanent magnetic moment. Since it is the electrons in the unclosed

TABLE 20.1

*Comparison of theoretical and measured values of $p^2$ for trivalent rare earth ions*

| No. of electrons in 4f shell | Ion | Ground spectroscopic state | Theoretical values | | | | | Average experimental value of $p^2$ |
|---|---|---|---|---|---|---|---|---|
| | | | $S$ | $L$ | $J$ | $g$ | $p^2 = g^2 J(J+1)$ | |
| 0 | La$^{+++}$ | $^1S_0$ | 0 | 0 | 0 | — | 0 | 0 |
| 1 | Ce$^{+++}$ | $^2F_{\frac{5}{2}}$ | $\frac{1}{2}$ | 3 | $\frac{5}{2}$ | $\frac{6}{7}$ | 6·43 | 6 |
| 2 | Pr$^{+++}$ | $^3H_4$ | 1 | 5 | 4 | $\frac{4}{5}$ | 12·8 | 12 |
| 3 | Nd$^{+++}$ | $^4I_{\frac{9}{2}}$ | $\frac{3}{2}$ | 6 | $\frac{9}{2}$ | $\frac{8}{11}$ | 13·1 | 12 |
| 4 | Pm$^{+++}$ | $^5I_4$ | 2 | 6 | 4 | $\frac{3}{5}$ | 7·2 | — |
| 5 | Sm$^{+++}$ | $^6H_{\frac{5}{2}}$ | $\frac{5}{2}$ | 5 | $\frac{5}{2}$ | $\frac{2}{7}$ | 0·71 (2·5) | 2·4 |
| 6 | Eu$^{+++}$ | $^7F_0$ | 3 | 3 | 0 | — | 0 (12) | 12·6 |
| 7 | Gd$^{+++}$ | $^8S_{\frac{7}{2}}$ | $\frac{7}{2}$ | 0 | $\frac{7}{2}$ | 2 | 63 | 63 |
| 8 | Tb$^{+++}$ | $^7F_6$ | 3 | 3 | 6 | $\frac{3}{2}$ | 94·5 | 92 |
| 9 | Dy$^{+++}$ | $^6H_{\frac{15}{2}}$ | $\frac{5}{2}$ | 5 | $\frac{15}{2}$ | $\frac{4}{3}$ | 113 | 110 |
| 10 | Ho$^{+++}$ | $^5I_8$ | 2 | 6 | 8 | $\frac{5}{4}$ | 112 | 110 |
| 11 | Er$^{+++}$ | $^4I_{\frac{15}{2}}$ | $\frac{3}{2}$ | 6 | $\frac{15}{2}$ | $\frac{6}{5}$ | 92 | 90 |
| 12 | Tm$^{+++}$ | $^3H_6$ | 1 | 5 | 6 | $\frac{7}{6}$ | 57 | 52 |
| 13 | Yb$^{+++}$ | $^2F_{\frac{7}{2}}$ | $\frac{1}{2}$ | 3 | $\frac{7}{2}$ | $\frac{8}{7}$ | 20·6 | 19 |
| 14 | Lu$^{+++}$ | $^1S_0$ | 0 | 0 | 0 | — | 0 | 0 |

The values given in parentheses for $Sm^{3+}$ and $Eu^{3+}$ are those calculated by Van Vleck allowing for population of excited states with higher values of $J$, at $T = 293°$ K.

shell which determine the magnetic properties, we should expect the paramagnetism to be typical of the ion, not the atom. Thus ions with the same electron configuration, even if formed from different atoms, have similar magnetic properties. These ions may be labelled by the spectroscopic description of the electron shell which is partly full; these are, 3d (iron group), 4d (palladium group), 4f (lanthanide group), 5d (platinum group), and 5f (actinide group). The titles in brackets are often used as being more descriptive, though less precise.

We consider first the 4f group, whose paramagnetism in the solid state is closest to that of an assembly of free ions. The spectroscopic states of the free ions of the 4f shell are shown in Table 20.1. It will be seen that they conform to Hund's rules, the values of first $S$ and then $L$ being the greatest possible consistent with the Pauli exclusion principle. The ground state has the smallest possible value of $J$ in the first half, and the largest value in the second half, as the spin-orbit coupling interaction changes sign when the shell is more than half full. The experimental values of $p^2$ have the following significance. If we assume that the susceptibility of a substance obeys Curie's law, we may write

$$\chi = \mu_0 n \mathrm{m}^2/3kT = \mu_0 n p^2 \beta^2/3kT. \tag{20.17}$$

Here $p$ is called the effective Bohr magneton number, and by comparison with equation (20.16) we see that for an assembly of free ions

$$p^2 = g^2 J(J+1).$$

It is convenient to give the experimental results in terms of $p^2$, since this facilitates comparison with the theory, but it must be remembered that though we can always calculate a value of $p^2$ from the susceptibility at a given temperature, it has little significance if the susceptibility does not obey Curie's law. The latter can be established by measuring the susceptibility over a range of temperature. In this connexion it must be emphasized that only measurements on 'magnetically dilute' salts are significant; by this phrase is meant salts where the paramagnetic ions are fairly far apart so that mutual interaction between them may be neglected (see Problem 20.2 and § 21.1). This condition is generally fulfilled for hydrated salts, and the values of $p^2$ in Tables 20.1, 20.2 are for salts where the effect of mutual interaction on the susceptibility is appreciable only at very low temperatures.

The calculated values of $p^2$ assume that only the ground state of angular momentum $J$ is occupied. Since states of different $J$ generally lie at several thousand °K, this is a good approximation at room temperature, except for the ions $4f^5$, $4f^6$ where excited levels with higher values of $J$ are exceptionally low-lying, and whose presence cannot be neglected. Van Vleck has shown that their inclusion gives much better agreement with experiment, and his values, calculated for $T = 293°$ K, are shown in parentheses.

The experimental values of $p^2$ for the other ions are in fair agreement with those calculated for an assembly of free ions with angular momentum $J$, but in fact these values have mostly been deduced by fitting the experimental measurements of susceptibility to a formula of the type

$$\chi = \frac{\mu_0 n p^2 \beta^2}{3k(T+\Delta)}. \tag{20.18}$$

This modification of equation (20.17) is known as the Curie–Weiss law (see § 21.1), but it is better to regard it as an expression which includes a term in $T^{-2}$ and is the start of a series expansion in inverse powers of

$T$, as can be seen by writing (20.18) in the form

$$\chi = \frac{\mu_0 np^2\beta^2}{3kT}\left(1 - \frac{\Delta}{T} + \cdots\right). \qquad (20.19)$$

The empirical values of $\Delta$ which give the best fit to the susceptibility in the region of room temperature are of order 10–20° K, but at low temperatures the susceptibility often departs quite markedly from any such simple formula. The reason for this is that we cannot neglect the influence of the charged ions which surround each paramagnetic ion in the solid state. In a magnetically dilute salt these immediate neighbours carry no permanent magnetic moment (they are diamagnetic ions such as $F^-$, $O^=$, etc.), but they are electrically charged, and have an electrostatic interaction with the $4f$ electrons which are responsible for the paramagnetism. To a good approximation the $4f$ electrons can be regarded as moving in an electric field set up by the neighbouring ions, known as the 'crystalline electric field'. The energy of interaction with this field is smaller, for ions of the $4f$ group, than the coulomb, exchange and spin-orbit interactions within the paramagnetic ion itself, and gives rise to a 'Stark' splitting of the $2J+1$ levels of the ion. This is similar in nature to the effect of an external electric field on the spectrum of an atom, first investigated in detail by Stark, but is considerably more complex because the electrostatic potential set up by the neighbours varies in a complicated way over the space occupied by the $4f$ electrons. The overall splittings of the $2J+1$ levels of a $4f$ ion are generally of the order of a few hundred °K. As can be seen in Fig. 20.10, the susceptibility is rather insensitive to such splittings, and approaches that of the free ion at temperatures where most of the levels are appreciably populated. At low temperatures where only the very lowest levels are populated, the susceptibility can be very different from that of the free ion, and in a single crystal may be highly anisotropic.

At first sight it may appear surprising that the crystalline electric field can have such a marked effect on the magnetic properties. The basic reason is that the wave functions corresponding to different values of the orbital magnetic quantum number $M_L$ have different angular dependencies; i.e. for each value of $M_L$ the distribution of electronic charge has a different shape, and hence acquires a different electrostatic energy in the crystalline electric field. Thus the primary interaction is associated with the electronic orbit, and the interaction is zero (except for a small residual effect due to a slight departure from pure Russell–Saunders coupling) for an ion such as $Eu^{2+}$ or $Gd^{3+}$ with a half-filled shell carrying no orbital angular momentum ($L = 0$). For the other ions the coupling together of $L$ and $S$ means that states of different $M_J$ have a different charge distribution, so that the crystalline electric field splits the $2J+1$ states which otherwise have the same energy in the absence of a magnetic field. An important restriction on this splitting occurs

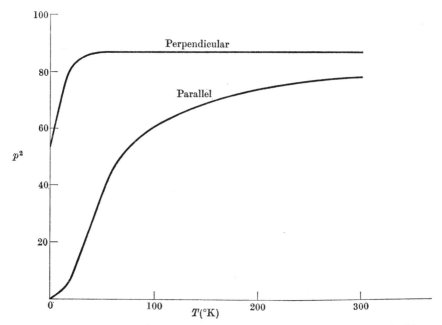

Fig. 20.10. The values of $p^2$ (parallel and perpendicular) for a single crystal of erbium ethylsulphate $Er(C_2H_5SO_4)_3,9H_2O$. This forms hexagonal crystals, and the susceptibility is symmetrical about the hexagonal axis. The ground state of the $Er^{3+}$ ion is $^4I_{\frac{15}{2}}$, and this is split by the crystalline electric field into eight doublets lying at 0, 61, 108, 159, 249, 301, 375, and 438 °K.

for ions with an odd number of electrons, which have half-integral values of $S$ and hence also of $J$; in this case the states occur always in pairs which have the same charge distribution and differ only in the orientation of the magnetic moment. Each pair must thus retain the same energy in an electric field, though they can be split in a magnetic field. This result was proved in a theorem of Kramers and the double degeneracy of such states in an electric field is known as 'Kramers' degeneracy'.

## 20.7. Susceptibility of paramagnetic solids—the $3d$ group

The spectroscopic ground states of the free ions of the $3d$ shell are shown in Table 20.2, whence it can be verified that they follow Hund's rules. An assembly of free ions would therefore give a susceptibility corresponding to $p^2 = g^2 J(J+1)$, but a comparison of the values of this quantity with the experimental values shows a striking disagreement. In fact the experimental values lie much closer to $p^2 = 4S(S+1)$, the value which would be expected if there were no orbital angular momentum and the magnetism were due entirely to the electron spin. This is

TABLE 20.2

| No. of electrons in 3d shell | Ion | Ground state | $S$ | $L$ | $J$ | $g^2 J(J+1)$ | $p^2$ (exper.) | $4S(S+1)$ |
|---|---|---|---|---|---|---|---|---|
| 0 | $K^+$, $Ca^{2+}$, $Sc^{3+}$, $Ti^{4+}$, $V^{5+}$ | $^1S_0$ | 0 | 0 | 0 | 0 | 0 | 0 |
| 1 | $Ti^{3+}$, $V^{4+}$ | $^2D_{\frac{3}{2}}$ | $\frac{1}{2}$ | 2 | $\frac{3}{2}$ | 2·4 | 2·9 | 3 |
| 2 | $V^{3+}$ | $^3F_2$ | 1 | 3 | 2 | 2·67 | 6·8 | 8 |
| 3 | $V^{2+}$, $Cr^{3+}$ | $^4F_{\frac{3}{2}}$ | $\frac{3}{2}$ | 3 | $\frac{3}{2}$ | 0·6 | 14·8 | 15 |
| 4 | $Cr^{2+}$, $Mn^{3+}$ | $^5D_0$ | 2 | 2 | 0 | 0 | (23·3) | 24 |
| 5 | $Mn^{2+}$, $Fe^{3+}$ | $^6S_{\frac{5}{2}}$ | $\frac{5}{2}$ | 0 | $\frac{5}{2}$ | 35 | 34·0 | 35 |
| 6 | $Fe^{2+}$ | $^5D_4$ | 2 | 2 | 4 | 45 | 28·7 | 24 |
| 7 | $Co^{2+}$ | $^4F_{\frac{9}{2}}$ | $\frac{3}{2}$ | 3 | $\frac{9}{2}$ | 44 | 24·0 | 15 |
| 8 | $Ni^{2+}$ | $^3F_4$ | 1 | 3 | 4 | 31·3 | 9·7 | 8 |
| 9 | $Cu^{2+}$ | $^2D_{\frac{5}{2}}$ | $\frac{1}{2}$ | 2 | $\frac{5}{2}$ | 12·6 | 3·35 | 3 |
| 10 | $Cu^+$, $Zn^{2+}$ | $^1S_0$ | 0 | 0 | 0 | 0 | 0 | 0 |

The values of $p^2$ (at 300° K) are for double sulphates of the type $M''M'_2(SO_4)_2,6H_2O$ or $M'''M'(SO_4)_2,12H_2O$ (where $M''$ = divalent paramagnetic ion, $M'''$ = trivalent paramagnetic ion, $M'$ = monovalent diamagnetic ion). In these salts the distance between nearest paramagnetic ions is at least 6 Å, and interaction between them is negligible. The value in parentheses is for $CrSO_4,6H_2O$ : no double sulphate of $Cr^{2+}$ has been measured.

clearly brought out in Fig. 20.11, in which average experimental values of $p^2$ are plotted together with the quantities $g^2 J(J+1)$ and $4S(S+1)$.

This phenomenon, known as the 'quenching' of the orbital magnetism, is a result of the crystalline electric field. In the lanthanide group the $4f$ electrons, which are responsible for the paramagnetism, are fairly deep seated in the atom, but in the iron group the $3d$ electrons are in an outer shell which has a very much larger interaction with the crystalline electric field of neighbouring charged ions. On the other hand the spin-orbit coupling in the $3d$ group is considerably smaller than in the $4f$ group. The result is that interaction between the orbit and the crystalline electric field is a good deal stronger than the spin-orbit coupling for $3d$ ions, so that the orbital momentum is primarily coupled to the crystal field, and it is no longer correct to regard $L$ and $S$ as coupled to form a resultant $J$. The quantitative expression of this situation is that the $2L+1$ orbital states are split in the crystal field, and have energies differing by about $10\,000$ cm$^{-1}$, which is much larger than the spin-orbit splittings (of order $100$–$1000$ cm$^{-1}$) between the states of different $J$ in the free ion. The simplest case to consider is that where the crystal field splitting of the orbital levels gives a singlet state as the lowest level. Such a state has no magnetic moment, and the orbital moment is completely 'quenched'. On the other hand the electron

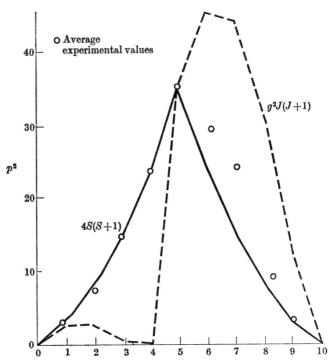

FIG. 20.11. Experimental (at $300°$ K) and calculated values of $p^2$ for the $3d$ group.

In the second half of the group the orbital angular momentum is less effectively quenched than in the first half, so that the values of $p^2$ lie noticeably above the spin only values.

spin has no direct interaction with the crystalline electric field, and remains free to orient itself in a magnetic field. Thus, in this case, the susceptibility would correspond exactly to the 'spin only' value of $p^2 = 4S(S+1)$ at all temperatures such that there is no appreciable population of an excited orbital state.

It can be seen from Fig. 20.11 that the values of $p^2$ do not follow exactly the 'spin only' values, particularly for ions with $d^6$ (Fe$^{2+}$) and $d^7$ (Co$^{2+}$) configurations. The basic reason for this is that the crystalline electric field does not always result in a singlet orbital state as the lowest state, but sometimes gives a group of low-lying orbital states which can make some contribution to the magnetic moment, though less than the full orbital contribution from a free ion. In principle we could calculate the splitting of the orbital levels, but in practice this is extremely difficult to do. However, the general features of the magnetic properties of salts of the 3d group are well understood, mainly through the work of Van

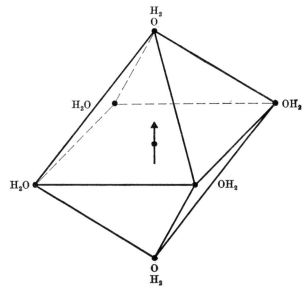

Fig. 20.12. Octahedron of water molecules round a paramagnetic 3d ion.

Vleck, and we will now attempt to outline the main results of the crystal field approach.

The size of an ion of the 3d group is such that six negatively charged ions can be packed round it; when these ions are identical, they are arranged in the form of an octahedron which is very nearly regular. In hydrated salts these six ions are commonly the oxygens of six water molecules, as shown in Fig. 20.12. These ions are known as the 'ligand ions', and in general there is a small amount of homopolar binding between them and the 3d ion. In the crystal field theory this is ignored, and the magnetic 3d electrons are assumed to be localized on the 3d ion, and to move in the electrostatic potential of the surrounding charged ligand ions. If the 3d ion is assumed to be at the point $(0, 0, 0)$, the ligand ions may be taken to lie at the points

$$(\pm a, 0, 0), \quad (0, \pm a, 0), \quad (0, 0, \pm a)$$

thus forming a regular octahedron. If we assign a charge $-2e$ to each oxygen ion, the electrostatic potential near the centre of the octahedron (see Problem 2.18) is

$$V = -\frac{12e}{4\pi\epsilon_0 a} - \frac{2e}{4\pi\epsilon_0}\left\{\frac{35}{4a^5}\right\}(x^4+y^4+z^4-\tfrac{3}{5}r^4), \qquad (20.20)$$

and this will change the energy of an electron on the central ion by an amount $\int \psi^*(-eV)\psi \, d\tau$, where $\psi$ is the electronic wave function. This energy change is a quantitative expression of the fact that, since the electrons on the magnetic ion are negatively charged, they will have a lower energy in states where they avoid the negatively charged ligand ions as much as possible, and a higher energy when they do not, because of the electrostatic repulsion. Taking linear combinations to give real wave functions, we can write $d$-orbitals as a radial function $f(r)$ times the following functions, which express the angular dependence in Cartesian coordinates instead of the spherical harmonics of § 2.2:

$$\left.\begin{array}{l} r^2C_{2,0} = \tfrac{1}{2}(2z^2-x^2-y^2) \\[2mm] \dfrac{1}{\sqrt{2}}r^2(C_{2,2}+C_{2,-2}) = \dfrac{\sqrt{3}}{2}(x^2-y^2) \end{array}\right\} \quad (d\gamma)$$

$$\left.\begin{array}{l} -\dfrac{j}{\sqrt{2}}r^2(C_{2,2}-C_{2,-2}) = \sqrt{3}\,xy \\[2mm] \dfrac{j}{\sqrt{2}}r^2(C_{2,1}+C_{2,-1}) = \sqrt{3}\,yz \\[2mm] -\dfrac{1}{\sqrt{2}}r^2(C_{2,1}-C_{2,-1}) = \sqrt{3}\,zx \end{array}\right\} \quad (d\epsilon).$$

The last three (known as $d\epsilon$ states) are each zero along two of the cubic axes (see Fig. 20.13), so that the charge density (which is proportional to the square of the wave function) is also zero along two of the axes. This gives a lower energy for these three states (by symmetry each must have the same energy in a cubic field, since $x$, $y$, $z$ are all equivalent if the octahedron is regular) than for the other two $(d\gamma)$ states which have a finite density along all three cubic axes. Hence we get a splitting of the $D(d)$ state as shown in Fig. 20.14 for $d^1$. The splitting is similar, but inverted, for $d^9$, which is one electron short of a filled $d$-shell. A filled shell has a spherical charge distribution, and the charge distribution for $d^9$ is equivalent to a filled shell plus a 'positive hole', for which the electrostatic energy in the crystal field has the opposite sign. A half-filled shell also has spherical symmetry, with $L = 0$; for this reason the ligand field plays virtually no role in affecting the paramagnetism

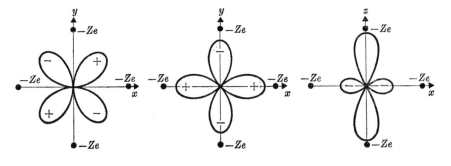

$(a) \quad \psi = \left(\frac{xy}{r^2}\right) f(r)$    $(b) \quad \psi = \left(\frac{x^2-y^2}{r^2}\right) f(r)$    $(c) \quad \psi = \left(\frac{2z^2-x^2-y^2}{r^2}\right) f(r)$

FIG. 20.13. Angular variation of $d$ wave functions. $(a)$ is a $d\epsilon$-state (the other two $d\epsilon$-states are similar but differently oriented); $(b)$ and $(c)$ are $d\gamma$-states. $d\epsilon$- and $d\gamma$-functions have different symmetry properties: $d\gamma$-functions do not change sign on reflection in any one of the cubic axes (i.e. $x \to -x$, or $y \to -y$, or $z \to -z$), while the $d\epsilon$-functions change sign for two such reflections but not for the third.

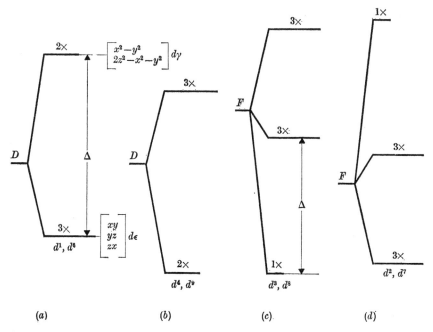

FIG. 20.14. Splittings of $D$ and $F$ states in a crystal field of octahedral symmetry. The overall splittings lie generally in the range 10 000–15 000 cm$^{-1}$. The strong colours of many paramagnetic compounds of the 3$d$ group are due to absorption bands in or near the visible region of the spectrum which arise from transitions between the ground state and excited states shown above, combined with vibrational effects.

of $d^5$ ions, whose ground state is $^6S_{\frac{5}{2}}$. However a $d^6$ ion, with one electron outside the half-filled shell, has a similar splitting to $d^1$, while $d^4$ corresponds to a positive hole in a half-filled shell and behaves like $d^9$ (see Fig. 20.14). Thus $d^1$, $d^4$, $d^6$, $d^9$ have a basically similar splitting pattern because each is equivalent to a single electron or single hole state, as far as the orbit is concerned (they do not all have the same spin).

Similarly, the remaining ions $d^2$, $d^3$, $d^7$, $d^8$ are orbitally equivalent to two-electron or two-hole states ($d^7 \equiv$ half-filled shell+2 electrons; $d^3 \equiv$ half-filled shell+2 holes; $d^8 \equiv$ filled shell+2 holes). They are all in $F$ states, with $L = 3$, which are split by a cubic crystal field into a singlet and two triplet levels, as shown in Fig. 20.14. In $d^3$ and $d^8$ the lowest level is a singlet (it corresponds to a wave function $xyz$, which has zero density along all three cubic axes), but in $d^2$ and $d^7$ the splitting pattern is inverted.

Using these crystal field splittings, we can distinguish between two separate cases:

(a) When the orbital ground state is a singlet, it has no component of angular momentum along any axis, so that the magnetism is due primarily to the spin. The susceptibility follows Curie's law very exactly (for example, the susceptibility of a chrome alum such as $CrK(SO_4),12H_2O$ does not deviate from Curie's law by more than 2 per cent between room temperature and $2°$ K). There are, however, two residual effects of the spin-orbit coupling: (1) the effective $g$-value differs from the free spin value by an amount of order $\lambda/\Delta$, where $\lambda$ is the spin-orbit coupling and $\Delta$ the splitting between the ground orbital level and the excited orbital states shown in Fig. 20.14. The spin-orbit constant $\lambda$ is positive if the $d$-shell is less than half-filled, and negative if it is more than half-filled. It is also larger for the ions at the end of the group because of the increased nuclear charge. Thus the effective value of $g$ is about 1 per cent smaller than the free spin value for $Cr^{3+}$, $d^3$, but 10 per cent higher for $Ni^{2+}$, $d^8$. (2) Where the spin is 1 or more, the $2S+1$ spin states may be split by amounts of order $(\lambda^2/\Delta)$, which is usually of order $0 \cdot 1$–$10$ cm$^{-1}$. This gives a specific heat anomaly, of which a typical example is shown in Fig. 20.15.

(b) When the ground state is not a singlet, there is a first-order contribution from the orbit to the paramagnetism, but less than that for the free ion. When the ground state is a triplet in Fig. 20.14, it behaves like a $P$-state with $L = 1$, and an effective $g_L$ which is $-1$ for $d^1$ and $d^6$, and $-\frac{3}{2}$ for $d^2$ and $d^7$. Thus it can interact with the spin through the spin-orbit interaction, giving states with an effective

$J$ of $S-1$, $S$, and $S+1$ if $S \geqslant 1$, or $\frac{1}{2}$ and $\frac{3}{2}$ if $S = \frac{1}{2}$. The splittings between these levels are of order $100 \text{ cm}^{-1}$ ($140° \text{ K}$), so that Curie's law is not obeyed because excited states become occupied as the temperature is raised. This is particularly noticeable for cobalt ($Co^{2+}$, $d^7$) salts, as shown in Fig. 20.16. The ions $d^4$, $d^9$ are exceptional because the

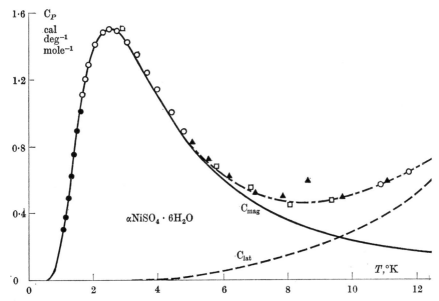

FIG. 20.15. Magnetic specific heat anomaly of $\alpha NiSO_4,6H_2O$ (after Stout and Hadley, 1964). The anomaly is associated with the spin triplet states, which lie at 0, 6·44, and 7·26° K respectively.

doubt orbital states left as their ground states by the octahedral field have effectively $g_L = 0$. Thus they behave rather like case ($a$). Figure 20.16 shows a typical cupric salt, $Cu^{2+}$, $d^9$, where Curie's law is obeyed closely, but the effective $g$-value is more than 10 per cent higher than the free spin value, giving $p^2 = 3·76$ instead of the value $4S(S+1) = 3$ we would expect for a single hole ($S = \frac{1}{2}$).

A striking effect in many single crystals of paramagnetic substances of the $4f$ group is the high anisotropy of the susceptibility; this arises because the surroundings of the paramagnetic ion in such crystals have only axial symmetry. For the regular octahedron shown in Fig. 20.12 there would be no anisotropy, but in the $3d$ group this octahedron is normally somewhat distorted, and as a result the orbital contributions to the magnetism depend on the direction in which the external field is applied relative to the crystal axes. The anisotropy is large when the splitting of the lowest orbital levels is small; that is, when there are also considerable departures from Curie's law, as in cobalt salts.

## 20.8. Susceptibility of paramagnetic solids—strongly bonded compounds

Much less is known in detail about the magnetic properties of salts of the $4d$ and $5d$ groups, but in many cases it appears that the binding to the ligand ions is covalent rather than ionic in character. This is true

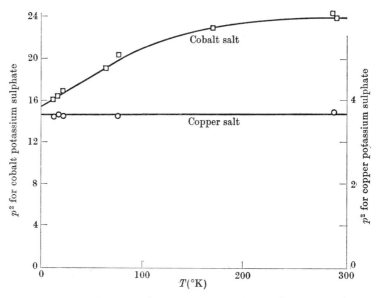

FIG. 20.16. Variation of $p^2$ with temperature for two iron group salts.

also for a few salts of the iron group, notably the complex cyanides such as $K_3Fe(CN)_6$. In the latter, and in salts such as $K_2IrCl_6$ where the magnetic $Ir^{4+}$ ion has the configuration $5d^5$, the ligand ions (six CN groups in the former case, six $Cl^-$ ions in the latter) are again arranged in the form of a very nearly regular octahedron. We shall confine the discussion to this type of compound, as it affords an interesting comparison with the pure crystal field approach.

In a covalent bond the electrons are shared between the two ions concerned, in contrast with a purely ionic case where the electrons are localized on each ion. The latter is an over-simplification, and in practice there is always a small amount of covalent bonding, so that we distinguish only between weak bonding, and strong bonding. In a complex with octahedral symmetry, the $d\gamma$ states have maximum density along the cubic axes (towards the ligand ions), and can form $\sigma$-bonds with the ligand ions, while the $d\epsilon$ states can only form $\pi$-bonds. In the formation of a bond, a $d$-state on the magnetic ion is combined with the appropriate bonding state of the ligand ion, and the overlap of the electronic wave functions gives a splitting of the combined levels, in the same way as pointed out in § 18.2. The overlap is greater for the $d\gamma$ states (forming $\sigma$-bonds) than for the $d\epsilon$ states (forming $\pi$-bonds), giving the energy level diagram shown in Fig. 20.17. The lower bonding states are all

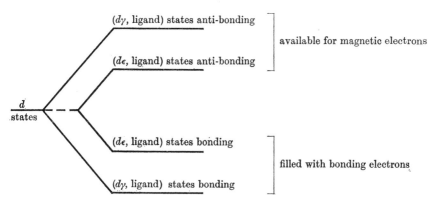

FIG. 20.17. Splitting of the $d$-states on the bonding model. The lowest (bonding) states are filled with electrons, and only the anti-bonding states are available for the magnetic electrons. In the crystalline electric field approach the bonding states play no role, and a cubic field splitting (see Fig. 20.14) of the $d$-states is obtained similar to that for the anti-bonding states above.

filled with electrons, and behave as filled sub-shells. Thus the states available for magnetic electrons are the anti-bonding states, which are split in the same way as by an octahedral crystal field. In weakly bonded compounds this splitting is about $10\,000$ cm$^{-1}$, as mentioned in the previous section, but in the strongly bonded compounds it is very much larger, so that the latter behave as though subjected to a very much stronger crystalline electric field. However, the approach from the bonding viewpoint is more correct, since it allows the magnetic electron wave functions to spread out from the central ion on to the ligand ions, for which there is direct experimental evidence from measurements of the hyperfine interaction between the magnetic electrons and the nuclear moments of the ligand ions.

In this more general approach, allowing for bonding, the splitting between the $d\epsilon$ states and the $d\gamma$ anti-bonding states is ascribed to the 'ligand field', and it is interesting to contrast the two cases of small and large ligand field. Here the comparison is with the electrostatic and exchange energy which is responsible for Russell–Saunders coupling, and when the ligand field splitting is large compared with this exchange energy we must regard the Russell–Saunders coupling as broken. The way in which the $d\epsilon$ and $d\gamma$ anti-bonding states are occupied by the magnetic electrons in the two cases is determined by the competition between the exchange energy (which favours parallel orientation of the

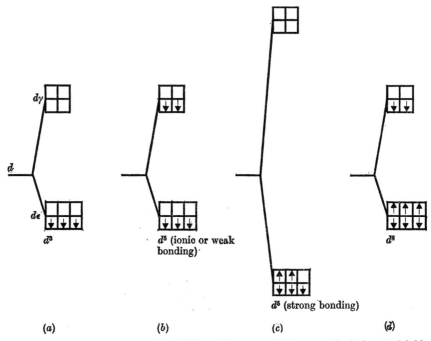

Fig. 20.18. Single electron model of filling of $d$-states split by an octahedral crystal field. The exchange energy forms parallel spin arrangements (subject to the exclusion principle); the crystal field splitting favours electrons in the $d\epsilon$ states.

electron spins) and the ligand field splitting (which favours electrons going into the $d\epsilon$ states because of their lower energy).

We may represent each orbital state by a pair of square boxes, as in Fig. 20.18, into each of which we can put one electron, with spin up or down. With one electron, the state of lowest energy will obviously be when this electron is in the $d\epsilon$ states. When further electrons are added they will also go into the $d\epsilon$ states, but with spins parallel in order to make the exchange energy a minimum; up to three electrons can be accommodated in this way. The $d\epsilon$ shell is then half full, and behaves like a state with zero orbital momentum (corresponding to the singlet orbital ground state for $d^3$ in Fig. 20.14) and $S = \frac{3}{2}$. When more electrons are added, they cannot go into the $d\epsilon$ shell with parallel spin, because this would violate the exclusion principle. There is therefore a competition between the exchange energy, which prefers parallel spin, and the ligand field energy, which prefers the $d\epsilon$ states. In the hydrated salts, the latter is less important, and the fourth and fifth electrons go into the $d\gamma$ states with parallel spin, making $d^5$ a state with $L = 0$, $S = \frac{5}{2}$ (a half-filled $d$-shell). In the more strongly-bonded salts the ligand field splitting is so large that no electrons go into the $d\gamma$ states, since they have a lower energy by occupying the $d\epsilon$ states with anti-parallel spin, as shown in Fig. 20.18 (c). Thus a strongly bonded $d^5$ salt behaves as if it had one hole in the $d\epsilon$ shell; for example, $K_3Fe(CN)_6$, where the $Fe^{3+}$ ion has a $d^5$ configuration, has magnetic properties quite different from hydrated ferric compounds, showing considerable departures from Curie's law, a susceptibility close to that of a single spin, and strong anisotropy in single crystals. With six electrons, $d^6$, strongly bonded, the $d\epsilon$ shell is completed, and the ion has no permanent magnetic dipole moment ($K_3Co(CN)_6$ has only a small temperature-independent paramagnetism). Any further electrons would have to go into the $d\gamma$ states, but these are so high in energy that such ions are usually chemically unstable. However, when the ligand field is less strong, the $d\gamma$ states are occupied, as shown in Fig. 20.18 (d) for a hydrated $Ni^{2+}$, $d^8$, ion. Here the $d\epsilon$ states are completely filled and the $d\gamma$ half-filled, giving again a ground state with no orbital momentum (cf. Fig. 20.14 (c)). On this single electron picture we can see that the orbital momentum is effectively quenched whenever the two sets of $d\epsilon$ and $d\gamma$ states are each either empty, half-filled, or completely filled with electrons; the reader can verify that a half-filled sub-shell, with all electron spins parallel, can be achieved by only one possible arrangement of the electrons in the various boxes, and therefore corresponds to a singlet orbital state. On the other hand, when the $d\epsilon$ states are occupied by one or two electrons, or four or five electrons, there are three equivalent ways of arranging them, giving a triply degenerate orbital state. This corresponds to the triplet state which is lowest for $d^1$, $d^2$, $d^6$, $d^7$ in Fig. 20.14.

## 20.9. Electronic paramagnetism—a summary

In conclusion we may summarize the magnetic properties as being the result of competition between the electrostatic (including exchange) interactions between electrons on the same ion, spin-orbit interaction between these electrons, and electrostatic (crystal field) or covalent bonding interaction with ligand ions. In the $4f$ group the latter is the weakest of the three, giving splittings of order $10^2$ cm$^{-1}$ while the spin-orbit coupling is $\approx 10^3$ cm$^{-1}$. In ionic $3d$ salts, the spin-orbit coupling ($\approx 10^2$ cm$^{-1}$) is too small to compete with the crystal field ($10^4$ cm$^{-1}$), but the latter is smaller than the exchange interaction (e.g. the mean separation between the quartet, $S = \frac{3}{2}$, states and the doublet, $S = \frac{1}{2}$, states for Cr$^{3+}$ is about $2 \times 10^4$ cm$^{-1}$). In the strongly bonded salts, interaction with the ligands outweighs the exchange and electrostatic interactions between the electrons within the magnetic ion, breaking down the Russell–Saunders coupling.

In the $5f$, or actinide group, the behaviour is generally similar to that of the $4f$ (lanthanide group), though only the salts of the first members of the group (U, Np, Pu) have been investigated in any detail because of the high radioactivity of the other members. An exception is the complex ions UO$_2$, NpO$_2$, etc., where strong covalent binding exists between the actinide ion and the two oxygen ions.

### 20.10. Nuclear moments and hyperfine structure

In § 20.1 it was mentioned that the nuclei of many types of atoms possess angular momentum. This is associated with a 'spin' of the nucleus about an internal axis, and the angular momentum is quantized just as in the case of the orbital and spin angular momenta of the electron. The fundamental nuclear particles ('nucleons') are the proton and the neutron, each of which possesses a spin of $\frac{1}{2}\hbar$, like the electron. All nuclei are regarded as assemblies of protons and neutrons bound together; the number of protons is equal to $Z$, the atomic number, since the nuclear charge is $Ze$, and the number of neutrons $N = (A-Z)$, where $A$ is the atomic mass number. The spin of any given nucleus is denoted by $I\hbar$, and $I$ is characteristic of any given isotope. The number of nucleons in a nucleus is equal to $A$, and the nuclear spin is half-integral or integral according to whether $A$ is odd or even. No simple rule can be given for calculating the nuclear spin a priori in a particular case, though the observed values can be fitted into a shell model not greatly different from that used in atomic theory. The most important rule is that all nuclei containing an even number of protons and an even number of neutrons have $I = 0$ in the ground state. This can be understood in terms of a 'pairing off' of the spins of protons and neutrons similar to that of a pair of electrons in an $s$-state. For nuclei with an odd proton or odd neutron the value of $I$ is attributed to the resultant of the intrinsic spin of $\frac{1}{2}$ for the odd nucleon and an 'orbital' momentum whose value is an integral number of units of $\hbar$, due to circulation of this odd nucleon within the nucleus. Relatively few stable nuclei exist which contain odd numbers of both protons and neutrons (such as $^2_1D$ and $^{14}_7N$) but these have integral values of $I$ other than zero, an exceptionally high value being $I = 7$ for $^{176}Lu$. The highest half-integral value so far observed is $\frac{9}{2}$. These values are for the ground states of nuclei. Investigation of nuclear structure has led to the assignment of spin values for many excited nuclear states, but these have not been observed directly, except in a few cases where the excited states have an abnormally long life.

All nuclei which have a non-zero value of the spin $I$ possess magnetic moments, and these are measured in terms of a unit called the 'nuclear magneton'. The value of this unit is $\beta_n = e\hbar/2M$, which is similar to that for the Bohr magneton except that the mass in the denominator is that of the proton instead of that of the electron. If the proton obeyed a similar wave equation to that for the electron, we would expect it to possess a moment of one nuclear magneton associated with its spin $\frac{1}{2}$, just as the electron has a moment of one Bohr magneton and spin $\frac{1}{2}$. In fact the moment of the proton is $+2\cdot793$ nuclear magnetons (n.m.), and the neutron (which, being uncharged, we should not have expected to possess a magnetic moment) has in fact a moment of $-1\cdot913$ n.m. Here the significance of the plus and minus signs is that the magnetic moments are respectively parallel and anti-parallel to the spin. Since the magnetic moment of neither neutron nor proton is an integral number of nuclear magnetons we should not expect the moments of more complicated nuclei to be simple integers. They do, however, follow the trend which the nuclear shell model would indicate (see Problem 20.5); in general we write the nuclear magnetic moment as $\mathfrak{m}_n = g_n\beta_n I$, where $g_n$ is the nuclear magnetogyric ratio.

Interactions between a nuclear magnet and its surroundings are small. In a magnetic field each of the $2m_I+1$ states corresponding to different orientations of the nuclear moment takes up a different energy

$$W_{m_I} = -\mathbf{m}_n.\mathbf{B} = -g_n\beta_n m_I B; \qquad (20.21)$$

in a field of 1 weber/metre$^2$ ($10^4$ gauss) the separation between successive levels corresponds to a frequency of order $10^7$ c/s. In an atom or ion which has a permanent electronic magnetic moment, the latter sets up a magnetic field at the nucleus which may be as much as $10^7$ gauss, being generally larger in the heavier atoms. This magnetic field is partly due to the electronic orbit and partly to the spin, but for most purposes we need consider only the steady component of the electronic field $\mathbf{B}_e$, which is parallel to and proportional to the resultant electronic angular momentum vector $\mathbf{J}$. Thus we have an additional 'hyperfine' energy

$$W = -\mathbf{m}_n \cdot \mathbf{B}_e = A\mathbf{J}.\mathbf{I}, \tag{20.22}$$

where $A$ is a constant whose order of magnitude can be estimated as follows. The electronic field $\mathbf{B}_e$ is of order $\mathbf{m}_e\langle R_e^{-3}\rangle = -g\beta\mathbf{J}\langle R_e^{-3}\rangle$, where $\langle R_e^{-3}\rangle$ is the mean inverse cube of the distance of the electron from the nucleus; since $\mathbf{m}_n = g_n\beta_n\mathbf{I}$, $A$ is of order $gg_n\beta\beta_n\langle R_e^{-3}\rangle$. In frequency units $A/h$ generally lies in the range $10^8$–$10^{10}$ c/s, so that the hyperfine energy may approach $1$ cm$^{-1} = 1.43°$ K.

In addition to possessing a magnetic moment, a nucleus may have a non-spherical distribution of electric charge. Its electrostatic potential can then be expanded as in § 2.3, giving an energy of interaction with the electrons of the form (see equations (2.30)–(2.34))

$$W = \frac{1}{4\pi\epsilon_0} \iint \frac{\rho_e \rho_n \, d\tau_e \, d\tau_n}{|R_e - r_n|}$$

$$= \frac{1}{4\pi\epsilon_0}\left\{ Ze \int \frac{\rho_e \, d\tau_e}{R_e} + \sum_{m=-2}^{+2}(-1)^{|m|}A_{2,m}B_{2,-m} + \text{etc.} \right\}. \tag{20.23}$$

Here the subscripts $e$, $n$ refer to the electrons and nuclei respectively; $Ze = \int \rho_n \, d\tau_n$ is the nuclear charge, so that the first term is the coulomb interaction due to a point charge at the nucleus, and the quantities in the second term are

$$A_{2,m} = \int \rho_n r_n^2 C_{2,m}(\theta_n, \phi_n) \, d\tau_n,$$

$$B_{2,-m} = \int (-1)^{|m|}\rho_e R_e^{-3} C_{2,-m}(\theta_e, \phi_e) \, d\tau_e.$$

This term represents the interaction between the electric quadrupole moments of the nucleus and of the electrons, whose nature is that of a tensor. The charge distribution is spherical for nuclei with $I = 0$ or $\frac{1}{2}$, and for electronic shells with $J = 0$ or $\frac{1}{2}$, so that the quadrupole interaction vanishes in either case. Since the nuclear charge is symmetric about the axis of nuclear precession, the nuclear terms can be expressed in terms of a single quantity

$$A_{2,0} = \int \rho_n \tfrac{1}{2}r_n^2 (3\cos^2\theta_n - 1) \, d\tau_n = \tfrac{1}{2}eQ\left\{\frac{3m_I^2 - I(I+1)}{I(2I-1)}\right\}, \tag{20.24}$$

where

$$Q = \frac{1}{e}\int \rho_n r_n^2(3\cos^2\theta_n - 1) \, d\tau_n \tag{20.25}$$

is called the nuclear electric quadrupole moment, and has the dimensions of an area of the same order as the (nuclear radius)$^2$. It is expressed in terms of the 'barn', a unit equal to $10^{-24}$ cm$^2$. The sign of $Q$ is positive for a prolate spheroid, and negative for an oblate spheroid, as illustrated in Fig. 20.19. The expression in parentheses in equation (20.24) gives the variation of $A_{2,0}$ with the nuclear magnetic quantum number $m_I$, and it is easily verified that in the states $m_I = \pm I$, $A_{2,0} = \frac{1}{2}eQ$.

In the absence of an external magnetic field, the electronic and nuclear angular momentum vectors $J$, $I$ are coupled together by the magnetic hyperfine energy (equation (20.22)) to form a resultant vector

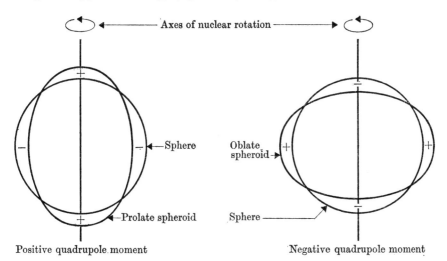

Positive quadrupole moment                    Negative quadrupole moment

FIG. 20.19. Representation of non-spherical charge distribution in nucleus as combination of sphere and quadrupole.

$F$. Different values of $F$ correspond to different energies, since the angle between $J$ and $I$ is changed, and from the vector model it can be shown that

$$W_F = \frac{1}{2}A\{F(F+1)-J(J+1)-I(I+1)\} \qquad (20.26)$$

so that the energies of successive states form an arithmetical progression (cf. Problem 20.7, for the corresponding case of spin-orbit coupling). This rule, known as the Landé interval rule, no longer holds when the electric quadrupole interaction is included, but it can be shown that then

$$W_F = \frac{1}{2}AC+B_Q\frac{\frac{3}{4}C(C+1)-I(I+1)J(J+1)}{2I(2I-1)J(2J-1)}, \qquad (20.27)$$

where

$$C = F(F+1)-I(I+1)-J(J+1); \quad B_Q = 2eQB_{2,0}/4\pi\epsilon_0 = eQ\,(\partial^2V/\partial z^2),$$

where $\partial^2V/\partial z^2$ is the field gradient set up by the electrons at the nucleus. The energy levels given by equation (20.27) for the case of $J = 1$, $I = \frac{3}{2}$ are shown in Fig. 20.20. In general the size of $B_Q$ is comparable with that of $A$, except in atoms where $J$ or $I$ is 0 or $\frac{1}{2}$, and $B_Q$ vanishes.

Nuclear spins can be found from observations of hyperfine structure in spectra, and values of the constants $A$ and $B_Q$ are obtained from the separations of the hyperfine levels. In magnetic resonance experiments (see § 23.6) the precision with which these constants can be determined is very high, and nuclear magnetic dipole and electric quadrupole

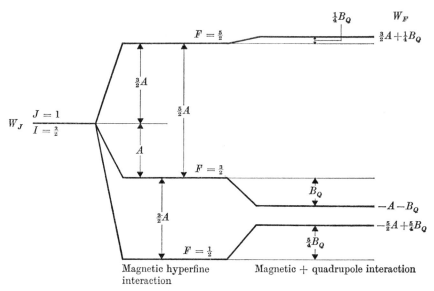

Fig. 20.20. Splitting of ground state of an ion with $J = 1$, $I = \frac{3}{2}$ due to magnetic dipole and electric quadrupole interaction. The figure is drawn for positive values of both $A$ and $B$. Note that (allowing for the multiplicity $2F+1$) the centre of gravity of the levels remains constant.

moments can be estimated with an accuracy generally limited by the lack of exact electronic wave functions from which the quantities $B_e$ in equation (20.22) and $\partial^2 V / \partial z^2$ must be calculated.

In the solid state an assembly of nuclear dipoles behaves as a simple paramagnetic substance, contributing an amount (cf. equation (20.16))

$$\chi_n = \frac{\mu_0 n g_n^2 \beta_n^2 I(I+1)}{3kT}, \qquad (20.28)$$

which is only about $10^{-6}$ of that of any electronic paramagnetic substance, since the susceptibility depends on the square of the magnetic dipole moment. The nuclear contribution has been detected by static susceptibility measurements in solid hydrogen, where the nuclear paramagnetism just outweighs the electronic diamagnetism at about $1°$ K (see Problem 20.9).

The nuclear susceptibility follows Curie's law, equation (20.28), only at temperatures such that $kT$ is large compared with any splittings of the nuclear levels. In substances without permanent electronic magnetic dipoles this means temperatures down to about $10^{-6}\,°\mathrm{K}$, except where the nuclear levels are split through an electric quadrupole interaction with the electrostatic field gradient (the 'crystal field') set up by neighbouring ions. In such cases the gradient $(\partial^2 V/\partial z^2)$ is fixed, unlike in a free atom where it follows the precessing electronic angular momentum vector for the orbit, which determines the orientation of the electronic charge cloud. Hence in a solid in which the local surroundings of a nucleus have symmetry about an axis (which we take to be the $z$-axis) the nuclear levels may be split according to the formula

$$W_{m_I} = \frac{1}{4\pi\epsilon_0} A_{2,0} B_{2,0} = eQ(\partial^2 V/\partial z^2)\frac{3m_I^2 - I(I+1)}{4I(2I-1)}. \qquad (20.29)$$

The splittings range from a few kc/s up to over 2000 Mc/s for $^{127}$I in $I_2$, solid iodine.

In substances containing ions with both electronic and nuclear magnetic dipoles the two contributions to the susceptibility are additive at temperatures such that $kT$ is large compared with any hyperfine structure splittings (in practice this usually means down to about $1°$ K). Such splittings arise from both nuclear magnetic dipole and electric quadrupole interactions in the same way as for free atoms, but the effects are more complicated because of the complex interaction of the electrons with the crystal or ligand field discussed in §§ 20.6–20.9. The hyperfine splittings usually correspond to temperatures in the range $10^{-3}$–$1°$ K, and affect both the electronic and nuclear contributions to the susceptibility in this temperature range and below.

## GENERAL REFERENCES

Coulson, C. A., 1952, *Valence* (Clarendon Press).

Kopfermann, H., 1958, *Nuclear Moments* (Academic Press Inc., New York).

Kuhn, H. G. 1964, *Atomic Spectra* (Longmans, Green & Co. Ltd, London).

## PROBLEMS

**20.1.** In statistical mechanics the partition function $Z$ is defined as

$$Z = \sum_i \exp(-W_i/kT),$$

where $W_i$ is the energy of the $i$th state. Show that for an assembly of non-interacting paramagnetic ions, each of angular momentum $J$, in a field $B$

$$Z = \frac{\sinh\{(2J+1)y/2J\}}{\sinh\{y/2J\}},$$

where $y = Jg\beta B/kT$.

The magnetization $M$ for an assembly of $n$ such atoms is given by the formula

$$M = nkT \frac{d}{dB}(\log_e Z).$$

Using this formula, derive the Brillouin function of equation (20.15).

**20.2.** Show that the energy of interaction of two magnetic dipoles $\mathfrak{m}$ a distance $r$ apart is of the order $\mu_0 \mathfrak{m}^2/4\pi r^3$.

In potassium chrome alum, each chromium ion carries a magnetic moment of 3 Bohr magnetons, and the mean distance apart is about $7.8 \times 10^{-8}$ cm. Assuming that serious departures from Curie's law will occur when the interaction energy between two neighbouring dipoles is $\approx kT$, show that this temperature is approximately $0.01°$ K. (In fact the levels of each chromium ion are split by about $0.2°$ K through a high order effect of the crystalline field, and this is more important than the magnetic dipole interaction between neighbouring ions; it also gives a specific anomaly at about $0.1°$ K of the type shown in Fig. 20.15.)

**20.3.** For a $Cu^{++}$ ion, $S = \frac{1}{2}$ and the energy levels of the ground state in a magnetic field $B$ are of the form $\qquad W = \pm\frac{1}{2}g\beta B - \frac{1}{2}\alpha B^2.$

Show that in small fields $(g\beta B/kT \ll 1)$ the partition function

$$Z = 2 + \alpha B^2/kT + g^2\beta^2 B^2/4(kT)^2 + ...,$$

and hence that $\qquad \chi/\mu_0 = n\{g^2\beta^2/4kT + \alpha\} = np^2\beta^2/3kT.$

This shows that the term $B^2$ in $W$ gives rise to a temperature-independent contribution to the susceptibility. Note that $p^2$ is then of the form $A + BT$. ($B$ is very small for $Cu^{++}$, but $Co^{++}$ ions obey this relation below $100°$ K—see Fig. 20.16.)

**20.4.** Show that for a system where the magnetic moment associated with orbital angular momentum $l\hbar$ is $g_l l\beta$ and that associated with spin $s\hbar$ is $g_s s\beta$ and $l$ and $s$ are coupled together to form a resultant $j$, the generalized Landé formula for the $g$-factor is

$$g = \frac{j(j+1)(g_l+g_s) + \{l(l+1)-s(s+1)\}(g_l-g_s)}{2j(j+1)}.$$

**20.5.** On the nuclear shell model the nuclear spin is due to the odd neutron or proton with spin $\frac{1}{2}$ moving in an orbit within the nucleus with angular momentum $l\hbar$. The observed nuclear spin $I$ is either $l+\frac{1}{2}$ or $l-\frac{1}{2}$. Apply the formula of the last question to calculate the magnetic moment, assuming that for a proton $g_l = 1$ and $g_s = 5.586$, and for a neutron $g_l = 0$ and $g_s = -3.826$. Show that the magnetic moment $\mathfrak{m} = g_n\beta_n I$ of a nucleus of spin $I$ is

(a) odd proton $\quad I = l+\frac{1}{2}, \qquad \mathfrak{m} = \beta_n(I+2.293),$

$\qquad\qquad\qquad\quad I = l-\frac{1}{2}, \qquad \mathfrak{m} = \beta_n I(I-1.293)/(I+1),$

(b) odd neutron $I = l+\tfrac{1}{2}$, $\quad \mathfrak{m} = -1\cdot913\beta_n = \mathfrak{m}_n$,

$\qquad\qquad I = l-\tfrac{1}{2}$, $\quad \mathfrak{m} = 1\cdot913\beta_n I/(I+1) = -\mathfrak{m}_n I/(I+1)$.

These formulae are known as the Schmidt limits. Observed nuclear moments follow the trend given by these formulae but generally lie between these limits.

20.6. The arrangement of parallel cylindrical conductors carrying equal and opposite currents of Problem 5.3 is used to give a large field gradient and deflect atoms in an atomic beam. Each cylinder carries a current of 1000 A and the axes of the cylinders are 1 cm apart. A beam of atoms in the $^2S_{\frac{1}{2}}$ state from an oven at 900° K travels parallel to the cylinders along the line where the inhomogeneous field is a maximum. Calculate the separation between the two components of the beam after travelling a distance of 20 cm.

(*Answer*: $\approx 0\cdot01$ cm.)

20.7. Use the vector model as in § 20.3 to show that, as a result of the spin–orbit coupling $\lambda \mathbf{L} . \mathbf{S}$ ($\equiv \lambda LS \cos ABC$ in Fig. 20.6), the energy of a state with total angular momentum $J$ is

$$W_J = \tfrac{1}{2}\lambda\{J(J+1)-L(L+1)-S(S+1)\},$$

so that $W_J - W_{J-1} = \lambda J$ (this is known as the Landé interval rule).

Show from the splittings of the $^4F$ multiplet given in Fig. 20.5 for the Cr$^{3+}$ ion that the value of $\lambda$ is about 87 cm$^{-1}$ (slightly higher values are obtained from the $^4P$ states, but these are perturbed by doublet states which are not far away).

20.8. Hydrogen molecules are of two types: (a) ortho-hydrogen, where the nuclear spin of $\tfrac{1}{2}\hbar$ of each proton is parallel to the other and the nuclear spin for the molecule is $I = 1$; (b) para-hydrogen, where the two proton spins are anti-parallel giving $I = 0$ for the molecule. Show that at high temperatures where the ratio of ortho- to para-hydrogen molecules is 3:1, the susceptibility due to the nuclear paramagnetism is identical with that of the same total number of hydrogen atoms with independent spin $I = \tfrac{1}{2}$. (Note that the equilibrium ratio of 3:1 corresponds to the fact that there are three quantum states for $I = 1$, associated with three possible orientations of the spin, each with the same *a priori* probability as the single state for $I = 0$.)

20.9. Calculate the paramagnetic susceptibility of a gramme molecule of hydrogen at 1° K due to the nuclear moments, assuming that the ortho-para ratio is still 3:1. Show that it is of the same order as the diamagnetic susceptibility due to the electrons, assuming that each of the two electrons is in an orbit for which the mean radius is the Bohr radius.

(*Answers*: $2\cdot2 \times 10^{-11}$ and $-2\cdot0 \times 10^{-11}$ (m.k.s.).)

20.10. The ground state of sodium is $^2S_{\frac{1}{2}}$, and the yellow $D$-lines are due to transitions to the ground state from the two lowest excited states $^2P_{\frac{1}{2}}$ and $^2P_{\frac{3}{2}}$. Show that the Landé $g$-factors of these two states are $\tfrac{2}{3}$ and $\tfrac{4}{3}$ respectively.

Hence show that one $D$-line will be split in a magnetic field $B$ into four components, with frequencies $D_1 \pm \tfrac{2}{3}\delta$, $D_1 \pm \tfrac{4}{3}\delta$; and the other $D$-line into six components with frequencies $D_2 \pm \tfrac{1}{3}\delta$, $D_2 \pm \delta$, $D_2 \pm \tfrac{5}{3}\delta$, where $\delta = \beta B/h$, when viewed normal to the field. (Only the $\Delta M = \pm 1$ components are seen when viewed parallel to the field.)

# FERROMAGNETISM

## 21.1. Exchange interaction between paramagnetic ions

In the discussion in §§ 20.5–20.9 of paramagnetism in the solid state, it was tacitly assumed that interactions between different paramagnetic ions could be neglected. Such interactions are of two types: (a) magnetic dipole-dipole interaction, arising from the magnetic field due to one dipole acting on another; (b) exchange interactions between the electrons in different paramagnetic ions, of the same nature as those between electrons within the same atom (giving rise to Russell–Saunders coupling) or between the electrons of different atoms in chemical binding. Of these two types of interaction, the latter greatly outweighs the former in ordinary substances. For example, the Curie point of nickel is 631° K (see Table 21.1). This is a rough indication of the temperature at which the interaction between neighbouring nickel ions (separation 2·5 Å) is of the order $kT$, whereas (Problem 20.2) the purely magnetic interaction of two atomic dipoles at this distance would be equivalent to $kT$ with $T$ less than 1° K. Exchange interaction decreases more rapidly than magnetic dipole interaction as the atomic separation is increased, though no simple law can be given for its rate of decrease. As an example, in paramagnetic salts of the $3d$ group the exchange interaction is more important than the magnetic dipole interaction until the separation between the paramagnetic ions is greater than about 6 Å, and then both are so small that they have an appreciable effect on the magnetic properties only well below 1° K.

The mechanism of exchange interaction, as originally proposed by Heisenberg in 1928, is one in which the forces involved are electrostatic in origin, but which, because of the constraints imposed by the Pauli exclusion principle, are formally equivalent to a very large coupling between the electron spins, of the type

$$W = -2\mathscr{J}\mathbf{s}_i.\mathbf{s}_j. \tag{21.1}$$

The quantity $\mathscr{J}$ is known as the exchange energy. Though several types of indirect exchange interaction have since been suggested (see § 21.9), they all lead to a basic coupling between the spins of this form, dependent on the cosine of the angle between the two spin vectors  For two separate

atoms with total spin vectors $\mathbf{S}_i$, $\mathbf{S}_j$ we may use the vector summations
to show that the total interaction energy is

$$W = -2\mathscr{J}\sum_i\sum_j \mathbf{s}_i.\mathbf{s}_j = -2\mathscr{J}\sum_i \mathbf{s}_i.\sum_j \mathbf{s}_j = -2\mathscr{J}\mathbf{S}_i.\sum_j \mathbf{s}_j = -2\mathscr{J}\mathbf{S}_i.\mathbf{S}_j$$
$$(21.2)$$

which depends only on the relative orientation of the two total spin
vectors $\mathbf{S}_i$, $\mathbf{S}_j$. An immediate result of equation (21.2) is that the
exchange interaction vanishes for any closed shell of electrons, since
then $\mathbf{S} = 0$. Thus we need consider only the partly filled shells which
are responsible for permanent magnetic dipole moments in atoms and
ions.

For an ion in which $\mathbf{J}$ is a good quantum number (such as ions of the
$4f$ group), we must project $\mathbf{S}$ onto $\mathbf{J}$; the reason for this is that $\mathbf{J}$ is a
constant of the motion, and hence so also is the projection of $\mathbf{S}$ onto $\mathbf{J}$.
The components of $\mathbf{S}$ normal to $\mathbf{J}$ are precessing rapidly, so that their
contribution to the scalar product $\mathbf{S}_i.\mathbf{S}_j$ is zero on a time average.
From the equivalences $\mathbf{L}+2\mathbf{S} \equiv g\mathbf{J}$ (where $g$ is the Landé factor),
$\mathbf{L}+\mathbf{S} \equiv \mathbf{J}$, we find at once that $\mathbf{S} \equiv (g-1)\mathbf{J}$; this result can be derived
in a lengthier but more satisfying way from the vector model (see
Problem 21.4). Thus, for a pair of such ions (assumed identical, with
the same values of $\mathbf{J}$ and $g$) we have

$$W = -2\mathscr{J}\mathbf{S}_i.\mathbf{S}_j = -2\mathscr{J}(g-1)^2\mathbf{J}_i.\mathbf{J}_j = -2\mathscr{J}'\mathbf{J}_i.\mathbf{J}_j. \quad (21.3)$$

This gives a coupling of the angular momentum vectors of the same
form as equation (21.2), but with a modified value of the apparent
exchange energy.

In a solid, any given magnetic ion is surrounded by other magnetic
ions, with each of which it will have an exchange interaction. The total
interaction for each ion will therefore be a sum of terms such as (21.3)
taken over all pairs of ions; the energy for atom $i$ is thus

$$W_i = -2\mathbf{J}_i.\sum_j \mathscr{J}'_{ij}\mathbf{J}_j.$$

The magnetic dipole moment of each ion is proportional to the angular
momentum $\mathbf{J}$, since $\mathbf{m} = g\beta\mathbf{J}$, so that the exchange energy can be
expressed in terms of the dipole moments, giving

$$W_i = -2\left(\frac{\mathbf{m}_i}{g\beta}\right).\sum_j \mathscr{J}_{ij}\left(\frac{\mathbf{m}_j}{g\beta}\right),$$

assuming again that all ions have the same Landé $g$-factor. In a ferromagnetic substance, or a paramagnetic substance subjected to an
external magnetic field, each ion will have an average dipole moment

in the direction of magnetization, together with fluctuating components in other directions whose time average is zero. In summing over the interaction with neighbouring ions, that part associated with the fluctuating components will tend to average out, since at any instant the contributions from different neighbours will be as often positive as negative. To a fair approximation we can therefore replace the vector sum over the neighbouring dipole moments by a sum over the average moment per neighbour $\overline{\mathbf{m}}_j$, and if we assume further that the only important interaction is with $z$ equidistant neighbours, each having the same interaction energy $\mathscr{I}'$, we can write

$$W = -2\left(\frac{\mathbf{m}}{g\beta}\right) \cdot \sum \mathscr{I}'\left(\frac{\overline{\mathbf{m}}_j}{g\beta}\right) = -2\left(\frac{\mathbf{m}}{g\beta}\right) \cdot \left(\frac{z\overline{\mathbf{m}}}{g\beta}\right)\mathscr{I}'$$

$$= -\left(\frac{2z\mathscr{I}'}{ng^2\beta^2}\right)\mathbf{m} \cdot \mathbf{M} = -\mathbf{m} \cdot \mathbf{B}_{\text{int}}. \qquad (21.4)$$

Here we have dropped the subscript $i$, since we assume all ions are identical, and the energy is the same for each; and we have replaced the mean moment per ion by the magnetization $\mathbf{M} = n\overline{\mathbf{m}}$, where $n$ is the number of ions per unit volume. The result is an equation formally identical with the potential energy of a dipole $\mathbf{m}$ in a field

$$\mathbf{B}_{\text{int}} = (2z\mathscr{I}'/ng^2\beta^2)\mathbf{M} = \lambda\mathbf{M};$$

we may therefore represent the effect of the exchange forces, to a good approximation, by an effective 'internal field' $\mathbf{B}_{\text{int}}$ which is proportional to the intensity of magnetization. This concept was first introduced by Weiss to account for the occurrence of spontaneously magnetized substances (ferromagnetics).

As a preliminary, we shall discuss the effect of this internal field in a paramagnetic substance. The total field acting on an ion is then $\mathbf{B}_0 + \mathbf{B}_{\text{int}} = \mathbf{B}_0 + \lambda\mathbf{M}$, where $\mathbf{B}_0$ is the external field. So long as the magnetization is small compared with the saturation value we may assume that Curie's law $\chi = C/T$ still holds if we replace $\mathbf{B}$ in our earlier theory by $\mathbf{B}_0 + \lambda\mathbf{M}$. Then we have

$$\mathbf{M} = (C/T)\mathbf{B}/\mu_0 = C(\mathbf{B}_0 + \lambda\mathbf{M})/\mu_0 T$$

and hence $\quad \chi = \mu_0 \mathbf{M}/\mathbf{B}_0 = C/(T - \lambda C/\mu_0) = C/(T - \theta). \qquad (21.5)$

This is known as the Curie–Weiss law, and represents the behaviour of paramagnetic substances at temperatures $T > \theta$ with fair accuracy; $\theta = \lambda C/\mu_0$ is often called the 'Weiss' constant.

The form of equation (21.5) shows that some radical change in the magnetic properties is to be expected at the temperature $\theta$, and we may interpret the infinite susceptibility which is predicted by equation (21.5) at this point in the following way. Since $\chi = \mu_0 \mathbf{M}/\mathbf{B}_0$, and the maximum value of $M$ is finite, being limited to the saturation moment obtainable when all the dipoles are aligned parallel to one another, we must assume $\mathbf{B}_0 = 0$; in other words, the substance is magnetized even in the absence of an external field. This 'spontaneous magnetization', due to the internal field, is a characteristic of ferromagnetism, and the temperature

TABLE 21.1

*Saturation moment and Curie point of some ferromagnetic materials*

| Substance | Saturation moment at 0° K | | Curie point (°K) |
|---|---|---|---|
| | (a) e.m.u./g | (b) Bohr magnetons/atom | |
| Fe . . . | 221·7 | 2·22 | 1043 |
| Co (> 670° K). | 162·6 | 1·715 | |
| (> 670° K). | (167·3) | (1·76) | 1394 |
| Ni . . . | 57·6 | 0·605 | 631 |
| MnBi . . | 75 | 3·52 | 630 |
| MnAs . . | 146 | 3·40 | 318 |
| Fe₂O₃ . . | 83·5 | 1·20 (per atom of Fe) | 893 |

*Notes*: Cobalt has a phase transition at about 670° K, being hexagonal in structure below that temperature, and face-centred cubic above. The values in brackets are obtained by extrapolation.

In the m.k.s. system, the saturation moment in ampere-metre²/kg is the same as the value given in column (a); in any system the values of $M_s$, the saturation moment per unit volume, may be obtained by multiplying the values per unit mass by the density.

$\theta$ is the boundary between paramagnetic behaviour at $T > \theta$ and ferromagnetic behaviour when $T < \theta$. The temperature below which spontaneous magnetization appears is known as the Curie point, and the experimental values for a number of substances are given in Table 21.1. The 'ferromagnetic Curie temperature' is defined as that below which spontaneous magnetization sets in, and it often differs by 10° or 20° from the value of $\theta$ determined in the paramagnetic region by fitting the observed susceptibility to equation (21.5). The latter value is sometimes called the 'paramagnetic Curie temperature'. On our simple theory there is no difference between the two Curie temperatures.

Since the Curie constant $C = \mu_0 ng^2\beta^2 J(J+1)/3k$, the value of the Weiss constant in equation (21.5) is

$$\theta = \lambda C/\mu_0 = (2z\mathscr{J}'/ng^2\beta^2) \times \{\mu_0 ng^2\beta^2 J(J+1)/3k\} \div \mu_0$$
$$= 2z\mathscr{J}' J(J+1)/3k \qquad (21.6)$$

and on simple theory this is also the value of the Curie temperature $T_C$. More sophisticated methods of calculation produce a somewhat different value of the numerical constant, and Rushbrooke and Wood (1958) show that the results can be fitted remarkably well by the empirical formula

$$T_c = \frac{5\mathscr{J}'}{96k}(z-1)\{11J(J+1)-1\}. \tag{21.7}$$

This predicts somewhat lower values for the Curie point than equation (21.6), and conversely, gives higher estimates of the exchange interaction. For example, nickel has its Curie point at 631° K; its crystal structure is face-centred cubic, for which the number of nearest neighbours is 12, which we take to be the value of $z$. If we make the further assumption that $J = S = \frac{1}{2}$, then we find that $\mathscr{J}'/k$ is 105° K from equation (21.6), and 150° K from (21.7). Thus the exchange energy (there is no difference between $\mathscr{J}'$ and $\mathscr{J}$ when we are dealing with spin-only magnetism), is about $10^{-2}$ electron volts. The magnitude of this interaction can perhaps be appreciated best by expressing it in terms of the internal field $\mathbf{B}_{int}$ of equation (21.4), which is found to be of order $10^7$ gauss ($10^3$ weber/metre²). This is over 100 times larger than any field which can easily be produced in the laboratory, so that external fields would be expected to have little effect on the spontaneous magnetization below the Curie point.

Equations (21.6) and (21.7) show that the sign of $\theta$ and $T_c$ is the same as that of $\mathscr{J}'$ (and hence also of $\mathscr{J}$, so long as we are dealing with identical ions). Thus a positive value of the exchange energy is required to give a vanishing denominator in the Curie–Weiss law (equation (21.5)), and a co-operative state in which the electron spins are parallel to each other. This ferromagnetic state is a direct consequence of the fact that the exchange coupling (equation (21.1)) gives a lower energy for any pair of electrons when their spins are parallel, provided the exchange energy $\mathscr{J}$ is positive. If it is negative, the state of lower energy is one with anti-parallel spins; the Weiss constant is also negative, and the denominator of the Curie–Weiss law does not vanish at any real temperature. Nevertheless a co-operative state does then occur, but one in which the basic arrangement is of anti-parallel spins. This phenomenon is called 'anti-ferromagnetism', and is discussed in Chapter 22.

## 21.2. The Weiss theory of spontaneous magnetization

Since the internal field in a ferromagnetic substance is so large, the magnetization will approach the saturation value even at ordinary temperatures. The assumption that the magnetization is small and proportional to the effective field, used in deriving equation (21.5) for the susceptibility above the Curie point, thus cannot be used below the Curie point. If we retain the concept of an internal field, the magnetization may be calculated using the Brillouin function (see equation (20.15)) which may be written in the form

$$M/M_s = \phi(y). \tag{21.8}$$

Here $M_s$ is the saturation magnetization per unit volume, and equals $ngJ\beta$, where $n$ is the number of atomic dipoles per unit volume. The argument of the Brillouin function may be written as

$$y = gJ\beta B/kT = M_s B/nkT$$

and $B$ must be taken as the sum of the external field $B_0$ and the internal field $\lambda M$. Hence we have

$$y = M_s(B_0 + \lambda M)/nkT, \tag{21.9}$$

which may be solved for $M$, giving

$$M/M_s = y(nkT/\lambda M_s^2) - (B_0/\lambda M_s). \tag{21.10}$$

The value of the magnetization under any given conditions of $B_0$ and $T$ may be found by eliminating the parameter $y$ between the two equations (21.8) and (21.10). It is clear that this cannot be done analytically, but the general behaviour of the magnetization can be found from a graphical solution. We shall begin by equating $B_0$ to zero, and finding the value of the spontaneous magnetization $M_0$ in zero field. To obtain a gra phical solution we then plot the two functions $M_0/M_s = \phi(y)$ (from equation (21.8)) and $M_0/M_s = y(nkT/\lambda M_s^2)$ (from equation (21.10)) against $y$, as in Fig. 21.1. The second function gives a straight line which passes through the origin and intersects the curve for $\phi(y)$ at this point. Thus one possible value of the magnetization is always zero. If the temperature $T$ is sufficiently high, the slope of the line $M_0/M_s = y(nkT/\lambda M_s^2)$ is so great that this is the only point of intersection, and the substance must therefore be unmagnetized in zero external field. This corresponds to the paramagnetic behaviour above the Curie point, discussed in the last section. As the temperature $T$ falls, the slope of the line given by equation (21.10) decreases, until at a certain temperature $T_C$ it is tangential to the curve $(a)$ at the origin. For small values of $y$,

$$\phi(y) = M/M_s = y(J+1)/3J,$$

and on equating this to the value of $M/M_s$ given by equation (21.10) with

$B_0 = 0$, the value of $T_C$ is found to be

$$T_C = \frac{\lambda M_s^2}{nk}\left(\frac{J+1}{3J}\right) = \frac{\lambda n g^2 \beta^2 J(J+1)}{3k} = C\lambda/\mu_0 = \theta, \qquad (21.6\text{ a})$$

where $\theta$ is the Weiss constant defined by equation (21.6). At still lower temperatures, the slope of the line is less than the initial slope of $\phi(y)$, and there will be two points of intersection, and two possible values of the magnetization, one zero and the other finite. It is easy to show that

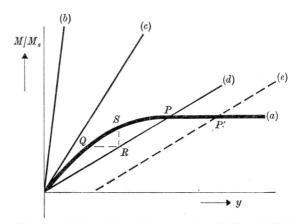

FIG. 21.1. Graphical solution of the equations (21.8) and (21.10) for spontaneous magnetization.

(a) is the Brillouin function $\phi(y)$ (equation (21.8));
(b), (c), (d) are the straight lines $M/M_s = y(nkT/\lambda M_s^2)$ for temperatures $T > T_C$, $T = T_C$, and $T < T_C$ respectively, where $T_C$ is the Curie point (all with $B_0 = 0$);
(e) is the function in equation (21.10); an external field $B_0$ is applied, with the temperature the same as for (d).

the former is unstable and the latter stable. For, if we imagine the magnetization at any instant to correspond to the point $Q$ on $\phi(y)$, then the internal field produced by the magnetization corresponds to the point $R$, and this field will produce the greater magnetization corresponding to the point $S$ on $\phi(y)$. Thus the magnetization will increase until the point $P$ is reached where the two curves intersect. Above $P$, the two curves cross and any further increase in the magnetization would produce an internal field insufficient to sustain the increased magnetization. It thus appears that the state of spontaneous magnetization corresponding to the point $P$ is stable, while the unmagnetized state is unstable.

Since the value of the spontaneous magnetization is determined by the intersection with $\phi(y)$ of the line corresponding to equation (21.10) (with $B_0 = 0$), and the slope of this line depends on the temperature, it is obvious that the whole of the curve $\phi(y)$ will be traced out as we lower the temperature from the Curie point to the absolute zero. From equation (21.6 a), $\lambda M_s^2/nk = 3\theta J/(J+1)$, and hence we may express equation (21.10) (with $B_0 = 0$) in the form

$$M_0/M_s = y\left(\frac{T}{\theta}\right)\left(\frac{J+1}{3J}\right).$$

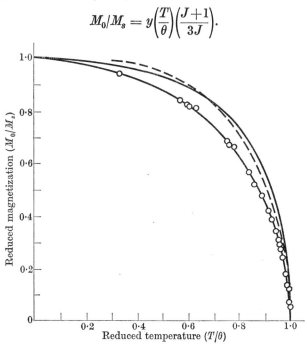

FIG. 21.2. Reduced equation of state for a ferromagnetic substance.
– – – – from the Weiss theory (equation (21.8)) for $J = \frac{1}{2}$.
———— experimental curve for nickel.
—○— experimental curve for a nickel–copper alloy (76%–24%).
(After Oliver and Sucksmith, 1953.)

Elimination of $y$ between this equation and equation (21.8) shows that a 'reduced equation' may be found of the form

$$M_0/M_s = f(T/\theta), \tag{21.11}$$

where the function $f(T/\theta)$ is the same for all substances with the same value of $J$. This function is plotted in Fig. 21.2 (broken line) for the special case of $J = \frac{1}{2}$; the curves for other values of $J$ lie slightly inside this curve at intermediate values of $(T/\theta)$. The experimental determination of $M_0/M_s$ and the verification of this 'Law of Corresponding States' will be discussed in § 21.6.

When a considerable external magnetic field $B_0$ is applied the effect on the magnetization can be found by a graphical solution of equations

(21.8) and (21.10), where the term in $B_0$ is retained in the latter equation. The straight line corresponding to a plot of $M/M_s$ against $y$ is now displaced to the right compared to that for $B_0 = 0$ at the same temperature. The intersection with $M/M_s = \phi(y)$ occurs at the point $P'$ in Fig. 21.1, and the magnetization is slightly increased over that corresponding to $P$, the value for zero external field. At temperatures well below the Curie point $M_0$ is already close to $M_s$ and $\phi(y)$ increases only very slowly, so that the effect of $B_0$ is small. At temperatures near the Curie point $P$ is on the steeper part of the curve for $\phi(y)$ near the origin and the increase in $M$ produced by an external field is more noticeable.

The theory outlined above is similar to the original theory of Weiss except that the Brillouin function has been substituted for the Langevin function. Its great success lies in the explanation of the presence of spontaneous magnetization in a ferromagnetic substance, but there are also difficulties. The fact that the unmagnetized state is unstable appears to be contrary to experience, since it is well known that a piece of iron can be demagnetized by dropping it. Moreover, in a single crystal the magnetization can be restored by applying an external field of less than 1 gauss, although the internal field is about $10^7$ gauss! We also require some explanation of the hysteresis curve. To overcome these difficulties Weiss introduced the concept of domains of magnetization within the specimen. Each domain contains some $10^{17}$–$10^{21}$ atoms, and a piece of unmagnetized iron contains many domains all spontaneously magnetized, but the directions of magnetization of different domains are oriented at random. The theory of spontaneous magnetization applies to a single domain, but the magnetization of the whole specimen depends on whether the domains themselves are aligned towards the field or whether they are randomly oriented. This theory, which was conceived before the nature of the exchange interaction which causes the spontaneous magnetization was known, is remarkably successful in explaining the main features of ferromagnetic substances. The existence of domains has been confirmed by the experiments of Bitter, briefly described in the next section, where we shall first consider what factors determine the size and shape of the domains.

## 21.3. Ferromagnetic domains

A considerable advance in the understanding of ferromagnetism occurred when it became possible to obtain single crystals of iron, cobalt, and nickel sufficiently large for their magnetization curves to be measured. In each case it was found that the crystals are anisotropic; that is, the magnetization depends on the direction the field makes with the crystal axes. Fig. 21.3 shows the curves for iron, which forms body-centred cubic crystals. The $M-B_0$ curve is found to rise more steeply when $B_0$ is parallel to the edge of the unit cube [100] than any other direction, such as a face diagonal [110] or a body diagonal [111]. The energy of magnetization is $\int B_0\, dM$, and is represented by the area between the magnetization

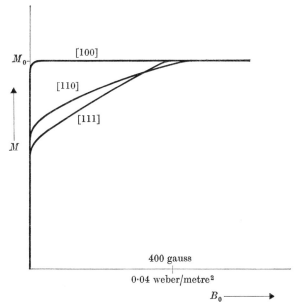

FIG. 21.3. Magnetization curves for a single crystal of iron. (Note that $B_0$ is the actual field inside the sample.)

The directions of easy magnetization are the cube edges (e.g. [100]). When the field is not along a cube edge, the initial process is of magnetization along the cube edges in directions nearest to that of the field; hence the curve for [110] breaks off roughly at $M_0/\sqrt{2}$, and that for [111] at $M_0/\sqrt{3}$, since further magnetization requires domain rotation against the anisotropy energy.

curve and the $M$-axis ($B_0 = 0$). This energy is least when the single crystal of iron is magnetized along the [100] direction (or its equivalents, [010] and [001]), and these are known as directions of easy magnetization. In the case of nickel, with a face-centred cubic structure, the directions of easy magnetization are the body diagonals, while for cobalt, with a hexagonal structure at room temperature, there is only one direction of easy magnetization, the hexagonal crystal axis.

The excess energy required to magnetize the substance in a hard direction is known as the anisotropy energy. It is clear that the anisotropy energy cannot arise from the exchange interaction, for the latter depends only on the mutual orientation of the dipoles and not on the angle which they make with the crystal axes. Its origin is thought to be similar to that of paramagnetic anisotropy (see end of § 20.7), arising from the combined effect of spin-orbit coupling and the electric field of the neighbouring charged ions. The anisotropy energy has the same symmetry properties as the crystal, and is smallest for crystals of high symmetry. Thus it is less for iron or nickel, which are both cubic, than

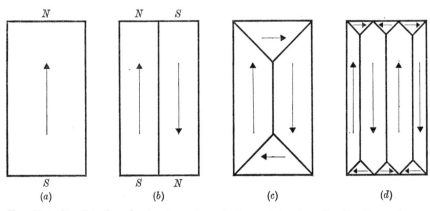

FIG. 21.4. Possible domain structures in a single crystal, where the directions of easy magnetization are along the edges of a cube.

(a) Single domain; external lines of field run from north to south pole and give large external field.
(b) Double domain, where external lines of field run mostly between adjacent north and south poles, and the energy stored in external field is much reduced.
(c) Arrangement with no free poles and no external field; the domains with perpendicular magnetization at top and bottom are called 'domains of flux closure'.
(d) As in (c), but with further subdivision into smaller domains.

for cobalt, which has only axial symmetry. The anisotropy energy also causes a change of length on magnetization (magneto-striction).

In zero field the specimen, whether it is a single crystal or an aggregate of crystals, will be in equilibrium when its potential energy is a minimum. In an unstrained crystal the important contributions are the exchange energy, the anisotropy energy, and the magnetostatic energy (the energy stored in the magnetic field). If the crystal consisted of one single domain, as in Fig. 21.4 (a), the 'free poles' at the ends would give rise to a large external magnetic field and to a large magnetostatic energy. This is reduced by having two domains oppositely magnetized as in Fig. 21.4 (b), when the two poles partially cancel one another. If there are no free poles on any surface the magnetostatic energy is reduced still further. For this to be the case, the field $\mathbf{B}$ at the surface of the crystal must always be parallel to the surface, and the normal component of **B** must be continuous across the boundary between two domains. If the two domains are magnetized in perpendicular directions the wall between them must run at an angle of 45° to each direction of magnetization, and Fig. 21.4 (c) shows a possible arrangement. The little surface domains which produce a closed circuit of **B** are called domains of closure, and are generally much smaller than the inner domains. The size of the domains

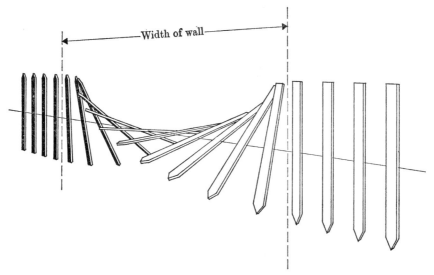

FIG. 21.5. Variation of spin orientation in a Bloch wall.

depends very much on the size and shape of the crystal, and this depends on the previous history of the substance. This fits in with the fact that the hysteresis curve is very sensitive to the composition and state of the specimen, since the domain structure must determine the shape of this curve.

The configuration in Fig. 21.4 (d) is an alternative to that of Fig. 21.4 (c) and one might expect the domains always to be very small in size and large in number; but energy is required to form the boundary between two domains, since the magnetization on either side is in opposite directions. The boundary between two domains is known as a 'Bloch wall'. It has a finite thickness, extending over a number of atoms whose spins change gradually in direction as we proceed through the wall (Fig. 21.5).

From equation (21.3) the exchange energy between neighbouring identical spins is approximately $\Delta W_e = -2\mathscr{J}'J^2\cos\psi$, where $\psi$ is the angle between the directions of the spin momentum vectors. Therefore, the total exchange energy in going through the wall is

$$W_e = -\sum_{i>j} 2\mathscr{J}' J^2 \cos \psi_{ij}.$$

If the wall thickness extends over many atoms, and the angle between neighbouring spins is small, we may write $\cos \psi_{ij} \simeq 1 - \psi_{ij}^2/2$, and the total increase in exchange energy because the spins are not exactly parallel is

$$W_e \approx \mathscr{J}' J^2 \sum \psi_{ij}^2.$$

For a wall which forms the boundary between two domains where the spins are anti-parallel, the total change in angle in going through the wall is $\sum \psi_{ij} = \pi$. If there is a line of $n'$ atoms in the thickness of the wall, and $\psi_{ij}$ is the same for all adjacent pairs of atoms, $n' \psi_{ij} = \pi$ and

$$W_e \approx n' \mathscr{J}' J^2 (\pi/n')^2 = \pi^2 \mathscr{J}' J^2/n'.$$

This equation shows that the exchange energy is reduced by making $n'$ large, and it would seem that the wall should be infinitely thick. This would increase the anisotropy energy $W_a$, however, since a number of spins in the wall are pointing at an angle to the direction of easy magnetization, and this number increases with the wall thickness. Thus $W_a$ is proportional to $n'$, and the total energy per unit area of wall in the substance is

$$W_e + W_a = \pi^2 \mathscr{J}' J^2/n' a^2 + K n' a, \tag{21.12}$$

where $K$ is a constant roughly equal to the anisotropy energy per unit volume. $a$ is the lattice constant of the substance, so that, for a simple cubic crystal, there are $1/a^2$ atoms per unit area of wall, and $n'a$ is the thickness of the wall.

The form of equation (21.12) shows that there will be a minimum value of the total energy for some value of $n'$, which by differentiation is found to be $n' = (\pi^2 \mathscr{J}' J^2/Ka^3)^{\frac{1}{2}}$. For nickel, $J = \frac{1}{2}$, $\mathscr{J}$ is about $10^{-14}$ ergs, $K$ is about $10^5$ ergs/cm$^3$, and $a^3$ is about $10^{-23}$ cm$^3$. Hence $n'$ is of the order of 100 atoms, and the thickness of the wall is a few hundred Ångström units. Substitution of the optimum value of $n'$ in equation (21.9) gives the expression $2\pi(\mathscr{J}' KJ^2/a)^{\frac{1}{2}}$ for the wall energy per unit area, whose order of magnitude is found to be about an erg/cm$^2$.

As the domain width decreases in the flux closure arrangement shown in Fig. 21.4 (d), the number of walls per unit area of the crystal surface increases, with a corresponding increase in the energy. The energy required to form a wall therefore tends to keep the domains small in number, and large in size. When $K$ is large, particles of about $10^{-4}$ cm diameter are found to consist of a single domain, because the energy required to form a wall is more than the reduction in the magnetostatic energy which would result from the subdivision into domains. In large crystals another factor which enters into the determination of domain size is that the domains of closure in Fig. 21.4 (d) may require to be magnetized in a hard direction, thereby increasing the anisotropy energy. The volume occupied by the domains of closure decreases as the width of the domains decreases, and the anisotropy energy therefore tends to reduce the domain size, while the wall energy tends to increase it. The optimum domain size is determined by a compromise between these two effects.

The most striking evidence for the existence of domains is provided by the Bitter patterns which are obtained when finely powdered iron or cobalt, or colloidal magnetite, is spread on the surface of the crystal. The surface must be very carefully prepared and electrolytically polished to remove irregularities. The particles deposit themselves along the domain boundaries since here there are strong local inhomogeneous magnetic fields which attract the particles. A typical Bitter pattern is shown in Fig. 21.6; the 'fir-tree' effect is obtained when the surface makes a small angle of 2 or 3 degrees with the true (100) crystal plane. The branches of the tree are the domains of closure which close the flux circuit over the primary domains below. On looking through a micro-scope the patterns can be seen to change as a magnetic field is applied. The direction of magnetization in a domain is found by making a tiny scratch on the surface with a fine glass fibre. If the scratch is parallel to the magnetization the pattern is unchanged, but if it is normal to it the pattern is distorted. This is because a scratch parallel to the field behaves as a long narrow cavity, with no free poles at the ends; a scratch perpendicular to the field will have induced poles on its sides, and there will be a strong field in the cavity so that the pattern is distorted. Experiments of this type, and others, in which the scattering of beams of electrons or polarized neutrons have been used to investigate domain structure, show that the theory outlined above is correct in its main features.

The changes in the domain structure which occur when a magnetic field is applied, and the correspondence between these changes and the various parts of the magnetization curve, have already been outlined in § 8.4. The initial portions of the magnetization curve are associated with movements of the Bloch walls, which are reversible in small fields but irreversible after larger fields have been applied. Where there are strains or inclusions of impurities the energy depends on the position of

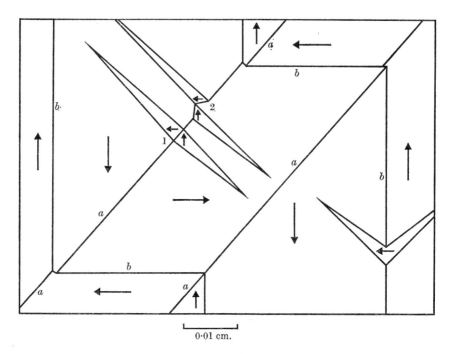

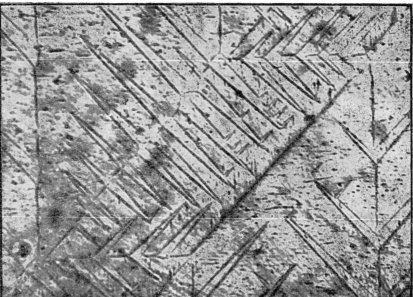

FIG. 21.6. Domain patterns on a demagnetized single crystal of silicon-iron (the surface is very nearly a (100) crystal plane).

The magnetization is normal to the fine scratches visible on the surface, and is directed as shown in the key diagram above. Domain walls labelled *a* form the boundary between domains magnetized in directions differing by 90°, and those labelled *b* are boundaries between domains differing by 180°. The 'fir-tree' closure domains arise because the surface is not exactly a crystal plane. Two different types of closure domain (labelled 1 and 2) can be seen on the 90° wall.

(Photograph by L. F. Bates and A. Hart.)

the wall, as can be seen from considering the effect of a small particle embedded in the material. Such a particle will be a small domain magnetized in one of its own easy directions of magnetization, which do not in general coincide with those of the surrounding material, or it may be a particle of a non-ferromagnetic substance. In the latter case there

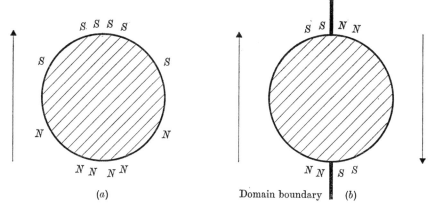

Fig. 21.7. Effect of a non-magnetic inclusion.

(a) In the middle of a domain.
(b) When intersected by a domain boundary.

will be free poles on its surface, as in Fig. 21.7 (a), and the field of these poles gives extra magnetostatic energy. If a Bloch wall intersects the particle, as in Fig. 21.7 (b), this energy will be reduced, just as in the case of free poles on the surface of a ferromagnetic substance in Fig. 21.4 (a, b). This gives a minimum of energy when a wall intersects as many inclusions as possible. In a small external field the wall is displaced slightly away from the minimum energy, but returns when the field is removed; this gives a reversible wall movement. In larger fields the wall may be shifted to a more distant position where the energy curve has passed through a maximum and then diminished; on removing the field the wall cannot cross the energy maximum and so is unable to return to its initial position. The displacement is then irreversible. The more free the material is from strains and inclusions, the greater the size of reversible wall movements, and the lower the field required to produce a movement, thus giving a large initial permeability, and a 'soft' magnetic material. With large strains and many inclusions the smaller is the possibility of boundary movement, and the higher the coercive force.

## 21.4. The gyromagnetic effect

It was pointed out in § 20.1 that the magnetic moment of an atom is proportional to the total electronic angular momentum of the atom. For a macroscopic system, the total magnetic moment **M** and the total electronic angular momentum $\mathbf{G}_e$ are formed by similar vector addition of the individual components, and they should therefore be related in the same way. Thus we have

$$\mathbf{M}/\mathbf{G}_e = \gamma = -g'(e/2m_0),$$

where $g'$ is an effective Landé factor. It follows from this that if we could measure in some way the change in electronic angular momentum associated with the change in magnetization of a specimen, the value of $g'$ would be determined. Since $g'$ differs by a factor of 2 according to whether the magnetic moments are associated with orbital or spin angular momentum, this affords a method of verifying our assumption that ferromagnetism in the $3d$ group is associated with the electronic spins.

Since no external couple is exerted on a specimen by the act of changing its magnetization, the total angular momentum of the system must remain unaltered. The change $\Delta G_e$ in the electronic angular momentum must therefore be accompanied by an equal and opposite change

$$\Delta G_{\text{lattice}} = -\Delta G_e$$

in the angular momentum of the 'lattice', defined as the rest of the specimen, apart from the electrons responsible for the magnetization. It is this latter change in angular momentum which is observed, but it is very small. In a cubic centimetre of nickel there are some $10^{23}$ electrons whose individual momenta can be changed by $\hbar \approx 10^{-34}$ newton-metre ($10^{-27}$ dyne-cm) by reversal of the spin. The total angular momentum thus imparted to the lattice is only about $10^{-11}$ newton-metre ($10^{-4}$ dyne-cm).

A variety of experimental methods have been used to determine $\gamma$, but only a short account will be given here (more details are given by the authors to whom references are made in this section). The methods fall into two classes. In one, an unmagnetized specimen is set into rotation and the resultant magnetization is measured. This is the Barnett effect, and typical experiments are those of Barnett (1944). Even with a large specimen, the magnetic moment induced is very small owing to the limited velocities of rotation which can be employed. In the second class, the magnetization is changed by a known amount and the change in angular momentum is determined; this is known as the Einstein- de Haas effect, though first suggested by Richardson. This method has the advantage that resonance can be used to enhance the effect. A ferromagnetic rod is suspended inside a long solenoid supplied with alternating current whose period is equal to the torsional oscillation period of the suspended rod. If $\mathfrak{I}$ is the moment of inertia of the rod, $b$ the damping constant, $c$ the torsion constant of the suspension, and $M \sin \omega t$ the magnetic moment of the specimen at any instant, the equation of motion is

$$\mathfrak{I}\frac{d^2\theta}{dt^2} + b\frac{d\theta}{dt} + c\theta = \frac{dG}{dt} = \frac{1}{\gamma}\omega M \cos \omega t.$$

At resonance, the amplitude of the angle of rotation is $(1/\gamma)(M/b)$; $b$ is found from the logarithmic decrement, and $M$ must be measured independently.

This method of measuring $\gamma$ was employed by Scott (1951) using a modification of the apparatus built for the determination of $e/m$ of the carriers of electric current (see § 3.1). The specimen, in the form of a rod, is suspended as a torsional pendulum. A coil is wound on the rod, and by reversing a current in this coil the magnetization of the rod can be reversed. The change in magnetization is measured by a null magnetometer placed half-way between the rod and a standard coil carrying a steady current which is simultaneously reversed with that in the specimen. This steady current is adjusted until a balance is obtained. The magnetometer is fitted with a mirror, and the light reflected from it falls on a twin photocell feeding an amplifier, a device similar to that used to amplify galvanometer deflexions. By this means a null magnetometer of great sensitivity is produced. A correction was made for the non-uniformity of magnetization of the rod, and the earth's field was neutralized by a system of Helmholtz coils. The period of oscillation of the rod was 26 sec, and its rotation was observed by reflections of a beam of light from a mirror mounted immediately above the specimen. The procedure used was to reverse the magnetizing current at a moment when the specimen passed through the centre of its swing. The direction of reversal was chosen so that for 60 current reversals the amplitude was increased, and then for 60 reversals it was decreased. With small damping, the progressive change in amplitude was very nearly linear, and the amplitude change for one reversal was obtained from the two slopes of the plot for 120 reversals.

A number of experiments of high precision have been carried out using both the Einstein–de Haas and Barnett effects, and a mean of the results obtained between 1944 and 1960 is given in a survey by Meyer and Asch (1961), who show also that there is good agreement with results of ferromagnetic resonance experiments using microwave radiation (see § 23.7). The results are shown in Table 21.2, and are expressed in terms of two quantities $g$ and $g'$, obtained from ferromagnetic resonance and gyromagnetic experiments respectively. When we have a mixture of orbit and spin, the magnetic moment and angular momentum may be written as $M = M_L + M_S = (e/2m_0)\{G_L + 2G_S\}$, $G = G_L + G_S$, and the ratio is

$$\gamma = \frac{M}{G} = \frac{e}{2m_0}\left\{\frac{G_L + 2G_S}{G_L + G_S}\right\} = g'\left(\frac{e}{2m_0}\right), \qquad (21.13)$$

The 'spectroscopic splitting factor' $g$ measured in a ferromagnetic resonance experiment has been shown by Kittel and Van Vleck to be defined by

$$\frac{M}{G_S} = \frac{e}{2m_0}\left\{\frac{G_L + 2G_S}{G_S}\right\} = g\left(\frac{e}{2m_0}\right), \qquad (21.14)$$

from which it follows that

$$\frac{1}{g} + \frac{1}{g'} = 1. \qquad (21.15)$$

The results given in Table 21.2 show that this relation is fulfilled within the experimental error for iron and nickel, and Meyer and Asch show that this is true also for a wide range of alloys of the $3d$ group. The fact that $g$, $g'$ are so close to 2 shows that the magnetism of the ferromagnetic metals of this group is almost entirely due to spin. This result

### TABLE 21.2

*Some values of the quantities $g'$ and $g$*

*The quantity $g'$ is derived from gyromagnetic (magneto-mechanical) experiments, the quantity $g$ from ferromagnetic resonance experiments; the values quoted are the means of a number of experimental results, given by Meyer and Asch (1961).*

| Substance | $g'$ | $g$ | $\dfrac{1}{g} + \dfrac{1}{g'}$ |
|-----------|------|-----|--------------------------------|
| Iron   | $1\cdot928 \pm 0\cdot004$ | $2\cdot094 \pm 0\cdot003$ | $0\cdot996 \pm 0\cdot004$ |
| Cobalt | $1\cdot854 \pm 0\cdot004$ | —                         | —                         |
| Nickel | $1\cdot840 \pm 0\cdot008$ | $2\cdot185 \pm 0\cdot010$ | $1\cdot001 \pm 0\cdot009$ |

is similar to that found for the paramagnetism of salts of $3d$ group ions (Chapter 20), and there is little doubt that it is due essentially to the same cause, 'quenching' of the orbital moment by electrostatic interaction with the neighbouring (ligand) ions.

### 21.5. Thermal effects in ferromagnetism

When a substance is magnetized, with all the electron spins pointing in one direction, it is in a state of greater order than when it is unmagnetized, with the spins pointing in random directions. The magnetized state is therefore one of lower entropy than the unmagnetized state, and in passing from the former to the latter there will be an increase in the entropy of the spin system. If the transition is accomplished by heating a ferromagnetic substance through its Curie point, the entropy change appears as an anomaly in the specific heat. If it is accomplished by the sudden (adiabatic) removal of a magnetic field, the entropy change appears as a fall in the temperature of the substance; this is known as the magneto-caloric effect. Both this effect and the specific heat anomaly have been used to obtain information about the ferromagnetic state.

The specific heat of a substance is $C = T(dS/dT)$, where the entropy change $dS$ is given by the relation

$$T\,dS = dU - \frac{1}{\rho}B\,dM; \tag{21.16}$$

$dU$ is the change in the internal energy, and $-B\,dM$ is the increase in the magnetic potential energy when the magnetization is increased by $dM$ at constant field $B$. The density $\rho$ appears because $M$ is the magnetization per unit volume, while the specific heat (and other thermal quantities) are per unit mass. In a ferromagnet, $B = B_0 + \lambda M$, and the specific heat is thus

$$C = T\frac{dS}{dT} = \frac{dU}{dT} - \left(\frac{B_0 + \lambda M}{\rho}\right)\left(\frac{dM}{dT}\right)$$

$$= C_M - \left(\frac{B_0 + \lambda M}{\rho}\right)\left(\frac{dM}{dT}\right). \tag{21.17}$$

Below the Curie point any external field $B_0$ is very small in comparison with the internal field $\lambda M$, so that we can write

$$C = C_M - \frac{1}{2}\left(\frac{\lambda}{\rho}\right)\frac{d(M^2)}{dT}. \tag{21.18}$$

Here $C_M$ is the specific heat of the substance at constant magnetization, while the second term arises from the change in magnetization with temperature. Since $M$ falls with increasing $T$, it gives a positive contribution to the specific heat (as the temperature rises, the degree of order in the magnetic system decreases, and the entropy associated with the magnetization increases). Reference to Fig. 21.2 shows that the rate of change of $M$ with temperature is greatest just below the Curie point, and the anomalous specific heat arising from the magnetic properties should be greatest at this point, followed by a sharp drop above the Curie point where $M$ becomes zero.

An experimental curve showing the variation of $C$ with $T$ for nickel is given in Fig. 21.8. The anomalous specific heat is appreciable only near the Curie point, but the drop above the Curie point spreads over a range of temperature, instead of appearing as a sharp discontinuity. In

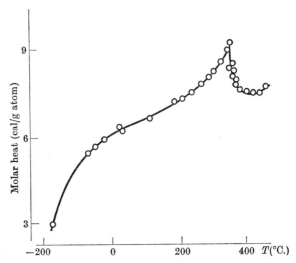

FIG. 21.8. The molar heat of nickel, from the measurements of Grew, 1934.

order to obtain a value for $\lambda$ from the specific heat anomaly, $C_M$ must be estimated and subtracted from the measured specific heat, so that only the magnetic contribution remains. Measurements are made at constant pressure, so that we can write $C_M = C_v + (C_p - C_v) + C_e$. $C_v$ is obtained by extrapolation, using the Debye formula, from measurements at low temperatures; $(C_p - C_v)$ may be found from the expansion coefficient and compressibility using a standard thermodynamical formula; $C_e$ is the electronic specific heat. This is abnormally large in a ferromagnetic metal and difficult to estimate since it is associated with a high electron density in the $3d$ band (see § 18.4). $dM^2/dT$ must be found by plotting $M^2$ as a function of temperature, and then $\lambda$ is obtained. This is not a very accurate method of finding $\lambda$ and the value does not agree too well with the value obtained from the magnetization curve, probably because of errors in $C_e$. However, the general form of the specific heat curve is not incompatible with theory and this also applies to iron and cobalt, although the measurements on these metals are less certain (for experimental details, see Grew, 1934). The general form of the specific heat anomaly ('lambda type') is typical of a 'co-operative' transition from an ordered to a disordered state.

If a field is applied to a magnetic substance, there is in general an increase in magnetization, and this results in a state of greater order than in zero field. In other words the entropy of the system has decreased, and the loss of (magnetic) potential energy of the dipoles in turning towards the field appears as heat of magnetization. If the field is switched off isothermally, heat is absorbed. If the field is switched off adiabatically the entropy of the system must remain constant; the increase in entropy due to increased disorder of the dipoles is then compensated by a decrease in the entropy associated with thermal agitation, and there is therefore a fall in temperature. This is the basis of the 'magnetic cooling' method for obtaining temperatures below $1°$ K using paramagnetic substances. This 'magneto-caloric' effect also has applications to ferromagnetics. Since $dS = 0$ in a reversible adiabatic process, we have from equation (21.17)

$$dT = \left\{\frac{B_0 + \lambda M}{\rho C_M}\right\} dM. \tag{21.19}$$

Above the Curie point saturation effects are negligible and $M/B_0$ is a constant at a given temperature, so that in a finite change of the magnetization we have

$$\Delta T = \left\{\frac{B_0/M + \lambda}{2\rho C_M}\right\} \Delta(M^2). \tag{21.20}$$

Below the Curie point we can neglect $B_0$ in comparison with $\lambda M$, and we obtain

$$\Delta T = \frac{\lambda}{2\rho C_M} \Delta(M^2). \tag{21.21}$$

If the external field is initially zero, so that the magnetization of each domain has the spontaneous value $M_0$, the temperature rise on applying a field is

$$\Delta T = \frac{\lambda}{2\rho C_M} (M^2 - M_0^2). \tag{21.22}$$

If $\Delta T$ is plotted as a function of $M^2$, a curve of the form shown in Fig. 21.9 is obtained. It becomes a straight line in the region where the external field is large enough to change the magnetization of the domains, with a curved tail at lower fields where the magnetization of the substance is mainly due to wall movements or the rotation of domains. Extrapolation of the straight portion to the axis $\Delta T = 0$ gives $M_0^2$ from the intercept.

The magneto-caloric effect may be used for a number of purposes, such as investigation of the hysteresis curve, one of the most important being the determination of the spontaneous magnetization $M_0$ near the Curie point. A good description of experimental technique is given by Oliver and Sucksmith (1953) in work on a copper-nickel alloy (24% Cu; 76% Ni).

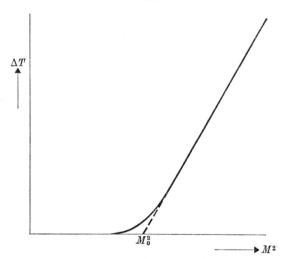

FIG. 21.9. Curve showing the variation of $\Delta T$ with $M^2$ in the magneto-caloric effect.

$$\Delta T = (\lambda/2\rho C_M)(M^2 - M_0^2).$$

## 21.6. Measurement of the spontaneous magnetization $M_0$ as a function of temperature

In § 21.2 it was shown that the spontaneous magnetization of a single domain should obey an equation of state which depends only slightly on $J$ (see Fig. 21.2). In order to test this relation it is necessary to determine the value of $M_0$ for a single domain at zero field over a wide range of temperature. Since in practice any specimen consists of a number of domains randomly oriented, so that (apart from remanence) the net magnetization will be zero, it follows that the spontaneous magnetization of a single domain cannot be directly measured. If we apply a sufficiently strong field, however, the various domains will rotate until they point in the direction of the external field, and the resultant magnetic moment will be close to the spontaneous magnetization of the individual domains. It will slightly exceed it, since the magnetization under these conditions corresponds, not to the point $P$ in Fig. 21.1, but to the point $P'$, the stable state in the presence of a magnetic field. In order to find the value corresponding to $P$, we must make measurements of $M$ for a range of values of the external field, and then extrapolate back to zero field. Since the fields which are applied are small compared with the internal field, the point $P'$ is never far from $P$, and the extrapolation required is not very great at temperatures well below the Curie point. Near the Curie point the magneto-caloric effect is used as described in the previous section.

In a number of magnetic materials the nucleus of the magnetic ion possesses a nuclear magnetic dipole moment $\mathbf{m}_n$, which interacts with the magnetic field $\mathbf{B}_e$ of the electrons (see § 20.10). (The field $\mathbf{B}_e$ is the actual magnetic field at the nucleus generated by the magnetic electrons, and is nothing to do with the effective molecular field $\mathbf{B}_{int}$ introduced by Weiss to explain ferromagnetism.) The interaction energy

$$W = -\mathbf{m}_n . \mathbf{B}_e$$

gives a hyperfine splitting of the nuclear levels, from observation of which $B_e$ can be found if the nuclear moment is known. In a ferromagnetic substance $B_e$ is parallel to the magnetization, and its time average value is proportional to the average magnetic moment on each ion (apart from some small corrections). Thus $B_e$ is proportional to the magnetization, and observation of the hyperfine structure separation as a function of temperature gives a convenient and accurate method of determining the saturation magnetization curve. This can be done in zero external field, since it is not necessary to line up the domains, and many of the difficulties of direct measurement of the bulk magnetization are avoided.

The magnitude of the electronic field $B_e$ lies generally between $10^5$ and $10^7$ gauss. The nuclear levels have energy $W_{m_I} = -g_n \beta_n m_I B_e$, where $m_I$ is the nuclear magnetic quantum number, and are equally separated by an amount corresponding to a frequency of $10^8$–$10^{10}$ c/s. Two methods are available for measuring this separation over a range of temperature. One of these is the Mössbauer effect, in which a low-energy $\gamma$-ray is emitted from a nucleus in an excited state and absorbed by a nucleus in the ground state. A $\gamma$-ray photon of energy $h\nu$ carries momentum $h\nu/c$, so that the emitting or absorbing nucleus is given a recoil momentum, and hence takes up energy which reduces the photon energy. If the nuclei are in a solid the recoil momentum is generally taken up by the solid as a whole, and the energy taken from the $\gamma$-ray is negligible. Thus in a solid, unlike a gas (see Problem 21.3), there is no spread in energy of the photon due to the varying amounts of energy taken up by the recoil.

Only those $\gamma$-rays which are extremely narrow are of use, since the width of the $\gamma$-ray must be smaller than the hyperfine splitting. For magnetic purposes, the 14·4 keV transition between the excited state $(I = \frac{3}{2})$ and the ground state $(I = \frac{1}{2})$ of the isotope $^{57}$Fe has been especially useful. This gives a line width of about 3 Mc/s, and the hyperfine levels and structure of the Mössbauer gamma-ray are shown in Fig. 21.10. The structure is exactly analogous to the Zeeman effect

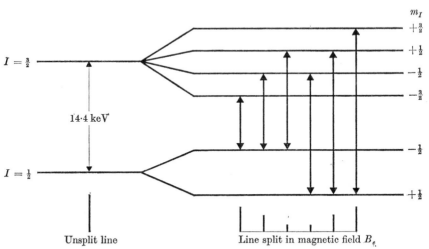

FIG. 21.10. Hyperfine splitting of the nuclear states of $^{57}$Fe in a magnetic field. The ground state $I = \frac{1}{2}$ has $g_n = +0·18$, and the excited state $I = \frac{3}{2}$ has $g_n = -0·010$; the allowed transitions are those for which $\Delta m_I = 0, \pm 1$. Note the gross disparity in scale; the hyperfine splittings are about $10^{-11}$ to $10^{-12}$ of the $\gamma$-ray frequency. In some substances there is also an electric quadrupole interaction in the $I = \frac{3}{2}$ state.

in an atomic transition. The splittings are a very small fraction of the $\gamma$-ray frequency, and their analysis is made by means of the Doppler effect produced by a relative motion of the source and absorber. It is convenient to use a source with no hyperfine structure, such as $^{57}$Fe (derived from the nuclear decay of $^{57}$Co) in stainless steel, which is non-magnetic, since this gives a single emission line, as shown on the left of Fig. 21.10. For this to be absorbed by a $^{57}$Fe nucleus in a magnetic substance, where six transitions are allowed with slightly different frequencies as on the right of Fig. 21.10, a Doppler shift is needed of the correct velocity to bring one of the transitions to the same frequency as the single line on the left. Thus the entire hyperfine pattern can be scanned by systematically changing the relative velocity of source and absorber (the velocity required is of order a few mm/sec). Of course source and absorber can be interchanged, and the choice is determined by experimental convenience.

The hyperfine field in metallic iron has been determined as a function of temperature by means of the Mössbauer effect; the results (see Fig. 21.11) of Nagle, Frauenfelder, Taylor, Cochran, and Matthias (1960) show close agreement with the saturation curve determined by conventional means. At sufficiently low temperatures for the magnetization to reach the saturation value, the hyperfine field is 330 kilogauss. On applying an external field parallel to the magnetization Hanna, Heberle,

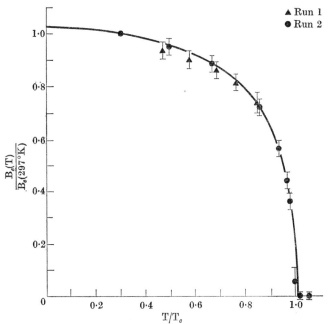

FIG. 21.11. The hyperfine magnetic field at a $^{57}$Fe nucleus in metallic iron, relative to that at room temperature, plotted against the reduced temperature $T/T_c$. The experimental points are measured by the Mössbauer effect, the solid line indicates the relative saturation magnetization as determined by a bulk measurement (see Nagle *et al.*, 1960).

Perlow, Preston, and Vincent (1960) found that the net field at the $^{57}$Fe nucleus was reduced, showing that the hyperfine field was in the opposite sense to the external field, and hence also to the magnetization.

The hyperfine splitting of the ground nuclear levels in a ferromagnetic substance has also been measured by the method of nuclear magnetic resonance (see § 23.5). For $^{57}$Fe this gives a direct observation of transitions between the states $m_I = +\frac{1}{2}$ and $-\frac{1}{2}$ of the ground state $I = \frac{1}{2}$, at a frequency such that

$$h\nu = W_{-\frac{1}{2}} - W_{+\frac{1}{2}} = g_n \beta_n B_e, \qquad (21.23)$$

where $g_n$ is the value for the ground state $I = \frac{1}{2}$. This gives a more precise measurement of $B_e$ than the Mössbauer method (in which the line width cannot be less than that determined by the lifetime of the excited state), and the resonance frequency, about 46 Mc/s in metallic iron near 0° K, can be found within a few kc/s. Benedek and Armstrong (1961) have made a careful study of the pressure and temperature dependence of the resonance frequency in iron, and have shown that the resonance frequency is not quite linearly proportional to the magnetization at higher temperatures, but the departure is less than 1 per cent at 300° C.

## 21.7. Foundations of the theory of ferromagnetism

The brief description of the chief properties of ferromagnetic substances given above shows that we possess a fairly good qualitative understanding of the basic phenomena. There is no doubt that ferromagnetism is due to exchange forces, but the quantitative theory of ferromagnetism contains many difficulties and can be treated only by approximate methods. We may distinguish between two separate problems: (a) the nature of the mechanism giving rise to exchange forces; (b) development of methods of treating the problem of an assembly of magnetic particles subject to exchange interaction. We shall outline the principal approaches to (b) first, and postpone consideration of (a) to § 21.9.

In the original Heisenberg model, the magnetic electrons are regarded as localized on each atom. This is clearly a good approximation in an ionic solid, such as the paramagnetic substances discussed in Chapter 20. In the 3d group, with which we are principally concerned, the crystal field interaction effectively 'quenches' the orbital magnetism, leaving only that due to the electron spin. The spins on adjacent atoms then interact through the exchange interaction. On this basis we should expect the saturation moment of a ferromagnetic to correspond to an integral number of spins per atom, and since a g value of 2 is associated with the spin, we should expect an integral number of Bohr magnetons per atom. Reference to Table 21.1 shows that this is by no means the case. Nickel has a saturation moment corresponding to 0·6 magnetons, iron 2·22, and cobalt 1·72 magnetons. These substances are, of course, metals, where the success of the band model for the conduction electrons suggests that it should be used as the basis of a theory of ferromagnetism.

The 'collective electron' model has been investigated principally by Bloch, Slater, Stoner, and Wohlfarth. As in the theory of metallic conduction, the electrons obey the Fermi–Dirac statistics, and the allowed energies fall into bands. The exchange interaction is introduced as an internal field $\lambda M$, proportional to the magnetization, as in the Weiss treatment. This gives a difference in energy between spin dipoles pointing parallel and anti-parallel to the internal field, which we may represent by dividing the energy band into two halves as in Fig. 18.13, but with the important difference that the effective field is now the internal field $B_{\text{int}}$ and not the external field. Hence the energy separation of the two halves of the band is $2\beta B_{\text{int}} = 2\beta(\lambda M) = 2\beta(\lambda\, 2x_0\,\beta) = 4x_0\,\lambda\beta^2$, where $x_0$ is the number of electrons transferred from one half-band to the other, giving an excess of $2x_0$ in the 'parallel' orientation and a net magnetization of $2x_0\,\beta$. Thus the energy separation is itself proportional to the number of electrons transferred. Reference to § 18.7 shows that the extra kinetic energy required by the $x$th electron to transfer it to a vacant level is approximately $2xw = 4x\{g(W)_F\}^{-1}$, where $\{g(W)_F\}$ is the number of levels per unit of translational energy at the top of the Fermi distribution. Hence the total kinetic energy required to transfer $x_0$ electrons is

$$\int_0^{x_0} 4x\{g(W)_F\}^{-1}\,dx = 2x_0^2\{g(W)_F\}^{-1}.$$ The change in magnetic energy is $-\tfrac{1}{2}M B_{\text{int}} = -\tfrac{1}{2}\lambda M^2 = -\tfrac{1}{2}\lambda(2x_0\,\beta)^2 = -2x_0^2\,\lambda\beta^2$. Hence the net change in energy of the system is

$$2x_0^2\left\{-\lambda\beta^2 + \frac{1}{g(W)_F}\right\},$$

and this will be negative provided that

$$\lambda\beta^2 g(W)_F > 1.$$

If the change in energy is negative, it follows that the magnetized state is one of lower energy and is therefore the stable state; if the energy change is positive the unmagnetized state will be stable and there will be no spontaneous ferromagnetism. It turns out that the values of $\lambda$ are such that ferromagnetism is possible for bands which have a small energy width, and hence a large value of $g(W)_F$.

In a simple case, such as sodium, we may use the relation

$$g(W)_F = 3n/2W_F$$

given by equation (4.13). Then we have

$$\frac{3\lambda\beta^2 n}{2W_F} > 1 \tag{21.24}$$

as the condition for ferromagnetism. For sodium, this requires a value of $\lambda$ about a hundred times larger than that observed in iron. In the $3d$ group the overlapping $3d$ and $4s$ bands produce a much higher value of $g(W)_F$ than that for sodium, and the effect of the overlapping is enhanced by the fact that $n$, the number of free electrons per unit volume, is also larger. It turns out that $g(W)_F$ is greatest when the $3d$ band is almost filled, a situation reached by iron, cobalt, and nickel, so that the condition for ferromagnetism is satisfied. Then the value of $x_0$ will rise until any further increase would raise the total energy instead

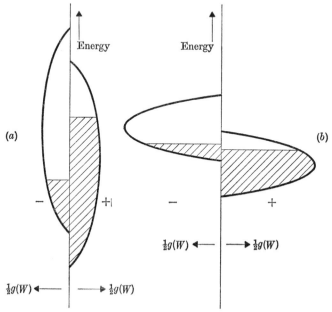

FIG. 21.12. Schematic diagram of energy bands with exchange interaction.

In both (a) and (b) equal numbers of electrons have been transferred from the anti-parallel (−) orientation to the parallel (+) orientation. As a result the (+) band is lowered in energy relative to the (−) band in each case by the same amount, determined by the size of the internal field set up. In case (a), with a wide energy band, the top of the Fermi distribution in the (+) band comes above that in the (−) band, showing that this displacement has a higher energy than if the numbers in the two bands were equal. In case (b), with a narrow energy band, the top of the distribution is higher in the (−) band, and more electrons will transfer to the (+) band, increasing the net magnetization still further. Hence (b) gives spontaneous magnetization while (a) does not.

of lowering it. Such an equilibrium state is possible because the effective value of $g(W)_F$ changes when we transfer an appreciable fraction of the total number of electrons from one orientation to the other, as one half-band is being emptied and the other filled (compare Fig. 21.12). It is obvious that there is no reason to expect that the saturation magnetic moment, determined by the position of this equilibrium, should correspond to an integral number of electron spins per atom.

Ferromagnetic substances have abnormally large electronic specific heats, as would be expected on the energy band picture from the large values of $g(W)_F$ required for ferromagnetism (see § 18.4). The 'collective electron model', as it is called, also accounts for the difference between the ferromagnetic and paramagnetic Curie points, and for the considerable difference in the effective Bohr magneton number derived from the slope of the Curie–Weiss law in the paramagnetic region from the value given by the saturation magnetic moment in the ferromagnetic region.

The 'collective electron' model of ferromagnetism has been criticized by Van Vleck (1953) on the grounds that it neglects the electrostatic repulsion of the electrons, which forms part of the 'correlation energy' mentioned at the end of § 18.2. In a simple metal the energy bands are rather wide, and the correlation energy has little effect on the ordinary conduction properties. However, ferromagnetism can occur only if the bands are rather narrow; this requires $d$- (or $f$-)electrons, which are more tightly bound and for which the energy needed to change the state of ionization is higher. Thus states of excessive ionization, which are allowed undue weight on the free electron theory, are very improbable, and fluctuations in the charge density on each ion are relatively small. In this respect a localized electron model may form a better starting point, and Van Vleck has put forward a generalization of this model in which there is on average a non-integral number of spins per atom, the spins being continually redistributed between different sites. For example, the low moment of nickel can be understood if we assume that 40 per cent of the nickel ions are in the non-magnetic $3d^{10}$ state, with closed shells, while the remaining 60 per cent are in $3d^9$ states, each contributing one Bohr magneton to the total moment. Since all nickel atoms are identical there is nothing to determine which atoms should be in the $3d^{10}$ state and which in $3d^9$; any given atom fluctuates rapidly from one to the other, so that on average it is in a $3d^{10}$ state for 40 per cent of the time, and $3d^9$ for 60 per cent. In fact neutron diffraction measurements yield a scattering pattern corresponding to each atom carrying an identical moment, so that fluctuations between states of different ionization must average out in a very short time. Van Vleck has refined this model to include states of higher ionization, typical values being 53% $d^{10}$, 35% $d^9$, 10% $d^8$, $1\frac{1}{2}$% $d^7$, 0·1% $d^6$, giving an average value of $3d^{9\cdot4}$. This gives a 'minimum polarity' for the ions, in contrast with the excessive polarity allowed in the free electron model.

The problem of the co-operative magnetic state in a conducting solid with itinerant electrons is extremely difficult to handle mathematically, and existing methods start from over-simplified models which are progressively refined. Ideally any theory should include not only the exchange interaction, but also the ligand field interaction (§§ 20.6–9), which is primarily responsible for 'spin only' magnetism in the iron group, and the spin-orbit interaction, which makes the $g$, $g'$ values discussed in § 21.4 different from the free spin value of 2. Considerably more progress has been made on the magnetic properties of electrically insulating materials, where the theoretical problems are somewhat easier, and magnetic resonance experiments provide much more detailed information; such compounds are mostly anti-ferromagnetic or ferri-magnetic, whose properties are discussed in Chapter 22. There is, however, one theoretical technique, originally developed for localized electrons, but which has since been shown to be valid for itinerant electrons; in it the collective excitations of the assembly of magnetic carriers, known as 'spin waves', are handled by means of expansions valid at low temperatures in the co-operative state. A brief outline of this method, first formulated by Bloch (1932), is given in the following section.

### 21.8. Spin waves

At $0°$ K, where the magnetization has the saturation value, all the spins are rigorously parallel, but this is obviously not so at a non-zero temperature where the magnetization is smaller. However, it would be incorrect to regard the reduction in magnetization as due to the reversal of any given individual spin, because any such deviation would be passed on to neighbouring spins through the exchange interaction in a time of order $(\mathcal{J}'/\hbar)$, so that it would not remain localized on any given atom. In fact the average deviation of each spin from exact parallelism is small, and can be analysed in terms of sinusoidal spatial variations throughout the crystal, known as 'spin waves'. In a spin wave of wave vector $\mathbf{k}_s$, the angle between adjacent spins a distance $\mathbf{r}_0$ apart is $\mathbf{k}_s . \mathbf{r}_0$, and since the exchange energy varies with the cosine of this angle, the extra energy required to excite a wave is proportional to $\mathcal{J}'(1-\cos \mathbf{k}_s . \mathbf{r}_0) = \frac{1}{2}\mathcal{J}'(\mathbf{k}_s . \mathbf{r}_0)^2 = \frac{1}{2}\mathcal{J}'k_s^2 r_0^2 \cos^2\theta_{k,r_0}$, where $\theta_{k,r_0}$ is the angle between $\mathbf{k}_s$ and $\mathbf{r}_0$. This must be summed over all neighbours, giving

$$W_k = \hbar\omega_k = Dk_s^2. \qquad (21.25)$$

This is the dispersion relation connecting the frequency and wavelength of a spin wave. $D$ is proportional to the exchange energy $\mathcal{J}'$, and in a cubic lattice with $z$ equidistant neighbours with angular momentum $J$.

$$D = \frac{1}{3}\mathcal{J}'zJr_0^2. \qquad (21.26)$$

The energy required to excite a spin wave is proportional to $k^2$, and at low temperatures only long waves will be excited; in the limit at $0°$ K the only wave present will be $k = 0$, which corresponds to all the dipoles being parallel. As the temperature rises more spin waves of shorter wavelengths will be excited, and the energy required for this shows up as an additional term in the specific heat. This is quite distinct from the abnormal electronic specific heat discussed above, and would be present in a ferromagnetic insulator. It is purely magnetic in origin, and constitutes the low-temperature tail of the magnetic specific heat anomaly discussed in § 21.5. Van Kranendonk and Van Vleck (1958) have shown that a spin wave behaves formally like a harmonic oscillator, its mean energy being

$$\overline{W}_k = \frac{\hbar\omega_k}{\exp(\hbar\omega_k/kT)-1} = \bar{n}\hbar\omega_k, \tag{21.27}$$

where $\bar{n} = \{\exp(\hbar\omega_k/kT)-1\}^{-1}$ is known as the 'occupation number'. The number of spin waves of wave vector $k_s$ (we have used $k_s$ to avoid confusion with Boltzmann's constant $k$ which occurs in equation (21.27) is $g(k_s)\,dk_s = (V/2\pi^2)k_s^2\,dk_s$, as can be seen from equation (4.8) by substituting $k_s = (2\pi/\lambda)$. Hence the internal energy at temperature $T$ is

$$U = \int \bar{n}(\hbar\omega_k)g(k_s)\,dk_s$$

$$= \frac{V}{2\pi^2} \int_0^\infty \frac{(Dk_s^2)k_s^2\,dk_s}{\exp(Dk_s^2/kT)-1}$$

$$= \frac{VD}{2\pi^2} \left(\frac{kT}{D}\right)^{\frac{5}{2}} \int_0^\infty \frac{x^4\,dx}{\exp(x^2)-1},$$

where we have made the substitution $x^2 = (Dk_s^2/kT)$. The integral can be taken to infinity at low temperatures, and is therefore just a numerical constant. Differentiation with respect to temperature gives

$$C_V = dU/dT = c(kT/D)^{\frac{3}{2}}, \tag{21.28}$$

where $c$ is a numerical constant whose value depends somewhat on the crystal structure; for a simple cubic lattice ($z = 6$) we have (per mole)

$$C_V = 0.113kV(kT/D)^{\frac{3}{2}} = 0.113k(V/r_0^3)(kT/2\mathscr{J}'J)^{\frac{3}{2}}$$

$$= 0.113R(kT/2\mathscr{J}'J)^{\frac{3}{2}}. \tag{21.29}$$

For the ordinary ferromagnetic metals this magnetic specific heat is small and difficult to measure in the presence of the abnormally large electronic specific heat, and the lattice specific heat. It has been detected in some non-conducting ferrimagnetic compounds (see § 22.3).

The departure of the magnetization from the absolute saturation value $M_s$ can be computed similarly, using the fact that each spin wave reduces the magnetic moment by an amount $g\beta\bar{n}$. Thus

$$M_s - M_0 = g\beta \sum \bar{n} = (g\beta V/2\pi^2) \int \frac{k_s^2\, dk_s}{\exp(Dk_s^2/kT) - 1}$$

$$= (g\beta V/2\pi^2)(kT/D)^{\frac{3}{2}} \int_0^\infty \frac{x^2\, dx}{\exp(x^2) - 1}.$$

On substituting for $D$ and using the fact that $g\beta(V/r_0^3) = M_s$, in a simple cubic lattice, one obtains the relation

$$M_0/M_s = 1 - a(kT/2\mathscr{J}'J)^{\frac{3}{2}}, \tag{21.30}$$

where $a = 0{\cdot}059/J$ in a simple cubic lattice. This result is the first term of a power series where the next terms are in $T^{\frac{5}{2}}$, $T^{\frac{7}{2}}$, and $T^4$. The terms in $T^{\frac{5}{2}}$ and $T^{\frac{7}{2}}$ have been verified in a special case where they are unusually large (see Gossard, Jaccarino, and Remeika, 1961), using nuclear magnetic resonance of the $^{53}$Cr nucleus in $CrBr_3$, where the nuclear resonance frequency is accurately proportional to the magnetization. In gadolinium metal, where the spontaneous magnetization has been measured by Elliott, Legvold, and Spedding (1953) by the bulk magnetization method, the $T^{\frac{3}{2}}$ law holds closely almost up to the Curie point, a result that has been explained as due to a near cancellation of the higher terms (Goodings, 1962). These experimental results for the variation of the magnetization with temperature confirm the validity of the spin wave method; in contrast, the collective electron model predicts a variation of the form
$$M_0/M_s = 1 - bT^2 + \ldots \tag{21.31}$$

while the molecular field model gives an exponential term (see Problem 21.1). Direct experimental confirmation of the existence of spin waves is obtained from magnetic resonance experiments in thin ferromagnetic films (see § 23.7).

## 21.9. Mechanisms of exchange interaction

In § 21.1 it was stated that ferromagnetism is due to exchange interaction; certainly we know of no other interaction of the correct form which is large enough in size to produce ferromagnetism. Though it is generally agreed that ferromagnetism is due to exchange interaction, attempts to make numerical calculations of its size have proved very difficult; more than one mechanism of exchange interaction has been proposed, each of which no doubt plays a role, but the absence of reliable quantitative information makes an assessment of their relative importance still rather speculative.

The original treatment of Heisenberg and Dirac deals with the interaction between two electrons on the same atom. If the two electrons
did not influence one another the solution of the wave equation would
be a simple product of the two solutions for a single electron, of the form

$$\psi_{\mathrm{I}} = \phi_k^{(1)} \phi_m^{(2)}.$$

The physical interpretation of this is that electron (1) is in orbital $k$,
and electron (2) is in orbital $m$. Since the two electrons are equivalent,
the energy is unchanged if the two electrons are interchanged, giving
another solution
$$\psi_{\mathrm{II}} = \phi_k^{(2)} \phi_m^{(1)}.$$

In general, any linear combination of these two solutions is allowed, the
correct combination being determined when we include the electrostatic
energy $e^2/r_{12}$ (where $r_{12}$ is the distance between the two electrons) of
repulsion between the two negatively charged electrons. The correct
solutions are then the symmetric and anti-symmetric combinations

$$\psi_{\mathrm{sym}} = (2)^{-\frac{1}{2}}(\psi_{\mathrm{I}} + \psi_{\mathrm{II}}),$$

$$\psi_{\mathrm{ant}} = (2)^{-\frac{1}{2}}(\psi_{\mathrm{I}} - \psi_{\mathrm{II}}).$$

These two solutions no longer have the same energy, because the symmetrical solution allows the wave function to have a large amplitude
if the two electrons are at the same point, while the anti-symmetric
wave function then vanishes because $\psi_{\mathrm{I}} = \psi_{\mathrm{II}}$. Thus the electrostatic
repulsive energy between the two electrons is larger in the first case
than in the second.

So far it has not been necessary to include the electron spin. With
two electrons, the spin states (two for each electron, hence four in all)
are divided between the triplet states ($S = 1$, $M_S = 1, 0, -1$) and the
singlet state $S = 0$, according to whether the two individual spins are
parallel or anti-parallel. The triplet states are symmetrical with respect
to interchange of the two electrons, the singlet state is anti-symmetrical.
Since only states whose overall symmetry is anti-symmetrical are
allowed in nature, the spin triplet states can only be combined with the
orbital $\psi_{\mathrm{ant}}$, and the singlet spin state with the orbital $\psi_{\mathrm{sym}}$. Thus the
difference in electrostatic energy between the symmetrical and anti-
symmetrical orbital states carries with it a corresponding energy difference between the spin singlet and triplet. This is formally similar to the
introduction of a coupling energy between the electron spins of the type
assumed in § 21.1.

For two electrons within the same atom, the exchange energy is always positive, so that the state of lower energy is with the spins parallel. This coupling is 'ferromagnetic' in nature, and is the justification for Hund's rule (§ 20.2) which makes the ground state of the atom the one with maximum multiplicity in the spin. In the phenomenon of ferromagnetism proper, however, we are concerned with exchange interaction between electrons on different atoms, and the electrostatic energy involved contains terms arising both from the repulsive forces between the two nuclei and between the two electrons and from the attractive forces between an electron on one atom and the nucleus of the other atom. (The much larger energy of attraction between an electron and the nucleus of its own atom has already been included in the wave equation for each electron.) In simple molecules like $H_2$ the overall exchange term is easily shown to be negative, in agreement with the ground state of the molecule being a singlet, but with more complex ions such as the $3d$ group, opinions have differed whether the net effect (which obviously varies with interatomic distance) would be positive or negative at the ionic separations typical of $3d$ group metals. Since improved wave functions have become available from electronic computers, attempts have been made to carry out calculations which might be reasonably realistic. Stuart and Marshall (1960) obtained a positive energy, though two orders of magnitude too small, but Freeman, Nesbet, and Watson (1962) find a negative energy. Thus 'direct exchange', due to direct overlap of the electronic wave functions, appears incapable of accounting for ferromagnetism. A negative exchange energy would give rise to 'anti-ferromagnetism' (see Chapter 22), where neighbouring spins are arranged anti-parallel rather than parallel.

In conducting solids an alternative mechanism has been proposed, which involves exchange interaction between the ferromagnetic $3d$ electrons (largely localized) and the itinerant conduction electrons. A conduction electron is spin-polarized by exchange interaction with one ion, then moves away to interact with another ion, carrying the memory of its polarization with it. This gives rise to an indirect exchange interaction between the two ions, involving the exchange interaction $\mathscr{J}_{sm}$ between the conduction electrons (or '$s$' electrons) and the ferromagnetic ('$m$') electrons, and the energy $W_F$ at the Fermi surface. The resultant interaction between the ions is proportional to $(\mathscr{J}_{sm})^2/W_F$, since the exchange interaction $\mathscr{J}_{sm}$ is involved twice, and the polarization of the conduction electrons is inversely proportional to the Fermi energy (see § 18.7). Since the wave function of a conduction electron spreads throughout the metal, at first sight this exchange interaction appears to be independent of distance, and necessarily ferromagnetic since $\mathscr{J}^2_{sm}/W_F$ must be positive. However, a proper calculation shows that it can be of either sign and does fall off with distance (though much less rapidly than direct exchange), being an oscillatory function of $x = 2k_F R$, where $k_F$ is the wave vector of a conduction electron at the Fermi surface and $R$ the inter-ionic distance.

In this mechanism the conduction electrons serve as a medium through which an interaction is transmitted between spins which are localized. In fact it was first proposed for nuclear spins, the hyperfine energy of interaction between the nuclear spin and a conduction electron appearing instead of the exchange interaction $\mathscr{J}_{sm}$ above; the oscillatory nature of the interaction was deduced by Rudermann and Kittel (1954). The exchange mechanism for electrons was proposed by Yosida (1957) and Kasuya (1956); it is generally thought to provide the mechanism for ferromagnetism in the lanthanide metals (see § 22.4), where the magnetic $4f$ electrons are quite localized. How large a role it plays in the $3d$ metals is uncertain.

*Exchange interaction in insulators*

In electrical insulators no conduction electrons exist to provide an exchange mechanism of the type just considered, but exchange interactions of considerable magnitude are found in compounds where the interionic distance is so large that direct exchange between electrons localized on the magnetic ions must be negligible. As an example we consider a simple compound such as an oxide MO, where M is a dipositive ion of the $3d$ group (e.g. $Mn^{2+}$, $Fe^{2+}$, $Co^{2+}$, $Ni^{2+}$). These have a face-centred cubic structure similar to that of NaCl, a typical plane of atoms being shown in Fig. 21.13. Here the circles are drawn in proportion to the ionic radii, and it can be seen that the much larger anions separate almost completely even the nearest neighbour cations. However, neutron diffraction results suggest that the stronger exchange interactions are between ions on next nearest neighbour sites such as $A$, $B$ rather than between nearest neighbour sites such as $A$, $C$. Direct overlap between the wave functions of magnetic electrons on the cation sites is very small, but a purely ionic model where the magnetic electrons are localized on the cations is an over-simplification. Some degree of covalent binding is always present, whereby the wave functions of the magnetic electrons spread over onto the adjacent anions. Direct overlap of the magnetic electrons from neighbouring cations can therefore take place on the intervening anions. Of course the degree of overlap depends on the amount of covalent bonding, and so also does the size of this 'indirect' exchange interaction; it is very much smaller for ions of the 4$f$ group, which take almost no part in covalent bonding, than for ions of the 3$d$ group (for example, the transition temperature of the lanthanide oxides is below 10° K, while those of the 3$d$ group oxides are over 100° K).

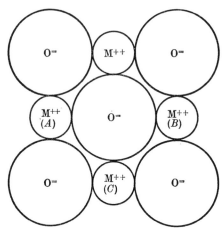

FIG. 21.13. A plane of atoms in an oxide MO, where M$^{++}$ is a dipositive ion of the 3$d$ group. The ions are drawn approximately to size, showing how the small cations (M$^{++}$) are well separated by the large anions (O$^{=}$).

Although this solves the problem of interaction between ions at relatively large distances, there are two difficulties. The first is that the potential energy due to the electrostatic repulsion between the magnetic electrons in the overlap region leads to a ferromagnetic interaction (as for electrons within the same atom, where it results in Hund's rules—see § 20.2), whereas the vast majority of insulating magnetic compounds have an anti-ferromagnetic interaction. Second, the interacting magnetic electrons form a partly-filled band, which according to the classification set out in § 18.3 should make the substance an electrical conductor. However, the energy band is narrow, and the fall in kinetic energy of an electron (cf. Fig. 18.2) on transferring from a localized state (which corresponds in energy to the centre of the band) to a conduction state at the bottom of the band is only ≈ 1 eV. On the other hand, because of the electrostatic repulsion between the electrons, their potential energy is least when they are uniformly distributed, giving each ion the same number of electrons. This potential energy is part of the 'correlation energy' mentioned at the end of § 18.2. For $s$-electrons, and to a smaller extent for $p$-electrons, the correlation energy is small because their wave functions are extended and the charge density within the atom is small; however, the extended wave functions give a larger overlap and greater bandwidth in the solid (cf. Fig. 18.7). Thus such electrons have a lower energy overall when they are non-localized, and become conduction electrons. For $d$-electrons the bandwidth is smaller and the correlation energy greater, making the latter correspondingly more important; the 'minimum polarity' model of Van Vleck discussed in § 21.7 for nickel is an attempt to allow for this. In compounds the disparity is even greater; the $d$-electron band width is not more than about 1 eV, while about 10 eV is required to transfer an electron from one ion to another (i.e. to create a pair of ions in $d^{n-1}$, $d^{n+1}$ states from a pair both in $d^n$ states). Thus it is energetically favourable for the electrons to remain localized and the substance is an electric insulator.

As a result of these conflicting energy considerations, the localization is not, however, absolutely complete. If $b$ is the reduction in kinetic energy which would result from moving from site to site, while $U$ is the potential energy required to overcome the electrostatic repulsion, the equilibrium state is one where the chance of such a movement is of order $b/U$, and the net reduction in kinetic energy is of order $b^2/U$. Through the exclusion principle this possibility of movement to adjacent sites is restricted nearly always to electrons with anti-parallel spin, which can therefore acquire a lower energy than those with parallel spin. This is equivalent to an anti-ferromagnetic exchange energy of order $b^2/U$, which is of order $10^{-2}$ to $10^{-1}$ eV (a few hundred °K).

The first explanation of how exchange interaction could arise between ions at the rather large inter-ionic distances found in compounds was put forward by Kramers (1934), and a number of subsequent attempts were made to arrive at more explicit interpretations. The theory outlined above is due to Anderson (1963), and though difficult to explain in simple terms, appears to be the most satisfactory in its general approach.

## REFERENCES

ANDERSON, P. W., 1963, *Advanc. Solid State Phys.* **14**, 99.
BARNETT, S. J., 1944, *Phys. Rev.* **66**, 224.
BENEDEK, G. B., and ARMSTRONG, J., 1961, *J. Appl. Phys.* **32**, 106s.
BLOCH, F., 1932, *Z. Phys.* **74**, 295.
ELLIOTT, J. F., LEGVOLD, S., and SPEDDING, F. H., 1953, *Phys. Rev.* **91**, 28.
FREEMAN, A. J., NESBET, R. K., and WATSON, R. E., 1962, ibid. **125**, 1978.
GOODINGS, D. A., 1962, ibid. **127**, 1532.

GOSSARD, A. C., JACCARINO, V., and REMEIKA, J. P., 1961, *Phys. Rev. Letters*, **7**, 122.

GREW, K. E., 1934, *Proc. Roy. Soc.* A, **145**, 509.

HANNA, S. S., HEBERLE, J., PERLOW, G. J., PRESTON, R. S., and VINCENT, D. H., 1960, *Phys. Rev. Letters*, **4**, 513.

KASUYA, T., 1956, *Prog. Theoret. Phys.* **16**, 45.

KRAMERS, H. A., 1934, *Physica*, **1**, 182.

MEYER, A. J. P., and ASCH, G., 1961, *J. Appl. Phys.* **32**, 330.

NAGLE, D. E., FRAUENFELDER, R. D., TAYLOR, R. D., COCHRAN, D. R. F., and MATTHIAS, B. T., 1960, *Phys. Rev. Letters*, **5**, 364.

OLIVER, D. J., and SUCKSMITH, W., 1953, *Proc. Roy. Soc.* A, **219**, 1.

RUDERMANN, M. A., and KITTEL, C., 1954, *Phys. Rev.* **96**, 99.

RUSHBROOKE, G. S., and WOOD, P. J., 1958, *Molec. Phys.* **1**, 257.

SCOTT, G. G., 1951, *Phys. Rev.* **82**, 542.

STUART, R., and MARSHALL, W., 1960, ibid. **120**, 353.

VAN KRANENDONK, J., and VAN VLECK, J. H., 1958, *Rev. Mod. Phys.* **30**, 1.

VAN VLECK, J. H., 1953, ibid. **25**, 220.

YOSIDA, K., 1957, *Phys. Rev.* **106**, 893.

# PROBLEMS

**21.1.** Show that for a substance consisting of atoms or ions in the $^2S_{\frac{1}{2}}$ state, the Brillouin function becomes

$$M/M_s = \tanh y, \quad \text{where } y = \beta B/kT.$$

Show that for such a ferromagnetic substance at low temperatures, where $y$ is large, the Weiss internal field treatment of § 21.2 leads to the formula

$$M_0/M_s = 1 - 2\exp(-2\lambda M_0 M_s/nkT)$$

for the spontaneous magnetization $M_0$ in zero field. Note that this does not lead to a simple power law such as in equations (21.30) or (21.31).

**21.2.** Using the result of Problem 6.11, show that the magnetostatic energy of a small spherical particle of nickel, of radius $b$ and magnetized to saturation ($M_s = 5\cdot1\ 10^5$ ampere/metre $= 510$ e.m.u./cm$^3$), is approximately $2 \times 10^5 b^3$ joules ($b$ in metres).

From the results of § 21.3, the energy required to form a Bloch wall increases with $b^2$ (for nickel the wall energy is about an erg/cm$^2$). Hence show that for particles whose radius is less than about $10^{-8}$ metres, the reduction in magnetostatic energy obtained by division into two domains is less than the energy required to form a wall.

**21.3.** The nucleus of an atom of mass $M$ moving with velocity $v$ emits a $\gamma$-ray of energy $h\nu$ in the forward direction. Show by considering the change in momentum and energy of the atom that the $\gamma$-ray energy is increased by a fraction $(v/c)$, provided that the $\gamma$-ray energy is small compared with the rest mass of the atom $[h\nu/Mc^2 \ll 1]$. Note that this is the same as the classical Doppler shift.

**21.4.** Show, from the vector model diagram of Fig. 20.6, that the ratio to $J$ of the projection of $S$ on $J$ is

$$\{S(S+1)\}^{\frac{1}{2}}\cos ACB/\{J(J+1)\}^{\frac{1}{2}} = g-1.$$

# ANTI-FERROMAGNETISM AND FERRIMAGNETISM

## 22.1. Anti-ferromagnetism

IN a paramagnetic substance the dipoles are free to orient themselves at random, and there is a correspondingly high entropy; if there are $2J+1$ levels having the same energy in the ground state, the entropy is $R\ln(2J+1)$. The substance would obey Curie's law down to $0°$ K if the ground state contains two or more levels with the same energy in the absence of an external field, but this would be a violation of the third law of thermodynamics, by which the entropy in a substance in thermodynamic equilibrium must be zero at $0°$ K. In practice there is always some mutual interaction between the dipoles (either through exchange or magnetic dipolar interaction), such that the internal energy $U$ of the system is lower when the dipoles are oriented in an orderly array than when they are randomly oriented. Thus, at the absolute zero, where the free energy $F = U - TS$ is equal to $U$, the equilibrium state of lowest *free energy* will be the ordered state with the lowest *internal energy*. At a sufficiently high temperature, on the other hand, the paramagnetic state, with its higher entropy corresponding to the random orientation of the dipoles, will have the lower free energy because of the second term in $F = U - TS$, and will thus be the equilibrium state. As the temperature falls, any substance where the dipoles still have some freedom of orientation (this excludes those paramagnetic substances which have a singlet ground state and a temperature-independent susceptibility) will make a transition from a disordered phase into an ordered phase. The ferromagnetic state discussed in the last chapter, in which all the dipoles are oriented parallel to one another at $0°$ K, is the state of lowest energy when the exchange energy $\mathscr{J}'$ has a positive sign. However, ferromagnetism is exhibited by relatively few substances, though there are many containing transition group ions.

It was suggested by Néel (1936) that in many substances the exchange interaction is large but negative, resulting in an ordered state where neighbouring dipoles are aligned in an anti-parallel arrangement. Such an arrangement for a simple cubic lattice is shown in Fig. 22.1; the dipoles at adjacent corners of each cubic cell point in opposite directions.

Another simple case is the body-centred cubic lattice, with an ion at the centre of each cube as well as at the corners; here all the ions at the corners have their dipoles parallel to each other, but anti-parallel to the ions at the centres. In each case a given dipole is surrounded by a number of equidistant dipoles all pointing in the opposite direction, while the next nearest neighbours point in the same direction again.

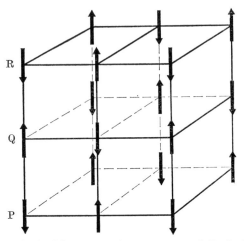

Fig. 22.1. Anti-ferromagnetic arrangement of dipoles in a simple cubic lattice.

The system may be thought of as consisting of two interlocking sub-lattices, one of which is spontaneously magnetized in one direction, while the other is spontaneously magnetized in the opposite direction. As in ferromagnetism, this spontaneous magnetization of the sub-lattices sets in only below a certain transition temperature, generally known as the 'Néel temperature'. Above this temperature the dipoles are randomly oriented, and the substance is paramagnetic, obeying a Curie–Weiss law with the Weiss constant of opposite sign to that found in ferromagnetism, as we should expect from the reversed sign of the exchange energy. The onset of spontaneous magnetization in the sub-lattices as the substance is cooled through the Néel temperature is accompanied by a specific heat anomaly of the co-operative type, as illustrated in Fig. 22.2. The substance as a whole exhibits no spontaneous magnetization in zero field, since the two sub-lattices are equally and oppositely polarized. When an external field is applied, a small magnetization occurs giving a positive susceptibility; the general behaviour of the susceptibility can be explained quite well on a molecular field model, as outlined below.

## 22.2. The molecular field—two sub-lattice model

Let the two sub-lattices be denoted by $A$ and $B$. Then a dipole in lattice $A$ is subject to an external field $B_0$ and an internal field proportional to the magnetization of sub-lattice $B$ which we may write as

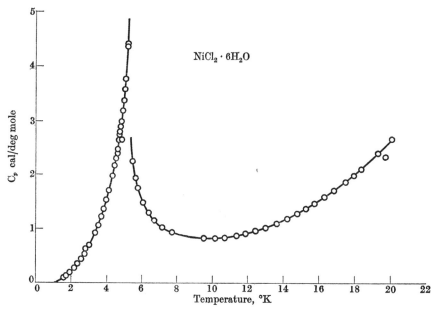

FIG. 22.2. Specific heat of $NiCl_2,6H_2O$ at low temperatures, showing the $\lambda$-type anomaly at the Néel temperature, $5 \cdot 34°$ K (after Robinson and Friedberg, 1960). The entropy in the anomaly is $R \ln 3$, corresponding to the threefold degeneracy of the $S = 1$ ground state of the $Ni^{++}$ ion. The rise at high temperatures is due to the lattice specific heat. Note the different shape of the co-operative anomaly from that due to a simple level splitting in another nickel salt (Fig. 20.15).

$-\lambda M_B$, where the minus sign appears because of the reversed sign of the exchange integral. The effective field acting on a dipole in $A$ is therefore

$$B_A = B_0 - \lambda M_B \left.\right\}$$
Similarly
$$B_B = B_0 - \lambda M_A \left.\right\} \qquad (22.1)$$

At high temperatures where the dipoles are randomly oriented the magnetization of each sub-lattice should obey Curie's law if we take the effective field instead of the external field. Thus we have

$$M_A = \tfrac{1}{2}CB_A/\mu_0 T, \qquad M_B = \tfrac{1}{2}CB_B/\mu_0 T, \qquad (22.2)$$

where $C$ is the Curie constant per unit volume, and the factor $\tfrac{1}{2}$ appears because only half of the dipoles are in a given sub-lattice. The total magnetization is then

$$M = M_A + M_B = \frac{C}{2\mu_0 T}\{2B_0 - \lambda(M_A + M_B)\} = \frac{C}{\mu_0 T}(B_0 - \tfrac{1}{2}\lambda M).$$

Hence
$$\chi = \frac{\mu_0 M}{B_0} = \frac{C}{T + (\lambda C/2\mu_0)} = \frac{C}{T + \theta}. \qquad (22.3)$$

This equation for the susceptibility above the Néel point is similar to that found in ferromagnetism except for the reversed sign of the Weiss constant $\theta$.

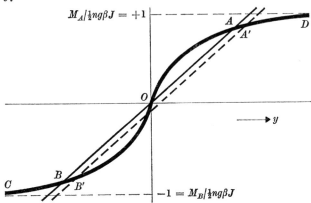

FIG. 22.3. Graphical solution of equations for spontaneous magnetization of an anti-ferromagnetic substance.

Curve $CBOAD$ is the Brillouin function $\phi(y)$, $BOA$ is the straight line
relation between $M$ and $y$ when the external field is zero, and $B'OA'$
is a similar line for the case when an external field is applied parallel
to the direction of the spontaneous magnetization.

In order to investigate the behaviour at low temperatures we cannot assume Curie's law to hold, since a large spontaneous magnetization will be set up in each sub-lattice by the internal field. We must use, instead of equation (22.2), modified forms of equation (21.8):

$$\left.\begin{array}{l} M_A = \tfrac{1}{2}ng\beta J\phi(y_A) \\ M_B = \tfrac{1}{2}ng\beta J\phi(y_B) \end{array}\right\}, \qquad (22.4)$$

where $y = (g\beta J/kT)\times$(effective field on sub-lattice), and $\phi(y)$ is the Brillouin function given by equation (20.15). The factor $\tfrac{1}{2}$ appears again because only half of the dipoles are in either lattice; we have also assumed that the magnetism is due to dipoles with angular momentum $J$.

In the absence of an external field the magnetization of each sub-lattice is given by the solution of equation (22.4) with

$$B_A = -\lambda M_B = -\lambda(-M_0) = +\lambda M_0,$$
$$B_B = -\lambda M_A = -\lambda(+M_0) = -\lambda M_0,$$

since the two sub-lattices $A$ and $B$ will have equal and opposite magnetization, $+M_0$ and $-M_0$ respectively. The equation may be solved graphically, as in ferromagnetism. The spontaneous magnetization is given by the points $A$ and $B$ in Fig. 22.3, which correspond to the stable condition, while the other possible solution $M_A = M_B = 0$ is unstable. The value of $M_0$ at any temperature is given by the root of the transcendental equation

$$M_0 = \tfrac{1}{2}ng\beta J\phi\left(\frac{g\beta J}{kT}\lambda M_0\right).$$

As the temperature rises the line $BOA$ becomes steeper, and the points $A$, $B$ move back towards the origin; the spontaneous magnetization

TABLE 22.1

| Substance | Néel temperature $T_N$ (°K) | $\theta/T_N$ | $\chi_0/\chi_{T_N}$ |
|---|---|---|---|
| Cr . . | 311 | — | — |
| alpha-Mn . | 100 | — | — |
| $MnF_2$ . . | 67 | 1·2 | 0·76 |
| $FeF_2$ . . | 78 | 1·5 | 0·72 |
| $CoF_2$ . . | 50 | — | — |
| $NiF_2$ . . | 73 | — | — |
| MnO . . | 116 | 4 to 5 | 0·69 |
| FeO . | 198 | 3 | 0·75 |
| $CuCl_2,2H_2O$ . | 4·3 | — | — |
| $NiCl_2,6H_2O$ . | 5·3 | — | — |

disappears at the Néel temperature $T_N$ where the line $AB$ is tangential to the Brillouin function at the origin. Since $\phi(y) = y(J+1)/3J$ for small values of $y$, we have

$$M_0 = \tfrac{1}{2}ng\beta J\left[\left(\frac{g\beta J}{kT_N}\right)\left(\frac{J+1}{3J}\right)\lambda M_0\right],$$

or        $$T_N = \tfrac{1}{2}\lambda ng^2\beta^2 J(J+1)/3k = \lambda C/2\mu_0 = \theta.$$

Thus on this simple theory, due to Van Vleck (1941), the Néel point $T_N$ should have the same value as the Weiss constant $\theta$. The values of both $\theta$ and $T_N$ are given in Table 22.1 for a number of substances now established as being anti-ferromagnetic. It will be seen that in general $\theta$ and $T_N$ are different, and this can be accounted for by an extension of the theory given above where interactions with next nearest neighbours belonging to the same sub-lattice are included (Van Vleck, 1951; see Problem 22.1). In addition other types of arrangement of the dipoles, where not all the nearest neighbours are anti-parallel, are possible.

When an external field is applied at a temperature below the Néel point, a positive magnetization results whose magnitude can be estimated from the theory given above. In general, the effect of applying a field is to change the magnetization of each sub-lattice slightly, so that we may write

$$\left.\begin{array}{l} \mathbf{M}_A = \mathbf{M}_0 + \delta\mathbf{M} \\ \mathbf{M}_B = -\mathbf{M}_0 + \delta\mathbf{M} \end{array}\right\}, \tag{22.5}$$

where these must be taken as vector equations if the external magnetic field is applied at an arbitrary angle to the direction of the spontaneous magnetization $\mathbf{M}_0$. If $\mathbf{B}_0$ is parallel to $\mathbf{M}_0$, so also will be $\delta\mathbf{M}$, and, if we

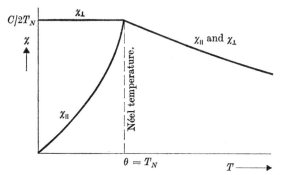

FIG. 22.4. Variation of $\chi_\parallel$ and $\chi_\perp$ on the simple theory of anti-ferromagnetism.

return to the graphical solution of our transcendental equation, we see that the magnetizations of the sub-lattices will be given by the intersection of the dotted line $B'A'$ in Fig. 22.3 with the Brillouin curve. For the effective fields become, using equation (22.1),

$$\mathbf{B}_A = \mathbf{B}_0 - \lambda(-\mathbf{M}_0 + \delta\mathbf{M}) = \lambda\mathbf{M}_0 + (\mathbf{B}_0 - \lambda\delta\mathbf{M}),$$
$$\mathbf{B}_B = \mathbf{B}_0 - \lambda(+\mathbf{M}_0 + \delta\mathbf{M}) = -\lambda\mathbf{M}_0 + (\mathbf{B}_0 - \lambda\delta\mathbf{M}).$$

The resulting net magnetization $2\delta\mathbf{M}$ will depend on the slope of the Brillouin function (for small fields) at the point $\mathbf{M}_0$. As $\mathbf{M}_0$ increases, this slope decreases, reaching zero at saturation. It follows that the susceptibility $\chi_\parallel$ (in the direction parallel to $\mathbf{M}_0$) decreases to zero as the temperature falls to zero, as illustrated in Fig. 22.4. The exact shape of the curve depends only slightly on the value of $J$, as in the case of the saturation curve for a ferromagnetic substance.

If the external field is applied perpendicularly to $\mathbf{M}_0$, we can evaluate the susceptibility more easily. In this case the magnetizations $\mathbf{M}_A$, $\mathbf{M}_B$ of each of the sub-lattices turn through a small angle $\alpha$ towards $\mathbf{B}_0$, as shown in Fig. 22.5. The effective field on a dipole now has the two components $B_z = \pm\lambda M_0$ (the upper sign for lattice $A$), and

$$B_x = B_0 - \lambda\delta M.$$

For small external fields the angle $\alpha$ is small, and the ratio of the magnetization components in the two directions will be

$$\frac{\delta M}{M_0} = \frac{B_x}{B_z} = \frac{B_0 - \lambda\delta M}{\lambda M_0},$$

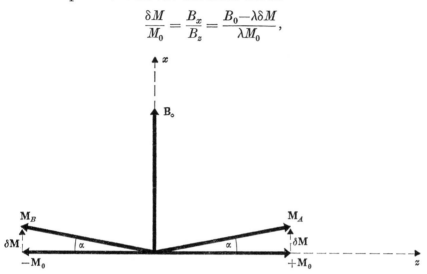

FIG. 22.5. Effect of applying a field $\mathbf{B_0}$ perpendicular to the spontaneous magnetization $\mathbf{M_0}$ in an anti-ferromagnetic substance.

from which $2\delta M = B_0/\lambda$, and the susceptibility will be

$$\chi_\perp = 2\mu_0 \delta M/B_0 = \mu_0/\lambda = C/2T_N. \tag{22.6}$$

Thus $\chi_\perp$ should be constant below the Néel point and equal to the value at the Néel point, as shown in Fig. 22.4. For a powdered specimen consisting of micro-crystals with random orientation, we have

$$\chi = \tfrac{1}{3}(\chi_\| + 2\chi_\perp),$$

and we should expect

$$\frac{\chi_{(T=0)}}{\chi_{(T=T_N)}} = \frac{2}{3}. \tag{22.7}$$

The values of this ratio for a number of powdered anti-ferromagnetics are also given in Table 22.1. A more direct check of the theory is obtained from measurements of the susceptibility of a single crystal; Fig. 22.6 shows the experimental points of Stout and Trapp (1963) for $MnF_2$. Here the $Mn^{++}$ ion is in a $^6S_{\frac{5}{2}}$ state, and the susceptibility shows negligible anisotropy above the Néel point, as would be expected. Below the Néel point $\chi_\|$ falls rapidly and approaches zero, while $\chi_\perp$ remains almost constant, as predicted by the theory.

The two sub-lattice model is valid for many anti-ferromagnetic substances, but in some cases there are more (in a face-centred cubic lattice there are generally four). As in ferromagnetism, the exchange interaction itself gives no preference to any particular orientation of the spins relative to the crystal axes; this arises from the anisotropy energy. In a simple tetragonal crystal such as $MnF_2$, the spins are aligned along

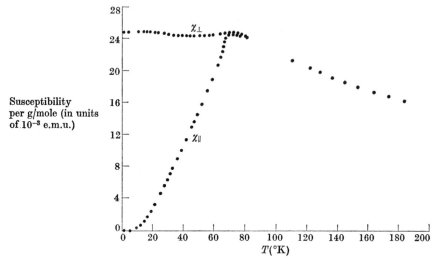

FIG. 22.6. Principal susceptibilities of a single crystal of $MnF_2$ (after C. Trapp and J. W. Stout, 1963).

the tetragonal axis in a simple two sub-lattice anti-parallel arrangement, but much more complicated arrangements are possible in which the vector sum of the dipole moments is zero—the distinctive feature of an anti-ferromagnetic.

## 22.3. Ferrimagnetism

The technical importance of magnetic materials in electrical industry has increased continuously, the ideal substance being one with a large magnetic moment at room temperature, which is also an electrical insulator. Ferromagnetic metals and alloys have been widely exploited, but their high electrical conductivity is a serious handicap in radio-frequency applications because of the eddy current losses. For this reason a number of magnetic oxides ('ferrites', of which magnetite, $Fe_3O_4$, is the most famous as the original 'lodestone') became of great technical interest because of their low electrical conductivity. They show spontaneous magnetization, remanence, and other properties similar to ordinary ferromagnetic materials, but the spontaneous moment does not correspond to the value expected for full parallel alignment of the dipoles.

In 1948 Néel put forward a theory for such materials; he suggested that they contain two sub-lattices in which the magnetizations are oppositely directed, but which give a net moment because the two sub-lattice moments are unequal. For this phenomenon he coined the word 'ferrimagnetism'. It can arise from a number of arrangements, of which the simplest are illustrated in Fig. 22.7. In (a) all the dipoles are equal in magnitude, but there are more on one sub-lattice than on

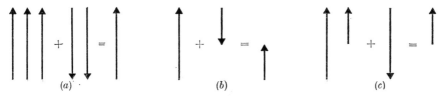

FIG. 22.7. Three possible arrangements of the dipole moments in a ferrimagnetic material.

    (a) Unequal numbers of identical moments on the two sub-lattices.
    (b) Unequal moments on the two sub-lattices.
    (c) Two equal moments and one unequal.

the other; the most notable example is yttrium iron garnet (YIG). The simple arrangement (b) with ions of unequal moments occurs rather rarely. The arrangement (c), with two equal and opposite moments, and a third moment on one sub-lattice is typical of ferrites such as $MnFe_2O_4$.

*Ferrites*

These have the typical formula $M^{++}Fe_2^{+++}O_4^{--}$ (equivalent to $MO,Fe_2O_3$), where $M^{++}$ is a dipositive ion, commonly $Mn^{++}$, $Fe^{++}$, $Co^{++}$, $Ni^{++}$, $Cu^{++}$, $Zn^{++}$, or $Mg^{++}$; other tripositive ions such as $Cr^{+++}$ can replace $Fe^{+++}$. The crystallographic structure is cubic and similar to the mineral spinel $(MgAl_2O_4)$, and the unit cell, with eight formula units, equivalent to $M_8Fe_{16}O_{32}$, contains eight cation sites with tetrahedral coordination (to four oxygen ions) and sixteen cation sites with octahedral coordination (to six oxygen ions), known as the $A$ and $B$ sites respectively. The division of cations between these sites is not unique, the limiting cases being:

|  | A sites (8) | B sites (16) |
|---|---|---|
| 'normal' structure | $8M^{++}$ | $16Fe^{+++}$ |
| 'inverse' structure | $8Fe^{+++}$ | $8M^{++}+8Fe^{+++}$ |

Intermediate arrangements are also found, and we will consider only the inverse structure. Each $Fe^{+++}$ ion is in a $^6S_{\frac{5}{2}}$ state with a moment of 5 Bohr magnetons; however, the moments on the $A$ and $B$ sites are anti-parallel. If $m_M$ is the moment of the $M^{++}$ ion, the net saturation moment at $0°$ K for the unit $MFe_2O_4$ will be

$$m = m_M + (m_{Fe})_B - (m_{Fe})_A = m_M + 5\beta - 5\beta = m_M. \qquad (22.8)$$

The moments calculated thus (assuming that the M ion has a 'spin only' moment) are compared with the observed moments in Table 22.2. The agreement is satisfactory; some orbital moment would be expected in the $Fe^{++}$, $Co^{++}$, $Ni^{++}$, $Cu^{++}$ ions, and in magnesium ferrite the structure is not completely inverse.

TABLE 22.2

| M | $m_M$ (spin only) | Observed moment | $T_N$ (°K) |
|---|---|---|---|
| Mn | 5 | 4·4–5·0 | 573 |
| Fe | 4 | 4·0–4·2 | 858 |
| Co | 3 | 3·3–3·9 | 793 |
| Ni | 2 | 2·2–2·4 | 858 |
| Cu | 1 | 1·3–1·4 | 728 |
| Mg | 0 | 0·9–1·1 | — |

The magnetic moments are in Bohr magnetons per unit $MFe_2O_4$.

Néel suggested that all the interactions in the ferrites are anti-ferromagnetic in sign, but that the $A-B$ interaction is considerably stronger than the $A-A$ or $B-B$ interactions. Thus in the inverse structure the dominating $A-B$ interaction makes the spins within each group parallel, despite their mutual anti-ferromagnetic interaction. This is supported by the fact that $ZnFe_2O_4$, which has the normal structure, has no net moment. Here the $A$ sites are entirely occupied by zinc ions, with no moment, so the $A-B$ interactions are zero. The ferric ions on the $B$ sites are then aligned anti-parallel through the anti-ferromagnetic $B-B$ interaction, in equal numbers, so that the compound is anti-ferromagnetic. Its Néel temperature ($9°$ K) is quite low, as would be expected if the $B-B$ interactions are weak.

*Garnets*

These have the typical formula $M_3Fe_5O_{12}$ (of which two units are equivalent to $5Fe_2O_3, 3M_2O_3$), where both the M cation and the Fe are tripositive ions; the $M^{+++}$ ion is commonly yttrium or a member of the $4f$ transition group. The crystallographic structure is cubic and similar to the mineral garnet, though this has cations of other valencies. The unit cell is complex, containing eight units of $M_3Fe_5O_{12}$; for simplicity we shall discuss mainly yttrium iron garnet, where the $Y^{+++}$ ion has a closed shell and carries no magnetic moment. The ferric ions occupy two types of site; in each unit $Y_3Fe_5O_{12}$ two $Fe^{+++}$ ions occupy '$a$' sites, coordinated to six oxygen ions, and three $Fe^{+++}$ ions occupy '$d$' sites, coordinated to four oxygen ions. The magnetic moments of the two '$a$' ions are antiparallel to those of the three '$d$' ions, giving the arrangement shown in Fig. 22.7 (a); the net moment per unit $Y_3Fe_5O_{12}$ is thus that of one $Fe^{+++}$ ion, or 5 Bohr magnetons (the best experimental value is $4\cdot96\beta$). The Néel temperature is 545° K.

Amongst other ferrimagnetic materials we mention only $BaFe_{12}O_{19}$ (equivalent to $BaO,6Fe_2O_3$). This has a hexagonal structure, with a number of inequivalent sites for the ferric ions. Of the twelve ferric ions per formula unit, the moments of eight are anti-parallel to the remaining four, giving a net moment of $4\times5 = 20$ Bohr magnetons; the Néel temperature is about 820° K. Barium ferrite, as it is frequently called, has a high value of $(BH)_{max}$ and is used as a permanent magnet material (cf. Chapter 8). Being hexagonal, it has a high anisotropy energy; it is used in the form of pressed oriented fine particles.

## Discussion

Néel's theory of ferrimagnetism had considerable success in explaining the anomalous behaviour of the susceptibility above the Néel point. Using a molecular field approximation with three constants representing the $A$–$B$, $A$–$A$, and $B$–$B$ interactions he deduced the relation

$$\frac{1}{\chi} = \frac{T}{C} + \frac{1}{\chi_0} - \frac{\sigma}{T-\theta} \qquad (22.9)$$

for a substance where all the magnetic ions have the same moment, such as YIG, or $MFe_2O_4$ when M carries no moment. Here $C$ is the usual Curie constant, but the other parameters are functions of the molecular field constants and the numbers of ions in each sub-lattice. The general behaviour of the inverse susceptibility given by Néel's relation as fitted to experiments on YIG is shown in Fig. 22.8. The theory also explains qualitatively the complex behaviour of the spontaneous magnetization curve below the Néel temperature. The magnetization does not always increase monotonically as the temperature falls, and in ferrimagnetic compounds containing more than one type of magnetic ion whose spontaneous magnetization varies in different ways with temperature a 'compensation point' may be observed, where the magnetization of the two sub-lattices is equal and opposite.

The magnetization curve of gadolinium iron garnet, $Gd_3Fe_5O_{12}$, is shown in Fig. 22.9, together with that of $Y_3Fe_5O_{12}$. The latter is not unlike that of a ferromagnetic, but at low temperatures the former has a much higher magnetization, falling to zero at the compensation point at about 295° K. At 0° K we would expect each $Gd^{+++}$ ion to have a moment of 7 Bohr magnetons; if these are mutually parallel, but opposed

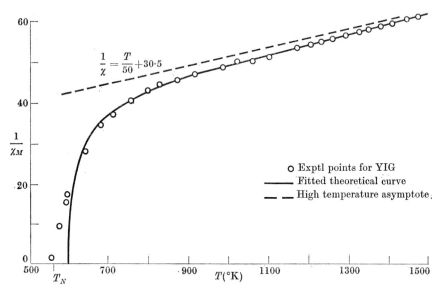

FIG. 22.8. Inverse magnetic susceptibility of the ferrimagnetic substance yttrium iron garnet, which has three and two $Fe^{+++}$ ions on the two sub-lattices (arrangement (a) in Fig. 22.7).

to the net ferric moment, we would expect an overall moment for the unit $Gd_3Fe_5O_{12}$ of $(3 \times 7 - \{3 \times 5 - 2 \times 5\})\beta = (21 - 5)\beta = 16\beta$; this is close to the observed moment. As the temperature rises the magnetization of the gadolinium ions, which are subjected to a comparatively weak interaction with the ferric ions, falls much more rapidly than that of the iron lattice with its strong mutual interactions between the ferric ions. In fact the behaviour of the Gd ions is not far from that of paramagnetic ions with $S = \frac{7}{2}$, subjected to an internal field generated by the iron lattice. The Néel temperature of $Gd_3Fe_5O_{12}$ (564° K) is not appreciably different from that of $Y_3Fe_5O_{12}$ (545° K), as would be expected on this basis.

Apart from their technical importance, ferrimagnetic materials have played a major role in advancing our understanding of magnetic problems; for this purpose the garnets are more favoured than the ferrites,

since the structure is unique and there are no uncertainties concerning
the sites occupied by the magnetic ions. The absence of conduction
electrons is a great asset, not only technically but also scientifically.
On the one hand we are dealing with localized magnetic moments, so
the theory rests on a much firmer foundation; on the other many
important experiments can be carried out to check the theory which

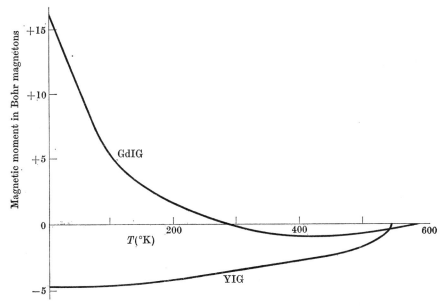

FIG. 22.9. Variation of the spontaneous moment with temperature for $Gd_3Fe_5O_{12}$ (GdIG)
and $Y_3Fe_5O_{12}$ (YIG) in Bohr magnetons per formula unit.

would otherwise be impossible. An obvious example is magnetic
resonance experiments (cf. Chapter 23) in the frequency range $10^{10}$–
$10^{13}$ c/s, which have been a very fruitful field both for ferrimagnetics
and for anti-ferromagnetics. The absence of conduction electrons plays
a less direct but no less important role in measurements of the magnetic
specific heat contribution predicted by spin wave theory. A term proportional to $T^{\frac{3}{2}}$ was first confirmed by Kouvel (1956) using $Fe_3O_4$ (it has
also been measured in compounds such as YIG), whereas in the ordinary
ferromagnetic metals it is obscured by the electronic specific heat.
Another experimental achievement is the optical demonstration of the
presence of domains, using the rotation of the plane of polarized light
propagated parallel to the direction of magnetization (the Faraday
effect); when a thin crystal of YIG is placed under a polarizing

microscope the domains are visible as light and dark regions whose motion can be observed under the action of an applied field.

## 22.4. The lanthanide ('rare earth') metals

Measurements of the susceptibilities of the lanthanide metals at high temperatures give generally a Curie–Weiss law where the size of the Curie constant agrees well with that expected for the tripositive ions. There are two notable exceptions to this: europium metal and ytterbium metal, which are cubic in structure with an ionic size indicating the presence of dipositive ions. In addition, cerium tends to show a phase transition at low temperatures to a cubic structure with $Ce^{4+}$ ions, dependent on the thermal history of the specimen. The $Ce^{4+}$ and $Yb^{++}$ ions have closed shells and no magnetic moment, so they are not of interest here; the $Eu^{2+}$ ion has a half-filled shell, ground state $S = \frac{7}{2}$, but the magnetic behaviour of the metal shows unexpected complications. We shall therefore restrict ourselves to the metals containing tripositive ions, data for which are given in Table 22.3.

No metal shows a co-operative state above room temperature, so that exchange interactions are small compared with the spin-orbit coupling. We may therefore regard the spin and orbit as coupled to give a resultant angular momentum $J$, as in the paramagnetic salts (cf. § 20.6). On this basis the saturation moment per ion at $0°$ K should be $gJ$ Bohr magnetons, where $g$ is the Landé factor appropriate to the ground state $J$ of the free tripositive ion. Values of $gJ$ are given in column 2 of Table 22.3, and are generally substantiated by the magnetic evidence for gadolinium and the heavier metals.

In considering the exchange interaction, we have to project the spin vector $\mathbf{S}$ onto the total angular momentum vector $\mathbf{J}$, as pointed out in § 21.1. The exchange interaction $-2\mathscr{J}\mathbf{S}_i.\mathbf{S}_j$ between the spins thus becomes equivalent to a coupling $-2\mathscr{J}'\mathbf{J}_i.\mathbf{J}_j$ between the total angular momenta, with $\mathscr{J}' = (g-1)^2\mathscr{J}$, as given by equation (21.3). If $\mathscr{J}$ were the same for all the lanthanon metals, we should expect the Curie points to vary as $(g-1)^2 J(J+1)$, from equation (21.6). This quantity is largest for $Gd^{+++}$, with a half-filled shell, and this metal shows co-operative effects at a higher temperature ($290°$ K) than any other lanthanide metal. Reference to Table 22.3 shows that the temperature at which co-operative effects appear varies qualitatively in accordance with this relation in the second half of the group. However, these metals show more than one ordered phase, being anti-ferromagnetic at higher temperatures and ferromagnetic at lower temperatures. This effect, which appears to require a reversal in sign of the exchange interaction as the temperature falls, was for a long time very puzzling.

The 4f electrons in the lanthanons belong to an inner shell, and their wave functions are much less extended than those of d-electrons. For

TABLE 22.3

*Magnetic data for the lanthanon metals, assuming* $Ln^{+++}$ *ions. For the values of g, J see Table 20.1. The value of gJ gives the moment per ion at* $0°$ *K assuming the ions are not subject to any crystal field effects. Pm has been omitted for lack of data (it has no radioactively stable isotopes); europium metal becomes anti-ferromagnetic below* $87°$ *K (and possibly ferromagnetic at a lower temperature), and appears to contain* $Eu^{++}$ *ions, with a half-filled shell and* $S = \frac{7}{2}$; *ytterbium metal contains* $Yb^{++}$ *ions with a filled shell and no magnetic moment.*

|    | $gJ$ | $(g-1)^2 J(J+1)$ | $T_N$ (°K) | $T_C$ (°K) |
|----|------|------------------|-----------|-----------|
| La | 0    | 0                | —         | —         |
| Ce | 2·14 | 0·18             | 12·5      | —         |
| Pr | 3·2  | 0·8              | 25        | —         |
| Nd | 3·17 | 1·84             | 7, 18     | —         |
| Sm | 0·71 | 4·5              | 14        | —         |
| Gd | 7    | 15·75            | —         | 290       |
| Tb | 9    | 10·5             | 228       | 220       |
| Dy | 10   | 7·1              | 179       | 85        |
| Ho | 10   | 4·5              | 125       | 40        |
| Er | 9    | 2·55             | 80        | 20        |
| Tm | 7    | 1·17             | 50        | 20        |
| Lu | 0    | 0                | —         | —         |

this reason direct exchange, involving overlap of f-electron wave functions on adjacent ions, is unlikely to be important, and the origin of exchange interaction observed in the lanthanon metals is ascribed to the second mechanism discussed in § 21.9, the conduction electrons being polarized by exchange interaction with the 4f shells, and serving as a medium whereby the orientation of the moment on one ion can influence that on neighbouring ions. We can thus regard the metals as consisting of ions with well-localized moments due to their 4f shells in a sea of conduction electrons formed from the valence electrons, which contribute little to the magnetic properties directly but provide the medium for exchange interaction.

Electrostatic interaction between the 4f electrons on a given ion and the charge on the adjacent ions provides a 'crystal field' interaction in the metals which would be expected to be of the same order as that in salts of the lanthanide group. Direct evidence for this comes from Schottky-type anomalies in the specific heats of the first members of the group; the excess 'magnetic' specific heat due to crystal field splittings of the $J = 4$ state of $Pr^{+++}$ in praseodymium metal is shown in Fig. 22.10. The overall splitting produced by the crystal field is in the region of a few hundred °K for Ce, Pr, Nd, and Sm; since the values

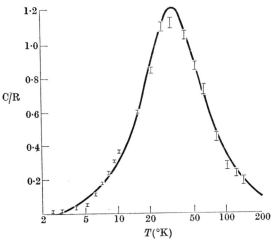

Fig. 22.10. The magnetic specific heat per mole of praseodymium metal, due to crystal field splittings of the $^3H_4$ ground state of the $Pr^{3+}$ ion (Bleaney, 1963).

of $(g-1)^2 J(J+1)$ are rather low, the exchange interaction is small compared with the crystal field. A co-operative phase is found only at temperatures below 25° K, and in praseodymium, where the crystal field splitting leaves a singlet as the ground state, the co-operative state has only a small moment.

The lanthanon metals (apart from those with $Ce^{4+}$, $Eu^{++}$, or $Yb^{++}$ ions) all form hexagonal crystals, but the structure changes slightly at gadolinium. In this and the heavier metals the crystal field is smaller than in the first metals of the group, while the value of $(g-1)^2 J(J+1)$ tends to be larger; thus exchange interactions preponderate over crystal field splittings, and the co-operative phase sets in at temperatures where crystal field effects are relatively less important. Such effects do, however, play a major part in determining the magnetic structure in the co-operative phase. They produce an 'anisotropy energy' which varies with powers of the magnetization up to the sixth degree, and is a complex function of orientation of the magnetic moment, reflecting the hexagonal symmetry of the lattice. This anisotropy energy favours orientation of the moments in certain crystallographic directions, while the exchange interaction favours a simple parallel orientation. At the lowest temperatures gadolinium and the heavier metals have a ferromagnetic phase in which the direction of magnetization is determined by the anisotropy energy. The latter is large, and the metals are magnetically hard, except in the case of gadolinium. The $Gd^{3+}$ ion, with a half-filled $4f$ shell is in an $^8S_{\frac{7}{2}}$ state with no orbital moment; it therefore has no first order interaction with the crystal field, and the anisotropy energy is relatively small.

At higher temperatures the co-operative phase of terbium and the following metals changes to an antiferromagnetic state, with no resultant magnetization. In some cases the moments lie in a spiral arrangement where the angle between successive layers is a function of the temperature, and in others the moment lies along the hexagonal axis but shows a spatial oscillatory variation in magnitude. The equilibrium state is that with the lowest free energy $F = U - TS$, and these complex arrangements have a lower free energy at higher temperatures because of their higher entropy. At still higher temperatures the paramagnetic phase becomes the equilibrium phase. Table 22.3 gives both the Néel temperature $T_N$ at which the anti-ferromagnetic phase sets in, and the Curie temperature $T_C$.

## 22.5. Neutron diffraction

A proper description of the theory and practice of neutron diffraction is outside the scope of this book, and only a brief outline can be given of the major role it has played in establishing the structure of the ordered state of a magnetic compound. Associated with a particle whose momentum is $p$ is a wavelength $\lambda = h/p$, where $h$ is Planck's constant; for neutrons of thermal energies, this wavelength is of the order of an Ångström unit (for neutrons in thermal equilibrium with a temperature of $0°$ C, the wavelength is $1·55$ Å). The nuclei of the atoms in a crystal lattice scatter neutrons, and diffraction patterns are formed in a similar way to those for X-rays. Neutrons can thus be used for the determination of crystal structures in much the same way as X-rays; in particular the positions of hydrogen ions (which, being just protons with no electrons, have virtually zero scattering power for X-rays) in crystal lattices can be determined accurately.

In magnetic materials, the permanent electronic magnetic moments give an additional scattering mechanism for neutrons which often outweighs the nuclear scattering, through the interaction between the electronic magnetic moment and the nuclear magnetic moment of the neutron. If the electronic moments are randomly oriented, as in a paramagnetic substance, the scattered neutrons are incoherent in phase and the result is an addition to the general background or diffuse scattering. Although some magnetic information can be obtained from careful measurements

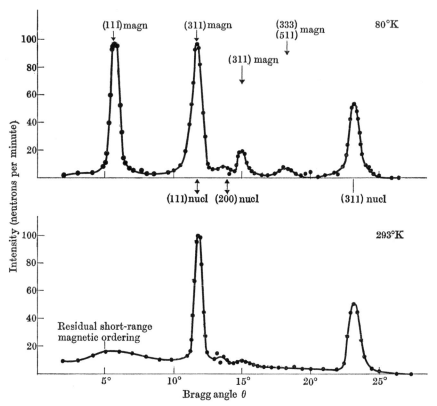

Fig. 22.11. The neutron diffraction patterns of MnO at 80° K, 293° K (below and above the Curie temperature of 116° K respectively). The low-temperature pattern shows extra antiferromagnetic reflections which can be indexed in terms of a magnetic unit with dimensions twice those of the chemical unit cell. (Shull and Smart, 1949.)

of the additional diffuse scattering, neutron diffraction provides much more striking and useful information when the magnetic dipoles are oriented in an ordered structure, as in most spontaneously magnetized substances. An ordered array of electronic dipoles gives rise to diffraction peaks in specific directions determined by the three-dimensional structure of the array. If the magnetic unit cell has the same dimensions as the chemical unit cell, the coherent magnetic diffraction peaks appear at the same angular positions as the peaks due to the nuclear scattering. In an anti-ferromagnetic the dimensions of the magnetic unit cell may differ from those of the chemical unit cell; for instance, in Fig. 22.1, the magnetic pattern only repeats in the distance $PR$, whereas the chemical pattern repeats at the distance $PQ$. Extra peaks therefore occur in the diffraction pattern of the ordered array (see Fig. 22.11), which are absent in the disordered array (the paramagnetic state). As with X-rays, neutron diffraction can be observed using powdered or polycrystalline substances, but fuller magnetic information is obtained with single crystals. Such information includes the symmetry of the magnetic array (i.e. the size of the magnetic unit cell and the relative orientation of the moments within it), the actual orientation of the moments relative to the crystal axes, and the size of the individual moments. Though details of the magnetic structure can often be inferred from other magnetic measurements, only neutron diffraction gives a direct determination. The more complicated the magnetic structure, the less likely it can be deduced indirectly; an obvious example is the helical moment structure of some lanthanon metals and other substances (in fact $MnAu_2$ was the first such structure discovered by neutron diffraction, in 1959). Many structural determinations of a simpler nature have been carried out, of which only two may be mentioned briefly. (a) Although some suggestions of a ferrimagnetic structure have been put forward for iron, neutron diffraction shows that every iron atom appears identical and carries the same moment, at any rate on a time average; (b) the series of compounds $MnF_2$, $FeF_2$, $CoF_2$, which are tetragonal, have been shown to have a simple anti-parallel arrangement of spins oriented along the tetragonal axis, but in $NiF_2$ the spins are canted away from this axis by about $10°$, giving a weak ferromagnetic moment (i.e. the spins are oriented as in Fig. 22.5, but through the anisotropy energy, not by a magnetic field).

## REFERENCES

BLEANEY, B., 1963, *Proc. Roy. Soc.* A, **276**, 39.
KOUVEL, J. S., 1956, *Phys. Rev.* **102**, 1489.
NÉEL, L., 1936, *Ann. Phys. Paris*, **5**, 256.
ROBINSON, W. K., and FRIEDBERG, S. A., 1960, *Phys. Rev.* **117**, 402.
SHULL, C. G., and SMART, J. S., 1949, ibid. **76**, 1256.
TRAPP, C., and STOUT, J. W., 1963. *Phys. Rev. Letters*, **10**, 157.
VAN VLECK, J. H., 1941, *J. Chem. Phys.* **9**, 85.
—— 1951, *J. Phys. Radium*, **12**, 262.

## PROBLEMS

**22.1.** The theory of anti-ferromagnetism can be extended by assuming that the molecular field acting on each sub-lattice contains a term due to exchange interaction with ions on the same sub-lattice as well as a term due to ions on the other sub-lattice. Show that in the paramagnetic state the equations

$$M_A = (C/2\mu_0 T)(B_0 - \lambda M_B - \lambda' M_A),$$
$$M_B = (C/2\mu_0 T)(B_0 - \lambda M_A - \lambda' M_B)$$

lead to a Curie–Weiss law for the susceptibility (equation (22.3)) with

$$\theta = (C/2\mu_0)(\lambda + \lambda').$$

**22.2.** The Néel temperature $T_N$ can be found by putting $B_0 = 0$ in the preceding question, and finding the condition that the pair of equations for $M_A$, $M_B$ still have a solution. ($T_N$ is the temperature at which a vanishingly small magnetization can exist when $B_0 = 0$, and the Brillouin function is approximated by Curie's law.) Show that this gives $T_N = (C/2\mu_0)(\lambda - \lambda')$.

# 23

## MAGNETIC RESONANCE

### 23.1. The magnetic resonance phenomenon

IT was shown in § 20.1 that when an atom or nucleus with a resultant angular momentum $\mathbf{G}$ and magnetic moment $\mathbf{m}$ is placed in a steady magnetic field $\mathbf{B_0}$ the equation of motion (obtained from equation (20.2) by multiplying by $\gamma$) is

$$d\mathbf{m}/dt = \gamma \mathbf{m} \wedge \mathbf{B_0}, \tag{23.1}$$

where $\gamma = \mathbf{m}/\mathbf{G}$ is the magnetogyric ratio. The motion represented by this equation consists of a precession of the angular momentum vector $\mathbf{G}$ and hence also of $\mathbf{m}$ about the direction of $\mathbf{B_0}$ with a uniform angular velocity $-\gamma \mathbf{B_0}$, which we shall denote by $\boldsymbol{\omega}_L$. If the system is undisturbed it will continue indefinitely in this state of uniform precession with $\mathbf{m}$ at a fixed angle to $\mathbf{B_0}$, and it is convenient to make use of rotating coordinate systems in considering this motion. It is shown in § A.10 that the rate of change $(d\mathbf{m}/dt)$ of any vector quantity such as $\mathbf{m}$ in the laboratory coordinate system is related to the rate of change $(D\mathbf{m}/Dt)$ in a system rotating with angular velocity $\boldsymbol{\omega}$ relative to the laboratory system, by the equation

$$d\mathbf{m}/dt = D\mathbf{m}/Dt + \boldsymbol{\omega} \wedge \mathbf{m}.$$

Substitution of this in equation (23.1) gives

$$D\mathbf{m}/Dt = \gamma \mathbf{m} \wedge \mathbf{B_0} - \boldsymbol{\omega} \wedge \mathbf{m}$$
$$= \gamma \mathbf{m} \wedge \mathbf{B_0} + \mathbf{m} \wedge \boldsymbol{\omega}$$
$$= \gamma \mathbf{m} \wedge \left(\mathbf{B_0} + \frac{\boldsymbol{\omega}}{\gamma}\right). \tag{23.2}$$

This result shows that in the rotating coordinate system the apparent magnetic field is $(\mathbf{B_0} + \boldsymbol{\omega}/\gamma)$, and the apparent precession velocity is $-\gamma(\mathbf{B_0} + \boldsymbol{\omega}/\gamma) = \boldsymbol{\omega}_L - \boldsymbol{\omega}$. Thus the apparent angular velocity is decreased by $\boldsymbol{\omega}$, as would be expected from simple considerations of relative angular velocity. If we write $\mathbf{B}' = -\boldsymbol{\omega}/\gamma$, the apparent field in the rotating system is $(\mathbf{B_0} - \mathbf{B}')$, and it is reduced if $\mathbf{B}'$ is positive (i.e. $\boldsymbol{\omega}$ has the same sign as $\boldsymbol{\omega}_L$) as shown in Fig. 23.1. Clearly, if $\mathbf{B}' = \mathbf{B_0}$, the apparent field $(\mathbf{B_0} - \mathbf{B}')$ and precession velocity $-\gamma(\mathbf{B_0} - \mathbf{B}')$

are both zero, and the vector **m** is stationary in the rotating coordinate system.

We shall now consider the effect of applying a small oscillating magnetic field $\mathbf{B}_1 \cos \omega t$ in the plane normal to the direction of the steady field $\mathbf{B}_0$. This oscillating field may be plane polarized or circularly polarized; in the latter case $\mathbf{B}_1$ is simply a vector, normal to $\mathbf{B}_0$, which is constant in length but which rotates about $\mathbf{B}_0$ with angular velocity $\boldsymbol{\omega}$. If the oscillating field is plane polarized, with a component say in the $x$-direction (taking $\mathbf{B}_0$ along the $z$-axis), it may be decomposed into two vectors rotating in opposite senses; thus there is no loss of generality in considering only the circularly polarized case.

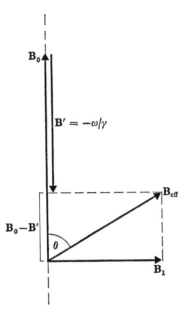

FIG. 23.1. Effective fields in a rotating coordinate system.

If we now transfer from the laboratory system to a system rotating with the angular velocity $\boldsymbol{\omega}$, then the vector $\mathbf{B}_1$ is stationary in this system, and can be represented by a constant vector $\mathbf{B}_1$ as shown in Fig. 23.1. In this system, the atom or nucleus feels an apparent magnetic field $(\mathbf{B}_0 - \mathbf{B}')$ parallel to the $z$-axis, together with the field $\mathbf{B}_1$ normal to this axis; thus the resultant field in this rotating system is the vector sum of these two fields, which is denoted by $\mathbf{B}_{\text{eff}}$ in Fig. 23.1. To an observer in this system, the dipole moment **m** will appear to precess about $\mathbf{B}_{\text{eff}}$ with angular velocity $-\gamma\mathbf{B}_{\text{eff}}$, and its projection on $\mathbf{B}_0$ will change as time goes on. If **m** were initially parallel to $\mathbf{B}_0$ (as we should expect in a macroscopic system), it would precess about $\mathbf{B}_{\text{eff}}$ and at some subsequent time would reach a maximum angle $2\theta$ with $\mathbf{B}_0$, where

$$\tan \theta = B_1/(B_0 - B').$$

If $\mathbf{B}_0 - \mathbf{B}' = 0$, $\mathbf{B}_{\text{eff}} = \mathbf{B}_1$ and $\theta = \frac{1}{2}\pi$, so that **m** will turn right over to reach a position anti-parallel to $\mathbf{B}_0$ before commencing to return. This occurs only when

$$\boldsymbol{\omega} = -\gamma\mathbf{B}' = -\gamma\mathbf{B}_0 = \boldsymbol{\omega}_L,$$

so that the frequency of the applied field is then the same as that of the Larmor precession. Thus the precession about $\mathbf{B}_{\text{eff}}$ is a forced resonance phenomenon, whose amplitude is greatest when the applied frequency $\omega$ is equal to the natural frequency $\omega_L$.

In the case of an atomic or nuclear system, the angular momentum is quantized, and so are its projections on $\mathbf{B}_0$, so that the energy $W = -\mathbf{m}.\mathbf{B}_0$ is also quantized. We shall consider first the nuclear case, assuming a nucleus of spin angular momentum $I\hbar$, and magnetic moment $\mathbf{m}$, where the magnetogyric ratio $\gamma = g_n(e/2M)$. Then the potential energy in a state whose magnetic quantum number is $m$ is

$$W_m = -\mathbf{m}.\mathbf{B}_0 = -\gamma\hbar\mathbf{I}.\mathbf{B}_0 = -\gamma\hbar m B_0. \tag{23.3}$$

Under the influence of an oscillating magnetic field polarized in the plane normal to $\mathbf{B}_0$, transitions between states with different values of $m$ may take place according to the selection rule $\Delta m = \pm 1$. The quantum of energy required is

$$\hbar\omega = W_m - W_{m-1} = -\gamma(h/2\pi)B_0. \tag{23.4}$$

This is the same for all transitions, as shown in Fig. 23.2. From this it follows that the frequency of the radiation must be

$$\nu = -\frac{\gamma}{2\pi}B_0 = +\omega_L/2\pi. \tag{23.5}$$

This is the resonance condition, which is the same as that given by the classical treatment above. The minus sign is significant only if circularly polarized radiation is used. If a system of nuclei with a positive value of $\gamma$ is to absorb energy from an applied oscillatory field, the selection rule for absorption is $\Delta m = -1$, and the vector $\mathbf{B}_1$ must rotate in the left-hand sense about $\mathbf{B}_0$, while if $\gamma$ is negative, the reverse holds. This gives a method of determining the sign of $\gamma$, but for many purposes this is immaterial and linearly polarized radiation may be used. Since this can be regarded as composed of two circularly polarized components rotating in opposite senses, transitions can be induced whatever the sign of $\gamma$. In the usual spectroscopic terminology these are 'magnetic dipole' transitions, corresponding to the fact that they are caused by the interaction of an oscillatory magnetic field with the magnetic dipole moments of the system. This phenomenon is generally known as 'magnetic resonance', and it offers a method of determining $\gamma$ directly from a measurement of a frequency and a magnetic field. The order of magnitude of the frequencies required may be found from the specific charge $(e/M)$ of the proton, if we assume that $g_n$ is around unity. The value of $e/M$ for the proton is nearly equal to the Faraday, i.e. it is about

$10^8$ coulombs/kg ($10^4$ e.m.u./g). Hence the frequency

$$\nu = -\frac{g_n}{2\pi}\left(\frac{e}{2M}\right)B_0$$

is $\approx 10^7$ c/s in a field of 1 weber/m$^2$ (10 kilogauss) in the case of a nuclear magnetic moment. Electronic magnetic moments are some 2000 times larger, owing to the smaller mass of the electron, while the

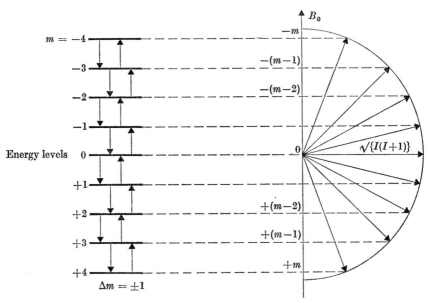

FIG. 23.2. Digram showing the nine energy levels and the allowed transitions between them for a nuclear spin $I = 4$ in a field $B_0$. Transitions can be induced by an oscillating field of frequency $\nu$ if $\nu = -(\gamma/2\pi)B_0$.

associated angular momentum is of the same order as in the nuclear case, so that the value of $\gamma$ and of the frequency required are higher in proportion. For an atom with a magnetic moment due only to electron spin, the wavelength of the radiation required for resonance in a field of 10 700 gauss is 1 cm (a frequency of $3 \times 10^{10}$ c/s).

The magnetic resonance phenomenon has been used to investigate systems of both atomic and nuclear magnetic moments, and we shall discuss first the latter. It makes possible a direct determination of the value of $\gamma$, and hence, for a nucleus whose spin $I$ is known, of the nuclear magnetic moment. The chief experimental difficulty lies in the smallness of the effect, and we shall describe first an ingenious method due to Rabi, where the phenomenon is detected by its effect on the path of a molecule in a molecular beam.

### 23.2. Molecular beams and nuclear magnetic resonance

The use of atomic beams for the measurement of atomic magnetic moments has been mentioned in § 20.4. The method depends on deflecting the atoms by passing them through an inhomogeneous magnetic field; the deflexion is proportional to the projection of the magnetic moment on the direction of the field gradient, and the initial beam is split into $(2J+1)$ beams if the total electronic angular momentum has quantum number $J$. The magnetic moment can be computed from the

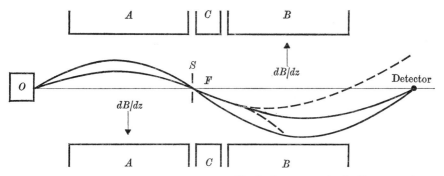

Fig. 23.3. Rabi's molecular beam apparatus. The broken curves in the $B$ magnet show the paths of molecules which have undergone a transition in the field $B_0$ of the $C$ magnet due to the r.f. field applied at $F$ perpendicular to $B_0$.

size of the deflexions if the magnitude of the field gradient is known. The main difficulty in achieving high precision is the spread in velocity of the atoms in the beam, since the deflexion is inversely proportional to the square of this velocity.

Application of this method to the determination of nuclear magnetic moments demands great refinements, since the size of the moment is some 2000 times smaller than that of an electron, and the deflexion is correspondingly smaller. For a direct measurement molecules such as $H_2$ or NaCl, with no electronic magnetic moment, must be used. Owing to the great difficulty of working with purely nuclear moments, methods were devised using atoms with a hyperfine structure due to magnetic interaction between the electronic moment and the nuclear magnetic moment. These are rather complicated, and such deflexion methods have now been superseded by others making use of magnetic resonance. The first of these was carried out by Rabi and his colleagues (1939).

A schematic diagram of the apparatus is shown in Fig. 23.3. Molecules from an oven $O$ emerge through a narrow slit, moving at small angles with the axis of the apparatus. They enter a region of inhomogeneous magnetic field in the $A$-magnet, and are deflected by an amount proportional to the projection of their magnetic moments on the direction of the field; thus some of them will pass through the collimating slit $S$. Neglecting for the moment the $C$-magnet, we follow the molecules through the $B$-magnet, which produces an inhomogeneous field exactly like that of the $A$-magnet except that the gradient is reversed. The force on the nuclear magnets in a molecule is therefore also reversed (provided that the orientation of these magnets is the same as it was when passing through the $A$-magnet), and the molecules are therefore deflected

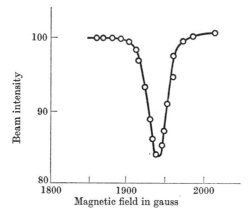

FIG. 23.4. Resonance curve for the $F^{19}$ nucleus in NaF obtained by Rabi with the apparatus in Fig. 23.3.

upwards and reach a detector. The proviso about the orientation is important, because if it changes between $A$ and $B$, then the deflexion produced by $B$ is different from that in $A$, and the molecules will not reach the detector. This gives a means of detecting a magnetic resonance phenomenon, since it can be used to cause a change in the orientation after leaving $A$ and before entering $B$. The $C$-magnet produces a uniform field $\mathbf{B_0}$, and between its pole faces is a conducting loop carrying an r.f. current which produces an oscillating field $B_1 \cos \omega t$ in a direction perpendicular to $\mathbf{B_0}$. When the resonance condition is fulfilled, transitions are induced within the Zeeman levels of the nuclear moment in the field $\mathbf{B_0}$, so that the orientation of the nuclear moment is changed. The beam current at the detector then falls, a typical example being shown in Fig. 23.4. Here the radio frequency is kept constant, and the magnetic field $\mathbf{B_0}$ is varied through the resonance. The value of $\gamma$ is found from the observed values of $\mathbf{B_0}$ (at the centre of the resonance) and the frequency. From the width of the resonance curve in Fig. 23.4 it can

be seen that the accuracy is very much greater than could be obtained
by a simple deflexion method.

An estimate of the width can be obtained as follows. If the nuclear
moment is initially parallel to $\mathbf{B_0}$, then at resonance it precesses about
$\mathbf{B_1}$ in the rotating coordinate frame with angular velocity $\gamma \mathbf{B_1}$, and in
a time $t$ it will exactly reverse its orientation provided that $\gamma B_1 t = \pi$.
This corresponds to the maximum in the resonance curve. When we
are off resonance, the moment precesses about $\mathbf{B_{eff}}$, and if $\mathbf{B_{eff}}$ is at an
angle $\theta = 45°$ to $\mathbf{B_0}$ the moment will only reach a maximum angle of
$2\theta = \tfrac{1}{2}\pi$ to $\mathbf{B_0}$. If we take this to define
the half intensity points on the reson-
ance curve, they correspond to

$$B_0 - B' = \pm B_1,$$

so that

$$\Delta\nu = \pm\gamma(B_0 - B')/2\pi = \pm 1/2t,$$

$$(23.6)$$

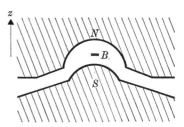

Fig. 23.5. Cross-section of the $A$ and
$B$ magnets used in Rabi's apparatus
of Fig. 23.3, normal to the path of the
beam (marked $B$ in the figure). The
curved parts of the pole pieces are
cylindrical, but the radius of curvature for the upper pole is larger than
for the lower one.

showing that the line width is simply
related to the time $t$ for which the dipole
moment is subjected to the oscillatory
field.

An experiment of this kind is by no
means easy, as can be seen from the fact
that the deflexion of a molecule is only about 0·05 mm in a magnet
with a field gradient of the order of $10^5$ gauss/cm. This is using a
magnet 50 cm long with pole faces of the shape shown in Fig. 23.5; the
curvature is adjusted to give a uniform value of $dB/dz$ over the width
of the beam. Because of the small deflexions the defining slits at $S$ and
the detector must be very narrow ($\approx 0·01$ mm) and the beam intensity
at the detector is very small, being determined by the solid angle which
the detector slit makes with the oven, some $1\tfrac{1}{2}$ metres away! Originally
the difficulty of detecting a beam of uncharged molecules limited the
method to hydrogen, deuterium, and the alkali metals, whose nuclear
moments were measured with a precision of a few parts per thousand
(see Table 23.1). The spectra of $H_2$ and $D_2$ are more complicated than
those of heavier molecules, for a rotating $H_2$ molecule has a rotational
magnetic moment of the same order as the nuclear moment; in addition
there is another interaction in the $D_2$ molecule, between the electric
quadrupole moment of the deuterium nucleus and the electric field
gradient of the electrons.

Present methods of detection depend on ionization of the molecule by electron bombardment; the resultant ion is then passed through a mass spectrometer to separate it from the background ion current. Finally it is accelerated onto the first plate of an electron multiplier, in which the secondary electrons ejected by its impact are amplified as in a photo-multiplier tube (§ 4.4).

TABLE 23.1

*Nuclear spins and magnetic moments of some common isotopes*

| Nucleus | Spin | Magnetic moment (nuclear magnetons) | |
|---|---|---|---|
| | | Molecular beam value | Nuclear resonance value |
| neutron | $\tfrac{1}{2}$ | $-1\cdot913$ | — |
| ¹H | $\tfrac{1}{2}$ | $+2\cdot789$ | $+2\cdot7927$ |
| ²H | 1 | $+0\cdot856$ | $+0\cdot8574$ |
| ³H | $\tfrac{1}{2}$ | — | $+2\cdot9788$ |
| *Alkali metals:* | | | |
| ⁶Li | 1 | $+0\cdot821$ | $+0\cdot8220$ |
| ⁷Li | $\tfrac{3}{2}$ | $+3\cdot253$ | $+3\cdot2563$ |
| ²³Na | $\tfrac{3}{2}$ | $+2\cdot215$ | $+2\cdot2175$ |
| ³⁹K | $\tfrac{3}{2}$ | $+0\cdot391$ | $+0\cdot3915$ |
| ⁴¹K | $\tfrac{3}{2}$ | $+0\cdot215$ | $+0\cdot2154$ |
| ⁸⁵Rb | $\tfrac{5}{2}$ | $+1\cdot340$ | $+1\cdot3527$ |
| ⁸⁷Rb | $\tfrac{3}{2}$ | $+2\cdot733$ | $+2\cdot7505$ |
| ¹³³Cs | $\tfrac{7}{2}$ | $+2\cdot558$ | $+2\cdot5789$ |
| *Halogens:* | | | |
| ¹⁹F | $\tfrac{1}{2}$ | $+2\cdot62$ | $+2\cdot6285$ |
| ³⁵Cl | $\tfrac{3}{2}$ | $+0\cdot819$ | $+0\cdot8218$ |
| ³⁷Cl | $\tfrac{3}{2}$ | $+0\cdot681$ | $+0\cdot6841$ |
| ⁷⁹Br | $\tfrac{3}{2}$ | $+2\cdot110$ | $+2\cdot1056$ |
| ⁸¹Br | $\tfrac{3}{2}$ | $+2\cdot271$ | $+2\cdot2696$ |
| ¹²⁷I | $\tfrac{5}{2}$ | — | $+2\cdot8090$ |

An experiment of this kind was carried out by Alvarez and Bloch (1940) to determine the magnitude of the magnetic dipole moment of the neutron. In this case it is not possible to use the method of deflexion in an inhomogeneous field because the number of neutrons reaching the detector, with the narrow slits required, is too small for detection. Instead, use was made of the fact that the absorption of neutrons in a ferromagnetic material, such as iron magnetized to saturation, is different for neutrons whose spin is parallel to the electron spins in the material from that for neutrons with anti-parallel spins. Two such magnetized blocks are therefore used as 'polarizer' and 'analyser' instead of the inhomogeneous field magnets $A$ and $B$. From the first of these a partially polarized beam of neutrons enters a homogeneous field $C$, where transitions are induced by the r.f. magnetic field at resonance. When resonance is achieved, it is detected by a drop in the neutron count of the beam emerging from the second block, since some of the neutrons have made transitions to the orientation having greater absorption in the iron. In later work the precision has been improved by measuring the field of the $C$-magnet by proton resonance (see § 23.3), so that by measuring the radio frequencies required for magnetic resonance of the proton and neutron in the same field, their relative magnetic moments are immediately determined (both neutron and proton have $I = \frac{1}{2}$). High precision can only be obtained with narrow resonance curves, and from equation (23.6) this requires a large value of $t$; i.e. a long path through the $C$-field. The corresponding requirement of high uniformity in the $C$-field is made less rigorous by the use of two separate oscillatory fields, one at each end of the $C$-field. With this arrangement, due to Ramsey (1949), only the average value of the $C$-field over the whole path is required to be the same as that at the position of the oscillatory fields. By means of this and other special techniques Cohen, Corngold, and Ramsey (1956) obtained the result (p.p.m. = parts per million)

magnetic moment of neutron/magnetic moment of proton

$$= 0 \cdot 685039 \ (\pm 25 \ \text{p.p.m.}).$$

By applying an electric field of about $2 \times 10^5$ V/cm parallel to and in the same region as the $C$-field, as suggested by Purcell and Ramsey (1950), it has been shown from the absence of any effect due to precession in the electric field that the upper limit of any electric dipole moment on the neutron is less than the charge on the electron multiplied by a length $5 \times 10^{-20}$ cm (Smith, Purcell, and Ramsey, 1957).

### 23.3. Nuclear magnetic resonance in bulk material

The molecular beam method of detecting nuclear magnetic resonance is experimentally very difficult, but it was used because at the time there seemed no prospect of detecting the resonance phenomenon directly; that is, by observation of the effect of emission or absorption of quanta on the oscillatory field. At radio frequencies the rate of spontaneous emission of quanta is negligibly small, and spectroscopic lines can be observed only in absorption. The magnitude of the absorption in nuclear magnetic resonance is very small, as can be seen from the following estimate. From the theory of anomalous dispersion (§ 17.4) the imaginary part of the susceptibility $\chi''$ at the centre of a narrow line is related to the static susceptibility $\chi_0$ by the formula (see Problem 23.1)

$$\frac{\chi''}{\chi_0} = \frac{\omega}{2\Delta\omega} = \frac{\nu}{2\Delta\nu}, \tag{23.7}$$

where $\Delta\nu$ is the distance from the centre of the line to a point where the intensity has fallen to half its maximum value. Now

$$\chi_0 = \frac{\mu_0\, ng_n^2\, \beta_n^2\, I(I+1)}{3kT},$$

and in a favourable case, such as the protons in water, the value of $\chi_0$ at room temperature is approximately $10^{-8}$ m.k.s./metre$^3$ ($\approx 10^{-9}$ e.m.u./cm$^3$). To estimate $\chi''$ we need an approximate value of $\Delta\nu$. The main cause of line broadening in our case is the random magnetic fields of neighbouring nuclear magnetic moments. The effect of these is to change the actual field at a given nucleus by an amount depending on the orientation and number of neighbouring magnetic dipoles: this causes a spread in the magnetic field acting on different nuclei, and so gives a finite line width. The spread in field $\Delta B$ is of the order of $\mu_0\, \mathfrak{m}/4\pi d^3$, where $\mathfrak{m}$ is the dipole moment of a neighbour, and $d$ its distance. The mean value of $d^3$ is just half the average volume occupied by the two protons in a water molecule, whence $\Delta B \approx 1$ gauss. Now $\nu/\Delta\nu = B_0/(\Delta B)$, so that at a field of 2000 gauss, $\chi''$ would be about $10^{-8}(2000/2) \approx 10^{-5}$ m.k.s./metre$^3$. For protons, the resonance frequency at this field would be $\approx 8.5$ Mc/s, and this would cause the power transmitted through 10 km of the substance to fall by only 1.8 per cent (see Problem 23.3), and so it is quite out of the question to use a transmission method. Instead the substance is inserted in the r.f. magnetic field generated in the coil of a tuned circuit for 8.5 Mc/s. The magnetic resonance phenomenon will then cause a change in $(1/Q)$, where $Q$ is the quality factor of the circuit, of magnitude (see Problem 23.2)

$$\Delta(1/Q) = \chi''/(1+\chi') \approx 10^{-5}. \tag{23.8}$$

The smallest value of $(1/Q_0)$, the reciprocal of the quality factor of the circuit in the absence of resonance, that we can expect is about $5 \times 10^{-3}$, so that to detect the resonance requires a measurement of a change in $Q$ of less than 1 per cent, which cannot easily be carried out using a $Q$-meter such as that described in § 15.3.

    In practice nuclear magnetic resonance can be observed using quite simple radio techniques. The sample is placed in the inductance of a tuned circuit which forms the grid circuit of a marginal oscillator as shown in Fig. 23.6. A marginal oscillator is one in which the level of oscillation is deliberately kept low so that its output level depends on the losses in the grid circuit, and thus falls when these are increased through the magnetic resonance phenomenon. A simple circuit which achieves a stable output at low level, due to Robinson (1959), is shown as a block diagram in Fig. 23.6. Essentially it consists of a tuned grid oscillator in which the feed-back voltage is obtained, not directly from

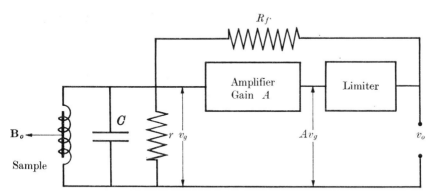

Fig. 23.6. Marginal oscillator circuit of Robinson (1959) for the detection of nuclear magnetic resonance. The level of oscillation is controlled by the voltage output $v_0$ from the limiter, and $r$, the parallel impedance of the tuned circuit, which falls when extra loss is introduced through magnetic resonance in the sample.

the oscillator output, but from the output of a subsequent limiter stage. If the voltage output from the latter is $v_0$, then the voltage fed back to the grid is $v_g = v_0 r/(r+R_f) \approx v_0(r/R_f)$ if $r \ll R_f$. Oscillations are sustained provided that $Av_g \geqslant v_0$, or $A(r/R_f) \geqslant 1$, where $A$ is the amplification factor (this condition is equivalent to $A\beta \geqslant 1$ in § 13.2), at a level $v_g \approx v_0(r/R_f)$ determined by the output voltage $v_0$ from the limiter. Here $r$ is the parallel impedance of the tuned circuit, so that $r = Q/\omega C$, and $v_g$ is linearly proportional to $Q$, giving (from equation (23.8))

$$\delta v_g/v_g = \delta Q/Q = -Q\delta(1/Q) = -Q\chi''.$$

From equation (16.7) the smallest value of $\delta v_g$ we can observe (corresponding to a signal to noise ratio of unity) is $(4kTr\,df)^{\frac{1}{2}}$, so that the smallest detectable value of $\chi''$ is

$$(\chi'')_{min} = \frac{1}{Qv_g}(4kTr\,df)^{\frac{1}{2}}. \tag{23.8 a}$$

If we take $Q = 10^2$, $r = 10^4$ ohm, $df = 10^3$ c/s, $v_g = 10^{-1}$ volt, we obtain $(\chi'')_{min} = 4\ 10^{-8}$, giving an ample margin of sensitivity compared with (23.8).

In an experiment the sample is placed in a coil whose axis (the direction of the oscillating field $\mathbf{B_1}$) is perpendicular to the steady field $\mathbf{B_0}$. The latter is then swept through resonance, at which point the voltage output $Av_g$ from the amplifier momentarily diminishes. A low frequency modulation is imposed on $\mathbf{B_0}$, so that the momentary drop in $Av_g$ is repeated in synchronism with this modulation, giving a low frequency modulation of $Av_g$. After detection, the modulation can be amplified (if necessary) and applied to the $Y$-plates of an oscillograph. The $X$-sweep is derived from the low frequency modulation, so that a given $X$-deflexion

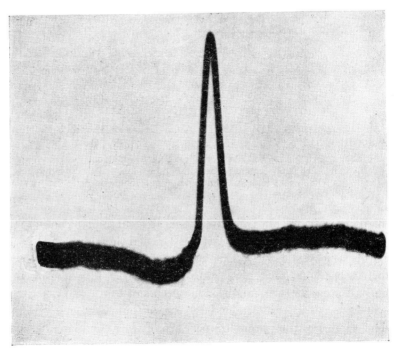

FIG. 23.7. Nuclear magnetic resonance signal from protons in liquid water, displayed on oscilloscope. The vertical deflexion is proportional to the strength of the absorption and the horizontal deflexion to the variation in the applied magnetic field.
(Photograph by R. A. Kamper.)

corresponds to a given change in $\mathbf{B_0}$ caused by the modulation. A typical resonance curve obtained in this way with liquid water as the sample is shown in Fig. 23.7. As the mean value of $\mathbf{B_0}$ (i.e. the field corresponding to the mid-point of the modulation) is slowly varied, the resonance line appears at one end of the trace, moves across, and disappears at the other end.

The first experiment of this kind was carried out by Purcell, Torrey, and Pound (1946). Simultaneously, the nuclear resonance was observed independently by Bloch, Hansen, and Packard (1946) using a slightly different principle, known as nuclear induction. To understand this we shall return to the rotating coordinate system used in Fig. 23.1. If there is some damping mechanism by which energy can be transferred from the system of nuclear spins to the outside world, the equilibrium state will be one where the net magnetization $\mathbf{M}$ will be parallel to the steady field $\mathbf{B_0}$. When a rotating field $\mathbf{B_1}$ is applied, the magnetization vector precesses at an angle $\delta$ about $\mathbf{B_0}$ with the angular velocity $\omega$ of the applied rotating field. Thus it is a constant vector in the rotating coordinate system, though not coplanar with $\mathbf{B_0}$ and $\mathbf{B_1}$ (this is the steady state solution of the forced precession of the damped system). Theory shows that, if $\Delta B$ is the line width, $\delta$ is given by

$$\tan \delta = \frac{B_1}{\{(B_0-B')^2+\Delta B^2\}^{\frac{1}{2}}}.$$

Hence $\delta$ is greatest at resonance ($\mathbf{B_0} = \mathbf{B'}$), and the rotating component $M \sin \delta$ is then also a maximum, leading the rotating field $\mathbf{B_1}$ by an angle $\frac{1}{2}\pi$. This component will induce a voltage in a coil placed at right angles to the main coil producing the driving field $B_1 \cos \omega t$. The induced voltage is an oscillatory one with the same frequency, and the detector coil must therefore be carefully oriented to reduce as far as possible any direct pick-up from the driving coil. Here again the steady field $\mathbf{B_0}$ is 'wobbled' at an audio frequency, since this differentiates between such stray pick-up, which will not be modulated at the wobble frequency, and the resonance effect, which is.

## 23.4. Relaxation effects in nuclear magnetic resonance

The Purcell method is generally known as 'nuclear resonance', and the Bloch method as 'nuclear induction'; they are alternative methods of detecting the same phenomenon, and have the same ultimate sensitivity. Both have been pushed to the limits of sensitivity in applications such as measurement of the value of $\gamma$ for rare isotopes. In this connexion line width is of great importance, since the intensity at the centre of an absorption line varies inversely as the line width (see equation (23.7)), and the accuracy with which the position of the centre of the line can be determined is also higher for a narrower line. It turns out that the line width varies very considerably with the nature of the sample, and we shall discuss this briefly first.

In the estimate of the line width for $H_2O$ made in § 23.3 the field due to one neighbouring proton was found to be about one gauss. This was an underestimate of the width to be expected, since there is more than one neighbour, and we would expect the full width ($2\Delta B$) to be about 10 gauss. In fact it is found to be about 16 gauss in ice at low temperatures. In liquid water, on the other hand, the resonance is extremely narrow; so narrow, that its actual width is very difficult to determine, as variation of the field produced by the external magnet over the volume of the sample is usually the limiting factor in determining the breadth. By working at low field strength, however, Brown and Purcell (1949) were able to show that the overall width was less than 0·007 gauss. The explanation for this striking difference from the width in ice is as follows. In water the molecules are not stationary, but on the average change their positions once every $10^{-11}$ sec or so, this figure being given by the relaxation time of the Debye absorption discussed in § 17.7. This means that at a given nucleus the field of a neighbouring nucleus will not be constant, but will change its value every $10^{-11}$ sec. This is a very much shorter time than that of the precession period in a field of, say, 2 kilogauss, which is $\approx 10^{-7}$ sec. At first sight the rapid fluctuations of the random fields of the neighbours might be expected to broaden the line, but in fact the nucleus cannot respond to changing fields whose duration is less than $T_2 = (\Delta\omega)^{-1} = (\gamma\Delta B)^{-1}$, the inverse line width: in the words of Purcell (1948), 'the nucleus rides out the storm like a well-balanced gyroscope on perfect gymbals'. It turns out that the more rapid the fluctuations the more closely does their effect average to zero. If the rate of fluctuation is lower, on the other hand, as it is in a liquid of high viscosity such as glycerine, the line width is not so effectively reduced, and increases rapidly if the viscosity is increased by lowering the temperature. When the Debye relaxation time becomes much longer than the characteristic time $T_2$, the full line width is attained. In many substances the line width does not have the expected width due to the random magnetic fields of other nuclear dipole moments even in the solid state. This is attributed to internal motion within the solid lattice, which 'averages out' the fields of the neighbours, and nuclear resonance has been used to investigate such internal motions in many cases·

A second question of considerable importance is the rate at which energy is transferred from the nuclear spin system to the lattice containing the nuclei. In the absence of an external magnetic field $\mathbf{B}_0$, the nuclear spins will point in random directions, and $\chi_0$ will be zero. If a field $\mathbf{B}_0$ is now applied, the energy levels corresponding to different nuclear spin or orientations will be split, as shown in Fig. 23.8. For simplicity, a spin $I = \frac{1}{2}$ is assumed, giving just two levels. Originally, the populations of these two levels were equal, and after $\mathbf{B}_0$ is switched on they will remain so until a number are transferred from the upper to the lower state to give the equilibrium Boltzmann distribution in which

$$n_2 = n_1 \exp(-W/kT).$$

This involves a transfer of energy from the system of spins to the lattice, and the magnetization approaches its equilibrium value $\mathbf{M}_0$ according to

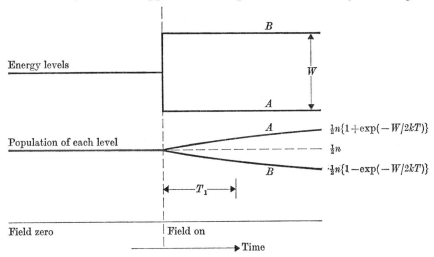

FIG. 23.8. The energy levels and the relative populations of a nucleus of spin $I = \frac{1}{2}$ before and after a magnetic field is switched on. The populations approach the new equilibrium values exponentially, with time constant $T_1$, the 'relaxation time'.

the exponential law (compare the corresponding equation for electric polarization in § 17.7)

$$d\mathbf{M}/dt = (\mathbf{M}_0 - \mathbf{M})/T_1,$$

which gives

$$\mathbf{M}_0 - \mathbf{M} = \mathbf{M}_0 \exp(-t/T_1) \tag{23.9}$$

if $\mathbf{M} = 0$ at $t = 0$. The parameter $T_1$ is known as the spin-lattice relaxation time, since it determines the rate at which energy is transferred from the magnetic dipoles of the system of nuclear spins to the crystal lattice in which they are embedded. Such a transfer requires that transitions be induced between the various nuclear levels corresponding to different orientations, and these can only be caused by the presence of an oscillating magnetic field whose frequency satisfies the condition for resonance. Furthermore, this oscillating field must originate in the thermal motion of the surroundings of the nucleus. In a liquid the Brownian motion of neighbouring molecules causes the local magnetic fields of their nuclei to fluctuate rapidly, and this random fluctuation contains components of the right frequency to cause transitions. For distilled water at 20° C,

Bloembergen, Purcell, and Pound (1948) found the value of $T_1$ to be about 2 sec. This can be shortened by dissolving a paramagnetic salt in the water, so that the protons interact with the much bigger electronic magnetic moments. Another feature is that one would expect the desired component of the randomly fluctuating magnetic fields to be greatest (and hence $T_1$ to be shortest) when the Debye relaxation time of the liquid $\tau$ is of the order $1/\omega_0$, where $\omega_0$ is the angular frequency of the magnetic resonance. This was verified by Bloembergen, Purcell, and Pound by measuring $T_1$ in glycerine over a range of temperatures, which gives a wide range of viscosity and hence of the Debye relaxation time $\tau$. In solids at low temperatures, where there is practically no thermal motion, we should expect $T_1$ to be very long, but in practice it turns out to be nothing like as long as the values predicted by theory. This is ascribed to the presence of paramagnetic impurities, where the electron spins turn over and so give a fluctuating field. Owing to their larger magnetic moments, very few such impurity ions are required, and the thermal contact between the electron spin (or orbit) and the lattice is much more intimate than that between a nuclear spin and the lattice (see § 23.7), so that a transfer of energy to the electron spins from the nuclei is effectively a transfer to the lattice itself.

The variation of $T_1$ with the Debye relaxation time $\tau$ for three substances is shown in Fig. 23.9. In ethyl alcohol, $\tau \ll (1/\omega_0)$ and $T_1$ decreases as $\tau$ increases. In glycerin $T_1$ passes through a minimum and increases again, while in ice, where $\tau \gg (1/\omega_0)$, $T_1$ is rising with increasing $\tau$. This variation of $T_1$ (with a corresponding increase in the line width towards the value calculated for an assembly of static dipoles as $\tau$ increases) confirms the internal molecular motion in ice indicated by the Debye relaxation. Internal motions exist in many other solids, and have been investigated by measurement of the relaxation time $T_1$ as well as the line width in nuclear magnetic resonance. Such experiments have added considerably to our knowledge of the solid state.

### 23.5. Applications of nuclear resonance

The most obvious application of nuclear resonance is to the measurement of $\gamma$ for all possible isotopes. A direct measurement of $\gamma$ involves a precise measurement of the frequency, which is comparatively easy, and of the magnetic field $B_0$, which is difficult. For this reason it is usual to measure instead the ratio of $\gamma$ for the unknown isotope to that for a standard isotope such as ${}^1H$, the proton. This may be accomplished by measuring the two frequencies of magnetic resonance in the same magnetic field. To achieve high accuracy, a single sample is used, such as a solution of a substance containing the unknown isotope in water. From the discussion of line width in § 23.4 it will be appreciated that a solution gives the narrowest lines, and hence the greatest accuracy as well as the greatest intensity at the centre of the line. The sample is surrounded by two coils, one for each of the two resonance frequencies, which are

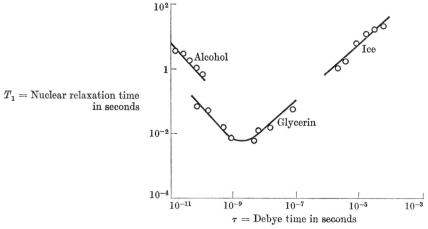

$T_1 =$ Nuclear relaxation time in seconds

$\tau =$ Debye time in seconds

FIG. 23.9. The thermal relaxation time $T_1$ for protons in ethyl alcohol, glycerin, and ice, measured at 29 Mc/s, plotted against the Debye relaxation time $\tau$, obtained from dielectric dispersion data. Note the logarithmic scales. The slope of the solid lines for alcohol and ice and the shape of the solid curve for glycerin have been drawn in accordance with theory.

usually arranged to be mutually perpendicular so as to minimize the mutual inductance between them. The accuracy which can be achieved in this way is illustrated by the ratio of the nuclear moments of the deuteron and the proton, found by Wimett (1953) to be

$$m_D/m_H = 0{\cdot}307012192 \pm 0{\cdot}000000015.$$

The measurement was made with compressed HD gas in order to avoid difficulties with 'diamagnetic shielding' (see below), and certain other small corrections.

A table of nuclear moments for hydrogen, the alkali metals, and the halogens is given in Table 23.1; a complete list would occupy many pages. The earlier values obtained by the use of molecular beams are shown for comparison; in the case of the neutron the value is that obtained by special beam methods outlined in § 23.2. The proton value is obtained from an absolute measurement of $\gamma$, described below, and other magnetic moments from the measured ratios of $\gamma$ to that for the proton.

The absolute measurement of $\gamma$ for one nucleus is obviously of considerable importance, the obvious choice being the proton (which has a high magnetic moment and gives a large signal) in liquid water. The principal difficulty is that of measuring the magnetic field with sufficient accuracy, which can most conveniently be carried out in a standards laboratory. The first such measurement was that of Thomas, Driscoll, and Hipple (1950) at the United States Bureau of Standards, who used a magnetic field of 4700 gauss, determined by means of the Cotton

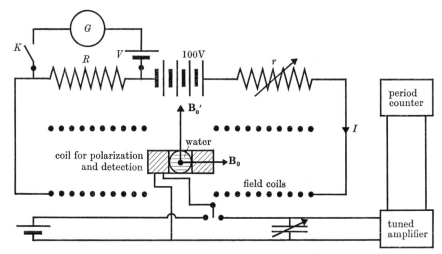

FIG. 23.10. Plan of the apparatus used by Vigoureux (1962) for measuring the frequency of nuclear precession of the proton in a weak magnetic field. The field $\mathbf{B_0}$ is provided by coils of known dimensions carrying a current $I$ measured by the voltage $V$ across a standard resistor $R$. The pulse of the polarizing field $\mathbf{B_0'}$ is provided by a subsidiary coil, in which the subsequent free precession induces a voltage which is amplified and whose frequency is determined by the period counter.

balance (see § 8.6). Later methods have used fields of order 10 gauss produced by a standard solenoid whose dimensions are accurately known, so that the field can be calculated from these dimensions and the current. To obtain sufficient signal at such low frequencies, the method of 'free precession' is used. By means of a subsidiary coil, a field $\mathbf{B_0'}$ of 100–1000 gauss is set up at the proton sample in a direction normal to the standard field $\mathbf{B_0}$. The subsidiary field $\mathbf{B_0'}$ is maintained for a short time ($> T_1$), long enough for the sample to acquire a nuclear magnetization parallel to the resultant field $(\mathbf{B_0}+\mathbf{B_0'})$ and proportional to it. On removing $\mathbf{B_0'}$ we have therefore a comparatively large magnetization $\mathbf{M} = (\chi/\mu_0)(\mathbf{B_0'}+\mathbf{B_0})$ which is almost normal to the standard field $\mathbf{B_0}$, and therefore precesses about $\mathbf{B_0}$ with angular frequency $\omega_\mathrm{p} = -\gamma_\mathrm{p}\mathbf{B_0}$.

During this process the magnitude of **M** decays towards the value $\mathbf{M_0}$ appropriate to the field $\mathbf{B_0}$ (in thermal equilibrium $\mathbf{M_0}$ will also be parallel to $\mathbf{B_0}$). The precessing magnetization induces an alternating voltage in a suitably oriented coil, whose frequency $(\omega_p/2\pi)$ can be determined with an accuracy limited by the number of cycles which elapse before the signal becomes too small to be observable.

TABLE 23.2

*Values of $\gamma_p = -\omega_p/\mathbf{B_0}$ as determined at some Standards laboratories. The last result is referred to the unit of electric current maintained at the N.P.L., rather than the absolute ampere, and on correction agrees with the measurement of Driscoll and Bender within 1·1 p.p.m. The values quoted do not include the diamagnetic correction*

| Method | $\gamma_p$ (in units of (gauss-sec)$^{-1}$) |
|---|---|
| N.M.R. (Thomas, Driscoll, and Hipple, 1950)    .    . | 26 752·3 ($\pm 22$ p.p.m.) |
| Free precession (Driscoll and Bender, 1958)    .    . | 26 751·3 ($\pm 7$ p.p.m.) |
| Free precession (Vigoureux, 1962)    .    .    .    . | 26 751·71 ($\pm 2$ p.p.m.) |

A plan view of the circuit used by Vigoureux (1962) of the United Kingdom National Physical Laboratory is shown in Fig. 23.10. The current $I$ through the field coils (solenoid) is equal to $V/R$, where $V$ is a standard cell and $R$ a standard resistor; to obtain $I$ in terms of the absolute ampere the ratio $V/R$ must be determined by means of a current balance. The results of three independent determinations of $\gamma_p$ (in liquid water) are given in Table 23.2, together with the estimated error in parts per million (p.p.m.). The two more recent results quoted agree within about 1 p.p.m.

The absolute determination of $\gamma_p$ is important not only because of its use in determining nuclear moments, but also because nuclear resonance offers a simple and accurate laboratory method of measuring a magnetic field. Only a frequency measurement is required, which can readily achieve an accuracy of 1 part in $10^4$ if a simple frequency meter with a quartz crystal oscillator check is used, or higher if a frequency standard is available. The main requirement is that the magnetic field must be uniform over the proton sample in order to avoid broadening the resonance, but this is not often a serious limitation. The free precession method can be used for very small fields, such as the earth's field, which can be measured to about 1 part in $10^5$. This accuracy is comparable with other methods such as the earth inductor which have the disadvantage of measuring only a component of the earth's field, so that the orientation of the sensing element must be known accurately (the advantage in this respect of a 'proton magnetometer' in finding the earth's field at the bottom of, say, the Atlantic Ocean can be readily appreciated).

In computing a nuclear magnetic moment from its precession frequency in an external field $\mathbf{B}_0$ a correction must be applied for 'diamagnetic shielding'. This effect is closely allied to diamagnetism, and arises from the precession of the closed shells of electrons about $\mathbf{B}_0$, which sets up a small field at the nucleus with the opposite sense to $\mathbf{B}_0$, thus making the actual field acting at the nucleus slightly smaller than the external field. The apparent value of $\gamma$, if no correction is made, is therefore less than the true value by a fractional amount of about $2 \cdot 8 \times 10^{-5}$ for hydrogen, rising to $10^{-2}$ for the heaviest elements. This correction has been computed, with a probable error rising to about 5 per cent (which is greater than the experimental error) in the heavy elements. This shielding effect, which makes the field in the interior of an atom different from that outside, must be distinguished from the 'demagnetizing field' (§ 5.4) and the 'local field', which can be evaluated sufficiently accurately for this purpose by the method due to Lorentz (cf. § 17.2). Each of these fields is proportional to the bulk diamagnetism of the sample, and in a spherical sample the demagnetizing field and the Lorentz field just cancel, so that the average local field is the same as the external field, apart from the diamagnetic correction.

The shift due to diamagnetic shielding depends on the local density of electrons, and may thus vary from compound to compound; in addition there may be shifts due to the induced paramagnetic moment in compounds which have temperature-independent paramagnetism such as $K_3Co(CN)_6$; these effects are known as 'chemical shifts'. The diamagnetic shielding may also vary between different nuclear sites in the same compound; for example, in $CH_3CH_2OH$ the resonances from protons in the $CH_3$, $CH_2$, and OH groups are separated in frequency by about 1 part in $10^6$. In very high resolution n.m.r. (1 part in $10^8$ may be obtained by special methods) further splittings due to interactions between neighbouring protons can also be resolved in liquids, with important chemical applications.

Such possibilities arise because the frequency of nuclear magnetic resonance is a measure of the magnetic field at the point in the compound occupied by the nucleus whose resonance is being observed. Large shifts are observed in strongly magnetic solids, making nuclear magnetic resonance an important tool in the investigation of magnetic compounds.

In general the electronic magnetic dipoles change their orientation very rapidly, either through relaxation effects due to the thermal fluctuations of the lattice or through interaction with neighbouring spins, and so long as this reorientation occurs many times in a time $T_2 = (\gamma_n \Delta B)^{-1}$ characteristic of the nuclear resonance line width $\Delta B$, relatively narrow n.m.r. lines are obtained, shifted in frequency by a local field which is proportional to the time average of the electronic magnetic moment. Thus the shift is temperature dependent and proportional to the average electronic magnetization; in a paramagnetic substance we can write for the nuclear precession frequency

$$\omega = -\gamma_n(\mathbf{B}_0 + a\mathbf{M}) = -\gamma_n \mathbf{B}_0(1 + a\chi/\mu_0),$$

showing that the fractional change in frequency is proportional to the susceptibility. In an ordered magnetic substance, where the magnetization is finite in the absence of an external field, nuclear magnetic resonance can be observed at a frequency which is very nearly proportional to the magnetization in a ferromagnetic substance, or to the sub-lattice magnetization in an anti-ferromagnetic or ferrimagnetic compound.

The nuclear magnetic moment of $^{19}F$ is quite large, and signals of high intensity have been observed from nuclear magnetic resonance of this nucleus in a number of magnetic compounds. It was found by Shulman and Jaccarino (1956) that in $MnF_2$ in the paramagnetic state, the $^{19}F$ resonance was shifted by an amount proportional to the electronic paramagnetic susceptibility. However, the magnitude of the shift was greater than would be expected from the dipolar magnetic field at the fluorine site due to the electronic magnetic moments, assuming them to be localized on the $Mn^{2+}$ ions; the larger field is consistent with a spread of the wave functions of the magnetic electrons onto the $F^-$ ions, due to a small amount of covalent bonding. In the anti-ferromagnetic state the electronic moments are fixed in orientation, and the field which they produce at the $F^-$ nucleus is quite high even when $\mathbf{B}_0 = 0$. At $0°$ K in $MnF_2$ the precession frequency of $^{19}F$ in this electronic field is $159 \cdot 99$ Mc/s falling, as the temperature rises, to zero at the Néel point, $67 \cdot 3°$ K. A comparison of the nuclear resonance frequency, which should be proportional to the sub-lattice magnetization, with the magnetization calculated from the molecular field theory, is shown in Fig. 23.11.

## 23.6. Electron magnetic resonance in atomic beams

Magnetic resonance experiments involving electronic magnetic moments can be carried out in analogous ways to experiments with nuclear magnetic moments. In general, experiments with electronic moments are easier, because the moments are so much larger and magnetic resonance is correspondingly easier to detect. In the analogue of Rabi's experiments (§ 23.2), beams of atoms with electronic magnetic dipole moments are used, for which appreciable deflexions in the inhomogeneous magnetic fields $A$, $B$ (see Fig. 23.3) can be achieved using relatively short magnets. The main interest of such experiments

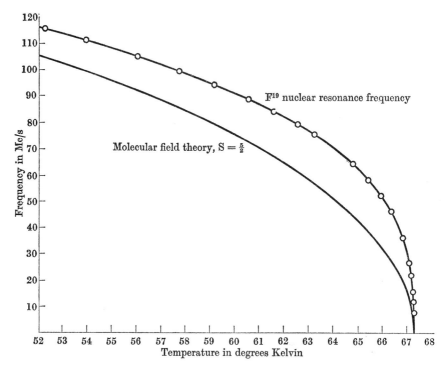

FIG. 23.11. Temperature dependence of the $^{19}$F nuclear magnetic resonance frequency in MnF$_2$ between 52° K and the Néel point, 67·3° K. The lower curve shows the variation expected if the sub-lattice magnetization, relative to that at 0° K, followed the curve computed from molecular field theory for $S = \frac{5}{2}$. (Heller and Benedek, 1962.) In this and other substances the resonance frequency varies near $T_N$ as $(T_N - T)^{\frac{1}{3}}$.

arises from the high precision which can be obtained by increasing the length of the $C$-field, since from equation (23.6) the width of the resonance curve depends on the time $t$ during which the atom is subjected to the radio-frequency field. If the velocity of atoms in the beam is $10^5$ cm/sec, and the length of the $C$-field is 3 cm, the value of $t$ is $3 \times 10^{-5}$ sec, and the corresponding line width $2\Delta\nu$ is about 30 kc/s. To achieve such a narrow line the $C$-field would have to be very homogeneous, since a variation of the field by as little as $10^{-2}$ gauss would change the electronic magnetic resonance frequency of an atom with $g = 2$ by 30 kc/s. The requirement of such high homogeneity is avoided by use of the two separated oscillatory fields method of Ramsey (1949), as mentioned in § 23.2.

For an atom with an electronic magnetic moment but no nuclear moment the magnetic resonance transitions occur at a frequency (cf. equation (23.5))

$$\nu = (\gamma/2\pi)B_0 = g_J(e/4\pi m)B_0 \qquad (23.10)$$

and determination of $\nu$ in a known field $B_0$ gives a precise measurement of $g_J$. As mentioned in § 20.2, there are corrections to equation (20.11) for $g_J$ due to diamagnetic shielding (cf. § 23.5) by other electrons and the relativistic increase in the mass of the electron, which amount to between 10 and 100 p.p.m. A more fundamental correction is due to the intrinsic magnetic moment of the electron spin being slightly greater than one Bohr magneton. First indications of this were obtained from atomic beam measurements of the hyperfine structure of hydrogen (see below), and from measurements of the ratio of the values of $g_j$ for two states of the same atom with the same $s$, $l$ but different $j$ (see Problem 23.6). The accepted value of $g_s$ is in agreement with that calculated using quantum electrodynamics by Sommerfield (1957):

$$g_s = 2(1+\alpha/2\pi-0\cdot328\alpha^2/\pi^2+...) = 2(1\cdot0011596), \qquad (23.11)$$

where $\alpha$ is the fine structure constant.

An important application of atomic beam magnetic resonance is the precise measurement of hyperfine structure in atoms. As pointed out in § 20.10, in an atom with both electronic and nuclear moments the nuclear magnetic moment precesses in the electronic magnetic field $\mathbf{B}_e$, and the electronic moment in the nuclear magnetic field $\mathbf{B}_n$, the result being a precession of each moment about the resultant angular momentum vector $\mathbf{F}$. This gives rise to a set of hyperfine energy levels, as illustrated in Fig. 20.20, where the effect of a nuclear electric quadrupole interaction is also shown. In magnetic resonance the transitions for which $\Delta F = \pm 1$ have an intensity associated with an electronic magnetic dipole moment, and can readily be observed; from measurements of the frequencies of two such transitions the values of the hyperfine constants $A$ and $B_Q$ can be determined. These require no magnetic field in the $C$-magnet, but in practice a small field $\mathbf{B}_0$ is generally used, whose effect (see Fig. 23.12) is to split each set of states with a given value of $F$ into $2F+1$ levels, provided that the Zeeman energy $g_J\beta(\mathbf{J}.\mathbf{B}_0)$ is small compared with the hyperfine energies. This corresponds to a precession of the vector **F** about **B₀** at a rate slow compared with the precession of **J**, **I** about **F**. The allowed transitions are then those for which $\Delta F = 0, \pm 1$; $\Delta m_F = 0, \pm 1$, but the $\Delta m = 0$ transitions occur only if the oscillatory field has a component parallel to **B₀** (the $\Delta m = \pm 1$ transitions require a component **B₁** perpendicular to **B₀**, as in Fig. 23.1).

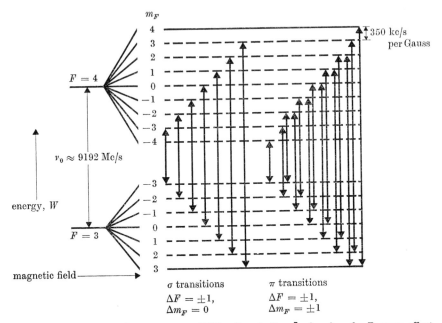

FIG. 23.12. The hyperfine structure of $^{133}$Cs, $S = \frac{1}{2}$, $I = \frac{7}{2}$, showing the Zeeman effect in a small field (note the difference in scale between the Zeeman splittings and the overall splitting) and the allowed transitions (after Essen and Parry, 1957).

The atomic beam magnetic resonance technique has been widely applied to measure the constants $A$, $B_Q$, and in a few atoms a further very weak interaction between a nuclear magnetic octupole moment and the second derivative of the electronic field **B₂** has been detected. It can also be used with radioactive isotopes, which can be measured by means of their radioactive emission after being collected at the detector. Only two examples will be discussed here; the hyperfine structure of caesium, which gives an atomic standard of frequency, and the hyperfine structure of hydrogen, because of its fundamental importance.

The ground state of the caesium atom is $^2S_{\frac{1}{2}}$, and the only stable isotope $^{133}$Cs has nuclear spin $I = \frac{7}{2}$. Since the electronic ground state is $S = \frac{1}{2}$, there is no electric quadrupole interaction, and in zero magnetic field there are two sets of hyperfine levels corresponding to $F = 3$ and

$F = 4$, as in Fig. 23.12. Caesium is fairly volatile, so that an atomic beam of sufficient intensity can be emitted from an oven at 200° C, and this combined with the rather high atomic mass gives a low thermal velocity and increases the time required to traverse the $C$-field, where a distance of about 50 cm is used between the separated oscillatory fields (see Essen and Parry (1957)). A small field of 0·05 gauss (this requires cancellation of the earth's field, which is about 0·5 gauss) is maintained as the $C$-field, and the resonance observed is the transition $(F, m_F) = (4, 0) \leftrightarrow (3, 0)$, which has only a second-order Zeeman effect

$$\nu = \nu_0 + 426 B_0^2 \text{ c/s} \quad (B_0 \text{ in gauss}).$$

Following collaboration between the Standards laboratories of the U.K. and the U.S., the value of $\nu_0$ is found to be (see Markowitz, Hall, Essen, and Barry (1958))

$$\nu_0 = 9\,192\,631\,770 \pm 20 \text{ c/s (Ephemeris time) at } 1957 \cdot 0.$$

The atomic frequency standards in the two countries have been found to agree within 1 part in $10^{10}$ in comparisons made over several years, and this accuracy (1 c/s) is higher than that which can be obtained in determining the mean rate of rotation of the earth. The variation in the length of the day, as measured at the National Physical Laboratory over a period of seven years against a caesium 'atomic clock', is shown in Fig. 23.13; the annual variation is about 1 millisecond per day (about 1 part in $10^8$) and there is a suggestion of a longer term change also. An international recommendation in 1964 makes the caesium 'clock' the new standard of frequency, the second being defined as the time interval containing exactly 9 192 631 770 cycles of the caesium hyperfine frequency in zero magnetic field.

The ground state of a hydrogen or alkali metal atom is $^2S_{\frac{1}{2}}$, so that the electronic field at the nucleus is due only to the electron spin of the odd electron, which is in an $s$-state. The electron density in such a state is spherically symmetric, with a maximum at the nucleus and falling exponentially with distance. The magnetic moment due to the electron spin is similarly distributed, and we can regard the atom as possessing a magnetization which (because of the negative electronic charge) is anti-parallel to the spin, and distributed in a spherically symmetric fashion. This is equivalent to a ferromagnetic sphere which is everywhere magnetized in the same direction but with a varying intensity

$$\mathbf{M} = -g_s \beta \mathbf{S} |\psi|^2,$$

where $\psi$ is the wave function for the $s$-state. The nuclear magnetic moment is then due to a small current loop immersed in this ferro-magnetic medium at the centre. The interaction between the two gives an energy $W = -\mathbf{m_n} \cdot \mathbf{B_e}$. In calculating $\mathbf{B_e}$ at the centre of the spherical distribution we note that the field at the centre due to a uniformly magnetized spherical shell is zero (see Problem 5.9), so that the whole contribution to $\mathbf{B_e}$ comes from the magnetization $\mathbf{M_0}$

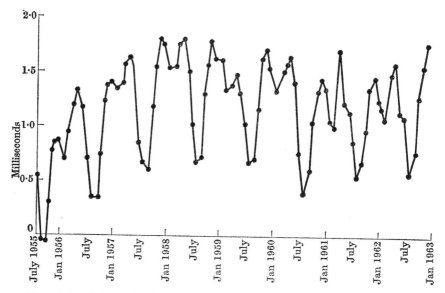

FIG. 23.13. Variation in the length of the day, as measured by the caesium atomic clock (courtesy of the Director, National Physical Laboratory).

at the centre. From equation (5.34), in the absence of an external field, we have $\mathbf{H} = -\tfrac{1}{3}\mathbf{M_0}$, so that $\mathbf{B_e} = \mu_0(\mathbf{H}+\mathbf{M_0}) = \tfrac{2}{3}\mu_0\mathbf{M_0}$. Hence

$$W = -\mathbf{m_n}\cdot\mathbf{B_e} = -(g_n\beta_n\,\mathbf{I})\cdot(-\tfrac{2}{3}\mu_0\,g_S\beta\mathbf{S}|\psi(0)|^2)$$
$$= \tfrac{2}{3}\mu_0 g_n g_S\beta\beta_n|\psi(0)|^2\mathbf{S}\cdot\mathbf{I} = A\mathbf{S}\cdot\mathbf{I}. \quad (23.12)$$

For atomic hydrogen in the $1s$-state, $|\psi(0)|^2 = 1/\pi a_0^3$, where $a_0 = $ Bohr radius, being the fraction of the electron to be found per unit volume at the nucleus. After inserting small relativistic and reduced mass correc-tions, the best value of $A/h$ obtained from the Cohen, Dumond, et. al. (1955) values of the atomic constants is (assuming $g_S = 2$ exactly)

$$A/h = 1418 \cdot 90 \pm 2 \text{ p.p.m. Mc/s}$$

and since $S = \tfrac{1}{2}$, $I = \tfrac{1}{2}$ this should be equal to the frequency of the single transition between the two states $F = 0$ and $F = 1$ of the hyperfine structure. The best experimental values are

1420·40573±0·035 p.p.m. Mc/s (Kusch, 1955),

1420·40580±0·04 p.p.m. Mc/s (Wittke and Dicke, 1956),

where the first result was obtained by an atomic beam method and the second by another method. The discrepancy with the theoretical value is well outside the experimental error, and it was the first discovery of this discrepancy in 1947–8 that led to the suggestion that $g_S$ is greater than 2.

A detailed theoretical treatment shows that some other small corrections besides that for $g_S$ are required in the formula for $A$, and the discrepancy with experiment has been removed. At almost the same time as this discrepancy was discovered an anomaly in the separation of the electronic $2s$ and $2p$ states of atomic hydrogen was established by the experiment of Lamb and Retherford (1947). This has also been explained by quantum electrodynamics. Experiments of the kind mentioned above and others are discussed in *The Spectrum of Atomic Hydrogen*, by G. W. Series.

### 23.7. Electron magnetic resonance in solids

Magnetic resonance experiments on substances containing permanent magnetic dipole moments due to electrons can be carried out in a manner analogous to those on nuclear dipoles, but there are a number of significant differences. If fields of a few kilogauss are used, the resonance frequency for electrons is in the vicinity of $10^{10}$ c/s, corresponding to wavelengths of a few centimetres. Frequencies of this order and higher are in fact used for a number of reasons:

(a) the sensitivity is high; this is partly through equation (23.7), and partly because a better filling factor can be obtained from a small sample by using it in a tuned circuit (a cavity resonator) which has similar dimensions;

(b) the electronic levels may have splittings of order $0·1$ cm$^{-1}$ or more due to crystal field effects (see § 20.7);

(c) line widths in the solid due to magnetic fields of neighbouring ions are of order $10^2$–$10^3$ gauss, and to achieve reasonable accuracy in determining the centre of a line measurements must be made using external fields as large as possible. Line width and shape are also affected by exchange interaction between the ions; this can be avoided by making measurements on 'diluted' crystals— crystals in which most of the paramagnetic ions have been replaced by diamagnetic ions. For example, a crystal of $K_2Zn(SO_4)_2,6H_2O$ containing a few tenths of a per cent of $Cu^{++}$ ($3d^9$) ions replacing $Zn^{++}$ ($3d^{10}$) ions gives a line width of about 10 gauss; this residual width is due mainly to the nuclear magnetic moments of the protons in the water of crystallization, and can be further reduced by growing crystals with $D_2O$ instead of $H_2O$ because of the smaller nuclear moment of the deuteron.

Another important feature of electron spin resonance in paramagnetic substances is that spin-lattice relaxation times may be extremely short. Obviously the electron, with its larger magnetic moment, will be in more intimate contact with the lattice vibrations than a nuclear dipole, but a much more important effect is that the lattice vibrations distort the local surroundings of a paramagnetic ion, and so produce a fluctuating modulation of the crystal electric field or the ligand field. The extent to which this affects the magnetic dipole depends on the degree of 'quenching' of the orbital moment: for an ion in an $S$-state, such as $Mn^{++}$ ($3d^5$, $^6S_{\frac{5}{2}}$) or $Gd^{3+}$ ($4f^7$, $^8S_{\frac{7}{2}}$), there is no orbital moment except through small departures from Russell-Saunders coupling, and the spin-lattice relaxation time $T_1$ varies from $\approx 10^{-6}$ sec at room temperature to $10^{-3}$ sec at liquid helium temperatures. For other ions the values of $T_1$ are very much smaller, and in many ions of the $4f$ group $T_1$ is so short and the lines so broad ($\Delta\omega = T_1^{-1}$) that magnetic resonance is unobservable, except at liquid helium or liquid hydrogen temperatures. The value of $T_1$ always increases as the temperature falls because the lattice vibrations die out, the variation being in general of the form

$$\frac{1}{T_1} = aT + bT^n + c\exp(\hbar\omega/kT). \tag{23.13}$$

The first term $aT$ is due to 'direct transitions' in which magnetic quanta are exchanged with lattice vibrations of the same frequency as the magnetic resonance frequency; the second term $bT^n$ (where $n = 5$, 7, or 9 according to the type of magnetic ion involved) is due to 'indirect' or 'Raman' processes in which any two lattice vibrations are involved whose frequency *difference* is equal to the magnetic resonance frequency ($\omega_{lattice} = \omega'_{lattice} \pm \omega_{resonance}$); the exponential term is due to lattice vibrations whose quanta $\hbar\omega$ coincide with the difference in energy between the ground state and an excited state of the magnetic ion. The second two processes are weaker than the first, and at liquid helium temperatures the first term almost always predominates.

A spin-lattice relaxation time $T_1$ will produce a line width of $2\Delta\nu$

between the half-intensity points of a line, where $2\pi\Delta\nu = \Delta\omega = T_1^{-1}$, and measurements of line width can be used to find $T_1$ when this is the dominant effect in the line width. For other purposes the need for high resolution in order to obtain accurate measurements makes it desirable, however, to work at temperatures where broadening due to spin lattice relaxation is negligible, and a typical apparatus for low temperature work is outlined in Fig. 23.14. Power from a microwave oscillator

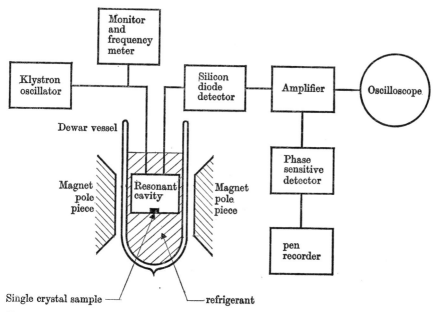

FIG. 23.14. Outline diagram of an electron spin resonance apparatus. Power from a klystron oscillator is fed through a waveguide to a loosely coupled resonant cavity containing the paramagnetic sample and immersed in a refrigerant between the poles of an electromagnet. A small fraction of the cavity signal is fed through a second waveguide to a silicon diode detector. The modulation due to the absorption is amplified and displayed on an oscilloscope or fed through a phase-sensitive detector to a pen recorder.

(usually a klystron) is carried by a waveguide or co-axial cable to a cavity resonator contained in a dewar vessel and placed between the poles of an electromagnet. When the latter is adjusted to resonance, power is absorbed in the paramagnetic sample, which is placed inside the cavity in a position of maximum oscillatory magnetic field. This additional power loss in the cavity produces a change in the signal reflected from the cavity, or in the signal transmitted through the cavity to another waveguide or co-axial line, which is detected by a silicon crystal rectifier. Normally the field of the electromagnet is modulated at an audio frequency, giving a corresponding modulation of the signal when the field for magnetic resonance is traversed; after detection, this modulation is amplified and displayed on an oscilloscope or a recorder. The sensitivity achieved is quite high, and signals from as few as $10^{13}$ electronic dipoles can be seen if the lines are narrow.

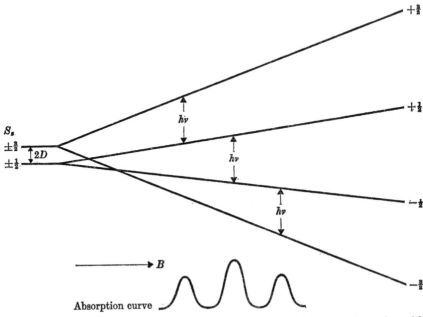

FIG. 23.15. Energy levels and absorption curve at constant frequency for an ion with $S = \frac{3}{2}$ and a crystal field splitting:

$$W = g\beta S_z\,B_z + D\{S_z^2 - \tfrac{1}{3}S(S+1)\};$$

when the magnetic field is parallel to the principal axis ($z$-axis) of the splitting term (for other directions the levels do not diverge linearly with field). The intensity of the $S_z \leftrightarrow (S_z - 1)$ transition is proportional to $\{S(S+1) - S_z(S_z - 1)\}$, giving the 3:4:3 intensity ratio shown in the figure.

The results of electron magnetic resonance in paramagnetic salts have greatly advanced the detailed understanding of the properties of paramagnetic ions subjected to ligand field interactions in solids. In general the resonance spectrum is very anisotropic, depending strongly on the angle between the external field and the crystal axes; for this reason single crystals must be used. In dilute salts the splittings of the levels due to the external field as a function of angle can be studied, together with any crystal field splittings of the same order as the microwave frequency (see Fig. 23.15). When the nucleus of the paramagnetic ion or of a ligand ion has a nuclear moment, a hyperfine structure may be observed, as in Fig. 23.16. A number of nuclear spins and moments have been determined from hyperfine structure in electron magnetic resonance, and the degree to which the wave functions of the magnetic electrons overlap onto the ligand ions because of covalent bonding effects (see § 20.8) can be estimated from the hyperfine structure due to interaction with the dipole moment of the ligand nucleus. In more concentrated salts the effect of magnetic dipole and exchange interaction between neighbouring dipoles can be studied, giving one of the few direct measurements of exchange interaction.

FIG. 23.16. Hyperfine structure of the $^{55}$Mn $(I = \frac{5}{2})$ nucleus in the electron spin resonance spectrum of a Mn$^{++}$ ion $(S = \frac{5}{2}$, transition $S_z = \frac{1}{2} \leftrightarrow -\frac{1}{2})$. The resonance condition is $h\nu = g\beta(B_0+B_n)$, where $B_n$ is the magnetic field due to the nucleus. In first approximation $B_n$ is proportional to the nuclear magnetic quantum number $I_z$; this gives a pattern of $2I+1 = 6$ lines, equally spaced and of equal intensity, since all nuclear orientations are equally probable at the temperature of the observation. The line shape is the derivative of the absorption curve; it is obtained by a sinusoidal modulation of $B_0$ with amplitude small compared with the line width. This gives a corresponding modulation of the signal (measured by a phase sensitive detector) whose amplitude is proportional to the slope of the absorption curve.

*Ferromagnetic resonance*

In substances where the exchange forces are strong magnetic resonance may be observed in the co-operative state below the transition temperature. Since all the dipoles are coupled together by the exchange forces it is convenient to work in terms of the magnetization **M**, which is the vector sum of the individual dipole moments **m**. By performing this vector sum over both sides of equation (23.1) we obtain the equation of motion for the magnetization

$$dM/dt = \gamma M \wedge B, \qquad (23.14)$$

where we have assumed that all dipoles have the same value of $\gamma$. Here we have written, not $B_0$ the external field, but **B** the field within the sample, since in a ferromagnetic substance demagnetizing fields may be quite important. We shall assume that $B_0$ is along the z-axis, and confine ourselves to certain sample shapes such that we can write for the components of **B**:

$$B_x = -\mu_0 D_x M_x; \qquad B_y = -\mu_0 D_y M_y; \qquad B_z = B_0 - \mu_0 D_z M_z.$$
$$(23.15)$$

On substituting into equation (23.14) we obtain

$$\left.\begin{array}{l} dM_x/dt = \gamma M_y\{B_0 + \mu_0 M_z(D_y - D_z)\} \\ dM_y/dt = -\gamma M_x\{B_0 + \mu_0 M_z(D_x - D_z)\} \\ dM_z/dt = \gamma\{\mu_0 M_x M_y(D_x - D_y)\} \end{array}\right\}, \qquad (23.16)$$

which are no longer linear in $M$. However, the equations can be solved in the limit of small amplitudes of precession, when the product $M_x M_y$ becomes vanishingly small and can be neglected. Then $dM_z/dt = 0$, and $M_z$ is constant, its value being equal to the static magnetization; this is large in a ferromagnetic substance, and the corrections to $B_0$ are important in determining the resonance frequency. By solving the equations for $M_x$, $M_y$ it is easily shown that the precession frequency is

$$\omega_L = -\gamma[\{B_0 + \mu_0 M_z(D_y - D_z)\}\{B_0 + \mu_0 M_z(D_x - D_z)\}]^{\frac{1}{2}}. \quad (23.17)$$

There are three simple cases of interest:

(a) a sphere, for which $D_x = D_y = D_z$; the precession velocity is $\omega_L = -\gamma B_0$, the same as if there were no demagnetizing fields;

(b) a thin plane film normal to $B_0$, for which $D_x = D_y = -1, D_z = 0$, giving
$$\omega_L = -\gamma\{B_0 - \mu_0 M_z\};$$

(c) a thin plane film parallel to $B_0$, for which $D_x = D_z = -1, D_y = 0$ (assuming the film to be normal to the $y$-axis), giving

$$\omega_L = -\gamma\{B_0(B_0 + \mu_0 M_z)\}^{\frac{1}{2}}.$$

This treatment assumes that the magnetization (including the precessing components) is uniform throughout the sample; this requires that the dimensions be small compared with the wavelength in the sample, and in a conducting sample this means small compared with the skin-depth. Hence spherical samples of metal must be very small, and colloidal samples (where the particles are assumed to be spherical because of surface tension effects in formation) have been used. Most work has been done on thin plane samples, which are attached to (but insulated from) one wall of the microwave cavity. The equations show that the magnetization must be known in order to determine $\gamma$; for simplicity it is usual to work at such high fields that the magnetization is equal to the saturation value. The phenomenon of ferromagnetic resonance was discovered experimentally by Griffiths (1946); the theory given above is due to Kittel (1948). Some values of $g$ measured by ferromagnetic resonance are given in Table 21.2.

*Spin wave resonance in ferromagnetic films*

The uniform precession mode assumed above corresponds to a spin wave with $k_s = 0$. It is possible to excite spin waves for which $k_s \neq 0$; since each spin wave corresponds to a unit change $\hbar$ in angular momentum, and hence to a change of $g\beta$ in magnetization, the energy required to excite a spin wave in a field $B$ (in the sample) is

$$\hbar\omega = g\beta B + Dk_s^2, \qquad (23.18)$$

where the constant $D$ is the same as that in equation (21.25). In a thin film of thickness $l$, the boundary conditions (assumed identical at the two faces of the film) limit the allowed values of $k_s$ to those for which the film thickness is an integral number of half-wavelengths; that is, $k_s = p\pi/l$, where $p$ is an integer. If magnetic resonance is observed at constant frequency, the value of the resonance field $B$ is found from equation (23.18) above to be

$$B = B_{k_s=0} - \left(\frac{D}{g\beta}\frac{\pi^2}{l^2}\right)p^2, \qquad (23.19)$$

so that a series of resonances corresponding to different values of $p$ should be observed on the low field side of the ordinary ferromagnetic resonance field $B_{k_s=0}$. A spin wave resonance curve is shown in Fig. 23.17 for a thin film of cobalt metal, of thickness approximately equal to 6000 Å. This is small compared with the skin depth, so that the oscillatory field is uniform within the sample, and the resonance intensity depends on the net magnetic moment in the direction of the oscillatory field. This is proportional to

$$\int_0^l \sin kx \, dx = \int_0^l \sin(p\pi x/l) \, dx = (l/p\pi)(1 - \cos p\pi).$$

This vanishes for even values of $p$, and decreases as $1/p$ for odd values, giving the intensity change shown in Fig. 23.17. The resonance field decreases accurately as $p^2$ (see Fig. 23.18), and the value of $D$ can be found if the thickness $l$ is known.

*Ferrimagnetic and anti-ferromagnetic resonance*

The presence of two sub-lattices in these substances makes the magnetic resonance phenomena in general much more complicated. One simple case occurs in ferrimagnetic substances with strongly coupled sub-lattices; the two sub-lattices can then precess together in such a way that the relative orientation of their two magnetic moments remains unaltered. This occurs at an angular velocity $\omega = -\gamma_{\text{eff}} B$; here $B$ is the field in the substance and $\gamma_{\text{eff}}$ is an average value obtained from the relation

$$\mathbf{M} = \sum_i \mathbf{M}_i = \sum \gamma_i\,\mathbf{G}_i = \gamma_{\text{eff}} \sum \mathbf{G}_i = \gamma_{\text{eff}}\,\mathbf{G},$$

where the summation is over all the individual ions. In both ferri- and anti-ferromagnetics more complicated modes of precession occur in

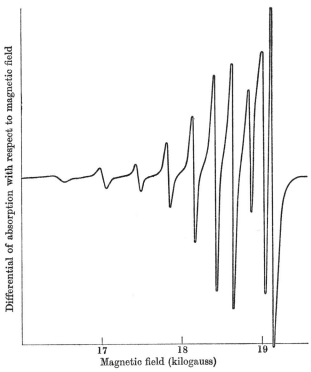

FIG. 23.17. Ferromagnetic spin wave resonance in a thin film (6000 Å thickness) of cobalt metal at room temperature and a frequency of 9370 Mc/s (3·2 cm wavelength). The line shape is that corresponding to the differential of the absorption curve. The intensity of resonance decreases towards lower field strength (higher values of $p$) irregularly because of lack of uniformity in the film thickness (Phillips and Rosenberg, 1964). $B_0$ is normal to the surface of the film, so that rather high values of $B_0$ are needed to satisfy the resonance condition

$$\omega_L = -\gamma\{B_0 - \mu_0\,M_z\}.$$

which the relative orientation of the sub-lattice magnetic moments is not preserved; the frequency of precession then depends on a number of parameters, including the exchange and anisotropy energies.

## 23.8. Cyclotron resonance with free charged particles

When a charged particle of mass $M$ and charge $q$ is moving in a uniform magnetic field $\mathbf{B}$, its equation of motion is

$$\mathbf{F} = q\mathbf{v} \wedge \mathbf{B}.$$

Since this force is always normal to its instantaneous velocity **v**, the particle will move in a circle of radius $r$ in the plane normal to **B** with angular velocity given by the equation

$$M\omega_c^2 r = q\omega_c rB,$$

i.e.
$$\boldsymbol{\omega}_c = (q/M)\mathbf{B}.$$

Thus if it is possible to determine the angular velocity **ω** in a known field **B**, the ratio of charge to mass of the particle may be found. The

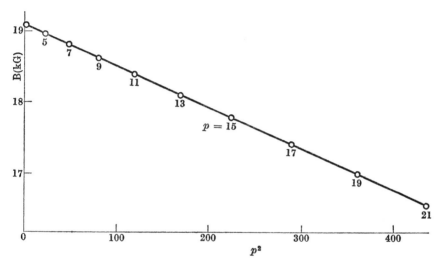

FIG. 23.18. Plot showing the linear relation between magnetic field and $p^2$ for ferromagnetic spin wave resonance in a thin film of cobalt (after Phillips and Rosenberg, 1964).

frequency $\omega_c/2\pi$ is often called the 'cyclotron frequency' since it is the frequency of the r.f. electric field required to accelerate charged particles in the cyclotron. The success of this device, which depends on resonance between the frequency of the oscillating electric field and the frequency of rotation of the particles in the field **B**, suggests that a similar principle may be used to determine the ratio of $q$ to $M$.

We begin by investigating the motion of a charged particle starting from rest under the action of a uniform induction **B** (whose direction we take to be the $z$-axis of a system of cartesian coordinates) and an oscillating electric field of frequency $\omega/2\pi$ polarized so that the lines of electric field are parallel to the $x$-axis. Then the equations of motion are

$$\left. \begin{aligned} M\ddot{x} &= qE\cos\omega t + q\dot{y}B \\ M\ddot{y} &= -q\dot{x}B \\ M\ddot{z} &= 0 \end{aligned} \right\}. \qquad (23.20)$$

The last of these equations shows that the $z$-component of the motion will be independent of $E$ and $B$, and does not appear in the other equations. The second equation can be integrated once giving

$$M\dot{y} = -qxB,$$

where the constant of integration has been equated to zero, corresponding to the assumption that the particle starts at rest from the origin. $\dot{y}$ may now be eliminated from the first equation giving

$$\ddot{x}+\omega_c^2 x = (q/M)E\cos\omega t,$$

where $\omega_c = (q/M)B$. The general solution of this equation is

$$x = \frac{(qE/M)\cos\omega t}{\omega_c^2-\omega^2} + C\cos\omega_c t + D\sin\omega_c t.$$

If the initial conditions are $x = 0$, $\dot{x} = 0$ at $t = 0$, the unknown constants are determined and we have

$$x = \frac{(qE/M)(\cos\omega t - \cos\omega_c t)}{\omega_c^2-\omega^2}$$

$$= \frac{2(qE/M)\sin\tfrac{1}{2}(\omega_c+\omega)t\sin\tfrac{1}{2}(\omega_c-\omega)t}{(\omega_c+\omega)(\omega_c-\omega)}$$

$$= \frac{qE}{M\omega'}\sin\omega't\left(\frac{\sin\tfrac{1}{2}\Delta\omega t}{\Delta\omega}\right), \qquad (23.21)$$

where $\omega' = \tfrac{1}{2}(\omega_c+\omega)$, $\Delta\omega = \omega_c-\omega$. If $\Delta\omega \ll \omega_c$, the factor $\sin\tfrac{1}{2}\Delta\omega t$ varies very slowly with respect to time compared with $\sin\omega't$, and $\omega'$ is very close to $\omega_c$, so that using the relation $\dot{y} = -\omega_c x$ we find approximately

$$y = \frac{qE}{M\omega'}\cos\omega't\left(\frac{\sin\tfrac{1}{2}\Delta\omega t}{\Delta\omega}\right). \qquad (23.22)$$

Examination of the equations for $x$ and $y$ shows that the path of the particle is a spiral with angular velocity $\omega'$ and radius

$$\left(\frac{qE}{M\omega'}\right)\left(\frac{\sin\tfrac{1}{2}\Delta\omega t}{\Delta\omega}\right).$$

If $\Delta\omega = 0$ (i.e. $\omega = \omega_c$) then the value of the factor $(\sin\tfrac{1}{2}\Delta\omega t)/\Delta\omega$ is $\tfrac{1}{2}t$, showing that the radius increases linearly with $t$. On the other hand, if $\Delta\omega \neq 0$, the radius has a maximum value $r_0$ (when the sine is unity) equal to $qE/M\omega'|\Delta\omega|$, which is very nearly equal to $qE/M\omega_c|\Delta\omega|$ when $\Delta\omega$ is small. Hence, if a collector is placed at a distance $R_0$ from the origin, only those ions will reach it for which $r_0 \geqslant R_0$, or

$$|\Delta\omega| \leqslant qE/M\omega_c R_0 = E/BR_0.$$

This is a measure of the precision with which $\omega_c$, and hence $q/M$, can be determined. The 'resolving power' will be

$$\omega_c/|\Delta\omega| = (qB/M)/(E/BR_0) = qB^2R_0/ME. \qquad (23.23)$$

Hence, for a given ion and a given field $B$, the precision is increased by
using a small amplitude of oscillating electric field $E$ and a large value
of $R_0$. It can be shown that our expression for the resolving power is
equal to $L/2R_0$ (see Problem 23.4), where $L$ is the total path traversed

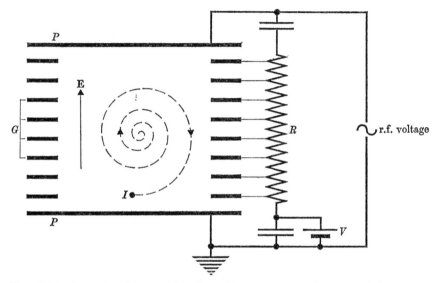

FIG. 23.19. Apparatus for measuring the cyclotron resonance frequency of the proton.
      **B**  is normal to the plane of the paper.
      *I*   ion collector.
      *V*  is a steady voltage of about 0·1 volt for focusing the ion beam.
      *R*  potentiometer system for guard rings.
      *G*  guard rings.
  *P, P*  plates.
      **E**  oscillatory electric field.

by the ion in its spiral journey from the origin to the collector. Thus
the resolving power primarily depends on the number of revolutions
which the ions make on their journey to the collector.

The apparatus used by Sommer, Thomas, and Hipple (1951) is shown
in Fig. 23.19. An oscillatory voltage is applied between two parallel
plates $P$, $P$ of size 3 cm $\times$ 5 cm, and separation 2 cm, with a number of
parallel guard rings. These rings are equally spaced, and by means of a
potentiometer system $R$ a fraction of the voltage proportional to the
distance from one end plate is applied to them so that a uniform r.f.
field is obtained. A small steady positive voltage of about 0·1 V is

applied to the guard rings relative to the end plates so as to retard the drift of positive ions in the direction parallel to the field **B**. The magnitude of **B** is determined by a nuclear magnetic resonance experiment, using an r.f. coil containing a sample of oil. Ions are produced along the axis of the apparatus by firing in a narrow beam of electrons of about 70 V energy, which cause ionization by collision with the residual gas. The pressure must be kept low ($\approx 10^{-6}$ mm Hg) in order to prevent scattering of the ions by collision. The whole assembly is enclosed in a glass tube of 4·7 cm diameter, which fits between the poles of an electromagnet.

In a typical experiment $B = 4700$ gauss, and the oscillatory field $E$ is about 0·1 V/cm at a frequency of about 7 Mc/s for the $H^+$ ion. With $R_0 = 1$ cm, the ions make about 7000 revolutions and attain an energy of about 1000 eV before reaching the ion collector, which is connected to an electrometer. The ion current at the peak of a resonance is about $3 \times 10^{-14}$ A while the background fluctuations are about $4 \times 10^{-16}$ A. Owing to the small positive voltage on the guard rings, and to space charge, a small radial electric field exists which displaces the resonant frequency slightly. In a radial field $E'$ the equation of motion is

$$M\omega^2 r + qE' = q\omega r B,$$

whence approximately     $$\omega = \omega_c\left[1 - \frac{E'M}{rqB^2}\right]. \qquad (23.24)$$

In practice it turns out that $E'$ increases linearly with $r$, and hence the shift in the resonance is independent of $r$, but proportional to $M$. Thus by making measurements both with $H^+$ and $H_2^+$ ions ($H^+$ and $D_2^+$ ions were also compared) the size of the shift can be determined.

Similar experiments have been carried out using an 'inverted' cyclotron, in which use is made of the ions which are retarded by the oscillatory field across the 'dees', rather than those which are accelerated, in order to obtain longer path lengths and higher resolution. These ions lose energy and spiral inwards until they reach a detector. This method, first used by Jeffries (1951), has been improved by the use of a modified system of decelerating electrodes in which the ions approach an asymptotic orbit in which the energy loss becomes zero (Sanders and Turberfield, 1963). The high resolving power thus obtained is further improved by using oscillatory fields at the eighth or sixteenth harmonic of the cyclotron frequency.

An alternative approach, used by Boyne and Franken (1961), is to detect the power absorbed by the ions from the oscillatory field, as in a nuclear resonance experiment. This has the advantage that low values of the oscillatory field can be used, so that the ion cloud is not appreciably disturbed by the power absorption. Boyne and Franken made measurements on $H_2^+$ ions at fields between 8 and 12·5 kilogauss, and corrected for electrostatic fields by using equation (23.24) and plotting $\omega$ back to $1/B^2 = 0$.

### Cyclotron resonance for free electrons

Analogous experiments can be carried out with electrons, the main difference in technique being due to the fact that in a field of a few kilogauss the resonance frequency is now at about $10^{10}$ c/s instead of about $10^7$ c/s. The first precise experiment (Gardner, 1951) was based on the fact that electrons moving in a narrow beam parallel to the magnetic field may gain energy from the cyclotron resonance effect and spiral outwards so that they fail to pass through a narrow slit guarding the collector. Thus the collector current should fall at resonance, but it was found that superimposed on this dip in current was a much sharper maximum, associated with space charge effects. In later experiments cyclotron resonance has been detected through the absorption of energy by free electrons from the oscillatory magnetic field, in a cavity resonator. Sanders, Tittel, and Ward (1963) used a current of about 1 $\mu A$ accelerated through about 1 V from a tungsten filament at one end of the cavity. Frequency shifts due to radial electric fields arising from space charge were eliminated by extrapolating the resonance frequency to zero current. Liebes and Franken (1959) carried out a similar experiment using some $10^4$–$10^5$ free electrons of about 1 eV energy, produced by photo-emission from a thin layer of potassium; they worked at field strengths between 750 and 1700 gauss, and extrapolated the resonance frequency to infinite field, as in the corresponding proton experiment.

### Results

In all such experiments the ratio of two frequencies in the same magnetic field is determined—the cyclotron resonance frequency of the electron ($\nu_e$) or proton ($\nu_c$), and the nuclear magnetic resonance frequency ($\nu_p$) of protons in water or a mineral oil. The main results are summarized in Table 23.3, which gives the ratios measured for protons and electrons, together with the quantity ($\nu_e/\nu_c$) obtained by combining a pair of these ratios, which should be equal to $M/m$, the ratio of masses of the proton and electron. If a correction of 28 p.p.m. is applied for diamagnetic shielding of the protons in the water or mineral oil sample, the measurements give the value of the nuclear magnetic moment of the proton in nuclear magnetons, since

$$\frac{\omega_{\rm p}}{\omega_{\rm c}} = \frac{2\pi\nu_{\rm p}}{2\pi\nu_{\rm c}} = \frac{g_n(e/2M)B}{(e/M)B} = \tfrac{1}{2}g_n$$

and the nuclear spin of the proton is $\tfrac{1}{2}$. If the cyclotron resonance of the electron is used instead of that of the proton, the nuclear moment of the proton is found in terms of the Bohr magneton. Apart from the

## Table 23.3

*Measurements of: column 1, ratio of proton magnetic resonance frequency $\nu_{\rm p}$ (in $H_2O$) to proton cyclotron resonance frequency $\nu_{\rm c}$; column 2, ratio of electron cyclotron frequency $\nu_{\rm e}$ to $\nu_{\rm p}$; column 3, ratio of $\nu_{\rm e}$ to $\nu_{\rm c}$ = ratio of masses of proton and electron, obtained from preceding ratios on the same line.*

| $\nu_{\rm p}/\nu_{\rm c}$ | | $\nu_{\rm e}/\nu_{\rm p}$ | | $\nu_{\rm e}/\nu_{\rm c} = M/m$ |
|---|---|---|---|---|
| 2·792 65(10) | J 1951 | | | |
| 2·792 68(6) | STH 1951 | 657·475(8) | G 1951 | 1836·12(5) |
| 2·792 83(6) | BF 1961 | 657·462(3) | LF 1959 | 1836·22(4) |
| 2·792 68(5) | ST 1963 | 657·462(2) | STW 1963 | 1836·08(3) |

The number in parentheses gives the probable error in the last digit; e.g. 1836·12(5) = 1836·12±0·05 (the accepted value is 1836·12(2)).

*References:*

| J | 1951 | Jeffries, 1951. |
|---|---|---|
| STH | 1951 | Sommer, Thomas, and Hipple (1951). |
| G | 1951 | Gardner (1951). |
| BF | 1961 | Boyne and Franken (1961). |
| LF | 1959 | Liebes and Franken (1959). |
| ST | 1963 | Sanders and Turberfield (1963). |
| STW | 1963 | Sanders, Tittel, and Ward (1963). |

cyclotron resonance experiment of Boyne and Franken, which gives a rather high value, the results agree closely, the mean value being

magnetic moment of proton = $2·79276(7)\beta_n = 1·521043(6)\times10^{-3}\beta$.

The ratios determined above may be written as

$$\frac{\omega_{\rm c}}{\omega_{\rm p}} = \frac{e/M}{\gamma_{\rm p}}, \qquad \frac{\omega_{\rm e}}{\omega_{\rm p}} = \frac{e/m}{\gamma_{\rm p}},$$

showing that by using the absolute value of $\gamma_{\rm p}$ measured at the Standards laboratories (see § 23.5) they give the specific charge of the proton $(e/M)$ and electron $(e/m)$ respectively. Multiplication of the former by the isotopic mass (1·00728) of the proton also gives the value of the Faraday, the charge required to liberate unit mass of an ion whose isotopic weight is unity. The results are all in good agreement with the accepted values.

### 23.9. Cyclotron resonance of charge carriers in semiconductors

It was pointed out in Chapters 18 and 19 that the equations of motion of electrons (and holes) in the periodic potential of a crystal lattice are similar to those of a free particle, provided that an effective mass $m^*$ is used instead of the true mass. This holds also for motion in a magnetic field, and the cyclotron resonance frequency therefore becomes

$$\omega_c = (q/m^*)B,$$

if the effective mass is isotropic. Determination of this frequency is thus of great importance since it gives a direct measurement of $m^*$. In principle, the experiment is similar to those described in the previous section: an oscillatory electric field is applied normal to the steady magnetic field, and either its frequency or the strength of the magnetic field is varied while the power absorbed is measured. However, the charge carriers in a solid make collisions at a rate which is usually comparable with (and often much higher than) the cyclotron resonance frequency; this gives a very important damping term, and the equation of motion may be written as (cf. Problem 3.9)

$$m^*\left\{\frac{d\mathbf{v}}{dt}+\frac{1}{\tau}\,\mathbf{v}\right\} = q\{\mathbf{E}+\mathbf{v}\wedge\mathbf{B}\}, \tag{23.25}$$

where $q = -e$ for electrons and $+e$ for holes.

To solve this equation we assume that $\mathbf{B}$ is along the $z$-axis of a Cartesian coordinate system, and $\mathbf{E}$ is an oscillatory field along the $x$-axis. We therefore write $E_x = E_0\exp(j\omega t)$, and look for the steady state solution corresponding to the driven motion at angular frequency $\omega$; we can then replace $d/dt$ by $j\omega$, and the equations become

$$\left.\begin{aligned}
\left(j\omega+\frac{1}{\tau}\right)v_x &= \frac{q}{m^*}\,(E_x+v_yB)\\[2mm]
\left(j\omega+\frac{1}{\tau}\right)v_y &= -\frac{q}{m^*}\,v_x B\\[2mm]
\left(j\omega+\frac{1}{\tau}\right)v_z &= 0
\end{aligned}\right\}. \tag{23.26}$$

The last equation shows that any momentary current in the $z$-direction dies away exponentially through collisions, and we may eliminate $v_y$ between the first two equations in order to find the oscillatory velocity $v_x$ in the direction of the applied electric field. This gives

$$v_x\left\{\omega_c^2-\omega^2+\frac{1}{\tau^2}+\frac{2j\omega}{\tau}\right\} = \frac{q}{m^*}\,E_x\left(\frac{1}{\tau}+j\omega\right),$$

where we have written $\omega_c$ for $(q/m^*)B$, the cyclotron resonance frequency. The conductivity of the solid at angular frequency $\omega$ in the $x$-direction is $\sigma_x = nqv_x/E_x$, where $n$ is the number of charge carriers per unit volume of mass $m^*$, and is given by the relation

$$\sigma_x = \frac{nq^2}{m^*}\left\{\frac{j\omega+1/\tau}{(\omega_c^2-\omega^2)+1/\tau^2+2j\omega/\tau}\right\}$$

$$= \sigma_0\left\{\frac{1+j\omega\tau}{1+2j\omega\tau+\tau^2(\omega_c^2-\omega^2)}\right\}, \tag{23.27}$$

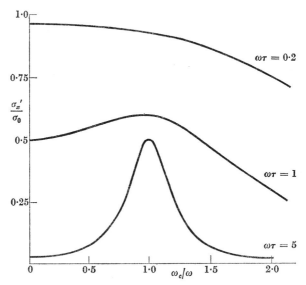

FIG. 23.20. Plot of the ratio of the r.f. conductivity to the d.c. conductivity against $(\omega_c/\omega)$. Cyclotron resonance measurements are usually made at constant $\omega$ and variable field; since $\omega_c$ is proportional to $B$, the curves show the conductivity against $B$ (on a reduced scale). Well resolved resonance curves are obtained when $\omega\tau$ is rather greater than unity.

where $\sigma_0 = n(q^2/m^*)\tau$ is the ordinary conductivity of the substance at zero frequency in the absence of a magnetic field. This equation shows that the high-frequency conductivity is complex; on solving for the real part $\sigma_x'$ of the conductivity, we find

$$\frac{\sigma_x'}{\sigma_0} = \frac{1+\tau^2(\omega_c^2+\omega^2)}{\{1+\tau^2(\omega_c^2-\omega^2)\}^2+4\omega^2\tau^2}. \tag{23.28}$$

The power absorption per unit volume of the sample is $\frac{1}{2}\sigma_x' E_x^2$; since it is usual to work at fixed frequency $\omega$ and measure the power absorption as $B$ (i.e. $\omega_c$) is varied, it is useful to plot the quantity $(\sigma_x'/\sigma_0)$ as a function of $(\omega_c/\omega)$ for various values of the parameter $\omega\tau$. This is shown in Fig. 23.20. When $\omega\tau$ is appreciably less than unity, the mean time between collisions is a small fraction of an r.f. period, and little change occurs until $\omega\tau$ approaches unity. However, when $\omega\tau$ is rather greater than unity, a distinct resonance effect is observed, with maximum power absorption at a point close to the cyclotron resonance frequency.

In a semiconductor or metal at room temperature the value of $\tau$ is about $10^{-12}$ to $10^{-14}$ seconds, so that even at a wavelength of 1 cm,

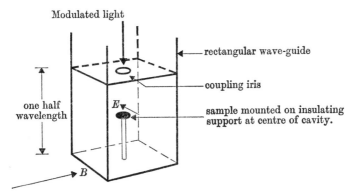

Modulated light

rectangular wave-guide

coupling iris

one half wavelength

$E$

sample mounted on insulating support at centre of cavity.

$B$

FIG. 23.21. Waveguide cavity resonator used in cyclotron resonance experiments, showing the sample mounted at the centre of the cavity where the oscillatory electric field is a maximum. Carriers can be excited in the sample by light passed down the waveguide and through the coupling iris linking the cavity to the guide.

where a magnetic field at resonance of about $10^4$ gauss would be needed if $m^* = m$, the value of $\omega\tau$ is about $2 \times 10^{-1}$ to $2 \times 10^{-3}$. However, the electron scattering is mainly due to phonons, and is reduced at low temperatures. In a semiconductor (see § 19.5) $\tau$ should vary as $T^{-\frac{3}{2}}$, and a factor of $10^3$ is gained in going from $300°$ to $3°$ K, making $\omega\tau \sim 2$ to 200. As can be seen from Fig. 23.20, this is sufficient for a fairly accurate determination of the resonance frequency. However, the number of charge carriers $n$, which (see § 19.5) varies as $T^{\frac{3}{2}} \exp(-W_g/2kT)$ for a pure semiconductor, becomes vanishingly small at helium temperatures. Dexter, Zeiger, and Lax (1956) overcame this difficulty by irradiating the sample with light of sufficiently short wavelength to lift electrons across the energy gap from the valence to the conduction band, thus creating both holes and conduction electrons. The main features of their apparatus are shown in Fig. 23.21. The sample, in the form of a thin disk some 3 mm in diameter and 0·5 mm thick, is mounted at a point in a waveguide cavity where the oscillatory electric field is as large as possible without producing serious carrier heating effects through acceleration of the carriers. This cavity terminates a wave-guide, and the change in the signal reflected by the cavity is a measure of the increased power absorption in the sample. The cavity is immersed in liquid helium in a dewar vessel placed between the poles of an electromagnet.

The most satisfactory method of detection is to modulate the light beam by passing it through a rotating disk pierced by a large number of holes. The lifetime of the carriers is short and they are present only for the duration of a light pulse; the reflected microwave signal is there-fore modulated at the same frequency (usually 100 to 1000 c/s). Instead of using irradiation by light, carriers can also be created through ioniza-tion of impurity levels by application of an electric field across the sample, or by the oscillatory microwave electric field. The latter method gives distorted line-shapes, however, since the number of secondary carriers created depends on the carrier energy and this is a maximum at resonance. It has the advantage that only electrons are created in $n$-type material, and holes in $p$-type, since the microwave energy is only sufficient to cause ionization across the small gap ($\sim 0 \cdot 01$ eV in Ge) of impurity levels, and not across the main gap $W_g$.

In many substances the effective mass is anisotropic (see § 18.2), and the ratio of cyclotron resonance frequency to magnetic field is a function of the orientation of the field relative to the crystal axes. For this reason a single crystal must be used, with either a special device for rotating it in the cavity, or for rotating the external magnetic field, so that a whole plane of directions relative to the external magnetic field can be explored. An absorption curve for a given orientation of germanium is given in Fig. 23.22; it is due to Dresselhaus, Kip, and Kittel (1955), who made the first observations of cyclotron resonance in semiconductors in 1953. When anisotropy is present, the equations of motion are modified and must be solved to find the relation between the cyclotron resonance frequency and the effective mass parameters; the following method for this is due to Shockley (1953).

When the energy surfaces are not spherical in $k$-space, they can be approximated near the band edges (see § 18.2) by equations such as

$$W = \tfrac{1}{2}\hbar^2 \left\{ \frac{k_x^2}{m_x} + \frac{k_y^2}{m_y} + \frac{k_z^2}{m_z} \right\} = \frac{1}{2} \left\{ \frac{p_x^2}{m_x} + \frac{p_y^2}{m_y} + \frac{p_z^2}{m_z} \right\},$$

provided that the directions of the $x$-, $y$-, $z$-axes are chosen correctly. Along these axes the components of the equation of motion have their usual form, so that in a magnetic field with components $B_x$, $B_y$, $B_z$ we have

$$m_x(dv_x/dt) = q(v_y B_z - v_z B_y), \quad \text{etc.}$$

To find the cyclotron resonance frequency for a particular energy surface we assume a sinusoidal motion with frequency $(\omega_c/2\pi)$; on

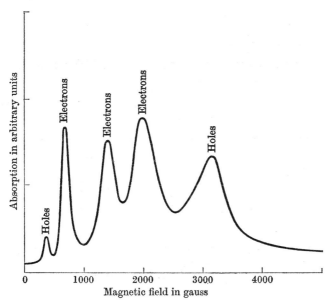

FIG. 23.22. Absorption curve for cyclotron resonance in a single crystal of germanium, at 24 000 Mc/s and 4° K. The static field is in a (110) plane at 60° from a [100] axis. Three electron resonance lines are observed because $B_0$ makes three different angles with the four [111] axes, which are the major axes of the four energy ellipsoids in Ge (after Dresselhaus, Kip, and Kittel, 1955).

replacing $d/dt$ by $j\omega_c$ we obtain the set of linear equations

$$j\omega_c m_x v_x - q v_y B_z + q v_z B_y = 0,$$
$$j\omega_c m_y v_y - q v_z B_x + q v_x B_z = 0,$$
$$j\omega_c m_z v_z - q v_x B_y + q v_y B_x = 0,$$

which have an allowed solution only if the determinant

$$\begin{Vmatrix} j\omega_c m_x & -qB_z & qB_y \\ qB_z & j\omega_c m_y & -qB_x \\ -qB_y & qB_x & j\omega_c m_z \end{Vmatrix} = 0.$$

This gives either $\omega_c = 0$ (corresponding to $\mathbf{v}$ parallel to $\mathbf{B}$), or

$$\omega_c^2 = \frac{q^2}{m_x m_y m_z}(m_x B_x^2 + m_y B_y^2 + m_z B_z^2). \qquad (23.29)$$

This equation shows that the cyclotron resonance frequency depends on the orientation of the magnetic field with respect to the crystal axes; in any given plane a plot of $\omega_c^2$ against angle gives a (cosine)$^2$ variation between the maximum and minimum values. When **B** is directed along one of the principal axes, such as the $z$-axis for an ellipsoidal energy surface, $(\omega_c)_z = qB/(m_x m_y)^{\frac{1}{2}}$; thus by measurement along each axis in turn, the principal values $m_x$, $m_y$, $m_z$ of the effective mass can be determined. The results for the elemental semiconductors Si, Ge, together with those for indium antimonide are shown in Table 23.4. For silicon

TABLE 23.4

*Effective masses in some semiconductors determined by cyclotron resonance, relative to the free electron mass*

| Substance | Electrons | | Holes | |
|---|---|---|---|---|
| | $m_L^*$ | $m_T^*$ | 'light' | 'heavy' |
| Si | 0·98 | 0·19 | 0·16 | 0·5 |
| Ge | 1·64 | 0·082 | 0·044 | 0·3 |
| InSb | 0·014 (isotropic) | | 0·02 | 0·4 |

*References*:

Si, Ge  R. N. Dexter, H. J. Zeiger, and B. Lax, 1956, *Phys. Rev.* **104**, 637.
InSb  Electrons—various authors.
  Holes—D. M. S. Bagguley, M. L. A. Robinson, and R. A. Stradling, 1963, *Phys. Letters* **6**, 143.

and germanium two of the principal values of the effective mass at the bottom of the conduction band are equal; this is known as the 'transverse mass', $m_T^*$, while the third (unequal) mass is called the longitudinal mass, $m_L^*$. In InSb the minimum of the conduction band occurs at $\mathbf{k} = 0$ (see § 19.4), and the effective mass is isotropic.

The position at the top of the valence band is more complicated. Two energy surfaces coincide at $\mathbf{k} = 0$, and at points near-by in $k$-space the energy surfaces for Si, Ge are given by the relation

$$W = Ak^2 \pm \{B^2k^4 + C^2(k_x^2 k_y^2 + k_y^2 k_z^2 + k_z^2 k_x^2)\}^{\frac{1}{2}}, \qquad (23.30)$$

which is also approximately correct for III–V semiconductors. If $C$ is small the two surfaces are nearly spherical, but with different curvature, corresponding to two different effective masses known as the 'light' and 'heavy' holes (see Table 23.4), giving resonance lines as in Fig. 23.22.

## 23.10. Azbel–Kaner resonance in metals

When a spectral line due to moving particles is observed, it is broadened through the Doppler effect, by an amount which is proportional to the random particle velocity. In a semiconductor at low temperatures, the electrons or holes have ordinary thermal velocities corresponding to energies of order $kT$, and broadening by the Doppler effect is not important. In a metal, on the other hand, the electron velocity is that at the Fermi surface; in copper, assuming $m^*/m = 1.5$ and $W_F = 4.7$ eV, this velocity is about $10^6$ m/sec, while the phase velocity in the metal of an electromagnetic wave with a free-space wavelength of 1 cm is only about $4 \times 10^4$ m/sec (from equation (10.30) it is equal to $\omega\delta$, where $\delta$ is the skin depth). Broadening through the Doppler effect thus makes it impossible to observe cyclotron resonance in metals by methods similar to those used for semiconductors. It can, however, be detected by a different method, originally due to Azbel and Kaner (1957, 1958).

As before, a reasonable degree of resolution is obtained only if $\omega\tau > 1$. This makes it essential to work at liquid helium temperatures, using very pure samples in which the residual resistivity due to electron scattering by impurities and imperfections is as small as possible ($10^{-3}$ to $10^{-5}$ of the room temperature resistivity). In copper the radius of the electron orbit in the magnetic field required to make the cyclotron resonance frequency equal to $3 \times 10^{10}$ c/s is about $5 \times 10^{-6}$ metres, and the mean path length of the electrons must be of this order in order to make $\omega\tau > 1$. This requires a conductivity greater than $10^{10}$ (ohm-metre)$^{-1}$, and the 'classical' skin depth given by equation (10.31) is about $3 \times 10^{-8}$ metres, which is small compared with the mean path length. This is the region of the 'anomalous skin effect', where the conductivity is effectively reduced because only those electrons moving at a small angle to the surface such that their free paths lie wholly within the skin depth contribute fully to the oscillatory current. However, even allowing for this, the 'anomalous' skin depth (see Problem 18.5) is about $2 \times 10^{-7}$ metre, which is still small compared with the radius of the cyclotron orbit. If then a magnetic field **B** is applied parallel to the surface of the metal, a certain number of electrons moving in helical orbits about **B** will enter the skin-depth region once per cycle, and while in this region they can be accelerated by the oscillatory electric field component normal or parallel to **B**. The latter geometry is illustrated in Fig. 23.23; an important difference from the conventional cyclotron is that acceleration occurs only once per revolution instead of twice. Electrons will gain energy steadily if the frequency of the electromagnetic wave incident on the surface of the metal is synchronous with the cyclotron resonance frequency, or is an integral multiple of it. Hence the resonance condition is

$$\omega = p\omega_c = p(q/m^*)B, \tag{23.31}$$

where $p = 1, 2, 3$, etc. It is usually convenient to work at a fixed frequency, making the metal sample one end of a cavity resonator as in ferromagnetic resonance (but with **B** normal or parallel to the oscillatory electric field instead of normal to the oscillatory magnetic field),

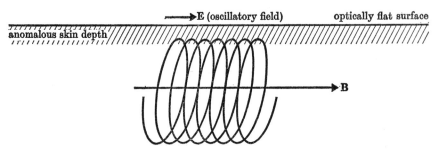

FIG. 23.23. Geometry of the steady magnetic field **B**, the oscillatory electric field and the cyclotron orbits in a metal for Azbel–Kaner resonance. The electrons are accelerated by the electric field only when their orbits take them into the skin depth.

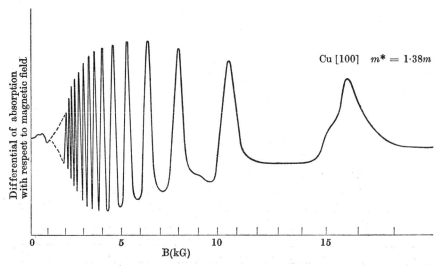

FIG. 23.24. Azbel–Kaner resonance at 4° K in a single crystal of copper (after Koch, Stradling, and Kip, 1964). The magnetic field is parallel to the surface and along a [100] direction; the frequency is 67 kMc/s (4·5 mm wavelength).

and maxima in the absorption of energy then occur at values of $B$ given by the relation

$$B_p = \frac{1}{p}\left(\frac{m^*\omega}{q}\right). \qquad (23.32)$$

To obtain a resonance peak the electrons must complete a cyclotron orbit without experiencing a collision. This condition can be written as $\omega_c\tau \geqslant 1$, and since $\omega_c = \omega/p$ it is a more stringent condition than $\omega\tau \geqslant 1$.

From equation (23.32) it follows that this condition is more difficult to satisfy at low values of $B$, but in experimental charts similar to Fig. 23.24 peaks have been observed down to magnetic fields of about 1 kilogauss (values of $p$ up to 30).

Samples of high purity are needed to give good resolution; ideally they must be so flat that surface irregularities are small compared with the anomalous skin depth. If the effective mass is anisotropic, single crystals must be used, cut in special orientations so that cyclotron resonance can be observed in all the principal directions. The steady magnetic field **B** must be accurately parallel to the surface, or electrons will move away from the surface because of their velocity components parallel to **B**. As the electrons can drift distances of the order of $10^{-5}$ metres in one cyclotron period and the skin depth is of the order $10^{-7}$ metres, the magnetic field must be aligned parallel to the surface to much better than $1°$; this is necessary to ensure that the electrons return to the same distance from the surface—otherwise they would experience a Doppler-shifted electric field. Grimes and Kip (1963) have found that the effective mass is isotropic in sodium and potassium, with values of $m^*/m$ equal to $1·24\pm0·02$ and $1·21\pm0·02$ respectively. In copper (Koch, Stradling, and Kip, 1964) the predominant absorption is due to electrons with $m^*/m$ about equal to $1·4$, with only slight anisotropy, but other very anisotropic values ranging from $0·4$ to $6$ are also observed, showing that the Fermi surface is rather complicated.

## REFERENCES

ALVAREZ, L. W., and BLOCH, F., 1940, *Phys. Rev.* **57**, 111.
AZBEL, M. YA., and KANER, E. A., 1957, *Soviet Phys. J.E.T.P.* **5**, 730.
—— —— 1958, *J. Phys. Chem. Solids*, **6**, 113.
BLOCH, F., HANSEN, W. W., and PACKARD, M., 1946, *Phys. Rev.* **69**, 127.
BLOEMBERGEN, N., PURCELL, E. M., and POUND, R. V., 1948, ibid. **73**, 679.
BOYNE, H. S., and FRANKEN, P. A., 1961, ibid. **123**, 242.
BROWN, R. M., and PURCELL, E. M., 1949, ibid. **75**, 1262.
COHEN, V. W., CORNGOLD, N. R., and RAMSEY, N. F., 1956, ibid. **104**, 283.
COHEN, E. R., DUMOND, J. W. M., LAYTON, T. W., and ROLLETT, R. S., 1955, *Rev. Mod. Phys.* **27**, 363.
DEXTER, R. N., ZEIGER, H. J., and LAX, B., 1956, *Phys. Rev.* **104**, 637.
DRESSELHAUS, G., KIP, A. F., and KITTEL, C., 1955, ibid. **98**, 368.
DRISCOLL, R. L., and BENDER, P. L., 1958, *Phys. Rev. Letters* **1**, 413.
ESSEN, L., and PARRY, J. V. L., 1957, *Phil. Trans.* A, **250**, 45.
GARDNER, J. H., 1951, *Phys. Rev.* **83**, 996.
GRIFFITHS, J. H. E., 1946, *Nature, Lond.* **158**, 670.
GRIMES, C. C., and KIP, A. F., 1963, *Phys. Rev.* **132**, 1991.
HELLER, P., and BENEDEK, G. B., 1962, *Phys. Rev. Letters* **8**, 428.
JEFFRIES, C. D., 1951, *Phys. Rev.* **81**, 1040.

KITTEL, C., 1948, ibid. **73**, 155.

KOCH, J. F., STRADLING, R. A., and KIP, A. F., 1964, ibid. **133**, A240.

KUSCH, P., 1955, ibid. **100**, 1188.

—— and FOLEY, H. M., 1948, ibid. **72**, 1256; **74**, 250.

LAMB, W. E., and RETHERFORD, R. C., 1947, ibid. **72**, 241.

LIEBES, S., and FRANKEN, P. A., 1959, ibid. **116**, 633.

MARKOWITZ, W., HALL, R. G., ESSEN, L., and PARRY, J. W. L., 1958, *Phys. Rev. Letters* **1**, 105.

PHILLIPS, T. G., and ROSENBERG, H. M., 1964, *Phys. Letters* **8**, 298.

PURCELL, E. M., 1948, *Science*, **107**, 433.

—— and RAMSEY, N. F., 1950, *Phys. Rev.* **78**, 699.

—— TORREY, H. C., and POUND, R. V., 1946, ibid. **69**, 37.

RABI, I. I., MILLMAN, S., KUSCH, P., and ZACHARIAS, J. R., 1939, ibid. **55**, 526.

RAMSEY, N. F., 1949, ibid. **76**, 996.

SANDERS, J. H., TITTEL, K. F., and WARD, J. F., 1963, *Proc. Roy. Soc.* A, **272**, 103.

SANDERS, J. H., and TURBERFIELD, K. C., 1963, ibid. **79**.

SHOCKLEY, W., 1953, *Phys. Rev.* **90**, 491.

SHULMAN, R. G., and JACCARINO, V., 1956, ibid. **103**, 1126.

SMITH, J. H., PURCELL, E. M., and RAMSEY, N. F., 1957, ibid. **108**, 120.

SOMMER, H., THOMAS, H. A., and HIPPLE, J. A., 1951, ibid. **82**, 697.

SOMMERFIELD, C. M., 1957, ibid. **107**, 328.

THOMAS, H. A., DRISCOLL, R. L., and HIPPLE, J. A., 1950, ibid. **78**, 787.

VIGOUREUX, P., 1962, *Proc. Roy. Soc.* A, **270**, 72.

WIMETT, T. F., 1953, *Phys. Rev.* **91**, 499.

WITTKE, J. P., and DICKE, R. H., 1956, ibid. **103**, 620.

## GENERAL REFERENCES

ANDREW, E. R., 1955, *Nuclear Magnetic Resonance* (C.U.P.).

INGRAM, D. J. E., 1955, *Spectroscopy at Radio and Microwave Frequencies* (Butterworth).

ROBINSON, F. N. H., 1959, *J. Scient. Instrum.* **36**, 481.

SANDERS, J. H. 1965, *The Fundamental Atomic Constants* (2nd edn., O.U.P.).

SERIES, G. W., 1957, *The Spectrum of Atomic Hydrogen* (O.U.P.).

## PROBLEMS

23.1. In a substance where the susceptibility is small and the Lorentz internal field can be neglected, show that equation (17.12) can be written in the form

$$\chi' - j\chi'' = \frac{n_0 e^2}{m\epsilon_0} \frac{1}{(\omega_p^2 - \omega^2) + 2j\omega\,\Delta\omega}.$$

If $\chi_0$ is the static susceptibility, and $\chi_p''$ is the imaginary part of the susceptibility when $\omega = \omega_p$, prove that

$$\chi_p''/\chi_0 = \omega_p/(2\Delta\omega) = \nu_p/(2\Delta\nu),$$

where $\nu_p$ is the frequency at the centre of the absorption line, and $\Delta\nu = \Delta\omega/2\pi$. Although this formula was derived for electric susceptibility it is equally valid for the magnetic case.

23.2. The work done per unit volume to increase the magnetization of a substance by $dM$ in a field $B$ is $dW = B\,dM$. If $B$ is an alternating field

$$B_1 \cos \omega t = \mathscr{R}\{B_1 \exp(j\omega t)\},$$

the magnetization may be written as

$$M = \mathscr{R}\{(\chi' - j\chi'')(B_1/\mu_0)\exp(j\omega t)\},$$

where $(\chi' - j\chi'')$ is the complex susceptibility. Show that the rate of doing work per unit volume is

$$B\frac{dM}{dt} = dW/dt = -\omega\chi'(B_1^2/\mu_0)\cos \omega t \sin \omega t + \omega\chi''(B_1^2/\mu_0)\cos^2\omega t$$

and the mean power dissipated per unit volume is $\frac{1}{2}\omega\chi''B_1^2/\mu_0$.

Use the definition $(f)$ for $Q$ given in § 9.3 to show that $1/Q = \chi''/(1+\chi')$ for a coil containing a magnetic substance in a tuned circuit with no other losses.

23.3. Adapt the results of Problem 10.6 to the case of the magnetic substance of the last problem (note that $\chi''/(1+\chi')$ is equivalent to $\epsilon''/\epsilon'$), and show that the power in an electromagnetic wave passing through such a medium would fall according to the law

$$W/W_0 = \exp(-2\pi\chi''x/\lambda)$$

if $\chi' \ll 1$.

Verify the figures given in § 23.3, that for $\lambda = 35$ metres and $\chi'' = 10^{-5}$, the power will fall by about 1·8 per cent in a distance of 10 km.

23.4. Show, from equations (23.21) and (23.22) that the instantaneous velocity of the charged particle in its spiral orbit is $(qE/M\Delta\omega)\sin(\frac{1}{2}\Delta\omega t)$. Hence show that the total length of path traversed by the particle in reaching its maximum radius $R_0$ when $\Delta\omega \neq 0$ is $L = 2qE/M(\Delta\omega)^2$, and verify that $L/2R_0$ is equal to the resolving power $\omega_c/\Delta\omega$.

23.5. Adapt the formula of Problem 20.4 to find the value of $g_F$ when $J$ and $I$ are coupled to form a resultant $F$, assuming that the nuclear magnetic moment can be neglected. Show that in the Zeeman splitting of Fig. 23.12,

$$g_{F=4} = -g_{F=3} = \tfrac{1}{8}g_J = \tfrac{1}{4}.$$

23.6. Kusch and Foley (1948), using the atomic beam method, determined the ratio of the value of $g_J$ in the $^2P_{\frac{3}{2}}$ and $^2P_{\frac{1}{2}}$ states of the gallium atom, and found it to be $2(1\cdot00172\pm0\cdot00006)$. Show, by writing $g_l = 1+\delta_l$ and $g_s = 2(1+\delta_s)$, that the ratio is equal to $2\{1+\frac{3}{2}(\delta_s-\delta_l)\}$, and hence that their result agrees within the experimental error with the accepted value $\delta_s = 0\cdot001160$ if $\delta_l$ is assumed to be zero.

23.7. A thin spherical shell of radius $r$, thickness $dr$ of electric charge density $\rho$ rotates with angular velocity $\boldsymbol{\omega}$ about a diameter. Show that the magnetic field $d\mathbf{B}$ at the centre is $-\frac{2}{3}\mu_0 \rho\boldsymbol{\omega}r\,dr$.

Use this result to show that the correction at the nucleus of a hydrogen atom in a magnetic field $\mathbf{B}$ due to diamagnetic shielding (see § 23.5) is

$$\frac{\delta B}{B} = -\frac{\mu_0 e^2}{12\pi m a_0},$$

given that the charge density at distance $r$ is

$$\rho = (-e/\pi a_0^3)\exp(-2r/a_0).$$

23.8. Show from equation (23.28) that the conductivity at zero frequency in the direction normal to a magnetic field $B$ varies as

$$\sigma_x'/\sigma_0 = 1/(1+aB^2),$$

where $a = (e\tau/m^*)^2$. This is the magneto-resistance effect, which becomes appreciable only at low temperatures where $\tau$ increases. (When only one type of carrier is present, the effect vanishes because the sideways force due to the magnetic field is exactly nullified by that due to the Hall voltage; when more than one type of charge carrier is present this cancellation does not occur.)

23.9. Show that in a cyclotron resonance experiment where $\omega\tau \gg 1$, the value of $\sigma_x'$ at resonance ($\omega_c/\omega = 1$) approaches $\frac{1}{2}\sigma_0$, and that the loss tangent of the specimen is then (writing $\Delta\omega_e$ for $\tau^{-1}$)

$$\tan\delta_e = \frac{ne^2}{2m^*\omega\epsilon\epsilon_0\Delta\omega_e}.$$

Use the result of Problem 23.1 to show that in an electron spin resonance experiment the magnetic loss tangent at resonance for a system of $n$ electrons with $S = \frac{1}{2}, g = 2$ is

$$\tan\delta_m = \frac{\chi_p''}{1+\chi_0} \approx \frac{\mu_0 n\beta^2\omega}{2kT\,\Delta\omega_m}$$

and hence prove that (taking $m^* = m$, $\Delta\omega_e = \Delta\omega_m$)

$$\frac{\tan\delta_e}{\tan\delta_m} = \frac{4mc^2kT}{\epsilon(\hbar\omega)^2}.$$

Hence verify that the inherent sensitivity of a cyclotron resonance experiment is very much higher than that of a spin resonance experiment, so that fewer electrons are needed.

Discuss whether the imaginary part of the conductivity (see equation (23.27)) can justifiably be neglected in the formula for $\tan\delta_e$.

# 24

## UNITS

### 24.1. Unrationalized c.g.s. systems

IN mechanics three quantities are required to define a system of units: standards of length, mass, and time. In the c.g.s. system these standards are the centimetre, the gramme, and the second respectively. Many alternative non-metric systems are in everyday use, but not in scientific use; it is obviously possible, however, to use different metric units as the standards, and the m.k.s. system is based on the metre, the kilogramme, and the second. For mechanical purposes either system will do, and units in one system are readily converted into those of the other system (they differ only by powers of 10). In electricity, a fourth standard quantity must be defined, and the multiplicity of systems of units is due to the varying choices of this standard which are in general use. Two alternative systems have survived, one based on the law of force between electric charges, and the other on the corresponding law between magnetic poles. Both of these systems are c.g.s. systems, since their units of length, mass, and time are the same, centimetre, gramme, and second respectively. All mechanical quantities, such as force or work, have the same units in either system, but the electrical units are quite different. Many of the units are of unsuitable size for ordinary work, and so another set of units, the practical system, has also come into common use. This is not a c.g.s. system, since mechanical quantities such as power, obtained from the product of current and voltage measured in practical units, are not in c.g.s. units. The basis of these three systems of units is outlined below.

*Unrationalized electrostatic units (e.s.u.)*

In this system the c.g.s. units of length, mass, and time are used, and a fourth unit, that of electrical charge, is defined by means of Coulomb's law (*in vacuo*)
$$F = q_1 q_2 / r^2, \tag{24.1}$$
where the unknown constant $C$ which appears in equation (1.1) has been set equal to unity. From equation (24.1) the electrostatic unit of charge is defined as that charge which, placed a distance of one centimetre away *in vacuo* from an exactly equal charge, repels it with a force of one dyne.

The unit of electric field is then defined by the equation

$$\mathbf{F} = q\mathbf{E} \tag{24.2}$$

as that field which exerts a force of one dyne on one unit of charge. Again, the potential at a point $B$ is one electrostatic unit higher than that at a point $A$ if one erg of work must be done to move unit charge from $A$ to $B$. Since the capacitance of a capacitor is the ratio of the charge on it to the potential difference between the plates, it follows that a capacitor has unit capacitance if, when unit charge is placed on it, unit potential difference is set up between the plates. Since potential has the dimensions of (work/charge), capacitance has the dimensions of (charge)²/work, and from equation (24.1) this reduces simply to a length. Hence the e.s.u. of capacitance is the centimetre.

The e.s.u. of electric dipole moment is defined as unit charge times unit distance (centimetre), and the potential which a dipole $\mathbf{p}$ produces at a distance $r$ is $V = p\cos\theta/r^2$. Polarization $\mathbf{P}$ is the dipole moment per unit volume, and hence has the dimensions (charge)/(length)², which are the same as those of electric field. In the absence of any polarizable medium, Gauss's theorem (equation (1.7 b)) becomes in e.s.u.

$$\int \mathbf{E}.\,d\mathbf{S} = 4\pi \sum q, \tag{24.3}$$

or in differential form $\qquad \text{div } \mathbf{E} = 4\pi\rho, \tag{24.4}$

where $\sum q$ is the total charge in the volume over which the integral is taken, and $\rho$ is the charge density. When a polarizable medium is present, the volume charge density becomes, on including the polarization charge, $\rho - \text{div } \mathbf{P}$, and hence Gauss's theorem takes the form

$$\int \mathbf{E}.\,d\mathbf{S} = 4\pi(\rho - \text{div } \mathbf{P}),$$

or $\qquad \int (\mathbf{E}+4\pi\mathbf{P}).\,d\mathbf{S} = \int \mathbf{D}.\,d\mathbf{S} = 4\pi\rho, \tag{24.5}$

so that the electric displacement $\mathbf{D}$ is defined as

$$\mathbf{D} = \mathbf{E}+4\pi\mathbf{P}. \tag{24.6}$$

We see that the factor $(4\pi)$, which does not appear in Coulomb's law, now appears in Gauss's theorem, and in the relation between $\mathbf{D}$, $\mathbf{E}$, and $\mathbf{P}$. Also, the units of $\mathbf{D}$, $\mathbf{E}$, and $\mathbf{P}$ all appear to be the same; this is true only in e.s.u. and is not true, for example, in e.m.u. The electric susceptibility $\chi_e$ and dielectric constant $\epsilon$ are defined by the relations

$$\mathbf{P} = \chi_e\,\mathbf{E}, \tag{24.7}$$

$$\mathbf{D} = \epsilon\mathbf{E}, \tag{24.8}$$

so that the relation between them is

$$\epsilon = 1 + 4\pi\chi_e. \qquad (24.9)$$

The dielectric constant is the same as in the m.k.s. system (it is simply the ratio of the capacitance of a capacitor filled with the dielectric to that of the same capacitor *in vacuo*), but the susceptibility differs by the factor $4\pi$. In the m.k.s. system the susceptibility of a substance (per unit volume = per metre$^3$) is a number a factor ($4\pi$) larger than the corresponding number in e.s.u. (per unit volume = per cm$^3$).

Since electric current is the rate at which charge flows past a given point, the e.s.u. of current is equal to a flow of one e.s.u. of charge per second. In current electricity and magnetism it is customary to work in e.m.u. instead of e.s.u., and we shall now discuss this second c.g.s. system.

*Unrationalized electromagnetic units (e.m.u.)*

Originally the electromagnetic system of units was based on Coulomb's law for the force between two magnetic charges (or magnetic poles) and the unit of pole strength was defined by setting the constant in the equation equal to unity, so that (*in vacuo*)

$$F = m_1 m_2 / r^2. \qquad (24.10)$$

Thus unit magnetic pole is that which exerts a force of 1 dyne on a similar pole a distance of one centimetre away *in vacuo*. The laws of magnetostatics are then developed formally in the same way as those of electrostatics, the quantities $\mathbf{B}$, $\mathbf{H}$, $\mathbf{M}$, $\mathbf{m}$, $\chi_m$, and $\mu$ playing similar roles to those of $\mathbf{D}$, $\mathbf{E}$, $\mathbf{P}$, $\mathbf{p}$, $\chi_e$, and $\epsilon$. For example

$$\mathbf{B} = \mathbf{H} + 4\pi\mathbf{M} \qquad (24.11)$$

and

$$\mu = 1 + 4\pi\chi_m. \qquad (24.12)$$

Hence the magnetic volume susceptibility of a substance in the m.k.s. system is a number larger by a factor ($4\pi$) than the corresponding number for the volume susceptibility in the e.m.u. system.

The connexion with electric current is made either by means of the magnetic field produced by the current, or by defining the equivalent magnetic dipole moment of a small coil of area $\mathbf{dS}$ carrying a current $I$ as

$$\mathbf{m} = I\,\mathbf{dS}. \qquad (24.13)$$

Since the units of $\mathbf{m}$ and $\mathbf{dS}$ are already defined, this fixes the unit of current. Alternatively, the electromagnetic system of units could be developed from the same starting-point as used in Chapter 5, the experiments of Ampère. Then the equivalent of equation (5.2) for the force between two current elements would be

$$\mathbf{dF}_1 = I_1 I_2 \{\mathbf{ds}_1 \wedge (\mathbf{ds}_2 \wedge \mathbf{r})\}/r^3 \qquad (24.14)$$

and the unit of current could be defined by means of the force between two equal currents in parallel conductors, as in § 5.1.

We have now two alternative units of current, the e.s.u. and the e.m.u., which we have no reason to suppose bear any simple relation to one another. If we assume that there are no dimensional constants in equations (24.1) or (24.10), we can work out the dimensions of electrical quantities in terms of length, mass, and time (they appear rather queer, involving (mass)$^{\frac{1}{2}}$ for example), and the dimensions of current in the two systems will also be different. The ratio of current in e.s.u. to current in e.m.u. has the dimensions of a velocity, and it turns out that the ratio of the quantities in the two systems is just the velocity of electromagnetic waves *in vacuo*, $c$ (in c.g.s. units). Hence

$$\frac{\text{number specifying current in e.s.u.}}{\text{number specifying same current in e.m.u.}} = c = 3 \times 10^{10} \text{ (approx.).}$$

In both e.s.u. and e.m.u. the product of current and potential is power in erg/second, and hence

$$\frac{\text{number specifying potential in e.s.u.}}{\text{number specifying same potential in e.m.u.}} = 1/c.$$

Hence the derived units, resistance, inductance, and (capacitance)$^{-1}$, all of which have the ratio of potential to current (apart from a dimension of time) all change in the same way; that is, as

$$\frac{\text{number specifying resistance in e.s.u.}}{\text{number specifying same resistance in e.m.u.}} = 1/c^2.$$

*Unrationalized mixed or Gaussian units*

In electromagnetic theory Maxwell's equations involve both electrical and magnetic units, and in the c.g.s. system they are generally written in mixed or Gaussian units. Electrical quantities $\mathbf{E}$, $\mathbf{D}$, $\rho$, and conductivity $\sigma$ are in e.s.u., while magnetic quantities $\mathbf{H}$, $\mathbf{B}$ and current density $\mathbf{J}$ are in e.m.u. Thus we must write $\mathbf{J} = (\sigma \mathbf{E})/c$, and the fundamental equations are

$$\left. \begin{aligned} \operatorname{div}\mathbf{D} &= 4\pi\rho, & \operatorname{div}\mathbf{B} &= 0 \\ \operatorname{curl}\mathbf{E} &= -\frac{1}{c}\frac{\partial\mathbf{B}}{\partial t}, & \operatorname{curl}\mathbf{H} &= 4\pi\mathbf{J}+\frac{1}{c}\frac{\partial\mathbf{D}}{\partial t} \\ & & &= \frac{1}{c}\left(4\pi\sigma\mathbf{E}+\frac{\partial\mathbf{D}}{\partial t}\right) \end{aligned} \right\} \qquad (24.15)$$

Elimination of either the electric or magnetic field leads to a wave equation

$$\nabla^2(\mathbf{E}, \mathbf{H}) = \frac{\epsilon\mu}{c^2}\frac{\partial^2}{\partial t^2}(\mathbf{E}, \mathbf{H}), \tag{24.16}$$

showing that the velocity of electromagnetic waves *in vacuo* is $c$.

## 24.2. Practical units

The electrostatic units of charge and current and the electromagnetic unit of potential are inconveniently small for practical use, and the coulomb, ampere, and volt are used instead. Originally these were defined in an arbitrary manner like the metre and the kilogramme (the coulomb was defined in terms of the mass deposited in electrolysis of

TABLE 24.1

To convert a quantity in practical units to a quantity in e.s.u. (or e.m.u.) multiply by the corresponding factor given in column I (or II)

| Quantity | Practical unit | (I) e.s.u. | (II) e.m.u. |
|---|---|---|---|
| Charge | coulomb | $3 \times 10^9$ | $10^{-1}$ |
| Current | ampere | $3 \times 10^9$ | $10^{-1}$ |
| Potential | volt | $1/300$ | $10^8$ |
| Power | watt | $10^7$ | $10^7$ |
| Resistance | ohm | $1/(9 \times 10^{11})$ | $10^9$ |
| Inductance | henry | $1/(9 \times 10^{11})$ | $10^9$ |
| Capacitance | farad | $9 \times 10^{11}$ | $10^{-9}$ |

In this table the ratios are exact where they are simple powers of 10, but elsewhere the factor $c$ has been taken as $3 \times 10^{10}$; more accurate values are obtained by taking $c$ as the velocity of light (in c.g.s. units) given in Appendix C.

a certain solution), but these old 'international units' have now been replaced by 'absolute units', related by powers of 10 to the electromagnetic units, which differ from the international units by amounts insignificant except in very accurate work. The factors required to convert a quantity given in practical units to the equivalent quantity in e.s.u. or e.m.u. are listed in Table 24.1. These can all be derived from the fundamental relations

one coulomb of charge $= 10^{-1}$ e.m.u. of charge,

one volt of potential $= 10^8$ e.m.u. of potential,

together with the fact that the ratios of these quantities in e.s.u. to e.m.u. are $c$ and $1/c$ respectively.

## 24.3. The rationalized m.k.s. system

Since the practical units are those in everyday use, it is convenient to make them the basis of a single consistent system. This is achieved in the m.k.s. system by adopting the metre, kilogramme, and second as the fundamental mechanical units, together with a fourth unit to define the electrical quantities. The definition of units of other mechanical quantities follows the usual rules. The units of velocity and acceleration are the metre/second and metre/second$^2$ respectively; unit force is that force which gives unit mass (1 kg) unit acceleration (1 m/sec$^2$). It is called the newton, and in magnitude is equal to $(10^3 \times 10^2) = 10^5$ dynes. Unit power is developed by unit force moving its point of application with unit velocity; hence the unit is newton-metre/second with magnitude $(10^5 \times 10^2) = 10^7$ erg/sec. Hence it is identical with the watt, and the unit of work is the watt-second or joule.

As the theory of electricity and magnetism has been developed in this book in rationalized m.k.s. units, it is unnecessary to do more than point out the difference between this system and the unrationalized m.k.s. system. The equations expressing Coulomb's law in electricity and magnetism, in our units, are

$$F = q_1 q_2/(4\pi\epsilon_0 r^2), \tag{24.17}$$

$$F = \mu_0 m_1 m_2/(4\pi r^2), \tag{24.18}$$

while Ampère's law of force between two current elements is

$$\mathbf{dF}_1 = \mu_0 I_1 I_2 \{\mathbf{ds}_1 \wedge (\mathbf{ds}_2 \wedge \mathbf{r})\}/(4\pi r^3). \tag{24.19}$$

These equations differ from the corresponding equations in unrationalized c.g.s. units (equations (24.1), (24.10), and (24.14)) not only in the introduction of unknown constants $\epsilon_0$, $\mu_0$ but also in the presence of the factors $4\pi$. The introduction of this factor in these equations, which makes it disappear from other equations such as the equivalents of equations (24.6), (24.9), (24.11), and (24.12), constitutes the process of 'rationalization'. (It can be applied also to c.g.s. units, but as rationalized c.g.s. units are not in common use we shall not discuss them.) We cannot just lump the factor $4\pi$ into the constants $\epsilon_0$, $\mu_0$ since the constants $\epsilon_0$ and $\mu_0$ appear without any factor $4\pi$ accompanying them in equations such as (*in vacuo*)

$$\mathbf{D} = \epsilon_0 \mathbf{E}, \tag{24.20}$$

$$\mathbf{B} = \mu_0 \mathbf{H}. \tag{24.21}$$

Rationalization gives a greater simplicity to various equations, notably those in electromagnetic theory, but it has the drawback of making the defining equations different from those in an unrationalized system, and hence the factors required to convert a quantity in the rationalized m.k.s. system to the equivalent quantity in an unrationalized c.g.s. system are not just simple powers of 10. The conversion factors required, together with two illustrations, are given in Table 24.2 and § 24.4.

A second important difference between the m.k.s. system and the older c.g.s. systems is that the constants $\epsilon_0$, $\mu_0$ are allowed to have dimensions. The reason for this is that a fourth unit (the coulomb (or ampere)) is introduced, which retains the dimension of charge (or current), whereas the absence of any dimensional constant in equations (24.1) and (24.10) made it possible to derive apparent dimensions for any electrical quantity in terms of mass, length, and time. Such derivations are not very illuminating, since they involve half integral powers, and the dimensions of any given electrical quantity are different in the two c.g.s. systems. Dimensions are very useful in checking any physical formula, and in electricity it is simpler to employ a system of four dimensions, such as the metre, kilogramme, second, and coulomb, than a three-dimensional system. Thus if we wish to check the equation

$$U = \tfrac{1}{2}\mathbf{D}.\mathbf{E}$$

by verifying that the product $(\mathbf{DE})$ has the dimensions of energy/volume, we proceed as follows: from equation (1.19) (Gauss's theorem) $\mathbf{D}$ has the dimensions of charge/area, while from the force equation (1.3) $\mathbf{E}$ has the dimensions force/charge. Hence $(\mathbf{DE})$ has the dimensions

$$\text{force/area} = \text{energy/volume}$$

and its units are joule/metre³.

The dimensions of the quantity $\epsilon_0$ are readily found from the fact that it is equal to the ratio $(\mathbf{D}/\mathbf{E})$. Using the alternative dimensions of (potential/length) for $\mathbf{E}$, we have

$$(\mathbf{D}/\mathbf{E}) = (\text{charge/area}) \div (\text{potential/length})$$
$$= (\text{charge/potential})/\text{length} = \text{capacitance/length}.$$

Hence $\epsilon_0$ is measured in units of farad/metre.

If we treated the coulomb as a standard of charge arbitrarily defined like the metre, kilogramme, and second, then both $\epsilon_0$ and $\mu_0$ would be constants to be determined by experiment, though they would still be linked (from electromagnetic theory) by the relation

$$\epsilon_0\mu_0 = 1/c^2$$

so that once one is measured the velocity of electromagnetic waves can be used to deduce the other. In practice we wish our units to be simply related to the older units, and we therefore take

$$\mu_0 = 4\pi\ 10^{-7}\ \text{henry/metre (exactly)}.$$

The size of the coulomb (or ampere) is then found by means of experiment. In fact all the quantities in everyday use are then measured in the practical units listed in Table 24.1.

The fact that the unit of energy in the m.k.s. system is the joule does not mean that an energy should never be quoted in ergs. Similarly there is no reason why a magnetic field should not be quoted in gauss, instead of weber/metre², in a book in m.k.s. units. This is only practical where the quantities in the two units bear a simple ratio to one another, and we have avoided doing this where the conversion involves a factor $(4\pi)$ as well as a power of 10. As far as possible we have endeavoured to make the text simple to follow for a person previously conversant only with the c.g.s. systems, and in the following sections additional tables are given for assistance.

### 24.4. Conversion factors from rationalized m.k.s. system

Since quantities such as susceptibility are generally given in tables in terms of the unrationalized c.g.s. systems, a list of conversion factors is given in Table 24.2 by means of which the value of a quantity given in the rationalized m.k.s. system can be multiplied to find the equivalent quantity in an unrationalized c.g.s. system, and vice versa. Because of the change in the defining equations consequent upon rationalization we cannot simply employ a 'ratio of the units', and we give two simple examples showing how the conversion between quantities in the different systems can be accomplished.

(a) In the rationalized m.k.s. system the formula for the magnetic field **H** at the centre of a circular coil of radius $a$ with one turn is

$$H = I/2a.$$

Hence a field of 1 A/metre is produced by a current of 1 A flowing in such a coil of radius $\frac{1}{2}$ metre.

In the unrationalized e.m.u. system, the corresponding formula is

$$H = 2\pi I/a.$$

With the same current and radius as before, we have $I = 10^{-1}$ e.m.u., $a = 50$ cm, and hence the same field in e.m.u. has the value

$$(2\pi\,10^{-1}/50) = 4\pi\,10^{-3}\ \text{e.m.u.}$$

Thus the unit of current has increased by a factor 10, and the unit of length by $10^{-2}$; but owing to the difference in the defining equation the factor by which we must convert the quantity is given by the equivalence

a field of 1 A/metre $\equiv$ a field of $4\pi\,10^{-3}$ e.m.u.

(b) An experiment is performed with Gouy's apparatus (§ 8.7) to measure the difference in the volume susceptibility of aluminium and air.

In the e.m.u. system, the force $F$ on a rod of cross-section $A$ with one end in a field $H$ and the other end in zero field is

$$F = \tfrac{1}{2}(\chi_1 - \chi_2)AH^2.$$

In a field $H = 4000$ oersted, a force $F$ of 4·92 dyne is measured on a rod for which $A = 1$ cm². Hence

$$\chi_1 - \chi_2 = 0{\cdot}615 \times 10^{-6} \text{ e.m.u.}$$

In our rationalized m.k.s. system, the expression for the force is

$$F = \tfrac{1}{2}\mu_0(\chi_1 - \chi_2)AH^2.$$

In the experiment (using the conversion factors of Table 24.2), the force $F = 4{\cdot}92 \times 10^{-5}$ newton, $A = 10^{-4}$ metre², $H = 4000/(4\pi\, 10^{-3}) = 10^6/\pi$ A/metre. Hence the difference of susceptibility is

$$\chi_1 - \chi_2 = \frac{2(4{\cdot}92 \times 10^{-5})}{(4\pi\, 10^{-7})(10^{-4})(10^6/\pi)^2} = 4\pi(0{\cdot}615 \times 10^{-6}) \text{ m.k.s.}$$

Thus we obtain a quantity in the m.k.s. system which is greater by a factor $(4\pi)$ than the corresponding quantity in the e.m.u. system. These are volume susceptibilities, and the unit of volume is the metre³ in the m.k.s. system and the centimetre³ in the c.g.s. system. The conversion factor for mass susceptibility is not just $(4\pi)$, because the conversion factor for density in the two systems is involved. Since

$$\chi_{\text{mass}} = \chi_{\text{volume}}/\text{density},$$

the conversion factor for $\chi_{\text{mass}}$ going from e.m.u. to m.k.s. is

$$(4\pi)/(10^3) = 4\pi\, 10^{-3},$$

or $10^3/4\pi$ going from m.k.s. to e.m.u.

## 24.5. Equivalent equations in unrationalized c.g.s. systems

Rationalization is the main difficulty which prevents simple rules being given for obtaining the equivalent equations in c.g.s. units to replace those in the text. In the following tables methods for effecting the transition are given for each chapter. These apply only to the numbered equations, but other expressions in the text may readily be modified by their help.

## TABLE 24.2

| Quantity | Unit in m.k.s. system | Unit in c.g.s. system | Factor by which quantity in m.k.s. system must be multiplied to convert to c.g.s. system |
|---|---|---|---|
| Length . . . . . | Metre | Centimetre | $10^2$ |
| Mass . . . . . | Kilogramme | Gramme | $10^3$ |
| Time . . . . . | Second | Second | 1 |
| Density . . . . | kg/metre³ | g/cm³ | $10^{-3}$ |
| Force . . . . | Newton or kg-metre-sec⁻² | Dyne | $10^5$ |
| Couple . . . . | Newton-metre | Dyne-cm | $10^7$ |
| Work . . . . | Joule or newton-metre | Erg | $10^7$ |
| Power . . . . | Watt, joule-sec⁻¹ or volt-ampere | Erg-second⁻¹ | $10^7$ |
| Charge $q$ . . . | Coulomb | e.m.u. | $\frac{1}{10}$ |
| Current $i$ . . . | Ampere | e.m.u. | $\frac{1}{10}$ |
| Potential $V$ . . . | Volt | e.m.u. | $10^8$ |
| Electric displacement **D** . | Coulomb-metre⁻² | e.s.u. | $12\pi \times 10^5$ |
| Electric intensity **E** . | Volt-metre⁻¹ or newton-coulomb⁻¹ | e.s.u. | $\frac{1}{3} \times 10^{-4}$ |
| Electric polarization **P** . . | Coulomb-metre⁻² | e.s.u. | $3 \times 10^5$ |
| Inductance $L$ . . . | Henry | e.m.u. | $10^9$ |
| Resistance $R$ . . . | Ohm | e.m.u. | $10^9$ |
| Capacitance $C$ . . . | Farad | e.s.u. | $9 \times 10^{11}$ |
| Magnetic field **B** . . . | Weber-metre⁻² | e.m.u. | $10^4$ |
| Magnetic field **H** . . . | Ampere-metre⁻¹ | e.m.u. | $4\pi \times 10^{-3}$ |
| Magnetomotive force . . | Ampere | e.m.u. | $4\pi/10$ |
| Magnetic flux $N$ . . . | Weber | e.m.u. | $10^8$ |
| Intensity of magnetization **M** | Ampere-metre⁻¹ | e.m.u. | $10^{-3}$ |
| Magnetic moment **m** . | Ampere-metre² | e.m.u. | $10^3$ |
| Volume susceptibility $\chi$ . | m.k.s./metre³ | e.m.u./cm³ | $1/4\pi$ |
| Mass susceptibility . | m.k.s./kg | e.m.u./g | $10^3/4\pi$ |
| Gramme-molar susceptibility | m.k.s./g-mole | e.m.u./g-mole | $10^6/4\pi$ |

Where a factor 3 appears in the table, it involves the approximation $c = 3 \times 10^{10}$ cm/sec. To the same approximation, since by definition

$$\mu_0 = 4\pi \, 10^{-7} \text{ henry metre}^{-1},$$

we have

$$\epsilon_0 = \frac{1}{36\pi} 10^{-9} \text{ farad metre}^{-1},$$

$$Z_0 \text{ (free space)} = 120\pi \text{ ohm}.$$

## Chapter 1

To obtain the equivalent equations in e.s.u. replace $\epsilon_0$ by $1/4\pi$ in:
2, 4, 5, 7 a, 7 b, 7 c, 8, 9, 10 a, 10 b, 11 a, 11 b, 12, 17, 24, 25, 29, 30, 31, 37.

The following equations are unchanged in e.s.u.:
3, 6, 13, 14, 15, 26, 27, 32, 33, 34, 35.

The other equations, expressed in e.s.u., become

$$\mathbf{P} = \chi\mathbf{E} \tag{1.16}$$

$$\mathbf{D} = \mathbf{E} + 4\pi\mathbf{P} = \epsilon\mathbf{E} \tag{1.18, 1.22}$$

$$\int \mathbf{D}.\,d\mathbf{S} = \int \operatorname{div}\mathbf{D}\,d\tau = 4\pi\int \rho\,d\tau \tag{1.19}$$

$$\operatorname{div}\mathbf{D} = 4\pi\rho \tag{1.20}$$

$$\epsilon = 1 + 4\pi\chi \tag{1.21}$$

$$\epsilon\mathbf{E} = \mathbf{D} = (q/r^3)\mathbf{r} \tag{1.23}$$

$$D = \epsilon E = 4\pi\sigma \tag{1.28}$$

and the right-hand sides of equations 36, 38, 39, and 40 must be multiplied by $(4\pi)^{-1}$.

## Chapter 2

To obtain the equivalent equations in e.s.u. replace $\epsilon_0$ by $1/4\pi$ in:

1, 3, 4, 5, 6, 29, 30, 31, 47, 48, 49, 50, 51, 52, 53, 54, 55.

All other numbered equations are unchanged.

## Chapter 3

All numbered equations are unchanged except

$$\left.\begin{array}{cc} \mathbf{D} = \epsilon\mathbf{E}, & \mathbf{J} = \sigma\mathbf{E} \\ \epsilon\operatorname{div}(\operatorname{grad}V) = 0, & \sigma\operatorname{div}(\operatorname{grad}V) = 0 \\ \int \mathbf{D}.\,d\mathbf{S} = 4\pi Q, & \int \mathbf{J}.\,d\mathbf{S} = I \end{array}\right\} \tag{3.10}$$

and

$$R \equiv \epsilon/4\pi\sigma C. \tag{3.11}$$

## Chapter 4

All numbered equations unchanged except: replace $\epsilon_0$ by $1/4\pi$ in 22, 43, 45, 46, 47, 48.

## Chapter 5

The equations in e.m.u. depend on the way the theory is developed. Using a parallel treatment to that in Chapter 5, to obtain the equivalent equations in e.m.u. replace $\mu_0$ by $4\pi$ in the following equations:

2, 3, 4, 5, 16, 17, 19, 23, 39, 46, 47, 49, 50, 53, 54, 58;

replace $\mu_0$ by 1 in:

10, 11, 15;

replace $4\pi$ by 1 in:

11, 12, 13, 14, 35, 36, 37, 38, 48, 59;

multiply by $4\pi$ on the right-hand side in:

21, 22, 26, 33, 55, 56, 57.

The following equations are unchanged in e.m.u.:

1, 6, 7, 8, 9, 18, 24, 25, 27, 28, 29, 32, 40, 41, 42, 43, 44, 45, 51, 52, 60, 61, 62, 63.

The remaining equations become:

$$\mathbf{B} = \mathbf{H} + 4\pi\mathbf{M} \qquad (5.20)$$

$$\mathbf{B} = \mu\mathbf{H} \qquad (5.30)$$

$$\mu = 1 + 4\pi\chi \qquad (5.31)$$

$$H_1 = H_0 - 4\pi M/3 \qquad (5.34)$$

*Chapter* 6

The numbered equations are unchanged in e.m.u. except:

11, 12, 15, 16, 17, 18 (replace $\mu_0$ by $4\pi$).

Also $\qquad U = \dfrac{1}{8\pi} \displaystyle\int (\mathbf{H}.\mathbf{B})\, d\tau \qquad (6.44)$

$$\delta U = \int \mathbf{J}.\delta\mathbf{A}\, d\tau = \frac{1}{8\pi} \int \mathbf{H}.\delta\mathbf{B}\, d\tau \qquad (6.45)$$

*Chapter* 7

All numbered equations unchanged in e.m.u. except:

13 (replace $\mu_0$ by 1).

*Chapter* 8

To obtain the equivalent equations in e.m.u.:

replace $\mu_0$ by 1 in:

7, 13, 24, 25;

replace $4\pi$ by 1 in:

21, 22.

The following equations are unchanged in e.m.u.:

1, 2, 3, 4, 5, 6, 9, 10, 11, 12, 14, 15, 16, 17.

The remaining numbered equations in e.m.u. become:

$$\chi = -2\cdot83 \times 10^{10} \sum \langle r^2 \rangle \qquad (8.8)$$

$$4\pi nI = \int \mathbf{H}.\mathbf{ds} = Hd_a + H_m d_m \qquad (8.18)$$

$$4\pi nI = BA_a \left[ \frac{d_a}{A_a} + \frac{d_m}{\mu A_m} \right] \qquad (8.19)$$

$$B = H = 4\pi M_s \sin^2\phi \cos\phi \log_e(b/a) \qquad (8.20)$$

$$W = \frac{1}{4\pi} \int H\, dB \qquad (8.26)$$

*Chapter* 10

The transition to c.g.s. units in this chapter is very complex because of the use of mixed units. The quantities $\mathbf{D}$, $\mathbf{E}$, $\rho$ (charge density or resistivity) and $\sigma$ (conductivity) are then in e.s.u., while $\mathbf{B}$, $\mathbf{H}$, and $\mathbf{J}$ are in e.m.u. We will deal with the various sections separately.

§§ 10.1 *to* 10.5 *inclusive*. Where different from the text, the fundamental equations become

$$\operatorname{div}\mathbf{D} = 4\pi\rho \tag{10.1}$$

$$\operatorname{curl}\mathbf{E} = -\frac{1}{c}(\partial\mathbf{B}/\partial t) \tag{10.3}$$

$$\operatorname{curl}\mathbf{H} = 4\pi\mathbf{J}' \tag{10.4}$$

$$\operatorname{div}\mathbf{J} = -\frac{1}{c}(\partial\rho/\partial t) \tag{10.5}$$

$$\mathbf{J}' = \mathbf{J} + \frac{1}{4\pi c}(\partial\mathbf{D}/\partial t) \tag{10.6}$$

$$\operatorname{curl}\mathbf{H} = \frac{1}{c}(4\pi\sigma\mathbf{E} + \partial\mathbf{D}/\partial t) \tag{10.7}$$

$$\operatorname{curl}\mathbf{E} = -\frac{1}{c}(\partial\mathbf{B}/\partial t) = -\frac{\mu}{c}(\partial\mathbf{H}/\partial t) \tag{10.10}$$

$$\operatorname{curl}\mathbf{H} = \frac{1}{c}(\partial\mathbf{D}/\partial t) = \frac{\epsilon}{c}(\partial\mathbf{E}/\partial t) \tag{10.11}$$

$$\mathbf{N} = \frac{c}{4\pi}(\mathbf{E}\wedge\mathbf{H}) \tag{10.23}$$

$$W = \tfrac{1}{4}c^2 J_0^2 \delta\rho = c^2 H_0^2 \rho/32\pi^2\delta \tag{10.34 a}$$

Of the other equations which are different, the equivalent equations can be found as follows:

replace $\epsilon_0$, $\mu_0$ by 1 in:

   8, 9, 19;

replace $(\epsilon_0, \mu_0)$ by $1/c^2$ in:

   12, 13, 14, 15, 17;

replace $\epsilon_0$ by $1/4\pi$, $\mu_0$ by $4\pi/c^2$ in:

   24, 26, 28, 29, 31, 33.

The following equations remain unaltered:

   2, 16, 18, 22, 27, 30, 34.

The modifications required in equations (10.25), (10.25 a) are readily found from equations 10.3), (10.7) above.

The situation as regards $Z_0$ is rather complex, since this quantity is not usually defined in the c.g.s. systems. In view of the equations $V = \int \mathbf{E} \cdot \mathbf{ds}, \; I = (4\pi)^{-1} \int \mathbf{H} \cdot \mathbf{ds}$, it would be natural to define $Z_0$ as

$$Z_0 = 4\pi(E_y/H_z) \quad \text{(all quantities in e.s.u. or all in e.m.u.)}.$$

In mixed units $Z_0$ (like $\rho$, $\sigma$) should be in e.s.u., and then

$$Z_0 = (4\pi/c)(E_y/H_z) \quad (Z_0, E_y \text{ in e.s.u.; } H_z \text{ in e.m.u.)}.$$

For a plane wave in a non-conducting medium, $E_y = (\mu/\epsilon)^{\frac{1}{2}} H_z$ in mixed units, and hence

$$Z_0 = (4\pi/c)(\mu/\epsilon)^{\frac{1}{2}} \quad (Z_0 \text{ in e.s.u.)}. \tag{10.20}$$

Then in equation (10.21) $Z_0$ must be replaced by $(\mu/\epsilon)^{\frac{1}{2}}$ in mixed units, but equation (10.32) gives $Z_0$ in e.s.u. if $\rho$, $\sigma$ are in e.s.u.

§ 10.6. All equations can be used in mixed units by replacing $Z$ by $(\mu/\epsilon)^{\frac{1}{2}}$.

§ 10.7. If the conductivity and resistivity are given in e.s.u., it is simplest to work in e.s.u., when only the modifications

$$Z_1 = 4\pi/c, \qquad t = 4\pi\sigma\delta/c$$

are required. Thus equation (10.56) becomes

$$\left|\frac{A'}{A}\right|^2 = 1 - 2\left(\frac{\mu f}{\sigma}\right)^{\frac{1}{2}} \quad (\sigma \text{ in e.s.u.)}.$$

§ 10.8. Unaltered.

§ 10.9. The significant alterations are

$$\mathbf{E} = -\frac{1}{c}\frac{\partial \mathbf{A}}{\partial t} - \operatorname{grad} V \quad (10.61)$$

$$\operatorname{div} \mathbf{A} = -\frac{\epsilon\mu}{c}\frac{\partial V}{\partial t} \quad (10.62)$$

$$H = (sI_0/r^2)\sin\theta\cos\omega(t-r/c) - (2\pi sI_0/r\lambda)\sin\theta\sin\omega(t-r/c). \quad (10.68)$$

Replace $\epsilon_0$ by $1/4\pi$, $\mu_0$ by $4\pi$ in:

63, 64, 65, 66, 67, 73, 74.

Replace $Z_0$ by $4\pi c$ to obtain equation in c.g.s.u. ($I_0$ in e.m.u.) in:

69, 70.

Replace $Z_0$ by $4\pi/c$, $\epsilon_0$ by $1/4\pi$, $\mu_0$ by $4\pi/c^2$ to obtain equation in e.s.u. ($R_r$, $p_0$ in e.s.u.) in:

71, 72.

*Chapters* 9, 13, 14, 15, 16, 18

The numbered equations are valid in e.m.u. or practical units, except:

valid only in e.m.u. (mechanical quantities in c.g.s.u.):

|  | |
|---|---|
| Chapter 14 | 9, 10; |
| Chapter 16 | 10, 11, 12, 13, 14, 15; |
| Chapter 18 | 21, 25; |

valid in e.s.u. (writing $Z_0 = 4\pi/c$):

|  | |
|---|---|
| Chapter 16 | 19, 20; |

replace $\mu_0$ by 1 to obtain equations in e.m.u. in:

|  | |
|---|---|
| Chapter 18 | 27, 28, 29, 30. |

*Chapter* 11

In equations 29, 30, 31 replace $\epsilon_0$ and $\mu_0$ by $1/c$ to convert to mixed units.

In equation 40 replace $Z_1$ by $(\mu/\epsilon)^{\frac{1}{2}}$ to convert to mixed units. Other numbered equations are unchanged.

*Chapter* 12

All numbered equations unchanged, except that $\epsilon_0$ should be replaced by $1/4\pi$ in 3 and 7.

*Chapter* 17

All numbered equations are unchanged in e.s.u. except that where it occurs $\epsilon_0$ should be replaced by $1/4\pi$, and the following equation becomes:

$$\mathbf{D} = \mathbf{E}_0 + 4\pi\mathbf{P} = \epsilon\mathbf{E}_0 \qquad (17.2)$$

and in equations 33 and 34 the equivalent expressions in e.s.u. are found by replacing $Z_0$ by $(4\pi/c)$.

*Chapter* 19

Replace $\epsilon_0$ by $1/4\pi$ to obtain equations in e.s.u. in:
32, 33, 34, 35, 36.

*Chapters* 20, 21, 22, 23

Replace $\mu_0$ by 1 to obtain equations in e.m.u. (except in 20.6: replace $\mu_0$ by $4\pi$).

Replace $\epsilon_0$ by $1/4\pi$ to obtain equations in e.s.u.

# APPENDIX A

# VECTORS

## A.1. Definition of scalar and vector quantities

MANY physical quantities are completely defined by magnitude alone. Examples are temperature, time, or length. These are called scalar quantities. They obey the ordinary laws of algebra, and are represented in the text by a symbol printed in italic type.

Other physical quantities, such as velocity, force, or acceleration are not completely defined unless the direction as well as the magnitude is given. Such quantities are called vectors. Vector quantities are printed in bold-face type in the text; a brief summary follows of the vector properties which are necessary for the understanding of the text.

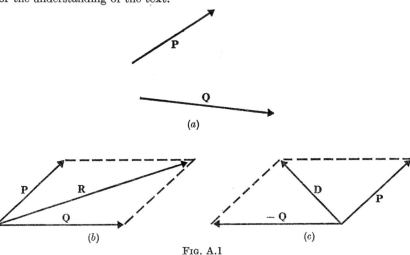

FIG. A.1

## A.2. Vector addition and subtraction

A vector may be represented graphically by an arrow pointing in the direction of the vector and of length equal to its magnitude. In Fig. A.1 (*a*), **P** and **Q** are two vectors. The addition of **P** and **Q** is effected by drawing them as in Fig. A.1 (*b*), in which the vectors form two sides of a parallelogram. The vector **R** defined by the equation **P**+**Q** = **R** is the diagonal of this parallelogram, and its magnitude and direction can be found by trigonometry if **P** and **Q** are known. Similarly, the vector **D** = **P**−**Q** is obtained from Fig. A.1 (*c*). In the special case only, that the vectors **P**, **Q** are parallel, then **R** is equal to the scalar sum of **P** and **Q**, and **D** is equal to the scalar difference, and **R** and **D** are parallel to **P** and **Q**.

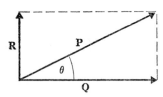

FIG. A.2. If **Q**, **R** are at right angles then $Q = P \cos \theta$, $R = P \sin \theta$.

The converse process is often useful. That is, a vector **P** (Fig. A.2) can be resolved into two vectors **Q** and **R** such that **P** is the diagonal of a parallelogram, and $\mathbf{Q}$ and $\mathbf{R}$ are two adjacent sides. Generally, $\mathbf{Q}$ and $\mathbf{R}$ are chosen to be at right angles, so that the parallelogram is then a rectangle. $\mathbf{Q}$ and $\mathbf{R}$ are called the components of $\mathbf{P}$. $\mathbf{P}$ may be resolved into three components parallel to the axes of Cartesian coordinates $x$, $y$, and $z$.

## A.3. Multiplication of vectors

(a) Multiplication of a vector $\mathbf{P}$ by a scalar quantity $m$ changes the magnitude of the vector by the factor $m$, but the direction is unaltered. Multiplication by $-m$ gives a vector of magnitude $m\mathbf{P}$ in the opposite direction, that is the vector $-m\mathbf{P}$. If $\mathbf{i}$, $\mathbf{j}$, and $\mathbf{k}$ are vectors of unit length parallel to the axes $x$, $y$, and $z$, we can write

$$\mathbf{P} = \mathbf{i}P_x + \mathbf{j}P_y + \mathbf{k}P_z,$$

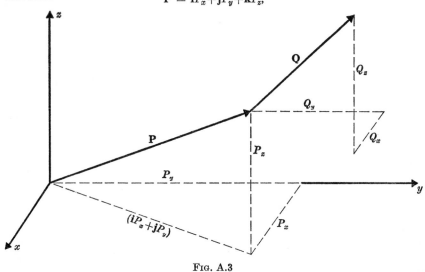

FIG. A.3

where $P_x$, $P_y$, and $P_z$ are scalar quantities giving the magnitude of the components of $\mathbf{P}$ parallel to the three axes (see Fig. A.3). Since $\mathbf{Q} = \mathbf{i}Q_x + \mathbf{j}Q_y + \mathbf{k}Q_z$ it follows that $\mathbf{P} + \mathbf{Q} = \mathbf{i}(P_x + Q_x) + \mathbf{j}(P_y + Q_y) + \mathbf{k}(P_z + Q_z)$.

(b) *The scalar product.* The scalar product of two vectors $\mathbf{P}$ and $\mathbf{Q}$ is written $\mathbf{P} \cdot \mathbf{Q}$ and is a scalar quantity numerically equal to the magnitude of one vector multiplied by the component of the other parallel to the direction of the first one. If the angle between $\mathbf{P}$ and $\mathbf{Q}$ is $\theta$

$$\mathbf{P} \cdot \mathbf{Q} = PQ \cos \theta = \mathbf{Q} \cdot \mathbf{P}$$

and 
$$\mathbf{P} \cdot (\mathbf{Q} + \mathbf{R} + \mathbf{S} + ...) = \mathbf{P} \cdot \mathbf{Q} + \mathbf{P} \cdot \mathbf{R} + \mathbf{P} \cdot \mathbf{S} + ....$$

The scalar product of two perpendicular vectors is zero. Therefore, for the unit vectors $\mathbf{i}$, $\mathbf{j}$, and $\mathbf{k}$, we have

$$\mathbf{i} \cdot \mathbf{j} = \mathbf{j} \cdot \mathbf{k} = \mathbf{k} \cdot \mathbf{i} = 0$$

and 
$$\mathbf{i} \cdot \mathbf{i} = \mathbf{j} \cdot \mathbf{j} = \mathbf{k} \cdot \mathbf{k} = 1.$$

An example of a scalar product is the work $dW$ done on a charge $q$ in moving a distance $\mathbf{ds}$ in a region where the electric field is $\mathbf{E}$, which is

$$dW = -q\mathbf{E} \cdot \mathbf{ds}. \tag{A.1}$$

(c) *The vector product.* The vector product of two vectors **P** and **Q** is defined as a vector perpendicular to both **P** and **Q** of magnitude $PQ \sin \theta$, where $\theta$ is the angle between **P** and **Q**. If **P** is perpendicular to **Q**, the vector product is $PQ$ but if **P** and **Q** are parallel the vector product is zero.

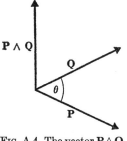

The direction of the vector product $(\mathbf{P} \wedge \mathbf{Q})$ is that in which a right-handed screw would move if turned from the first vector **P** towards the second vector **Q**, as shown in Fig. A.4. Hence we have

$$(\mathbf{P} \wedge \mathbf{Q}) = -(\mathbf{Q} \wedge \mathbf{P}).$$

Also,

$$\mathbf{P} \wedge (\mathbf{Q} + \mathbf{R} + \mathbf{S} + ...) = (\mathbf{P} \wedge \mathbf{Q}) + (\mathbf{P} \wedge \mathbf{R}) + (\mathbf{P} \wedge \mathbf{S}) + ....$$

FIG. A.4. The vector $\mathbf{P} \wedge \mathbf{Q}$ s normal to the plane containing **P** and **Q**.

The formula for a vector product in terms of the vector components may be conveniently expressed as a determinent. For the unit vectors along a set of right-handed Cartesian coordinates, we have

$$\mathbf{i} \wedge \mathbf{i} = \mathbf{j} \wedge \mathbf{j} = \mathbf{k} \wedge \mathbf{k} = 0,$$

$$\mathbf{i} \wedge \mathbf{j} = \mathbf{k} = -\mathbf{j} \wedge \mathbf{i}, \text{ etc.}$$

Hence $\quad \mathbf{P} \wedge \mathbf{Q} = (\mathbf{i}P_x + \mathbf{j}P_y + \mathbf{k}P_z) \wedge (\mathbf{i}Q_x + \mathbf{j}Q_y + \mathbf{k}Q_z)$

$$= \mathbf{i}(P_y Q_z - P_z Q_y) + \mathbf{j}(P_z Q_x - P_x Q_z) + \mathbf{k}(P_x Q_y - P_y Q_x),$$

which can be written as

$$\mathbf{P} \wedge \mathbf{Q} = \begin{vmatrix} \mathbf{i} & \mathbf{j} & \mathbf{k} \\ P_x & P_y & P_z \\ Q_x & Q_y & Q_z \end{vmatrix}.$$

An example of the use of a vector product is the equation for the force **dF** on an element **ds** of a wire carrying a current $I$ in a magnetic field **B**. The force is normal to **ds** and to **B**, and of magnitude $I\,ds\,B \sin \theta$. It is specified both in magnitude and direction by the vector equation

$$\mathbf{dF} = I\,(\mathbf{ds} \wedge \mathbf{B}).$$

Products of three vectors are occasionally met with, and can be evaluated from the foregoing rules. The scalar triple product

$$\mathbf{P} . (\mathbf{Q} \wedge \mathbf{R}) = \text{scalar product of } \mathbf{P} \text{ and } (\mathbf{Q} \wedge \mathbf{R})$$

is a scalar quantity equal in magnitude to the volume of the parallelepiped whose sides are constructed from the three vectors **P**, **Q**, **R** (see Fig. A.5). Clearly,

$$\mathbf{P} . (\mathbf{Q} \wedge \mathbf{R}) = (\mathbf{P} \wedge \mathbf{Q}) . \mathbf{R}$$

and this is often written simply as **PQR**. We have

$$\mathbf{PQR} = \mathbf{QRP} = \mathbf{RPQ} = -\mathbf{PRQ} = -\mathbf{QPR} = -\mathbf{RQP}.$$

The change of sign on inverting the order of any two of the vectors follows also from the determinantal form

$$\mathbf{PQR} = \begin{vmatrix} P_x & P_y & P_z \\ Q_x & Q_y & Q_z \\ R_x & R_y & R_z \end{vmatrix}.$$

The formula for the vector triple product may be expressed in the form

$$\mathbf{P} \wedge (\mathbf{Q} \wedge \mathbf{R}) = \mathbf{Q}(\mathbf{P} . \mathbf{R}) - \mathbf{R}(\mathbf{P} . \mathbf{Q}).$$

This may be verified by expressing the vectors in terms of their components along three Cartesian axes.

## A.4. Differentiation and integration of vectors

Vector quantities are often expressed as functions of scalar variables. For example, the electric field $\mathbf{E}$ can be expressed as a function of the position coordinates $x$, $y$, and $z$. The vector may be differentiated and integrated with respect

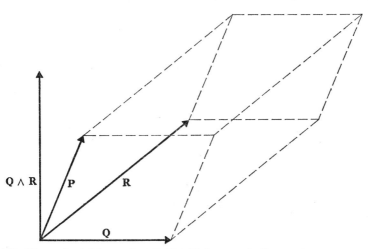

FIG. A.5. The scalar triple product $\mathbf{P}.(\mathbf{Q} \wedge \mathbf{R})$ is numerically equal to the volume of the parallelepiped whose sides are the vectors $\mathbf{P}$, $\mathbf{Q}$, and $\mathbf{R}$.

to these variables. The differential of $\mathbf{P}$ with respect to a scalar variable $u$ is defined as

$$\frac{d\mathbf{P}}{du} = \lim_{\Delta u \to 0} \frac{\mathbf{P}(u + \Delta u) - \mathbf{P}(u)}{\Delta u}.$$

When a force $\mathbf{F}$ acts for a small distance $\mathbf{ds}$, the work done is $dW = \mathbf{F}.\mathbf{ds}$ and if the total work done over a finite distance is required, we can write

$$W = \int \mathbf{F}.\mathbf{ds} = \int F \cos \theta \, ds,$$

where $ds$ is the component of $\mathbf{ds}$ parallel to $\mathbf{F}$ at any point.

This integral occurs frequently and is called the line integral of $\mathbf{F}$ along the curve. The line integral along the curve $AB$ is illustrated in Fig. A.6. If the integration is carried out round a closed path, returning to the original point $A$, it is written $\oint \mathbf{F}.\mathbf{ds}$.

The surface integral $\int \mathbf{F}.\mathbf{dS}$ is also important. $\mathbf{F}.\mathbf{dS}$ is the flux through the element of area $\mathbf{dS}$ due to the field $\mathbf{F}$, and the integral over a surface gives the total flux through that surface. If the vector $\mathbf{F} = \mathbf{v}$

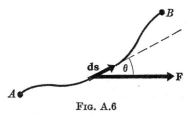

FIG. A.6

represents the velocity of flow of a fluid, $\int \mathbf{v}.\mathbf{dS}$ gives the total volume of fluid passing through the area $S$ in unit time. If $\mathbf{F}$ is the electric displacement $\mathbf{D}$, the integral gives the number of lines of displacement crossing the surface $S$.

In many problems in physics a scalar quantity is used which is a single-valued function of the position coordinates of the system. For example, in electrostatics the electric potential $V$ is a function of $x$, $y$, and $z$ in a Cartesian coordinate system. The change in potential corresponding to an infinitesimal displacement **ds** is given by Taylor's theorem, that is

$$dV = (\partial V/\partial x)\, dx + (\partial V/\partial y)\, dy + (\partial V/\partial z)\, dz$$

and
$$\mathbf{ds} = \mathbf{i}\, dx + \mathbf{j}\, dy + \mathbf{k}\, dz.$$

The rate of change of $V$ with the displacement **s** is expressed in terms of a new quantity grad $V$ which is defined by the equation

$$dV = (\text{grad } V) . \, \mathbf{ds},  \tag{A.2}$$

where
$$\text{grad } V = \mathbf{i}(\partial V/\partial x) + \mathbf{j}(\partial V/\partial y) + \mathbf{k}(\partial V/\partial z).$$

grad $V$ is a vector quantity and is an abbreviation for 'the gradient of $V$'. When grad $V$ is parallel to **ds**, $dV$ is a maximum, so that grad $V$ is in the direction of the greatest rate of change of $V$ with respect to the coordinates, and is normal to an equipotential surface. From equation (A.1) the work done on unit charge in moving a distance **ds** in a field **E** is $-\mathbf{E}.\,\mathbf{ds}$ and this is equal to $-dV$. Therefore we have $\mathbf{E} = -\text{grad } V$ and the electric field is equal to the gradient of the potential at any point, and is in the direction of the maximum rate of change of potential with respect to the space coordinates.

The operator $\mathbf{i}(\partial/\partial x) + \mathbf{j}(\partial/\partial y) + \mathbf{k}(\partial/\partial z)$ is often denoted by the symbol $\nabla$ (pronounced 'del'), so that
$$\text{grad } V \equiv \nabla V.  \tag{A.3}$$

The operator $\nabla$ can be regarded as a vector operator, which operates on both scalar and vector quantities, and forms scalar and vector products. Thus equation (A.2) can be written
$$dV = (\nabla V) . \, \mathbf{ds}.  \tag{A.4}$$

In general, any scalar potential function $\phi$, which is finite, single-valued, and free from discontinuities (these conditions must apply also to the first and second derivatives of $\phi$ w.r.t. the space coordinates), can be related to a field of force **F**, where
$$\mathbf{F} = -\text{grad } \phi,$$

so that once $\phi$ is everywhere determined, **F** is known at all points. Also, the line integral of **F** between any two points $A$ and $B$ is independent of the path taken between those points since

$$\int_A^B \mathbf{F}.\,\mathbf{ds} = -\int_A^B (\text{grad } \phi).\,\mathbf{ds} = -\int_A^B d\phi = \phi_A - \phi_B$$

by analogy with equation (A.2). Similarly, the line integral round a closed path is zero.

## A.5. The divergence of a vector

The divergence of a vector **P** is written div **P**. It is an operator used to describe the excess flux leaving an element of volume in space. The flux may be flow of liquid in hydrodynamics, heat in a thermal field of varying temperature, or electric flux. In the latter case, the excess flux leaving the volume element is related to the total charge enclosed by Gauss's theorem. In Fig. A.7 there is a varying electric charge density $\rho$ throughout space. Gauss's theorem is applied to a volume element $dx\,dy\,dz$ at the point $(x, y, z)$ in a Cartesian coordinate system.

The total charge enclosed is $\rho\,dxdydz$. The total flux through the faces normal to the $x$-axis is

$$\left[\left\{D_x+\frac{\partial}{\partial x}(D_x)\,dx\right\}-D_x\right]dydz = \frac{\partial D_x}{\partial x}dxdydz,$$

where $D_x$ is the component of the electric displacement parallel to the $x$-axis at the point $(x,y,z)$. Writing similar expressions for the flux through the other two

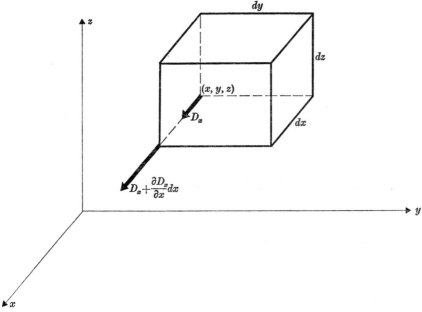

FIG. A.7

pairs of faces, Gauss's theorem becomes

$$\frac{\partial D_x}{\partial x}+\frac{\partial D_y}{\partial y}+\frac{\partial D_z}{\partial z} = \rho,$$

where $D_x$, $D_y$, and $D_z$ are the components of the electric displacement along the three axes at $(x,y,z)$.

The expression on the left-hand side of this equation is written $\operatorname{div}\mathbf{D}$, and is the divergence of the vector $\mathbf{D}$ at this point.

Now using the operator $\nabla$, we have

$$\nabla\cdot\mathbf{D} = \left(\mathbf{i}\frac{\partial}{\partial x}+\mathbf{j}\frac{\partial}{\partial y}+\mathbf{k}\frac{\partial}{\partial z}\right)\cdot(\mathbf{i}D_x+\mathbf{j}D_y+\mathbf{k}D_z)$$

$$= \frac{\partial D_x}{\partial x}+\frac{\partial D_y}{\partial y}+\frac{\partial D_z}{\partial z}.$$

Therefore                    $\nabla\cdot\mathbf{D} \equiv \operatorname{div}\mathbf{D}.$                    (A.5)

The divergence of a vector is a scalar quantity, since it represents the net amount of flux, or the number of lines of induction, coming out of a volume element. If $\operatorname{div}\mathbf{D} = 0$, the total flux entering the element $dxdydz$ is balanced by that leaving it. A vector satisfying this condition is said to be *solenoidal*.

### A.6. The curl of a vector

The curl (or rotation) of a vector $\mathbf{P}$ is written $\operatorname{curl}\mathbf{P}$ (or $\operatorname{rot}\mathbf{P}$). It arises in problems where a line integral of a vector round a closed path is related to the flux through the surface enclosed by the path of the line integral. For example, Ampère's law for the magnetic field due to a current is

$$\oint \mathbf{H} . \mathbf{ds} = \int \mathbf{J} . \mathbf{dS}.$$

Let us apply this equation to an element $dy\,dz$ at the point $(x, y, z)$ in a Cartesian coordinate system (Fig. A.8). For the $x$-component of the current, $J_x$, the line

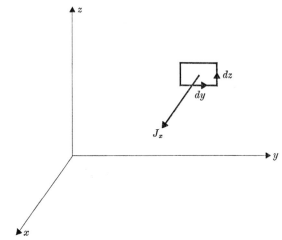

Fig. A.8. Application of Ampère's law in Cartesian coordinates.

integral of $\mathbf{H}$ in the $y, z$ plane is positive in an anti-clockwise direction, and we have

$$J_x\,dy\,dz = \left[H_y - \frac{\partial H_y}{\partial z}\frac{dz}{2}\right]dy + \left[H_z + \frac{\partial H_z}{\partial y}\frac{dy}{2}\right]dz - \left[H_y + \frac{\partial H_y}{\partial z}\frac{dz}{2}\right]dy - \left[H_z - \frac{\partial H_z}{\partial y}\frac{dy}{2}\right]dz$$

$$= \left(\frac{\partial H_z}{\partial y} - \frac{\partial H_y}{\partial z}\right)dy\,dz,$$

where $H_y$ and $H_z$ are the components of $\mathbf{H}$ parallel to the $y$- and $z$-axes respectively. Therefore

$$J_x = \frac{\partial H_z}{\partial y} - \frac{\partial H_y}{\partial z},$$

and similarly

$$J_y = \frac{\partial H_x}{\partial z} - \frac{\partial H_z}{\partial x} \quad \text{and} \quad J_z = \frac{\partial H_y}{\partial x} - \frac{\partial H_x}{\partial y}.$$

These equations are written

$$J_x = \operatorname{curl}_x\mathbf{H}, \qquad J_y = \operatorname{curl}_y\mathbf{H}, \qquad J_z = \operatorname{curl}_z\mathbf{H}$$

or simply

$$\operatorname{curl}\mathbf{H} = \mathbf{J},$$

where $\operatorname{curl}\mathbf{H}$ is a vector quantity whose components are expressed by means of the determinant

$$\operatorname{curl}\mathbf{H} = \begin{vmatrix} \mathbf{i} & \mathbf{j} & \mathbf{k} \\ \dfrac{\partial}{\partial x} & \dfrac{\partial}{\partial y} & \dfrac{\partial}{\partial z} \\ H_x & H_y & H_z \end{vmatrix}, \tag{A.6}$$

i.e.
$$\operatorname{curl} \mathbf{H} = \mathbf{i}\left(\frac{\partial H_z}{\partial y} - \frac{\partial H_y}{\partial z}\right) + \mathbf{j}\left(\frac{\partial H_x}{\partial z} - \frac{\partial H_z}{\partial x}\right) + \mathbf{k}\left(\frac{\partial H_y}{\partial x} - \frac{\partial H_x}{\partial y}\right).$$

Also
$$\nabla \wedge \mathbf{H} = \left(\mathbf{i}\frac{\partial}{\partial x} + \mathbf{j}\frac{\partial}{\partial y} + \mathbf{k}\frac{\partial}{\partial z}\right) \wedge (\mathbf{i}H_x + \mathbf{j}H_y + \mathbf{k}H_z)$$
$$= \mathbf{i}\left(\frac{\partial H_z}{\partial y} - \frac{\partial H_y}{\partial z}\right) + \mathbf{j}\left(\frac{\partial H_x}{\partial z} - \frac{\partial H_z}{\partial x}\right) + \mathbf{k}\left(\frac{\partial H_y}{\partial x} - \frac{\partial H_x}{\partial y}\right)$$
$$= \operatorname{curl} \mathbf{H}. \tag{A.7}$$

## A.7. Laplace's operator

Another operator which occurs in Laplace's and Poisson's equations in electrostatics is the operator div grad.

If $V$ is a scalar function, div grad $V = \nabla.(\nabla V)$, and from equations (A.3) and (A.5)

$$\nabla.(\nabla V) = \left(\mathbf{i}\frac{\partial}{\partial x} + \mathbf{j}\frac{\partial}{\partial y} + \mathbf{k}\frac{\partial}{\partial z}\right).\left(\mathbf{i}\frac{\partial V}{\partial x} + \mathbf{j}\frac{\partial V}{\partial y} + \mathbf{k}\frac{\partial V}{\partial z}\right) = \frac{\partial^2 V}{\partial x^2} + \frac{\partial^2 V}{\partial y^2} + \frac{\partial^2 V}{\partial z^2}.$$

But $\nabla.(\nabla V) = \nabla.\nabla(V) = \nabla^2 V$, treating $\nabla$ as a vector. The operator div grad is therefore equivalent to
$$\nabla^2 = \frac{\partial^2}{\partial x^2} + \frac{\partial^2}{\partial y^2} + \frac{\partial^2}{\partial z^2},$$

which is called Laplace's operator (pronounced 'del squared').

By expressing the operators div, grad, and curl in terms of the operator $\nabla$, a number of useful relations can be established. The reader should verify for himself those listed below (remember that the order of an operator and its operand must not be altered).

curl grad $V \equiv \nabla \wedge (\nabla V) = 0.$

grad div $\mathbf{P} \equiv \nabla(\nabla.\mathbf{P}).$

div curl $\mathbf{P} \equiv \nabla.(\nabla \wedge \mathbf{P}) = 0$    (cf. the scalar triple product is zero if two of the vectors are identical).

curl curl $\mathbf{P} \equiv \nabla \wedge (\nabla \wedge \mathbf{P}) = \operatorname{grad} \operatorname{div} \mathbf{P} - \nabla^2 \mathbf{P}.$

div $m\mathbf{P} = m\operatorname{div}\mathbf{P} + \mathbf{P}.\operatorname{grad} m$    where $m$ is a scalar.

curl $m\mathbf{P} = m\operatorname{curl}\mathbf{P} - \mathbf{P} \wedge \operatorname{grad} m.$

div$(\mathbf{P} \wedge \mathbf{Q}) \equiv \nabla.(\mathbf{P} \wedge \mathbf{Q}) = \mathbf{Q}.\operatorname{curl}\mathbf{P} - \mathbf{P}.\operatorname{curl}\mathbf{Q}.$

## A.8. Stokes's theorem

In Fig. A.9 the line integral of the vector $\mathbf{H}$ is taken round a closed path bounding an unclosed surface $S$. This integral is $\oint \mathbf{H}.\mathbf{ds}$. If the surface is divided up into small elements of area $\mathbf{dS}$, then from § A.6

$$\oint \mathbf{H}.\mathbf{dl} = \operatorname{curl}\mathbf{H}.\mathbf{dS},$$

where $\oint \mathbf{H}.\mathbf{dl}$ is the line integral of $\mathbf{H}$ round one small element of area $\mathbf{dS}$. If this equation is now summed over all the elementary areas, all the boundaries within the surface will cancel out on the left-hand side, and the result is the line integral round the circuit bounding the surface. Therefore

$$\oint \mathbf{H}.\mathbf{ds} = \int \operatorname{curl}\mathbf{H}.\mathbf{dS}. \tag{A.8}$$

This is Stokes's theorem. It is necessary for $\mathbf{H}$ and its derivatives to be well-behaved continuous functions, but in the cases normally arising in electro-magnetism, these conditions are satisfied.

Conversely, if the line integral of **H** round a closed curve is equal to the surface integral of **P** over a surface bounded by the curve, irrespective of what curve or surface are used, then **P** = curl **H**.

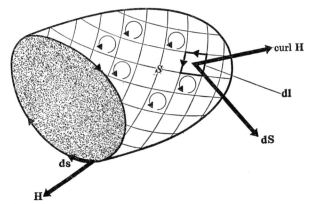

FIG. A.9. Illustrating Stokes's theorem.

### A.9. The divergence theorem

$S$ in Fig. A.10 is a closed surface in a region where there exists a vector field **F**. The flux through an element of area **dS** is **F . dS**, and the total flux through the surface is $\int$ **F . dS**. The total flux diverging from an element of volume $d\tau$ inside $S$ is, from § A.5 above, div **F** $d\tau$, where **F** is the value of the force field at this

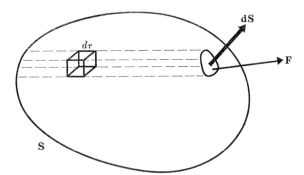

FIG. A.10. Illustrating the divergence theorem.

point. The integral $\int$ div **F** $d\tau$ throughout the whole volume enclosed by $S$ must give the total flux through the surface, since for any two adjacent volume elements the flux through a common face gives equal positive and negative contributions. Hence

$$\int \operatorname{div} \mathbf{F} \, d\tau = \int \mathbf{F} . \mathbf{dS},\qquad(\text{A.9})$$

which is the theorem of divergence. Again, the vector field **F** must be a well-behaved function. Conversely if the surface integral of a vector **F** is equal to the volume integral of a scalar function $P$ over the volume enclosed by the surface, whatever the surface, then we may conclude that

$$P = \operatorname{div} \mathbf{F}.$$

## A.10. Transformation from a rotating coordinate system

When dealing with the effect of an applied magnetic field on an atomic system it is often convenient to transform to a rotating coordinate system. Vector methods make this transformation simple, as can be seen from the following treatment.

Suppose we are concerned with some vector quantity $\mathbf{A}$, which to start with we will suppose to be fixed in the rotating coordinate system (a line on a spinning top is an example, but we do not have to restrict $\mathbf{A}$ to be simply a radius vector). The angular motion of the coordinate system is represented by a vector $\boldsymbol{\omega}$, whose magnitude is equal to the angular velocity and whose direction is parallel to the axis of rotation. Its sense is that in which a right-handed screw would advance if rotated in the same sense as the angular motion. If $\mathbf{A}$ is fixed in the rotating system, then in a time $\delta t$ the end point of the vector is displaced by an amount $\delta\mathbf{A}$ relative to a fixed coordinate system, as shown in Fig. A.11. It is clear that the motion of the end point is a simple rotation about the axis defined by $\boldsymbol{\omega}$. Hence

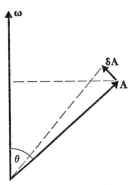

FIG. A.11. Change $\delta\mathbf{A}$ in time $\delta t$ of a vector $\mathbf{A}$ rotating with velocity $\boldsymbol{\omega}$.

$$\delta\mathbf{A} = (\omega\,\delta t)\,A\sin\theta = (\boldsymbol{\omega}\wedge\mathbf{A})\,\delta t.$$

Hence the velocity of $A$ relative to the fixed system is

$$\lim_{\delta t\to 0}(\delta\mathbf{A}/\delta t) = (d\mathbf{A}/dt) = (\boldsymbol{\omega}\wedge\mathbf{A}). \qquad (A.10)$$

If we now suppose that $\mathbf{A}$ is not fixed in the rotating system, but has a velocity $(D\mathbf{A}/Dt)$ relative to that system, then we have, from the vector addition of the two velocities

$$d\mathbf{A}/dt = (D\mathbf{A}/Dt) + (\boldsymbol{\omega}\wedge\mathbf{A}). \qquad (A.11)$$

This relation may be applied to any vector $\mathbf{A}$, and hence it may be applied to the vector $(d\mathbf{A}/dt)$ to find the second differential of $\mathbf{A}$. Retaining the notation that $(d/dt)$ refers to rate of change in the fixed coordinate system, and $(D/Dt)$ to rate of change relative to the rotating system, we have (since $\boldsymbol{\omega}$ is a constant)

$$\frac{d^2\mathbf{A}}{dt^2} = \frac{d}{dt}\left(\frac{d\mathbf{A}}{dt}\right) = \left(\frac{D}{Dt}+\boldsymbol{\omega}\wedge\right)\left(\frac{d\mathbf{A}}{dt}\right) = \left(\frac{D}{Dt}+\boldsymbol{\omega}\wedge\right)\left(\frac{D\mathbf{A}}{Dt}+\boldsymbol{\omega}\wedge\mathbf{A}\right)$$

$$= \frac{D^2\mathbf{A}}{Dt^2}+2\left(\boldsymbol{\omega}\wedge\frac{D\mathbf{A}}{Dt}\right)+\boldsymbol{\omega}\wedge(\boldsymbol{\omega}\wedge\mathbf{A}). \qquad (A.12)$$

## A.11. Larmor's theorem

Suppose that a charge $q$ is moving in a field of force (such as the attraction of a positively-charged nucleus) whose value at any moment is described by the vector $\mathbf{F}$. When a magnetic field is applied, the equation of motion is

$$m\frac{d^2\mathbf{r}}{dt^2} = \mathbf{F}+q\mathbf{v}\wedge\mathbf{B}, \qquad (A.13)$$

where $m$ is the mass associated with the charge, and $\mathbf{v}$ is the instantaneous velocity $(= d\mathbf{r}/dt)$. This is the equation of motion in vector form in a set of axes at rest with respect to the observer. Let us now change to a set of axes rotating with angular velocity $\boldsymbol{\omega}$ about the direction of $\mathbf{B}$. In transforming to rotating axes (see § A.10) we have the relation

$$m\frac{d^2\mathbf{r}}{dt^2} = m\frac{D^2\mathbf{r}}{Dt^2} + 2m\left[\boldsymbol{\omega}\wedge\frac{D\mathbf{r}}{Dt}\right] + m[\boldsymbol{\omega}\wedge(\boldsymbol{\omega}\wedge\mathbf{r})], \qquad (A.14)$$

where $D^2\mathbf{r}/Dt^2$, $D\mathbf{r}/Dt$ are the acceleration and velocity in the rotating coordinate frame, and $\boldsymbol{\omega}$ is the angular velocity expressed as a vector parallel to the axis of rotation, the direction of $\mathbf{B}$. The second term on the right-hand side is the 'Coriolis force' which appears if the particle is moving in the rotating system, and the last term is the centrifugal force normal to the axis of rotation. If $(\boldsymbol{\omega}\wedge\mathbf{r})$ is small compared with $D\mathbf{r}/Dt$ (as we shall show below to be the case), the centrifugal force will be small compared with the Coriolis force, and in the first approximation equations (A.13) and (A.14) give

$$m\frac{D^2\mathbf{r}}{Dt^2} = \mathbf{F} + q\mathbf{v}\wedge\mathbf{B} - 2m\boldsymbol{\omega}\wedge\frac{D\mathbf{r}}{Dt} = \mathbf{F} + q\mathbf{v}\wedge\mathbf{B} + 2m\mathbf{v}\wedge\boldsymbol{\omega}, \qquad (A.15)$$

where we have neglected the small difference between $\mathbf{v}$ and $(D\mathbf{r}/Dt)$ (the velocity in the rotating frame) since they differ only by the quantity $(\boldsymbol{\omega}\wedge\mathbf{r})$ which we have already assumed to be small in comparison. It is apparent that if we choose the rate of rotation of the axes such that

$$\boldsymbol{\omega} = -(q/2m)\mathbf{B} \qquad (A.16)$$

the last two terms in (A.15) will vanish and the equation of motion is the same as if the magnetic field were absent. Thus to an observer rotating with the angular velocity given by (A.16) the motion of the charge appears to be the same as it would to a stationary observer in the absence of a magnetic field. Hence we may regard the motion of an electron of charge $-e$ in the field $\mathbf{B}$ as unchanged except for a precession with angular velocity $\boldsymbol{\omega} = +(e/2m)\mathbf{B}$ about the axis of $\mathbf{B}$. This is commonly known as the 'Larmor precession'.

The fact that it is justifiable to neglect the last term in equation (A.14) can be seen as follows. When the electron is bound in the atom, it executes a periodic motion in its orbit whose frequency is of the same order as that of visible light. This corresponds to an angular frequency $\omega_0$ of the order of $10^{15}$ radians/sec. The terms $D^2\mathbf{r}/Dt^2$ and $D\mathbf{r}/Dt$ are then of order of magnitude $\omega_0^2 r$ and $\omega_0 r$ respectively, so that successive terms in equation (A.14) decrease in magnitude by the ratio $(\omega/\omega_0)$. Since $\omega$ is only about $10^{11}$ radians/sec even in a field of 1 weber/metre$^2$ (10 000 gauss), the centrifugal force term is an order of magnitude smaller than the Coriolis force. In other words, the force on the electron due to the field $\mathbf{B}$ is small compared with the force exerted by the positively-charged nucleus; if it were not, it would tear the atom apart.

The central force assumed above is that responsible for the orbital motion of an electron in an atom, and the angular velocity given by equation (A.16) is identical with the angular velocity of precession (see § 20.1) of an electronic orbital magnetic moment in a magnetic field $\mathbf{B}$.

# THE UNIQUENESS THEOREM

THE uniqueness theorem states that if a potential function $V_1$ is a solution of Laplace's equation which satisfies the boundary conditions, then it is the only solution.

If this were not so, then there exists another solution $V_2$ and we write $V = V_1 - V_2$, where, since $V_1$ and $V_2$ are each a solution, $V$ also satisfies Laplace's equation. If $V$ can be shown to be zero, then $V_1 = V_2$ and is a unique solution.

Consider the relation (cf. § A.7)

$$-\mathrm{div}(V\,\mathbf{E}) = \nabla.\,(V\,\nabla V) = (\nabla\,V)^2 + V\,\nabla^2 V$$

in the form

$$\int (\epsilon\epsilon_0\,\mathrm{grad}\,V.\,\mathrm{grad}\,V)\,d\tau = \int \mathrm{div}(V\epsilon\epsilon_0\,\mathrm{grad}\,V)\,d\tau - \int V\,\mathrm{div}(\epsilon\epsilon_0\,\mathrm{grad}\,V)\,d\tau,$$

where the integral is taken over all space outside the conductors where there are no free charges. Then the second integral on the right-hand side is zero by equation (2.1). The first integral is equal to $\int (V\epsilon\epsilon_0\,\mathrm{grad}\,V).\,\mathbf{dS}$ taken over the surfaces of the conductors and the limiting sphere at infinity. On the conductors either $V = 0$ or $\int \epsilon\epsilon_0(\partial V/\partial r).\,\mathbf{dS} = 0$, since either the potential or the charge on each conductor must be fixed. For a set of finite conductors, $V \to 0$ as $r \to \infty$; thus $V$ must vary as $r^{-n}$ where $n \geqslant 1$, and grad $V$ as $r^{-n-1}$, so that $\int V\,\mathrm{grad}\,V.\,\mathbf{dS}$ varies as $r^{-2n+1}$ and vanishes at $r = \infty$.

This shows that $\int (\epsilon\epsilon_0\,\mathrm{grad}\,V.\,\mathrm{grad}\,V)\,d\tau = 0$, so that grad $V = 0$ since the integrand is always positive, Hence $V = \mathrm{constant} = V_1 - V_2$. But $V_1 = V_2 = 0$ at $r = \infty$; whence $V = 0$ and $V_1 = V_2$ everywhere, showing that $V_1$ is a unique solution of Laplace's equation.

# NUMERICAL VALUES OF THE FUNDAMENTAL CONSTANTS (TO FOUR SIGNIFICANT FIGURES)

As recommended by the Committee on Fundamental Constants of the National Academy of Sciences—National Research Council, U.S.A. (1964)

| | | |
|---|---|---|
| $c$ | velocity of light *in vacuo* | $2 \cdot 998 \times 10^8$ m/sec |
| $N$ | Avogadro's number | $6 \cdot 023 \ 10^{26}$ (kg mole)$^{-1}$ |
| | | $= 6 \cdot 023 \ 10^{23}$ (g mole)$^{-1}$ |
| $e$ | electronic charge | $1 \cdot 602 \ 10^{-19}$ coulomb |
| $m$ | electron rest mass | $9 \cdot 109 \ 10^{-31}$ kg |
| $M$ | proton rest mass | $1 \cdot 673 \ 10^{-27}$ kg |
| $M/m$ | ratio of proton to electron mass | $1 \cdot 836 \ 10^3$ |
| $h$ | Planck's constant | $6 \cdot 626 \ 10^{-34}$ joule sec |
| $\hbar$ | Planck's constant$/2\pi$ | $1 \cdot 055 \ 10^{-34}$ joule sec |
| $F$ | Faraday's constant $(Ne)$ | $9 \cdot 649 \ 10^7$ coulomb/kg |
| $e/m$ | charge/mass for electron | $1 \cdot 759 \ 10^{11}$ coulomb/kg |
| $e^2/m$ | | $2 \cdot 819 \ 10^{-8}$ coulomb$^2$/kg |
| $a_0$ | Bohr radius | $5 \cdot 292 \ 10^{-11}$ m |
| $Rc$ | Rydberg constant $\times c$ | $3 \cdot 290 \ 10^{15}$ sec$^{-1}$ |
| $R$ | Rydberg constant | $1 \cdot 097 \ 10^7$ m$^{-1}$ |
| | | $= 1 \cdot 097 \ 10^5$ cm$^{-1}$ |
| $k$ | Boltzmann's constant | $1 \cdot 380 \ 10^{-23}$ joule/deg |
| | Bohr magneton | $9 \cdot 273 \ 10^{-24}$ A m$^2$ |
| | | $= 9 \cdot 273 \ 10^{-21}$ e.m.u. |
| $\beta_n$ | nuclear magneton | $5 \cdot 051 \ 10^{-27}$ A m$^2$ |
| $\alpha$ | fine structure constant | $(137 \cdot 0)^{-1}$ |
| $\epsilon_0$ | permittivity of free space $= (\mu_0 c^2)^{-1}$ | $8 \cdot 854 \ 10^{-12}$ farad/m |
| $4\pi\epsilon_0$ | | $10^7/c^2 = 10^{-9}/9$ approximately |
| $\mu_0$ | permeability of free space (by definition) | $4\pi \times 10^{-7}$ henry/m exactly |
| $Z_0$ | intrinsic impedance of free space | $3 \cdot 767 \ 10^2$ ohm |
| eV | electron volt | $1 \cdot 602 \ 10^{-19}$ joule |
| $kT$ | energy for $T = 290°$ K | $4 \cdot 003 \ 10^{-21}$ joule |

1 electron volt is equivalent to:

wavelength $\lambda = 1 \cdot 240 \times 10^{-6}$ m

frequency $\nu = 2 \cdot 416 \ 10^{14}$ sec$^{-1}$

wave number $\tilde{\nu} = 8 \cdot 066 \ 10^3$ cm$^{-1}$

temperature $T = 1 \cdot 161 \times 10^4$ °K

energy $W = 1 \cdot 602 \ 10^{-19}$ joule

1 cm$^{-1}$ is equivalent to:

wavelength $\lambda = 1$ cm

temperature $T = 1 \cdot 439°$ K

# SOME ATOMIC FORMULAE IN M.K.S. UNITS

Rydberg's constant $\times c$ 
$$Rc = \frac{me^4}{8\epsilon_0^2 h^3} = \frac{me^4}{64\pi^3 \epsilon_0^2 h^3}$$

Bohr radius 
$$a_0 = \frac{4\pi\epsilon_0 \hbar^2}{me^2}$$

Fine structure constant 
$$\alpha = \frac{e^2}{4\pi\epsilon_0 \hbar c}$$

Bohr magneton 
$$\beta = \frac{e\hbar}{2m}$$

Nuclear magneton 
$$\beta_n = \frac{e\hbar}{2M}$$

# INDEX

**A**, magnetic vector potential, 143, 161, 281.
Absorption, non-resonant, 497.
— resonant, 486.
Acceptor level, 537.
Admittance, 234.
Ammeter, 181.
Ampère, 130.
Ampère's law, 135, 137.
— theory of magnetism, 195.
Amplification factor of vacuum tube, 340, 342.
Amplifier, audio-frequency, 351.
— efficiency of, 357.
— power, 355.
— push-pull, 356.
— radio-frequency, 359.
Amplitude modulation, 375.
Anderson bridge, 428.
Anisotropy energy, 628.
Anode resistance of vacuum tube, 342.
Anti-ferromagnetism, 657.
Atomic beam, 681.
— clock, 701.
Attenuation on filter, 294.
— on transmission line, 312.
— in waveguide, 318.
Azbel-Kaner resonance, 722.

**B**, magnetic field, 126–30.
Band theory, 506–10.
Barn, 43.
Barnett effect, 634.
Base electrode, 571.
Biot and Savart's law, 142.
Bitter magnet, 213.
— patterns, 631.
Block wall, 628.
Bohr magneton, 577.
Bolometer, 420.
Boundary conditions for **D** and **E**, 20.
— for **B** and **H**, 138.
Brewster's angle, 273.
Bridge, alternating current, 424.
— Anderson, 428.
— Hartshorn mutual inductance, 429.
— Schering, 426.
— Wien, 435.
Brillouin function, 593, 623.
— zone, 513.
Brownian motion, 452.

Capacitance, 22.
— of sphere, 23.

Capacitance of two infinite cylinders, 54.
Capacitor, 22.
Cathode-follower, 388.
Cathode, oxide-coated, 330.
Cathode ray oscillograph, 415.
Cavity resonator, 325.
Characteristic of vacuum tube, 340, 348, 349.
Charge, electric, 4.
Child's law, 333.
Clausius–Mossotti formula, 479.
Coefficient of coupling $k$, 163, 246.
Coercive force, 205.
Collective electron model in ferromagnetism, 644.
Collector junction, 570.
Conductance, 234.
— input, for tube, 390.
Conduction band, 537.
Conduction current, 257.
Conductivity, electrical, 521–8.
— extrinsic, 538.
— intrinsic, 536.
— specific, 64.
— thermal, 521–8.
Contact potential, 95.
Continuity, equation of, 63, 257.
Coriolis force, 754.
Correlation energy, 514, 647.
Corresponding states, law of, 625.
Coulomb, unit of charge, 4.
Coulomb's law of inverse squares, 3, 19.
— — experimental proof of, 10.
Coupled circuits, 243.
Coupling coefficient $k$, 163, 246.
— Russell–Saunders, 582.
Crystal diode, 411.
Curie, method of measuring $\chi_m$, 217.
Curie's law, 201, 593.
Curie–Weiss law, 203, 620.
Curl of a vector, 750.
Current balance, 192.
— generator circuit, 354.
Cyclotron resonance, 710.
— — for electrons, 715.
— — for protons, 713.
— — in semi-conductors, 717.
Cylindrical harmonic functions, 47.

Damping, of galvanometer, 184.
Daniell cell, 113.
de Broglie relation, 89, 505.
Debye absorption, 497.

Debye unit, 476.
de Haas–van Alphen effect, 532.
Demagnetizing factor, 141.
— field, 209.
Detection, 376.
Detector, crystal diode, 411.
— diode, 375.
— standing-wave, 432.
Diamagnetism, 195, 198–201.
— of conduction electrons, 529.
Dielectric constant $\epsilon$, 19.
— — measurement of, 442.
— — theory of, 16, 475.
— — variation with frequency, 483.
— — — temperature, 480.
Diffusion length, in semi-conductor, 560.
Diode, thermionic, 331,
— transistor, 565–9.
Dip, angle of, 223.
Dipole, electronic, 13, 39.
— magnetic, 196.
— radiation, 281.
Discriminator, 385.
Dispersion, 483–8.
Displacement current, 257.
— electric $D$, 18, 19.
Divergence of a vector, 748.
Domain, ferromagnetic, 206, 626.
Donor level, 537.
Drude's theory, 85.
Dynamometer, 183, 419.

$e/m$ measurement for current carriers, 62.
— for electrons, 716.
$e/M$ measurement for proton, 716.
Earnshaw's theorem, 31.
Effective mass, 510.
— — measurement of, 717, 722.
Einstein–de Haas effect, 635.
Electrical conductivity, 521–8.
Electrochemical equivalent, 110.
Electrolyte, 110.
Electromagnet, 210.
Electromagnetic balance, 215.
— units, 731.
— waves, 256–87.
— — impedance of, 262.
— — propagation of, in conductors, 265.
— — — in dielectrics, 260.
— — reflection and refraction of, 269.
— — velocity of, 259, 445.
Electrometer, 32.
Electromotive force, 66.
Electron, 1.
— $e/m$, 62.
— in metals, classical theory, 85.
— — — quantum theory, 88.
— magnetic resonance, 698, 703.

Electron optics, 75–81.
— volt, 89.
Electrostatic units, 3, 729.
Emitter junction, 570.
Energy bands, 506–10, 516.
— of current circuit, 143, 144, 172.
— of electromagnetic wave, 263.
— of electrostatic field, 26.
— — — system of charges, 25, 42.
— — magnetic dipole, 143.
— — — field, 175.
Equipartition of energy, 452.
Equivalent circuit, 343.
Exchange interaction, 582, 609, 618, 630, 650.
Exciton, 550.
Exhaustion range, 538.

Farad, 23.
Faraday constant, 111.
— laws of electrolysis, 110.
— — of electromagnetic induction, 158.
Feedback, negative, 354.
— positive, 364.
Fermi energy, 91, 94.
— surface, 513.
— level, of metal, 94.
— — of semiconductor, 545.
Ferrimagnetic resonance, 709.
Ferrimagnetism, 664.
Ferrites, 665.
Ferromagnetic resonance, 707.
Ferromagnetism, 195, 618–55.
— classical theory, 204–7.
Field, electric, 4, 19.
— emission, 99.
— magnetic, 137.
— — measurement of, 214, 695.
— — production of, 207.
Filters, 289–301.
— band-pass, 299.
— high-pass, 298.
— low-pass, 297.
— $m$-derived, 301.
Flip-flop circuit, 389.
Flux, electric, 19.
— magnetic, 143.
Fluxmeter, 186.
Foner's magnetometer, 219.
Force, on moving charge, 152.
— between current circuits, 174.
Frequency, changing, 380.
— measurement, 441.
— modulation, 383.
— resonant, 229, 236, 240.
— standard, 701.
Fresnel's formulae, 275.

Galvanometer, 179.
— ballistic, 186.
— damping, 184, 454–6.
Garnets, 666.
Gauss' theorem, in free space, 8.
— — in dielectrics, 18.
— — in e.s.u., 730.
$g$, Landé factor, 588.
$g_s$ for electron, 579, 699.
$g_n$ for nucleus, 611.
Gouy, method of measuring $\chi_m$, 218.
Gradient of a vector, 748.
Grid, 339, 347.
Gruneisen's formula, 523.
Guided waves, 315–26.
Gyromagnetic, ratio, 575.
— effect, 634.

H, magnetic field, 136.
Half-power points, 237, 495.
Hall effect, 528, 552.
Harmonic generator, 375.
Hartley oscillator, 369.
Heisenberg model in ferromagnetism, 618, 644.
Helmholtz coils, 156.
Henry, 162.
Hole, positive, 512, 529, 536.
Hund's rules, 582, 652.
Hyperfine structure, 612.
Hysteresis, 205, 221–3.

Images, electrical, 48.
Impedance, 229.
— characteristic, 297, 304.
— of free space, 262.
— of a metal, 267.
— input, for transmission line, 309.
— — for triode, 344.
Impurity level, 537.
Inductance, mutual, 161, 429.
— self, 161, 428.
Intensity of magnetization, M, 135.
Ionization potential, 121.
Isotope, 1.
Iterative impedance, 296.

Johnson noise, 454.
Junction transistor, 569.

k, space, 513.
— wave vector, 89.
Kelvin's bridge, 83.
Kipp relay, 370.
Kirchhoff's laws, 68.
Klystron oscillator, 400.
— reflex, 405.
Kramers' theorem, 598.

Landé $g$-factor, 588.
Langevin, theory of paramagnetism, 201.
Lanthanide metals, magnetic properties of, 670.
Laplace's equation, 33, 66, 140.
Larmor's theorem, 199, 576, 753.
Lecher wire oscillator, 396.
Legendre, equation of, 35.
— associated functions, 36.
Lenz's law, 158.
Limiter, 385.
Line charges, 52.
— of force, 7.
Logarithmic decrement, 171, 187.
Lorentz, theory of local field, 478.
Lorenz force, 152, 529.
— number, 524.
Loss tangent, tan $\delta$, 236.

Magnetic field, due to current circuits, 148.
— — measurement of, 214–16, 695.
— — production of, 207.
— focusing of ions, 153.
— induction, 126.
— moment, 131, 195, 574.
— — of free atoms, 585, 593.
— — nuclear, 610.
— permeability, 139.
— resonance, 677.
— shell, 130.
— susceptibility, 139.
— vector potential, 143.
Magnetism, terrestrial, 223.
Magnetization, M, 139.
Magneto-caloric effect, 639.
Magnetogyric ratio, 196.
Magnetometer, Foner's, 219.
Magnetomotive force, 134.
Magneton, Bohr, 577.
— nuclear, 611.
Magnetron, 405.
Mass spectrometer, 154.
Maximum power theorem, 68, 356.
Maxwell stress tensor, 28.
Maxwell's equations, 256.
Metal-semiconductor junctions, 560.
Mho, 235.
m.k.s. units, 4.
Mobility, 65.
— of electrons in metals, 86.
— — in semiconductors, 553.
— of gaseous ion, 118.
— measurement of, 555.
— variation with temperature, 556.
Modulation, amplitude, 375.
— frequency, 383.
— index, 384.
Molecular beam, 681.

Momentum space, 90.
Mössbauer effect, 641.
Multipole expansions, 39.
Multivibrator, 372.
Mutual conductance of vacuum tube, 342.
Mutual inductance, 162.
— — bridge, 429.

n-type semiconductor, 537.
Néel temperature, 658.
Negative feed-back, 354.
— resistance, 366.
Neumann's formula, 162.
Neutron, 1.
— diffraction, 673.
— magnetic moment, 611, 684.
Noise figure, 462.
— Johnson, 454.
— measurement of, 470.
— shot, 462.
Nuclear induction, 689.
— magnetic moments, 610, 616.
— resonance, 685.

Ohm's law, 64.
Onsager, local field theory, 491.
Orbital quantum number, 577.
Oscillator, Hartley, 369.
— power, 368.
— quartz crystal, 437.
— strength, 486.
— tuned-anode, 364.
— tuned-grid, 367.

p–n junction, 565.
p-type semiconductor, 537.
Paramagnetism, 195.
— classical theory, 201–4.
— of conduction electrons, 529.
— Pauli, 532.
Paramagnetic resonance, 705.
Parity, 40.
Partition function, 615.
Paschen's law, 122.
Paschen–Back effect, 590.
Pauli exclusion principle, 88, 90, 580.
— paramagnetism, 532.
Peltier effect, 103.
Pentode, 349.
Permeability, of free space, $\mu_0$, 129.
— magnetic, $\mu$ 139.
Permittivity of free space $\epsilon_0$, 4.
Phase-shifter, 254.
Phonon, 522.
Photo-conductivity, 551.
Photoelectric emission, 97, 99.
Piezo-electric effect, 437.
Planck's constant, $h$, 89.

Plane wave in conductors, 265.
— — in dielectrics, 259.
— — reflection and refraction of, 269–278.
Plasma oscillations, 123.
— frequency, 124.
Poisson's equation, 33.
Polar gases, 480.
— liquids, 491.
— — radio-frequency dispersion in, 493.
— molecule, 109, 480.
Polarizability, 17, 478.
Polarization, electric, 17, 478.
— magnetic, 135.
Positive hole, 512.
Potential, electric, 4–6.
— magnetic vector, 143–9, 161, 175, 281.
— magnetostatic, 134.
Potentiometer, 73.
Power factor, 230.
— amplifier, 355.
— oscillator, 368.
Poynting vector, 263.
Practical units, 733.
Precession, 199, 574, 677, 708.
Pressure of electromagnetic radiation, 278.
Proton, 1.
— $e/M$, 716.
— magnetic moment, 611.

Quadrupole, electric, 14, 30, 43.
— nuclear, 612.
Quality factor $Q$, 171, 237, 242.
— — of transmission line, 315.
— — of waveguide, 325.
Quantum number, 577.
Quarter-wave line, 310.
Quartz crystal oscillator, 437.
Quenching of orbital momentum, 600, 609.
Quincke, method of measuring $\chi_m$, 219.

Rabi, molecular beam apparatus, 681.
Radiation resistance, 285.
Radio receiver, 386.
Raman effect, 502.
Rare earth metals, magnetic properties of, 670.
Rationalized units, 733.
Rayleigh scattering, 500.
Reactance, 232.
Reciprocity theorem, 70.
Rectifier, diode, 336, 338.
— p–n junction, 568.
— semiconductor–metal, 564.
Reflecting film, 311, 327.
— power, 275, 277.
Reflection coefficient for transmission line, 307.
— — of plane wave, 269–78.

Reflection coefficient, total internal, 276.
Refraction at dielectric boundary, 21.
— of plane wave, 269–78.
Refractive index, 260.
— — variation with frequency, 487.
Relaxation time of electrons in metals, 84.
— — — in paramagnetic solids, 703.
— — of nuclei, 690.
Reluctance, magnetic, 210.
Remanence, 205.
Resistance, absolute measurement of, 190.
— high frequency, of wire, 269.
— negative, 366.
— of radiating dipole, 285.
— residual, 523.
— specific, 64.
— temperature coefficient of, 64.
Resonant frequency, 229, 236, 240.
Resonance potential, 119.
Ripple voltage, 337.
Rotating cordinate system, 753.
Russell–Saunders coupling, 582.

Scalar product, 745.
Scattering of electromagnetic waves, 498–501.
— of electrons in metals, 522.
Schering bridge, 426.
Screen grid, 347.
Secondary emission, 101.
Seebeck effect, 103.
Selectivity $Q$, 171.
— of transmission line, 315.
— of cavity resonator, 325.
Semiconductor, 65, 536.
— absorption edge, 548.
— degenerate, 547.
— Fermi level, 545.
— $n$-type, 537.
— non-degenerate, 547.
— $p$-type, 537.
Shot noise, 462.
Sidebands, 384.
Skin depth $\delta$, 267.
— — anomalous, 528, 534.
Snell's law, 270.
Space charge, 332.
— — smoothing factor, 464.
Specific heat of conduction electrons, 517.
— — of a ferromagnet, 637.
Spherical harmonic functions, 36, 38.
— — — expansion of, 40.
Spin-orbit interaction, 583.
Spin quantum number, electronic, 579.
— — — nuclear, 610.
Spin-waves, 648, 709.
Stern-Gerlach experiment, 590.
Stokes's theorem, 751.

Stress, at surface of dielectric, 26.
— tensor, 28.
Superconducting magnet, 214.
Superconductivity, 527.
Susceptance, 234.
Susceptibility, electric, $\chi_e$, 17, 19.
— magnetic, $\chi_m$, 139, 200.
— — of conduction electrons, 529.
— measurement of $\chi_m$, 216–21.

Terrestrial magnetism, 223.
Tetrode, 347.
Thermal conductivity, 521–8.
Thermionic emission, 97.
Thermocouple, 107.
Thermoelectricity, 103–9.
Thévenin's theorem, 83.
Thomson effect, 103.
— — measurement of, 108.
Three-halves power law, 332.
Time-base, 417.
Townsend discharge, 121.
Transformer, 163.
— high frequency, 243.
— low frequency, 247.
— quarter-wave, 311.
— transmission line, 310.
Transients, 165–72.
Transistor, 569–72.
Transit time, 393.
Transmission line, 302–15.
Travelling wave tubes, 412.
Triode, 339.
Tuned circuits, 236–42.

Uniqueness theorem, 34, 755.
Units, 729–43.

Vacuum-tube voltmeter, 336, 422.
Valence band, 537.
Van Leeuwen's theorem, 592.
Vector model of atom, 576, 586.
— product, 746.
Velocity of electromagnetic waves, 259.
— of wave on transmission line, 304, 312.
— measurement of, 445.
— of wave in waveguide, 318.
Volt, 7.
Voltage amplification, 343.
Voltage standing wave ratio, 308, 431.
Voltmeter, 181.
— vacuum-tube, 336, 422.

Watt, 67.
Wattmeter, 183, 420.
Wave equation, 259.
— vector, $\mathbf{k}$, 89.
— velocity, 259.

Wave-guides, 321–6.
Wave-meter, 437.
Weber, 143.
Weiss constant, 203, 620, 661.
Wheatstone's bridge, 71.

Wiedemann's law, 86, 200, 524.
Wien's bridge, 435.
Work function, 92, 95.

Zeeman effect, 588.